# ANNUAL REVIEW OF PHYSIOLOGY

# ANNUAL REVIEW OF PHYSIOLOGY

**JULIUS H. COMROE, Jr.,** *Editor*
University of California Medical Center, San Francisco

**RALPH R. SONNENSCHEIN,** *Associate Editor*
University of California, Los Angeles

**KENNETH L. ZIERLER,** *Associate Editor*
Johns Hopkins Medical School

*VOLUME 36*

*1974*

ANNUAL REVIEWS INC.     4139 EL CAMINO WAY     PALO ALTO, CALIFORNIA 94306

ANNUAL REVIEWS INC.
Palo Alto, California USA

International Standard Book Number: 0–8243–0336–9
Library of Congress Catalog Card Number: 39–15404

Assistant Editor       Kathleen A. Gardner
Indexers               Mary Glass
                       Susan Tinker
Subject Indexers       Victor E. Hall
                       Francis M. Hall

PRINTED AND BOUND IN THE UNITED STATES OF AMERICA

# CONTENTS

# SOME BIOPHYSICAL EXPERIMENTS FROM FIFTY YEARS AGO

*Georg von Békésy*
Laboratory of Sensory Sciences, 1993 East-West Road, Honolulu, Hawaii

*. . . was man ist, das blieb man andern schulding.*

*Torquato Tasso*, Act 1, Scene 1
Johann Wolfgang Goethe

## Editor's Note

Georg von Békésy died June 13, 1972. In early March of that year, the Editors and Editorial Committee members of the Annual Review of Physiology invited him to write the prefatory chapter for this 1974 volume. He accepted promptly and added "I am sure I will have it finished long before your deadline of June 1973." He mailed us his completed manuscript three weeks later, early in April 1972, two months before his death.

Professor von Békésy received the Nobel Prize for Physiology and Medicine in 1961. In the presentation speech, Professor C. G. Bernhard of the Karolinska Institute said

The field of Physiological acoustics has a noble ancestry. von Békésy's distinction is to have recorded events in a fragile biological miniature system. Authorities in this field evaluate the elaborate technique which he developed as being worthy of a genius. By microdissection, he reaches anatomical structures difficult of access, uses advanced tele-technique for stimulation and recording, and employs high magnification stroboscopic microscopy for making apparent complex membrane movements, the amplitudes of which are measured in thousandths of a millimeter.

Professor von Békésy, your outstanding genius has given us an intimate knowledge of the elementary hearing process. As a whole this is a unique contribution. The main reasons for the award are, however, your fundamental discoveries concerning the dynamics of the inner ear. With reference to Nobel's intentions it is also a great satisfaction to be able to award the prize for outstanding discoveries which are entirely the result of one single scientist's work.

At the time of his death, Georg von Békésy was Professor of Sensory Sciences, University of Hawaii.

1

## Introduction

I like to read the history of science, especially of medicine. It describes the fight between man and nature, which consists of a continuing series of successes and failures. Unfortunately, the majority of present day scientific papers are written in a cold, impersonal style. In earlier times many case histories were presented and by reading them it was possible to make a connection between the conclusion and the actual situation. Today case histories are no longer published and reviews sometimes sound almost like autopsy reports.

Some researchers are of the opinion that it is no longer necessary to study the history of science because science has progressed so fast and always linearly, that earlier experiences are of no value. I do not believe this, but believe, like many of my otological colleagues, that scientific progress is more like a spiral, as in the cochlea of the ear, which always progresses in one direction but with many ups and downs and with many repetitions of earlier forms. I was therefore very pleased to receive from the Editors of this series an invitation to write a free-form article that includes whatever autobiographical, anecdotal, or philosophical comments I wish to make. The invitation encouraged inclusion of personal reminiscences and presentation of my views of any aspects of physiological science of special personal significance. In writing such an article, the pattern of ups and downs, advances and setbacks in my research and other endeavors may be revealed. The Editors believe that this and other prefatory chapters, taken together, will provide a valuable historical perspective of physiology in the twentieth century.

I quote these instructions from the Editor's letter in an effort to eliminate some misunderstandings that can occur when reviewing earlier periods. One possible mistake is that we do not like the time just past. In art it is very well known that the style of twenty to forty years ago is generally disliked today; you can find the best art objects of this period in junk shops and attics. This held also for art Nouveaux until some seventy years had passed, after which the art of that period became collector's items. Such aversion to art of the recent past probably results from our rejection of the opinions of our parents and older people and the desire to change, to do something new and better. In not succeeding so well we start to dislike the earlier period.

Another mistake is exactly the opposite of the first—sometimes we tend to make the past more attractive than it really was, omitting the unpleasant parts. And a third problem, ever present in an autobiography, is making your life more important than it really was. I tried to avoid this because it is misleading for the younger generation and can foster mistrust and dislike of autobiographies. I hope I have been successful in avoiding these errors.

One reason my biography is a little different is that my parents were not immigrants, as were the parents of many scientists in this country. I come from a well known Hungarian family of means and therefore our circumstances in general became worse and worse with time. Certainly there were not such improvements as with families who came to the United States and started life fresh.

## South Germany and Switzerland Before World War I

I received my basic education in Munich and Switzerland. Munich then belonged to the kingdom of Bavaria and had a certain freedom from the North German atmosphere. At that time South Germany and Switzerland were among the leading countries in science. It was Munich that had the first automatic telephone and it was Munich where garbage was collected in three different cans: one for paper, one for spoilable material, and one for the rest.

In Munich there was much interest in paintings and sculpture, and it was there that I, as a schoolboy at the age of about 8, first saw a well known sculptor, who lived in our neighborhood in the Königinen Strasse, work on a live model. The cooperation between the model and the sculptor was something that I will never forget. Both of them worked on the opposite end of the problem, but they helped each other and produced an exceptional work.

Munich had a museum for the history of science, unique at that time, and many museums for fine arts. The people knew how to live and how to let other people live and how to work. Formally it was a kingdom, but in behavior it was perhaps the best democracy I have even seen.

Switzerland was more commercially oriented. The schools were excellent and life was well organized. There were many refugees from Russia and other countries, mostly revolutionaries like Lenin. They were free to do and say what they wanted. But it is extremely difficult to make a revolution in Switzerland. The intended revolutionaries would listen to the speeches but at noon when the church bells started to ring all over the town, most would remember that they had steaming soup on their table at home and leave. Revolution just does not work after a hot meal.

Life was comfortable and some groups in Berne, the capital, were accused of not doing any work at all. The Imperial and Royal Embassy of Austria and Hungary belonged in this category and it was said that the chancellery of this Embassy had written a sign on the door, "Office hours from 12 to 1."

But despite the apparent beautiful and friendly atmosphere there was tremendous tension in 1913 because everybody expected a war. Even Switzerland had a large military buildup to protect her borders, and the students were drafted periodically because the front between France and Germany could easily be extended into Switzerland if there were no proper defense lines.

## World War I

The impossibility of avoiding a war in the next years influenced every boy's thinking. At that time it seemed to make no sense to study mathematics or theoretical physics when you could be drafted a year later into the war. It was known even in 1912 that the Siberian Russian Army had moved partially to the border of Germany and Austria-Hungary. Such masses of soldiers and material were involved that there was no way to stop it. My colleagues in Germany, those who were not Swiss citizens, tried to emigrate from Europe. One of my best friends committed suicide as he simply could see no other way out. Perhaps the worst feeling about the future was the fear that after World War I had ended there would be nothing left of Europe.

Given some of the preparations on both sides, France and Germany, it was obvious that the war would last very, very long, in spite of some of the military who felt they could occupy each other's capital in a week.

Only a few students favored the war. I had one friend from Prague who wanted to serve there so he could participate in the liberation of the Czechs from Austria-Hungary. He volunteered for military service in Prague but unfortunately the regiment to which he was assigned revolted. The liberation force was immediately crushed by the Austrian Army and every tenth member of the regiment was shot. My friend was one of them.

After this and similar experiences, I became an outspoken coward. I did not want to live from day to day waiting for a tragedy, so I made a program for my future life. Once you do so, all your behavior is directed against the disturbing factors that you want to avoid and in this way I completely lost my enthusiasm for military achievements.

Another disturbing factor was the question of a career in music. My piano teacher was like an income tax accountant—very precise, checking everything constantly. His technique was superb. He envied me to a certain degree because the span between my thumb and my small finger, as a boy at that time, was already larger than his, and because I had "good bones" in my hand. I could get from a concert piano about the maximum it could give.

But the real issue was that he played Chopin, for instance, with the precision of a Swiss watch. He realized that my way of playing, with a little Hungarian twist, was much more interesting for the Swiss public. There were things I could not explain to him. For instance, some of the very fast runs across the whole keyboard impressed him very much and I could not tell him that these are always somebody's own manufacture and have nothing to do with the notes which are written on paper. It was Liszt who used them extremely successfully, and knowing about four to five variations, could ornament a piano piece exactly so that it fit the group of listeners. My teacher told me in a very clear way that a concert pianist needed a repertoire of about six pieces and no more, and could travel all through Europe by having only that small knowledge. It would take about two or three years, he said, until I would play them so that I would be a top performer for two or three pieces.

My opinion was that I did not know how to play the piano at all but I did know what the public wanted. However, on this basis I would not start a life career. Another point which for me was very disturbing was the fact that music stuck with me. On hearing a good musical melody, I had to hum it for days and weeks. A painting or a sculpture never stuck with me. I could look at it and draw it and after a few minutes it somehow faded out; but music was different, it occupied my brain and that handicapped good logical thinking on my part. So for this reason, I gave up the playing of music even as a sideline.

## Education in Switzerland

Education was developed mainly by Pestalozzi, a simple, practical teacher who worked out new methods of transmitting information from an older man to a young student. I had the good fortune to be educated in a private school, the Institute

Minerva in Zurich. The great advantage of that gymnasium was that it used the so-called mobile class system, in which there were four to six classes in each subject but on different levels of progress. It was therefore often necessary to have six or more professors simultaneously teaching the same thing. A student had free choice to select the class on a level that fit him the best. This type of impedance matching, as we would call it today in electronics, was very useful and generally avoided inferiority complexes in the students and frustration in the teacher. If somebody failed in one subject, he could study the same subject for another year and not be disturbed in his progress in other subjects. In this way I finished my course in physics in about two years so I was able to do experiments at home in my own style and pace. Therefore when I did attend the university I had a definitely better education than many others. I was very poor in English and even more so in German. Unfortunately, Hungarian is a language which has few similarities to other languages, except Finnish, so knowing it did not help in learning other languages.

The University in Berne is financed by the citizens of the Kanton of Berne, a very small group of people. The capital of Switzerland, Berne, had only 50,000 inhabitants at the time. Therefore it was taken as an honor to be able to study at the University. When I first shook hands with the Rector Magnificus he made it clear that to be a chemist and to learn at the University cost the University, as far as I remember, about 5000 Swiss francs per year, although the education of a lawyer there cost the University only around 600 Swiss francs per year. This made it obvious to students that the few chemistry students were using a large amount of the citizens' money for their study and, therefore, the citizens of Berne expected the chemists to produce something of importance.

As a student I had the impression that it was most important to study mathematics. I found out that at the University, just as in most universities, there are very good courses in elementary and in highly advanced mathematics but nothing in-between. This made it extremely difficult to learn the subject. I ended up learning four dimension tensor analysis, which at that time seemed to be important in the treatment of the relativity theory. But finally I had to admit to myself that this was a very poor choice. Mathematics, and so geometry, makes a few assumptions and builds an empire based on these assumptions; it is a sort of closed circuit performance. It does not teach anything about what and how to observe.

From mathematics I went for a short time into astronomy, in which I wanted to stay but unfortunately the nights in the cool observatories produced a trememdous physical strain on me. Later on I went into chemistry. Unfortunately, of all the chemistry professors at the University, only one was really original. He was a colloid chemist who was disliked by everybody and who hated to teach. He gave only one lecture every week on colloid chemistry. But looking back at the things that I learned at the University of Berne, I have to say that he did teach me more than any other professor. The reason for this was that he was teaching his own experiences. For his lectures he had one book which he used as a framework, but everything else was his own, and these personal experiences stuck much better than the logically built up performances in the textbooks. Probably one of his most valuable pieces of advice was given to me when I asked him for help on a problem I could not solve: he listened for a while and then told me simply that the library was on the second floor and walked away. I was shocked that first day, but having learned in the military that if you want to complain about somebody you should do so after a night's sleep, I slept and the next morning realized that he had given me very valuable advice. Since I did not know the answers and he also did not know the answers, the solution of the problem could be in the library.

At the University of Berne, the student had complete freedom to select lectures. There was not even a minimum number of lectures he had to attend. I had, therefore, a chance to compare the different professors. Besides the colloid chemist, an anatomist was the most interesting. He was able to draw with both hands simultaneously. His drawings of the nervous system and circulatory system were almost as beautiful as the world famous drawings of Leonardo da Vinci.

The more I stayed at the University, the clearer it became that the subject a person chooses practically decides his future. I did not have a chance to become the assistant of a Nobel Prize winner who could show me the road on which he walked so it would have been easy to continue. My most important decision became how to select something of good quality. I asked practically everybody questions on that subject and I found that the art dealers are probably the best advisers in this field.

I asked an art dealer how can you learn which is an original art object and which is a fake. He smiled and told me there is only one solution—to constantly compare. You should never buy the things you like but buy one type, and then buy many different pieces of the same type. Then you will be able to decide on the first look which is genuine and which is fake without really being able to give a reason for the decision. I had real success with this method when comparing bronze statues. I bought several bronze statues from the Byzantine period. The bronzes in Anatolia have a very well defined patina, but in an antique shop it was never possible to tell if that patina is the same that fits into the Byzantine period. Having borrowed the piece and putting it together with all the other Byzantine pieces, there was no difficulty at all in deciding if that patina was a Byzantine type patina or not. If it had the same patina it was sure to be a Byzantine; if it did not, it still could be a genuine Byzantine piece but it may have been cleaned or somthing else could have happened. I learned to leave out such pieces even when they were extremely attractive.

To me this method of comparing seems to almost guarantee success over a longer period of time. But I paid a very high price in working hours because comparing involves studying the ideas of several people, not just one; a great number of people whose work I studied and learned to know were simply dropped later, along with all of the work I had done in their interest, simply because the comparison revealed their work to be of lesser importance. But I think the process is worthwhile since, as any archeological excavation shows, it is the quality which determines if something remains or is lost.

As a student I was very unjust toward my professors. At the end of every semester I made a sort of inventory of what I learned and what of the learned material could be useful in later years. Such an inventory showed an unbelieveable lack of efficiency. There were lectures at which I spent three or four hours per week without taking anything useful home. One reason for this was that they were very hard to memorize. The more I studied what is memorized and what is forgotten, I came to the conclusion that the Arab way of teaching by telling anecdotes, used around 1200 to 1400 A.D., was a very good method. It cannot be used in chemistry or mathematics but certainly it can be used much more than is done today. Today we mistrust anecdotes because somehow they do not represent a statistical mean value, but in general they do represent certain principles. I still remember very well the fairy tales my mother told me, scientific diaries such as of Faraday's, and some of the books on the beginning of electrophysiology. The anecdotes seemed to be successful because they rounded up in small, meaningful units what the memory can use and keep.

Listening to illuminated films, let us say on the method of doing certain surgery, never taught me anything useful because I could not remember the details. If I watched the actual surgery I went from landmark to landmark with the surgeon and could remember the landmarks. In most movies on surgery the landmarks are never even mentioned so they were, in spite of the huge amount of work invested in them, of very little practical use.

After the revolution in 1918, my family lost practically everything. I could have stayed in Switzerland and continued my studies, since the Swiss were very nice and they even offered me a job to sustain myself, but I had the feeling that I should somehow help to reconstruct Hungary. That is the optimism of a young man of 20 years. I misjudged tremendously the speed with which a country is able to rebuild and I misjudged also the new situation in Europe, which was more and more approaching financial chaos. There were no experts on economy in Hungary, only excellent people in science.

I received my PhD from the University of Hungary; my thesis dealt with a method to determine the diffusion coefficient of fluids in a very short time (sometimes less than three minutes). From the diffusion coefficient the molecular weight could be determined. It was a method I should not have given up but should have developed much further.

My general feeling at the University was that I wasted my time, especially the years which were the most valuable for a young man, namely when memory is still good and judgment becomes more and more objective. This feeling was further increased when it was impossible in Hungary for a PhD in physics to get a job. I visited factories and laboratories one after another and I was always told the same thing—what do you want us to do with a physicist. This was probably the most difficult time of my life and it was my mother who kept me going.

After a certain time I decided to look around systematically and find out which was the best equipped laboratory in Budapest. I found that it was the laboratory of the government controlling the research in long distance telephones, telegraphy, and radio stations. Hungary was in the middle of Europe and therefore communication was a very important feature. The government was forced by peace treaties to spend a certain amount of money to keep the transmission lines in good shape. To do so, they constructed a laboratory and gave the laboratory a certain amount of money to buy the necessary equipment. It was this financial support which started my research. There was a fixed income to the laboratory with no questions asked as to how it was spent. I still think that this is the basis of every big discovery.

The laboratory gave me a salary that was the lowest of all of the 80 people in the laboratory group; it was less than the salary of a carpenter in those days. But I tremendously enjoyed the possibility of learning new things. Every day was a new experience. On one day the telephone line between Prague and Belgrade would be down, on another day the radio station would have some problems. So I had the chance to study large fields of very different background. Sometimes chemistry became important because the cables, with lead mantle, corroded. Or there were stray currents in the ground and they produced trouble. This was the field where I learned to pick up and make conclusions from stray ground current about a sort of large scale encephalography. In some cases I was very successful; for instance, at that time it was necessary to check the condition of international transmission lines. To do so from Budapest a loop was made to London and from London back to Budapest, and the input of the voltage transmitted to London and back was measured in the loop arriving at Budapest. From this, conclusions were made about the state of the transmission lines. In general this measurement took about 15 or 20 minutes. Since there was a great number of telephone lines of this type, there was much excitement every morning in the control room while the lines were being checked. I developed a new method by which I could check the telephone line in a loop in one second. My new method consisted of not using sinusoidal tones, in general use at that time, but by using the transients. By looking up the transients it was immediately possible to see not only the amplitude distortions in the telephone line but also their phase distortions, and the phase distortions were much more sensitive and gave a much better control of the stability of the telephone line. With such small tricks I was able to escape much of the routine work, and I later applied them in the field of hearing.

## How I Became Interested in Hearing

Of all the developments after the war, communication became one of the most progressive. Hungary was constantly forced to build cables of international quality. They tried to standardize them in endless international meetings, but they were just as unsuccessful as the peace treaties.

In trying to fulfill the often very strict requirements, the government always had to ask for several bids. I was very much surprised to learn in reviewing some of these bids that those submitted by different companies for cables to connect the same two cities differed by less than 1%. At first everyone thought there was a secret agreement among the companies since most of them were controlled by financial groups outside Hungary. However, after having reviewed all their calculations, beginning with the price of copper, paper, and lead, from which the cable is made, I was sure that the mathematics of cable construction was so well developed that it was amazingly precise.

A more difficult point resulted from the fact that a communication line consists of three parts: the telephone apparatus, the cables, and the central switchboard. The cost of the switchboard did not play a very important role in the calculations of cost, but the price of the telephone sets, because of the large number of them in a city, was comparable in importance to the price of the cables. Therefore, the question was, if we wanted to improve the quality of a telephone transmission, where should we invest the money—in telephone sets or in cable? This was purely a question of economics, but I had the feeling that only the ear could supply the answer. It was a bioeconomical question.

It was possible to calculate the cost of improving the cable compared to that of the telephone set. Unknown, however, was which improvement the ear would most appreciate. My first experiment was to show that the ordinary telephone membrane vibrates in a much more distorted way than does the eardrum; to have a perfect transmission system, the telephone membrane should vibrate in such a way that the quality and the damping is comparable to that of the eardrum. These observations were again made with transients and they gave a clear answer as to where to invest further improvements—international cables or the local telephone system. After settling this question, I received all the financial support I needed to investigate the mechanical properties of the ear and to match the earphone to the membrane of the ear in such a way that sound transmission would be optimal.

My first conflict was with the institute of anatomy where I wanted ears so that I could measure the mechanical properties of the middle ear. In general it was said that the physicist, even if he does not have a job as a physicist, should not get involved in anatomy. Especially as i .as employed by an engineering laboratory, they did not want me present at autopsies. Unfortunately I had no alternative and so used the simple fact that the anatomical institute had two doors: one front door with a beautiful stairway used by professors and a back door where I was able to walk in and out with a few temporal bones. Naturally, there were difficulties because removing parts of human bodies (I had been taking them outside the anatomical institute) was improper conduct. The institute made it clear to me several times that if the police became involved I would have difficulty proving I used the bones only for scientific purposes. But in time everything quieted down and I was able to extend my research further to live anesthetized animals. I think this was real biophysics.

It is an extremely peculiar situation that a completely exposed nerve trunk (the chorda tympani) runs across the middle ear. That seemed to be one of the best places to measure the velocity of electrical transmission in the nerve fibers. The professor of physiology at the University of Budapest, Dr. Beznak, heard of my interest in the chorda tympani and immediately brought an anesthetized cat to my lab so we could do the measurements. Measurements at that time were quite difficult because we recorded with a Siemens loop oscillograph. Any time there was an overload on the loop it simply burned out this very expensive equipment; but we found that by putting a glow lamp parallel to the loop with a transformer, we could do peak clipping. I do not know who discovered peak clipping but we used it extensively before it was described in the literature. It made the oscilloscope and the Edelman galvanometer foolproof. Today, I think the biggest discovery is the oscilloscope because it has the advantage that it never burns out. You can use any voltage without damage to electronic beams. It has one disadvantage in that anyone, even if he knows nothing about electronics, can suddenly become an expert. It was the beginning of the age of bioelectronics.

Experiments with the first cat were a shock to the professor of physiology and to me. The professor said the chorda tympani serves mainly to stimulate the salivary glands with electric discharges. Therefore he put a tube in the salivary gland duct, and under a microscope it was possible to see that every time a small condenser discharge was transmitted through the chorda tympani the fluid in the capillary tube moved along one or two millimeters. It was a beautiful, clear experiment, very impressive to me because it showed that the secretion in a gland is just as precise as the reading in a voltmeter.

Unfortunately, my idea was that the chorda tympani picks up the stimulation of the taste nerves, and the transmission of the electric line is in the opposite direction. We could not agree and finally we gave up the experiment. Seemingly it turned out that the chorda tympani does both things and in different cats the distribution is very different. The chorda tympani is thus not the best object of research.

I was very lucky that I had this failure because it focused, for all my life, my interest on the importance of the material used for experiments. There are animals on which certain experiments cannot be done. That became clear in these conditions and therefore the selection of the right animal, just as it happened later with the squid or the limulus eye, is just as important as is the development of new methods in research.

## The Elasticity of the Membranes in the Cochlea

I had the impression that the rapid development of electroacoustical and telephone engineering methods would make it possible to retest the different fields of hearing and biophysics, and I decided, therefore, to direct my attention to the theory of hearing. At that time, around 1930, there were about five different theories of hearing, just as we have today. Also at that time one of the main questions concerned the form of the vibration pattern of the basilar membrane for a pure tone. Since this is a purely physical question, I felt that this could be solved with the modern method.

Helmholz had looked at the basilar membrane 150 years earlier, as had Corti. But they prepared the basilar membrane by chipping off the bones. Since the cochlea is embedded in the hardest bone of the human body, the basilar membrane was generally displaced during preparation and this prevented making precise measurements. In Corti's preparations, the whole cochlea dried out almost completely by the end of the dissection and this resulted in distortion of its structures. With Helmholz it was probably the same way. To avoid this drying, it is best to do the entire anatomical dissection under water or physiological solution. Therefore I used a square bath and let the fluid flow in one side and out the other. The fluid stream was kept constant in the whole cross section and by using a drill instead of scissors for dissecting it was possible to slowly peel off thin layers of the bone. Any time the drill was used, a formation of bone dust clouded the water, but the streaming water washed it away in a few seconds and the whole field of view was again clear and ready for new dissections. This method of underwater dissection was very convenient. If there was a membrane to be lifted, it was picked up with forceps and, by using an underwater (plankton) microscope with a magnification of 180 or even a little greater, the membrane could be pulled off carefully. By opening the forceps the membrane piece which was pulled off flowed away with the water. It was a pleasure to do dissection that way. It had the advantage too that there was no danger in dissecting an infected ear. With the drill it was very easy to expose one full turn on the tip of the cochlea allowing good observations of the basilar membrane.

The next question was whether we could make an opening in the cochlea without disturbing the vibrations of the basilar membrane. I spent too much time in developing an underwater glue which could fasten a window over the opening that I made in the cochlea. Later it turned out that the best way to fix a window on the cochlea opening is to use a highly viscous fluid, perhaps physiological solution with gelatin. Being highly viscous it is still moveable for DC displacement but not so for frequencies above 30 cycles per second, when it becomes almost completely rigid. Under stroboscopic illumination this could easily be checked.

In almost no time it was possible to show that there are traveling waves on the basilar membrane going from the stapes to the softer parts of the membrane. It is quite interesting that traveling waves were not readily accepted mainly because of the mathematics of the whole problem. Even today, most of the mathematical treatments of this problem have so many omissions and simplifications that they do not describe the movement of the basilar membrane properly. Even for me the traveling wave looked a little strange at the beginning, but as time went on it was obvious that whenever a system changes its mechanical properties continuously there is always a traveling wave. It is the only wave form by which energy is transmitted in systems with a lateral extension. Therefore, the traveling wave is the natural transmission form for the cochlea. After a while the theory and the whole measuring process were simplified so that by the simple means of testing the deformation of the basilar membrane under the DC pressure of a needle tip, it was possible to determine that the basilar membrane in the human cochlea should have vibrations corresponding to a traveling wave and not to resonance or other type of vibrations.

After having done measurements on the temporal bone of human cochleas, the question was whether these measurements were reliable. To answer this question it was necessary to make the vibration amplitude of the basilar membrane so large that we could see it with a magnification of 200 under a stereoscopic microscope with stroboscopic illumination. Once this was accomplished, the additional question was raised as to whether these vibrations would be the same as those in the basilar membrane if the amplitude was about 100,000 times smaller. This is the question of nonlinearity and it is quite clear that if we listen to a very weak tone at 1000 cycles, we can increase it almost 100,000 times and still the tone is unchanged. In all my measurements I never went to a higher amplitude of vibration than the vibrations of a pure tone. This can easily be checked if we keep the middle ear intact because the moment the amplitude goes higher we will have a tickling in our ear and a change in the vibration pattern in the middle ear. In general I used a sound producer attached to a $T$ tube. On one side was the preparation and on the other side was my own ear. Since in my own ear I heard a pure tone for that amplitude, there was no good physical reason to assume that anything would be different in the preparation.

Another question was, is the elasticity of a living basilar membrane different from that of a basilar membrane without a blood supply? As far as I could see there was no real difference. I developed a very peculiar and very sensitive method of stroboscopic illumination which again did not measure the amplitude but rather the phase of the vibration. It could be shown that a vibration pattern measured in a live lightly anesthetized guinea pig did not change when the animal was killed by an overdose of pentobarbital or by inhalation of nitrogen. It was stated many times in the literature that the tissues change their physical properties in ten to twenty minutes after death, but I never could prove that. There is some change, for instance in the eardrum, produced by the stopping of the blood supply, but since the eardrum consists of three thin layers, when blood flow stops the humidity in the ear channel is immediately decreased and the eardrum starts to dry out.

If a patient is taken to an operating room, he is usually rolled into the room receiving a continuous intravenous perfusion of physiological solution. In animal surgery, this is seemingly seldom done and therefore in all animal experiments dehydration is a problem. The smaller the animal, the faster it dehydrates because the surface relative to the weight is increased. It is incredible how many severely dehydrated cats I have seen, with almost brittle tongues, on which records from the cortex and the inner ear were made.

In time, I came to the conclusion that the dehydrated cats and the application of Fourier analysis to hearing problems became more and more a handicap for research in hearing. Therefore, my interest went more into the psychological questions. I am very thankful to one otologist who, in cases in which the labyrinth had to be taken out because of disturbance in the vestibular organ, gave me a few minutes before the operation to test the mobility and the difference between DC displacement and vibration transmission in the middle ear on patients who were under anesthesia but whose blood supply, and therefore humidity, were normal.

At this point I had a well developed and productive laboratory. Unfortunately all my work was interrupted by World War II.

## World War II and After

At the start of World War II our impression in Hungary was that a scientific laboratory would never be bombed by American airplanes. But it was not so: on the second day we found out that the American airplanes really did not hit a specific target at all. Instead, they used the tactic of carpet bombing, in which the leading airplane makes a circle and the following airplanes throw all their bombs inside that circle. The bombing was extremely inefficient; it killed people who had very little to do with the war and, in many cases, were definitely opposed to it.

A few days later a building near my lab and most of my equipment and writings were completely destroyed. It is interesting to note that the largest destruction was not done by the bomb itself but by the air suction produced by the explosion wave.

It pulled out the windows and everything in the cabinets and built it up into a mess which could not be separated.

The Russian attack came on the ground. They fought man against man. Toward the end, it seemed to be one German against eight Russians. Everything was depressing because there was no visible reason or logic in the whole behavior. The Russian Army worked like a machine; every morning at 7 o'clock they started with the Haubitzen to shoot and destroy one section after another very systematically. At 5 o'clock they stopped, had their supper, and the next morning they moved ahead again and went sometimes a few miles, sometimes only a few hundred feet. At the end the whole section under attack was destroyed, including the section where I lived, near the Danube. The highest wall left was about one meter high. I had many friends living in that section so I visited them before I decided to leave. I shouted their names under the blue sky but nobody came out so I went from one opening to another as I knew they had to come out for water. In some of these openings you could see the tragic history of Budapest. On the upper level was the modern type of buildings built in the nineteenth century, something of a modern empire style. One layer deeper you could see a clear empire style and going deeper in the layers there was the Baroque style in the staircases and cuttings of the stones on which the buildings and the cellar was based. If you went even deeper, there was a definite Gothic cutting of the stones and later a Romanesque style. It showed that Budapest had its history beginning from Rome up to modern times and it was destroyed several times during the last 2000 years. But every time it was built up again on the same place.

I have been asked several times why Hungarians are relatively successful compared with other people, especially in science. I have the impression that this sticking to one place and to one aim is the main reason why in the long run Hungary still produces important contributions to the culture of this world.

Since it was obvious that I would not be able to continue my scientific work, I decided to leave Hungary. Professor G. Holmgreen from Stockholm invited me to Sweden and from Sweden I went to Harvard where Professor S. S. Stevens took me into his laboratory.

Unfortunately, while at Harvard a great tragedy for my research occurred when the tower of Memorial Hall burned down. My entire working place in the basement of Memorial Hall was flooded and I lost the most cherished writings and old books, that I collected after I left Hungary.

I have found, on numerous occasions in my life, that it is impossible to rewrite the same idea the second time with the same freshness and logic as it was done the first time. After the fire in Memorial Hall some of my writings lost their precision because of the destruction of most of my data. To write a paper takes me, in general, one or two years. It takes almost one year to formulate the question that I would like to answer. It takes a half year to carry out the experiments and a half year to put it in the correct shape. I work on several problems simultaneously and the older I got the more problems I had to work on; this takes away the freshness of the logical buildup. Lately, the ordering of equipment, working on the financial aspects, getting an award from the funding agency, and receiving and setting up equipment in the laboratory can take two or three years, even in the case of a simple experiment. This has completely changed my way of building up an experiment and my method of working, which was not to collect data but to collect different methods, and not to do every observation many times but to do the same observation with different equipment and different methods. This approach now has become almost impossible to carry out. In earlier times I had no difficulty in measuring, for instance, the elasticity of the basilar membrane with three or four different methods. In general I published one method which I figured out was the most simple and the most reliable one. It always amused me when later somebody picked from all the possible methods exactly that method I had found most unsatisfactory and introduced it as a totally new method.

## Life in the United States of America

I really had very little information about the situation in the United States of America when I lived in Europe and a large part of the information was distorted. For instance, American films of good quality were so expensive that they did not reach Hungarian theaters. Those we saw were cowboy films and gave a relatively distorted picture compared with the German films which were excellent and of philosophical value. When I arrived in Sweden I was sure I would get good information about the US and I found the booklet given by the United States Army to their soldiers when they went to France. It contained instructions on how to behave when contacting French people and on the difference between a Frenchman and an American. The interesting thing was that at the end of this booklet was a chapter on how to survive in the United States. My first clear information came from that booklet. Unfortunately this information was also useless to me, being rules for survival of an American, not for a European who just arrived in the United States.

I could read English very well at that time, especially the technical language, but I could not speak the language at all and there were many incidents which were quite amusing, at least in looking back. The entry for a Hungarian into the United States was at that time quite difficult. Having arrived at La Guardia Airport after a long, long flight on a two-engine airplane with a long stopover at Laborador, I approached the officer of the Health Department. He looked at my passport and then he asked me if I was healthy and I told him no. He asked me again if I was healthy and again I told him no. Then he just put his hand on my shoulder, pushed me across the line, and I was in the United States. I was very much disturbed that already in the first seconds in the USA, I had probably made a very big mistake. My English-German dictionary soon made clear that I had mistaken the word healthy for wealthy. Since I had only $100 in my pocket and was thinking about the Rockefeller fortune, I was not able to tell him yes to his misunderstood question.

This small incident right at the beginning gave me an inferiority complex for which even today I am not really able to compensate. At Harvard University my colleagues were very friendly and helped me with my English. I learned from them good classical English. I still cannot write a good paper but I can judge if a paper is good or not. The secretary at the laboratory told me several times that I should read Churchill's book on the English speaking people[1] because it is written in beautiful English. I bought the book and I agree the English is just magnificent, but I did not like it for two reasons. One was the fact that it did not correspond exactly to the situations I had first-hand knowledge of and the other was that Churchill is a very poor painter. My general theory is that if a person is really bright and is good in his own field, he is bright in his amateur field also. It was a peculiar experience that a year later I was told to forget Churchill. I had an inkling that Churchill published at that time his controversial volume on the American revolution.

The American attitude toward science was very different from that to which I was accustomed in Europe. In Europe there was a certain pessimism about the degree of progress scientists can achieve, and there was an important difference in the role which financial support plays in new discoveries. In Europe you were born to be either an artist, a scientist, or a banker. You had to inherit the specific qualities which made you important in that field. In America everybody could learn to draw, everbody could make a million or lose it, and everybody could make excellent new discoveries. It was quite difficult to switch from one style to another style, especially after a certain age. My opinion was that both of these assumptions were extreme. The consequence of my optimism was incredible. Biophysics, which had been more biomechanics, became suddenly molecular physics, an absolutely new field with a tremendous potential for new ideas. Some old telephone experiments were developed into information theory. It was quite clear that in this field the optimism really paid off. But sometimes optimism went too far: a fund raiser told me that if he succeeded in raising $9 million, he would solve the cancer problem—that was about twenty years ago.

In the beginning the most interesting events of my life in the United States were trips to meetings. I met people whom I had known only from books and papers, and I saw the country and the large museums which contained collections I had never seen before. I soon enlarged my field of view and became very interested in the West Coast because it was so different from Boston. Eventually I decided to live in Hawaii and build a laboratory there. The decision was a good one and in the last six years we have made a few measurements which I think are new. Hawaii is basically just as different from the mainland as Europe is from the United States. The United States is very impressive for anyone who comes from Europe because it is so large and varied. In the United States you can have almost anything that you want, it is only a question of money. It was not so in Europe. In Hawaii you cannot have anything you want, but you can have things that you never expected before. Living in paradise, as it turns out, is not a very simple thing. It is so beautiful that there is really too much beauty and too much color. It is well known that the nervous system is more sensitive to variations than to continuous stimuli because of the role of adaptation. The same holds true for the life circumstances.

The University of Hawaii is a new university and therefore tradition does not play any role. This can produce many differences. For instance when I first came to

[1]Churchill, Winston Leonard Spencer. *A History of the English-Speaking Peoples,* Vol. 3: *The Age of Revolution.* New York: Dodd, Mead.

Hawaii I was very much surprised by the fact that between lectures the students walked on the grass of the campus and not on the beautifully planned roads. On the Harvard campus all the students walked on the roads, never on the grass. It took me a long time to explain this phenomenon. Obviously, the architect who designed the roads of the Hawaii campus did not know the different doors to the lecture halls, so the students had to make shortcuts. When I went back to Harvard I was told that the roads were there 200 years ago. Originally all the different houses on the campus were homes of professors and every professor owned a cow. These roads were selected by the cows when they went to and from the pasture. The cows had very good sense in making shortcuts, much better than the modern architects; and I have a very high respect for Harvard in that if something is good, they keep it, completely independent of who made it first.

Lately it seems that the different places in the United States are becoming more and more similar to each other, which makes life less and less interesting, and I have come to the conclusion that the most fascinating things today can be found mainly in museums. That is the one thing I enjoyed so much on the East Coast. The museums taught me in many ways how to look at the great diversity that human genius has produced during the past milleniums.

# TRANSPORT PATHWAYS IN BIOLOGICAL MEMBRANES

*Hans H. Ussing*

Institute of Biological Chemistry A, University of Copenhagen, Copenhagen, Denmark

*David Erlij*

Departmento de Biologia Cellular, Centro de Investigacion del IPN, Apartado Postal 14–740, Mexico 14, D. F.

*Ulrik Lassen*

Zoophysiological Laboratory B, August Krogh Institute, University of Copenhagen, Copenhagen, Denmark

## INTRODUCTION

This review deals with transport through biological membranes. The term "membrane" is used in a purely pragmatic sense: a sheet of unstirred material separating two solutions that can be considered well stirred. What unifies the concept of membrane is its physical function as a barrier as well as the methods by which such structures can be studied. The definition therefore covers, for instance, capillary walls and kidney tubule walls as well as plasma membranes. In recent years there has been a tendency to replace the above "classical" definition of a membrane by one based on the appearance of the structure in an electron microscopic preparation. Thus a biological membrane would be something that appears as a dark double line, for instance, a plasma membrane.

Such a restriction of the definition is not advisable, however. Even membranes with apparently simple appearance may show evidence of functional sandwich structure. Thus the permeability properties of nerve membranes can be greatly changed by, say, adsorbed inorganic ions (25). Such adsorption, although not changing the total membrane potential, may modify the potential profile across the membrane, drastically changing the potential shift necessary to trigger electric activity. The permeability may also be modified by the presence of mucopolysaccharides and proteins, if for no other reason than because such substances produce unstirred layers. Functionally, unstirred layers, whether or not supported by such

17

colloids, may be considered as integral parts of the membrane. Problems concerning the correction for thin layer effects have been treated recently by several authors (see 73, 157).

This review deals with new developments in transport pathways, both through "simple" cell membranes and through epithelia. Epithelia may be treated as "black box membranes," but much of the recent work has been centered around resolving the transport properties on the basis of events in an outward and inward facing membrane of the epithelial cell. But even that approach is an oversimplification.

The organization of epithelial cells in sheets with more or less occluded spaces between them provides the entire array with certain properties that are absent on the single cell level, and there are additional complications arising from coupling between neighboring cells (see 109).

Studies of epithelial pathways owe much of their recent success to the combination of biophysical and histological approaches. As far as plasma membranes are concerned, the word "pathway" is mainly operational, being based on kinetic data. Some workers prefer to ascribe the permeability properties to an assumed, more or less homogenous "membrane phase" (151). The prevailing trend, for which much experimental evidence can be mustered, is, however, toward explaining a large fraction of transport in terms of specific sites, channels, or carriers. For pathways in mitochondrial membranes, for example, see (95, 122).

## FLUX RATIO ANALYSIS AS A TOOL FOR CHARACTERIZING PATHWAYS

Among the methods being used to characterize specific pathways, the kinetics of tracer permeation has played a central role. Among tracer methods the flux ratio analysis has been used extensively for deciding whether a certain species penetrates by "simple" diffusion, exchange diffusion, single file diffusion, or active transport. Likewise it has been used to characterize solvent drag (3).

The theoretical aspects of the flux ratio approach have been treated in several recent papers. Thus it has been shown that the flux ratio for an independently diffusing species is independent of the membrane structure, even if the latter varies in three demensions (141).

Another extension of the theory (166) is concerned with non–steady-state conditions. If two tracers for the same substance are added to either side of the membrane, the ratio between the amounts of the two tracers crossing the membrane is the same as the steady-state flux ratio. The conditions are such that the resistance and potential profiles across the membrane remain constant during the period considered. If the flux ratio changes with time it indicates the existence of more than one transport path.

It has been argued (35) that one cannot use deviations from ideal flux ratios to characterize, say, carrier mediated exchange diffusion because the deviations may arise from interactions between fluxes. However, the word "interaction" is only another word for deviation from expected behavior. The concept behind the term "membrane carrier" is one of the possible molecular interpretations of such deviations.

The correct determination of fluxes and flux ratios is critically dependent on well defined boundary conditions. Notably the condition of ideal stirring on either side of the membrane may become a difficult technical problem. Difficulties are often encountered in dealing with rapidly diffusing substances like gases (157) and water (73). For instance, it has been realized recently that antidiuretic hormone (ADH) increases the water permeability of the luminal side of the toad bladder much more than hitherto assumed (73). Thus, during the hormone action the unstirred layers become a sizable fraction of the total resistance to diffusion of water. Total resistance becomes a complex function of inward and outward facing cell membranes, the cytoplasm, the basement membrane, the connective tissue of the chorium, and the unstirred water films.

Which of these resistances is the more important may vary from one experimental condition to the other. Recently it has been demonstrated (128) by a fast labeling technique that, at some distance from the luminal surface there is a relative barrier to water diffusion which becomes rate limiting when the diffusion resistance of the outer barrier has been reduced by antidiuretic hormone. This finding is in keeping with the observation that the degree of swelling of the frog skin epithelium becomes a function of the molality of the outside solution during the action of ADH, whereas normally it is determined exclusively by the osmolality of the inside bathing solution (see 163).

Deviation from the ideality of the flux ratio for water and certain hydrophilic test substances has been used in the past to indicate passage through pores, for instance in toad skin and urinary bladder. Some of the early studies undoubtedly gave flux ratios that were too high because the net osmotic flow is less sensitive to unstirred layers than is the isotope diffusion.

At least in toad skin and frog skin this error is practically nonexistent for larger molecules like amides, glycerol, and sucrose, so that for these tissues the theory can be applied. It should be kept in mind, however, that these predictions are ambiguous by the very nature of the approach. When a deviation from ideality is observed, the reason may be that the test substance is subject to solvent drag in a pore somewhere along the path, but the region of rapid hydraulic flow need not be a pore in a cell membrane. The large deviations from ideality, seen for instance in toad skin in connection with osmotic flow (31), do require a high linear flow rate that cannot be ascribed to a stagnant layer of unstirred solution. Although there is no clear-cut evidence against the possibility of the site of the drag effect being pores in the outward facing membrane of the epithelium, it is perhaps more likely that the drag effect is exerted by solution flowing through the interspaces of the epithelium. This view is supported by the finding of very high flux ratios (as high as 18/1) for sucrose in toad skin when the outside medium is 1/10 Ringer's solution and the inside medium ordinary Ringer's solution. It is more likely that sucrose passes through leaky zonulae occludentes and is swept along by the osmotic water stream than that the sucrose should pass through the cell membranes (167).

## COUPLING OF ACTIVE Na AND K TRANSPORT ACROSS THE CELL MEMBRANE

Active transport of alkali metal ions is a well-established fact that does not need further documentation at this point (163). Before considering the relatively compli-cated situation of the location of the active transport mechanism in epithelial and other cells with transcellular transport, it may be advantageous to summarize some data on transport in single cells with the special aim of elucidating the possible coupling between active transport of Na out of the cell and K into the cell.

The nearly general occurrence of the combination of high intracellular K, low intracellular Na, and a negative electrical potential inside the cell indicates that at least Na ions are far from electrochemical equilibrium. Consequently, it was proposed that active transport of only Na might account for the uneven distribution of K that, due to electrostatic forces, was then drawn into the cell (159). This suggestion represents in fact an extreme, where there is no direct coupling between the extrusion of Na and the uptake of K. In such a case, active transport of Na would supply a current, rendering the cell interior negative due to a constant removal of positive charge. In response to the current, the K ions would redistribute themselves (provided a reasonably large permeability) until attainment of equilibrium (77). Only if transport of K ions were also active (e.g. by coupling to the sodium pump) could a membrane potential more negative than the Nernst potential for K be encountered. Kernan (92) found that the membrane potential of frog muscles, loaded with Na after prolonged cooling, transiently had membrane potentials which were more negative than the corresponding $E_K$ values. Similar findings have occa-sionally been reported, but, as discussed below, contributions of an eventual electro-genic sodium pump are small when the cells are in a steady state where the analyses of intracellular ion concentrations are sufficiently reliable. For this reason the bulk of evidence for an electrogenic Na pump comes from more indirect types of experi-ments.

Early experiments by Ritchie & Straub (138) showed that marked hyperpolariza-tion of mammalian nonmyelinated nerve fibers follows prolonged tetanus, a fact later confirmed in extensive studies by Rang & Ritchie (133). This type of experi-ment has been performed on a number of excitable tissues (see 152) and has yielded a general pattern: inhibition of metabolism (e.g. by DNP) or inhibition of active Na transport by cardiac glycosides will abolish the post-tetanic hyperpolarization. These results are interpreted as a stimulation of an electrogenic pump by the Na that entered the cell during tetanus. If such a pump stimulation gives rise to a hyperpo-larization, the pump must cause a flow of positive current out of the cell, i.e. it is electrogenic. As demonstrated by Thomas (152) in his recent review, from studies of a variety of excitable tissues there is evidence of electrogenic ion transport.

From the above evidence, active transport of Na could be a strict Na pump without coupling to K transport. However, there is a large number of observations suggesting that K ions are pumped into the cell concomitantly with the extrusion of Na. One of the clearest examples is the active transport of Na and K in red cells. In these cells, the membrane potential is approximately –15 mV [as determined on giant erythrocytes from *Amphiuma* (78)]. This value should be compared to an $E_K$ of typically –100 mV and $E_{Na}$ of +50 mV. Thus both K and Na are far from equilibrium, meaning that K also must be actively transported. By blocking the active transport with ouabain, Post & Jolly (131) proved in an early publication that not only are the active movements of Na and K coupled, but apparently the coupling is such that each pump cycle transports 3 Na out of the cell and 2 K into the cell. Despite the coupling, the activity of the pump results in a positive outward-going current as in the aforementioned examples. As in other cells, this "pump current" is shunted in the steady state by passive leakage of ions. Contrary to the case in nerve and muscle, the pump in red cells, despite being electrogenic, does not contribute measurably to the membrane potential. For elucidation of the characteristics of the electrogenic pump the study by Kerkut & Thomas (93) and later by Thomas (see 152) on mollusc neurones plays a major role. The application of Na through intracellular electrodes elicited a marked hyperpolarization that was sensitive to extracellular ouabain or removal of K on the outside of the cell. During injection of Na there was a linearly rising, outward-going positive current under voltage clamp conditions. Using an elegant intracellular Na-sensitive electrode Thomas (153) showed that the rise in the clamp current was associated with an increase in intracellular Na activity, and the subsequent exponential decrease in current reflected a decreasing Na activity. Once more the electrogenic nature of the pump was firmly established. But as noted also in numerous other studies, the active transport of Na not only needs Na on the inside of the membrane but K (or $NH_4^+$) on the outside of the cell membrane is necessary to activate the pump (see 138). This fact, together with studies on purified ATPase from cell membranes (145), provides strong evidence that the outward pumping of Na is accompanied by inward pumping of K.

The question now arises as to what extent the coupling has a fixed ratio between the active transports of Na and K. If the ratio is not fixed, within what range can it vary? And especially, does the active transport of K ever exceed that of Na? Mullins & Brinley (124) have investigated Na and K fluxes at various internal Na concentrations in perfused squid axons. In accordance with earlier investigators they found that Na efflux varied linearly with $[Na]_i$. But the active influx of K from media with constant K concentration depended in a nonlinear fashion on $[Na]_i$, indicating a variable degree of coupling between the active fluxes of Na and K. At low internal Na concentrations, the ratio Na/K via the pump was close to unity, but at higher (up to 80 m$M$) $[Na]_i$ the ratio was 3/1 or even higher. The problem of the coupling ratio has been investigated recently by Kostyuk et al (100) using snail neurones. From continuous current/voltage curves before and after Na injection it was concluded that the electrogenecity of the pump disappeared at potentials more negative than the normal resting potential, equivalent to a Na/K ratio of unity. At less negative clamp potentials the ratio of the integrated pump current to the injected Na ions, which was ∿0.3 in the experiments of Thomas, varied from 0.02 to 0.7. If it is assumed that 0.3 of the injected charge appears as charge transfer via the pump, these data are consistent with the abovementioned ratio of 3 Na to 2 K transported through the pump system. This ratio does not seem fixed. It is suggested by Kostyuk et al (100) that the ratio varies with the thermodynamic work involved in transporting the K ions. Reduction of the electrochemical potential difference for K may lead to equal amounts of Na and K being pumped (i.e. lack of electrogenic effect of the pump).

The evidence mentioned so far states that Na loading of cells may lead to hyperpolarization of the cell membrane when the pump is active. In the past, the steady state contribution of the pump to the resting potential has been discussed repeatedly. In low impedance membranes, like squid axon, little or no effect of the pump on the resting potential can be detected (see 152). Carpenter (21) recently reported that the specific membrane resistance of the squid nerve cell bodies is 27 times higher than that of the axon. In the nerve cell body the contribution of the electrogenic pump to the resting potential was found to be about –13 mV. The idea that a high impedance membrane reveals a larger contribution to the resting potential by the electrogenic pump is in accordance with the theoretical considerations by Rang & Ritchie (133) and Christoffersen (26). This can be understood intuitively, as an electrogenic pump hyperpolarization will be shunted by passive (leak) currents by an amount proportional to the membrane resistance. Thomas (152) has calculated the maximal obtainable contribution to the membrane potential by the pump, given that the cell is in total steady state and the the Na/K ratio is 1.5. In this case the maximum contribution by the pump is a hyperpolarization of less than 20 mV, very much in accordance with the data of Christoffersen (26).

Until this point, only the "common" active transport of alkali metal ions has been mentioned. Harvey & Nedergaard (72) have described an active, primarily K-transporting system in the midgut of the silkworm. This system has not yet been characterized in sufficient detail to allow comparison to the electrogenic pump described above.

For further details about electrogenic Na pump in nerve and muscle cells the reader is referred to an excellent recent review by Thomas (152).

## PATHWAYS FOR CHLORIDE TRANSPORT ACROSS THE RED CELL MEMBRANE

This section on a highly specialized cell, the erythrocyte, is included to illustrate that tracer fluxes of a given ion may be very far from giving meaningful information about the ionic conductance across a membrane. But given a discrepancy between the tracer and the net charge movement, valuable information can be obtained about the mechanism of the transport.

Under normal circumstances the distribution of Cl ions indicates that the ions are in thermodynamic equilibrium across the red cell membrane. As expected in a Donnan system, the cell Cl (and H ions) change with pH in a predictable fashion (see 69). Furthermore, Tosteson (156) and later Dalmark & Wieth (34) reported a very fast exchange of labeled Cl across the red cell membrane. Net changes of Cl in the cells seemed to be limited only by the net movement of cations, provided that the Cl did not exchange with other anions. Scarpa et al (140) studied the net movement of Cl ions in red cells where the cation permeability was greatly enhanced by the addition of gramicidin. Under such conditions the net salt loss was now limited by the Cl permeability. The Cl conductance (carrying net charge) was much smaller than expected from the velocity of exchange of labeled Cl.

By increasing the K permeability of the human red cell membrane, Hunter (85) calculated the Cl conductance of the membrane to be $10^4$–$10^5$ times smaller than the apparent "Cl resistance" calculated from the tracer exchange. In this approach the change in membrane potential was estimated from the flux ratio of K after addition of valinomycin, because no direct determinations of the membrane potential were available. At this point it was desirable to obtain direct estimates of the membrane resistance of the red cell membrane. Such measurements are technically difficult due to the electrical short circuit induced as a microelectrode is inserted into the cell (see 103). But despite these limitations, direct measurement with current injection through the microelectrode has given values for the specific membrane resistance of *Amphiuma* red cells of more than 2000 $\Omega$ cm$^2$. This value should be compared to about 4 $\Omega$ cm$^2$ which is the calculated "chloride resistance" of the same type of cells (102) (measured at 0°C and corrected to 17°C). In unpublished experiments, using an oil-gap technique, Rathlev et al (see 102) have found values up to 5 X $10^4$ $\Omega$ cm$^2$ by passing current through an *Amphiuma* red cell with the ends sucked into two pipettes. The comparable tracer Cl resistance was in this case 1–4 $\Omega$ cm$^2$. So both for human red cells and for *Amphiuma* red cells it seems safe to conclude that only $10^{-4}$ to $10^{-5}$ of the Cl passing the membrane does so as a free ion. The remainder of the transport is an anion-anion exchange transport with typical characteristics of a carrier system (see 69). Gunn (68) has proposed that the carrier is titrable by H ions and that the same carrier system may be responsible for the transport of both divalent and monovalent anions. At low pH values (with relatively much H$^+$ bound to the carrier molecule) the carrier is relatively more efficient in transporting the divalent anions. At higher pH values the carrier has an increased affinity towards monovalent anions (like the halides). Such a model will in a satisfactory way predict other properties of the transport system (see 69), but the molecular mechanism is still far from being clarified.

## TRANSPORT ACROSS EPITHELIA

Since it is practically impossible to discuss all the developments of the last few years in the field of epithelial transport, we have chosen to cover only a few topics from the vast amount of available material on epithelial transport. We have put a greater emphasis on two aspects of epithelial transport: (*a*) the three-compartment model for salt transport as illustrated mainly by the frog skin and other related epithelia and (*b*) the role of the intercellular space in some properties of epithelia. Other current problems are discussed only briefly; additional information can be found in several recent collections of articles (30, 65, 74, 94) on transepithelial transport.

### The Three-Compartment Model for Transepithelial Transport

The hypothesis that the transport of solutes across epithelia involves the movement of substances across two different barriers placed in series originated from observations of Na transport in the frog skin (98). The model proposes that Na first moves across a Na-selective barrier into the cytoplasm of the epithelial cells and then is actively transported across the inner barrier into the inside solution. Since it was proposed, this model has been applied to many other epithelia. Still, an important fraction of the experiments designed to establish the properties of the individual components of the salt transport system have been concentrated on the frog skin. The interpretation of several of the results obtained in this tissue are complicated because its epithelium is formed by several cell layers (48, 120). This problem is partially overcome when studying other epithelia having a similar Na-transport system, like the toad urinary bladder or the duct of the rabbit (96) salivary gland, which are formed by a single layer of cells. Other problems related to the structure arise, however, when studying these tissues. The area of epithelial membrane of the urinary bladder included in a chamber will markedly depend on the degree of stretch of the tissue, and we do not yet have a good method of standardizing this area. Furthermore this epithelium is formed by cells of different types which may have markedly different properties. The salivary gland duct, on the other hand, is a tubular organ of relatively small dimensions that has received relatively little attention in spite of its potential usefulness (96). Obviously we do not yet possess the ideal epithelium with which to solve all the problems of Na transport and we must pool the results obtained from different sources to improve our image of the transport process.

## The Outer Barrier

Since the epithelium of the frog skin is formed by several layers of cells, one of the initial problems is to determine the anatomical localization of the outer barrier of the transport compartment. The problem is complicated because, in addition to having several layers of cells in the epithelium, tight junctions sealing the extracellular spaces are found in at least two cell layers: the cornified cell layer and the outermost layer of cells in the stratum granulosum (48, 120). For a time there was some discrepancy as to which of these cell layers formed the outer border of the transport compartment. Recent evidence, however, indicates that the cornified cell layers are "dying" cells whose membranes have lost the capacity to exclude from their interior those substances that do not penetrate normal cell membranes, and that the outer Na selective barrier corresponds to the outside border of the cells in the outermost layer of the stratum granulosum.

The evidence for this conclusion comes from three groups of experiments. The first group showed that ionic lanthanum, which does not go into the cytoplasma of normal cells, readily penetrates the interior of the cells of the stratum corneum (120). In the second group the time course of the potential change following a rapid increase of Na concentration in an ion exchange membrane was compared with that observed at the outside surface of the skin (59). The time course of the potential change was found to be slower in the skins than in the ion exchange membranes. The difference in the time course could be accounted for if it was assumed that an additional diffusion layer in the skins of about $5\mu$ thickness was interposed between the outer Na-selective barrier and the bulk solution. That this layer is probably formed by the cornified cells was suggested by studying skins immediately after a moult, or skins in which the cornified cells had been partially removed by enzymatic treatment. Under these conditions the differences in the time course of the potential response between the skin and the ion exchanger became minimal (59).

In the third group, observations were made with an electron microprobe on freeze-dried sections of frog skin. This method allows the determination of ion concentrations in single cells. Analysis for Na, K, and Cl show that the cornified cells have the same composition as the outside bathing solution while cells in other layers maintain the high K and low Na concentrations typical of animal cells (64).

Recently a method for measuring directly the movement of Na across the outer barrier of the frog skin has been proposed (11, 139). It is based on exposing for a brief period ($<$45 sec) the outside of the skin to a solution labeled with radioactive Na. The total radioactive Na recovered from the skin consists of two parts: that which has penetrated the epithelium and that which adheres to the outer surface of the skin. This second fraction can account for as much as 90% of the total. In the initial experiments the second fraction was corrected for by inulin as a marker of extracellular space (11). However, the inulin method seriously underestimated the amount of Na remaining outside the outer barrier of the transport compartment, making quantitative measurements of Na entry very difficult to interpret. Mannitol has been shown to be a better marker for the extracellular space at the outer border of the skin (13, 42, 46).

The better values obtained with mannitol as a marker have been used to clarify one of the more puzzling findings made in the earlier experiments in which inulin was the marker. These experiments demonstrated that the flux ($J_{12}$) of Na from the outer solution (component 1) into the epithelium (component 2) was almost seven times larger than the Na flux ($J_{13}$) from the outside solution into the inside solution (component 3). The use of mannitol as a marker has shown that the large difference between $J_{12}$ and $J_{13}$ results from the Na remaining outside the outer border of the epithelium, and not accounted for when inulin was used as a tracer (42, 46).

The early finding that the plot of Na uptake ($J_{12}$) versus Na concentration was described by the sum of a linear and a saturable component must also be reconsidered when the mannitol corrections are made (42, 47). Clearly, most of the linear component resulted from uncorrected Na outside the outer barrier (42, 46). The question of whether or not a small linear component remains is difficult to answer. In the first place the detection of the linear component is very dependent on the determinations made with the higher Na concentrations. Because these measurements require larger corrections for Na remaining outside the epithelium, they are less reliable. Secondly, the shape of the relationship between outside Na and trans-epithelial Na transport varies somewhat from experiment to experiment and with the substances used for Na substitution (50).

The rapid uptake method has also been used to determine the effects of several agents on $J_{12}$. As indicated above, the results obtained with high outside Na (115 m$M$) and with either inulin as an extracellular space marker or no marker at all are not reliable; furthermore, even when mannitol is used as a marker and $J_{12}$ is relatively low, determination of $J_{12}$ may become uncertain if the correction for the amount of Na in the extracellular space is too large compared with the amount that penetrated the tissue (42, 46). Provided these considerations are taken into account, it is possible to assess the effects of the agents described below.

One of the most interesting features of the actions of inhibitors on $J_{12}$ is that both amiloride, an agent that probably acts at the outer border of the skin (see below), and ouabain, an inhibitor of the Na + K ATPase that has been postulated to be localized at the inner barrier of the transport compartment, inhibit Na uptake almost completely (12, 46, 123).

The similarity between the effects of amiloride and ouabain can be interpreted in several ways. For example it has been suggested that they act at the same step of transepithelial Na transport, namely the outside barrier of the transport compartment, and that indeed the transport of Na across this barrier is the single active step involved in the transepithelial movement of Na (123). However, it is also possible that the effects of ouabain on $J_{12}$ are mediated by the alterations of intracellular electrolyte composition caused by the glycoside. This conclusion is supported by findings made in skins incubated with high concentrations of ouabain for a long period in Na-free solutions (46). Under these conditions $J_{12}$ is not blocked by ouabain although it is still sensitive to amiloride. Possibly this finding arises from a reduction in ouabain binding during exposure to Na-free solutions. Some observations suggest that this is not the case. Amiloride-sensitive potential and short circuit current transients were observed when Na was added to the outside solution bathing skins equilibrated with ouabain in Na-free solutions or skins whose transport had been previously inhibited by ouabain in Na-containing solutions and then washed for long periods in low Na-solutions containing the glycoside (46).

These experiments suggest that amiloride and ouabain act at different steps in the transport mechanism since the blocking effects of ouabain on $J_{12}$ are probably mediated by modifications of intracellular electrolyte composition (46).

Other interesting features of $J_{12}$ are that it is inhibited in $O_2$-free solutions (12) and is increased by antidiuretic hormone (23). Furthermore, K and Li competitively inhibit Na entry at this step (11, 139).

Some recent measurements of the resistance of the outer membrane are in remarkable agreement with these findings of Na uptake. Thus ouabain, amiloride, and cyanide all increase the resistance between a microelectrode tip localized in the cells and the outer solution, indicating a decrease in the sodium conductance of the outer membrane (87).

Measurements of acidification of the outside solutions by skins of whole frogs and the simultaneous uptake of Na have shown a striking correspondence between $H^+$ secretion and Na uptake (62). From these data it has been suggested that the primary process involved in Na movement across the outer border of the skin is an exchange of $H^+$ for $Na^+$ (62). This interpretation cannot be accepted without reservations as it has been shown more recently in isolated skins that it is possible to modify the $H^+$ movements across the outer border of the skin without affecting the Na movements and vice versa (40, 43).

Furthermore, in the toad urinary bladder, where Na uptake is also an amiloride-sensitive process, this substance blocked Na transport while $H^+$ secretion into the lumen was not inhibited (54, 110).

## The Transport Compartment

According to the three-compartment model, after crossing the outside barrier Na penetrates into an intermediate compartment, probably the cell cytoplasm, from which it is actively transported into the inside solution. The questions related to this passage of Na through the cytoplasm that have received most attention are: 1. What are the cytoplasmatic concentrations of Na (and Li) during different transport conditions? and 2. Which layers or types of cells are involved in the transport process?

Some progress toward answering these questions has been made by the use of preparations in which most of the nonepithelial elements present in the organs have been removed. In the case of the frog skin two types of preparations have been used. One involves cutting slices of epithelium parallel to the surface with a freezing microtome (71). The other consists of the isolated epithelium obtained by the combined use of an enzymatic treatment and hydrostatic pressure (2, 82, 132). With this procedure the epithelium preserves its function and tansports Na from the outside into the inside solution. In the case of toad urinary bladder, isolated separated epithelial cells are obtained by scraping them from the mucosal surface (63). In all cases it is necessary to account for the electrolytes remaining in the extracellular fluid by using adequate extracellular space markers.

The last procedure mentioned gave the result that the Na concentration in the cell water (48 m$M$/1 cell water in toad bladder; 24 m$M$/1 cell water in skin epithelium) found by analysis and correction for the Na in the extracellular space is well above the Na concentrations in the outside solution from which the skin or the bladder can readily pump Na into the inside solution (2, 114, 184). Similar findings are made when Li is used (71, 76, 104). The intraepithelial concentrations of this cation can reach up to 10 times the outside solution concentrations. These findings raise the possibility that Na and Li may be pumped from the outside solutions into the cytoplasm, particularly if we consider that the measured potential differences both in open and short circuited skins are insufficient to account for the movement of either Na or Li into the epithelium (9, 10).

Other observations show that the amount of Na coming from the outside solution that equilibrates with the cytoplasm is only a small fraction of the total Na in the cytoplasm (2). This finding, taken together with the results described immediately above, led to questions concerning the state of Na in the epithelium and whether or not all the layers of cells participate in the transepithelial transport process.

If a great fraction of the intracellular Na is either bound or sequestered in a subcellular compartment, the penetration of Na from the outside solution could be explained without the need of postulating an active transport process at the outer barrier. This assumption would also explain why only a small fraction of the total intracellular Na equilibrates with Na in the outside solution (41). Determinations with ion-selective microelectrodes are still scarce, and although Na activities are clearly lower inside the epithelial cells (90, 105) than in free solution, it is not yet clear whether the magnitude of the reduction in activity is sufficient to explain the observations.

Another particularly attractive explanation in the case of the frog skin epithelium is to propose that only a single layer of cells, namely the cells in the outer layer of the stratum granulosum, participates in the transport process (41, 169). This explanation has the advantage of accounting for the finding that a large proportion of the intraepithelial Na equilibrates with Na coming from the inside solution. There is a group of morphological findings that lend support to the idea that only a single layer of epithelial cells participates in transepithelial transport. It has been found that during the increase in transepithelial transport of Na, caused by short circuiting the skin, there is an increase in cell volume, restricted almost exclusively to the outer layer of the stratum granulosum (169, 172). This finding can be interpreted as indicating that Na moves only through this cell layer and that it has a very active transport mechanism. The increase of volume could be interpreted as resulting from the entry of Na through the outside surface and of Cl through the inside membrane. Finally determinations with the electron microprobe of Na in cells in different layers show that during the action of amiloride or after incubating skins with Na-free outside solution, there is a reduction in [Na], confined almost exclusively to the cells in the outer layer of the stratum granulosum (64).

A very recent observation (170) does indeed speak in favor of at least one cellular compartment in excess of the cytosol being involved in the active Na transport. When the hydrostatic pressure on the inside of an isolated frog skin is raised slightly (10–40 cm $H_2O$) over that on the outside, there is an expansion of the interspaces and at the same time one observes small vacuoles or blisters in the outermost living cell layer. Once the skin has reached the critical pressure for vacuole formation, it turns out that the number of vacuoles is strictly correlated to the short circuit current. It is tempting to speculate that at least part of the Na entering the cells from the outside is transported into the vacuoles. Similar vacuoles, only smaller, may be present at all times. Whatever their specific function, they may contain a sizable fraction of the cellular Na.

Although the single layer mechanism would explain the limited equilibration with outside Na and the changes of cell volume and Na concentration during changes in the transport rate, there are some findings that, for the time being, could be explained more readily by assuming that all the epithelial cells are connected by bridges that allow diffusion from cell to cell in different layers. Of course a combination of the two mechanisms is also possible, i.e. during some conditions only the outer layer serves as a transepithelial path, while under other conditions, Na could penetrate to the subjacent layers.

The main findings that favor cell to cell coupling and must be accounted for are:

(a)    When a microelectrode is advanced through the epithelium several potential steps are recorded (135), which suggests some kind of electrical coupling between the cells. The postulated bridges may have a relative high resistance or be relatively scarce since marked jumps in potential are observed between different levels.

(b)    Determinations of the ac impedance of the skin give normal values (about 2 $\mu F$ cm$^{-1}$) for the outer membrane but the enormous value of 65 $\mu F$ cm$^{-2}$ for the inner membrane. This finding could be interpreted as showing that membranes of more than one cell layer contribute to the capacitance (146).

(c)    Although the Na equilibration measurements can be explained by assuming the participation of a single layer, the amount of Li that penetrates into the epithelia from the outside is very large (71, 104). This finding is more difficult to explain on the basis of equilibration with a single layer of cells. Since very little Li moves into the inside solution, the best explanation is that it moves from cell to cell through intercellular bridges equilibrating with all cell layers.

(*d*)   The energy consumption associated with transepithelial transport is high. It seems that there is insufficient "fuel" in a single layer of cells to support Na transport for extended periods at the observed rate.

There may be one serious drawback to the proposal of extensive direct cell to cell communication. Very few gap junctions, the specialized contacts responsible for cell to cell communication, are found in transmission electron micrographs of the frog skin epithelium (47, 120). However, it is necessary to confirm this observation with freeze etching studies, because this technique can show the presence of gap junctions in tissues where it has been difficult to detect them with transmission electron microscopy.

Clearly it is difficult to propose a unifying hypothesis that will account for all the available observations on the outer barrier and the cation distribution within the epithelium. However, it is useful to summarize the properties of the Na channels at the outer barrier, taken together with the available information on the cell compartment:

1. Na and Li move across the outer barrier by a saturable process.
2. $Li^+$ and $K^+$ competitively inhibit Na entry into the channels.
3. Na and Li movements are selectively inhibited by amiloride.
4. The movements are markedly increased by antidiuretic hormone.
5. Na movements are inhibited by ouabain and metabolic poisons. The inhibition by ouabain is probably mediated by changes in the cell composition and/or potential.
6. The system may accumulate cations actively. Alternatively, Na (or Li) ions which have entered passively are actively taken up by intracellular compartments.
7. Under most experimental conditions Na transport across the outer barrier does not involve an exchange of $Na^+$ for $H^+$.

A most interesting property of these transport sites is that their function is not normally detectable in the membranes facing the inside of the frog skin, as Na movements across this surface are very low. However, the Na channels can rapidly appear when these inside facing membranes reach the outer border of the skin, since soon after a moult the outside facing membrane gains its special features (86).

## The Inside Barrier

In the original model for transepithelial transport it was assumed that the inward facing barrier of the epithelial transport system has a very low passive permeability to Na. This has recently been verified (14).

Another assumption was that the active transport was brought about by a tightly coupled exchange of one Na for one K at the pump site. Since then evidence has been obtained which suggests that, although coupling exists, the coupling ratio is less than one. A recent study on the isolated frog skin epithelium provides measurements of the coupling ratio (14). Reducing outside Na from 115 m$M$ to 1 m$M$ was found to reduce exchange with the inside bathing solution by about one third, from 0.302 to 0.183 $\mu$eq $\times$ hr$^{-1}$ $\times$ cm$^{-2}$. Simultaneously, the short circuit current was reduced from 0.819 to 0.065 $\mu$eq $\times$ hr$^{-1}$ $\times$ cm$^{-2}$.

If the reduction in K flux results from stopping the operation of a coupled pump due to lack of Na coming from the outside, the coupling ratio Na:K would be about 6:1.

Experiments with stimulation of the transport by antidiuretic hormone gave additional support to such a figure: When a coupling ratio was computed from the increment in short circuit current over the increment in K exchange, a value around 6:1 was again obtained (14).

When the Na transport was inhibited by amiloride the situation became less clear. This drug inhibited the short circuit current by about 93% with no significant reduction of the K exchange. The effects of dinitrophenol and ouabain were also measured. Both inhibitors depressed K exchange to lower levels than those observed with reduction of the outside Na concentration. The inhibitors might have blocked K transport in cells not associated with the transepithelial Na transport.

The technique used in the above studies as well as in previous attempts at measuring the coupling ratio in epithelia may well underestimate the true K exchange, thus giving figures for the coupling ratio which are too high. If most or all of the transepithelial Na transport is performed by the outermost living cell layer it is only the K exchange of these cells which is correlated to the short circuit current. Now, considering the fact that the outermost interspaces are very narrow with a total K content which is small compared to the net Na transport, there is every chance that the K ions in this region will be recycled through the transporting cells before they have a chance to exchange with the inside bathing solution via the rather long and narrow interspace system and the basement membrane. Furthermore, the nonactive cells of the epithelium will act as an ion exchange column which will attenuate the signal that may come from the outermost cell layer in the form of shifts in the K flux.

Still, it is likely that the coupling ratio is higher than unity so that the pump is partly electrogenic, as it has turned out to be in many cell types (see above).

On the other hand, it is clear from the foregoing that we are not dealing with a pure electrogenic Na pump. This conclusion is also supported by experiments where the normally K-tight outward-facing membrane has been made leaky with the polyene antibiotic amphotericin B (125).

Under conditions where K can pass right through the skin the outward flux of K becomes many times higher than the inward flux, even during short circuiting. This situation can be maintained for many hours, and the total K transported is larger than the K content of the skin. Thus we are dealing with an active outward transport of K. The transport seems to be Na sensitive and is inhibited by ouabain. This finding is exactly what one should expect from the original three-compartment model for epithelial transport when it is assumed that the pump only appears as a pure Na pump because the outward facing cell membrane is tight to K.

## Amiloride

One of the most useful tools in the study of transepithelial transport across frog skin and toad bladder is the diuretic amiloride (39). This diuretic probably acts on the outside surface of the epithelium by reversibly blocking the entry of Na or Li. Apart from exerting its effects from the outside surface only, its speed of action is extremely rapid (12). An important fraction of the time required for its effects can be accounted for by the diffusion delay at the outer border of the skin (12). As described above, direct measurements of Na uptake at the outer border of the epithelium show that the process is blocked when amiloride is added to the outside solution (12, 46, 123). It has been shown recently that after chelation of Ca in the outside solution the inhibitory effects of amiloride on the short circuit current are severely reduced or abolished (32). Other ions ($Mg^+$, $Sr^+$, $La^{2+}$, and $Mn^{2+}$) and $Ca^{2+}$ itself can restore the inhibitory effects of amiloride (32). An interesting possibility suggested by these observations is that amiloride may form a ternary complex with $Ca^{2+}$ and the membrane sites responsible for Na movements across the outside border of the skin.

In another set of experiments the binding of [14]C-amiloride has been measured by a dilution method. It was estimated that there are about 400 binding sites of amiloride per $cm^2$. From these measurements it was calculated that each amiloride-sensitive site can handle up to 8000 sodium ions/sec (33).

## Antidiuretic Hormone (ADH)

Since it was orginally observed (60, 164), the stimulation of salt transport across amphibian epithelia by ADH has been the object of considerable attention. It was postulated very early that the effects of ADH result mainly from an increase in permeability of the outer membrane to Na. The increase in Na transport caused by the hormone would be the result of a rise in the amount of Na in the transport compartment derived from the outside solution. Attempts to obtain further evidence in support of this proposal by measuring Na in the epithelial cells have resulted in contradictory findings. In the isolated cells from toad bladder, two groups of investigators (70, 115) have detected an increase in Na coming from the outside solution and a decrease in K during the action of the hormone, while a third group detected no significant changes in ion composition (107). One investigation in which ADH was used (2) with the isolated frog skin epithelium showed no change in Na coming from the outside. However, in other experiments studying the transport of Li, which is also enhanced by posterior hypophysis hormones, oxytocin was observed to increase the concentration of Li within the epithelium (104). Furthermore, ADH also stimulates Na uptake from the outside solution into the epithelium (23).

The hormone clearly stimulates Na movements across the outer border of the skin. However, it may have as an additional effect the stimulation of the pump at the serosal side of the epithelium, independently of changes in intracellular Na. The proposal, which would conciliate the contradictory findings described above, has some experimental support. Frog urinary bladders equilibrated with mineral oil in their lumen presumably have no Na at this surface, yet ADH can increase the Na efflux across the serosal surface (89, 90). Also, after loading with Na by amphoteri-cin treatment, the cells in the toad urinary bladder are stimulated by ADH to release their Na load (51).

## Anions and Transport

The participation of active Cl transport in the function of epithelia may be more widespread than hitherto assumed. Besides the well established active Cl transport in gastric mucosa (80), the process also plays an important role in the epithelium of frog cornea (183) and it has recently been discovered that the salt transport in the ascending limb of the loop of Henle is due to active transport of Cl rather than Na (8). Here only the handling of anions in frog skin and toad bladder are discussed.

Two questions concerning the role of anions in transepithelial transport in frog skin and toad urinary bladder have received the most attention. One is whether they are actively transported, and the other concerns the influence of the anion on the active cation transport process.

Except for observations in the South American frog *Leptodactylus ocellatus* (182), the determinations of Cl movements on skins bathed with Cl-Ringer's solution on both sides showed that Cl fluxes were essentially passive (97). More recently an inward active transport of Cl has been detected when skins of many species are incubated in low Cl solutions (41, 101, 119). The failure to observe active transport at high Cl concentrations is probably due to the presence of large flows of Cl through passive pathways that mask the small active Cl transport. The contribution of this active transport to the short circuit current is negligible. An active Cl transport can also be detected in the toad urinary bladder bathed in K-free solutions (52). There is pharmacological evidence showing that the Cl and Na active transport systems are independent. Amiloride or ouabain blocks Na transport without inhibiting Cl active movements (41, 101). The converse is observed with $Br^-$ and $SCN^-$ and with acetazolamide, an inhibitor of carbonic anydrase. Active Cl transport is inhibited without modifying Na transport (41, 101).

In a series of experiments the tissue pools for $Cl^-$ and $SO_4$ were determined when the appropriate isotope was added to either the outside or the inside solution (101). Two findings are of interest. The $Cl^-$ pool determined from the outside is larger than the pool determined from the inside. Furthermore, the $SO_4$ pools determined from either side are small and of a similar size to that found for $Cl^-$ on the inside. An additional finding was that the saturable fraction of the Cl transport is not modified by transepithelial potential changes. All these findings, taken together, suggest that Cl is actively transported across the outer sensitive barrier of the epithelium into the cells, forming an apparently neutral complex with a membrane component. Furthermore they suggest that $Cl^-$ efflux and $SO_4$ movements have a common pathway and that this pathway is different from the active Cl transport system (101).

The passive permeation of Cl through the isolated frog skin may take a cellular as well as an intercellular route. It has just been found (99) that Cu at a concentration of $10^{-5}$ $M$ in the solution bathing the outside of a frog skin (*Rana temporaria*) will reduce the Cl permeability drastically, provided that the frog has been kept at room temperature for a couple of days. Under these conditions the sulfate and sucrose permeabilities are unchanged or even slightly increased during the presence of Cu. This strongly suggests that Cl primarily takes a cellular route and the two other test substances an intercellular route. However, when the frog was kept cold right up to the time of the experiment, the Cu treatment did not significantly change the Cl permeability. Under these conditions, then, Cl would appear to be mainly following the same route as sulfate and sucrose, presumably the intercellular one.

Another interesting feature of the relationship between transport and the anions present in the solutions bathing the epithelium is the fact that the rate of Na transport is markedly dependent on the anion species in the bathing solution. The most striking effect found in the skin is that substitution of Cl by $SO_4$ in isotonic solutions leads to a marked depression of transepithelial transport (1, 31, 49, 83). An important part of this effect may be related to changes in cell volume (174). It is known that reduction in the volume of epithelial cells results in depression of transepithelial transport rate (see 163). It is also known that the cells are permeable to K and Cl from the inside; therefore, removal of Cl in the inside solution should result, due to a Donnan effect, in shrinkage of the cells. That this is the case for the skin is demonstrated by the finding that hypotonic $SO_4$ solutions will not depress transepithelial Na transport (49).

Another interesting effect of anions is observed in the toad urinary bladder. Several organic anions, particularly propionate, stimulate transepithelial Na transport in this organ (142). This stimulation does not seem to be mediated through metabolic stimulation (143). Substitution of $Cl^-$ for other anions showed that short circuit current and transport are markedly dependent on anion composition. The relative abilities of mucosal anions to stimulate Na transport were $SCN > I > NO_3 > Br > Cl >$ propionate $>$ acetate $>$ tartrate $>$ citrate $> SO_4 > HPO_4 > F > N_5$ (144).

Because this sequence reflects neither anion size nor mobility in free solution and is similar to the lytropic series, it was suggested that it is related to an interaction with fixed charged groups. It is also interesting that these anions have a similar sequence of effectivity from the inside solution, suggesting that the site for anion action is accessible from both sides of the epithelium (144).

## PERMEATION PATHS IN EPITHELIA

### The Route for Passive Permeation

It has been recognized for some time that there are large differences between transmural resistance values among different epithelia (28). Moreover, determinations in the epithelia with lower resistance showed that the resistance values of the cell membranes are well above those for transepithelial resistance, indicating the presence of a large paracellular shunt pathway in this type of tissue (15, 56, 57, 81, 111, 176). It was proposed quite early that the large shunt could be within the zonulae occludens, the belt-like regions where the membranes of neighboring cells come into closest apposition, with the cells acting as seals. This proposal was, however, only cautiously accepted since the membranes in the regions of apposition within the zonulae occludens appear under the electron microscope to be equally closed in most epithelia, regardless of their transepithelial resistance value (47). Furthermore, the possibility that the shunts could be localized elsewhere had been considered. Notably the sites of physiological or traumatic cell desquamations or some particular cell type could be involved (28).

Several recent findings, however, have established that the zonulae occludens are indeed a major route for paracellular passive permeation in low resistance epithelia. 1. In an elegant study it was shown that in necturus gall bladder the low electrical resistance pathway and the regions of cell contact coincide (57). 2. At least the main routes available for La permeation across the living tissue can be vizualized with the electron microscope after equilibration of living epithelia with ionic La ($0.5-1\,mM$) (120). This technique has shown that La moves through the zonulae occludens of several low resistance epithelia but not in high resistance epithelia (22, 45, 113, 120, 121, 154, 175). 3. There are a number of properties that suggest a paracellular shunt pathway, although by themselves they are not absolutely conclusive. They are (a) a high value for the ratio of cell membrane resistance over transepithelial resistance (15, 16, 56, 57, 81, 111, 176), (b) different values for relative ionic permeability coefficients across the cell membranes and the whole epithelia (58, 178), (c) symmetrical potential responses to changes in ion concentration gradients (6, 178), (d) a very narrow range of permeabilities from the most permeant to the least permeant alkali cation indicating a very hydrated permeation route (6, 178), (e) a linear current-voltage relationship over a large range of voltages (6, 178).

Table 1 shows a number of properties of epithelia, some of them particularly indicative of the tightness of their junctions as a function of membrane resistance. The resistances shown in the table spread over an almost continuous range of values. So far the highest resistance (150–300 $\Omega$ cm$^2$) determined in an epithelium (116) whose junctions are permeable to La is the distal tubule of the rat kidney (121, 154). The resistance values are not in sharp disagreement with the morphological findings, as a calculation of the resistance of the path formed by the junctions together with lateral spaces placed in series gives a value of around 300 $\Omega$ cm$^2$ (121). These publications do not specify which portion of the distal tubule was studied. This is a point that must be specifically mentioned, as there is now good evidence indicating that the proximal and distal portions of the distal tubule have different electrical properties (181). Nevertheless, at least when the examples at the extremes of the table are considered there is a clear-cut relationship between low transmural resistance and permeable junctional complexes on the one hand, and high transmural resistance and junctional complexes with high resistance for passive ion permeation on the other.

The table does not include what are probably interesting cases of epithelial organization. In two reports on the morphology of the salt glands in marine animals evidence has been found indicating that the tight junctions are absent (38, 168). These epithelial tissues transport salt at very high rates (38, 168).

The simplest explanation for the continuous range of values is to postulate that the same sealing mechanism operates in all epithelia; the variations would then result from different ratios between junctional areas that have more or less perfect seals and areas occupied by faulty seals.

**Table 1**  Physiological properties and junctional tightness[a]

| Epithelium | R $\Omega$ cm$^2$ | E mV | $C_1 C_2$[b] | OSM[c] | EM[d] |
|---|---|---|---|---|---|
| **Proximal Tubule** | | | | | |
| dog | 5.6 (15) | 2 | – | 1 | – |
| rat | 6.7 (58) | 0 | 1.3 | 1 | L (154) |
| frog | – | – | – | 1 | L (175) |
| **Gallbladder** | | | | | |
| rabbit | 30 (178) | 0 | 12 | 1 | L (116) |
| **Choroid Plexus** | | | | | |
| frog | 75 (180) | 0 | – | 1 | – |
| cat | – | – | – | 1 | L (22) |
| **Intestine** | | | | | |
| rabbit ileum | 100 (56) | 4 | 1.6 | 1 | L (116) |
| **Distal Tubule** | | | | | |
| rat | 150–300 (121) | 19–45 | – | – | L (121, 154) |
| dog | 600 (15) | 43 | – | – | – |
| **Frog Stomach** | 500 (79) | 30 | 1,000,000 | 1 | – |
| **Collecting Tubule** | | | | | |
| rabbit | 860 (75) | 25 | – | >1 | – |
| rat | – | – | – | – | T (121, 154) |
| **Urinary Bladder** | | | | | |
| toad | 1500 (27) | 60 | 600 | >1 | T (45) |
| **Frog Skin** | 3600 (165) | 90 | 10,000 | >1 | T (120) |

[a]The numbers in parentheses indicate the articles from which the data were taken.
[b]Maximum concentration ratio compatible with active transport.
[c]Osmolarity of the transported fluid as compared to the bathing solutions.
[d]Whether the junctions are tight (T) or leaky (L) as judged by the La technique.

Many of the ultrastructural features can be interpreted in agreement with this proposal. In low resistance epithelia the zonulae occludens are formed by a number of focal punctate junctions interrupted by stretches of separation between the two membranes that leave open spaces between them (18, 47). In high resistence epithelia the zonulae occludens are deeper than in low resistance epithelia. Also, the membranes of neighboring cells are in close opposition for almost all the depth of the zonulae occludens, separating only at a few points if at all. In freeze cleave studies of a number of epithelia a branching network of threads or chains of small globular subunits is found within the regions of the zonulae occludens (24, 29, 55, 150). It has also been observed that the complexity of this network can be correlated with the relative electrical leakiness of the epithelia, the leakier epithelia having a much less extensive network than the tight tissues (29). It is naturally attractive to propose that the subunits are in some way connected with the formation of close membrane appositions and that as the number of subunits increases the possibility of faults in the seal decreases.

Although it is obvious that the epithelia with leakier junctions have a lower transepithelial resistance we as yet have no clear understanding of the relationship between junctional leakiness and the absorption of solutes and water by the epithelia. When a number of epithelia are examined (see Table 1 and ref. 58) it appears that the tight epithelia can maintain steeper solute gradients and still transport actively from the dilute side.

Other correlations seem to exist. For example, in the leakier epithelia the transported solution is usually isotonic with respect to the bathing solutions and in tighter epithelia it is markedly hypertonic; however, the stomach secretes an isotonic fluid although the available evidence suggests that its junctions represent a high resistance pathway. Other correlations can be attempted but none will be free of exceptions. Perhaps important differences between tight and leaky epithelia will appear when more detailed studies are made on the ability of epithelia to modify their function in response to changes in the composition of the extracellular medium. For example, leakier epithelia can markedly alter their function when the oncotic pressure on their serosal surface is modified, while the tight epithelia generally do not respond dramatically to such small changes in osomotic pressure.

## The Shunt Pathway in the Leakier Epithelia

The relative permeabilities of anions and cations across the leakier epithelia with a paracellular shunt differ markedly from their relative mobilities in free solution (6, 56, 178). Two types of basic mechanism have been found in artificial membranes that could serve as possible models accounting for permeability differences between cations and anions or among ions of the same sign (5). One is the ion exchange membrane which contains ionized sites with net charge confined within the membrane and balanced by mobile ions of the opposite sign from the bathing solution. The second mechanism is found in the so-called neutral membranes, i.e. those lacking sites with net charge. In this case the sites controlling permeability are dipolar groups such as the carbonyl, ether, or hydroxyl group (5). Because the forms of several of the relations between ion fluxes and external driving forces differ between ion exchanger and neutral membranes it ought to be possible in principle to distinguish the type of sites controlling the permeability of a given membrane (5, 6, 56, 178) from the study of these relationships. A detailed analysis of the expected differences in behavior between these two types of membranes has been performed, the analysis also discusses properties that discriminate between a "thick" and a "thin" membrane and whether the sites controlling ion permeation are mobile or fixed (5). The application of the analysis to leaker epithelia might help in identifying the type of sites controlling permeation within the tight junctions since the overall passive epithelial properties are controlled by the low resistance pathway. To apply the analysis to epithelia the following measurements must be performed: 1. the current voltage relation (5, 6, 178, 180), 2. the dependence of conductance or permeability on salt concentration in the bathing solutions (56, 178), 3. an estimation of relative anionic and cationic permeabilities and their dependence on salt concentration in the solutions (5, 6, 56, 180), and 4. the determination of the relative permeabilities to several nonelectrolytes (147, 177).

The results obtained and their interpretation can be summarized as follows:

The current voltage relationship is linear over a long range of voltages (178, 180). Measurement of the current-voltage relation in asymmetrical solutions can distinguish between "thin" and "thick" membranes. The current-voltage ($I/V$) curve in asymmetrical solutions or in the presence of a single salt concentration gradient is linear for a thick membrane and nonlinear for a thin membrane (5). In the gall bladder and the choroid plexus the $I/V$ curve is linear over a long range of voltages (178, 180). This finding indicates that the behavior of the paracellular pathway is that of a thick membrane. Since cell membranes behave as thin membranes, the tight junction is the structure most easily identified with a region that could behave as a thick membrane.

The relationship between conductance and concentration taken together with estimations of ion selectivity can serve to distinguish between a fixed charge membrane and a so-called neutral site membrane. In leaky epithelia the relationship between conductance and concentration is linear (56, 178, 180). This behavior was initially taken to indicate that the selectivity of the membrane arose from neutral sites, i.e. dipolar groups that carry no net charge. In spite of the initial good fit of predicted theoretical properties and experimental findings, later experimental findings indicate that the neutral fixed site hypothesis is not acceptable in its original form. It has been observed that thorium and several other polyvalent cations and low pH can convert the gall bladder from a cation selective to an anion selective membrane (6, 112, 178). This effect is similar to what would be expected from an ion exchange membrane where either $H^+$ or the polycation would neutralize fixed negative charges that serve as fixed counterions for cations. To get around this difficulty three possible alternative models (178) have been proposed: (a) the tight junction may be composed of very short regions carrying net charge separated by wide aqueous regions, (b) the junction may be composed of a short region carrying a net charge in series with the long neutral site pore, or (c) the selectivity may result from binding of either anions or cations to the ends of dipoles in the neutral fixed sites. In the original publications a distinction was also made between two kinds of neutral sites: either the sites are fixed within a polar pore or the sites are mobile within a hydrocarbon-like membrane. The first possibility was selected as more likely mainly from considerations of the excessive size required by an hypothetical carrier (6).

Two other sets of comparisons are useful in the deduction of properties of the shunt pathway: 1. comparison of alkali cation selectivity isotherms of epithelia with the isotherms observed in single cells (6) and 2. comparison of the permeability ratios of large polar nonelectrolytes with the ratios of their diffusion coefficients in free solutions and also measurements of their respective activation energies (147). These comparisons show that (a) the leaky epithelia have a smaller range of ion selectivity than single cell membranes (6, 56, 180) and (b) large nonpolar electrolytes move across leaky epithelia with the same ratio of permeabilities as the ratio of their free solution diffusion coefficient (14, 177). Furthermore, activation energies for the movement of large nonelectrolyte across epithelia are similar to those observed in free solution (147). All these findings suggest that the permeation pathway across the tight junction is highly hydrated.

In summary, for the time being one may conclude that the route for passive permeation across leaky epithelia is formed by highly hydrated channels lined with sites that, at neutral pH, confer cation selectivity to the path.

Several approaches have been used to calculate the distribution and the radius of the hydrated pores localized within the tight junctions. The estimations have been based on the following assumptions:

1.  If all the large hydrophilic nonelectrolytes diffuse through the hydrated channels, the fractional area of the membrane occupied by the pores and the pore radius that will allow the passage of the test molecules can be calculated (147).
2.  If almost all the current crosses through the pores, the formula $A = pl/R$ can be used. In this formula $A$ is the total channel area; $p$ the specific resistivity of the solution in the channel, $l$ the length of the junction, and $R$ the electrical resistance of the epithelium.
3.  If all the water flow generated by an osmotic gradient goes through the junction, calculations based on the Poiseuille law can give an estimation of pore size (7).

Calculations based on assumption 1 and on the measurement of sucrose and inulin permeabilities across the gall bladder show that these substances permeate across 0.2% of the total area of the mucosal surface and that the pores ought to have a radius slightly larger than 12 Å (147). These calculations can be fitted quite well to the values for electrical resistance. Pores that have a radius of 12 Å, filled with saline and distributed about every 1000 Å along the cell edges, would account for the transepithelial electrical resistance of the gall bladder (179). Calculations based on measurements made on *necturus* proximal tubule and assumptions 2 and 3 are also not far from a reasonable fit (7, 16). In this epithelium, Poiseuille calculations show that if 100% of the osmotic water flow passed through the tight junction the width should be 34 Å (7). The resistance calculation using this width gives a value of 1.84 $\Omega$ cm$^2$. This value is far from the observed level of 70 $\Omega$ cm$^2$. Two reasons for this deviation can be proposed: (a) only a fraction of the osmotic water flow goes through the junction or (b) the contribution of the lateral intercellular spaces as a resistance in series with that of the junction is very important in determining transepithelial resistance. Some recent calculations suggest that the second proposal fits the available evidence (16).

## The Shunt Pathway in the Tighter Epithelia

Evidence regarding the properties of the paracellular pathway of unaltered high resistance epithelia is relatively scarce. The only systematic efforts in this direction are some recent experiments on the frog skin (117, 118). The permeability to urea of this tissue has been found to markedly increase when depolarized to –100 mV, independently of the activity of the Na pump. In skins with the Na pump poisoned by ouabain the fluxes of Na, K, Cl, and mannitol change in parallel with urea movements. The ion fluxes under these conditions and their responses to potential are described by the constant field equation. This finding suggests that the path has the properties of a single barrier, rather than of two or more barriers of different properties in series. Furthermore, the movement of mannitol follows very closely the behavior of the other solutes tested. Since this substance hardly penetrates cell membranes in the frog skin, it was suggested that the behavior of the solutes tested may represent their movement through an extracellular pathway. The selectivity of the proposed shunt is Cl > urea > K > Na > mannitol. Permeability of the shunt is decreased by outside $Ca^{2+}$ and increased by elevated external ionic strength (117, 118). (For cellular shunt path see *Anions and Transport* above.)

## Effects of Hypertonic Solutions and Other Agents

It has been known for some time that increasing the osmolarity of the mucosal solution causes a reversible reduction of transepithelial resistance and potential in a number of high resistance epithelia such as frog skin (106, 165), toad urinary bladder (158, 173), dog gastric mucosa (4), and sheep rumen (149). The phenomenon has been studied in greater detail in frog skin where the drop in resistance is associated with a large increase in the permeability to anions and cations (165) and also to large hydrophilic nonelectrolytes that normally do not penetrate cell membranes (10, 53, 161). From these findings it was proposed that hyperosmotic solutions cause an opening of the tight junctions. Direct evidence in agreement with this proposal has been obtained using ionic La as a tracer in frog skin and toad urinary bladder (44, 45). Under control conditions $^{140}$La moves at a very slow rate or not at all across these epithelia (44, 120). However, during the action of hypertonic solutions the tracer movement is markedly increased (44). Examination with the electron microscope of the epithelia fixed during treatment of the outside solution with hypertonic solutions and the tracer show that La is localized all along the intercellular spaces of the epithelium and that the occluding zonules that normally prevent the inward movement of La are open (44, 45).

In addition to the opening of the tight junctions, other morphological alterations are observed during the action of the hypertonic solution. Numerous vacuoles appear within the cytoplasm of the cells (44, 173). These vacuoles are not accessible to La in the mucosal solution and, although they appear simultaneously with the opening of the junctions, evidently are not the main shunt pathway. Another morphological feature observed particularly in toad bladders is the presence of very large blisters within or very near the junctional regions (37, 45, 173). These blisters could indeed represent opening of the junction; however, many junctions are open, as shown by the presence of La or $BaSO_4$ within them, without any evidence of blistering (45, 173). On the other hand, blisters very near or within the junction many times are not accessible to La. Therefore, although marked junctional blistering is concomitant with opening of the tight junctions, it is not yet finally settled whether or not this deformation is an indispensable event in the opening of the junctions, since open junctions can be found without blistering and sometimes the deformation is not associated with a junction permeable to the tracers.

An interesting phenomenon has been observed in association with the opening of tight junctions by hypertonic solutions in frog skin (10, 53, 161). During the action of the hypertonic solutions there is an asymmetric movement of sucrose and other hydrophilic solutes. This results in an inward net transport of the sucrose or the other solutes added in addition to the hypertonic agent (10, 53, 161). This asymmetric movement has been looked for but not observed in the urinary bladder (158). Two explanations have been proposed for this effect. One postulates that it is the result of solute-solute interactions in the aqueous spaces (10, 53). The second suggests that the transport is coupled to the local circulation of water in the interspace (129, 162).

Another site in which tight junctions are opened by hypertonic solution is the cerebral capillaries (134). Evans blue bound to plasma proteins normally does not leave the lumen of the brain capillaries. However, after applying hypertonic solutions to the brain, the protein bound dye leaves the capillaries and moves into the cerebral cortex, indicating an opening of the intercellular pathways.

In the frog skin the opening of the junction is produced only when the outside solution is hypertonic with respect to the inside solution (106, 160, 162). This finding indicates that the opening is not the result of cell shrinkage, but that the osmotic gradient across the epithelium plays an important role in the process. Furthermore, not all solutes are equally effective. When sucrose, mannitol, acetamide, urea, thiourea, $Na_2SO_4$, and $K_2SO_4$ were tested, thiourea and urea were the most effective in the series (106). When a series of polyhydric alcohols going from methanol to mannitol were tested, adonitol with 5 carbons was the most effective (106). Also, $D_2O$ was found to have effects similar to those of hypertonic solutions.

In the urinary bladder the effects of hypertonic urea and other solutes (methylurea, 1,3-dimethylurea, acetamide, thiourea, thioacetamide, glycerol, dimethyl sulfoxide) are observed only when they are added to the mucosal solution (158). Hypertonic solutions of mannitol, sucrose, raffinose, NaCl, and Na isethionate increase the permeability of the bladder to water when added either on the outside or on the inside of the epithelium (137, 158). Although we do not yet understand the mechanism of these effects of hypertonic solutions on the junctional complex, they are an interesting tool for exploring the mechanisms by which the cells are held close together at the tight junction.

Another interesting way to modify the junctional complex has been found in guinea pig ileum. In this epithelium horseradish peroxidase does not move normally through the tight junction. However, when the ileum is subjected to both surgical trauma and the action of large proteins, the junctions become permeable to horseradish peroxidase (136). It is tempting to speculate that in these experiments the release of a humoral factor is responsible for the opening of the junctions.

## The Lateral Intercellular Spaces as a Route for Water and Solute Permeation

Since it was observed that the lateral intercellular spaces widely dilate during isotonic water transport across the rabbit gall bladder (91, 155) considerable attention has been devoted to these spaces as a route for solute and water permeation.

The more recent findings on the role of intercellular spaces in epithelial function have served as the basis for ascribing the following properties to these spaces.

(a)  The intercellular spaces may dilate during active salt transport even in the virtual absence of transepithelial water movements.

(b)  The intercellular spaces are an important route for passive flow of water and solutes across epithelia.

(c)  Some of the alterations in water and salt absorption in the proximal tubule of the kidney and in the small intestine may be mediated by changes in the lateral spaces and/or leakiness of the tight junctions.

In this section we summarize the evidence on which these conclusions are based.

(a)  Expansion of the lateral spaces associated with increasing Na transport has been observed in the short circuited frog skin bathed by solutions of equal osmolarity on both sides (171). Under these conditions transepithelial water flow is negligible (1–5 $\mu$l/hr cm$^{-2}$). However, there is a linear relationship between short circuit current and the area of the intercellular spaces measured with the light microscope after fixation of the skin (171). This relationship holds when results are pooled from control and ADH stimulated skins (171).

(b)  Expansion of the intercellular spaces concomitant with the flow of water along an osmotic gradient across the ADH-treated urinary bladder of the toad was observed some time ago (19, 20, 67, 126, 130).

Expansion of extracellular spaces also has been observed during the transepithelial water flow that follows ADH treatment of isolated collecting kidney tubules perfused with a dilute solution through the lumen (61). In this epithelium the spaces also dilate when water flows from the cell to the peritubular medium during the change in cell volume that follows the substitution of peritubular fluid from a hypotonic to an isotonic solution (66). It has been suggested that the increase in intercellular space width that follows ADH treatment in toad urinary bladder may be the result of mechanical deformation due to changes in muscle tone (36). Evidently mechanical factors will influence intercellular space width. However, it is clear that changes of the interspaces during ADH-induced osmotic water flows can occur independently of changes in muscle tone, since they are observed in the isolated collecting tubules of the kidney (61, 66) or in a preparation of the toad bladder in which the muscle layers have been removed by dissection (127).

In several leaky epithelia (small intestine, proximal tubule of the kidney, gall bladder) it has been found that when the lumen solution is hypotonic with respect to the blood side solution, there is a widening of the lateral extracellular spaces concomitant with the water flow from lumen to blood side (7, 108, 148). When the sign of the osmotic gradient is inverted, i.e. the lumen solution is hypertonic with respect to blood side, the direction of water flow reverses, while the lateral extracellular spaces collapse (7, 108, 148). Furthermore, it has been observed that during the collapse of the extracellular spaces in the gall bladder there is a reduction of hydraulic conductivity, transepithelial electrical conductance, and permeability to nonelectrolytes (148). These findings, taken together with the changes in extracellular space dimension described above, are the basis for concluding that the lateral extracellular spaces are an important route for passive water and solute movement across epithelia, since the spaces dilate when there is water flow across the tissue. The converse is also true: when lateral extracellular space width is reduced, the hydraulic conductivity and the permeability to ions and nonelectrolytes are reduced (148, 179).

(c) There are many observations showing that saline infusion depresses net reabsorption of Na in the proximal tubule of the kidney and the small intestine. Several types of explanations have been advanced for this finding. First, it has been proposed that the effect is mediated through the liberation of a humoral agent with natriuretic effects. A second proposal is that the depression is mediated by changes in peritubular hemodynamics and oncotic pressure.

A detailed discussion of the merits of these hypotheses is outside the scope of this review. However, there is now convincing evidence that changes in oncotic pressure can directly modify the function of isolated proximal tubules (88) and that this effect may be mediated by either changes in lateral intercellular space width or in the permeability of the tight junction (17, 84). Thus in Necturus the proximal tubule transepithelial resistance falls markedly after isotonic extracellular volume expansion (17), while peritubular resistance remains unchanged. Simultaneously the permeability coefficients for NaCl and raffinose increase markedly (17). Because the lateral extracellular pathway is the main extracellular resistance across the tubule it was postulated that an increase in its width could explain the reduced resistance (17). Furthermore, it was also postulated that the reduction in salt absorption under these circumstances is the result of an increase in Na back flux along the paracellular path (17).

In the small intestine, where extracellular volume expansion likewise results in decreased salt and water absorption, there is also a simultaneous increase in inulin flux across the epithelium (84). Since this solute normally does not penetrate cell membranes one can infer that its increased flux results from an increase in the permeabilities of paracellular pathways (84).

*Literature Cited*

1. Aceves, J., Erlij, D., Edwards, C. 1968. Na$^+$ transport across the isolated skin of ambystoma mexicanus. *Biochim. Biophys. Acta* 150:744–46
2. Aceves, J., Erlij, D. 1971. Sodium transport across the isolated epithelium of the frog skin. *J. Physiol. London* 212:195
3. Andersen, B., Ussing, H. H. 1957. Solvent drag on nonelectrolytes during osmotic flow through isolated toad skin and its response to antidiuretic hormone. *Acta Physiol. Scand.* 39:228–39
4. Altamirano, M. 1969. Action of concentrated solutions of nonelectrolytes on the dog gastric mucosa. *Am. J. Physiol.* 216:33–40
5. Barry, P. H., Diamond, J. M. 1971. A theory of ion permeation through membranes with fixed neutral sites. *J. Membrane Biol.* 4:295–330
6. Barry, P. H., Diamond, J. M., Wright, E. M. 1971. The mechanism of cation permeation in rabbit gallbladder. Dilution potentials and biionic potentials. *J. Membrane Biol.* 4:358–94
7. Bentzel, C. J., Parsa, B., Hare, D. K. 1969. Osmotic flow across proximal tubule of necturus: correlation of physiologic and anatomic studies. *Am. J. Physiol.* 217:570–80
8. Berliner, R. W. 1973. Problems in current methods for studying transtubular transport. *Alfred Benzon Symposium V,* ed. H. H. Ussing, N. A. Thorn, 512–22. Copenhagen: Munksgaard
9. Biber, T. U. L., Chez, R. A., Curran, P. F. 1966. Na transport across frog skin at low external Na concentrations. *J. Gen. Physiol.* 49:1161–76
10. Biber, T. U. L., Curran, P. F. 1968. Coupled solute fluxes in toad skin. *J. Gen. Physiol.* 51:606–20

11. Biber, T. U. L., Curran, P. F. 1970. Direct measurement of uptake of sodium at the outer surface of the frog skin. *J. Gen. Physiol.* 56:83-99

12. Biber, T. U. L. 1971. Effect of changes in transepithelial transport on the uptake of sodium across the outer surface of the frog skin. *J. Gen. Physiol.* 58:131-44

13. Biber, T. U. L., Cruz, L., Curran, P. F. 1972. Sodium influx at the outer surface of frog skin. Evaluation of different extracellular markers. *J. Membrane Biol.* 7:365-76

14. Biber, T. U. L., Aceves, J., Mandel, L. J. 1972. Potassium uptake across serosal surface of isolated frog skin epithelium. *Am. J. Physiol.* 222:1366-73

15. Boulpaep, E. L., Seely, J. F. 1971. Electrophysiology of proximal and distal tubules in the autoperfused dog kidney. *Am. J. Physiol.* 221:1084-96

16. Boulpaep, E. L. 1971. Electrophysiological properties of the proximal tubule: Importance of cellular and intercellular transport pathways. *Electrophysiology of Epithelial Cells,* ed. G. Giebisch, 91. Stuttgart: Verlag

17. Boulpaep, E. L. 1972. Permeability changes of the proximal tubule of Necturus during saline loading. *Am. J. Physiol.* 222:517-31

18. Brightman, M. W., Reese, T. S. 1969. Junctions between intimately apposed cell membranes in the vertebrate brain. *J. Cell Biol.* 40:648-77

19. Carasso, N., Favard, P., Bourguet, J., Jard, S. 1966. Rôle du flux net d'eau dans les modifications ultrastructurales de la vessie de grenouille stimulée par l'oxitocine. *J. Microsc. Paris* 5:519

20. Carasso, N., Favard, P., Valérien, J. 1962. Variations des ultrastructures dans les cellules épitheliales de la vessie du crapaud après stimulation par l'hormone neurohypophysaire. *J. Microsc. Paris* 1:143-47

21. Carpenter, D. O. 1973. Electrogenic sodium pump and high specific resistance in nerve cell bodies of the squid. *Science* 179:1336-38

22. Castel, M., Sahar, A., Erlij, D. 1972. Extracellular route for passive permeation in choroid plexus epithelium. *Isr. J. Med. Sci.* 8:1762

23. Cereijido, M., Rotunno, C. A. 1971. The effect of antidiuretic hormone on Na movement across frog skin. *J. Physiol. London* 213:119-33

24. Chalcroft, J. P., Bullivant, S. 1970. An interpretation of liver cell membrane and junction structure based on observation of freeze-fracture replicas of both sides of the fracture. *J. Cell Biol.* 47:49-60

25. Chandler, W. K., Hodgkin, A. L., Meves, H. 1965. The effect of changing the internal solution on sodium inactivation and related phenomena in giant axons. *J. Physiol. London* 180:821-36

26. Christoffersen, G. R. J. 1972. Steady state contribution of the Na, K-pump to the membrane potential in identified neurons of a terrestrial snail, *Helix pomatia. Acta Physiol. Scand.* 86:498-514

27. Civan, M. M., Frazier, H. S. 1968. The site of the stimulatory action of vasopressin on sodium transport in toad bladder. *J. Gen. Physiol.* 51:589-605

28. Clarkson, T. W. 1967. The transport of salt and water across isolated rat ileum. Evidence for at least two distinct pathways. *J. Gen. Physiol.* 50:695-727

29. Claude, P., Goodenough, D. A. 1972. The ultrastructure of the zonula occludens in tight and leaky epithelia. *J. Cell Biol.* 55:46a

30. Schultz, S. G., Frizzell, R. A., Nellans, H. N. 1974. Ion transport by mammalian small intestine. *Ann. Rev. Physiol.* 36:51-91

31. Cuthbert, A. W., Painter, E., Prince, W. 1969. The effects of anions on sodium transport. *Brit. J. Pharmacol.* 36:97-106

32. Cuthbert, A. W., Wong, P. Y. D. 1972. The role of calcium ions in the interaction of amiloride with membrane receptors. *Mol. Pharmacol.* 8:222-29

33. Cuthbert, A. W. 1973. An upper limit to the number of sodium channels in frog skin epithelium. *J. Physiol. London* 228:681-92

34. Dalmark, M., Wieth, J. O. 1970. Chloride and sodium permeabilities of human red cells. *Biochim. Biophys. Acta* 219:525-27

35. DeSousa, R. C., Li, J. H., Essig, A. 1971. Flux ratios and isotope interaction in an ion exchange membrane. *Nature* 231:44-45

36. DiBona, D. R., Civan, M. M. 1970. The effect of smooth muscle on the intercellular spaces in toad urinary bladder. *J. Cell. Biol.* 46:235-44

37. DiBona, D. R. 1972. Passive intercellular pathway in amphibian epithelia. *Nature, New Biol.* 238:171-81

38. Dunson, W. A., Packer, R. K., Dunson, M. K. 1971. Sea snakes: An unusual salt gland under the tongue. *Science* 173:437-41

39. Eigler, J., Kelter, J., Renner, E. 1967. Wirkungscharakteristika eines neuen Acylguanidins-Amilorid-HCl

(MK 870) an der isolierten Haut von Amphibien. *Klin. Wochenschr.* 14:737, 738

40. Emilio, N. G., Machado, M. N., Menano, H. P. 1970. The production of a hydrogen ion gradient across the isolated frog skin. Quantative aspects and the effect of acetazolamide. *Biochim. Biophys. Acta* 203:394–409

41. Erlij, D. 1971. Salt transport across isolated frog skin. *Phil. Trans. Roy. Soc. London B* 262:153–61

42. Erlij, D., Smith, M. W. 1971. Sodium uptake by the outside surface of the frog skin. *J. Physiol. London* 218:33–34P

43. Erlij, D., Machen, T., Martínez-Palomo, A. 1972. Structure and function of the outer border of the frog skin. *Role of Membranes in Secretory Processes*, ed. L. Bolis, H. Wilbrandt, R. Keynes. Amsterdam: North-Holland

44. Erlij, D., Martínez-Palomo, A. 1972. Opening of tight junctions in frog skin by hypertonic urea solutions. *J. Membrane Biol.* 9:220–40

45. Erlij, D., Martínez-Palomo, A. 1973. Opening of tight junctions in toad urinary bladders by hypertonic solutions. *Fed. Proc.* 32:218 Abstr.

46. Erlij, D., Smith, M. W. 1973. Sodium uptake by frog skin and its modification by inhibitors of transepithelial sodium transport. *J. Physiol. London* 228:221–39

47. Farquhar, M. G., Palade, G. E. 1963. Junctional complexes in various epithelia. *J. Cell Biol.* 17:375–412

48. Farquhar, M. G., Palade, G. E. 1965. Cell junctions in amphibian skin. *J. Cell Biol.* 26:263–91

49. Ferreira, K. T. G. 1968. Anionic dependence of Na transport in the frog skin. *Biochim. Biophys. Acta* 150:587–98

50. Ferreira, K. T. G., Guerreiro, M. M., Ferreira, H. G. 1973. Kinetic characterization of the chloride dependence of sodium transport in the frog skin. *Biochim. Biophys. Acta* 291:269–73

51. Finn, A. L. 1968. Separate effects of sodium and vasopressin on the sodium pump in the toad bladder. *Am. J. Physiol.* 215:849–56

52. Finn, A. L., Handler, J. S., Orloff, J. 1967. Active chloride transport in the isolated toad bladder. *Am. J. Physiol.* 213:179–84

53. Franz, T. J., Van Bruggen, J. T. 1967. Hyperosmolarity and the net transport of nonelectrolytes in frog skin. *J. Gen. Physiol.* 50:933–49

54. Frazier, L. W., Vanatta, J. C. 1972. Mechanics of acidification of the mucosal fluid by the toad urinary bladder. *Biochim. Biophys. Acta* 290:168–77

55. Friend, D. S., Gilula, N. B. 1972. Variations in tight and gap junctions in mammalian tissues. *J. Cell Biol.* 53:758–76

56. Frizzell, R. A., Schultz, S. G. 1972. Ionic conductances of extracellular shunt pathway in rabbit ileum: influence of shunt on transmural Na transport and electrical potential differences. *J. Gen. Physiol.* 59:318–46

57. Frömter, E. 1972. The route of passive ion movement through the epithelium of Necturus gallbladder. *J. Membrane Biol.* 8:259–301

58. Frömter, E., Diamond, J. 1972. Route of passive ion permeation in epithelia. *Nature, New Biol.* 235:9–13

59. Fuchs, W., Gebhardt, U., Lindemann, B. 1972. Delayed voltage responses to fast changes of (Na)₀ at the outer surface of frog skin epithelium. *Passive Permeability of Cell Membranes*, Series Biomembranes, Vol. 3, ed. F. Dreuzer, J. F. G. Sleger, 483–98. New York, London: Plenum

60. Fuhrman, F. A., Ussing, H. H. 1951. A characteristic response of the isolated frog skin potential to neurohypophysial principles and its relation to the transport of sodium and water. *J. Cell Comp. Physiol.* 38:109–30

61. Ganote, C. E., Grantham, J. J., Moses, H. L., Burg, M. B., Orloff, J. 1968. Ultrastructural studies of vasopressin effect on isolated perfused renal collecting tubules of the rabbit. *J. Cell Biol.* 36:355–67

62. Garcia-Romeu, F., Salibian, A., Pezzani-Hernández, S. 1969. The nature of the in vivo sodium and chloride uptake mechanisms through the epithelium of the children frog *Calyptocephella gayi. J. Gen. Physiol.* 53:816–35

63. Gatzy, J. T., Berndt, W. O. 1968. Isolated epithelial cells of the toad bladder: their preparation, oxygen consumption and electrolyte content. *J. Gen. Physiol.* 51:770–84

64. Gehring, K., Dorge, A., Nagel, W., Thurau, K. 1972. Analysis and localization of electrolytes in frog skin epithelial cells by electron microprobe with an energy dispersive system. *J. Cell Biol.* 55:82a, No. 163

65. Giebisch, G., Ed. 1971. *Electrophysiology of Epithelial Cells.* Stuttgart: F. K. Schattauer Verlag

66. Grantham, J. J., Ganote, C. E., Burg, M. B., Orloff, J. 1969. Paths of transtubular water flow in isolated renal collecting tubules. *J. Cell Biol.* 41:562–76

67. Grantham, J. J., Cuppage, F. E., Fanestil, D. 1971. Direct observation of toad bladder response to vasopressin. *J. Cell Biol.* 48:695–99

68. Gunn, R. B. 1972. A titrable carrier model for both mono- and divalent anion transport in human red cells. *Oxygen Affinity of Hemoglobin and Red Cell Acid Base Status, Alfred Benzon Symposium IV,* ed. M. Rorth, P. Astrup, 823–927. Copenhagen: Munksgaard

69. Gunn, R. B., Dalmark, M., Tosteson, D. C., Wieth, J. O. 1973. Characteristics of chloride transport in human red blood cells. *J. Gen. Physiol.* 61:185–206

70. Handler, J. S., Preston, A. S., Orloff, J. 1972. Effect of ADH, aldosterone, ouabain and amiloride on toad bladder epithelial cells. *Am. J. Physiol.* 222:1071–74

71. Hansen, H. H., Zerahn, K. 1964. Concentration of lithium, sodium and potassium in epithelial cells of the isolated frog skin during active transport of lithium. *Acta Physiol. Scand.* 60:189–96

72. Harvey, W. R., Nedergaard, S. 1964. Sodium independent active transport of potassium in the isolated midgut of Cecropia silkworm. *Proc. Nat. Acad. Sci. USA* 51:757–65

73. Hays, R. M. 1972. The movement of water across vasopressin-sensitive epithelia. *Current Topics in Membranes and Transport,* ed. F. Bronner, A. Kleinzeller, 3:339–66. New York: Academic

74. Heinz, E., Ed. 1972. *Na-linked Transport of Organic Solutes.* Berlin, Heidelberg, New York: Springer. 201 pp.

75. Helman, S. I., Grantham, J. J., Burg, M. B. 1971. Effect of vasopressin on electrical resistance of renal cortical collecting tubules. *Am. J. Physiol.* 220:1825–32

76. Herrera, F. C., Egea, R., Herrera, A. M. 1971. Movement of Li across toad urinary bladder. *Am. J. Physiol.* 220:1501–08

77. Hodgkin, A. L. 1947. The effect of potassium on the surface membrane of an isolated axon. *J. Physiol. London* 106:319–40

78. Hoffman, J. F., Lassen, U. V. 1971. Plasma membrane potentials in amphibian red cells. *Int. Congr. Physiol. Sci., 25th,* Abstract

79. Hogben, C. A. M. 1955. Active transport of chloride by isolated frog gastric epithelium. *Am. J. Physiol.* 180:641–49

80. Hogben, C. A. M. 1955. Biological aspects of active chloride transport. *Electrolytes in Biological Systems,* ed. A. M. Shanes, 176–204. Washington DC: Am. Physiol. Soc.

81. Hoshi, T., Sakai, F. 1967. A comparison of the electrical resistance of the surface cell membrane and cellular wall in the proximal tubule of the newt kidney. *Jap. J. Physiol.* 17:627–37

82. Hoshiko, T., Parsons, R. H. 1972. Isolation of large sheets of frog skin epidermis. *Experientia* 281:795–96

83. Huf, E. G. 1972. The role of Cl⁻ and other anions in active Na⁺ transport in isolated frog skin. *Acta Physiol. Scand.* 84:366–81

84. Humphreys, M. H., Earley, L. E. 1971. The mechanism of decreased intestinal sodium and water absorption after acute volume expansion in the rat. *J. Clin. Invest.* 50:2355–67

85. Hunter, M. J. 1971. A quantitative estimate of the nonexchange-restricted chloride permeability of the human red cell. *J. Physiol. London* 218:49P–50P

86. Hviid Larsen, E. 1970. Sodium transport and dc resistance in the isolated toad skin in relation to shedding of the strutum corneum. *Acta Physiol. Scand.* 79:453–61

87. Hviid Larsen, E. 1973. Effect of amiloride, cyanide and ouabain on the active transport pathway in the toad skin. *Alfred Benzon Symposium V,* ed. H. H. Ussing, N. A. Thorn. Copenhagen: Munksgaard

88. Imai, M., Kokko, J. P. 1972. Effect of peritubular protein concentration on reabsorption of sodium and water in isolated perfused proximal tubules. *J. Clin. Invest.* 51:314–25

89. Janáček, K., Rybová, R. 1967. Stimulation of the sodium pump in frog bladder by oxytocin. *Nature* 215:992–93

90. Janáček, K., Morel, F., Bourguet, J. 1968. Etude expérimentale des potentiels électriques et des activités ioniques dans les cellules épithéliales de la vessie de grenouille. *J. Physiol. Paris* 60:51–66

91. Kaye, G. I., Wheeler, H. O., Whitlock, R. T., Lane, M. 1966. Fluid transport in the rabbit gallbladder: a combined physiological and electron microscopic study. *J. Cell Biol.* 30:237–68

92. Kernan, R. P. 1962. Membrane potential changes during sodium transport in frog sartorium muscle. *Nature London* 193:986–87

93. Kerkut, G. A., Thomas, R. C. 1965. An electrogenic sodium pump in snail nerve cells *Comp. Biochem. Physiol.* 14:167–83

94. Keynes, R. D. 1971. A discussion on active transport of salts and water in living tissues. *Phil. Trans. Roy. Soc. London B* 262:83–342
95. Klingenberg, M. 1970. Mitochondrial metabolic transport. *Fed. Eur. Biochem. Soc.* 6:145–54
96. Knauf, H., Frömter, E. 1971. Studies on the origin of the transepithelial electrical potentials difference in salivary duct epithelium. *Electrophysiology of Epithelial Cells,* ed. G. Giebisch, 187–99. Stuttgart: F. K. Schattauer Verlag
97. Koefoed-Johnsen, V., Levi, H., Ussing, H. H. 1952. The mode of passage of chloride ions through the isolated frog skin. *Acta Physiol. Scand.* 25:150–63
98. Koefoed-Johnsen, V., Ussing, H. H. 1958. The nature of the frog skin potential. *Acta Physiol. Scand.* 42:298–308
99. Koefoed-Johnsen, V., Lyon, J., Ussing, H. H. 1973. Effect of Cu ion on permeability properties of isolated frog skin (Rana temporia). *Acta Physiol. Scand. Suppl.* 396:102
100. Kostyuk, P. G., Krishtal, O. A., Pidoplichko, V. I. 1972. Potential-dependent membrane current during the active transport of ions in snail neurons. *J. Physiol. London* 226:373–92
101. Kristensen, P. 1972. Chloride transport across isolated frog skin. *Acta Physiol. Scand.* 84:338–46
102. Lassen, U. V. 1972. Membrane potential and membrane resistance of red cells. See Ref. 68, 291–304
103. Lassen, U. V., Nielsen, A.-M. T., Pape, L., Simonsen, L. O. 1971. The membrane potential of Ehrlich ascites tumor cells, microelectrode measurements and their critical evaluation. *J. Membrane Biol.* 6:269–88
104. Leblanc, G. 1972. The mechanism of lithium accumulation in the isolated frog skin epithelium. *Pfluegers Arch.* 337:1–18
105. Lee, C. O., Armstrong, W. McD. 1972. Activities of sodium and potassium ions in epithelial cells of small intestine. *Science* 175:1261–64
106. Lindley, B. D., Hoshiko, T., Leb, D. E. 1964. Effects of $D_2O$ and osmotic gradients on potential and resistance of the isolated frog skin. *J. Gen. Physiol.* 47:773–93
107. Lipton, P., Edelman, I. S. 1971. Effects of aldosterone and vasopressin on electrolytes of toad bladder epithelial cells. *Am. J. Physiol.* 221:733–41
108. Loeschke, K., Bentzel, C. J., Csaky, T. Z. 1970. Asymmetry of osmotic flow in frog intestine: functional and structural correlation. *Am. J. Physiol.* 218:1723–31
109. Loewenstein, W. R. 1966. Permeability of membrane junctions. *Ann. N.Y. Acad. Sci.* 137:441–72
110. Ludens, J. H., Fanestil, D. D. 1971. Amiloride induced negative potentials in the toad bladder. *Fed. Proc.* 30:421 (Abstr.)
111. Lundberg, A. 1957. The mechanism of establishment of secretory potentials in sublingual gland cells. *Acta Physiol. Scand.* 40:35–58
112. Machen, T. E., Diamond, J. M. 1972. The mechanism of anion permeation in thorium-treated gall bladder. *J. Membrane Biol.* 8:63–96
113. Machen, T. E., Erlij, D., Wooding, F. B. P. 1972. Permeable junctional complexes. The movement of lanthanum across rabbit gallbladder and intestine. *J. Cell Biol.* 54:302–12
114. Macknight, A. D. C., DiBona, D. R., Leaf, A., Civan, M. M. 1971. Measurement of the composition of epithelial cells from the toad urinary bladder. *J. Membrane Biol.* 6:108–26
115. Macknight, A. D. C., Leaf, A., Civan, M. M. 1971. Effects of vasopressin on the water and ionic composition of toad bladder epithelial cells. *J. Membrane Biol.* 6:127–37
116. Malnic, G., Giebisch, G. 1972. Some electrical properties of distal tubular epithelium in the rat. *Am. J. Physiol.* 223:797–808
117. Mandel, L. J., Curran, P. F. 1972. Chloride flux via a shunt pathway in frog skin: apparent exchange diffusion. *Biochim. Biophys. Acta* 282:258–64
118. Mandel, L. J., Curran, P. F. 1972. Response of the frog skin to steady-state voltage clamping. I. The shunt pathway. *J. Gen. Physiol.* 59:503–18
119. Martin, D. W., Curran, P. F. 1966. II. Reversed potentials in isolated frog skin. Active transport of chloride. *J. Cell Physiol.* 67:367–74
120. Martínez-Palomo, A., Erlij, D., Bracho, H. 1971. Localization of permeability barriers in the frog skin epithelium. *J. Cell Biol.* 50:277–87
121. Martínez-Palomo, A., Erlij, D. 1973. The distribution of lanthanum in tight junctions of the kidney tubule. *Pfluegers Arch.* In press
122. Mitchell, P. 1970. *The Molecular Basis of Membrane Function,* ed. D. C. Tosteson. Englewood Cliffs, N.J.: Prentice Hall
123. Moreno, J. H., Reisin, I. L., Rodríguez Boulan, E., Rotunno, C. A., Cereijido,

M. 1973. Barriers to sodium movement across frog skin. *J. Membrane Biol.* 11:99–115

124. Mullins, L. J., Brinley, F. J. 1969. Potassium fluxes in dialysed squid axons. *J. Gen. Physiol.* 53:704–40

125. Nielsen, R. 1971. Effect of amphotericin B on the frog skin in vitro. Evidence for outward active potassium transport across the epithelium. *Acta Physiol. Scand.* 83:106–14

126. Pak Poy, R. F. K., Bentley, P. J. 1960. Fine structure of the epithelial cells of the toad urinary bladder. *Exp. Cell Res.* 20:235–37

127. Parisi, M., Ripoche, P., Bourguet, J., Carasso, N., Favrad, P. 1969. This isolated epithelium of frog urinary bladder. *J. Microsc. Paris* 8:1031–36

128. Parisi, M., Piccinni, Z. F. 1973. The penetration of water into the epithelium of toad bladder and its modification by oxytocin. *J. Membrane Biol.* 12:227–46

129. Patlak, C. S., Rapoport, S. I. 1971. Theoretical analysis of net tracer flux due to volume circulation in a membrane with pores of different sizes. Relation to solute drag model. *J. Gen. Physiol.* 57:113–24

130. Peachey, L. D., Rasmussen, H. 1961. Structure of the toad's urinary bladder as related to its physiology. *J. Biophys. Biochem. Cytol.* 10:529–33

131. Post, R. L., Jolly, P. C. 1957. The linkage of sodium, potassium, and ammonium active transport across the human erythrocyte membrane. *Biochim. Biophys. Acta* 25:118–28

132. Rajerison, R. M., Montegut, M., Jard, S., Morel, F. 1972. The isolated frog skin epithelium: permeability characteristics and responsiveness to oxytocin, cyclic AMP and theophylline. *Pfuegers Arch.* 332:302–12

133. Rang, H. P., Ritchie, J. M. 1968. On the elctrogenic pump in mammalian non-myelinated nerve fibres and its activation by various external cations. *J. Physiol. London* 196:183–221

134. Rapoport, S. I., Hori, M., Klatzo, I. 1971. Reversible osmotic opening of the blood-brain barrier. *Science* 173:1026–28

135. Rawlins, F., Mateu, L., Fragachan, F., Whittembury, G. 1970. Isolated toad skin epithelium: transport characteristics. *Pfuegers Arch.* 316:64–80

136. Rhodes, R. S., Karnovsky, M. J. 1971. Loss of macromolecular barrier function associated with surgical trauma to the intestine. *Lab. Invest.* 25:220–29

137. Ripoche, P., Bourguet, J., Parisi, M. 1973. The effect of hypertonic media on water permeability of frog urinary bladder. Inhibition by catecholamines and prostaglandin $E_1$. *J. Gen. Physiol.* 61:110–24

138. Ritchie, J. M., Straub, W. R. 1957. The hyperpolarization which follows activity in mammalian non-medullated fibres. *J. Physiol. London* 136:80–97

139. Rotunno, C. A., Vilallonga, F. A., Fernández, M., Cereijido, M. 1970. The penetration of sodium into the epithelium of the frog skin. *J. Gen. Physiol.* 55:716–35

140. Scarpa, A., Cecchetto, A., Azzone, G. F. 1970. The mechanism of anion translocation and pH equilibration in erythrocytes. *Biochim. Biophys. Acta* 219:179–88

141. Schwartz, T. L. 1971. The validity of the Ussing flux ratio equation in a three-dimensionally inhomogeneous membrane. *Biophys. J.* 11:596–602

142. Singer, I., Sharp, G. W. G., Civan, M. M. 1969. The effect of propionate and other organic anions on sodium transport across toad bladder. *Biochim. Biophys. Acta* 193:430–43

143. Singer, I., Divan, M. M., Sharp, G. W. G. 1970. Studies on the mode of action of propionate in toad bladder. *Am. J. Physiol.* 219:1273–78

144. Singer, I., Civan, M. M. 1971. Effects of anions on sodium transport in toad urinary bladder. *Am. J. Physiol.* 221:1019–26

145. Skou, J. C. 1972. The relationship of the $(Na^+ + K^+)$-activated enzyme system to transport of sodium and potassium across the cell membrane. *Bioenergetics* 4:203–32

146. Smith, P. G. 1971. The low-frequency electrical impedance of the isolated frog skin. *Acta Physiol. Scand.* 81:355–66

147. Smulders, A. P., Wright, E. M. 1971. The magnitude of nonelectrolyte selectivity in the gall bladder epithelium. *J. Membrane Biol.* 5:297–318

148. Smulders, A. P., Tormey, J. McD., Wright, E. M. 1972. The effect of osmotically induced water flows on the permeability and ultrastructure of the rabbit gallbladder. *J. Membrane Biol.* 7:164–97

149. Stacy, B. D., Warner, A. C. I. 1972. Acute effects of hypertonicity on the potential difference across the rumen wall in sheep. *Comp. Biochem. Physiol. A* 43:637–41

150. Staehelin, L. A., Mukherjee, T. M., Williams, A. W. 1969. Freeze-etch ap-

pearance of the tight junctions in the epithelium of small and large intestine of mice. *Protoplasma* 67:165–84

151. Tasaki, J. 1968. Nerve excitation: *A Macromolecular Approach.* Springfield, Ill.: Thomas

152. Thomas, R. C. 1972. Electrogenic sodium pump in nerve and muscle cells. *Physiol. Rev.* 52:563–94

153. Thomas, R. C. 1972. Intracellular sodium activity and the sodium pump in snail neurones. *J. Physiol. London* 220:55–71

154. Tisher, C. C., Yarger, W. E. 1973. Lanthanum permeability of the tight junction (zonule occludens) in the renal tubule of the rat. *Kidney Int.* 3:238–50

155. Tormey, J. McD., Diamond, J. M. 1967. The ultrastructural route of fluid transport in rabbit gallbladder. *J. Gen. Physiol.* 50:2031–60

156. Tosteson, D. C. 1959. Halide transport in red cells. *Acta Physiol. Scand.* 46:19–41

157. Tosteson, D. C. 1973. Ion Transport across thin lipid bilayer membranes. See Ref. 88, 28–42

158. Urakabe, S., Handler, J. S. Orloff, J. 1970. Effect of hypertonicity on permeability properties of toad bladder. *Am J. Physiol.* 210:1179–87

159. Ussing, H. H. 1949. Transport of ions across cellular membranes. *Physiol. Rev.* 29:127–55

160. Ussing, H. H. 1965. Relationship between osmotic reactions and active sodium transport in the frog skin epithelium. *Acta Physiol. Scand.* 63:141–55

161. Ussing, H. H. 1966. Anomalous transport of electrolytes and sucrose through the isolated frog skin induced by hypertonicity of the outside bathing solution. *Ann. N.Y. Acad. Sci.* 137:543–55

162. Ussing, H. H. 1969. The interpretation of tracer fluxes in terms of membrane structure. *Quart. Rev. Biophys.* 1:365–76

163. Ussing, H. H., Kruhoffer, P., Hess Thaysen, J., Thorn, N. A. 1960. *The Alkali Metal Ion in Biology, Handb. Exp. Pharmakol.,* Vol. 13, ed. O. Eichler, A. Farah. Heidelberg: Springer

164. Ussing, H. H., Zerahn, K. 1951. Active transport of sodium as the source of electric current in the short-circuited isolated frog skin. *Acta Physiol. Scand.* 23:110–27

165. Ussing, H. H., Windhager, E. E. 1964. Nature of shunt path and active sodium transport path through frog skin epi-

thelium. *Acta Physiol. Scand.* 61:484–504

166. Ussing, H. H. 1972. The use of the flux ratio equation under non-steady state conditions. *Perspectives in Membrane Biophysics. A Tribute to Kenneth S. Cole,* ed. D. P. Agin. New York: Gordon and Breach

167. Ussing, H. H. 1973. The effect of antidiuretic hormone on the transport paths through the isolated toad skin. See Ref. 8, 11–16

168. Van Lennep, E. W. 1968. Electron microscopic histochemical studies on salt-excreting glands in elasmobranchs and marine catfish. *J. Ultrastruct. Res.* 25:94–108

169. Voûte, C. L., Ussing, H. H. 1968. Some morphological aspects of active sodium transport. The epithelium of the frog skin. *J. Cell Biol.* 36:625–38

170. Voûte, C. L. 1973. Morphophysiological evidence for a two step active transport path for sodium in the epithelium of the frog skin (R. temporaria). *Experientia.* In press

171. Voûte, C. L., Ussing, H. H. 1970. Quantitative relation between hydrostatic pressure gradient, extracellular volume and active sodium transport in the epithelium of the frog skin (R. temporaria). *Exp. Cell Res.* 62:375–83

172. Voûte, C. L., Hänni, S. 1973. Relation between structure and function in frog skin. See Ref. 88, 86–93

173. Wade, J. B., Revel, J. P., DiScala, V. A. 1973. Effect of osmotic gradients on intercellular junctions of the toad bladder. *Am. J. Physiol.* 224:407–15

174. Watlington, C. O. 1972. Regulation of sodium transport by alteration of chloride conductance. *Biochim. Biophys. Acta* 288:482–85

175. Whittembury, G., Rawlins, F. A. 1972. Evidence of a paracellular pathway for ion flow in the kidney proximal tubule: Electron microscopic demonstration of lanthanum precipitate in the tight junction. *Pfluegers Arch.* 330:302–9

176. Windhager, E. E., Boulpaep, E. L., Giebisch, G. 1967. Electrophysiological studies on single nephrons. *Proc. Int. Congr. Nephrol., 3rd, Washington, 1966,* 1:35. New York: Karger, Basel

177. Wright, E. M., Prather, J. W. 1970. The permeability of the frog chloroid plexus to nonelectrolytes. *J. Membrane Biol.* 2:127–49

178. Wright, E. M., Barry, P. H., Diamond, J. M. 1971. The mechanism of cation permeation in rabbit gallbladder. Con-

ductances, the current-voltage relation, the concentration dependence of anion-cation discrimination, and the calcium competition effect. *J. Membrane Biol.* 4:331–57

179. Wright, E. M., Smulders, A. P., Tormey, J. M. 1972. The role of the lateral intercellular spaces and solute polarization effects in the passive flow of water across the rabbit gall bladder. *J. Membrane Biol.* 7:198–219

180. Wright, E. M. 1972. Mechanisms of ion transport across the choroid plexus. *J. Physiol. London* 226:545–71

181. Wright, F. 1971. Increasing magnitude of electrical potential along the renal distal tubule. *Am. J. Physiol.* 220:624–38

182. Zadunaisky, J. A., Candia, O. A., Chiarandini, J. 1963. Origin of the short-circuit current in the isolated skin of the south american frog Leptodactylus Ocellatus. *J. Gen. Physiol.* 47:392–402

183. Zadunaisky, J. A. 1972. Sodium activation of chloride transport in the frog cornea. *Biochim. Biophys. Acta* 292:255–57

184. Zerahn, K. 1969. Nature and localization of the sodium pool during active transport in the isolated frog skin. *Acta Physiol. Scand.* 77:272–81

# ION TRANSPORT BY ❖1105
# MAMMALIAN SMALL INTESTINE[1]

*Stanley G. Schultz, Raymond A. Frizzell, and Hugh N. Nellans*

Department of Physiology, University of Pittsburgh, School of Medicine, Pittsburgh, Pennsylvania

## INTRODUCTION

The investigation of intestinal transport processes using in vitro preparations has two principal goals. One is to elucidate general principles of membrane physiology that are applicable to all epithelia and, in some instances, to nonepithelial cells as well. The other is to gain a deeper understanding of the mechanisms responsible for intestinal absorptive and secretory processes in vivo. The first goal might be classified under the general area of membrane physiology, whereas the second would more properly fall within the realm of gastrointestinal physiology; needless to say, these goals are not divorced, but, on the contrary, have proven to be highly synergistic.

The primary emphasis of this review will be gastroenterologic. We will attempt to examine critically observations and models that have emerged from relatively recent studies of intestinal function in vivo and to relate these to results of studies on in vitro preparations. In this way, we hope to identify areas of convergence where in vitro studies have provided insight into the mechanisms responsible for in vivo observations, and, equally important, to identify areas of divergence where in vivo observations are not readily reconcilable with in vitro observations; possible explanations for these divergences will be suggested in the hope that they will stimulate further investigation aimed at their resolution.

This review will focus on sodium, chloride, bicarbonate, and potassium transport by mammalian small intestine and the interaction between sodium transport and the transport of nonelectrolytes, with stress on developments that have emerged since these subjects were last reviewed in detail (56, 57, 155, 156). References to the literature will be selective rather than exhaustive; and those readers interested in a more complete compilation of the relevant literature should consult the excellent

[1]The studies reported from the authors' laboratories were supported by research grants from the National Institute of Arthritis, Metabolism and Digestive Diseases, and the American Heart Association.

51

abstract service issued by the Biomedical Information Project of the University of Sheffield.

Finally, because of space limitations, any attempt at a comprehensive review of recent progress in the area of intestinal ion transport would, of necessity, be superficial. For this reason, we will address ourselves to only three areas that have witnessed major new developments and that portend important consequences for the future. These are (a) recently suggested models for transepithelial ion transport (b) new developments with respect to the interactions between ion transport and the transport of nonelectrolytes, and (c) the recognition that the small intestine is capable of active secretion and is a "target organ" for the action of bacterial enterotoxins and gastrointestinal secretogogues.

## MODELS OF SMALL INTESTINAL ION TRANSPORT

Since the studies of Ussing & Windhager (182) it has become increasingly clear that solute transport across all epithelia may partake of two routes, a transcellular route that involves movements across at least two membranes arranged in series and an extracellular route that circumvents the membranes surrounding the epithelial cells. The latter route is referred to as the "shunt" pathway and there is compelling evidence that this pathway comprises the tight junctions and the underlying lateral intercellular spaces (68). Although the relative contributions of the shunt pathway and the transcellular route to ion and solute movements across epithelial tissues varies over a wide spectrum, there is little doubt that the shunt plays a major role in the movement of ions, small nonelectrolytes, and, in all likelihood, water across small intestine. Indeed, this pathway appears to play a major role in all tissues characterized by relatively low transepithelial electrical potential differences (PDs), low resistances, high hydraulic conductivities, and isotonic absorbates or secretions (68). For this reason, a quantitative appreciation of the properties of the shunt pathway across small intestine is prerequisite to any attempt to define the transport properties of the epithelial cells themselves.

### The Shunt Pathway Across Small Intestine

IONIC PERMEABILITIES AND TRANSEPITHELIAL POTENTIAL DIFFERENCES    Recently three lines of evidence have been presented for the presence of relatively high conductance shunt pathways across in vitro preparations of small intestine. First, electrophysiologic studies on rabbit (148) and bullfrog (184) small intestine have disclosed that changes in the PD across the mucosal and basolateral membranes in response to the addition of actively transported sugars or amino acids to the mucosal solution can be reconciled only with an equivalent electrical circuit model featuring a relatively low resistance shunt pathway which permits electrical coupling between the electromotive forces across the two limiting membranes of the epithelial cells. Similar results have been reported for the proximal renal tubule of the newt (121) where there is direct electrophysiologic evidence for the presence of low resistance transepithelial shunt pathways (92). Second, studies on the effect of an imposed transepithelial PD on the unidirectional influxes[2] of Na, Cl, and K across the luminal surface of rabbit ileum have disclosed that the total influx of each ion is comprised of two components. The first behaves as if it crosses the mucosal membranes and does not conform to the laws of diffusion. The second component conforms to the laws of simple ionic diffusion and behaves as if the ion simply enters a water-filled, neutral, polar pore (62). Similar observations have been made on rat jejunum (Munch & Schultz, unpublished observations). Finally, Machen et al (119) have demonstrated that the tight junctions of rabbit ileal mucosa are permeable to lanthanum, an ion whose size is not much larger than that of Na; similar findings have been reported by Whittembury & Rawlins (185) for proximal tubule of toad kidney. Thus it seems safe to conclude that the "tight junctions" are permeable to some small ions (and as we shall see below, small nonelectrolytes) and that the junctional complexes, together with the underlying lateral intercellular spaces, comprise the anatomic counterpart of the shunt pathway disclosed by electrophysiologic and influx studies. Compelling evidence for the same conclusion has been presented for renal proximal tubule (16) and gall bladder (68).

Several properties of the shunt pathways across rabbit ileum and rat jejunum are particularly relevant to the present discussion. First, in rabbit ileum the total ionic conductance of the shunt pathway accounts for at least 85% of the total tissue conductance (62). In other words, in response to driving forces such as concentration gradients and electrical potential differences, transepithelial movements through the shunt pathway should exceed flows through the transcellular route by a factor of 7–10. Second, the shunt pathways across rabbit ileum and rat jejunum do not sharply distinguish between Na and K but are cation-selective; the relative ionic permeabilities of the former are $P_K:P_{Na}:P_{Cl} = 1.14:1.00:0.55$, and for rat jejunum, $P_{Cl}/P_{Na} = 0.2$–0.25. These relative ionic permeabilities, when compared to the relative ionic mobilities in free solution, suggest that the shunt pathway affords an aqueous environment for the diffusion of ions in their hydrated forms and is characterized by an anionic field strength of intermediate to low intensity. In rabbit ileum the shunt pathway is only minimally permeable to tetraethylammonium (TEA) ($P_{TEA}/P_{Na} \approx 0.02$), a spherical molecule with a radius of approximately 4 Å, and is impermeable to lysine (129); the shunt across rat jejunum is impermeable to TEA, lysine, and diaminobutyric acid (Munck & Schultz, unpublished observations). Thus the diameter of this pathway appears to be approximately 10–15 Å, a value similar to that proposed by Bentzel et al (10) for the shunt pathway in proximal tubule of *Necturus*. Third, analysis of the equivalent electrical circuit corresponding to an epithelial tissue characterized by a single cell layer and low resistance intercellular shunts (62, 148) indicates that 1. in the absence of transepithelial ionic gradients, the shunt pathway markedly attentuates the difference between the electromotive forces across the mucosal and basolateral membranes so that these tissues will, in general, be characterized by small transepithelial PDs; and

---

[2]The terms *influx* and *efflux* refer to unidirectional solute movements; in particular, the term influx when applied to the mucosal membrane refers to the zero-time rate of uptake of a solute from the mucosal solution into the epithelium as described by Schultz et al and modified by Frizzell & Schultz (62).

2. in the presence of transepithelial ionic gradients, the transepithelial PDs will predominantly reflect diffusion PDs resulting from the permselective properties of the shunt (62). Finally, influx into the shunt pathway from the mucosal solution closely agrees with the unidirectional serosa-to-mucosa flux of Na in rabbit ileum (62, 159) and rat jejunum (128, Munck & Schultz, unpublished observations) suggesting that 1. most, if not all, of the back-flux of Na from the serosal solution to the mucosal solution takes place through the shunt; 2. the basolateral membranes of these two epithelia are essentially impermeable to Na; and 3. the active Na extrusion mechanism responsible for the movement of Na from the cell into the serosal solution is virtually completely rectified.

These findings offer possible, if not probable, explanations for a number of previously reported findings on in vitro and in vivo preparations of small intestine. First, it is now clear that the large bidirectional fluxes of Na observed in rabbit (50, 67, 159) and rat (128) small intestine under short-circuit conditions may be predominantly attributed to ionic diffusion through the shunt pathway. The net (active) flux under short-circuit conditions is but a small difference between two large numbers and, as suggested by Clarkson (34), probably represents a rectified movement through the transcellular route from mucosa to serosa only. Similar arguments probably apply to the relatively large bidirectional fluxes of Na observed in human (123, 171) and canine (36) small intestine in vivo.

Second, in vivo perfusion of the human jejunum with distilled water results in a rapid entry of Na and Cl into the lumen (152). Similarly, perfusion of human small intestine with a Na-free hypertonic mannitol solution results in a rapid influx of water, Na, and Cl into the lumen; after 30 min, the mean concentrations of NaCl were 50 mM in the upper jejunum, 34 mM in the lower jejunum, and 10 mM in the ileum (59). In addition, Fordtran et al (58) have demonstrated that Na absorption by normal human jejunum ceases when the luminal concentration is lowered to approximately 130 mM and that Na secretion ensues at lower luminal concentrations; in human ileum, net Na absorption ceases when the luminal concentration is ~30 mM and a slow but significant secretion of Na into the lumen is observed at lower luminal Na concentrations. All of these data suggest that the human small intestine is highly permeable to Na and that the permeability decreases progressively from the upper jejunum to the ileum. A similar progression is observed with respect to the spontaneous transepithelial PD, which is lowest in the jejunum and reaches maximal values in the ileum (58). Finally, Turnberg et al (180) have reported that when NaCl in the luminal fluid perfusing normal human ileum is lowered by isotonic replacement with mannitol, the lumen becomes electrically positive with respect to the serosal solution and the relation between the PD and the NaCl concentration is consistent with a diffusion potential in which $P_{Cl}/P_{Na} = 0.3$, a value close to those found for the shunt pathways across isolated rabbit and rat jejunum.

All these data are entirely consistent with the notion that the movement of NaCl into the lumen of human small intestine, in response to concentration gradients, bulk flow (solvent drag), or both, takes place largely via the shunt pathway and that the accompanying PD reflects the permselective properties of that pathway. The rate of NaCl diffusion, the concentration gradients against which net Na absorption can take place, and the spontaneous transepithelial PD in the absence of ionic gradients could simply reflect the ionic conductances of the shunts in the various regions of the small intestine. Properties of the transcellular pathway need not be invoked to explain any of the findings reported above.

INTERACTIONS BETWEEN SOLUTE MOVEMENTS AND BULK FLOW  A number of groups have recently examined the effects of spontaneous water absorption and osmotically-incuded water absorption or secretion on the movements of solutes across small intestine in vivo and in vitro. In most instances, the formal analysis of the coupling between solute and solvent flows has followed the approach proposed by Kedem & Katchalsky (98). Thus,

$$J_s = (1 - \sigma_s) \, J_v \bar{C}_s + \omega RT \Delta C_s \qquad\qquad 1.$$

where $J_s$ is the flow of solute, $J_v$ is the volume flow, $\omega RT$ is the traditional "permeability coefficient" ($P_s$) of the solute, $\sigma_s$ is the reflection coefficient (which may vary from 1 for a totally impermeant solute to 0 for a solute whose permeability is equal to that of $H_2O$), $\bar{C}_s$ is the mean concentration, and $\Delta C_s$ is the concentration difference across the barrier. Thus when $\Delta C_s = 0$

$$J_s = (1 - \sigma_s) \, J_v C_s \qquad\qquad 2.$$

The diffusive-convective model proposed by Lifson and co-workers (113–115) essentially parallels this analysis except for the use of different terminology and symbols, and Equation 1 is expressed as $J_s = \phi J_v C_s' + \alpha \Delta C_s$ where $C_s'$ is the mean luminal concentration when volume is being absorbed and $C_s$ is the plasma (or serosal) concentration during secretion. Thus, when $\Delta C_s$ is small, $\phi$ is essentially equal to $(1 - \sigma_s)$ and provides a reasonable estimate of the coupling between $J_s$ and $J_v$.

It should be stressed that the demonstration of a relation between solute movement and volume flow in the apparent absence of a concentration difference need not mean that the underlying mechanism is solvent drag through water-filled pores. Volume flow could also influence solute movements as a result of the presence of unstirred and poorly stirred regions that surround the epithelial cell layer. Thus water flow from mucosa to serosa (lumen to plasma) will tend to concentrate solutes in the unstirred layers adjacent to the brush border and dilute (or "wash out") solutes in the lateral spaces, subepithelial tissues, the capillary network in the villus core, the central lacteals, and possibly within the epithelial cells themselves. Preexisting concentration differences may be increased and presumably absent concentration differences may be established by this "sieving effect" regardless of the direction of water flow. Thus $\Delta C_s$ and the contribution of diffusional flows accompanying bulk flow may be seriously underestimated. This "concentrating" and "washing out" effect is observed in highly stirred artificial membrane systems, is inevitable in less well stirred in vitro preparations of small intestine, and is likely to play a maximal role in in vivo studies that provide minimal stirring. In the light of these considerations, the use of Equations 1 and 2 to determine reflection coefficients is subject to error and the observation of an increase in solute movement in response to an increase in water flow cannot be indiscriminantly attributed to solvent drag. For this reason, the term *apparent reflection coefficient* ("$\sigma$") will be employed in the ensuing discussion.

Fordtran et al (58) reported that Na and urea movements across human jejunum are markedly affected by bulk flow; the apparent reflection coefficients for both solutes are approximately 0.5 regardless of the direction and magnitude of water movement. In contrast, in the normal human ileum water movement did not significantly affect Na transport and only mimimally affected urea movements; thus the apparent reflection coefficients for these solutes in ileum are close to unity. These data are in good agreement with the results of previous studies on the osmotic effectiveness of various solutes (compared to mannitol) in inducing water movement into the lumen of human small intestine. In the jejunum, the apparent reflection coefficients for NaCl, urea, and erythritol are 0.6, 0.5, and 0.6, respectively, and in the ileum they are 1.0, 0.9, and 1.0, respectively (59). An analysis of these data using the Renkin equation suggested that the "equivalent pore radius" in human jejunum is 7–9 Å and that for human ileum is 3–4 Å. Similar values for human small intestine have been reported by Soergel et al (170). However, as will be discussed below, these values may be underestimates because of the technique employed. In any event, the large pore radii estimated for human jejunum on the basis of these studies virtually excludes the possibility that the transcellular route plays a significant role in convective solute flow and osmotically induced bulk flow. Turnberg (179) has recently reported that K movements across human jejunum are also markedly affected by bulk flow; the apparent reflection coefficient ("$\sigma$") for K is approximately 0.4 regardless of the direction of water flow. Thus, "$\sigma$"$_{Na}$/"$\sigma$"$_K$ in human jejunum is approximately 1.2, a value in close agreement with the relative permeabilities of the shunt pathway across rabbit ileum for Na and K.

Lifson and co-workers (80, 113–115) have evaluated the convective and diffusive components of a variety of nonelectrolytes in canine jejunum. Using an in vitro preparation they found that the apparent reflection coefficient for urea was near zero during spontaneous water absorption and when water secretion was induced by the application of a hydrostatic pressure to the serosal solution (80). Similar conclusions were drawn for $D_2O$ suggesting that neither urea nor $D_2O$ is subject to significant sieving by the epithelium (115). Using perfused in vivo loops of canine jejunum, these investigators (113) found an apparent reflection coefficient of 0.2 for urea, and for arabinose, xylose, and glucose the coefficients are approximately 0.4 during spontaneous water absorption. These values are consistent with convective flow through channels having an equivalent pore radius of approximately 15 Å. On the other hand, the diffusive components for xylose, arabinose, and glucose were considerably lower and are consistent with a pore radius of approximately 5 Å. Further, these authors found that the convective components of xylose and arabinose are negligible during osmotically induced water secretion; their data suggest that under these conditions the channel for convective flow has a radius of approximately 3.5 Å. Thus bulk flow was considerably less effective in producing solute movement when water secretion was brought about by rendering the luminal solution hypertonic than during spontaneous water absorption.

The most reasonable explanation for these findings emerges from the investigations of Loeschke et al (117), who found that the hydraulic conductivity ($L_p$) of the bullfrog small intestine is larger when water flow is directed from mucosa to serosa

than when water is secreted into a hypertonic muscosal solution. Ultrastructural studies indicated that the lateral intercellular spaces were widely distended when fluid movement was directed from mucosa to serosa but were collapsed during osmotically-induced volume secretion. Studies by Loeschke et al (118) on 3-O-methylglucose (3-MG) diffusion across frog jejunum in the presence of phlorizin indicated that in the absence of water flow, the permeability coefficient was equal in the two directions. When the serosal solution was rendered hypertonic the permeability coefficients for 3-MG diffusion in both directions were increased severalfold and there was a net absorption of this sugar attributed to solvent drag. In contrast, when the mucosal solution was rendered hypertonic there was no increase in the permeability coefficient and no solvent drag effect was observed. Somewhat similar results have been reported by Wright et al (187) and Smulders et al (169) for rabbit gall bladder. These investigators found that during spontaneous water absorption the lateral interspaces were distended, and that rendering the serosal solution hypertonic further dilated these spaces but did not increase tissue conductance or the permeability to sucrose. On the other hand, when the mucosal solution was made hypertonic the lateral interspaces collapsed, total tissue resistance increased and the permeability to sucrose decreased. Further, the hydraulic conductivity of the tissue was significantly greater when osmotically-induced bulk flow was directed from mucosa to serosa than when it was directed from serosa to mucosa.

All of these observations indicate conclusively that the small intestinal epithelium must be treated as a mosaic membrane, characterized by parallel (as well as series) inhomogenieties. The tight junctions and lateral intercellular spaces appear to provide the major parallel pathway for transepithelial water flow, either spontaneous (i.e. coupled to net solute absorption) or resulting from osmotic gradients. The dimensions of this pathway appear to vary with species, region of small intestine, and the experimental techniques employed. In the human and canine jejunum in vivo, the equivalent pore radius of this pathway during water absorption appears to exceed 10–15 Å. In human ileum the dimensions of this shunt appear to be somewhat smaller. However, the technique employed by Fordtran et al (59) and Soergel et al (170) (i.e. rendering the muscosal solution hypertonic) may have resulted in an underestimate of the shunt dimensions or, stated in another way, an overestimate of the apparent solute reflection coefficients, since the permeability of the shunt pathway appears to be determined by factors that influence the width of the lateral interspaces and the "tightness" of the junctional complexes. Water flow from mucosa to serosa, either spontaneous or induced by serosal hypertonicity, appears to widen this pathway, increase the hydraulic conductivity of the tissue, and enhance convective solute flow. On the other hand, the reverse of these effects accompanies water flow from serosa to mucosa resulting from mucosal hypertonicity. Thus the experimental techniques employed must be considered in any attempt to characterize this pathway in terms of either apparent reflection coefficients or equivalent pore radii.

Finally, this concept is entirely consistent with the findings of Lifson et al (113, 114) that the dimensions of the pathways for solute diffusion are considerably smaller than those for convective flow. If the principal pathway for bulk water flow

is through the junctional complexes and lateral interspaces, the apparent reflection coefficients will be determined predominantly by the dimensions of this extracellular route. On the other hand, if solute diffusion takes place through both the extracellular and transcellular routes, the overall permeability coefficient will be the area-weighted average of the permeabilities of these two routes. The fractional area of the mucosal membranes vastly exceeds that of the shunt pathway. Thus the finding that the equivalent pore radius consistent with nonelectrolyte diffusion is considerably smaller than that for convective flow is readily explicable, in view of the likelihood that the mucosal membranes (like almost all plasma membranes) are relatively impermeable to solutes having four or more carbon atoms (solutes with radii greater than 4 Å). This argument is entirely consistent with Kedem & Katchalsky's (99) formal analysis of the behavior of mosaic membranes characterized by parallel inhomogenieties.

THE ROLE OF THE SHUNT PATHWAY IN HOMEOSTATIC MECHANISMS    Evidence has recently been presented that saline infusion rapidly depresses Na and water absorption by rat (97), dog (86), and cat (78) small intestine. In the rat, volume expansion through infusion of isotonic saline was associated with an increased movement of Na from plasma to lumen and a significant increase in the permeability of the epithelium to inulin. Further, volume expansion by infusion of hyperoncotic albumin partially reversed the inhibitory effect of saline infusion on intestinal absorption of salt and water. In addition, Mailman & Ingraham (120) have reported that 12–25% hemorrhage and upward head tilting significantly enhanced salt and water absorption by canine ileum.

These observations appear to be explicable in the light of recent studies by Hakim & Lifson (81) on the effects of pressure on water and solute transport across canine jejunum in vitro. These investigators found that increasing the hydrostatic pressure of the mucosal solution (with respect to the serosal solution) up to 22 cm $H_2O$ did not affect fluid absorption. In contrast, when the serosal pressure was increased by only 2–6 cm $H_2O$ (1.5–4.5 mm Hg) fluid absorption was abolished and further increases in the serosal pressure resulted in fluid secretion. In addition, the Na, Cl, and glucose concentrations in the secreted fluid closely approximated those in the serosal solution indicating little or no sieving of these solutes during the secretory process (the apparent reflection coefficients were approximately zero). Finally, in the presence of moderate serosal pressures, inulin was transported into the mucosal solution and Evans blue, ferritin, and even erythrocytes entered the mucosal solution when the serosal pressure was raised to only 10 cm $H_2O$. These findings should be contrasted with the results of Levitt et al (113) which indicated that convective flow of pentoses from plasma to lumen was abolished when fluid secretion was elicited by mucosal hypertonicity.

Thus it seems reasonable to conclude that whereas mucosal hypertoncity results in a collapse of the lateral interspaces, fluid secretion resulting from an increase in serosal interstitial tissue pressure is associated with a widening of these interspace and an increase in the permeability of the junctional complexes. In vivo, the inters

tial tissue pressure in the villus cores will be strongly influenced by the balance of hydrostatic and oncotic pressures of the villus capillary bed (the "Starling forces"). Thus the effects of volume expansion with either isotonic saline or hyperoncotic albumin and the effects of hemorrhage on small intestinal fluid absorption can be explained in terms of their effects on interstitial tissue pressure in the villus cores and, in turn, on the width and permeability of the shunt pathway. In short, the physical factors responsible for alterations in the absorptive function of the small intestine in response to changes in extracellular fluid volume appear to parallel closely those postulated for the renal proximal tubule (9, 17, 153) and appear to be mediated, at least in part, by changes in the properties of the shunt pathway.[3]

## Transcellular Ion Transport by Small Intestine

MODELS FOR ION TRANSPORT BY JEJUNUM  Although it has long been established that mammalian jejunum is capable of absorbing Na, Cl, and $HCO_3$, the only detailed investigation of possible underlying mechanisms has been carried out by Fordtran and co-workers (58, 181) on human jejunum in vivo. These investigators found that the rate and direction of Na flow are markedly affected by bulk water flow. However, when the lumen was perfused with a solution containing 140 m$M$ Na and 100 m$M$ Cl ($SO_4$ was employed to isotonically replace Cl) so that transepithelial concentration differences for these ions were abolished 1. the electrical potential difference (PD) between the lumen and abraded skin was small (approximately 2.5 mV, lumen negative) and 2. in the absence of water absorption, NaCl absorption was abolished. Thus, under these conditions, active Na absorption was not detected. However, in spite of the fact that transepithelial concentration gradients for Na and Cl were eliminated, the role of the transepithelial PD may have been underestimated. Although a PD of 2.5 mV is generally not impressive, it could provide an important driving force in epithelia characterized by low resistance shunt pathways (62, 154). The failure to observe net transepithelial Na absorption could have been the result of active transcellular Na absorption balanced by a "backflux" of Na through the shunt pathway driven by the transepithelial PD. Thus, although concentration differences were eliminated, the electrochemical potential was not abolished; in the absence of active Na absorption, one might have expected to observe net Na secretion. On the other hand, following the addition of $HCO_3$ to the perfusate, both Na and $HCO_3$ were absorbed against their respective electrochemical potential gradients so that demonstrable net active Na absorption appears to depend upon the presence of $HCO_3$ in the lumen. Further, using achlorhydric, pernicious anemia patients these investigators found that the disappearance of $HCO_3$ from the lumen was associated with a significant increase in luminal $P_{CO_2}$; this suggested that

[3]Recent studies by Lee (Effects of pressure on water absorption and secretion in rat jejunum. *Am. J. Physiol.* 224:1338–44, 1973), in which he used an in vitro vascularly perfused segment of rat jejunum, provide support for the notion that the balance between capillary hydrostatic pressure and colloid osmotic pressure in the villus core strongly influences the direction of fluid transport across small intestinal epithelium.

the apparent $HCO_3$ absorption was in reality the result of H secretion. This process was inhibited by acetazolamide and under no circumstances was a statistically significant change in the (PD) detected between the lumen and abraded skin.

On the basis of these observations, the authors suggested that active Na absorption is the result of a neutral exchange between Na and H, with the latter reacting with luminal $HCO_3$. The failure to actively absorb Na in the absence of $HCO_3$ was attributed to the fact that the luminal contents are acidified and the possiblilty that active H secretory process (responsible for Na absorption) is pH-gradient limited. Thus, in essence, the authors propose that this mechanism brings about the overall absorption of Na and $HCO_3$, the latter being formed within the cell and extruded preferentially across the basolateral membranes. Although they did not address themselves directly to Cl absorption, we assume that they attribute this to 1. Cl diffusion, since volume absorption will establish a concentration gradient for Cl directed from lumen to plasma, and 2. solvent drag secondary to water absorption associated with the net transepithelial movements of Na and $HCO_3$. If so, the failure to detect a significant change in the transepithelial PD would imply that the diffusive and convective pathways for Na and Cl movements are equally permeable to these two ions. However, this implication is apparently contradicted by other data presented by these authors which will be discussed below.

Sladen & Dawson (166) have confirmed that the presence of $HCO_3$ in a perfusate of isotonic saline markedly enhances Na absorption by normal human ileum compared to that observed in the absence of $HCO_3$. However, in the $HCO_3$-free experiments, the saline was buffered with 24 m$M$ phosphate so that the pH ranged between 7.45–7.61 and did not differ significantly from that of the $HCO_3$-containing perfusate. Thus these investigators concluded that the stimulatory effect of $HCO_3$ is independent of luminal pH and that their results do not support the notion of a pH-gradient limited active secretion of H in exchange for Na. Finally, Hellier et al (85) have reported recently that perfusion of human jejunum with isotonic NaCl alone resulted in secretion of water and electrolytes.

Unfortunately, to date there are few in vitro studies on mammalian jejunum that can assist in providing some insight into underlying mechanisms; indeed, the results of these studies do not provide a consistent picture of the behavior of mammalian jejunum in vitro. Fluid transport by rat (54) and canine (82) jejunum appears to depend on the presence of glucose, even in the presence of bicarbonate. More recently, Munck (128) has reported that in the absence of bicarbonate and an actively transported sugar or amino acid, short-circuited preparations of rat jejunum actively secrete Cl and absorb Na; the former accounts for approximately two-thirds of the total short-circuit current and the latter accounts for the remainder. Fromm (67) reported that in the presence of $HCO_3$-Ringer, short-circuited preparations of proximal rabbit jejunum actively secrete Na, and that the addition of actively transported sugars such as glucose or 3-O-methylglucose reversed this process and resulted in active Na absorption. Studies by Binder (personal communication) on short-circuited human jejunum indicate a small but significant active absorption of Na in the absence of $HCO_3$ which was markedly stimulated by glucose or 3-O-methylglucose.

In any event, to date there has been no direct evaluation of the effect of $HCO_3$ per se on ion transport across in vitro mammalian jejunum using the same preparation and experimental conditions. There are, therefore, no data comparable to those presented by Turnberg et al (181) and Sladen & Dawson (166). Nevertheless, it seems clear that in the absence of $HCO_3$, actively transported sugars, or a combination of these, both in vivo and in vitro preparations of mammalian ileum either exhibit minimal salt and water absorption or actually secrete electrolytes and water into the lumen. Finally, it should be noted that $HCO_3$ stimulates Na transport across a number of epithelia in vitro including frog skin (69) and rabbit gall bladder (40), but the mechanisms underlying these observations are as yet unclear.

MODELS FOR ION TRANSPORT BY ILEUM    One of the principal distinctions between jejunal and ileal function in vivo is that the former absorbs NaCl and $HCO_3$, while in vivo preparations of rat (94, 95, 135) and canine (175) ileum actively secrete $HCO_3$. Turnberg et al (180) have demonstrated in normal human ileum in situ that 1. Na and Cl are absorbed and $HCO_3$ is secreted, and all three movements take place against steep transepithelial electrochemical potential differences; 2. the rate of active $HCO_3$ secretion equals that of active Cl absorption only when there is no net Na transport; 3. with increasing Na absorption, the rate of $HCO_3$ secretion (or recovery from the luminal solution) declines, and, with further increases in the rate of Na absorption, there is apparent $HCO_3$ absorption from a balanced Ringer's solution; 4. Cl is actively absorbed from solutions containing low $HCO_3$ concentrations, but when the latter exceeds approximately 60 m$M$, Cl is secreted; and 5. when the perfusate contained 25 m$M$ $HCO_3$, but $SO_4$ was substituted for Cl, the rate of Na absorption decreased, $HCO_3$ was absorbed rather than secreted, and the pH of the luminal fluid declined.

These observations suggested a model featuring two independent neutral exchange mechanisms (Figure 1$a$), one that brings about an exchange of Na for H and another that leads to an exchange of Cl for $HCO_3$. The Cl-$HCO_3$ exchange process is presumed to be reversible inasmuch as high luminal concentrations of $HCO_3$ can result in Cl secretion. Further, the Na-H exchange might be pH-gradient limited as suggested for jejunum; in the absence of Cl, $HCO_3$ was absorbed, the lumen was acidified, and Na absorption was reduced. The decrease in apparent $HCO_3$ secretion with increasing Na absorption is attributed to the interaction between secreted H and secreted $HCO_3$ so that $HCO_3$ recovery is reduced. Finally, it is clear that according to this model, human ileum can display a wide spectrum of transport activities. If both exchange mechanisms operate at the same rates, the net result would be NaCl absorption. If the Cl-$HCO_3$ exchange mechanism operates at a faster rate than the Na-H mechanism, NaCl absorption and $HCO_3$ secretion would occur.

The model suggested by Turnberg et al (180) is consistent with observations on a patient with congenital chloridorrhea (11). The results suggest that the Cl-$HCO_3$ exchange mechanism is no longer capable of active Cl absorption and active $HCO_3$ secretion, but responds in an entirely passive manner to the apparent electrochemical potential gradients for these ions (Figure 1$b$). In contrast, the active Na-H exchange process is unimpaired. Consequently, this individual secretes H and Cl and

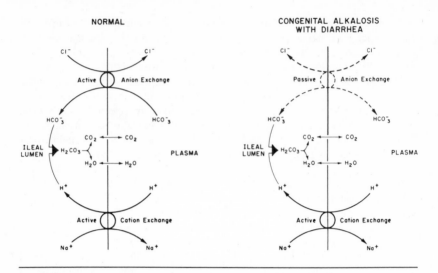

*Figure 1 (Left) a* Double exchange model for normal human ileum. *(Right) b* Model for human ileal function in congenital chloridorrhea. From Turnberg et al (180) and Bieberdorf et al (11).

absorbs Na and $HCO_3$, and these effects lead to a metabolic alkalosis. The defect in this condition is closely simulated by perfusion of normal human ileum with a Cl-free solution (180).

The principal shortcoming of these in vivo studies is that they treat the intestinal epithelium as a single membrane separating the lumen from the plasma. This "black box" approach certainly can provide important information regarding the overall operation of the epithelium with respect to net movements into or out of the lumen, and it is difficult to conceive of an alternate method for the study of human intestinal function in vivo. But, as discussed by Schultz & Frizzell (157), the results of such studies are not amenable to a definitive analysis of the mechanisms responsible for these movements. The epithelial cell layer comprises at least five cell types (178) and each cell is bounded by at least two membranes, the mucosal and the basolateral, arranged in series. Active transepithelial transport must result from the different transport properties of these membranes. Thus terms such as "coupled exchange," "electrogenic," etc, have little significance in terms of underlying biochemical or physical mechanisms unless the processes responsible for net absorption or secretion can be specifically localized to one or the other of the limiting membranes. In addition, because in vivo preparations cannot be short-circuited, significant net movements could take place via the low resistance shunt pathway. Further, the black box approach may, in some instances, incorrectly identify the initial and final states of an ion leading to an incorrect assignment of conjugate driving forces, i.e. electrochemical potential differences. For example, there is reasonable evidence that $HCO_3$ secreted by ileum and colon is derived partly from intracellular metabolism

MODEL FOR TRANSCELLULAR Na AND Cl TRANSPORT

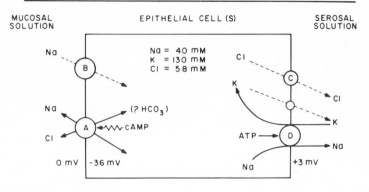

*Figure 2* Model for Na, Cl, K, and HCO$_3$ transport by in vitro rabbit ileum.

(c.f. 25); thus the conjugate driving force for movement across the mucosal membrane into the lumen is the electrochemical potential difference of HCO$_3$ across that membrane rather than the electrochemical potential difference of HCO$_3$ between the plasma and the lumen.

In recent years, ion transport across rabbit ileum has been extensively investigated by a variety of in vitro techniques. Most recent studies employing the short-circuit technique have used preparations of ileal mucosa from which the muscle layers and much of the submucosal tissues have been stripped. This preparation affords better oxygenation of the epithelial cell layer (18, 63). In most instances, the short-circuit current can be accounted for by active Na absorption, a smaller component of active Cl absorption, and a "residual current" that appears to be due to active HCO$_3$ secretion (48, 50). The latter ranges between 1–3 $\mu$moles cm$^{-2}$ hr$^{-1}$ and closely corresponds to the rate of HCO$_3$ production by mucosal strips of rabbit ileum (63). Short-circuited stripped human ileal mucosa displays active Na absorption and a residual current presumably due to active HCO$_3$ secretion, but no significant net movements of Cl (3); indeed, active Cl absorption by short-circuited rabbit (15, 162) and rat (34, 35) ileum has not been a consistent finding. Possible explanations for these observations are discussed below.

The results of studies on intracellular ion concentrations (108, 161), the electrical potential profile (148), ion influxes across the brush border (62, 66, 131), and transepithelial movements of Na and Cl across short-circuited rabbit ileum (132) are consistent with the model illustrated in Figure 2. In the absence of actively transported sugars or amino acids, Na may cross the brush border via two routes. One (*A*) is tightly coupled to Cl influx and is inhibited by intracellular cAMP and acetazolamide; the second (*B*) is Cl-independent and is unaffected by cAMP. In both instances, Na entry is down a steep electrochemical potential difference (108, 110, 148, 161) and is not inhibited by ouabain or metabolic inhibitors (33). Process

$A$ appears to be a neutral NaCl influx mechanism whose kinetic properties conform to a classical carrier model featuring a random combination of Na and Cl with a membrane component (or "carrier") (131). As discussed below, there is reason to believe that this process is reversible and may mediate the efflux of NaCl, $NaHCO_3$ or both out of the cell into the mucosal solution; indeed, there is good evidence that this process plays a central role in ileal secretory processes. The nature of process $B$ is unclear; it may be simply diffusional or it may be mediated by a carrier mechanism. If the latter is the case, process $B$ may be responsible for the Na-H exchange postulated by Turnberg et al (180).

Cl entry into the cell appears to be restricted to process $A$ inasmuch as active Cl absorption is abolished in the absence of Na. In the absence of Cl, active Na absorption is reduced but not abolished (132). Further, this process appears to result in the net movement of Cl into the cell against an apparent electrochemical potential difference (66). Inasmuch as influx via process $A$ does not seem to be directly linked to metabolic energy (131), net Cl entry via process $A$ may be driven by the Na gradient as postulated for actively transported sugars and amino acids (156). Alternatively, net Cl entry via this process could be driven by an outwardly directed $HCO_3$ electrochemical gradient. Such a model would be consistent with the apparently close link between $HCO_3$ secretion and the presence of Cl in the mucosal solution reported for rat ileum (94, 95) and colon (137). Finally, the apparent uphill entry of Cl from the mucosal solution into the cell could, of course, derive the required energy from a combination of Na and $HCO_3$ electrochemical potential differences across the mucosal membrane. In any event, if the net entry of Cl from the mucosal solution into the epithelial cell is linked to $HCO_3$ secretion, as postulated for rat (94, 95) and human (180) ileum, the failure to observe active Cl absorption by short-circuited, unstripped preparations of rabbit (162) and rat (34, 35) ileum may be attributed to the fact that oxidative metabolism and the rate of $HCO_3$ production by these preparations are markedly impaired by the presence of the muscle layers and serosal tissues (18, 63).

Na extrusion from the cell into the serosal solution (process $D$) is certainly an active transport process dependent upon a direct link to a source of metabolic energy. It is inhibited by ouabain in the serosal solution (159) (ouabain in the mucosal solution alone is ineffective), so it seems reasonable to infer that this process is mediated by a Na-K ATPase similar to that found in virtually all animal cells. This inference, including localization of the enzyme, is supported by recent studies on fractionated small intestinal cells (70, 71, 143) as well as autoradiographic studies (173) that indicate that most, if not all, of the Na-K stimulated, ouabain-sensitive ATPase is located in the basolateral membranes. In addition, active Na absorption is inhibited by ethacrynic acid, which is more effective when present in the mucosal solution than in the serosal solution (32). However, ethacrynic acid does not inhibit Na influx across the mucosal membranes and current evidence suggests that its inhibitory effect on transepithelial transport may be attributable to a direct effect on the Na-K ATPase as well as possible impairment of intracellular metabolic processes (32). Cassidy (30) has demonstrated that 1 m$M$ ethacrynic acid is more effective in inhibiting the Na-K ATPase of rat intestinal epithelium than 0.1 m$M$

ouabain, though less effective than 0.1 m$M$ scillaren. Electrophysiologic studies have provided strong evidence that process $D$ is "electrogenic" (or preferably, as discussed below, "rheogenic") and, as reported in several other instances, does not result in a neutral exchange of Na for K; instead, the rate of active Na extrusion appears to exceed the rate of coupled active K uptake (62, 148, 154). Finally, as pointed out previously, the basolateral membranes appear to be essentially impermeable to Na and process $D$ seems to be essentially completely rectified since the serosa-to-mucosa unidirectional flux of Na is attributable to simple diffusion through the extracellular shunt pathway (62).

The process ($C$) by which Cl leaves the absorptive cells is as yet unclear. In view of the admittedly indirect evidence that the electrochemical potential of intracellular Cl exceeds that in the serosal solution (66), simple diffusion might suffice; there is no reason at present to invoke a more complex mechanism.

Finally, compelling evidence has been presented, using in vivo human jejunum and ileum (123, 179) and canine small intestine (136), for the idea that K transport across the epithelium is a passive process driven by electrochemical potential differences; in human jejunum net K movements are strongly influenced by solvent drag (179). K transport across in vitro preparations of rat jejunum (75) and short-circuited rabbit ileum (M. Field, personal communication) also appears to be entirely passive. For rabbit ileum the route of transepithelial K transport appears to be restricted to the shunt pathway. In view of the fact that in rabbit ileum the intracellular electrochemical potential for K exceeds that in the surrounding media (108, 148, 161), these observations imply either ($a$) that there is a pump-leak system located in the mucosal membrane, capable of active K accumulation, which balances that at the basolateral membranes or ($b$) that the mucosal membrane is essentially impermeable to K and that the steady-state intracellular K concentration is maintained by a pump-leak system located exclusively at the basolateral membranes. Currently, there is no evidence for the former alternative; instead, the preponderance of evidence suggests that the steady-state intracellular K concentration is maintained by the pump-leak system illustrated in Figure 2 and that transepithelial K movements in response to electrochemical potential differences or bulk flow are restricted to the extracellular route.

EFFECTS OF ACETAZOLAMIDE ON ION TRANSPORT   In 1956 Parsons (135) reported that the carbonic anhydrase inhibitor, acetazolamide, depressed Na, Cl, and $HCO_3$ absorption by in vivo rat jejunum and inhibited Na and Cl absorption and $HCO_3$ secretion by in vivo rat ileum; indeed, in ileum perfused with a bicarbonate-Ringer's solution, the presence of acetazolamide brought about $HCO_3$ absorption. Subsequently, Kinney & Code (105) demonstrated that acetazolamide inhibits active Cl absorption by canine jejunum in vivo as a result of a decrease in the lumen-to-plasma flux with no change in the plasma-to-lumen flux. Turnberg et al have demonstrated that acetazolamide depressed Na and $HCO_3$ absorption (or, according to their interpretation, H secretion) by human jejunum (181) and Na and Cl absorption by human ileum (180) (which, according to their model, is the result of H and $HCO_3$ secretion).

Studies on the effect of acetazolamide on Na and Cl influx across the brush border of rabbit ileum indicate that this agent inhibits the neutral coupled NaCl influx process ($A$) and that the effect is observed within 30 sec. In addition, observations on short-circuited stripped rabbit ileum indicate that acetazolamide abolishes active Cl absorption and reduces, but does not eliminate, active Na absorption. Thus the effect of acetazolamide resembles that of Cl removal and appears to be due to a competitive inhibition of the neutral Na-anion transport mechanism located at the brush border (66, 131, 132).

The mechanism underlying this inhibitory effect is as yet unclear. Carter & Parsons (28, 29) have demonstrated that the carbonic anhydrase activity in guinea pig ileum is small but not negligible and that a significant fraction of carbonic anhydrase activity in colonic mucosa is present in the brush border. Thus the possibility that carbonic anhydrase, bound to the brush border, is intimately involved in the neutral NaCl influx process and the Na-anion (Cl or $HCO_3$) efflux process (process $A$) cannot be dismissed. Alternatively, it is possible that the effect of acetazolamide is exerted on a brush border carrier mechanism that possesses an "active" site that simply resembles that of carbonic anhydrase. The finding that acetazolamide does not inhibit $HCO_3$ production by mucosal strips of rabbit ileum (63) as well as the rapidity with which it inhibits Cl influx (66) would seem to favor the latter alternative.

SOME CONCLUDING REMARKS CONCERNING ION TRANSPORT BY IN VIVO AND IN VITRO PREPARATIONS OF SMALL INTESTINE    In contrast to mammalian jejunum where few in vitro studies have been carried out that shed light on underlying mechanisms of ion transport, recent studies on in vitro mammalian ileum have not only disclosed many similarities with ileal function in vivo, but have also provided some insight into specific transport processes and their location. Indeed, the model illustrated in Figure 2 is capable of satisfying many, if not all, of the observations reported by Turnberg et al (179, 180). The two major areas that require additional investigation in vitro are those of H and $HCO_3$ transport; these studies pose formidable technical problems inasmuch as they do not lend themselves to the traditional tracer techniques that have proved so useful in the analysis of Na, Cl, and K movements.

One major area of contention revolves about the "electrogenicity ' of active Na absorption. The position supported by Fordtran and his collaborators (11, 58, 180, 181) is that active Na absorption (and, for the case of ileum, active Cl absorption and $HCO_3$ secretion) are consequences of neutral exchange processes and are not associated with changes in the transepithelial PD. At the same time, these authors acknowledge that the techniques employed may not be sufficiently accurate to detect a change in transepithelial PD of 2–3 mV. In this respect, it should be stressed that in the presence of a high conductance shunt pathway, which accounts for approximately 90% of the total tissue conductance (and perhaps more in normal human jejunum), a change in the electromotive force across the basolateral membranes due to non-neutral or rheogenic active Na extrusion will be attenuated tenfold and could easily fall within the limits of reliability of the in vivo techniques. For example, a

20 mV increase in the electromotive force across the basolateral membranes resulting from increase in active Na extrusion from the cell by means of a rheogenic mechanism could go undetected. Second, and perhaps more important, as discussed above, the models proposed by Fordtran and his collaborators describe overall absorptive and secretory processes and depict the intestine as a homogeneous membrane separating the lumen from the plasma (as exemplified by Figure 1). Consequently, the term electrogenic as employed by these (and other) authors does not refer to a specific transport process, but to an overall phenomenon. Although Na entry into the cell from the lumen may be the result of neutral exchange mechanisms similar to those postulated by Fordtran and his collaborators, there is every reason to believe that Na extrusion from the cell, which is the process responsible for active Na absorption, is mediated by a Na-K, ouabain-sensitive, ATPase. Evidence has been obtained from a number of systems (particularly the human erythrocyte) that this process does not bring about a neutral exchange of Na for K but that the rate of Na extrusion exceeds the rate of K uptake (76, 100). In addition, studies on the human erythrocyte suggest that the stoichiometry of this process is variable and is influenced by intracellular as well as extracellular factors (76). As discussed above, there is compelling evidence that the active Na extrusion mechanism in rabbit ileum is rheogenic (process $D$, Figure 2) (62, 148, 154).

In the light of these observations, we propose the following terminology:

1. The term "electrogenic" should be reserved for any procedure, process, etc, that results in a change in the PD across a tissue or single membrane, without implication as to the mechanism responsible for the change in PD. The term "nonelectrogenic" should be used with caution when one is dealing with tissues characterized by low resistance shunt pathways, inasmuch as a small and perhaps statistically insignificant change in transepithelial PD may be the result of a major change in the electromotive force across one or both of the limiting membranes.

2. As suggested by Schwartz (163), the term "rheogenic" should be reserved to characterize specific non-neutral or current-generating transport processes.

Clearly, electrogenic processes may be the result of diffusion potentials (nonrheogenic), electrokinetic phenomena (i.e. streaming potentials), rheogenic transport processes, or a combination of these. Further, depending on the passive permeability of the membrane, rheogenic transport processes need not be associated with large changes in the transmembrane or transepithelial PD; that is, the current generated by such processes could be shunted by passive ionic flows. Finally, rheogenicity need not be an invariant characteristic of a specific transport process inasmuch as the coupling coefficient or stoichiometry of exchange processes (e.g. the Na-K active transport mechanism) may not be fixed.

It should be stressed that our distinction between "rheogenic" and "electrogenic" is not intended to diminish the importance of the latter in describing overall changes in transepithelial or transmembrane PDs, as these PDs may provide an important driving force for the transepithelial movement of charged species. Instead, we wish to make the point that the descriptive term "electrogenic" as generally employed does not characterize an identifiable process. Transepithelial PDs may result from diffusion potentials across the cellular membranes, diffusion potentials across the shunt pathway, streaming potentials, and rheogenic pumps. Changes in transepithelial PDs can arise from changes in any of the above processes as well as changes in the resistances of the barriers involved. Further, the absence of a significant change in PD may be the result of the interaction of a conglomerate of opposing factors. For example, an increase in transepithelial active Na transport mediated by a rheogenic Na pump at the basolateral membranes would be expected to increase the transepithelial PD. However, the associated increase in water absorption would be expected to distend the lateral interspaces, reduce the resistance of the shunt pathway, and diminish the transepithelial PD. These two opposing factors could balance each other, within the limits of experimental error, and lead to the conclusion that active Na absorption is nonelectrogenic in spite of the fact that the mechanism responsible for the absorptive process is rheogenic. Thus, unless all of the processes that can, in principle, take part in determining transepithelial PDs are taken into account, arguments over whether or not a specific transport process is capable of generating a PD are not meaningful and could lead to unnecessary and nonproductive disputes.

## SODIUM TRANSPORT AND THE TRANSPORT OF NONELECTROLYTES

There is abundant evidence that actively transported sugars and amino acids stimulate Na absorption across in vivo and in vitro preparations of small intestine from a wide variety of species (156). This phenomenon cannot be attributed to an increase in the energy supply to the absorptive cells because it can be elicited in vitro by nonmetabolized sugars and amino acids and there is no reason to believe that in vivo preparations are energy limited. The relation between Na and the transport of other solutes has recently been reviewed in detail (156) so that the following discussion focuses on issues that have been raised or clarified since that review.

THE MECHANISM OF ENHANCED SODIUM ABSORPTION    Three models have been proposed to account for the mechanism by which actively transported sugars or amino acids stimulate Na absorption by small intestine.

Schultz & Zalusky (160) extended the model proposed by Bihler et al (13) and suggested that the presence of actively transported sugars or amino acids in the mucosal solution enhances the entry of Na into the villus absorptive cells by formation of a ternary complex at the brush border; the Na coupled to the influx of sugars or amino acids is then extruded from the cell by the same ouabain-sensitive active transport mechanism operant in the absence of nonelectrolytes. The enhancement of Na influx across the luminal surface of rabbit ileum and rat jejunum by a variety of actively transported sugars and amino acids has subsequently been directly demonstrated by tracer techniques (156; Munck & Schultz, unpublished observations). Further, electrophysiologic studies by Rose & Schultz (148) and White & Armstrong (184) are consistent with the notion that the coupled entry of Na and sugars or neutral amino acids is a rheogenic process that results in a prompt depolarization of the PD across the brush border as well as an increase in transepithelial PD. Similar findings have been reported by Maruyama & Hoshi (121) for the proximal tubule of newt kidney, and indirect evidence for a rheogenic coupling of Na and glucose movements in both directions across the brush border of toad small intestine has been reported by Hoshi & Komatsu (91). Analyses of the equivalent electrical circuit of small intestinal epithelium and newt proximal renal tubule indicate that the observed changes in PD cannot be attributed to Na entry into a shunt pathway or the stimulation of a rheogenic Na extrusion mechanism at the basolateral membranes alone, but that a depolarization of the electromotive force across the brush border must be involved.

Conflicting results have been reported for tortoise (74, 186), hamster (186), and rat jejunum (8) where the increase in transepithelial PD was attributed solely to an increase in the PD across the basolateral membranes. Several points should be noted with respect to the latter studies. First, the initial PDs across the mucosal membranes were very low and, as pointed out by Rose & Schultz (148), the expected change in PD following the addition of sugars or amino acids is linearly related to the magnitude of the initial PD. Second, in most instances the effects of sugars or amino acids were not examined during impalement of the same cell and, in view of the fact that the predicted change in PD across the mucosal membrane is very small, it could have been obscured by averaging the results of impalements of different populations of cells before and after the addition of the actively transported nonelectrolyte. Finally, as concluded by Rose & Schultz (148) and Frizzell & Schultz (62), the increment in transepithelial PD almost certainly results predominantly from an increase in the electromotive force across the basolateral membranes because the shunt pathway markedly attenuates the change in PD across the brush border. Nonetheless, the fact that actively transported sugars and amino acids depolarize the PD across the brush border in rabbit ileum and small intestine (as well as newt proximal tubule) is indisputable; further study on tortoise, hamster, and rat are indicated to determine whether the apparent discrepancies are related to species differences or to some of the technical problems mentioned above.

A second model has been proposed by Kimmich as a result of studies on suspensions of isolated small intestinal cells from chickens (103, 104). This author has suggested that brush border transport processes for sugars, amino acids, Na, and K all compete for a common energy source, namely an ouabain-sensitive, Na-K ATPase. The ATPase would, either directly or through a high energy intermediate $(E_2 \sim P)$, provide energy for the uphill movement of sugars, amino acids, and K into the cell, and the active extrusion of Na from the cell across the brush border. According to the model, the inhibitory effect of ouabain would be exerted at the brush border and inhibition of organic solute transport by removal of Na would be due to depletion of intracellular Na. Further, the active transport of sugars or amino acids would deplete some of the energy for active Na extrusion from the cell across the brush border, increase the intracellular Na transport pool, and, in turn, enhance active Na absorption. Subsequently, Kimmich (104) has revised his original model to include a Na dependence for the membrane components or "carriers" responsible for sugar or amino acid entry, but he has not explicitly revised his views regarding the energetics involved in active Na, sugar, and amino acid transport.

Although the data presented by Kimmich are challenging and certainly require explanation, the predictions of his model are inconsistent with the following observations. 1. Depletion of cell Na does not affect sugar or amino acid influx when Na is present in the mucosal solution, but results in a marked inhibition of these processes when the mucosal solution is Na free. Therefore, these influx processes appear to depend predominantly on extracellular rather than intracellular Na (156). 2. The presence of sugars or amino acids increases Na influx across the brush border and there is no evidence that Na efflux across this boundary is decreased. On the contrary, cellular alanine increases Na efflux across the brush border presumably by reversing the direction of the coupled mechanism (156). 3. The coupled interaction between Na influx and the influxes of sugars or amino acids across the brush border is unaffected by ouabain or metabolic inhibitors (33, 148, 156); according to the Kimmich model, the presence or absence of Na should be irrelevant if the cell is energy depleted or the ATPase activity is inhibited by ouabain. 4. K influx across the luminal surface is unaffected by sugars or amino acids under conditions where Na influx is enhanced (64); according to the Kimmich model, K influx should be decreased. 5. Field et al (53) demonstrated that active alanine transport across short-circuited rabbit ileum is abolished when ouabain is present in the serosal solution alone; the presence of ouabain in the mucosal solution alone is ineffective. In the erythrocyte (88) and squid axon (24), ouabain is effective only when present in the extracellular medium. If the same is true for rabbit ileum, the observation of Field et al (53) would by itself invalidate the Kimmich model. 6. Finally, there is no compelling evidence for the presence of an ouabain-sensitive ATPase in the brush border of the villus absorptive cells (70, 71, 143, 173).

It should be stressed that Kimmich's concern has focused largely on the adequacy of the Na (or ion)-gradient hypothesis with respect to the active accumulation of sugars and amino acids by the isolated intestinal cell preparation; the mechanism by which these solutes enhance active Na absorption is a secondary consequence of his model. The results of recent studies on amino acid accumulation by Ehrlich ascites tumor cells suggest that the Na and K gradients alone are insufficient and that some additional direct or indirect energetic contribution from intracellular metabolic processes is required. However, in view of the fact that ouabain invariably inhibits Na-coupled active solute transport, it is reasonable to postulate that this additional metabolic requirement serves to energize the Na-K dependent, ouabain-sensitive ATPase. Although a discussion of the ion gradient hypothesis is beyond the scope of this review, it should be pointed out that the operation of the Na-K ATPase does more than merely establish transmembrane gradients for Na and K. ATPase activity generates H ions which may contribute to one of the ion gradients involved in the accumulation of sugars and amino acids (61). Further, the evidence cited above indicates that the coupled entry of Na with either sugars or amino acids in small intestine of rabbit and bullfrog is rheogenic and thus must be influenced by the PD across the brush border. If the same obtains for Ehrlich ascites tumor cells and if the Na-K active transport process in this cell is rheogenic, the operation of this mechanism could contribute an electrical driving force for the accumulation of amino acids; this driving force would not be duplicated by artificially established

Na and K gradients in energy depleted cells. Not only could these additional functions of the Na-K active exchange mechanism explain the apparent requirement for some metabolic input, apart from the Na and K gradients, but they are consistent with the fact that ouabain invariably abolishes these active accumulation processes. This problem, for the case of ascites cells, has been discussed in some detail by Schafer & Heinz (151) and Eddy and co-workers (73, 144). In this respect, it should be stressed that the suspension of isolated intestinal cells employed by Kimmich closely resembles Ehrlich ascites cells experimentally inasmuch as the polarity of the intestinal cell is obscured; that is, there is no definitive way of distinguishing between mechanisms located at the brush border and those located at the basolateral membranes. Thus many of Kimmich's observations linking the operation of an ouabain-sensitive, Na-K ATPase to the active accumulation of sugars and amino acids may be ascribable to the ATPase located in the basolateral membranes rather than to metabolic events located at the brush border.

Finally, Fordtran et al (58) have proposed that the enhanced small intestinal absorption of Na and water by human jejunum elicited by glucose or galactose is a consequence of solvent drag in response to sugar-stimulated water absorption. They found that the addition of glucose or galactose to the solution perfusing normal human jejunum increased water absorption, Na absorption, urea absorption, and the transepithelial PD (plasma positive). The concentrations of Na and urea in the absorbates are consistent with previous (59) estimates of the apparent reflection coefficients for Na and urea (approximately 0.5) and with the apparent reflection coefficient for Na derived from the effects of bulk flow on Na movements across jejunum in the absence of sugars (58). Thus the conclusion that the enhanced NaCl absorption is a consequence of solvent drag and that the increased PD is due to a streaming potential is apparently consistent with their data.

As discussed above, however, $HCO_3$ in the perfusate also stimulates water absorption without a discernable effect on the PD (58, 181). Under these conditions, solvent drag should also have enhanced NaCl absorption and, according to the argument of Fordtran et al (58), a streaming potential should have been established. The observations and conclusions that (a) sugars stimulate water absorption, (b) NaCl absorption is a consequence of solvent drag, and (c) the increased PD is the result of a streaming potential, are difficult to reconcile with the observation that water absorption stimulated by the presence of $HCO_3$ in the perfusate did not affect the transepithelial PD. In addition, these authors reported that glucose or galactose did not enhance Na or urea movements across in vivo human ileum, although it increased water absorption and markedly increased the transepithelial PD (lumen became more negative). The failure of bulk flow to stimulate Na and urea absorption is consistent with the minimal effect of bulk flow on Na and urea movements in ileum in the absence of sugars, as well as with previous estimates of an apparent reflection coefficient, close to unity, for each of these solutes (58, 59); the mechanism of the increased PD, however, remains unexplained.

There is no major inconsistency between the proposed model and the data collected by Fordtran et al in a series of ingenious experiments. Nonetheless, their data are in apparent conflict with other observations on in vivo human and canine jejunum. Thus, Sladen & Dawson (167) demonstrated that glucose stimulates Na and water absorption by human jejunum but that the concentration of Na in the absorbate was essentially equal to that in the perfusate, suggesting the absence of significant sieving or, stated otherwise, an apparent reflection coefficient for Na close to zero. Similar findings have been reported by Adibi (2) with respect to the effect of leucine on Na and water absorption by human jejunum in vivo, and by Heaton & Code (83) on the effect of glucose on Na and water absorption by canine jejunum in vivo. Further, Hellier et al (85) have demonstrated that alanine (as well as dipeptides) enhances fluid and electrolyte absorption by human jejunum and that in the presence of alanine, the absorbate is isotonic; these findings suggest little or no sieving of Na during alanine-induced fluid absorption. Finally, Holdsworth & Dawson (90) have shown that glucose and galactose absorption by normal human jenunum is accompanied by a marked increase in water absorption whereas fructose absorption was far less efficient in enhancing water absorption. These observations are inconsistent with the model suggested by Fordtran et al (58) which would have predicted that at equivalent rates of solute transport all three sugars should have had the same effect on Na and water absorption. Instead, these findings are consistent with the notion that glucose and galactose enhance Na influx across the brush border and, in turn, active Na absorption. On the other hand, fructose influx across the brush border of rabbit ileum is not Na-dependent (158) nor does the presence of fructose in the mucosal solution result in an increase in transepithelial PD (160) or a depolarization of the PD across the brush border (148). Thus the lack of an equivalent effect of fructose on water absorption can be attributed to the failure of this sugar to stimulate active Na absorption via the transcellular route.

Modigliani & Bernier (123) have recently examined the effect of glucose on net and unidirectional fluxes of water, Na, K, and Cl across human jejunum and ileum in vivo; they used an intestinal perfusion technique that employed a proximal occluding balloon. In the jejunum, glucose stimulated net absorption of water and NaCl but did not significantly affect the net movement of K. These effects were attributable to increases in the lumen-to-plasma unidirectional fluxes of water, Na, and K, and, although the plasma-to-lumen fluxes of water and K were increased, there was no significant increase in the "backflux" of Na. In the ileum, glucose increased water absorption but did not affect the net movements of Na or Cl, and it brought about a net secretion of K. These net effects were attributed to equivalent increases in the bidirectional fluxes of Na, an increase in the plasma-to-lumen flux of water that did not match the increase in the opposite direction, and a significant increase in the plasma-to-lumen movement of K. The authors concluded that the movements of K are entirely passive and are driven by the transepithelial PD and solvent drag. That is, the increased luminal negativity increased to plasma-to-lumen flow of K and, at the same time, the increased water absorption increased the lumen-to-plasma flow of K. In the jejunum, these two opposing effects were balanced so that no net K movement was observed. In the ileum, an excess of the electrical driving force over the solvent drag effect resulted in net K secretion.

With respect to Na, these authors (123) concluded that the increased lumen-to-plasma flow in jejunum could be accounted for by a direct coupling of the movements of sugar and Na through the transcellular route as well as by solvent drag (presumably via extracellular routes). In the ileum, the increased lumen-to-plasma flow of Na was attributed to a direct coupling via the transcellular route, and the increased plasma-to-lumen flow was attributed to the increased electrical negativity of the lumen; these two opposing movements cancelled each other so that there was no discernable net Na movement. The findings of these investigators are thus in general agreement with those of Fordtran et al (58). The analysis of unidirectional ion fluxes as well as of the effects of water flow and the transepithelial PD moreover serve to reconcile the models proposed by Schultz & Zalusky (160) and Fordtran et al (58). In addition, these studies illustrate the difficulties involved in interpreting net movements across perfused, in vivo preparations in terms of underlying mechanisms. The addition of actively transported sugars (and presumably amino acids) to the perfusate results in a conglomerate of events. These include an increase in water absorption which would tend to increase lumen-to-plasma ion movements and decrease tissue resistance, and an increase in the transepithelial PD (serosa positive) which would tend to decrease the lumen-to-plasma flow of cations. Studies of net movements alone cannot disentangle these opposing driving forces and, therefore, cannot yield definitive insights into the processes responsible for the observed overall phenomena.[4]

In vitro studies on the effects of actively transported sugars or amino acids on active Na transport across short-circuited rabbit ileum (46, 50, 156) and human jejunum (Binder, personal communication) have invariably indicated an increase in the mucosa-to-serosa flux with no significant effect on the serosa-to-mucosa flux. These results suggest that enhancement of active Na absorption cannot be attributed to solvent drag alone since this would be expected to decrease the backflux (160). Further, Frizzell et al (64) have demonstrated that, whereas actively transported sugars and amino acids enhance Na influx across the brush border, K influx is unaffected in spite of the fact that the shunt pathway is slightly more permeable to K than to Na. [As noted above, Turnberg (179) arrived at the same conclusion with respect to the relative effects of solvent drag on Na and K across in vivo human jejunum.] An increase in K influx would have been expected if solvent drag through the shunt pathway contributed significantly to the enhanced Na influx.

In conclusion, it should be stressed that the models proposed by Schultz & Zalusky (160) and that of Fordtran et al (58) are not mutually exclusive. There is little doubt that actively transported sugars and amino acids enhance the influx of Na across the brush border of the mature villus absorptive cells, which appear to be principally responsible for the absorption of these nonelectrolytes (106). In turn, this enhancement of Na influx results in an increased rate of active Na absorption via the transcellular route. However, in view of the evidence that the shunt pathway is highly permeable to Na, K, Cl, and small water soluble nonelectrolytes, particularly when the interspaces are widened by water absorption, it is quite likely that

[4]For example, in the studies of Modigliani & Bernier (123) the finding that the plasma-to-lumen flux of Na was unaffected by glucose could be attributed to opposing effects of solvent drag and the glucose-induced increase in transepithelial PD.

the transepithelial movements of electrolytes and organic solutes such as urea (58), thiourea (43–45, 128), and acetamide (43–45) will be enhanced by solvent drag, wash out effects, etc. The extent to which Na absorption will be secondarily enhanced by water absorption will depend upon a variety of factors such as the permeability of the shunt pathway, the rate of water absorption and its effect on tissue permeability, the role of unstirred layers, and the opposing effect of the increased electrical potential difference which would tend to increase the backflux of Na. All of these parameters are likely to vary with different species, different regions of small intestine, the use of in vitro or in vivo preparations, etc.

THE ROLE OF INTRALUMINAL SODIUM IN ACTIVE SUGAR AND AMINO ACID ABSORPTION    There is abundant evidence that active intracellular accumulation and active transepithelial absorption of sugars and amino acids by small intestine from a wide variety of species is abolished in the absence of Na (104, 156). In most instances where transmural movements were studied both bathing media were rendered Na free. Csaky & Thale (38), however, demonstrated that the presence of Na in the mucosal solution was essential for active transport of 3-O-methylglucose transport across toad small intestine in vitro, and that replacement of Na in the serosal solution alone did not abolish this process. Further, the absence of Na in the external solution has been shown to inhibit the downhill entry of sugars and amino acids into a wide variety of epithelial and, for the case of amino acids, nonepithelial cells (156). Thus, Na is not only necessary for the active transport of these solutes, but it also plays an important role in the entry process itself, albeit downhill. In small intestine, the available evidence suggests that the movement of amino acids across the basolateral membrane is Na-independent (79); similar findings have been reported for sugar movement across the peritubular membrane of flounder kidney tubules in vitro (107).

Studies on the effect of luminal Na on active sugar absorption under in vivo conditions where the Na concentration in the plasma is unaltered have resulted in some controversy. Csaky & Zollicoffer (39) demonstrated that replacement of Na with Li, K, or Mg in the solution perfusing in vivo rat small intestine inhibited active glucose absorption by 91%, 86%, and 75% respectively; perfusion of the lumen with isotonic mannitol inhibited glucose absorption by only 40% (37). Annegers (6) reported a significant inhibition of glucose and galactose absorption by canine jejunum and ileum when Na in the perfusate was replaced with K, but only a minimal inhibitory effect when $NH_4$ was employed as the substitute cation; replacement of Na did not affect the absorption of fructose, sorbose, or glycine. Fleshler & Nelson (55) have reported a 20–40% decrease in alanine absorption by canine Thiry-Vella loops when the Na in the luminal solution was replaced isosmotically with mannitol. Adibi (2) demonstrated that leucine absorption by human jejunum was unaffected when the perfusion solution was initially Na free. Olsen & Ingelfinger (134) demonstrated a small but significant inhibition of glucose absorption by human jejunum and ileum when Na in the perfusate was replaced with either mannitol or Tris and the intraluminal glucose concentration was less than ~3 m$M$; when the luminal glucose concentration exceeded 6 m$M$, Na replacement had no effect.

Saltzman et al (149) have recently reported that replacement of Na with mannitol did not affect active glucose absorption by in vivo human or canine ileum and that replacement of Na with either mannitol or K did not inhibit active glucose absorption by in vivo rat ileum. The latter observation differs from that reported by Csaky & Zollicoffer (39) and Csaky (37). Finally, Förster & Hoos (60) have reported that replacement of Na with xylitol did not markedly inhibit glucose absorption by in vivo perfused rat small intestine.

At present these observations do not lend themselves to a definitive explanation, but several possibilities must be entertained. Species differences with respect to the observations on in vivo human and rat small intestine can be dismissed inasmuch as active sugar transport by rat (156) and human (41, 42) small intestine in vitro has been shown to be Na dependent; we are unaware of any comparable studies on in vitro canine small intestine. The most plausible explanation for these findings is that during in vivo perfusion the luminal contents cannot be maintained Na free in spite of the fact that the initial perfusate is Na free. Thus, although Na-free solutions were infused in the studies reported by Adibi (2), the mean final concentration of Na in the jejunum was 55 m$M$, and in the studies of Olsen & Ingelfinger (134) the concentration of Na in human jejunum and ileum rose to as high as 55 m$M$ and 25 m$M$ respectively. In Fleshler & Nelson's study (55) the final mean luminal Na concentrations were 29 m$M$ after 5 min and 42 m$M$ after 10 min. Saltzman et al (149) reported that the mean luminal Na concentrations were quite low and averaged $\sim$ 15 m$M$ in human ileum (in some instances as low as 2.5 m$M$), 10–15 m$M$ in rat ileum, and 10 m$M$ in canine ileum. In this respect, it is of interest that in the in vivo experiments by Csaky and his co-workers, where Na replacement significantly inhibited sugar absorption, "no measurable quantity of sodium" was detected in the perfusing solution (37).

Since it is difficult, if not impossible, to maintain the lumen Na free during in vivo perfusion studies, even though the initial perfusate is Na free, two possible explanations for these in vivo findings are suggested. First, in all instances extremely slow perfusion rates were employed; for example, when 30 cm of human small intestine are perfused at a rate of 16 ml min$^{-1}$ the linear flow of perfusate is only 0.05 ml cm$^{-2}$ min$^{-1}$, a value several orders of magnitude lower than that obtained with the short-circuit apparatus described by Schultz & Zalusky (159) (120 ml cm$^{-2}$ min$^{-1}$). Consequently, in vivo, large unstirred or very poorly stirred layers adjacent to the brush border are inevitable. This notion is strongly supported by the observations of Modigliani & Bernier (122) that the rate of glucose absorption by perfused human jejunum increases with increasing perfusion rate and that the apparent "half-saturation" value for absorption is not a function of glucose concentration but of glucose "load." Presumably, more rapid rates of perfusion resulted in more efficient stirring. These observations provide a possible explanation for the fact that the reported half-saturation concentrations ("apparent Michaelis constants for transport") for sugar and amino acid absorption by perfused human small intestine are often an order of magnitude greater than those reported for in vitro systems (1, 134, 149). Thus the concentration of the transported solute at the brush border may be as much as 10 times lower than that in the bulk solution. Conversely, when the in vivo intestine is perfused with a solution that is initially Na free, the concentration of Na at the brush border due to backflux from plasma to lumen may be several times greater than that found in the aspirate.[5]

The problem of the inevitable existence of unstirred layers is compounded by the likelihood that the brush border possesses a net negative fixed charge so that the ionic atmosphere adjacent to this boundary (the Gouy-Chapman diffuse double layer) will be characterized by an excess of mobile cations. This likelihood is supported by studies on the electrophoretic mobility of human intestinal cells (183) as well as the findings of Hogben et al (89) which are consistent with the notion that the pH adjacent to the brush border may be approximately one unit lower than that of the bulk luminal solution. The combined effects of a large unstirred layer and the Gouy-Chapman effect could well result in a Na concentration adjacent to the brush border that is many times greater than that in the bulk solution. The consequences of these effects will, of course, be compounded by the sugar-enhanced transepithelial PD which would increase the rate of Na diffusion from plasma to lumen.

In short, the finding that low concentrations of Na in the bulk luminal fluid do not markedly inhibit sugar and amino acid absorption in vivo may be due to significant underestimation of the effective Na concentration at the brush border. This explanation is speculative, however, and a definitive resolution of this problem requires further investigation. The use of more rapid perfusion techniques, the use of multivalent cations that might bind to fixed negative charges on the brush border as replacements for Na (rather than mannitol), and procedures that reduce the backflux of Na into the lumen might be helpful.

Finally, the active absorption of sugars and amino acids possibly also depends to some extent on the presence of Na in the serosal solution. Smulders & Wright (168) reported that partial replacement of Na in the serosal solution alone with mannitol significantly inhibited active galactose absorption by in vitro short-circuited hamster small intestine and that this effect was irreversible. These findings await confirmation and a definitive explanation.

## ACTIVE ION SECRETION BY THE SMALL INTESTINE

Although the small intestine has been customarily viewed as an absorptive organ with respect to the movements of ions and water, there is now no doubt that it can actively secrete ions under pathological conditions and, probably, under physiological conditions as well. This secretory capability has emerged as one of the most active areas of investigation after almost a quarter of a century of dormancy, spurred largely by attempts to define the mechanisms responsible for the massive intestinal losses of salts and water associated with cholera and other enterobacterial infestations. Intestinal secretion was the subject of an excellent review by Hendrix &

[5]A recent formal analysis by Winne (Unstirred layer, source of biased Michaelis constant in membrane transport. *Biochim. Biophys. Acta* 298:27–31, 1973) clearly demonstrates that the differences between "Michaelis constants" obtained from in vivo and in vitro absorption studies may be attributable, at least in part, to the larger unstirred layers encountered in the in vivo perfusion studies.

Bayless (84) in 1970 and the following discussion attempts to summarize subsequent developments in this area.

THE ROLE OF CYCLIC 3',5' ADENOSINEMONOPHOSPHATE (cAMP)    In 1968 Soergel et al (171) demonstrated that administration of antidiuretic hormone (ADH) inhibited NaCl absorption by human jejunum and ileum in vivo and in some instances resulted in salt and water secretion; the same effect was observed when endogenous ADH secretion was elicited by dehydration of the subject. The reduction of Na absorption was the result of a decrease in the lumen-to-plasma unidirectional flux with no significant change in the backflux. During the same year, Field et al (52) reported that ADH, theophylline, and cAMP increased the short-circuit current across a stripped preparation of rabbit ileum; they suggested that both theophylline and cAMP bring about active secretion of Cl and $HCO_3$ by this in vitro preparation. Subsequent studies by Field (46) confirmed that theophylline and cAMP abolish active Na absorption by reducing the mucosa-to-serosa flux without significantly affecting the serosa-to-mucosa flux and that they elicit active Cl secretion primarily by decreasing the mucosa-to-serosa flux; neither agent significantly affected the residual current which appears to be attributable to $HCO_3$ secretion (48). These observations have been confirmed by Nellans et al (132).

Pierce et al (138) demonstrated that infusion of prostaglandins and theophylline into the mesenteric artery results in a cholera-like secretion of water and electrolytes by in vivo canine jejunum and that the effects of the two agents are synergistic. Subsequently, Kimberg et al (102) demonstrated that prostaglandins increase the intracellular levels of cAMP in rabbit and guinea pig small intestine and mimic the effect of theophylline on the short-circuit current across guinea pig ileum. Further, evidence was presented by these investigators that the effects of both theophylline and the prostaglandins on the short-circuit current are mediated by cAMP. These observations were extended by Al-Awqati & Greenough (4) who demonstrated that the effects of prostaglandins on Na and Cl transport across isolated rabbit ileum are virtually identical to those of cAMP. Thus there appears to be no doubt that theophylline and prostaglandins, which increase intestinal cAMP levels, abolish active Na absorption (and in some instances may promote a small active secretion of Na) and elicit active Cl secretion by in vivo as well as in vitro preparations of small intestine.

RELATION TO CHOLERA AND OTHER BACTERIAL ENTERITISES    Compelling evidence has been presented that the effects of purified as well as crude cholera toxin on transport across in vitro rabbit (51, 102, 141) and human ileum (3) mimic those of theophylline and cAMP, and that cholera toxin increases cAMP levels in rabbit (102, 165), guinea pig (102), and canine small intestine (150). In addition, the amount of intracellular cAMP in biopsied small intestine from patients suffering from clinical cholera is higher than the levels found in these patients following recovery or convalescence (31). Further, it has recently been found that cholera toxin also stimulates prostaglandin synthesis by small intestinal epithelium, but that this is a parallel effect and is not prerequisite for the toxin-induced increase in cAMP

(Kimberg et al, personal communication). There is thus little doubt that intracellular cAMP plays a central, if not sole, role in reversing the normal small intestinal absorptive processes and eliciting the active secretory state characteristic of clinical cholera. Furthermore, the mechanism responsible for intestinal secretion in patients suffering from prostaglandin-secreting tumors appears to be clarified. At least one significant problem remains to be resolved. It is well established that, in vivo, the principal anion secreted by rabbit (111, 112, 133) and canine (27, 124) ileum in response to cholera toxin is $HCO_3$ rather than Cl; that is, the normal secretory rate of $HCO_3$ by mammalian ileum is significantly increased. On the other hand, studies on in vitro rabbit ileum do not disclose an increase in residual current or $HCO_3$ secretion in response to cholera toxin or theophylline (46–48, 51). A possible explanation for this apparent discrepancy is discussed below. For further information on the mode of action of cholera toxin and its relation to cAMP, the reader is referred to the excellent reviews by Field (47), Pierce et al (139), Carpenter (26), and Greenough et al (77).

Finally, evidence has recently been presented that enterotoxins or cell-free filtrates of *Escherichia coli* (5, 23), *Shigella dysenteriae* (101), and staphylococci (174) are capable of eliciting small intestinal secretion that in some respects resembles that resulting from challenge with cholera toxin. Although we are unaware of any evidence linking these enterotoxins to intestinal cAMP levels, such evidence may be forthcoming in the not too distant future.[6]

MODELS FOR cAMP-INDUCED INTESTINAL SECRETION    As discussed above, recent studies by Nellans et al (131) on the unidirectional influxes of Na and Cl across the brush border of rabbit ileum have disclosed the presence of a neutral NaCl influx mechanism that is noncompetitively inhibited by theophylline and cAMP. There is currently no evidence that theophylline affects any other brush border transport process for Na or Cl. Amino acid influx across the brush border of rat jejunum appears to be slightly inhibited by theophylline (B. G. Munck, personal communication), and Field and his collaborators (personal communication) have demonstrated at 25% decrease in the rate of active alanine transport across short-circuited rabbit ileum in the presence of theophylline.

The inhibitory effects of cAMP on the influx and transepithelial transport of these amino acids are as yet unexplained; in view of the fact that Na-coupled amino acid influx appears to be rheogenic, changes in the PD across the mucosal membrane may be involved. Nonetheless, the coupling between the influxes of actively trans-

[6]Since the completion of this manuscript, our attention was drawn to a paper by Evans et al (Stimulation of adenyl cyclase by *Escherichia coli* enterotoxin. *Nature New Biol.* 236:137–38, 1972) in which a heat-labile enterotoxin obtained from a noninvasive species of *E. coli,* which elicits massive diarrhea in humans, was shown to increase adenyl cyclase activity in rabbit ileal mucosa. The similarity between the enterotoxins elaborated by some strains of *C. vibrio* and *E. coli* with respect to the induction of intestinal secretion and enhancement of adenyl cyclase activity has been recently confirmed for canine small intestine by Guerrant et al (Effect of *Escherichia coli* on fluid transport across canine small bowel. *J. Clin. Invest.* 52:1707–14, 1973).

ported sugars, amino acids, and Na across the brush border appears to be largely intact, as does the active Na extrusion mechanism at the basolateral membranes. This follows from the fact that actively transported sugars and amino acids enhance active Na absorption by in vitro (46, 51, 57) and in vivo (133) rabbit ileum and in vivo canine jejunum (27) in the presence of theophylline, cAMP, or cholera toxin. Furthermore, perorally administered glucose or glucose-amino acid mixtures diminish salt and water secretion in clinical cholera and often restore net salt and water absorption (87, 130). There is thus no evidence that the ability of small intestine to absorb Na actively is significantly impaired by cAMP. In addition, there is compelling evidence that the passive permeability of the epithelium is not increased by exposure to cholera toxin (116, 147); on the contrary, much of the available evidence suggests that, if anything, the transepithelial conductance, which is largely attributable to the ionic permeability of the shunt pathway, is slightly reduced (46, 132, 141).

Thus it seems evident that cholera toxin, or other agents that elevate intracellular cAMP levels, affects carrier-mediated transport processes of the mucosal epithelium without significantly impairing the active Na extrusion mechanism(s) at the basolateral membranes. Nellans et al (132) have found that (a) replacement of Na with choline abolishes active Cl secretion in the presence of theophylline and (b) replacement of Cl with $SO_4$ restores active Na absorption in the presence of theophylline. Moreover, evidence has been presented that acetazolamide inhibits salt and water secretion induced by cholera toxin (112, 133) and, as discussed above, the effect of acetazolamide on ion transport across rabbit ileum appears to be largely restricted to the inhibition of the coupled NaCl influx process at the brush border. These observations suggest the models for rabbit ileum illustrated in Figure 3. Under control conditions, the brush border features 1. a Cl-independent, cAMP-insensitive mechanism that results in net Na entry approximately 2 $\mu$moles cm$^{-2}$ hr$^{-1}$, and 2. a bidirectional neutral NaCl transport process that mediates the influx of 4 $\mu$moles cm$^{-2}$ hr$^{-1}$ of NaCl and the efflux of 2 $\mu$moles cm$^{-2}$ hr$^{-1}$ of NaCl. Under steady-state conditions the net movements across the basolateral membranes must result in the net active absorption of Na and Cl of 4 $\mu$moles cm$^{-2}$ hr$^{-1}$ and 2 $\mu$moles cm$^{-2}$ hr$^{-1}$, respectively (132). The removal of Cl or the presence of acetazolamide inhibits the neutral NaCl transport process at the brush border, thereby abolishing active Cl absorption and reducing active Na absorption. In the presence of theophylline the neutral NaCl influx mechanism is inhibited, but the neutral efflux mechanism need not be affected. Thus, in the presence of Cl, Na is simply recycled across the brush border and no net transepithelial movement occurs; however, in the absence of Cl the neutral efflux process is abolished and active Na absorption is restored.

These models imply that brush border transport processes are the major determinants of transepithelial Na and Cl movements, regardless of their direction, and that ileal absorption or secretion are two extremes of a continuous spectrum of potential activities. In other words, there appear to be opposing absorptive and secretory processes at the mucosal and basolateral membranes, which determine the direction of net movement. Inhibition of processes that contribute to absorption may result

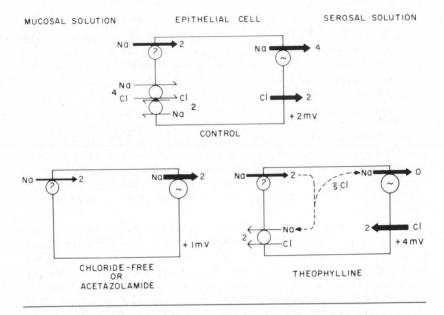

*Figure 3* Models depicting the relation between transport of Na and Cl across the brush border of in vitro rabbit ileum and active transepithelial transport. The bold arrows at the mucosal and serosal membranes designate net movements. The dashed pathways shown in the model for ion transport in the presence of theophylline illustrate the fate of Na in the presence and absence ($\bar{s}$) of Cl. The zero value for active transepithelial Na transport represents the situation in the presence of Cl. Data from Nellans et al (132, and unpublished observations).

in secretion, and, as is discussed below, inhibition of processes that contribute to secretion may result in enhanced absorption. In short, there is no reason to postulate that the secretion elicited by elevated cAMP levels involves de novo mechanisms that are not operant under normal absorptive conditions; however, this notion requires further investigation.

This is an admittedly oversimplified model which is nonetheless consistent with the data of Nellans et al (132) and the observations of Powell et al (141) on Na and Cl transport across short-circuited rabbit ileum in the presence of theophylline and cholera toxin. In addition, the notion of opposing carrier mediated processes, one at the brush border that can mediate the neutral secretion of Na and an anion (either Cl or $HCO_3$) and one at the basolateral membranes that results in the rheogenic absorption of Na (and at the same time may provide the electrochemical driving force for the downhill diffusion of Cl into the serosal solution), is consistent with the findings of Taylor et al (176) and Munck (128) on secretion induced by sugars and amino acids in rat jejunum in vitro, Powell et al (14, 140, 142) on the spontaneous secretion observed in guinea pig ileum, Binder et al (15) on ion transport by rabbit ileum, and Norris et al (133) on the effects of cholera toxin on ion transport across rabbit ileum in vivo. The adequacy of this model, the need to invoke cAMP-induced effects at the basolateral membranes, and the mechanism responsible for $HCO_3$ secretion certainly require further investigation. Suffice it to say that the models illustrated in Figure 3 satisfy most of the data currently available and relate brush border transport processes to overall transepithelial movements of Na and Cl under a variety of conditions.

As mentioned above, one significant difference between the effects of cholera toxin on in vivo and in vitro preparations of mammalian ileum is that the former respond with a marked increase in the rate of $HCO_3$ secretion whereas the latter show an increase in Cl secretion and no detectable change in $HCO_3$ secretion. Studies by Frizzell et al (63) indicate that under control conditions the rate of $HCO_3$ production by mucosal strips of rabbit ileum is approximately 1.5–2.5 $\mu$moles $cm^{-2}$ $hr^{-1}$. These values agree well with the rate of $HCO_3$ secretion across in vitro rabbit ileum observed by Field & Dietz (48) and with the residual currents across short-circuited rabbit ileum reported by several groups of investigators. These observations suggest that most, if not all, of the secreted $HCO_3$ is derived from endogenous oxidative metabolism. Theophylline does not increase the rate of $HCO_3$ production by mucosal strips of rabbit ileum (63) so that, if the above reasoning is correct, an increase in $HCO_3$ secretory rate is precluded. There is compelling evidence that unstripped preparations of rabbit ileum are anoxic inasmuch as stripping the muscle layers away triples the rate of oxygen consumption and $CO_2$ production (63). It is not unreasonable to suspect that even stripped preparations of rabbit ileum are less well oxygenated than in vivo preparations, where the villus cores are characterized by a highly ramified capillary network. Thus cholera toxin or theophylline may be unable to increase $HCO_3$ secretion in vitro because the rate of oxidative metabolsim by these preparations is a limiting factor.

Finally, it should be stressed that Figure 3 depicts the small intestinal epithelium as if it were comprised of a single cell type. On the contrary, at least five cell types have been identified (178) and suggestive evidence has been presented that the intervillus crypt cells may be responsible for ion secretion induced by cholera in rabbit ileum (84, 146, 164) and neutral NaCl secretion induced by some sugars and amino acids in rat jejunum (128). For example, Serebro et al (164) have presented evidence that cycloheximide, at doses that produce histologic changes in the crypt cell population, inhibits secretion by in vivo rabbit small intestine in response to cholera toxin. On the other hand, Frizzell et al (65) have demonstrated that cycloheximide also inhibits a variety of carrier-mediated influx processes in rabbit ileum, some of which do not involve the crypt cells, and Lecount & Grey (109) have reported that cycloheximide produces transient shortening of the microvilli of the mature villus cells in chicken duodenum. Thus, although there is little doubt that the villus cells are primarily responsible for sugar and amino acid absorption (106) and the associated enhancement of Na absorption, further investigation is needed to identify definitively those cells which possess the neutral NaCl influx process and the adenylcyclase activity that responds to cholera toxin, and which are responsible for cAMP-induced intestinal secretion.

EFFECTS OF OTHER HORMONES ON INTESTINAL ION MOVEMENTS   Field and co-workers (48, 49) have reported that catecholamines enhance active Na and Cl absorption by in vitro short-circuited rabbit ileum and at the same time abolish the residual current and $HCO_3$ secretion. The absolute increases in net Na and Cl movements from mucosa to serosa are approximately equal, and the inhibition of $HCO_3$ secretion appears to be principally responsible for the observed change in short-circuit current. These effects are not observed when a $HCO_3$-free buffer aerated with 100% $O_2$ is employed, so that the action of catecholamines appears to be dependent upon the presence of $HCO_3$ and/or $CO_2$. Preliminary studies by Fizzell et al (unpublished observations) indicate that the catecholamines, at the same concentrations employed by Field & McColl (49), do not affect Cl influx across the brush border. This finding has been confirmed by Field and his collaborators (personal communication). Therefore, it seems reasonable to speculate that the enhanced Na and Cl absorption and the elimination of $HCO_3$ secretion may be attributable to an inhibition of the neutral Na-anion (Cl or $HCO_3$) efflux process illustrated in Figures 2 and 3. Field & McColl have suggested that the effects of cAMP on transepithelial ion movements are opposite to those of the catecholamines (49). This suggestion is consistent with the models that relate brush border events to transepithelial transport, since the effects of cAMP can be explained if its only action is an inhibition of the coupled NaCl influx process. On the other hand, the effects of the catecholamines are consistent with the notion that they are limited to an inhibition of the Na-anion efflux process. Further investigation is needed to test this hypothesis and to elucidate the underlying biochemical events involved.

Strong evidence has recently been presented that some, if not all, of the gastrointestinal hormones affect absorptive or secretory processes in the small intestine. Gardner et al (72) demonstrated that gastrin, secretin, and cholecystokinin inhibit water and NaCl absorption by everted sacs of hamster distal small intestine; the effects of these hormones differed in other regions. Stening et al (172) observed that isolated pouches of dog and cat duodenum, containing Brunner's glands, secrete water and electrolytes profusely in response to intravenously administered porcine secretin; lower rates of secretion were obtained with pure porcine gastrin II, cholecystokinin, and caeurlein. According to Barbezat & Grossman (7), vasoactive intestinal peptide, gastric inhibitory peptide, glucagon, and pentagastrin elicit secretion by Thiry-Vella loops of canine jejunum and ileum, whereas secretin and the COOH-terminal octapeptide of cholecystokinin do not. Finally, Moritz et al (126) have recently demonstrated that porcine secretin and cholecystokinin inhibit fluid absorption by perfused human jejunum.

One difficulty with many of the studies of the type cited above is their failure to distinguish between physiologic and pharmacologic effects of the administered hormones. This question appears to have been resolved for the small intestinal response to secretin, gastrin, and cholecystokinin. Secretin does not seem to affect absorption by in vivo rat (93) and dog (21, 22) small intestine at doses sufficient to elicit maximal pancreatic secretion, but at higher doses it inhibits absorption by in vivo rat intestine (96). Needless to say, assay techniques for plasma secretin levels are required to determine whether the concentration sufficient to elicit maximal pancreatic secretion is a valid criterion for a physiologic response. Bynum et al (22) reported that both exogenous and endogenous gastrin (evoked by instillation of acetylcholine in the stomach) inhibited water and salt absorption by in vivo loops of canine jejunum and ileum (see also 127). Similarly, Bussjaeger & Johnson (19) have demonstrated that exogenous cholecystokinin and cholecystokinin released following instillation of fats in the duodenum inhibit fluid absorption by in vivo loops of dog small intestine. Current evidence thus suggests that the effects of gastrin and cholecystokinin are truly physiologic whereas the effect of secretin may be pharmacologic. Whether glucagon and the other inhibitory peptides play a physiologic role in regulating intestinal function remains to be resolved. These observations may provide some insight into the findings of Tidball (177) that cholinergic drugs elicit water and active Cl secretion by in vivo loops of dog jejunum. This response may have been induced directly by bethanechol, but it may have been, at least in part, secondary to the release of gastrointestinal hormones by the cholinergic stimulus.

As we have recently stressed (157), in vivo studies of net disappearance from the lumen cannot distinguish between changes due to the inhibition of absorptive processes and those resulting from the stimulation of secretory processes, so that the mechanisms responsible for the observations cited above are as yet unclear. Inasmuch as cAMP appears to be implicated in the actions of many of the gastrointestinal secretagogues (12, 20, 125, 145), the observed inhibition of absorption may result from stimulation of secretion mediated by the adenylcyclase-cAMP system in the small intestinal cells. Indeed, the physiologic role of the "receptor-site adenylcyclase system" in small intestine may be to interact with the gastrointestinal hormones, inhibit the overall absorption of fluid, and maintain liquid luminal contents during the processes of digestion and absorption of nutrients. It would be a cruel accident of nature of the only function of this system were to render the small intestine susceptible to the pathologic actions of bacterial enterotoxins. Clearly, studies on the mechanism of action of these hormones on in vitro preparations and their effects on intestinal cAMP or prostaglandins would assist in resolving this issue.

## CONCLUDING REMARKS

Until recently, reviews of small intestinal function pictured this organ as a black box capable of absorbing water and electrolytes, and relatively unresponsive to humoral or neural stimuli. As aptly pointed out by Hendrix & Bayless (84), the subject of intestinal secretion (with the exception of $HCO_3$ secretion by ileum) was almost entirely ignored. In the past few years, the results of in vitro and in vivo studies have rendered this picture archaic. In many respects, the black box has been opened: specific transport processes that may be responsible for absorptive, as well as secretory, processes via both transcellular and extracellular transepithelial routes have been identified. In addition, the recognition that small intestinal function is subject to humoral and neural stimuli, and that cAMP and prostaglandins appear to play a central role in modulating absorptive and secretory flows, has opened a new frontier whose exploration will undoubtedly profoundly enhance our understanding of intestinal transport under both physiological and pathological conditions. In a sense, one chapter in the investigation of intestinal function has been closed and a new chapter, whose ultimate implications are yet to be realized, has been opened.

ACKNOWLEDGMENTS

The authors are grateful to Drs. M. Field, D. Kimberg, and H. J. Binder for providing data prior to publication. We also wish to acknowledge useful discussions with Drs. J. S. Fordtran and G. Kimmich which were of great assistance in our attempt to meet the aims of this review.

*Literature Cited*

1. Adibi, S. A. 1969. The influence of molecular structure of neutral amino acids on their absorption kinetics in the jejunum and ileum of human intestine in vivo. *Gastroenterology* 56:903–13
2. Adibi, S. A. 1970. Leucine absorption rate and net movements of sodium and water in human jejunum. *J. Appl. Physiol.* 28:753–57
3. Al-Awqati, Q., Cameron, J. L., Greenough, W. B. III. 1973. Electrolyte transport in human ileum: Effect of purified cholera exotoxin. *Am. J. Physiol.* 224:818–23
4. Al-Awqati, Q., Greenough, W. B. III. 1972. Prostaglandins inhibit intestinal sodium transport. *Nature London* 238:26–27
5. Al-Awqati, Q., Wallace, C. K., Greenough, W. B. III. 1972. Stimulation of intestinal secretion in vitro by culture filtrates of *Escherichia coli. J. Infec. Dis.* 125:300–03
6. Annegers, J. H. 1964. Some effects of cations and of water absorption on intestinal hexose, glycine and cation absorption. *Proc. Soc. Exp. Biol. Med.* 116:933–38
7. Barbezat, G. O., Grossman, M. I. 1971. Intestinal secretion: Stimulation by peptides. *Science* 174:422–24
8. Barry, R. J. C., Eggenton, J. 1972. Membrane potentials of epithelial cells in rat small intestine. *J. Physiol. London* 227:201–16
9. Bentzel, C. J. 1972. Proximal tubule structure-function relationships during volume expansion in *Necturus. Kidney Int.* 2:324–35
10. Bentzel, C. J., Parsa, B., Hare, D. K. 1969. Osmotic flow across proximal tubule of *Necturus.* Correlation of physiologic and anatomic studies. *Am. J. Physiol.* 217:570–80
11. Bieberdorf, F. A., Gorden, P., Fordtran, J. S. 1972. Pathogenesis of congenital alkalosis with diarrhea. Implications for the physiology of normal ileal electrolyte absorption and secretion. *J. Clin. Invest.* 51:1958–68
12. Bieck, P. R., Oates, J. A., Robinson, G. A., Adkins, R. B. 1973. Cyclic AMP in the regulation of gastric secretion in dogs and humans. *Am. J. Physiol.* 224:158–64
13. Bihler, I., Hawkins, K. A., Crane, R. K. 1962. Studies on the mechanism of intestinal absorption of sugars. VI. The specificity and other properties of Na$^+$ dependent entrance of sugars into intestinal tissue under anaerobic conditions in vitro. *Biochim. Biophys. Acta* 59:94–102
14. Binder, H. J., Powell, D. W., Curran, P. F. 1972. Effect of hexoses on ion transport in guinea pig ileum. *Am. J. Physiol.* 223:538–44
15. Binder, H. J., Powell, D. W., Tai, T. H., Curran, P. F. 1973. Electrolyte transport in rabbit ileum. *Am. J. Physiol.* In press
16. Boulpaep, E. L. 1971. Electrophysiological properties of the proximal tubule: Importance of cellular and intercellular transport pathways. In *Electrophysiology of Epithelial Cells,* ed. G. Giebisch, 91–112. Stuttgart: F. K. Schattauer Verlag
17. Boulpaep, E. L. 1972. Permeability changes of the proximal tubule of *Necturus* during saline loading. *Am. J. Physiol.* 222:517–31
18. Bronk, J. R., Parsons, D. S. 1965. The polarographic determination of the respiration of the small intestine of the rat. *Biochim. Biophys. Acta* 107:397–404
19. Bussjaeger, L. J., Johnson, L. R. 1973. Evidence for the humoral regulation of

intestinal absorption by cholecystokinin. *Am. J. Physiol.* 224:1276–79

20. Butcher, R. W., Carlson, L. A. 1970. Effects of secretin on fat mobilizing lipolysis and cyclic AMP levels in rat adipose tissue. *Acta Physiol. Scand.* 79:559–63

21. Bynum, T. E., Jacobson, E. D., Johnson, L. R. 1971. Effect of gastrin on intestinal absorption. *Gastroenterology* 60:767

22. Bynum, T. E., Jacobson, E. D., Johnson, L. R. 1971. Gastrin inhibition of intestinal absorption in dogs. *Gastroenterology* 61:858–62

23. Bywater, R. J. 1970. Some effects of *Escherichia coli* enterotoxin on net fluid, glucose and electrolyte transfer in calf small intestine. *J. Comp. Pathol.* 80:565–73

24. Caldwell, P. C., Keynes, R. D. 1959. The effect of ouabain on the efflux of sodium from a squid axon. *J. Physiol. London* 148:8P

25. Carlinsky, N. J., Lew, V. L. 1970. Bicarbonate secretion and non-Na component of the short-circuit current in the isolated colonic mucosa of *Bufo arenarum*. *J. Physiol. London* 206:529–41

26. Carpenter, C. C. J. Jr. 1971. Cholera enterotoxin—Recent Investigations yield insights into transport processes. *Am. J. Med.* 50:1–7

27. Carpenter, C. C. J., Sack, R. B., Feeley, J. C., Steenberg, R. W. 1968. Site and characteristics of electrolyte loss and effect of intraluminal glucose in experimental canine cholera. *J. Clin. Invest.* 47:1210–20

28. Carter, M. J., Parsons, D. S. 1971. The isoenzymes of carbonic anhydrase: Tissue, subcellular distribution and functional significance with particular reference to the intestinal tract. *J. Physiol. London* 215:71–94

29. Carter, M. J., Parsons, D. S. 1972. The isoenzymes of carbonic anhydrase: Kinetic properties with particular reference to the functions in the intestinal tract. *J. Physiol. London* 210:465–78

30. Cassidy, M. M. 1970. Characteristics of the (Na + K)-stimulated ATPase of rat jejunum. *J. Physiol. London* 210:53–54P

31. Chen, L. C., Rohde, J. E., Sharp, G. W. G. 1972. Properties of adenyl cyclase from human jejunal mucosa during naturally acquired cholera and convalescence. *J. Clin. Invest.* 51:731–40

32. Chez, R. A., Horger, E. O., Schultz, S. G. 1969. The effect of ethacrynic acid on sodium transport by isolated rabbit ileum. *J. Pharmacol. Exp. Ther.* 168:1–5

33. Chez, R. A., Palmer, R. R., Schultz, S. G., Curran, P. F. 1967. Effect of inhibitors on alanine transport in isolated rabbit ileum. *J. Gen. Physiol.* 50:2357–75

34. Clarkson, T. W. 1967. The transport of salt and water across isolated rat ileum. Evidence for at least two distinct pathways. *J. Gen. Physiol.* 50:695–727

35. Clarkson, T. W., Toole, S. R. 1964. Measurement of short-circuit current and ion transport across the ileum. *Am. J. Physiol.* 206:658–68

36. Code, C. F., Bass, P., McClary, G. B. Jr., Newnum, R. L., Orvis, A. L. 1960. Absorption of water, sodium and potassium in small intestine of dogs. *Am. J. Physiol.* 199:281–88

37. Csaky, T. Z. 1963. A possible link between active transport of electrolytes and nonelectrolytes. *Fed. Proc.* 22:3–7

38. Csaky, T. Z., Thale, M. 1960. Effect of ionic environment on intestinal sugar transport. *J. Physiol. London* 151:59–65

39. Csaky, T. Z., Zollicoffer, L. 1960. Ionic effect on intestinal transport of glucose in the rat. *Am. J. Physiol.* 198:1056–58

40. Diamond, J. M. 1964. Transport of salt and water in rabbit and guinea pig gall bladder. *J. Gen. Physiol.* 48:1–14

41. Eggermont, E., Loeb, H. 1966. Glucose-galactose intolerance. *Lancet* 2:343

42. Elsas, L. J., Hillman, R. E., Patterson, J. H., Rosenberg, L. E. 1970. Renal and intestinal hexose transport in familial glucose-galactose malabsorption. *J. Clin. Invest.* 49:576–85

43. Esposito, G., Faelli, A., Capraro, V. 1969. Effect of sodium on passive permeability of non-electrolytes through the intestinal wall. *Experientia* 25:603–4

44. Esposito, G., Faelli, A., Capraro, V. 1970. Effect of sodium on passive permeability of non-electrolytes through the intestinal wall. In *Permeability and Function of Biological Membranes,* ed L. Bolis, 74–85. Amsterdam: North-Holland

45. Esposito, G., Faelli, A., Capraro, V. 1972. A sodium dependent non-carrier mediated transport of a passive diffusing substance across the intestinal wall. In *Sodium-Linked Transport of Organic Solutes,* ed. E. Heinz, 170–76. New York: Springer-Verlag

46. Field, M. 1971. Ion transport in rabbit ileal mucosa. II. Effects of cyclic 3', 5'-AMP. *Am. J. Physiol.* 221:992–97

47. Field, M. 1971. Intestinal secretion: Effect of cyclic AMP and its role in cholera. *N. Engl. J. Med.* 284:1137–44
48. Field, M., Dietz, J. 1973. Ion transport in rabbit ileal mucosa. IV. Bicarbonate secretion. *Am. J. Physiol.* In press
49. Field, M., McColl, I. 1973. Ion transport in rabbit ileal mucosa. III. Effects of chatecholamines. *Am. J. Physiol.* In press
50. Field, M., Fromm, D., McColl, I. 1971. Ion transport in rabbit ileal mucosa. I. Na and Cl fluxes and short-circuit current. *Am. J. Physiol.* 220:1388–96
51. Field, M., Fromm, D., Al-Awqati, Q., Greenough, W. B. III. 1972. Effect of cholera enterotoxin on ion transport across isolated ileal mucosa. *J. Clin. Invest.* 51:796–804
52. Field, M., Plotkin, G. R., Silen, W. 1968. Effects of vasopressin, theophylline and cyclic adenosine monophosphate on short-circuit current across isolated rabbit ileal mucosa. *Nature London* 217:469–71
53. Field, M., Schultz, S. G., Curran, P. F. 1967. Alanine transport across isolated rabbit ileum. *Biochim. Biophys. Acta* 135:236–43
54. Fisher, R. B. 1955. The absorption of water and some small solute molecules from the isolated small intestine of the rat. *J. Physiol. London* 130:655–64
55. Fleshler, B., Nelson, R. A. 1970. Sodium dependency of L-alanine absorption in canine Thiry-Vella loops. *Gut* 11:240–44
56. Fordtran, J. S., Dietschy, J. M. 1966. Water and electrolyte movement in the intestine. *Gastroenterology* 50:263–85
57. Fordtran, J. S., Ingelfinger, F. J. 1968. Absorption of water, electrolytes and sugars from the human gut. *Handb. Physiol., Sect. 6, Aliment. Canal,* ed. C. F. Code, 3:1457–90. Washington D.C.: Am. Physiol. Soc.
58. Fordtran, J. S., Rector, F. C. Jr., Carter, N. W. 1968. The mechanisms of sodium absorption in the human small intestine. *J. Clin. Invest.* 47:884–900
59. Fordtran, J. S., Rector, F. C. Jr., Ewton, M. F., Soter, N., Kinney, J. 1965. Permeability characteristics of the human small intestine. *J. Clin. Invest.* 44: 1935–44
60. Förster, H., Hoos, I. 1972. The excretion of sodium during the active absorption of glucose from the perfused small intestine of rats. *Hoppe-Seyler's Z. Physiol. Chem.* 353:88–94
61. Frizzell, R. A., Schultz, S. G. 1970. Effects of monovalent cations on the sodium-alanine interaction in rabbit ileum: Implication of anionic groups in sodium binding. *J. Gen. Physiol.* 56: 462–90
62. Frizzell, R. A., Schultz, S. G. 1972. Ionic conductances of extracellular shunt pathway in rabbit ileum: Influence of shunt on transmural sodium transport and electrical potential differences. *J. Gen. Physiol.* 59:318–46
63. Frizzell, R. A., Markscheid-Kaspi, L., Schultz, S. G. 1974. Oxidative metabolism of rabbit ileal mucosa. *Am. J. Physiol.* In press
64. Frizzell, R. A., Nellans, H. N., Schultz, S. G. 1973. Effects of sugars and amino acids on sodium and potassium influx in rabbit ileum. *J. Clin. Invest.* 52:215–17
65. Frizzell, R. A., Nellans, H. N., Acheson, L. S., Schultz, S. G. 1973. Effects of cycloheximide on influx across the brush border of rabbit small intestine. *Biochim. Biophys. Acta* 291:302–7
66. Frizzell, R. A., Nellans, H. N., Rose, R. C., Markscheid-Kaspi, L., Schultz, S. G. 1973. Intracellular Cl concentrations and influxes across the brush border of rabbit ileum. *Am. J. Physiol.* 224: 328–37
67. Fromm, D. 1973. Na and Cl transport across isolated proximal small intestine of the rabbit. *Am. J. Physiol.* 224: 110–16
68. Frömter, E., Diamond, J. 1972. Route of passive ion permeation in epithelia. *Nature New Biol.* 235:9–13
69. Funder, J., Ussing, H. H., Wieth, J. O. 1967. The effects of $CO_2$ and hydrogen ions on active Na transport in isolated frog skin. *Acta Physiol. Scand.* 71:65–76
70. Fujita, M., Matsui, H., Nagano, K., Nakao, M. 1971. Asymmetric distribution of ouabain-sensitive ATPase activity in rat intestinal mucosa. *Biochim. Biophys. Acta* 233:404–8
71. Fujita, M., Ohta, H., Kawai, K., Matsui, H., Nakao, M. 1972. Differential isolation of microvillus and baso-lateral plasma membranes from intestinal mucosa: Mutually exclusive distribution of digestive enzymes and ouabain-sensitive ATPase. *Biochim. Biophys. Acta* 274:336–47
72. Gardner, J. D., Peskin, G. W., Cerda, J. J., Brooks, F. P. 1967. Alterations of in vitro fluid and electrolyte absorption by gastrointestinal hormones. *Am. J. Surg.* 113:57–64
73. Gigg, L. E., Eddy, A. A. 1972. An electrogenic sodium pump as a possible factor leading to concentration of amino

acids by mouse ascites tumor cells with reversed sodium ion concentration gradients. *Biochem. J.* 129:979–81

74. Gilles-Bailien, M., Schoffeniels, E. 1965. Site of action of L-alanine and D-glucose on the potential difference across the intestine. *Arch. Int. Physiol. Biochim.* 73:355–57

75. Gilman, A., Koelle, E., Ritchie, J. M. 1963. Transport of potassium in the rat's intestine. *Nature London* 197:1210–11

76. Glynn, I. M., Hoffman, J. F., Lew, V. L. 1971. Some partial reactions of the sodium pump. *Phil. Trans. Roy. Soc. London* 262:91–102

77. Greenough, W. B. III., Carpenter, C. C. J., Bayless, T. M., Hendrix, T. R. 1970. The role of cholera exotoxin in the study of intestinal water and electrolyte transport. *Progress in Gastroenterology*, ed. G. B. J. Glass, II:236–51. New York: Grune and Stratton

78. Gutman, Y., Benzakein, F. 1970. Effect of saline loading on absorption from the cat ileum in vivo. *Isr. J. Med. Sci.* 6:195–200

79. Hajjar, J. J., Khuri, R. N., Curran, P. F. 1973. Alanine efflux across the serosal border of turtle intestine. *J. Gen. Physiol.* 60:720–34

80. Hakim, A. A., Lifson, N. 1964. Urea transport across dog intestinal mucosa in vitro. *Am. J. Physiol.* 206:1315–20

81. Hakim, A. A., Lifson, N. 1969. Effects of pressure on water and solute transport by dog intestinal mucosa in vitro. *Am. J. Physiol.* 216:276–84

82. Hakim, A., Lester, R. G., Lifson, N. 1963. Absorption by an in vitro preparation of dog intestinal mucosa. *J. Appl. Physiol.* 18:409–13

83. Heaton, J. W. Jr., Code, C. F. 1969. Sodium-glucose relationships during intestinal sorption in dogs. *Am. J. Physiol.* 216:749–55

84. Hendrix, T. R., Bayless, T. M. 1970. Digestion: Intestinal secretion. *Ann. Rev. Physiol.* 32:139–64

85. Hellier, M. D., Thirumalai, C., Holdsworth, C. D. 1973. The effect of amino acids and dipeptides on sodium and water absorption in man. *Gut* 14:41–5

86. Higgins, J. T. Jr., Blair, N. P. 1971. Intestinal transport of water and electrolytes during extracellular volume expansion in dogs. *J. Clin. Invest.* 50:2569–79

87. Hirschhorn, N. et al 1968. Decrease in net stool output in cholera during perfusion with glucose-containing solutions. *N. Engl. J. Med.* 279:176–81

88. Hoffman, J. F. 1966. The red cell membrane and the transport of sodium and potassium. *Am. J. Med.* 41:666–80

89. Hogben, C. A. M., Tocco, D. J., Brodie, B. B., Schanker, L. S. 1959. On the mechanism of intestinal absorption of drugs. *J. Pharmacol. Exp. Ther.* 125:275–82

90. Holdsworth, C. D., Dawson, A. M. 1964. The absorption of monosaccharides in man. *Clin. Sci.* 27:371–79

91. Hoshi, T., Komatsu, Y. 1970. Effects of anoxia and metabolic inhibitors on the sugar-evoked potential and demonstration of sugar-outflow potential in toad intestine. *Tohoku J. Exp. Med.* 100:47–59

92. Hoshi, T., Sakai, F. 1967. A comparison of the electrical resistances of the surface cell membrane and cellular wall in the proximal tubule of the newt kidney. *Jap. J. Physiol.* 17:627–37

93. Hubel, K. A. 1967. Effect of secretin on bicarbonate secretion in fluid perfusing the rat ileum. *Experientia* 23:337

94. Hubel, K. A. 1967. Bicarbonate secretion in rat ileum and its dependence on intraluminal chloride. *Am. J. Physiol.* 213:1409–13

95. Hubel, K. A. 1969. Effect of luminal chloride concentration on bicarbonate secretion in rat ileum. *Am. J. Physiol.* 217:40–45

96. Hubel, K. A. 1972. Effects of secretin and glucagon on intestinal transport of ions and water in the rat. *Proc. Soc. Exp. Biol. Med.* 139:656–58

97. Humphreys, M. H., Earley, L. E. 1971. The mechanism of decreased intestinal sodium and water absorption after acute volume expansion in the rat. *J. Clin. Invest.* 50:2355–67

98. Kedem, O., Katchalsky, A. 1958. Thermodynamic analysis of the permeability of biological membranes to nonelectrolytes. *Biochim. Biophys. Acta* 27:229–46

99. Kedem, O., Katchalsky, A. 1963. Permeability of composite membranes: Part 2. Parallel elements. *Trans. Faraday Soc.* 488:1931–40

100. Kernan, R. P. 1970. Electrogenic or linked transport. *Membranes and Ion Transport*, ed. E. Bittar, Vol. I, Chap. 10. London: Wiley-Interscience

101. Keusch, G. T., Grady, G. F., Mata, L. J., McIver, J. 1972. The pathogenesis of *Shigella* diarrhea. I. Enterotoxin production by *Shigella dysenteriae 1. J. Clin. Invest.* 51:1212–18

102. Kimberg, D. V., Field, M., Johnson, J., Henderson, A., Gershon, E. 1971.

Stimulation of intestinal mucosal adenyl cyclase by cholera enterotoxin and prostaglandins. *J. Clin. Invest.* 50: 1218–30

103. Kimmich, G. A. 1970. Active sugar accumulation by isolated cells. A new model for sodium-dependent metabolite transport. *Biochemistry* 9:3669–77

104. Kimmich, G. A. 1973. Coupling between Na and sugar transport in small intestine. *Biochim. Biophys. Acta* 300: 31–78

105. Kinney, V. R., Code, C. F. 1964. Canine ileal chloride absorption: Effect of carbonic anhydrase inhibitor on transport. *Am. J. Physiol.* 207:998–1004

106. Kinter, W. B., Wilson, T. H. 1965. Autoradiographic study of sugar and amino acid absorption by everted sacs of hamster intestine. *J. Cell Biol.* 25: 19–39

107. Kleinzeller, A., McAvoy, E. M. 1973. Sugar transport across the peritubular face of renal cells of the flounder. *J. Gen. Physiol.* 62:169–84

108. Koopman, W., Schultz, S. G. 1969. The effect of sugars and amino acids on mucosal Na and K concentrations in rabbit ileum. *Biochim. Biophys. Acta* 173:338–40

109. Lecount, T. S., Grey, R. D. 1972. Transient shortening of microvilli induced by cycloheximide in the duodenal epithelium of the chicken. *J. Cell Biol.* 53: 601–5

110. Lee, C. O., Armstrong, W. McD. 1972. Activities of sodium and potassium ions in epithelial cells of small intestine. *Science* 175:1261–464

111. Leitch, G. J., Burrows, W. 1968. Experimental cholera in the rabbit ligated intestine: ion and water accumulation in the duodenum, ileum and colon. *J. Infec. Dis.* 118:349–59

112. Leitch, G. J., Iwert, M. E., Burrows, W. 1966. Experimental cholera in the rabbit ligated ileal loop: Toxin-induced water and ion movement. *J. Infec. Dis.* 116:303–12

113. Levitt, D. G., Hakim, A. A., Lifson, N. 1969. Evaluation of components of transport of sugars by dog jejunum in vivo. *Am. J. Physiol.* 217:777–83

114. Lifson, N., Hakim, A. A. 1966. Simple diffusive-convective model for intestinal absorption of a nonelectrolyte (urea). *Am. J. Physiol.* 211:1137–46

115. Lifson, N., Gruman, L. M., Levitt, D. G. 1968. Diffusive-convective models for intestinal absorption of $D_2O$. *Am. J. Physiol.* 215:444–54

116. Lifson, N., Hakim, A. A., Lender, E. J. 1972. Effects of cholera toxin on intestinal permeability and transport interactions. *Am. J. Physiol.* 222:1479–87

117. Loeschke, K., Bentzel, C. J., Csaky, T. Z. 1970. Asymmetry of osmotic flow in frog intestine: functional and structural correlation. *Am. J. Physiol.* 218: 1723–31

118. Loeschke, K., Hare, D., Csaky, T. Z. 1971. Passive sugar flux across frog jejunum in vitro. *Pfluegers Arch.* 328: 1–20

119. Machen, T. E., Erlij, D., Wooding, F. B. P. 1972. Permeable junctional complexes: The movement of lanthanum across rabbit gallbladder and intestine. *J. Cell Biol.* 54:302–12

120. Mailman, D. S., Ingraham, R. C. 1971. Effects of hemorrhage and tilting on Na, Cl and $H_2O$ absorption from the intestine. *Proc. Soc. Exp. Biol. Med.* 137:78–81

121. Maruyama, T., Hoshi, T. 1972. The effect of D-glucose on the electrical potential profile across the proximal tubule of Newt kidney. *Biochim. Biophys. Acta* 282:214–25

122. Modigliani, R., Bernier, J. J. 1971. Absorption of glucose, sodium and water by the human jejunum studied by intestinal perfusion with a proximal occluding balloon and at variable flow rates. *Gut* 12:184–93

123. Modigliani, R., Bernier, J. J. 1972. Effects of glucose on net and unidirectional movements of water and electrolytes in the human small intestine. *Biol. Gastro-Enterol.* 5:165–74

124. Moore, W. L. Jr., Bieberdorf, F. A., Morawski, S. G., Finkelstein, R. A., Fordtran, J. S. 1971. Ion transport during cholera-induced ileal secretion in the dog. *J. Clin. Invest.* 50:312–18

125. Morisset, J. A., Webster, P. D. 1971. In vitro and in vivo effects of pancreozymin, urecholine, and cyclic AMP on rat pancrease. *Am. J. Physiol.* 220:202–8

126. Moritz, M., Finkelstein, G., Meshkinpour, H., Fingerut, J., Lorber, S. H. 1973. Effect of secretin and cholecystokinin on the transport of electrolyte and water in human jejunum. *Gastroenterology.* 64:76–80

127. Moshal, M. G., Broitman, S. A., Zamcheck, N. 1970. Gastrin and absorption: A review. *Am. J. Clin. Nutr.* 23:336–42

128. Munck, B. G. 1972. Effects of sugar and amino acid transport on transepithelial fluxes of sodium and chloride of short circuited rat jejunum. *J. Physiol. London* 223:699–717

129. Munck, B. G., Schultz, S. G. 1969. Lysine transport across isolated rabbit ileum. *J. Gen. Physiol.* 53:157–82
130. Nalin, D. R., Cash, R. A., Rahman, M., Yunus, M. D. 1970. Effect of glycine and glucose on sodium and water absorption in patients with cholera. *Gut* 11:768–72
131. Nellans, H. N., Frizzell, R. A., Schultz, S. G. 1973. Coupled sodium-chloride influx across the brush border of rabbit ileum. *Am. J. Physiol.* 225:467–75
132. Nellans, H. N., Frizzell, R. A., Schultz, S. G. 1974. Brush border processes and transepithelial Na and Cl transport by rabbit ileum. *Am. J. Physiol.* In press
133. Norris, H. T., Curran, P. F., Schultz, S. G. 1969. Modification of intestinal secretion in experimental cholera. *J. Infec. Dis.* 119:117–25
134. Olsen, W. A., Ingelfinger, F. J. 1968. The role of sodium in intestinal glucose absorption in man. *J. Clin. Invest.* 47:1133–42
135. Parsons, D. S. 1956. The absorption of bicarbonate-saline solutions by the small intestine and colon of the white rat. *Quart. J. Exp. Physiol.* 41:410–20
136. Phillips, S. F., Code, C. F. 1966. Sorption of potassium in the small and the large intestine. *Am. J. Physiol.* 211:607–13
137. Phillips, S. F., Schmalz, P. F. 1970. Bicarbonate secretion by the rat colon: Effect of intraluminal chloride and acetazolamide. *Proc. Soc. Exp. Biol. Med.* 135:116–22
138. Pierce, N. F., Carpenter, C. C. J. Jr., Elliott, H. L., Greenough, W. B. III. 1970. Effects of prostaglandins, theophylline, and cholera exotoxin upon transmucosal water and electrolyte movement in the canine jejunum. *Gastroenterology* 60:22–32
139. Pierce, N. F., Greenough, W. B. III., Carpenter, C. J. J. Jr. 1971. *Vibrio cholerae* enterotoxin and its mode of action. *Bacteriol. Rev.* 35:1–13
140. Powell, D. W., Binder, H. J., Curran, P. F. 1972. Electrolyte secretion by the guinea pig ileum in vitro. *Am. J. Physiol.* 223:531–37
141. Powell, D. W., Binder, H. J., Curran, P. F. 1973. Active electrolyte secretion stimulated by choleragen in rabbit ileum in vitro. *Am. J. Physiol.* In press
142. Powell, D. W., Malawer, S. J., Plotkin, G. R. 1968. Secretion of electrolytes and water by the guinea pig small intestine in vivo. *Am. J. Physiol.* 215:1226–33
143. Quigley, J. P., Gotterer, G. S. 1969. Distribution of (Na + K)-stimulated ATPase activity in rat intestinal mucosa. *Biochim. Biophys. Acta* 173:456–68
144. Reid, M., Eddy, A. A. 1971. Apparent metabolic regulation of the coupling between the potassium ion gradient and methionine transport in the mouse ascites-tumour cell. *Biochem. J.* 124:951–52
145. Robison, G. A., Butcher, R. W., Sutherland, E. W. 1971. *Cyclic AMP.* New York: Academic
146. Roggin, G. M., Banwell, J. G., Yardley, J. H., Hendrix, T. R. 1972. Unimpaired response of rabbit jejunum to cholera toxin after selective damage to villus epithelium. *Gastroenterology* 63:981–89
147. Rohde, J. E., Chen, L. C. 1972. Permeability and selectivity of canine and human jejunum during cholera. *Gut* 13:191–96
148. Rose, R. C., Schultz, S. G. 1971. Studies on the electrical potential profile across rabbit ileum: Effects of sugars and amino acids on transmural and transmucosal electrical potential differences. *J. Gen. Physiol.* 57:639–63
149. Saltzman, D. A., Rector, F. C. Jr., Fordtran, J. S. 1972. The role of intraluminal sodium in glucose absorption in vivo. *J. Clin. Invest.* 51:876–85
150. Schafer, D. E., Lust, W. D., Sircar, R., Goldberg, N. D. 1970. Elevated concentration of adenosine 3', 5'-cyclic monophosphate in intestinal mucosa after treatment with cholera toxin. *Proc. Nat. Acad. Sci. USA* 67:851–56
151. Schafer, J. A., Heinz, E. 1971. The effect of reversal of Na and K electrochemical potential gradients on the active transport of amino acids in Ehrlich ascites tumor cells. *Biochim. Biophys. Acta* 249:15–33
152. Schedl, H. P., Clifton, J. A. 1963. Solute and water absorption by the human small intestine. *Nature London* 199:1264–67
153. Schrier, R. W., De Wardener, H. E. 1971. Tubular reabsorption of sodium ion: Influence of factors other than aldosterone and glomerular filtration rate. *N. Engl. J. Med.* 285:1231–43
154. Schultz, S. G. 1973. Shunt pathway, sodium transport and the electrical potential profile across rabbit ileum. *Transport Mechanisms in Epithelia*, ed. H. H. Ussing, N. A. Thorn, 281–94. Copenhagen: Munksgaard

155. Schultz, S. G., Curran, P. F. 1968. Intestinal absorption of sodium chloride and water. See Ref. 57, 3:1245–75

156. Schultz, S. G., Curran, P. F. 1970. Coupled transport of sodium and organic solutes. *Physiol. Rev.* 50:637–718

157. Schultz, S. G., Frizzell, R. A. 1972. An overview of intestinal absorptive and secretory processes. *Gastroenterology* 63:161–70

158. Schultz, S. G., Strecker, C. K. 1970. Fructose influx across the brush border of rabbit ileum. *Biochim. Biophys. Acta* 211:586–88

159. Schultz, S. G., Zalusky, R. 1964. Ion transport in isolated rabbit ileum. I. Short-circuit current and Na fluxes. *J. Gen. Physiol.* 47:567–84

160. Schultz, S. G., Zalusky, R. 1964. Ion transport in isolated rabbit ileum. II. The interaction between active sodium and active sugar transport. *J. Gen. Physiol.* 47:1043–59

161. Schultz, S. G., Fuisz, R. E., Curran, P. F. 1966. Amino acid and sugar transport in rabbit ileum. *J. Gen. Physiol.* 49:849–66

162. Schultz, S. G., Zalusky, R., Gass, A. E. Jr. 1964. Ion transport in isolated rabbit ileum. III. Chloride fluxes. *J. Gen. Physiol.* 48:375–78

163. Schwartz, T. L. 1971. Direct effects on the membrane potential due to "pumps" that transfer no net charge. *Biophys. J.* 11:944–60

164. Serebro, H. A., Iber, F. L., Yardley, J. H., Hendrix, T. R. 1969. Inhibition of cholera toxin action in the rabbit by cycloheximide. *Gastroenterology* 56:506–11

165. Sharp, G. W. G., Hynie, S. 1971. Stimulation of intestinal adenyl cyclase by cholera toxin. *Nature London* 229:266–69

166. Sladen, G. E., Dawson, A. M. 1968. Effect of bicarbonate on sodium absorption by the human jejunum. *Nature London* 218:267–68

167. Sladen, G. E., Dawson, A. M. 1969. Interrelationships between the absorptions of glucose, sodium and water by the normal human jejunum. *Clin. Sci.* 36:119–32

168. Smulders, A. P., Wright, E. M. 1971. Galactose transport across the hamster small intestine: The effect of sodium electrochemical potential gradients. *J. Physiol. London* 212:277–86

169. Smulders, A. P., Tormey, J. McD., Wright, E. M. 1972. The effect of osmotically induced water flows on the permeability and ultrastructure of the rabbit gallbladder. *J. Membrane Biol.* 7:164–97

170. Soergel, K. H., Whalen, G. E., Harris, J. A. 1968. Passive movement of water and sodium across human small intestinal mucosa. *J. Appl. Physiol.* 24:40–48

171. Soergel, K. H., Whalen, G. E., Harris, J. A., Geenen, J. E. 1968. Effect of antidiuretic hormone on human small intestinal water and solute transport. *J. Clin. Invest.* 47:1071–82

172. Stening, G. F., Grossman, M. I. 1969. Hormonal control of Brunner's glands. *Gastroenterology* 56:1047–52

173. Stirling, C. E. 1972. Radioautographic localization of sodium pump sites in rabbit intestine. *J. Cell Biol.* 53:704–14

174. Sullivan, R., Asano, T. 1971. Effects of staphylococcal enterotoxin B on intestinal transport in the rat. *Am. J. Physiol.* 220:1793–97

175. Swallow, J. H., Code, C. F. 1967. Intestinal transmucosal fluxes of bicarbonate. *Am. J. Physiol.* 212:717–23

176. Taylor, A. E., Wright, E. M., Schultz, S. G., Curran, P. F. 1968. Effect of sugars on ion fluxes in intestine. *Am. J. Physiol.* 214:836–42

177. Tidball, C. S. 1961. Active chloride transport during intestinal secretion. *Am. J. Physiol.* 200:309–12

178. Trier, J. S., Rubin, C. E. 1965. Electron-microscopy of the small intestine: A review. *Gastroenterology* 49:574–603

179. Turnberg, L. A. 1971. Potassium transport in the human small bowel. *Gut* 12:811–18

180. Turnberg, L. A., Bieberdorf, F. A., Morawski, S. G., Fordtran, J. S. 1970. Interrelationships of chloride, bicarbonate, sodium and hydrogen transport in the human ileum. *J. Clin. Invest.* 49:557–67

181. Turnberg, L. A., Fordtran, J. S., Carter, N. W., Rector, F. C. Jr. 1970. Mechanism of bicarbonate absorption and its relationship to sodium transport in the human jejunum. *J. Clin. Invest.* 49:548–56

182. Ussing, H. H., Windhager, E. E. 1964. Nature of shunt path and active sodium transport path through frog skin epithelium. *Acta Physiol. Scand.* 61:484–504

183. Vassar, P. S. 1963. The electric charge density of human tumor cell surfaces. *Lab. Invest.* 12:1072–77

184. White, J. F., Armstrong, W. McD. 1971. Effect of transport solutes on membrane potentials in bullfrog small intestine. *Am. J. Physiol.* 221:194–201

185. Whittembury, G., Rawlins, F. A. 1971. Evidence of a paracellular pathway for ion flow in the kidney proximal tubule: Electromicroscopic demonstration of lanthanum precipitate in the tight junction. *Pfluegers Arch.* 330: 302–9

186. Wright, E. M. 1966. The origin of the glucose dependent increase in the po-

tential difference across the tortoise small intestine. *J. Physiol. London* 185:486–500

187. Wright, E. M., Smulders, A. P., Tormey, J. McD. 1972. The role of the lateral intercellular spaces and solute polarization effects in the passive flow of water across rabbit gallbladder. *J. Membrane Biol.* 7:198–219

# REFLEX AND CENTRAL MECHANISMS INVOLVED IN THE CONTROL OF THE HEART AND CIRCULATION[1]

♦1106

*Orville A. Smith*

Department of Physiology and Biophysics and Regional Primate Research Center, University of Washington, Seattle

Most of the topics presented in this article have not been reviewed since 1970. Several have never received exposure in *Annual Reviews* at all. For this reason the literature to be covered is truly enormous.

The baroreceptor literature by itself would have consumed the whole article; therefore I have selected only the aspect of interactions of the reflex with central neural activity or behavior. The chemoreceptors, cerebral circulation, and reflexes with vagal afferents were omitted because each was covered in a recent review article (17, 85, 114). Other topics omitted were simply victims of lack of space, time, or expertise of the reviewer.

I have selected for review those areas where the central nervous system and behavior interact with the cardiovascular system. The particular areas chosen were those in which a significant amount of recent literature has accumulated since 1970 and on which there is enough history to present a somewhat cohesive story. I have also taken this opportunity to expose the physiological audience to the fringe of integrative physiology where behavior becomes a critical element in overall regulation. Two other areas were selected because some particularly good groups of papers in these areas deserved to be covered as a unit.

In addition to the reviews mentioned, the Milan conferences (14, 160), the FASEB symposium (4), and the biofeedback series (12, 79, 137, 148) represent major accumulations of work in this field.

---

[1]Preparation of this review was supported in part by NIH Grants RR 00166 and HL 04741.

## CNS-BEHAVIORAL INTERACTIONS WITH BAROREFLEXES

The year 1959 saw a major landmark in an evolving field of science: central nervous system control of circulation. In that year an international symposium, under the auspices of the National Academy of Sciences – National Research Council, brought together the many relevant disciplines of cardiovascular physiology, neurophysiology, medicine, neuroanatomy, psychology, pharmacology, and bioengineering (then in its infancy). The symposium established this special area of study as real and important and, in effect, announced publicly that neural control was critical to understanding cardiovascular physiology. The influence of such a meeting on subsequent ideas and research is difficult to assess, but Philip Bard (13), in his opening paper, pointed the way for the next fourteen years of research by asserting that suprabulbar influences must inhibit baroreceptor function when an organism maintains an elevated heart rate in the face of an elevated arterial pressure, as happens during periods of stress or exercise.

Twenty years earlier, Moruzzi (109) had performed an experiment demonstrating that the carotid sinus reflex could be inhibited by stimulation of the anterior vermis of the cerebellum; but, although the experiment demonstrated central neural influence over this reflex, it was not directed toward the problem of simultaneously elevated pressure and heart rate during behavioral extremes. This latter concern was first addressed experimentally in 1961 by Wilson et al (158), who, despite the text figure which showed obvious reduction of the cardiac component of the baroreceptor reflex during hypothalamic stimulation, concluded that the hypothalamic and reflex effects were independent and simply additive.

In 1962 Reis & Cuénod (127) approached the problem in a more general fashion. Employing decerebrations, decerebellations, brainstem transections, and electrical stimulations, they provided evidence for extensive central neural influence on baroreflexes (128, 129). In 1965 Hilton (68) published positive results on inhibiting a baroreceptor response by stimulating the hypothalamic "defense area." In 1966 Smith & Nathan (142), while attempting to discover the significance of the repeated presence of degenerating nerve fibers in the inferior olive after lesions of pressor-cardioaccelerator areas of the diencephalon, provided evidence that stimulation of the olive could inhibit the bradycardic and sometimes the depressor components of the carotid sinus reflex. The following year the same point was made for stimulating the diencephalic areas projecting to the olive (143). It is probably no coincidence that the effective point in the olivary complex can be shown anatomically to project to the vermal region of the cerebellum, where Moruzzi (109) had obtained positive results.

An important consideration in this sort of investigation is the clear demonstration that true neural inhibition is occurring and that the effect is not simply a peripheral summation of opposing effects. Weiss & Crill (154) provided good evidence that true neural inhibition was involved on the basis of presynaptic inhibition. They demonstrated primary afferent depolarization of the carotid sinus nerve following a conditioning stimulus delivered to the fields of Forel just dorsolateral to the mammillary bodies.

A different approach was used by Gebber & Snyder (61) to determine whether the suppressive effect of hypothalamic stimulation upon the baroreceptor reflex is true neural inhibition or is merely a sympathetic override of the cardiac inhibitory effect at a peripheral locus. Using cats, they elicited the reflex in each animal either by carotid stretch, by stimulation of the sinus nerve, or by administration of pressor doses of norepinephrine, and recorded mean arterial pressure, heart rate, and electrical activity of a postganglionic sympathetic nerve. The unique contribution of this approach was that by performing a high cervical spinal section they eliminated all peripheral sympathetic effects while retaining all central neural processes at the medullary level. Also, the vagus nerve was thereby left intact to mediate the cardiac effects of baroreceptor activation. They found that every location in the hypothalamus that produced elevated pressure and tachycardia during electrical stimulation before spinal section also inhibited the baroreceptor-produced bradycardia in the "encephale isole" preparation, thus contradicting the belief that the inhibitory influence is produced only by stimulation of the defense area of the hypothalamus. They also found that in cats with intact neuraxis, the hypothalamic stimulation would inhibit the bradycardia, but had no effect upon the depressor component. This accords with Wilson's finding (158), but contrasts with Hilton's results (68). In addition, they were able to facilitate the hypothalamically produced pressor effect by carotid artery occlusion and vice versa, thereby demonstrating the suprabulbar modulation of the baroreceptor response to increased or decreased systemic pressure. Klevans & Gebber (84) then proceeded to complete the possible combinations of influence by providing evidence that stimulation of septal, preoptic, or anterior hypothalamic areas that showed little or no change in heart rate or pressure would, however, markedly facilitate the bradycardia evoked by injection of norepinephrine, sinus stretch, or aortic nerve stimulation. In a summary paper Gebber & Klevans (60) reviewed some of these results, and added a series of studies involving stimulation of medullary sites that inhibited the sinus reflex. These sites included the inferior olive, verifying the earlier Smith & Nathan results (143). Recordings from the vagus nerve and nucleus solitarius allowed comparisons of the facilitatory effects of septal and amygdalar stimulation on baroreceptor-induced bradycardia. Stimulation of the amygdala produced action potentials in the vagus while septal stimulation did not; however, septal stimulation did enhance the synaptic component of the compound action potential in the nucleus solitarius in response to sinus nerve stimulation. This implies that septal stimulation is a powerful subliminal facilitatory input for the vagal portion of the baroreceptor reflex.

The results reported by Hilton (68) have prompted several investigators to study the influence exerted by the interactions of the hypothalamic defense area upon the baroreceptor reflex. Lisander (92), in a summary of five papers (44, 45, 51, 87, 93), demonstrated that simultaneous defense area stimulation and carotid sinus stretch led to complete inhibition of the cardiac slowing, but the reflex modulation of the peripheral vascular beds was usually unchanged. This cardiac-specific action of defense area stimulation was examined further by studying cardiac output under similar conditions. The efficiency of the heart was improved as a function of the interaction of these two neural inputs to the cardiovascular (CV) system because the increased drive to the heart from defense area stimulation was maintained, while the vascular bed pattern of responses still came under baroreflex control. This is particularly important for muscle blood flow which receives a triple advantage of (a) increased cardiac output as the result of a maintained heart rate due to inhibition of the vagus with defense area stimulation, (b) a decreased sympathetic vasoconstrictor tone due to baroreflex influences, and (c) an active vasodilatation due to defense area activation of the sympathetic cholinergic vasodilator system.

These studies, under certain conditions, showed maintained arterial pressure during baroreceptor activation with hypothalamic stimulation. These results accord with Hilton's observations (68), but not with Wilson's (158) nor with Gebber's preparations (61) in which the neuraxis and vagal nerves were intact. In another study Humphreys, Joels & McAllen (74) reported a failure to influence the depressor response of the baroreceptor reflex while stimulating the defense area. Such differences emphasize the extreme complexity of the hypothalamus: some stimulation sites possibly involve the defense reaction area and others do not, or possibly involve differential interactions with anesthesia and stimulation parameters.

A major concern in understanding neural contributions to cardiovascular control is that most studies are done using circulatory variables instead of neural activity as the dependent variable. Although these measurements are easier to make and quantify, they bear no necessary relation to the neural activity at the effector site. The work of Wilson et al (159) exemplifies the efforts to look directly at neural activity: they used whole nerve electroneurograms that were integrated to give an index of sympathetic neural activity to a particular organ or bed to study the interaction of hypothalamic stimulation and baroreceptor reflex interactions on activity in the renal nerve. The results show a decrease in renal nerve activity to noise levels after producing a large pressure increase by *l*-epinephrine injection. Superimposing hypothalamic stimulation, which by itself produced a large increase in renal nerve activity, had no effect on the renal nerve response until arterial pressure began to decline; then the effect of hypothalamic stimulation was directly a function of how much the aortic pressure (i.e. the pressure seen by the baroreceptor) had been reduced. They concluded that ". . . the range of linear operation of the baroreceptor reflexes was increased . . . by simple additive interaction with hypothalamic stimulus effects." After sectioning baroreceptor afferents, the hypothalamically induced changes in renal nerve activity were the same regardless of arterial pressure level, thereby proving the efficacy of baroreceptor input on the reduction of the hypothalamically produced renal nerve response. Keeping arterial pressure at various levels and then superimposing hypothalamic stimulation gave similar results, i.e. slopes of effects from varying frequencies of hypothalamic stimulation were constant and simply shifted along the axis in accordance with the level of arterial pressure maintained during stimulation. Despite their convincing argument for linear additive interaction between the two inputs, they recognized that three of the twelve hypothalamic stimulation locations gave nonlinear results.

In a similar study Bagshaw, Iizuka & Peterson (11), giving good reasons for the use of hemodynamic rather than neural measurements, recorded renal flow and pressure and then, using Fourier analysis, calculated renovascular input impedance.

Their results showed that peak renal resistance at all hypothalamic stimulation intensity levels decreased as carotid sinus pressure increased. They concluded that posterior hypothalamic stimulation did modulate the renal vasomotor response to baroreceptor activation in a fashion that produced a nonalgebraic effect on the renal resistance.

The difference in conclusions between these two studies may be due to activation of different fiber systems in the hypothalamus, nonlinearities in the transfer from neural activity to renovascular impedance, the difficulty of assuring complete neural activity measurement from whole nerve preparation, species difference, or anesthetic difference.

The hypothalamic-medullary vasomotor center interactions have been standard investigational fare for years, but usually with the assumptions that the vasomotor center is a relatively independent operator, self-sufficient for the homeostasis of the organism, and that the hypothalamus projects onto it, influencing it to some degree. The concept may well be a holdover from the primitive concept of the organization of the CNS as divided into centers of one kind or another, each with its own "deus." There have been some doubters, however, and in Randall's 1963 symposium *Nervous Control of the Heart* (123) some specific contrary ideas were presented by Peiss (115) and Manning (100). After stating that evidence for the dominant vasomotor center in the medulla was inconclusive, they provided experimental and theoretical evidence to support the idea that supramedullary structures provide tonic and phasic influences on CV activity and that the final integrator is the intermediolateral cells in the spinal cord that receive inputs from all levels of the CNS, of which the medulla is only one. This heretical notion has met substantial resistance but, far from dead, is enjoying a resurgence of support from several sources. Hilton(69) has marshalled the most recent evidence in favor of a longitudinal organization of the integrative structures ranging from cortex to spinal cord. Hilton & Spyer (70) have precisely mimicked the baroreceptor response by stimulating a depressor point in the anterior hypothalamus. Also, when this area is ablated, the baroreceptor response is decreased or eliminated if the ablation is preceded by medullary lesions. Spyer (146) has recorded the action potentials of single neurons in the hypothalamus in response to increases in carotid sinus pressure. He found 21 neurons that responded to high levels of pressure and concluded that the anterior hypothalamus plays a role in the integration of the baroreceptor reflex. This is the same area that Klevans & Gebber (84) found to facilitate the carotid stretch reflex.

Kent, Drane & Manning (80) have refined earlier work on the influence of decerebration on the baroreceptor reflex by comparing the vascular responses to a wide range of sinus pressures and applying elaborate mathematical treatments to the results. They found the major effect of brainstem transection to be a decrease in the effective range over which arterial pressure could be varied by changes in sinus pressure.

Korner et al (86) have taken all of these studies to task on the basis of their use of anesthesia. In his chronic unanesthetized preparations—thalamic, pontine, or sham operated rabbits—he found some alteration of median blood pressure and gain, but very little effect on range of pulse interval. These analyses were carried out on stimulus-response curves over a mean arterial pressure range of 70–130 mm Hg. He attributes differences in results from those of other investigators to the effects of anesthesia.

In the majority of papers cited so far, there has been an assumption of known, clear-cut relationships between the various neural structures concerned in the regulation of the baroreceptor reflexes. However, the last section has shown that the organization of the central autonomic pathways may well be poorly understood or even misunderstood. In a recent strikingly good paper, Gebber, Taylor & Weaver (62) studied this problem with an electrophysiological approach. Using cats, decerebrate or under dial-urethane-monoethylurea anesthesia, they selected a postganglionic sympathetic fiber bundle, which by all available criteria contained no vasodilator fibers and whose evoked potential was in sympathetic fibers subserving a vasoconstrictor function. The responses analyzed were monophasic evoked potentials which were summed with an average-response computer. The neuraxis from cervical cord to posterior hypothalamus was explored with small concentric stimulating electrodes, and the influence of baroreflex activation on the recorded potentials was measured. In the medulla, responses were obtained from periventricular gray, dorsolateral reticular formation, and the lateral portion of nucleus reticularis ventralis. The potentials could be divided into two major groups: those with latencies longer than 50 msec, which were always inhibited by baroreceptor reflex activation, and those with latencies of 34–44 msec, which were not.

In the spinal cord three groups of potentials were discriminated: (a) those with long latencies (60–120 msec) derived from dorsal funiculus (presumably ascending afferents) that were completely blocked by baroreceptor activity and eliminated by cord transection, (b) those with latencies of 36–52 msec that were partially blocked by baroreceptor action, and (c) those with short latencies (26–42 msec) that were not inhibited during a rise in arterial pressure.

These results demonstrate the existence of two systems of central pathways over which vasoconstrictor outflow is distributed, distinguishable on the basis of sensitivity to blockade by baroreceptor activation. Another important discovery is the existence of a site in the spinal cord at which inhibition from the baroreceptors occurs. Also, the fact that many responses elicited from hypothalamus and midbrain were not influenced by baroreceptor activity indicates that vasoconstrictor elements exist above the medullary level that are not under the influence of the vasomotor center-baroreceptor system.

Interpretation of these results must be qualified since the results are derived from a single postganglionic nerve (supplying the carotid artery) and hence may be somewhat specific to the vasculature supplied. Also the use of averaged potentials always carries some dangers in interpretation. However, in view of the physical impossibility of recording from all postganglionic sympathetics simultaneously and the equal impossibility of recording each postganglionic single fiber in a trunk, these results stand as important both in their immediate information content and in the hypotheses they may generate for future investigations.

In the final analysis the objective of all this research is to know how the CV system is regulated in the routine behavior of organisms, especially in man. Studies in this area have been thwarted by the difficulty of making measurements in man at all, aggravated by the problem of rarely being able to control systematically the independent variable so that something approaching an experiment can be done. In the past few years the Oxford group has used the vasoconstrictor effect of angiotensin or phenylephrine to elicit an increased arterial pressure and thereby produce a baroreflex. The change in heart rate interval plotted against systolic pressure during the reflex provides a measure of reflex sensitivity. When an artery is cannulated in awake humans, the CV effects of inducing a baroreflex during relatively normal behavior can be recorded. This approach was used by Smyth, Sleight & Pickering (145) to study pressure regulation during sleep. EEG records were taken to determine the stage of sleep, and measurements were made before, during, and after sleep. They found that of ten subjects, seven had significantly increased baroreflex sensitivity, one had a decreased sensitivity, and the other two had no change. No consistent changes in sensitivity occurred during various stages of sleep except during REM sleep when sensitivity was maximal. The same technique showed that baroreflex sensitivity is decreased in hypertensive patients (24). Baroreceptor-decreased sensitivity also decreased with age in a manner independent of arterial pressure level (65). Along a more behavioral line the influence of exercise (23) on reflex sensitivity was studied. In every case the sensitivity of the reflex was decreased during exercise and was found to decrease systematically with increased work levels. At heart rates of 150 beat/min no cardiac reflex effects were found despite increases of 25–30 mm Hg in arterial pressure. Results using this unique technique are provocative. Hopefully, what is being seen is the behavioral reflection of the hypothalamic influence on baroreflexes discussed earlier. This is a leap which is not unreasonable, but which is untestable in the human. Smith (141), using a technique developed by Scher et al (132), has developed a procedure for doing similar experiments in monkeys trained to perform a series of behavioral tasks on signal. Hydraulic occluders are placed around the terminal aorta; when the occluder is activated suddenly, arterial pressure increases abruptly by 25–30 mm Hg. In this fashion a systematic innocuous baroreflex is superimposed on any of the animal's own behavior. By plotting heart rate instead of interval against pressure, changes in sensitivity have been shown to occur with various behaviors, of which sleep is the most and eating the least sensitive reflex condition.

The use of animals of course allows more elaborate measuring devices and subsequent invasive manipulations which are denied with human subjects. The epitome of instrumentation to investigate baroreflexes during normal behavior is found in the studies of Vatner et al (151, 153). Using dogs, they implanted flow meters on the aorta and mesenteric, renal, iliac, and coronary arteries, pressure gauges in the aorta, and radiofrequency pacemakers to stimulate the carotid sinus nerves. During rest, sinus nerve stimulation produced decreased pressure, rate, total peripheral resistance, mesenteric, iliac, and renal resistance, and an increased iliac flow. Cardiac output was only slightly decreased. During exercise (4 mph treadmill) nearly identical percentage changes were produced in these variables, giving no support to the notion of a decreased reflex sensitivity as was found in the human studies. In the sleep studies, however, good evidence for increased reflex sensitivity was obtained: decreases in aortic pressure were identical, while heart rate decreased significantly more during sleep. Other changes did not differ greatly from the rest condition. In dogs anesthetized with pentobarbital, they noted prolonged recovery time (several dogs failed to recover from sinus nerve stimulation and died) and less vasodilatation, most significantly in the coronary and iliac beds.

All of these studies contain inherent problems. There is no way to guarantee that what is observed is a sensitivity change in the CNS organization of the reflex rather than a peripheral sympathetic competition with the vagal action (118). This is particularly critical when the behavior may be producing cardiac acceleration at the same time the reflex activation is occurring, but is of little importance during the steady sleep situations. The problem of just where the response of a particular animal in a particular situation is located on the sensitivity curve for the reflex (sigmoid pressure-rate curve) is difficult to determine. The technique for eliciting the reflex with drugs that stimulate alpha receptors is unsettling because of other possible sites of action for the drug, including the wall of the carotid artery itself or the CNS. The occlusion technique, of course, stops flow completely to a portion of the vascular tree for a brief period. The sinus nerve stimulation probably involves chemoreceptor reflex activation as well and suffers from the existence of the aortic arch buffer nerves that are attempting immediately to counteract the pressure changes produced by the carotid sinus nerve stimulation.

Systems analyses on the hemodynamics or control of the CV system are no longer new. But the use of this analytic approach in the unanesthetized preparation is new and important. Scher et al (132) have summarized baroreflex control of heart rate in the unanesthetized dog, baboon, and man. Sinusoidal changes in arterial pressure were produced in animals by inflating and deflating an occluder cuff around the aorta or vena cava, and in humans by sinusoidally tilting or changing suction to a lower body box. The vagal-sympathetic balance of control was determined by the time constant of the rate changes, the influence of propranolol, and the change in phase relationship with atropine. Their findings indicate that the dog's heart rate is entirely vagally controlled during increases of pressure; the human shows more sympathetic control, and the baboon has the greatest sympathetic control. The same order of relationship holds for decreases in pressure.

## OPERANT CONDITIONING AND BIOFEEDBACK IN CARDIOVASCULAR REGULATION

I remember in 1959 walking across the campus of Indiana University talking with a graduate student about his thesis work. He told me that he intended to use human subjects, record their heart rate, and when the rate changed in a predetermined direction reinforce this change. I immediately offered the opinion that it would not work because that sounded like "backward conditioning" and everyone back to Pavlov knew that backward conditioning did not work. The student patiently explained that his approach was one of instrumental or operant conditioning, not classical conditioning, despite his using an autonomic response, and that indeed it did seem to be working. The student was Donald M. Shearn and the positive results

presented in his thesis (139) set the stage for an almost frenetic burst of experimentation on instrumental visceral learning throughout the sixties continuing to the
present. Because of the potential implications inherent in the approach, the field has
captured the imagination of scientist and layman alike and has now spread to a point
that rests uncomfortably close to mysticism.

The basic principle in operant conditioning is that if any response of an organism
is followed by a positive reinforcer, i.e. something that the organism seeks out such
as money, food, praise, etc, then the probability that the response will be repeated
is increased. The same increased probability occurs if the organism's behavior is
contingent upon avoidance of a negative reinforcer. This principle has been B. F.
Skinner's basic tenet and has been shown to work for somatic responses of every
kind in almost any kind of organism. Shearn's unique contribution was to apply the
same principle to autonomic responses. Miller (104) spelled out the possible implications of this approach, and with DiCara (his graduate student) produced some of
the most exciting animal work in the middle sixties (40).

To show that the autonomic nervous system obeys the same laws of learning as
the somatic nervous system, it was critical that no "voluntary" or somatic responses
such as muscle tensing or respiration be allowed to influence the autonomic responses being studied. With humans, somatic mediation of the response was mini-
mized by techniques such as breathing in rhythm with a flashing light (22). These
approaches were not possible with animals, so the appeal to absolute somatic control
—curarization—was made (150). Curarization, however, results in another problem: how to reinforce an animal that cannot eat, drink, or seek safety (all proven
positive reinforcers). Trowill's study (150) provided a brilliant solution for this
problem: he used intracranial stimulation of the "pleasure center" of the hypothalamus as a reinforcer. With these techniques he guardedly reported differential
learning to either speed or slow the heart. Hothersall & Brener (72) introduced the
feedback principle to the animal studies (giving the animal a signal when his heart
was doing the "correct" thing) which seemed to improve the results. In rapid
sequence, Miller & DiCara showed (a) that this visceral learning acted much like
somatic learning (105), (b) that vasomotor responses could be conditioned (41), and
(c) that vasodilation in the skin of one ear could be learned simultaneously with
vasoconstriction in the other ear (43), a result far beyond Cannon's conception of
how the autonomic nervous system ought to function. They also showed that blood
pressure increases or decreases which were independent of heart rate changes could
be learned (42).

A few years earlier a series of human studies by Hnatiow & Lang (71) and Engel
(47) yielded positive results. One of the critical factors highlighted by the human
studies is "feedback," or knowledge of results. If subjects have feedback about
whether their response is either correct or incorrect, then their performance is better
even if they don't know precisely what it is they are supposed to be doing. Brener
& Hothersall (21) proved the importance of this factor and it became a standard
part of the paradigm for these experiments.

Investigation of blood pressure was delayed because of technical difficulties in
obtaining continuous information about pressure in humans. In 1969 Shapiro et al

(138) reported success in conditioning an average 4 mm Hg decrease in systolic pressure, but not for increases in pressure using a positive reinforcer. With monkeys, large increases in blood pressure have been produced using shock avoidance as the reinforcer (67, 120). Benson et al (15) showed that, by making avoidance of the electric shock contingent on increasing pressure, mean pressure could be elevated 20–40 mm Hg. By reversing the contingency, i.e. avoiding shock by decreasing pressure, a 10–20 mm Hg drop below basal level could be obtained. These reversals in direction of response using the same stimuli are important to assure that the learning process accounts for the changes rather than some other systematically changing variable.

Now that CV variables can be brought under environmental control by operant techniques, recent work has been directed toward applying these techniques in an attempt to ameliorate pathological conditions and, conversely, attempting to produce large changes which might result in pathologic states. Benson et al (16) selected a group of seven patients with a diagnosis of moderate or severe hypertension, telling them only that they would be paid a sum of money to come to the laboratory and have their pressures measured for hourly sessions. Their pressures were recorded with an automated cuff system recording Korotkoff sounds. After a series of control sessions, conditioning sessions began in which an occurrence of lowered systolic pressure was signaled to the patient by a flash of light and a brief tone. The subjects were told that these signals were good and that attempts should be made to turn them on. After each 20 occurrences of the signals, the subjects were reinforced with the equivalent of a small sum of money. When no further decreases in pressure occurred over five consecutive sessions, the conditioning was terminated. The average median systolic pressure was 164.9 mm Hg at the end of the control sessions and 148.4 mm Hg at the end of the conditioning trials. Only one subject did not show a decrease; the others showed decreases of 3.5–33.8 mm Hg. One would be scientifically happier with this study if it had an equivalent control group and clinically happier if there had been some indication that the decrease persisted after conditioning. However, the demonstrated effectiveness as a potential therapeutic approach is encouraging.

Weiss & Engel (155) achieved about the same degree of success in training patients with premature ventricular contraction (PVC) to control their heart rates within restricted limits and thereby reduce the incidence of PVCs. Followup studies showed that 4 of the 5 positive cases maintained a persistent decrease in PVCs for as long as 21 months. In this study the patients were told the reason for the study, as one of the main purposes was to train the patients to recognize when PVCs were occurring so that they might take appropriate behavioral measures to stop them.

To obtain models of hypertension, investigators in several laboratories have attempted to use these avoidance conditioning techniques to produce a maintained high blood pressure in animals. The results have not been overly encouraging. Brady and his associates have been very active in these attempts (5, 20, 66), but despite yeoman efforts, they have not succeeded in developing a long-term hypertension model in the dog or baboon. Some degree of success has been achieved by Herd et al (67) in the squirrel monkey and by Forsyth (52) in the rhesus monkey.

In these recent studies, particularly those involving therapeutic approaches or pathology-model production, there has been a shift away from the original theoretical concern of whether the autonomic nervous system obeys the same laws of learning as the somatic nervous system, and is therefore amenable to instrumental conditioning procedures. Biofeedback is now a big concern, supported by a series of recent books (12, 79, 137, 148). Biofeedback, of course, has nothing to do with the theoretical issue at hand, being used simply as a tool to improve results. In actuality, by using feedback, a subject can learn much more readily to make somatic adjustments that will influence the circulatory variables under consideration and thereby subvert the original theoretical concern.

The declining interest in the original problem has another more fundamental reason: the original observations with curarized animals do not seem to be standing the test of repeatability. Miller (see 77) has acknowledged that each time experiments have been done and controlled more closely, the differences have been smaller. The results of some experiments simply cannot be duplicated.

Even if the experiments of Miller and DiCara are eventually verified, the question for CV control may become academic: in the end, it may simply be that the somatic and CV responses are inseparable because of somatic and autonomic control overlap at a critical CNS level. Clarke, Smith & Shearn (29) have shown in completely muscle-blocked monkeys that stimulation of motor neocortex in the leg area will result in increased blood flow to the contralateral leg, not to the arm nor the ipsilateral leg, i.e. there is topographical autonomic representation of the vasculature in the motor cortex as well as somatic topography. If the output of the motor cortex is directly involved in the control of voluntary movement, then these results indicate that when signals are sent to the ventral horn cells (involving some other intermediaries as well) to produce muscle movement, signals are simultaneously sent to the intermediolateral cell column cells to produce vascular changes in those muscles that are going to move. Anatomic evidence for this possibility has been presented (143). The intent or the effort to make a somatic movement may possibly be accompanied by an obligatory CV response; the fact that the actual motor movement is blocked at the muscle motor end plate by curare may be unimportant.

Another more recent study by Goodwin, McCloskey & Mitchell (64) gives even greater support to the importance of the "central command." In this study human subjects were asked to maintain a constant tension in the biceps or triceps muscle of an arm and were given visual feedback of their accuracy. CV and respiratory variables were continuously monitored during the task. The experiment involved changing the central command to maintain that tension without altering the actual tension or energy expenditure and then comparing the accompanying cardiorespiratory responses. The change in central command was achieved by applying a vibratory stimulus to the tendon of either the active muscle or its antagonist. Vibratory input is a powerful stimulus to muscle spindle primary endings. Applying this stimulus to a muscle (e.g. biceps) being held at a given tension level and therefore at a given central command level would reflexly increase the tension in the muscle via the monosynaptic connections of the afferents. The central command would then have to be decreased to maintain tension at the stimulated level. By applying the vibrator to the antagonist muscle (e.g. triceps) the tension in the active muscle (biceps) would be reflexly decreased via disynaptic inhibition. In this case the central command would have to be increased in order to maintain the stipulated level of tension in biceps. Arterial pressure, ECG, ventilation, and end tidal $CO_2$ were measured and the results were straightforward: when central command was increased, the cardiorespiratory variables increased; when central command was decreased, they decreased. These changes were produced even when no increased work was being done by the individual and no greater degree of tension was being produced in the muscle (therefore not increasing the discharge in those muscle afferents concerned in cardiorespiratory reflexes).

This brilliantly conceived and elegantly executed study is of obvious importance, demonstrating that through central effort, circulatory responses can be dissociated from accompanying somatic muscle movement or tension. This, of course, means that the problem of "somatic mediation" in operant conditioning of visceral responses is completely confounded at the most basic central neural level, possibly the cortical level as suggested above. These physiological results bear directly upon the longstanding contention by Obrist et al (113) and Goesling & Brener (63) that movement and circulatory responses are initiated from the same central neural source. A psychophysiological study by Schwartz & Higgins (135), demonstrating identical cardiac responses to actual motor action of pushing a key or simply thinking "push," is in the same domain.

Regardless of the fate of the theoretical problem of visceral instrumental conditioning, we still retain the potential utility of biofeedback as a means of controlling the CV system or other systems as well. That changes can be produced is well substantiated; the degree to which changes can be produced in particular individuals is still in doubt, and the potential utility of biofeedback as a therapeutic technique needs to be pursued further. It may well be, as one eminent physiologist opined, that the use of operant conditioning to reduce high blood pressure, etc is all a Lucy van Pelt phenomenon; when Charlie Brown comes to the psychiatrist's booth, the advice he receives from Lucy is "Relax, Charlie Brown; that'll be five cents." On the other hand, if biofeedback or its neighbors, transcendental meditation, Zen, or whatever, can teach Charlie Brown how to relax to the point that his health is improved, then the whole effort will have been worthwhile.

## CNS—BEHAVIORAL INTERACTIONS IN REGULATION OF CARDIOVASCULAR RESPONSES TO EXERCISE AND EMOTION

### Exercise

As long as cardiovascular physiologists do research, there will be studies on exercise. CV control systems exist primarily to adjust the circulation to changing work loads of all types, and exercise is a simple, repeatable, easily measurable way to vary a very common type of work load. The long-term steady state CV responses to exercise have been studied in great detail. The initial response, involving extremely rapid increases in heart rate and blood pressure at the onset of exercise, has been less well studied. The genesis of these changes has been variously attributed to carotid and aortic chemoreceptor activation, to increased venous return effects on right heart reflexes, to metabolic products in muscle producing local and/or spinal reflex changes, and to a preorganized central neural output.

That these changes in heart rate are characteristically rapid has been known since the beginning of the century, but has been largely a matter of speculation rather than investigation. In 1970 Petro, Hollander & Bouman (117) attempted to determine the timing between onset of a muscular contraction and increase in heart rate in human subjects instructed to make a maximal isometric flexion of the elbow against a fixed resistance at the onset of an auditory stimulus. The brevity of this elapsed time ($\sim$ 0.5 sec) points directly to a neural effect. Inasmuch as stimulation of the vagus nerve requires 0.2–0.3 sec to produce slowing, a remarkably short period of about 200 msec is left for all other changes and reactions leading to this point, as indicated by Borst, Hollander & Bouman (19) in a followup study. Both of these studies eliminated anticipation or respiration as possible factors and both noted that the brief latency almost assuredly eliminates metabolite production as a stimulus. The Borst study also compared cardiac responses to varying levels of isometric contraction and found that a weak contraction elicited a relatively large fraction of the cardiac acceleration, strengthening the argument against a metabolic mediator. Both studies concluded that abrupt inhibition of vagal tone accounts for the instantaneous cardiac acceleration at the beginning of exercise. It has been suggested that the source lies either in reflex activity originating in muscle spindles or in motor cortex. McCloskey, Matthews & Mitchell (101) have effectively eliminated the muscle spindles as serious contenders in this regard.

Somewhat antedating these studies, Freyschuss (58) had been conducting an extensive series of investigations in which heart rate, arterial pressure, right atrial pressure, and venomotor reactions measured with the occluded limb technique were recorded in supine humans performing isometric contraction. This study verified the brevity of the cardiac response and the presence of increased arterial pressure, and denied the possible involvement of right atrial receptors by demonstrating a failure of right atrial pressure to change in a consistent fashion with muscular contraction. However, consistent increases in venous pressure were recorded. A series of pharmacological studies (59) was done using atropine and phentolamine separately and in combination. The results showed that the immediate heart rate increase was due to withdrawal of vagal tone and that both increased heart rate and sympathetic vasoconstrictor activity contributed to the increased arterial pressure. The CV responses of tetraplegic patients (deprived of descending sympathetic influence from the vasomotor center or elsewhere) to contraction of their neck muscles or remaining functional upper limb flexor muscles were identical to those of normal subjects (58). Another series of critical studies involved blocking neuromuscular transmission in the contracting arm and then asking the subject to attempt to produce the same isometric tension as in the unblocked state. The criteria of full block were no movement or electromyographic activity in response to stimulation of the ulnar nerve and no electromyographic activity accompanying the intended hand grip. CV responses similar to the unblocked state were produced with only a reduction in magnitude as the major differentiating characteristic. Heart rate increases were 64% as large as normal and pressure was 55% normal. During trials when the neuromuscular block was wearing off, increasing degrees of force actually could be produced with the same central effort. The CV response, however, was identical in each case, thus speaking strongly for central neural control and against a metabolic basis for the changes. This result was verified in a succeeding series in which subjects were required to double their effort by gripping with both hands, thereby doubling the contracting muscle mass. The CV responses were not different in the two situations. These results substantiate the earlier observations of Lind & McNicol (89).

All of Freyschuss' results point directly toward a prepatterned output of the CNS in the initial CV responses that accompany isometric exercise. The inhibition of the baroreceptor reflex as part of this pattern was suggested by Lind et al (90) and tested by the Oxford group (37). They used three kinds of exercising, bicycling, 30% maximum voluntary isometric contraction, and rhythmic hand grip. They elicited the baroreflex by phenylephrine injection as described previously and found that in each kind of exercise there was a decreased sensitivity of the reflex. Studying subjects with equivalent starting heart rate levels, they found that the sustained isometric contraction produced maximal loss of sensitivity. Their additional maneuver was to occlude the circulation to the exercising arm, observing that upon cessation of exercise the heart rate dropped rapidly to resting level while arterial pressure remained elevated (3). At the same time baroreceptor sensitivity was still partially reduced, indicating a possible influence of arterial pressure directly upon the baroreceptor sensitivity.

Two nearly identical studies (31, 102) approached the problem of analyzing the possible role of reflex changes in determining the circulatory response to exercise by using stimulation of the lumbar ventral roots of anesthetized cats. This procedure produced increased blood pressure, but very small heart rate changes. By sectioning dorsal roots and applying appropriate blocking agents, it was proved that the circulatory response was the result of a reflex originating in contracting muscle. In these experiments a direct relation was shown between magnitude of the CV response and amount of tension developed. They also demonstrated by two different approaches that the reflex was not associated with muscle spindle or Golgi tendon organ activity. The conclusion is that the reflex has its source in the accumulation of metabolites of exercising muscle, and is mediated by Group III and IV afferents. This, of course, accounts nicely for the sustained pressure response after cessation of muscular activity when circulation is occluded and washout of metabolites is not permitted.

These studies concluding that metabolites are the critical factor might seem to conflict with those of Freyschuss (58), Petro et al (117), and Borst et al (19), where definite evidence was presented for a central origin of the pattern. However, McCloskey & Mitchell (102) acknowledge that the central irradiation effects should be considered as part of the whole pattern. To begin with, obviously the central command for exercise cannot be present in exercise brought about by direct stimulation of ventral roots of anesthetized cats. Second, the real focus of attention differed for the two sets of studies, the first mostly concerned with heart rate changes which were large compared with the arterial pressure changes and the second just the opposite. Third, the time span being examined was very different, with Freyschuss and others measuring responses the first few seconds of exercise and Coote et al (31) studying the longer duration responses. The baroreflex sensitivity studies bridge the two beautifully.

Collectively, these studies set the stage for an explanation of the circulatory response to exercise by specifying the elegant interaction of the initial central command to both autonomic and somatomotor control systems (including baroreflex inhibition) and the later peripheral reflexes produced by metabolites of active muscle. The later changes in increased venous return, chemoreceptor action, reactive hyperemia, temperature effects, etc, will collectively contribute to the whole complex pattern accompanying exercise.

## Emotion

Since the time of Cannon the idea has been generally accepted that during strong emotion heart rate increases, arterial pressure is elevated, blood flow to the viscera decreases, and probably blood flow to the muscles even increases. Psychologists in the Pavlov tradition have shown repeatedly, in situations that could be defined as "emotion-producing," that heart rate can go either direction depending on species of the subject, the situation, or individual perversity. When chronic measuring techniques came into use, increases in terminal aortic blood flow (111, 144, 147) and arterial pressure (52) were demonstrated in similar situations. In all these observations, a major concern was whether these were primary changes or secondary, mediated by activity and respiratory changes. Black, Carlson & Solomon (18) showed in studies of dogs under curare that CV changes occurred in response to conditional stimuli and electric shock.

Along another very active line Hilton (68) and colleagues have observed that the sympathetic cholinergic vasodilator response in skeletal muscle is elicited from the same hypothalamic location that Hess had found to produce behavior he described as "defense reaction." This active sympathetic vasodilation has become the sine qua non of the defense reaction: ". . . the vasodilator fibers to skeletal muscle are not known to participate in any other physiological response, the vasodilatation itself is the sole feature which is characteristic of the defense reaction" (68). Using this physiological response as a defining characteristic, a whole series of studies has been done which have related many CV responses to the "defense reaction," including augmented cardiac contraction (131), renal vasoconstriction (50), gut vasoconstriction (30), constriction of skin vessels (91), as well as the increased arterial pressure, heart rate, and, of course, dilation of skeletal muscle.

Recently Caraffa-Braga et al (28) and Pinotti (119) have used chronically instrumented dogs to study blood flow distribution during emotional stress. The behavioral situations, which included response to unexpected loud noise, water spray, or presentation of a cat, produced increased arterial pressure, heart rate, and iliac blood flow, with decreased mesenteric and renal blood flow. The increased muscle blood flow was concluded to be a result of active vasodilation. In contrast, Adams et al

(2), Zanchetti et al (161), and Baccelli et al (10) observed different responses in cats fighting and preparing to fight. Stimulating electrodes implanted in the mesence-phalic gray of one member of a pair of cats produced attack behavior toward the unsuspecting cagemate cat in the test box. A plastic panel separated the animals until the experimenter decided to allow contact. The nonstimulated cats were instrumented for aortic, mesenteric, and iliac flow and blood pressure. The "defending" cats fought the attacking cats in two ways, either by standing on their hind legs or by continuing to lie down and striking back only with the forepaws. In the first case all expectations for the CV pattern of emotion were fulfilled except that arterial pressure increased only slightly. In the second case, however, where the cat did not use his hind legs, iliac flow and conductance decreased during the whole preparatory and actual fighting period. This is in contrast to the very large increases seen in these variables when the muscles supplied by the iliac artery were being used during the fighting. When the standing fighting responses were compared to treadmill exercise responses, they were found to be the same. When the transparent panel separating the two animals was left in place so that the defending cat only prepared for fighting, but did not actually engage in fighting, the patterns were very different, including iliac vasoconstriction, decreased cardiac output, and frequently, bradycardia. The authors pointed out that circulatory changes due to natural emotional behavior are decidedly different from those due to stimulation of the hypothalamic defense area, in regard both to preparation for fighting and to fighting with only the forelegs. The major point, obviously, is that this truly defensive behavior does not involve a cholinergic muscle vasodilation; on the contrary, a vasoconstriction is produced.

To extend these observations the cats were exposed to different "emotion-producing" stimuli. When the limbs were not exercised, the iliac vessels constricted when the stimulus was the attacking cat and vasodilated when it was a barking dog or edible mouse. The dilation was blocked by methylatropine. Additional studies emphasized the importance of movement in producing cholinergic vasodilation. This was checked experimentally by classically conditioning cats, instrumented with flow sections on both iliac arteries, by following a tone with a painful electric shock to only one paw. On those trials when no conditioned flexion was produced, there was bilateral vasoconstriction in response to the tone, but when a flexion did occur, there was a vasodilation in the moving leg and a vasoconstriction in the quiet leg. After atropinization both the moving and quiet legs showed vasoconstriction regardless of movement. Either these results must be explained as species or situtational differences, or else a new concept of the role of sympathetic vasodilators in normal behavior must be developed. The relatively short duration of sympathetic vasodilation and the rapid vasodilation of muscle beds by the powerful action of local metabolites potentially diminish the theoretical utility of this system in normal muscle vasodilating during a specific kind of behavior.

## CNS—BEHAVIORAL CONTROL OF FLOW DISTRIBUTION

A major contribution to the understanding of neural-behavioral regulation of flow distribution has been made through the technological advancements of radioactive microsphere injections and refinements of electronic flowmeter recordings. The disadvantages of the former technique are that it measures organ flow at one single point in time—although the possibility of using up to five different radioactive nuclides compensates somewhat here, and that it requires killing the animal. Moreover it leans heavily upon the assumption of complete trapping of the microspheres in the various organs. The flowmeter technique has the advantage of continuous recording, but is still difficult to use on the smaller vessels and requires major surgical procedures on the animals, with consequent risks of damage to nerves or other important tissues.

Forsyth (55) has applied the microsphere technique to unanesthetized monkeys and has used his psychological expertise to control and manipulate the monkey's behavior with great precision. He has shown that the distribution of cardiac output in resting monkeys is roughly equivalent to that in humans with the exception that the rhesus monkey has a higher fraction delivered to skeletal muscle and less to brain and kidney. The pentobarbital anesthetized monkey (56) has decreased cardiac output concomitant with an increased percentage flow to kidney, skin, lungs, and bone at the expense of brain, skeletal muscle, and adrenals. Hemorrhage in the unanesthetized monkey (57) results in increased fractions of cardiac output delivered to brain, heart, adrenal gland, and the bed of the hepatic artery at the expense of skin, spleen, and pancreas. Changes in distribution during stimulation of pressor points in the hypothalamus (53) showed marked increases to skeletal muscle at the expense of all the viscera. Oddly, the changes were much the same regardless of the locus of the hypothalamic stimulation, which suggests a generalized sympathetic discharge. This study also confirmed that there is no cholinergic component in the dilation of primate skeletal muscle. Psychological stress studies (54) involving short (20 min) and long term (72 hr) shock avoidance produced maintained levels of systemtic arterial pressure which during the short term was a function of increased cardiac output and during the long term was produced by increased peripheral resistance. During short term avoidance, increases in blood flow to skeletal muscle, heart, and liver were prominent; during long term avoidance increases in blood flow to the heart, spleen, pancreas, and liver occurred at the expense of skeletal muscle, kidneys, and gut.

The chronically implanted blood flow transducer technique in the tradition of Rushmer, Franklin & Van Citters has been used in several of the studies reported earlier in this article. In addition to those studies, Vatner et al (152) have measured coronary flow and arterial pressure in unrestrained baboons continuously for periods of 48 hours duration. Minimum coronary flow and maximum resistance occurred at night while the animals were asleep. With movement, coronary flow increased and resistance decreased. Maximal flow and minimal resistance were observed when the animals were excited by interaction with another baboon or by teasing. During the night when the baboons were asleep, spontaneous 100% increases in coronary flow and decreases in coronary resistance occurred in the absence of significant changes in pressure or rate. This last observation combined with the demonstration that stimulation of the carotid sinus nerve resulted in coronary dilatation despite simultaneous reductions of blood pressure and rate lends naturalistic corroboration of neural control of coronary circulation which has been so elegantly demonstrated in the laboratory by Feigl (48, 49).

In a provocative study Millard et al (103) recorded renal blood flow responses in normal dogs and in dogs with experimental heart failure. They measured renal flow bilaterally with one normal and one denervated kidney. In normal dogs, severe exercise resulted in an increase of arterial pressure of about 50%; in the innervated kidney renal resistance transiently increased by 130%, then returned to a steady state level of 50% increase; in the denervated kidney renal resistance showed no initial transient increase and during steady state increased to 50% above normal. After alpha receptor blockade, the renal resistance showed the same magnitude of increase, indicating that the steady state changes were probably not neurally mediated. In dogs with experimental congestive heart failure the pressor response to exercise was small and the renal resistance change in the denervated kidney approximated the increase in the normal dogs. However, a dramatic increase in resistance of 360% with a flow reduction from 148 ml/min to 46 ml/min occurred in the innervated kidney. With phentolamine these changes were nearly eliminated. This study strongly supports the previous findings of this group showing no reduction in renal flow during exercise in the normal dog. This paper has provided a raison d'etre for the profuse sympathetic innervation the kidney is known to have: it is apparently called into play during occasions of abnormal CV stress much more severe than that of strenuous exercise. Very recent studies[2] have shown severe reductions in renal flow during "emotional" responses in baboons which fit nicely with Feigl's earlier description of renal flow decreases during activation of the "defense reaction" in the acute preparation (50). There still needs to be some clarification of the experimental differences found between the reduction in renal flow during exercise in humans and the failure to find it in dogs. A species difference may be the answer, but errors in measurement are still a possibility.

Although the recent review by Betz (17) on the regulation of cerebral blood flow makes similar coverage here redundant, since the appearance of Betz's article there has been a major contribution to the proposition that neural effects can exert a major control on cerebral blood flow. D'Alecy & Feigl (38) have executed a tour de force in producing a preparation in which all outflows from the cerebrum except one were eliminated and flow through that vessel was measured during stimulation of the stellate ganglion. Extreme care was taken to assure that all other outflows (except a very minor loss through the diploic veins) were indeed eliminated and this was checked terminally by injection of acrylic material which would have revealed any leaks in the system. Any preparations showing incomplete occlusions or anastomotic veins (44 dogs) were eliminated from the study leaving 17 animals, on which the results are based. Flow decreases averaging 80% were found in response to stellate stimulation and were maintained for up to 1.5 min despite decreased $Po_2$, increased $Pco_2$, and increased pH during stimulation. It is difficult to determine

[2]Smith, O. A., Stephenson, R. B., Randall, D. C. Range of control of cardiovascular variables by the hypothalamus. *Recent Studies in Hypothalmic Function,* ed. K. Lederis, K. E. Cooper. Basel: Karger. In press.

what teleologic benefit to the organism is provided by this capability of the nervous system to produce such major decreases in cerebral blood flow. Some degree of job security should be provided to the individuals accepting the task of determining such.

In a study similar to that of Gebber, Taylor & Weaver (62), the effects of hypothalamic stimulation on sympathetic nerve activity in the renal, splenic, inferior cardiac, and leg skeletal muscle nerves were examined by Ninomiya et al (112). It has been implicitly assumed that there should be a relationship between the great variety of CV patterns elicitable on stimulating the hypothalamus and the great variety of behavior with which the hypothalamus is concerned. It would make sense that the pattern of CV responses, including variations in distribution of flow, be integrated at some neural level and be coordinated with the behavior that is to be carried out. Different CV patterns are known to accompany different behavior or environmental demands, but whether these patterns emerge full blown from the hypothalamic "forehead of Zeus" or are produced largely by action and reaction from the periphery is certainly one of the fundamental problems in understanding circulatory physiology. Ninomiya's study (112) addresses this problem using pentobarbital anesthetized cats and electroneurogram (whole nerve) recordings from the nerves listed above during stimulation of punctate single and combination points in the hypothalamus. Several statistical indices of relationship were used for analysis. In general, they found a nonuniform contribution of stimulus effects to the four organs and no indication of organ-specific effects. These are the results one would desire from an integrative structure with the capability of making fine adjustments and developing varying patterns of response.

These kinds of studies are very difficult to do. They are also prone to objections: that the effect of anesthetic agents is unknown, that there is no precise knowledge of the number and kinds of impulses being recorded by the electrode, and that electrical stimulation is itself artificial. However, these studies are very important and must be continued and refined as new techniques permit. Obviously the ideal would be the recording of these peripheral outputs in unanesthetized animals during ongoing behavior.

## CENTRAL AND PERIPHERAL AUTONOMIC NEUROANATOMY

Much confusion about the regulation of the CV system stems from inadequate knowledge of how the neural portions of the control mechanism are organized and physically arranged, both within the CNS and in the periphery. The anatomical relationships have been difficult to study because of the small size of the fibers that comprise the autonomic system (at least in the periphery), the frequent occurrence of mixed sympathetic and parasympathetic fibers in a single bundle, the ubiquitous distribution of the sympathetic fibers and their remarkable proclivity for regeneration. Histochemical techniques will be of tremendous future advantage, but they will provide only one kind of information. Additional information must be gained by electrical stimulation, recording, and other approaches.

A truly outstanding series of investigations in peripheral autonomic innervation has come from the Loyola University group. Under Randall's guidance, they have studied the innervation of the heart in minute detail mostly in dogs (124, 125), but also in baboons (121, 126). They have examined the distribution of both sympathetic and parasympathetic fibers and their influence on both inotropic and chronotropic functions, and they have examined the endocardial as well as the epicardial distribution. They have found highly localized inotropic responses to stimulation of discrete small nerve bundles, which suggests a mechanism for a fine degree of neural control of the myocardium, and have found the endocardial surface to have equally discrete innervation. They have also described four major vagosympathetic projections into the left heart and five to the right heart. Stemming from this work, Armour et al (9) looked at some of the integrative aspects of this innervation in conjunction with adrenal activity, and in an initial long-term project using the trained baboon, Randall & Smith (122) assessed the influence of sympathetic nerve activity on the control of right and left ventricular contractility during exercise and emotional responses. Armour et al (8) have also made a significant contribution based on these studies to the understanding of the potential importance of sympathetic nerve activity in the genesis of cardiac arrhythmias.

Concerning the other major fraction of cardiac innervation, the chronotropic effects, Levy (88) has summarized the extremely complicated situation that actually exists at the points of interaction of the sympathetic and parasympathetic system, e.g. the paradoxical effects of cardioacceleration after vagal or cholinergic type interventions. Although the evidence is far from complete, Iano, Levy & Lee (75) have provided evidence that there is an acceleratory effect of acetylcholine on the cells of the S-A node existing concurrently with the deceleratory effects. The reason the vagus is a cardiac deceleratory nerve is that the negative effect is dominant.

A deceleratory dominance is also very evident in the sympathetic-parasympathetic competition at the S-A node where the effects of the two inputs are simply not at all additive, as is so often mistakenly assumed. A small vagal effect can override a large sympathetic effect. This factor is critical when one attempts to interpret the inhibition of baroreflexes by central neural manipulations in a situation where the two inputs elicit competing cardiac effects. However, the direction of effect of this nonadditive interaction should help to identify the central neural locus of the inhibitory effect when it is the vagal component of the reflex that is being inhibited.

Weiss & Priola (156) have used sympathectomized dogs after atropine block to find loci in the brainstem which might mediate the vagal cardioaccelerator effect. When they stimulated the brainstem in such dogs the major cardiac acceleratory effects were localized to the tractus solitarius, dorsal motor nucleus of X, and nucleus ambiguus. Subsequent vagotomy had no effect on the acceleratory effect derived from stimulating the motor nucelus of the vagus or the solitary tract. The responses continued to be of undiminished large magnitude and had a very long latency ( ~13 sec) to onset. These acceleratory responses were, however, eliminated after ligation of the adrenal vein. In contrast, the tachycardia originating from stimulation of nucleus ambiguus, which had a very brief latency (2 sec) to onset, was not abolished by adrenal vein ligation and was immediately abolished by ipsilateral section of the vagus. This study established the nucleus ambiguus as the critical locus of origin of the vagal cardioacceleration. Other observations suggested that the fibers responsible for this acceleration represent a separate population within the vagus, e.g. ipsilateral vagal section eliminated the cardioacceleration effect, but in the normal animal, bilateral vagotomy was required to eliminate the bradycardia; also, the stimulation thresholds for the effects were different.

Although the knowledge of peripheral autonomic anatomy is meager, the amount of information on central autonomic anatomy is critically deficient. Because of the polysynaptic nature of some of the pathways, the usual degeneration techniques, which stain only to the first synapse, are of little value. The only effective way to study polysynaptic pathways is by electrophysiological analysis which carries the danger of current spread and recording artifact, but when used judiciously usually provides some functional as well as anatomical information.

In 1964 Humphrey (73) used an electrophysiological technique to provide the most complete description to that date of the intramedullary course of the carotid sinus nerve afferents. He found the expected direct projections to the nucleus and tractus solitarius; in addition, he recorded the activity of a group of cells, lying in the medial reticular formation at the same medullary level, that fired in response to sinus nerve stimulation with latencies 7–8 msec longer than those in nucleus solitarius and that followed on an average of only 13 pulses/sec. His interpretation was that these cells were influenced over polysynaptic paths mediated through the primary synapse in the nucleus solitarius. The anatomical studies of Cottle (35), Kerr (81), and Rhoton et al (130) support these results. Later Crill & Reis (36) verified this reticular projection. They, however, found evidence indicating that these cells are monosynaptic with sinus nerve fibers. Miura & Reis (106) subsequently verified the presence of this monosynaptic pathway as well as the polysynaptic path described by Humphrey and localized the active cells more precisely to the paramedian reticular nucleus.

This discovery of the potential importance of the paramedian reticular nucleus in mediating baroreceptor reflexes led Miura & Reis (107) to investigate the major input to this nucleus, the fastigial nucleus of the cerebellum. They discovered that stimulation of the nucleus fastigius produced a very consistent, surprisingly large pressor effect. This pressor response was eliminated by bilateral lesions of the restiform body, the fastigiobulbar tract, or the paramedian reticular nucleus, thereby establishing the source, route, and first synaptic termination of this pressor effect. Achari & Downman (1) provided evidence that accompanying this pressor effect there was also decreased flow to muscle, kidney, and intestine. Lisander & Martner (94) found fastigial stimulation to produce a pattern of responses similar to a baroreceptor response to decreased pressure. The predicted inhibitory interaction between fastigial and baroreceptor fibers on the cells of the paramedian nucleus was not found in a degree sufficient to make a strong case for true synaptic interaction (108). Only 10–16% of the recorded cells showed inhibitory interactions and very few paramedian cells responded to both inputs. Nathan (110) did show that on the final output side (splanchnic nerve activity) there was an overlapping of neurons used to mediate the responses from the two nuclei.

Doba & Reis (46) have attempted to clarify the functional significance of this fastigial pressor response by making elaborate measurements of hemodynamics and general sympathetic activity in cats. The consistent pattern of response included increased systolic, diastolic, mean, and pulse pressure; no change in venous pressures; small increases in heart rate and contractile force; a decrease in calculated stroke volume; no change in cardiac output; increased resistance and decreased flow in the femoral, axillary, renal and mesenteric arteries; increased flow with no change in resistance in the common carotid artery; and no change in pupil size. These changes reflect widespread activity of the sympathetic nervous system involving both alpha and beta adrenergic systems. However, it is not a massive total sympathetic discharge as evidenced by the lack of change in venous pressures and pupillary diameter. It is a consistently repeatable pattern which Doba & Reis (46) concluded resembles most the integrated CV response to assuming an upright posture. This hypothesis carries with it a convincing psychological factor because of the well known involvement of the cerebellum in posture and motor control: some integration with the CV system would be essential. Although the original thought (107) was that the fastigial effect might be one of inhibition of the baroreceptor reflex, the hemodynamic (arterial pressure) results dispute anything more than an algebraically summative effect. However, in each of the above studies, evidence can be found for the presence of inhibition of the cardio-vagal component of the reflex. This inhibition may be responsible for the maintained cardiac output resulting from fastigial stimulation despite the potential counter forces of increased peripheral resistance and, secondarily, the baroreceptor reflex itself.

Illert & Gabriel (76) have used stimulation techniques in spinal cats to resurvey the spinal cord for CV effects. The dorsal columns were relatively free of autonomic influence; pressor effects and increased sympathetic nerve activity were evoked from the lateral and dorsal part of the lateral funiculus and lamina II to IV in the gray matter. Decreased blood pressure and reduced neural activity were evoked by stimulation of the ventral funiculus and ventral portion of the lateral funiculus. Trouth, Loeschcke & Berndt (149) have reexamined the medulla and have specified the cardiovascular-respiratory interactions at this level.

In studying the higher portions of the nervous system, Jurf & Blake (78) observed that stimulating the diencephalon resulted in neurogenically mediated renal vasoconstriction and that stimulating the septal area resulted in inhibition of sympathetic renal constriction. Humorally mediated decreases in flow also were controlled by these areas. Calaresu & Mogenson (27) also mapped the septal area for pressor responses; they found pressor and depressor responses from stimulation of the lateral and medial septum respectively, and they documented the reversal in the direction of these responses when the kind of anesthetic was changed. This last result emphasizes once again the dangers inherent in assuming function from data derived by electrical stimulation of the brain in an anesthetized animal.

In two papers Schramm, Honig & Bignall (134) and Schramm & Bignall (133) have reexamined the cholinergic sympathetic vasodilator pathways in the cat and have made a comparison with the noncholinergic vasodilation produced in the squirrel monkey by stimulating homologous loci (primarily along the route of the lateral spinothalamic tract). They concluded that there is a primate homologue of the cholinergic sympathetic vasodilator system which can be defined anatomically instead of pharmacologically.

The intimate anatomical relationship between the lateral spinothalamic tract and the route of the sympathetic vasodilator system has bothered me for fifteen years. The possibility that the CV effects are sequelae of stimulating pain fibers has never been investigated to my knowledge. It would be possible for the CV effects of stimulating pain-afferent pathways to be retained even if the animal is anesthetized or decerebrate.

## SPINAL AND INTERACTIVE REFLEXES

In a set of three papers, Corbett, Frankel & Harris (32–34) surveyed the autonomic reflex control remaining in humans after complete cervical cord transection. The patients were under 40 years of age, all had had the transection for a minimum of 4.5 months, the transections were clinically complete, and all patients were free from other disease processes. Arterial pressure was measured via a percutaneously introduced arterial catheter. Calf and hand blood flow were measured plethysmographically and venomotor changes were determined via a venous catheter during hand or foot occlusion.

In one study (32) the circulatory changes accompanying muscle spasm were found to produce increased arterial pressure, venoconstriction, decreased heart rate, and decreased hand and calf blood flow. These changes began 2–3 sec after the start of the contraction. Considerations of possible explanatory mechanisms led them to conclude that only the venoconstriction and the skin and muscle blood flow reductions can definitely be attributed to spinal reflexes. There are other possible, though not definitive, explanations for the other changes. As mentioned previously, however, in studies with spinal cats, Coote et al (31) and McCloskey & Mitchell (102) proved that muscle contraction reflexly produces increased arterial pressure.

Corbett, Frankel & Harris (33) also studied the effects of cutaneous and visceral stimulation. Cold pack and pin prick produced slightly increased mean arterial pressure, and decreased hand and calf blood flow. Deep inspiration produced a transient increased blood pressure and heart rate, followed by variable responses. Bladder percussion consistently produced increased arterial pressure, decreases in heart rate and calf and hand blood flow, and venoconstriction. Again the authors concluded that there is evidence for spinal reflex activity influencing the peripheral vessels, but no necessary evidence for postulating a cardiac reflex.

In the final paper (34) the effect of tilting was studied. Head up tilt produced progressive decreases in arterial blood pressure and increased heart rate leveling off after about 2 min. Reductions in forearm blood flow dropped to unrecordable levels at times. A marked venoconstriction also occurred.

Collectively, these data support the notion that the spinal cord can mediate vasomotor cardiovascular reflexes. However, to obtain more specific answers to some of the questions and to perform some manipulations not possible in man, it seems that studies of chronically spinal transected monkeys may be in order.

Kirchner, Sato & Weidinger (83) and Khayatin & Lukoshkova (82) contributed additional electrophysiological evidence for the presence of active reflexes, most probably vasomotor in nature, in cats with spinal cord transection.

Over the past three years an important series of papers has been produced by a fortunate combination of talents from Milan, Italy, and Salt Lake City, Utah. After Brown (25) observed the sensory effects of coronary artery occlusion and Malliani et al (95, 99) made electrophysiological observations, these principals collaborated on studies of sympathetic discharge in the white ramus of the third thoracic ganglion and the inferior cardiac nerves (26). They found that increases in coronary flow increased the preganglionic firing recorded from the central end of the severed white ramus of T3 or inferior cardiac nerve. These were efferent fibers and the responses disappeared after stellectomy. Afferent fibers from the peripheral end of the nerves gave similar discharges to increased coronary pressure, myocardial ischemia, and coronary sinus occlusion. These studies were all done in spinal cats so that the reflexes were independent of any influence of the medulla or higher center. In checking the functional significance of these electrophysiological results, Peterson & Brown (116) found that stimulation of the central end of the cut inferior cardiac nerve increased arterial pressure. The pressure rise was further increased after vagotomy and the response persisted although it was decreased in magnitude after spinal cord section at C1. Stimulation of the pericoronary nerve to localize the origin of the effects closer to the coronary artery gave a pressor response after vagotomy, and the response was abolished after stellectomy. In looking at another potential cardiac target for these reflexes, Malliani et al (97) recorded the rate of change of left ventricular pressure $dP/dt$ in response to electrical stimulation of cardiac afferent fibers or to chemical stimulation of their cardiac receptor endings. Positive inotropic effects were found in this situation which were still present after spinal cord section. The reflex nature of the response was established by apropriate maneuvers. The next variable examined was heart rate (96). The previous studies all had involved sodium pentobarbital as the anesthetic agent; in this study the use of chloralose and minimal surgical procedures allowed the appearance of increased heart rate as a response to the stimulation of the cardiac afferent nerves. This was produced after vagotomy and spinal cord section, thereby once again assuring the nature of the response as a spinal sympathetic cardiocardiac reflex. Interactions of this reflex with vagal discharge have been recently examined by recording single vagal and cardiac sympathetic fibers (136). The neural discharge of 28 cardiac vagal efferent fibers was either abolished or greatly reduced during stimulation of the cut central end of the left inferior cardiac nerve. Stimulation of the opposite vagus, however, increased the vagal discharge. These responses were maintained after decerebration.

Malliani et al (98) have also considered the possible involvement of the afferent cardiac fibers in supplying continuous information to the spinal cord about the normal cardiac events. Recordings were made of single afferent fibers until one was found that fired in phase with the heart beat. Terminally, the inner and outer walls of each heart chamber were probed until the nerve fiber could be made to fire repeatedly from one locus. The ventricular fibers so identified were found to fire in synchrony with the time of contraction. The atrial fibers could be activated by either contraction or stretch. Also, all of the fibers were influenced by alterations of left coronary flow and pressure.

Collectively, these papers on spinally mediated CV reflexes serve to emphasize how much potential control resides at the spinal level. When these data are considered with the data of Spyer (146) and Hilton (69) and the older data from Peiss (115) and Manning (100), it is evident that the idea of an all-important vasomotor center in the medulla controlling the spinal outflow has been too highly emphasized.

In the area of interactions of reflexes and integration of complex reflexes the work of Daly and Angell-James stands preeminent. In a recent summary paper Daly (39) considered the complex interaction of arterial chemoreceptors, pulmonary reflexes, baroreflexes, and trigeminal reflexes. Angell-James & Daly have also presented an excellent review and analysis of the diving reflex (6). They have very recently (7) attacked the knotty problem of how the respiratory response is inhibited during diving when the carotid body chemoreceptors, stimulated by progressive hypoxia and hypercapnia, should produce increased respiration. They found that stimulation of the nasal mucosa inhibited the chemoreceptor-respiratory response, and greatly facilitated the slowing of heart rate. White & McRitchie (157) have looked at interactions of nasopharyngeal reflexes, baroreceptors, and lung inflation and determined the neural loci for these interactions.

*Literature Cited*

1. Achari, N. K., Downman, C. B. B. 1970. Autonomic effector responses to stimulation of nucleus fastigius. *J. Physiol.* 210:637–50
2. Adams, D. B., Baccelli, G., Mancia, G., Zanchetti, A. 1971. Relation of cardiovascular changes in fighting to emotion and exercise. *J. Physiol.* 212:321–36
3. Alam, M., Smirk, F. H. 1937. Observations in man upon a blood pressure raising reflex arising from the voluntary muscles. *J. Physiol.* 89:372–83
4. American Physiological Society Symposium. 1972. Neural regulation of the cardiovascular system. *Fed. Proc.* 31:1197–1252
5. Anderson, D. E., Brady, J. V. 1971. Preavoidance blood pressure elevations accompanied by heart rate decreases in the dog. *Science* 172:595–97
6. Angell-James, J. E., Daly, M. deB. 1972. Some mechanisms involved in the cardiovascular adaptions to diving. *Symp. Soc. Exp. Biol.* 26:313–41
7. Angell-James, J. E., Daly, M. deB. 1973. The interaction of reflexes elicited by stimulation of carotid body chemoreceptors and receptors in the nasal mucosa affecting respiration and pulse interval in the dog. *J. Physiol.* 229:133–49

8. Armour, J. A., Hageman, G. R., Randall, W. C. 1972. Arrhythmias induced by local cardiac nerve stimulation. *Am. J. Physiol.* 223:1068–75
9. Armour, J. A., Randall, D. C., Randall, W. C., Priola, D. V., Stekiel, W. J. 1972. Sympathoadrenal regulation of the cardiovascular system in the baboon. *Am. J. Physiol.* 222:480–88
10. Baccelli, G., Ellison, G. D., Mancia, G., Zanchetti, A. 1971. Opposite responses of muscle circulation to different emotional stimuli. *Experientia* 27:1183–84
11. Bagshaw, R. J., Iizuka, M., Peterson, L. H. 1971. Effect of interaction of the hypothalamus and the carotid sinus mechanoreceptor system on renal hemodynamics in the anesthetized dog. *Circ. Res.* 29:569–85
12. Barber, T. X. et al, Eds. 1971. *Biofeedback and Self-Control 1970.* Chicago: Aldine-Atherton. 546 pp.
13. Bard, P. 1959. Anatomical organization of the central nervous system in relation to control of the heart and blood vessels. *Physiol. Rev.* 40(Suppl. 4): 3–26
14. Bartorelli, C., Zanchetti, A., Eds. 1971. *Cardiovascular Regulation in Health and Diseases.* Milano: Instituto di Ricerche Cardiovascolari. 339 pp.

15. Benson, H., Herd, J. A., Morse, W. H., Kelleher, R. T. 1969. Behavioral induction of arterial hypertension and its reversal. *Am. J. Physiol.* 217:30–34
16. Benson, H., Shapiro, D., Tursky, B., Schwartz, G. E. 1971. Decreased systolic blood pressure through operant conditioning techniques in patients with essential hypertension. *Science* 173: 740–42
17. Betz, E. 1972. Cerebral blood flow: its measurement and regulation. *Physiol. Rev.* 52:595–630
18. Black, A. H., Carlson, N. J., Solomon, R. L. 1962. Exploratory studies of the conditioning of autonomic responses in curarized dogs. *Psychol. Monogr.* 76, No. 29. 31 pp.
19. Borst, C., Hollander, A. P., Bouman, L. N. 1972. Cardiac acceleration elicited by voluntary muscle contractions of minimal duration. *J. Appl. Physiol.* 32: 70–77
20. Brady, J. V., Anderson, D. E., Harris, A. H. 1972. Behavior and the cardiovascular system in experimental animals. *Neural and Psychological Mechanisms in Cardiovascular Disease*, ed. A. Zanchetti, 47–74. Milano: Casa Editrice "Il Ponte"
21. Brener, J., Hothersall, D. 1966. Heart rate control under conditions of augmented sensory feedback. *Psychophysiology* 3:23–28
22. Brener, J., Hothersall, D. 1967. Paced respiration and heart rate control. *Psychophysiology* 4:1–6
23. Bristow, J. D. et al 1971. Effect of bicycling on the baroreflex regulation of pulse interval. *Circ. Res.* 33:582–92
24. Bristow, J. D., Honour, A. J., Pickering, G. W., Sleight, P., Smyth, H. S. 1969. Diminished baroreflex sensitivity in high blood pressure. *Circulation* 39: 48–54
25. Brown, A. M. 1967. Excitation of afferent cardiac sympathetic nerve fibers during myocardial ischemia. *J. Physiol.* 190:35–53
26. Brown, A. M., Malliani, A. 1971. Spinal sympathetic reflexes initiated by coronary receptors. *J. Physiol.* 212: 685–705
27. Calaresu, F. R., Mogenson, G. J. 1972. Cardiovascular responses to electrical stimulation of the septum in the rat. *Am. J. Physiol.* 223:777–82
28. Caraffa-Braga, E., Granata, L., Pinotti, O. 1973. Changes in blood-flow distribution during acute emotional stress in dogs. *Pfluegers Arch.* 339:203–16
29. Clarke, N. P., Smith, O. A., Shearn, D. W. 1968. Topographical representation of vascular smooth muscle of limbs in primate motor cortex. *Am. J. Physiol.* 214:122–29
30. Cobbold, A., Folkow, B., Lundgren, O., Wallentin, I. 1964. Blood flow, capillary filtration coefficients and regional blood volume responses in the intestine of the cat during stimulation of the hypothalamic "defence" area. *Acta Physiol. Scand.* 61:467–75
31. Coote, J. H., Hilton, S. M., Perez-Gonzalez, J. F. 1971. The reflex nature of the pressor response to muscular exercise. *J. Physiol.* 215: 789–804
32. Corbett, J. L., Frankel, H. L., Harris, P. J. 1971. Cardiovascular changes associated with skeletal muscle spasm in tetraplegic man. *J. Physiol.* 215:381–93
33. Corbett, J. L., Frankel, H. L., Harris, P. J. 1971. Cardiovascular reflex responses to cutaneous and visceral stimuli in spinal man. *J. Physiol.* 215:395–410
34. Corbett, J. L., Frankel, H. L., Harris, P. J. 1971. Cardiovascular responses to tilting in tetraplegic man. *J. Physiol.* 215:411–31
35. Cottle, M. K. 1964. Degeneration studies of primary afferents of IXth and Xth cranial nerves in the cat. *J. Comp. Neurol.* 122:329–45
36. Crill, W. E., Reis, D. J. 1968. Distribution of carotid sinus and depressor nerves in cat brain stem. *Am. J. Physiol.* 214:269–76
37. Cunningham, D. J. C., Petersen, E. S., Peto, R., Pickering, T. G., Sleight, P. 1972. Comparison of the effect of different types of exercise on the baroreflex regulation of heart rate. *Acta Physiol. Scand.* 86:444–55
38. D'Alecy, L. G., Feigl, E. O. 1972. Sympathetic control of cerebral blood flow in dogs. *Circ. Res.* 31:267–83
39. Daly, M. deB. 1972. Interaction of cardiovascular reflexes. *Sci. Basis Med.* 20:307–32
40. DiCara, L. 1970. Learning in the autonomic nervous system. *Sci. Am.* 222: 31–39
41. DiCara, L. V., Miller, N. E. 1968. Instrumental learning of peripheral vasomotor responses by the curarized rat. *Commun. Behav. Biol.* 1:209–12
42. DiCara, L. V., Miller, N. E. 1968. Instrumental learning of systolic blood pressure responses by curarized rats: dissociation of cardiac and vascular changes. *Psychosom. Med.* 30:489–94

43. DiCara, L. V., Miller, N. E. 1968. Conditioning of vasomotor responses in curarized rats: learning to respond differentially in the two ears. *Science* 159:1485–86

44. Djojosugito, A. M., Folkow, B., Kylstra, P. H., Lisander, B., Tuttle, R. S. 1970. Differentiated interaction between the hypothalamic defence reaction and baroreceptor reflexes. *Acta Physiol. Scand.* 78:376–85

45. Djojosugito, A. M., Folkow, B., Lisander, B., Sparks, H. 1968. Mechanism of escape of mucle resistance vessels from the influence of sympathetic cholinergic vasodilator fibre activity. *Acta Physiol. Scand.* 72:148–56

46. Doba, N., Reis, D. J. 1972. Changes in regional blood flow and cardiodynamics evoked by electrical stimulation of the fastigial nucleus in the cat and their similarity to orthostatic reflexes. *J. Physiol.* 227:729–47

47. Engel, B. T., Hansen, S. P. 1966. Operant conditioning of heart rate slowing. *Psychophysiology* 3:176–88

48. Feigl, E. O. 1967. Sympathetic control of coronary circulation. *Circ. Res.* 20:262–71

49. Feigl, E. O. 1969. Parasympathetic control of coronary blood flow in dogs. *Circ. Res.* 25:509–19

50. Feigl, E., Johansson, B., Löfving, B. 1964. Renal vasoconstriction and the "defense reaction." *Acta Physiol. Scand.* 62:429–35

51. Folkow, B., Lisander, B., Tuttle, R. S., Wang, S. C. 1968. Changes in cardiac output upon stimulation of the hypothalamic defence area and the medullary depressor area in the cat. *Acta Physiol. Scand.* 72:220–33

52. Forsyth, R. P. 1969. Blood pressure responses to long-term avoidance schedules in the restrained rhesus monkey. *Psychosom. Med.* 31:300–9

53. Forsyth, R. P. 1970. Hypothalamic control of the distribution of cardiac output in the unanesthetized rhesus monkey. *Circ. Res.* 26:783–94

54. Forsyth, R. P. 1971. Regional blood-flow changes during 72-hour avoidance schedules in the monkey. *Science* 173:546–48

55. Forsyth, R. P. 1972. Sympathetic nervous system control of distribution of cardiac output in unanesthetized monkeys. *Fed. Proc.* 31:1240–44

56. Forsyth, R. P., Hoffbrand, B. I. 1970. Redistribution of cardiac output after sodium pentobarbital anesthesia in the monkey. *Am. J. Physiol.* 218:214–17

57. Forsyth, R. P., Hoffbrand, B. I., Melmon, K. L. 1970. Redistribution of cardiac output during hemorrhage in the unanesthetized monkey. *Circ. Res.* 27:311–20

58. Freyschuss, U. 1970. Cardiovascular adjustment to somatomotor activation. *Acta Physiol. Scand.* 79, Suppl. 342. 63 pp.

59. Freyschuss, U. 1970. Elicitation of heart rate and blood pressure increase on muscle contraction. *J. Appl. Physiol.* 28:758–61

60. Gebber, G. L., Klevans, L. R. 1972. Central nervous system modulation of cardiovascular reflexes. *Fed. Proc.* 31:1245–52

61. Gebber, G. L., Snyder, D. W. 1970. Hypothalamic control of baroreceptor reflexes. *Am. J. Physiol.* 218:124–31

62. Gebber, G. L., Taylor, D. G., Weaver, L. C. 1973. Electrophysiological studies on organization of central vasopressor pathways. *Am. J. Physiol.* 224:470–81

63. Goesling, W. J., Brener, J. 1972. Effects of activity and immobility conditioning upon subsequent heart-rate conditioning in curarized rats. *J. Comp. Physiol. Psychol.* 31:311–17

64. Goodwin, G. M., McCloskey, D. I., Mitchell, J. H. 1972. Cardiovascular and respiratory responses to changes in central command during isometric exercise at constant muscle tension. *J. Physiol.* 226:173–90

65. Gribbin, B., Pickering, T. G., Sleight, P., Peto, R. 1971. Effect of age and high blood pressure on baroreflex sensitivity in man. *Circ. Res.* 29:424–31

66. Harris, A. H., Findley, J. D., Brady, J. V. 1971. Instrumental conditioning of blood pressure elevations in the baboon. *Cond. Reflex.* 6:215–26

67. Herd, J. A., Morse, W. H., Kelleher, R. T., Jones, L. G. 1969. Arterial hypertension in the squirrel monkey during behavioral experiments. *Am. J. Physiol.* 217:24–29

68. Hilton, S. M. 1965. Hypothalamic control of the cardiovascular responses in fear and rage. *Sci. Basis Med.* 217–38

69. Hilton, S. M. 1971. A critique of current ideas of the nervous system control of circulation. See Ref. 14, 57–62

70. Hilton, S. M., Spyer, K. M. 1971. Participation of the anterior hypothalamus in the baroreceptor reflex. *J. Physiol.* 218:271–93

71. Hnatiow, M., Lang, P. J. 1965. Learned stabilization of heart rate. *Psychophysiology* 1:330–36

72. Hothersall, D., Brener, J. 1969. Operant conditioning of changes in heart rate in curarized rats. *J. Comp. Physiol. Psychol.* 68:338–42

73. Humphrey, D. R. 1967. Neuronal activity in the medulla oblongata of cat evoked by stimulation of the carotid sinus nerve. In *Baroreceptors and Hypertension,* ed. P. Kezdi. New York: Pergamon

74. Humphreys, P. W., Joels, N., McAllen R. M. 1971. Modification of the reflex response to stimulation of carotid sinus baroreceptors during and following stimulation of the hypothalamic defence area in the cat. *J. Physiol.* 216: 461–82

75. Iano, T. L., Levy, M. N., Lee, M. H. 1973. An acceleratory component of the parasympathetic control of heart rate. *Am. J. Physiol.* 224:997–1005

76. Illert, M., Gabriel, M. 1972. Descending pathways in the cervical cord of cats affecting blood pressure and sympathetic activity. *Pfluegers Arch.* 335: 109–24

77. Jonas, G. 1972. Profiles: Visceral learning—II. *New Yorker* 48:30–57

78. Jurf, A. N., Blake, W. D. 1972. Renal response to electrical stimulation in the septum and diencephalon of rabbits. *Circ. Res.* 30:322–31

79. Kamiya, J. et al, Eds. 1971. *Biofeedback and Self-Control.* Chicago: Aldine-Atherton. 806 pp.

80. Kent, B. B., Drane, J. W., Manning, J. W. 1971. Suprapontine contributions to the carotid sinus reflex in the cat. *Circ. Res.* 29:534–41

81. Kerr, F. W. L. 1962. Facial, vagal and glossopharyngeal nerves in the cat. *Arch. Neurol.* 6:264–81

82. Khayutin, V. M., Lukoshkova, E. V. 1970. Spinal mediation of vasomotor reflexes in animals with intact brain studied by electrophysiological methods. *Pfluegers Arch.* 321:197–222

83. Kirchner, F., Sato, A., Weidinger, H. 1970. Central pathways of reflex discharges in the cervical sympathetic trunk. *Pfluegers Arch.* 319:1–11

84. Klevans, L. R., Gebber, G. L. 1970. Facilitatory forebrain influence on cardiac component of baroreceptor reflexes. *Am. J. Physiol.* 219:1235–41

85. Korner, P. I. 1971. Integrative neural cardiovascular control. *Physiol. Rev.* 51:312–67

86. Korner, P. I., Shaw, J., West, M. J., Oliver, J. R. 1972. Central nervous system control of baroreceptor reflexes in the rabbit. *Circ. Res.* 31:637–52

87. Kylstra, P. H., Lisander, B. 1970. Differentiated interaction between the hypothalamic defence area and baroreceptor reflexes. *Acta Physiol. Scand.* 78:386–92

88. Levy, M. N. 1971. Brief reviews: Sympathetic-parasympathetic interactions in the heart. *Circ. Res.* 29:437–45

89. Lind, A. R., McNicol, G. W. 1967. Circulatory response to sustained hand grip contractions performed during other exercise, both rhythmic and static. *J. Physiol.* 192:595–607

90. Lind, A. R., Taylor, S. H., Humphreys, P. W., Kennelly, B. M., Donald, K. W. 1964. The circulatory effects of sustained voluntary muscle contraction. *Clin. Sci.* 27:229–44

91. Lindgren, P. 1955. Mesencephalon and the vasomotor system. *Acta Physiol. Scand.* 35, Suppl. 121

92. Lisander, B. 1970. Factors influencing the autonomic component of the defence reaction. *Acta Physiol. Scand.* 78, Suppl. 351:1–42

93. Lisander, B., Martner, J. 1970. Cerebellar suppression of the autonomic components of the defence reaction. *Acta Physiol. Scand.* 81:84–95

94. Lisander, B., Martner, J. 1971. Interaction between the fastigial pressor response and the baroreceptor reflex. *Acta Physiol. Scand.* 83:505–14

95. Malliani, A., Pagani, M., Recordati, G., Schwartz, P. J. 1970. Evidence for a spinal sympathetic regulation of cardiovascular functions. *Experientia* 26:929–1048

96. Malliani, A., Parks, M., Tuckett, R. P., Brown, A. M. 1973. Reflex increases in heart rate elicited by stimulation of afferent cardiac sympathetic nerve fibers in the cat. *Circ. Res.* 32:9–14

97. Malliani, A., Peterson, D. F., Bishop, V. S., Brown, A. M. 1972. Spinal sympathetic cardiocardiac reflexes. *Circ. Res.* 30:158–66

98. Malliani, A., Recordati, G., Schwartz, P. J. 1973. Nervous activity of afferent cardiac sympathetic fibres with atrial and ventricular endings. *J. Physiol.* 229:457–69

99. Malliani, A., Schwartz, P. J., Zanchetti, A. 1969. A sympathetic reflex elicited by experimental coronary occlusion. *Am. J. Physiol.* 217:703–9

100. Manning, J. W. 1965. Intracranial representation of cardiac innervation. In *Nervous Control of the Heart,* ed. W.

C. Randall, 16–33. Baltimore: Williams & Wilkins

101. McCloskey, D. I., Matthews, P. B. C., Mitchell, J. H. 1972. Absence of appreciable cardiovascular and respiratory responses to muscle vibration. *J. Appl. Physiol.* 33:623–26

102. McCloskey, D. I., Mitchell, J. H. 1972. Reflex cardiovascular and respiratory responses originating in exercising muscle. *J. Physiol.* 224:173–86

103. Millard, R. W., Higgins, C. B., Franklin, D., Vatner, S. F. 1972. Regulation of the renal circulation during severe exercise in normal dogs and dogs with experimental heart failure. *Circ. Res.* 31:881–88

104. Miller, N. 1969. Learning of visceral and glandular responses. *Science* 163:434–45

105. Miller, N., DiCara, L. V. 1967. Instrumental learning of heart rate changes in curarized rats: shaping and specificity to discriminative stimulus. *J. Comp. Physiol. Psychol.* 63:12–19

106. Miura, M., Reis, D. J. 1969. Termination and secondary projections of carotid sinus nerve in the cat brain stem. *Am. J. Physiol.* 217:142–53

107. Miura, M., Reis, D. J. 1970. A blood pressure response from fastigial nucleus and its relay pathway in brainstem. *Am. J. Physiol.* 219:1330–36

108. Miura, M., Reis, D. J. 1971. The paramedian reticular nucleus: a site of inhibitory interaction between projections from fastigial nucleus and carotid sinus nerve acting on blood pressure. *J. Physiol.* 216:441–60

109. Moruzzi, G. 1940. Paleocerebellar inhibition of vasomotor and respiratory carotid sinus reflexes. *J. Neurophysiol.* 3:20–32

110. Nathan, M. A. 1972. Vasomotor projections of the nucleus fastigii to the medulla. *Brain Res.* 41:194–98

111. Nathan, M. A., Smith, O. A. Jr. 1968. Differential conditional emotional and cardiovascular responses—a training technique for monkeys. *J. Exp. Anal. Behav.* 11:77–82

112. Ninomiya, I., Judy, W. V., Wilson, M. F. 1970. Hypothalamic stimulus effects on sympathetic nerve activity. *Am. J. Physiol.* 218:453–62

113. Obrist, P. A., Webb, R. A., Sutterer, J. R., Howard, J. L. 1970. The cardiac somatic relationship: some reformulations. *Psychophysiology* 6:569–87

114. Paintal, A. S. 1973. Vagal sensory receptors and their reflex effects. *Physiol. Rev.* 53:159–227

115. Peiss, C. N. 1965. Concepts of cardiovascular regulation: past, present and future. See Ref. 100, 154–97

116. Peterson, D. F., Brown, A. M. 1971. Professor reflexes produced by stimulation of afferent cardiac nerve fibers in the cardiac sympathetic nerves of the cat. *Circ. Res.* 33:605–10

117. Petro, J. K., Hollander, A. P., Bouman, L. N. 1970. Instantaneous cardiac acceleration in man induced by a voluntary muscle contraction. *J. Appl. Physiol.* 29:794–98

118. Pickering, T. G., Gribbin, B., Strange Petersen, E., Cunningham, D. J. C., Sleight, P. 1972. Effects of autonomic blockade on the baroreflex in man at rest and during exercise. *Circ. Res.* 30:177–85

119. Pinotti, O. 1971. Cardiovascular responses to excitement in dogs. See Ref. 14, 43–50

120. Plumlee, L. 1969. Operant conditioning of increases in blood pressure. *Psychophysiology* 6:283–90

121. Randall, D. C., Armour, J. A., Randall, W. C. 1971. Dynamic responses to cardiac nerve stimulation in the baboon. *Am. J. Physiol.* 220:526–33

122. Randall, D. C., Smith, O. A. 1971. Heart rate, pressure, and myocardial contractility responses to exercise and emotional conditioning in the nonhuman primate. *Physiologist* 14:213

123. Randall, W. C., Ed. 1965. *Nervous Control of the Heart.* Baltimore: Williams & Wilkins. 251 pp.

124. Randall, W. C. 1971. New insights into the sympathetic innervation of the heart. See Ref. 14, 49–118

125. Randall, W. C., Armour, J. A., Geis, P. W., Lippencott, D. B. 1972. Regional cardiac distribution of the sympathetic nerves. *Fed. Proc.* 31:1199–1208

126. Randall, W. C., Armour, J. A., Randall, D. C., Smith, O. A. 1971. Functional anatomy of the cardiac nerves in the baboon. *Anat. Rec.* 170:183–98

127. Reis, D. J., Cuénod, M. R. 1962. Evidence for supramedullary influence on carotid baroreceptor reflexes. *Trans. Am. Neurol. Assoc.* 87:229–31

128. Reis, D. J., Cuénod, M. 1964. Tonic influence of rostral brain structures on pressure regulation mechanisms in the cat. *Science* 145:64–65

129. Reis, D. J., Cuénod, M. 1965. Central neuroregulation of carotid baroreceptor reflexes in the cat. *Am. J. Physiol.* 209:1267–77

130. Rhoton, A. L. Jr., O'Leary, J. L., Ferguson, J. P. 1966. The trigeminal, facial, vagal, and glossopharyngeal nerves in the monkey. *Arch. Neurol.* 14:530–40

131. Rosen, A. 1961. Augmented cardiac contraction, heart acceleration and skeletal muscle vasodilation produced by hypothalamic stimulation in cats. *Acta Physiol. Scand.* 52:291–308

132. Scher, A. M., Ohm, W. W., Bumgardner, K., Boynton, R., Young, A. C. 1972. Sympathetic and parasympathetic control of heart rate in the dog, baboon and man. *Fed. Proc.* 31:1219–25

133. Schramm, L. P., Bignall, K. E. 1971. Central neural pathways mediating active sympathetic muscle vasodilation in cats. *Am. J. Physiol.* 221:754–67

134. Schramm, L. P., Honig, C. R., Bignall, K. E. 1971. Active muscle vasodilation in primates homologous with sympathetic vasodilation in carnivores. *Am. J. Physiol.* 221:768–77

135. Schwartz, G. E., Higgins, J. D. 1971. Cardiac activity preparatory to overt and covert behavior. *Science* 173:1144–46

136. Schwartz, P. J., Pagani, M., Lombardi, F., Malliani, A., Brown, A. M. 1973. A cardiocardiac sympathovagal reflex in the cat. *Circ. Res.* 32:215–20

137. Shapiro, D. et al, Eds. 1973. *Biofeedback and Self-Control 1972.* Chicago: Aldine. 534 pp.

138. Shapiro, D., Tursky, B., Gershon, E., Stern, M. 1969. Effect of feedback and reinforcement on the control of human systolic blood pressure. *Science* 163:588–89

139. Shearn, D. W. 1962. Operant conditioning of heart rate. *Science* 137:530–31

140. Smith, O. A. Jr. 1965. Anatomy of central neural pathways mediating cardiovascular functions. See Ref. 100, 34–53

141. Smith, O. A. 1972. Personality and cardiovascular disease: contributions from nonhuman primates: See Ref. 20, 297–303

142. Smith, O. A. Jr., Nathan, M. A. 1966. Inhibition of the carotid sinus reflex by stimulation of the inferior olive. *Science* 154:674–75

143. Smith, O. A. Jr., Nathan, M. A., Clarke, N. P. 1967. Central nervous system pathways mediating blood pressure changes. In *Hypertension, Vol. XVI: Neural Control of Arterial Pressure,* ed. J. E. Wood, 9–22 New York: Am. Heart Assoc.

144. Smith, O. A. Jr., Stebbins, W. C. 1965. Conditioned blood flow and heart rate in monkeys. *J. Comp. Physiol. Psychol.* 59:432–36

145. Smyth, H. S., Sleight, P., Pickering, G. W. 1969. Reflex regulation of arterial pressure during sleep in man. *Circ. Res.* 24:109–21

146. Spyer, K. M. 1972. Baroreceptor sensitive neurones in the anterior hypothalamus of the cat. *J. Physiol.* 224:245–57

147. Stebbins, W. C., Smith, O. A. Jr. 1964. Cardiovascular concomitants of the conditioned emotional response in the monkey. *Science* 144:881–83

148. Stoyva, J. et al, Eds. 1972. *Biofeedback and Self-Control 1971.* Chicago: Aldine-Atherton. 565 pp.

149. Trouth, C. O., Loeschcke, H. H., Berndt, J. 1973. Topography of the circulatory responses to electrical stimulation in the medulla oblongata. *Pfluegers Arch.* 339:185–201

150. Trowill, J. A. 1967. Instrumental conditioning of heart rate in the curarized rat. *J. Comp. Physiol. Psychol.* 63:7–11

151. Vatner, S. F., Franklin, D., Braunwald, E. 1971. Effects of anesthesia and sleep on circulatory response to carotid sinus nerve stimulation. *Am. J. Physiol.* 220:1249–55

152. Vatner, S. F. et al 1971. Coronary dynamics in unrestrained conscious baboons. *Am. J. Physiol.* 221:1396–1401

153. Vatner, S. F., Franklin, D., Van Citters, R. L., Braunwald, E. 1970. Effects of carotid sinus nerve stimulation on blood-flow distribution in conscious dogs at rest and during exercise. *Circ. Res.* 32:495–504

154. Weiss, G. K., Crill, W. E. 1969. Carotid sinus nerve: primary afferent depolarization evoked by hypothalamic stimulation. *Brain Res.* 16:269–72

155. Weiss, T., Engel, B. T. 1971. Operant conditioning of heart rate in patients with premature ventricular contractions. *Psychosom. Med.* 33:301–21

156. Weiss, G. K., Priola, D. V. 1972. Brainstem sites for activation of vagal cardioaccelerator fibers in the dog. *Am. J. Physiol.* 223:300–4

157. White, S. W., McRitchie, R. J. 1973. Nasopharyngeal reflexes: integrative analysis of evoked respiratory and cardiovascular effects. *Aust. J. Exp. Biol. Med. Sci.* 51:17–31

158. Wilson, M. F., Clarke, N. P., Smith, O. A., Rushmer, R. F. 1961. Interrelation between central and peripheral mechanisms regulating blood pressure. *Circ. Res.* 9:491–96

159. Wilson, M. F., Ninomiya, I., Franz, G. N., Judy, W. V. 1971. Hypothalamic stimulation and baroreceptor reflex interaction on renal nerve activity. *Am. J. Physiol.* 221:1768–73

160. Zanchetti, A., Ed. 1972. *Neural and Psychological Mechanisms in Cardiovascular Disease.* Milano: Casa Editrice "Il Ponte." 387 pp.

161. Zanchetti, A., Baccelli, G., Mancia, G. 1971. Cardiovascular effects of emotional behavior. See Ref. 14, 17–32

# HEMODYNAMICS

❖1107

*Dali J. Patel,[1] Ramesh N. Vaishnav,[2] Barry S. Gow,[3] and Peter A. Kot[4]*

## INTRODUCTION

McDonald (69) defined hemodynamics as the study of "the physical aspect of the cardiovascular system" which includes, among other things, blood flow characteristics, rheology of the vessel wall, and blood-wall interactions; it is these latter aspects of hemodynamics that we intend to emphasize in this review. In view of the recent exhaustive review on hemodynamics by Taylor (102) and the current research effort on the role of hemodynamic factors in the pathogenesis of atherosclerosis, we restrict our coverage essentially to those aspects of the field that have a direct bearing on the understanding of the disease processes.

The hemodynamic era of the early 1950s was dominated by quantitative studies of steady pressure, steady flow, and the peripheral vascular resistance (15). Also in the 1950s McDonald, Womersley, and Taylor (68) were active in quantitative investigation of pulsatile phenomena in the cardiovascular system. Stimulated by their efforts, hemodynamic research in the 1960s continued as a quantitative study of pulsatile phenomena in the arterial system (2). A number of recent books and review articles capture various aspects of the thinking during this era. Specifically, we cite the following: *The Physiology and Biophysics of Circulation* by Burton (15) is an introductory text which explains the fundamental concepts of circulatory physics in a very clear manner. *Blood Flow in Arteries* by McDonald (68) represents the next level of sophistication and deals mainly with pulsatile pressure-flow phenomenon. A new and updated version of this book is soon to appear. *Cardiovascular Fluid Dynamics,* edited by Bergel (7), is a more advanced treatise based on recent research in hemodynamics.

Among the review articles surveying various aspects of hemodynamics, we cite the following: Bergel & Shultz (6) have reviewed the most recent work in arterial elasticity and details of flow fields. Fung (45), in a scholarly survey, discusses blood

[1]National Heart and Lung Institute, National Institutes of Health, Bethesda, Maryland.

[2] Department of Civil and Mechanical Engineering, The Catholic University of America, Washington DC.

[3]Physiology Department, University of Sydney, Australia.

[4]Department of Physiology and Biophysics, Georgetown University Medical School, Washington DC.

rheology and biophysics of red blood cells, nonlinear phenomena in the blood vascular system, and flow problems peculiar to the microcirculation, such as capillary sheet flow. Lighthill (63) attempts to lure the fluid dynamicist into biology by showing him the variety of unsolved and challenging problems presented by the cardiovascular system. In the process he sheds light on some of the difficult but important problems in circulatory mechanics, e.g. entrance flow, distribution of wall shear in branching systems, and lubrication theory for the passage of red cells through narrow capillaries.

The body of knowledge covered in the foregoing has dealt with relatively pure hemodynamic concepts, with only incidental efforts to relate these to disease. A new era of hemodynamic research appears to be emerging with a somewhat different emphasis, one in which the concepts and tools of the hemodynamicist are being deliberately shaped to be targeted on questions of importance in the pathogenesis of disease. Most notable of these efforts have been the recent advances in our knowledge of the interrelationships among hemodynamic events, serum lipoproteins, and the genesis of atherosclerosis, the number one cause of death in affluent societies (30). A large number of workers believe that hemodynamic forces are one of the more important localizing factors in this disease process. Examination of the evidence for this view will be our first task so that the relevance of much of the material presented subsequently can be placed in a more lucid and hopefully more interesting perspective, particularly for the reader from other fields.

## ARTERIAL RESPONSE TO HEMODYNAMIC STRESSES

The evidence that hemodynamic events can play an important role as a localizing factor in atherogenesis is both circumstantial and direct. The fact that the atherosclerotic process tends to be a highly discrete one localized in the regions of orifices, bends, and vessel entrances is strong circumstantial evidence for a hemodynamic role since these are also the places that can be exposed to intense and variable stresses from the adjacent blood flow. Evidence of a more direct nature is the strong correlation between elevation in blood pressure and acceleration of the atherosclerotic process. Moreover, areas exposed to jets from diseased heart valves or through arteriovenous shunts develop characteristic intimal fibromuscular hyperplasia very similar to that seen in atherosclerotic lesions occurring elsewhere.

The most direct evidence implicating hemodynamic forces in the atherosclerotic process comes from studies of experimental atherosclerosis in animals in which the hemodynamic patterns have been deliberately altered. For example, Sako (95) showed that surgically constructed coarctations of the aorta were associated with greatly accelerated disease above and relatively less disease below the coarctation. Sako and later Flaherty et al (36) studied surgically induced arteriovenous fistulas and demonstrated dramatically increased incidence of atherosclerosis in the arteries supplying the arteriovenous shunt as compared to the contralateral control arteries.

We conclude from the foregoing that the atherosclerotic process is a highly localized and topographically consistent process, indicating that strong localizing factors are at play. Moreover, there is clear evidence that both an increase in pressure and an increase in flow in an artery will greatly accelerate the atherosclerotic process. Observations such as these have been the stimulus for a large variety of hypotheses (38, 44, 53, 90, 103) which attempted to explain the mechanisms involved, as well as a large body of new research to test these hypotheses. We shall attempt to summarize these new developments, not only because of their inherent interest to the hemodynamicist but also because they point the way to areas of important future research.

There appears to be a growing consensus that the atherosclerotic process occurs at points where there is an increased flux of plasma substances, particularly lipoproteins, into the intimal tissues. As we shall see, an increased flux can occur in areas of histologically normal endothelial cells as well as in areas of injury. We shall arbitrarily refer to the former as the physiologic response and to the latter as the pathologic response of the arterial wall to hemodynamic stresses.

## Nature of Hemodynamic Stresses

Hemodynamic stresses can be resolved into two types: normal and shearing. Examples of various types of stresses that can occur in the vascular system have been summarized by Fry (42). The normal stresses that counterbalance intravascular pressure and vascular tethering are basically of three types: a tensile stress in the circumferential direction; a tensile stress in the longitudinal direction; and a compressional stress in the radial direction with a radial pressure gradient acting from within outward in the vessel wall. The radial stress is always nonuniform, whereas the circumferential and longitudinal stresses tend to be uniform except in areas of bends and branches.

Shearing stresses are most prominent at the vascular interface and are related mostly to the friction of the adjacent blood flow. The shearing stress on the endothelial surface is proportional to the blood velocity gradient at the wall as shown in Figure 1. In a well-developed Poiseuille flow in a straight long segment of blood vessel, the shearing stress on the wall is relatively low (Figure 1b). However, in the areas where the velocity profile is relatively blunt, e.g. in the entrance region where the flow is not fully developed (Figure 1a), near the crotch of a bifurcation, and at the adjacent inner wall of the branches, the shearing stress on the wall is high (Figure 1d). The wall shear tends to be low at the outer wall of the branch distal to a bifurcation (Figure 1c), provided the flow remains stable. However, the flow can become unstable in such regions, forming local vortices and turbulence. Under these circumstances it is very difficult to predict wall stresses in this area short of actual measurements which are not yet available. The next set of velocity profiles shows the effect of bends and protuberances in the path of the blood flow. Around a bend such as the arch of the aorta, the wall shear will be high near the outer curvature (Figure 1g) and low or high on the inner curvature (Figure 1h) depending on the stability of flow. Near a protuberance from the wall such as an atheroma (Figure 1f) the wall shear will be increased. When the flow increases as in an arteriovenous fistula, the shearing stress on the wall is high (Figure 1j); if the velocity becomes high enough, turbulence can develop resulting in a very high shearing stress on the wall (Figure 1i). Thus we have a rather large variety of

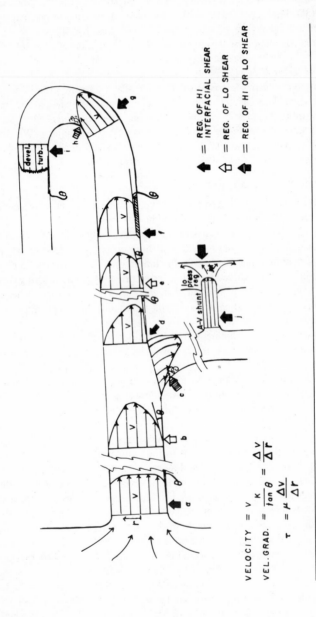

*Figure 1* Schematic diagram indicating velocity profiles and shearing stress in an artery for various geometric configurations; $\tau$ = shear stress, $\mu$ = viscosity of blood, K = an arbitrary constant. (From Fry, D. L. 1969. *Circulation* 39, 40: Suppl. IV 38–59)

hemodynamic situations that might arise in the vascular tree. In light of the possible relationship of these situations to the development of vascular disease, it is of interest to review the various ways in which the arterial tissue has been shown to respond to some of these events.

## Physiologic Response of the Arterial Wall

Although arterial tissue changes secondary to hemodynamic events are generally regarded as pathologic changes, Rodbard (91) and Fry (44) have suggested that many of these changes are of a compensatory nature and are more appropriately thought of as physiologic responses of the conduit system to altered flow conditions. Fry speculates that the central purpose of these changes is to continuously restructure the arterial conduit system to maintain stable flow configurations where these exist and to alter structure to correct unstable ones when they occur. During this set of physiologic processes there are certain phases during which endothelial permeability is increased; it is during such periods that the deposition of lipid probably occurs.

The relationship of local hemodynamic events to the flux of plasma substances into the normal arterial wall has been studied by several workers (20, 36, 44). These may be divided into studies of the acute and studies of the chronic effects of hemodynamic stresses on the transendothelial flux of macromolecules.

ACUTE RESPONSE    The permeability of the endothelial surface to proteins has been shown to be increased acutely by exposure to an elevated level of shearing stress at the wall, by exposure to disturbed or turbulent flow, and by wall stretch (20, 21, 32, 44). The underlying mechanisms responsible for these important observations are undoubtedly complex and at present are poorly understood.

As a conceptual device to simplify and organize the experimental evidence in this area of research, Fry (43) suggested a simple model which is useful to describe the overall transport process for a given molecular species:

$$J = k \nabla \mu \qquad \qquad 1.$$

where $J$ is the flux in moles per unit cross-sectional area per unit time, $\nabla \mu$ is the driving force or energy gradient along which the molecules flow, and $k$ is the proportionality constant representing the overall conductance. The conductance, $k$, may be visualized as describing the barrier property of the blood-vascular interface and the vessel wall. Although the structural properties and components of this barrier system have not been identified, it has been shown that a large portion of the barrier is associated with the normal endothelial surface. For example, the barrier can be greatly decreased by subtle mechanical insults like touching the endothelial surface with a wet camel's-hair brush which only damages the endothelial cells, leaving the rest of the wall intact.

Caro et al (20, 22) follow a more classical chemical engineering approach to transvascular transport. They consider a more specialized model in which they subdivide the overall conductance $k$ into $k_1$, $k_2$, and $k_3$ to represent specifically the conductances of the diffusion boundary layer in the fluid near the vessel wall, the blood-wall interface, and the wall itself. Thus

$$\frac{1}{k} = \frac{1}{k_1} + \frac{1}{k_2} + \frac{1}{k_3} \qquad\qquad 2.$$

The use of Equation 1 permits us to separate the transport problem into factors altering the driving force and factors affecting the conductance or permeability of the vascular interface.

*Factors altering the driving force*    The concentration gradient of a particular molecular species is the most obvious contributor to the driving force, $\nabla\mu$, for transport. However, other energy sources such as mechanical, thermal, or electrical, can also contribute to $\nabla\mu$ (43, 46). We shall consider only the effect on $\nabla\mu$ of concentration gradient, blood velocity gradient, disturbed flow conditions, and transmural pressure.

(*a*) *Concentration gradient*    An increased concentration gradient from blood to wall is probably the most important driving force for lipid transport into the wall both in human and in experimentally induced disease. Flaherty et al (36) explain the increased intimal lipid deposition and medial spread observed in their hyperlipemic pigs and dogs on this basis. The severity and topographic incidence of the disease correlated well with the product of level of blood cholesterol and the duration of exposure to hyperlipemia.

(*b*) *Velocity gradient*    Caro et al (20), on the basis of pathological findings in human aortas, report that in the natural disease process atherosclerotic lesions occur in regions where the wall shear is relatively low. They cite the following evidence: the abdominal aorta is more severely affected than the arch or the descending thoracic aorta; and near bifurcations and branches there is relative sparing of the flow divider and heavy involvement of the outer walls of the junctions. To explain these findings they adopt the following working hypothesis. The primary mode of movement of lipids across the blood-wall interface is by mass diffusion and the diffusion boundary layer provides the primary resistance to the passage of invading molecules, i.e. $k_1 \ll k_2$ or $k_3$ in Equation 2. It can be shown that for this kind of transport (11, 22) the concentration gradient across the diffusion boundary layer will depend on the associated velocity gradient near the wall. Thus an increased velocity gradient in the boundary layer would steepen the concentration gradient for lipid transport. If the lipid concentration is higher in the wall, because of either previous deposits or cholesterol synthesis in the wall, then lipid will be washed away from the wall in high shear regions and tend to accumulate in low shear regions.

If this hypothesis were valid, one would expect a greater flux of lipids in areas of steeper concentration gradients than in areas of flatter gradients. With this rationale in mind, Caro & Nerem (22) and Caro (21) carried out experiments where the concentration gradient gradually changed from steep to flat in the diffusion boundary layer. Specifically, they constructed an assembly of a segment of dog's carotid artery with its upstream end connected to a long stainless steel tube.

Through this assembly they passed serum containing $^{14}$C-4-cholesterol tagged lipoproteins. The flow was designed to stay laminar throughout the assembly with a constant momentum boundary layer and wall shear. In this system a diffusion boundary layer begins to grow at the upstream end of the arterial segment, having a steep concentration gradient at this end which then flattens out downstream to a constant value. However, when they measured the uptake of the radioactive material by the vessel wall, it was found to be essentially uniform throughout the segment. Moreover, the calculated diffusion coefficient from experimental data was approximately three orders of magnitude lower than that predicted by theory. These findings indicate that the diffusion boundary layer could not be rate controlling, i.e. it could not provide the largest resistance to the passage of the invading species. Moreover, in experiments on paired arteries, Caro noted that the uptake of radioactive material increased with an increase in wall shear. From these data the authors concluded that the permeability of the interface was rate controlling and that it was shear dependent; this is in agreement with the earlier studies of Fry (42).

(c) *Disturbed blood flow conditions*    Turbulence in blood flow adjacent to the wall can increase convection of matter to and from the vessel wall and thus effectively increase $\nabla \mu$ in Equation 1 (43). Moreover, it is possible that the ballistic effect of heavy molecules in unsteady flow systems, as might occur in regions of severe turbulence, may be of importance in increasing $\nabla \mu$. The kinetic energy of very large molecules such as lipoproteins in these disturbed flow regions may approach their thermal energy. Therefore, in a highly turbulent flow pattern these molecules can momentarily increase the energy with which they strike the barrier by an amount equivalent to raising their temperature to higher levels, thus making their apparent chemical potential larger.

(d) *Transmural pressure*    The effect of pressure as a driving force for protein transport across the interface of the thoracic aorta of dogs has been studied by Duncan et al (32) and Fry (43, 44) with essentially similar results. Fry concluded that a pressure difference of 280 cm $H_2O$ did not alter the protein flux in preparations either with intact or with damaged endothelial cells. Since the transmural pressure can play a significant role in protein transport across a capillary wall, it was thought that the buttressing property of the arterial intima and media bore the entire pressure gradient, thus insulating the endothelial surface from the direct effect of increased pressure. Therefore, pressure may be a significant driving force in various pathologic situations where the buttressing effect of the media has been decreased, such as in regions of medial defects and fragmented internal elastic lamellae.

*Factors affecting the conductance*    The conductance of the vascular interfacial region ($k$ in Equation 1) appears to be sensitive to a variety of physical and chemical factors. The physical factors normally encountered in the circulatory system are the hemodynamic stresses, and these have been studied by Fry (40–44). It has been shown, for example, that either stretching or compressing the tissue can increase the permeability of the barrier. It is likely that the increased permeability of the vascular interface associated with increased arterial pressure is related to the resultant increase in circumferential stretch rather than to the pressure itself. Shearing stresses from the adjacent blood flow also affect the conductance of the wall. An increase in wall shear has been shown to increase the permeability of the barrier even prior to any histological damage to the endothelial cells. In these studies the flux of protein across the interface correlated well both with the time-smoothed value of shearing stress and to a lesser extent with the intensity of the high frequency components of turbulence. These changes in permeability of the interface under such a wide variety of conditions led Fry to hypothesize concerning a unifying mechanism governing this process. He proposed that an increase in internal energy density of the surface, from whatever source, will facilitate macromolecular transport across the barrier. The added energy may be viewed as decreasing the cohesive energy of the barrier so that an invading molecule will now require relatively less energy to penetrate the system. The experimental interventions cited above (compressional or elongating stresses, time-smoothed shearing stress, or stress due to high frequency components of turbulence) will tend to increase the internal energy of the surface for at least two reasons: (a) the deformations resulting from these stresses will increase the strain energy density, i.e. the elastic energy stored per unit volume of the tissue, in the intimal region; and (b) tissue, being viscoelastic, will generate heat during deformation. Although this concept appears to be a unified and consistent way of explaining the experimental findings cited above, it does not exclude the existence of pores or interfacial thinning as other mechanisms which may play a modifying role in altering interfacial permeability.

Indirect evidence for the "energy density" concept was provided by Carew (18) who studied in vitro the effect of shearing stress due to adjacent blood flow on the transport of albumin across the endothelial surface of the thoracic aorta in dogs. The results showed that the albumin flux into the intima was linearly related to the square of the shearing stress. It is interesting to note that the energy stored in a linearly elastic surface deformed in shear is also proportional to the square of the shearing stress.

Some of the chemical factors to which the endothelial interface might be exposed are alcohol, normal saline, sodium pentobarbital, and other pharmacologic agents. These also affect the conductance of the interface as shown below: 1. Fry (43, 44) demonstrated that exposure of the endothelial surface to alcohol, acetone, normal saline, or anesthetic agents like sodium pentobarbital increased the protein flux across the interface. 2. Constantinides & Robinson (24) had observed that vasoconstrictor agents such as angiotensin opened endothelial cell junctions and increased the permeability of the vascular interface. In a more recent study (25) Constantinides perfused the femoral arteries of rats and rabbits with various concentrations of epinephrine and norepinephrine for 30 sec and examined the endothelial surface with an electron microscope. He observed opening of many endothelial junctions by both drugs at a concentration of 10 $\mu$g/ml in rabbits; at lower concentrations (200 ng/ml) he observed intracellular edema, blebbing, and microvillus formation in endothelial cells. At comparable concentrations these pressor amines had no significant effect in rats. 3. Rosen et al (93) described the effect of shearing stress on the synthesis of histamine in the endothelial region. They subjected freshly isolated and cultured bovine endothelial cells to known amounts of shearing stress and studied the histidine decarboxylase (HD) activity of the cells. Results showed that HD activity of cultured cells subjected to a mean shear stress of 65 dyne/cm$^2$ for 1 hr was several orders of magnitude greater than those of control cultured cells or of freshly isolated cells. The data suggest that histamine is produced by the endothelial cell in response to the shearing stress in the physiologic range. Histamine can accelerate pinocytosis and cause endothelial contraction, thus increasing the permeability of the interface, and edema formation in the arterial wall. 4. Jorgensen et al (58) examined aortas from rabbits and pigs infused with Evans blue dye (EBD) and found focal areas of blue staining which were associated with intimal edema, leukocyte accumulation within intima, and surface deposition of platelets. Platelets are known to accumulate near the vascular interface in regions of flow separation and vortex formation (47) and, under appropriate conditions, these platelets could react with the vessel wall and release a number of substances which in turn could injure the vessel wall and increase its permeability.

So far we have only talked about the transport of material across the interface. Not much is known about the passage of macromolecules through the wall substance. Recently, Brown et al (12) have devised a method to study this transport in vivo by injecting into the aortic wall tiny lipid crystals of known dimensions tagged with $^{14}$C. The animal is sacrificed after a few days to six months, and the test region is examined microscopically and autoradiographically. Preliminary results indicate that the major mechanism for removal of cholesterol and its esters is by diffusion, although there is some macrophage activity.

CHRONIC RESPONSE    The chronic response of the arterial wall to hemodynamic stresses can be observed as permeability changes or structural changes. The permeability changes have been studied by Fry (44) and Flaherty et al (36) in dog and pig. Fry, in collaboration with his associates, studied the topography of blue staining of the endothelial surface in dogs and pigs following infusion of EBD. They carefully examined the regions near orifices and branch sites and observed that the leading edges of the flow dividers, exposed to high shear stress, were spared of staining whereas the adjacent entrance regions and more distal portions of flow dividers, exposed to relatively lower shear stress, were stained blue. Flaherty et al noted a similar pattern of Sudanophilia near flow dividers. These changes in permeability were associated with certain structural changes in the intimal region. The spared areas were characterized by a dense, oriented layer of subendothelial collagen, presumably generated in response to chronic unidirectional stresses. In the adjacent, more permeable areas, oriented collagen was not stimulated to develop, perhaps because the previous stress patterns were too unsteady. These latter areas were also characterized by increased population of smooth muscle cells, connective tissue cells, poorly oriented collagen fibers, and a high predilection for lipid deposition (44).

Another manifestation of chronic response to hemodynamic stresses is observed in the nuclei of endothelial cells. Flaherty et al (37) studied the endothelial nuclear patterns in dogs from *en face* photomicrographs. The vessel segments were taken immediately postmortem, stretched to in vivo dimensions, and stained with EBD. Results showed that in uniform vessel segments, such as the descending thoracic aorta where blood flow is known to be more or less stable (44), the endothelial nuclei were highly elliptical and were oriented with their major axis parallel to the axis of the blood vessel. In the ascending aorta and in entrance regions of major branches, where flow is known to be unstable (44), the nuclei were more circular with a less ordered orientation. In regions such as the veins, which are exposed to mild hemodynamic forces, the nuclei were round in shape. The authors also studied chronic in vivo preparations in which a segment of the descending thoracic aorta was removed, opened longitudinally, and reclosed to form a tube with a new longitudinal axis 90° from the original vessel axis. They found that within 70 days the nuclear orientation in the grafted area, initially at right angles, became once more reoriented parallel to the blood stream. Although this study establishes the role of hemodynamic forces in orienting the endothelial cells, it does not quantify these forces; it would be important to do so.

## Pathologic Response of the Arterial Wall

ACUTE RESPONSE   The experimental evidence for such response is summarized below. Fry (40, 42) studied in vivo effects of wall stresses in the thoracic aorta of dogs following infusion of EBD. He introduced a solid cylindrical plug having a 3 cm long, narrow, uniform channel on its surface. The endothelial surface covering the channel was thus exposed to a wide range of known shearing stresses produced by the accelerated blood flow. Results indicated that: (*a*) beyond a critical value of shear stress ($378 \pm 85$ dyne/cm²), the surface begins to deteriorate histologically leading to a loss of endothelial cells and deposition of fibrin; (*b*) continued exposure to high stress can produce erosion of the subjacent tissue matrix, adherence of blood cellular elements, and deposition of fibrin on the eroded surface; and (*c*) high frequency stress components of turbulence also damaged the endothelial cells. In all cases, the protein flux across the interface increased. Since the time constant of this process is minutes to hours, one wonders about the effect of physiologically occurring peak stresses in the circulatory system.

Carew & Patel (19) investigated in vitro the effect of changes in pressure and flow on the endothelial surface of the left coronary artery of dogs following infusion of EBD. Their results showed that the flux of EBD across the endothelial surface increased with an increase in intravascular pressure or circumferential stress as well as with an increase in shearing stress at the wall, the former effect being more marked (74%).

Gutstein & Farrell (54) studied in vivo the flow pattern near the aortic bifurcation area in young Yorkshire swines, using a hot-wire anemometer. The flow pattern near the lateral wall at the junction was markedly disturbed with high frequency components superimposed on the usual pulse wave form. Normal flow patterns were seen in the terminal aorta and the iliac artery. The animals were sacrificed after 10 months and the endothelial surface was examined with an electron microscope on the test side as well as on the contralateral side. Endothelial cell damage accompanied by inflow of plasma into the arterial wall was seen only at the ilioaortic junction. The authors conclude that this area of spontaneous injury could be considered a likely future site for atherosclerotic lesions.

Another interesting pathological response of the arterial wall to hemodynamic stresses is the post-stenotic dilatation (PSD). In many clinical situations, such as pulmonary or aortic valvular stenosis or stenosis in a peripheral artery, the arterial segment distal to the stenosis is known to dilate. Roach and associates have carried out extensive experimental work to elucidate the hemodynamic factors responsible for PSD, and their work is summarized in a recent review by Roach (87). Their principal findings were: 1. PSD could be produced with moderate stenosis within 10 days and could be reversed in 24 hr after removal of the constriction; 2. turbulence was a necessary requirement for producing PSD; 3. in a study of the effect of vibrations alone on the arterial wall in isolated, nondistended iliac arteries of man, frequencies under 400 Hz increased the distensibility of the wall; and 4. elastin was more susceptible to vibrations than collagen.

CHRONIC RESPONSE   The dominant features in the histologic picture of atherosclerosis are intimal fibromuscular thickening and lipid deposition. Although lipid deposition is frequently associated with intimal fibromuscular hyperplasia, it is important to realize that each of these processes can occur independently. Another important feature in the pathogenesis of atherosclerotic lesions is the sequence of initial injury to the endothelial surface and subsequent tissue repair processes set in motion. In this section we illustrate some of these features.

*Arteriovenous shunts*   It is possible to produce a chronically increased flow in certain uniform, paired sets of vessels in the body by constructing arteriovenous shunts. The symmetry of the iliofemoral arteries and carotid arteries make these vessel systems particularly well suited to this type of experiment. If one creates an arteriovenous shunt in either of these systems, a disproportionately large blood flow occurs in the artery supplying the shunt. This increased blood flow is associated with an increased shearing stress on the endothelial surface of the supply artery and, if the Reynolds number is high enough, perhaps also with high frequency stress components produced by turbulence. It is possible to examine the structural changes associated with this increased exposure to stress by comparing the structure of the artery leading to the shunt with its contralateral control artery. In eight dogs from their colony of atherosclerotic animals Flaherty et al (36) created arteriovenous shunts in the ileofemoral artery and/or the carotid artery on one side. Between 8 and 12 weeks after surgery the dogs were anesthetized to measure pressure and flow in control and test areas and then sacrificed for histological studies. The flow conditions in these sets of arteries were comparable, but the histologic responses were quite different. The iliac artery with the shunt showed erosion of the endothelial surface, highly disorganized connective tissue with no preferred direction of orientation, and lipid deposition. In contrast, the carotid shunt artery showed marked intimal fibromuscular hyperplasia with an ordered deposition of longitudinally oriented collagen and essentially no lipid deposition; the endothelial cells appeared normal. Fry (44) has speculated as to why these two sets of arteries under comparable flow conditions responded so differently: one pathologically and the other more or less physiologically. He suggests the possibilities that the flow fields in these arteries, though comparable during anesthesia, might have been quite different in the awake animal owing to changing diurnal metabolic demands, or that there was disturbed flow in the iliac artery, or that the endothelial-intimal tissue in the two arterial systems had inherently different properties and responses.

*Endothelial injury and repair*  Stemerman & Ross (100) produced lesions in monkeys by selective removal of the vascular endothelium from the abdominal aorta and the iliac artery with an intra-arterial balloon catheter. The animals were allowed to recover for various periods from 10 min to 6 months, after which they were sacrificed and the vessels examined both by light and electron microscopy. Results indicated that the denuded area was covered immediately with a platelet layer; this thrombus was then gradually removed and the vessel re-endothelialized in 7 days. Beginning on day 4, smooth muscle cells were seen to migrate into the intima where they proliferated. By 28 days, the intimal lesion consisted of multiple layers of smooth muscle cells surrounded by elastic and collagen fibers and basement-like material. In 3 months these lesions were markedly hyperplastic and contained new extracellular connective tissue. With no further injury, in 6 months the lesions decreased in size, suggesting potential reversibility of the lesion. The authors emphasize the importance of initial endothelial injury which exposes the medial smooth muscle to plasma constituents in initiating this sequence of events. Fry (44), in collaboration with Ferrans, has also demonstrated a similar pattern of endothelial injury and repair in the thoracic aorta of dogs. In a related study Kern et al (59) reported intimal proliferation in aortic-coronary saphenous vein grafts in man. Within 2 to 29 months, the graft showed considerable intimal fibrosis, presumably in response to the increased hemodynamic stresses to which the venous endothelium was exposed.

Before leaving this section, we emphasize the need to quantify the topography of various atherosclerotic lesions so that average patterns of lesions in animal or man can be established. Although beginnings are made in this direction (20, 36) more work is needed, particularly near bends, branches, and orifices, so that hemodynamic and tissue factors can be examined in critical areas. Recent work of Roach & Cornhill (89) is important in this regard. These authors present a simple method for quantifying orifice lesions in atherosclerotic rabbit aorta. Photographs of orifices and the surrounding lesions are first projected onto a polar coordinate grid. The distance from orifice to outer edge of the plaque and the angular location of the plaque with respect to the orifice are then measured and replotted, one as a function of the other, on a rectangular coordinate grid. The authors feel that the two-dimensional analysis can be easily extended to three dimensions to include the height of the plaque from the endothelial surface.

## BLOOD FLOW FIELDS

Having established that hemodynamic stresses play a significant role in the pathogenesis of atherosclerotic processes, we now review recent developments in nonlinear theories of blood flow, finite element methods in hemodynamics, details of local flow fields, flow studies in artificial models, hemodynamics of coronary blood flow, and newer techniques for measurement of blood flow fields.

## Nonlinear Theories of Blood Flow

Ling & Atabek (64) used an approximate numerical method for calculating flow profiles in arteries. Their theory included nonlinear convective acceleration terms of the Navier-Stokes equations as well as nonlinear behavior and large deformations of the arterial wall. They simplified the complicated boundary value problem by assuming that the radial arterial motion is primarily governed by the pressure wave, that the longitudinal wall motion is negligible, and that velocity profiles are developed locally as the pressure gradient wave propagates forward. The authors solved the resulting simplified equations by the method of finite differences. They applied the theory to the flow through a distensible model of the circulatory system and compared their results of velocity profiles with those measured experimentally in the model with good agreement. The method constitutes an improvement over the previously used linear theories (68), particularly in determining velocity profiles and flow waves in distensible vessels under large pulse pressures.

In a subsequent recent publication Ling et al (65) applied the preceding theory to describe the characteristics of pulsatile flow in living dogs. The measurement of the mean blood flow by a pressure gradient technique is difficult, since it requires accurate measurement of the mean pressure gradient within $\pm$ 0.001 mm Hg/cm. Their technique, called the forward-backward switching technique, to achieve such accuracy is one of the most important aspects of their paper and represents a significant experimental advance. To obtain pressure gradient information at a point along the aorta, proximal and distal taps are made through intercostal orifices. These taps are connected to two pressure transducers through nylon catheters and a special duplex three-way valve. Using this valve either tap can be connected to its respective transducer, or the connections can be reversed. By taking the difference of forward and backward pressure gradient signals, the static error is essentially eliminated. The same system could be used for measurement of dynamic pressure gradient, provided the lengths of the stiff nylon tubing connecting the pressure gauges to the sites of measurement are equal and the system is free of leaks and microbubbles. With these pressure gradient data, along with data on pressure-radius function, pressure wave, wall taper, and blood viscosity, detailed flow fields within the aorta could be calculated and compared with measured flow data using other techniques. The method was found capable of accurately predicting flow field in the descending thoracic aorta of dogs. Under conditions of increased flow the computed value of the peak shearing stress was approximately 270 dyne/cm$^2$; this value is close to the value 379 dyne/cm$^2$ of critical stress for the endothelial cells quoted by Fry (40).

Wemple & Mockros (108) formulated the pressure-flow behavior of the systemic arterial system by solving the nonlinear momentum and continuity equations. Their model included geometric and elastic taper of the aorta, nonlinear elastic properties of the arteries, side flows, and a complex distal impedance. Solution of the equation for realistic parametric values gave results for pressure wave shape, impedances, and wave velocities that compared favorably with results reported in the literature. They found that reflections, and not the geometric taper, were the major factor determining the shape and distal amplification of the pressure wave in the arterial tree. Elastic taper and nonlinear elasticity of the vessel wall were found to be of minor significance in determining pressure and flow profiles. Highly nonlinear as the system was, it behaved in a somewhat linear fashion for low frequency components. Although their model is not as anatomically extensive as the electronic model of Westerhof et al (110) and requires a considerable amount of computer time, it is superior to the Westerhof model in that it includes nonlinear convective acceleration terms and other nonlinear effects resulting from the dependence of cross-sectional area and compliance on pressure.

## Finite Element Methods in Hemodynamics

Most of the work in physiological fluid mechanics has been done so far using classical methods based on solution of differential equations subject to appropriate boundary conditions, the solution method itself being analytical, numerical, or by finite differences. These classical methods enjoy a power and sophistication adequate to solve a variety of difficult problems. However, they have certain shortcomings mostly associated with the complexity of geometrical shapes and incorporation of nonlinearities. Of late, increasing effort is being directed to the so-called finite element methods different in principle and spirit from the classical methods in that, instead of using differential equations as their starting point, they use a chosen small, but finite, convenient geometrical element and apply directly to it the physical principles used to derive the corresponding differential equation without actually deriving the latter. The advantage of these methods lies in the fact that the physics of the problem is more transparent and hence intuition and a physical feel for the problem can be used to better advantage in formulation and solution of the problem. Moreover, these methods are directly amenable to numerical computations involving high speed digital computers.

We cite three recent papers in which these methods have been used. Davids & Cheng (28) analyzed the entry problem, the transient problem, and the problem of viscous flow in ducts of noncircular cross sections, such as rectangular, elliptic, and bicircular. Davids & Mani (29) considered blood flow turbulence including the problems of turbulent entry wall shear stresses. Cannon & Greenfield (17) used computer graphics to display the results of a finite element analysis of viscous flow in tubes, with a view to investigating the relationships of turbulence in blood flow to the pathogenesis of atherosclerosis and to the sites of predilection of atherosclerotic lesion formation. The range of problems considered by these authors shows the potential of the method. The real success of this method, however, will depend on validation of computed results by comparison with experimentally measured quantities.

## Local Flow Fields

Important as is the knowledge of average hemodynamic parameters such as pressure, flow, average velocity, and wave velocity, it is the measurement of local details that is relevant to the discrete disease processes. Accordingly, increasing attention is being directed toward measurement of velocity profiles at various sites in the vascular bed and measurement of flow disturbances including vortex formation, separation, and turbulence, especially at branches, bends, and bifurcations. For a visual understanding of such complicated flow events, we recommend a series of films by the National Committee of Fluid Mechanics and a companion book (75).

VELOCITY PROFILES IN THE AORTA    Schultz (97) has reviewed this subject in detail. More recently, Falsetti et al (34), using hot-film anemometry, mapped velocity profiles in the ascending and descending aorta of living dogs. By careful measurements they obtained sequential profiles over a full cardiac cycle. They confirmed the previous observation of essentially flat velocity profiles but reported a significant variation from dog to dog, probably as a consequence of a variety of geometrical factors such as valve inlet geometry, curvature of the aortic arch, and the branches from the descending aorta. The shapes of the profiles also changed with position along the aorta, and with time at a given position. Because of the difficulty in obtaining a zero-flow condition, these authors caution against using their values in the absolute sense but claim that the normalized profiles are dependable. They caution against temptation to infer wall shear from the slopes of their velocity profiles, since the data points near the wall are of limited accuracy, because of, among other things, the relatively large size of the probe.

TURBULENCE IN THE AORTA    Nerem & Seed (76) carried out in vivo experiments on small dogs to quantify the parameters controlling the degree of disturbance in flow. Using a hot-film anemometer with a direction-sensing probe they measured velocity waveforms in the aortic arch and in the ascending and descending thoracic aorta. By changing heart rate and peak velocity in various ways, they could vary Reynolds number, $Re$, and frequency parameter, $\alpha$, defined as

$$Re = UD/\nu \qquad\qquad\qquad 3.$$

and

$$\alpha = R \, (\omega/\nu)^{1/2} \qquad\qquad\qquad 4.$$

where $U =$ mean flow velocity, $D =$ vessel diameter, $\nu =$ blood viscosity, $R =$ vessel radius, and $\omega =$ the fundamental circular frequency of the pulsatile flow. They classified the velocity waveforms into three categories: undisturbed, disturbed, and highly disturbed. The waveform with high frequency disturbances throughout the systolic phase was termed highly disturbed and considered representative of turbulence. Their results indicated that the degree of disturbance in flow depended on $\alpha$ as well on $Re$. The dependence of the degree of disturbance on $Re$ is well understood; the dependence on $\alpha$ can be explained by considering that a larger value of $\alpha$ corresponds with an increase in frequency, $\omega$, which decreases the time available in one cardiac cycle for disturbances to grow. These authors provide us with a brief and lucid tutorial on the phenomenon of turbulence.

## Flow Studies in Artificial Models

Since available studies of flow fields in animal or man are limited to straight segments of blood vessels, there is a tendency to study more complicated geometries in artificial models. Such investigations can be helpful provided one is careful about the interpretation of the results and does not directly extend them to real situations in animals; this is particularly true when pulsatile blood flow is modelled with rigid tubes. For unsteady flow in rigid tubes, the flow at a given location depends strongly on the convected flow from upstream; however, for such flows in distensible tubes, a part of the flow at a given location can be generated by a passing pressure gradient wave. With this in mind, we describe the following model studies.

FLOW DISTURBANCE AT BIFURCATIONS   Ferguson & Roach (35) and Roach et al (88) photographed steady state flow patterns in water flowing through glass models of aortic bifurcations with various angles. The patterns of flow were observed by injecting a dilute solution of EBD through a fine needle axially and in the boundary layer. The axial stream impinged directly upon the apex of the bifurcations and was reflected into the branches. The dye stream in the boundary layer separated from the wall at the bend and reattached downstream at low Reynolds numbers ($Re = 200$–$500$). As the flow rate increased, a helical pattern arose which was particularly obvious in the wide-angled bifurcations, the flow pattern being neither laminar nor turbulent. Further increase in flow rate resulted in turbulence which was localized to the upstream portion of the bifurcation leg, the flow in the distal portion being again streamlined. A still further increase in flow rate resulted in turbulence throughout the bifurcation leg, the flow rate in the stem and in the region of the apex remaining streamlined. The authors were able to achieve a critical $Re$ of 2500 for steady flow and 2100 for pulsatile flow in straight tubes. Bifurcations, however, lowered the critical $Re$; pulsatile flow and flow reversal lowered it even further.

Analytical solution of the bifurcation problem has not been obtained so far. For the two-dimensional analog, however, various solutions, on the basis of different assumptions, have been given by Lew (62) and Lynn et al (66).

FORMATION OF PLATELET AGGREGATES ON VESSEL WALL   Goldsmith (47) reported the presence of platelet thrombi on vessel walls in vivo, downstream from bifurcations, sharp bends, and constrictions. He attributed such platelet thrombus formation to fluid mechanical factors such as separation of streamlines from the wall and formation of vortices. To test the hypothesis, he used 2 $\mu$ latex spheres as models of platelets in 40 to 50% suspensions of human biconcave ghost cells in plasma and found that the latex spheres had a marked tendency for transverse displacement, occasionally colliding with the wall. When dilute suspensions of red cells and latex spheres were caused to flow through 1 mm diameter glass tubes partially blocked with 0.5 and 0.8 mm polystyrene spheres fused to the inner wall, the red cells described spiral paths in the vortex formed downstream from the obstruction. Aggregates of latex spheres adhered only to the surface of the obstruction that was close to the tube wall. Conditions within the vortex may thus make it possible for platelets, once activated, to adhere to the vessel wall.

STRESSES CAUSED BY FLOW The stresses induced by blood within the vessel wall can be computed using various assumptions but cannot be directly measured. This becomes more difficult if one wishes to know details of stress distribution in the vicinity of a region with slightly complicated geometry. Rodbard & Farbstein (92) used photoelastic analysis to estimate mechanical stresses caused by blood flowing through a blood vessel. They constructed channels of a compliant birefringent material made by mixing gelatin and agar. The channel was cast into a chosen shape and covered with a transparent cover. Water flowing under pressure caused stresses in the channel which in turn formed photoelastic fringes; from these, maximum shear stress in the channel wall could be estimated by standard methods of photoelastic analysis. The stress patterns varied with the local stresses generated by the fluid pressure and local stream velocity.

## Coronary Blood Flow

Considering the importance of coronary blood flow in atherosclerosis, we now review some recent work on the hemodynamics of coronary circulation. The development of suitable techniques for direct flow measurements in large branches of the coronary artery has permitted detailed study of total and phasic coronary blood flow changes in a variety of activities. Telemetry allows these measurements to be performed in unrestrained animals. Using a Doppler ultrasonic flow probe, Vatner et al (106) recorded phasic and mean blood flow continuously in the left circumflex coronary artery of unanesthetized baboons. The characteristic phasic coronary blood flow pattern of minimal flow in systole and maximal flow in early diastole was obtained. The flow was at its minimum while the animal was sleeping and markedly increased during excitement or fright. Periodic fluctuations in coronary vascular resistance and flow were observed in the absence of any alteration in heart rate or arterial pressure, suggesting that the responses might be mediated by neural mechanisms. This study constitutes an excellent example of the use of hemodynamics in an objective evaluation of emotional factors affecting the coronary circulation.

Gregg et al (52) studied the effects of chronic cardiac denervation on coronary blood flow in conscious dogs. Denervation of the hearts was substantiated by demonstrating a lack of cardiac response to intravenous tyramine or to cardiac sympathetic nerve stimulation. When the animals were sacrificed, catecholamine content of the myocardium was shown to be markedly reduced. The coronary blood flow as well as oxygen usage by the myocardium were diminished in denervated animals in the resting state and during exercise and excitement. The differences observed in the denervated preparation as compared to the intact animal are probably related to the manner in which the heart adjusts its performance in the absence of catecholamine release by the sympathetic nerves.

To evaluate what proportion of the augmentation of coronary blood flow observed in exercise was due to heart rate changes, Vatner et al (107) paced the hearts of resting conscious dogs to the same level of tachycardia that was normally achieved in spontaneous exercise. Approximately one third of the increase in coronary flow could be attributed to heart rate changes. When complete heart block was produced in dogs so that tachycardia could not develop during exercise, coronary blood flow increased to twice the resting value, presumably as a result of alterations in myocardial contractility and wall tension.

The technique of intra-aortic balloon counterpulsation, which is based on reasonably sound hemodynamic principles, has been used to assist the coronary circulation in cardiogenic shock (96). The hemodynamic changes associated with counterpulsation (77) are a decrease in aortic systolic pressure and an increase in aortic diastolic pressure, an increase in coronary blood flow due primarily to an augmentation of flow in diastole, and an increase in cardiac output with a decrease in the calculated tension-time index. Improvement of the hemodynamic and clinical status of patients while on counterpulsation, including improvement by the new external noninvasive technique, has been documented in several recent papers (33, 67, 74). Thus, counterpulsation appears to be a dependable interim measure to support the circulation during cardiogenic shock.

## Measurement of Blood Flow Fields

In view of two recent reviews on cardiovascular instrumentation, one has an almost up-to-date account of the advances in the field (70, 102). Consequently, in this section, consistent with the main theme of the review, we discuss only the use of hot-film anemometry and ultrasonic techniques for measurement of local flow fields. Unfortunately, despite its importance, no precise method exists for measurement of wall shear in critical areas of the vascular system. The difficulty arises from our inability to measure velocity close to the endothelial surface of a vessel which is moving during a cardiac cycle.

The principle of the technique of hot-film anemometry is simply that the amount of cooling of a heated object placed within a moving fluid can be related to the rate at which heat is conducted away and therefore to the fluid velocity. The sensing element of the instrument, which consists of a hot film, is usually maintained at a constant temperature of about 5°C above that of the blood. The use of this technique has already been illustrated in the section on local flow fields.

The ultrasonic flowmeters appear promising because of their noninvasive nature. However, the state of the art does not appear to have advanced far enough to permit accurate estimate of wall shear. Earlier instruments based on measurement of the transit time of an ultrasonic pulse have largely been replaced by instruments employing the Doppler shift principle, which essentially states that when a beam of ultrasound is directed into a moving stream of blood, the beam reflected from the particles in the stream is shifted in frequency, the shift being proportional to the velocity of the stream.

Baker (4) describes the use of a comb-type gate which allows flow velocity to be sampled from a series of gates generated sequentially. Hence, a train of echoes is received, each successive one representing reflection from an interface farther from the probe.

Recently, the pulsed ultrasonic Doppler technique has been used by Morris et al (72) and Histand et al (55) to measure blood velocity profiles transcutaneously in canine arteries at various locations. By proper electronic gating of a reflected ultrasound beam they could obtain velocity data from a rather small sample volume of 1–2 mm$^3$ for a gate of 2 $\mu$sec using a 2 mm diameter transducer. Histand et al measured velocity profiles in the iliac, femoral, and carotid arteries, and the abdominal and thoracic aorta, at 21 equally spaced intervals during the cardiac cycle. They found velocity profiles to be generally symmetric in straight, uniform segments, but distinctly skewed near branch points, bifurcations, or sites of abrupt vessel curvature. Owing to the finite sample volume, there was a slight broadening of the velocity profiles at the wall. Thus the method should be used with caution for calculation of wall shear. Better beam focusing techniques and smaller range increments should reduce these errors.

The Doppler shift principle has also been employed for measurement of flow field using lasers (48, 94). Unfortunately this method requires use of a transparent conduit. Finally, Stiles & Bischoff (101) have described an electrochemical method to measure wall shear resulting from flow in a rigid model of the canine abdominal aorta and its branches including the trifurcation area. The measurement of shear was based on the use of a chemical reaction in which the transport to the wall of a reacting ion (ferricyanide) depended on the velocity gradient and could be measured electrically. The authors mapped the velocity gradient in the model at 75 locations. Unfortunately, their method can be used only in rigid models.

# RHEOLOGY OF VASCULAR TISSUE

Proper characterization of mechanical properties of the vascular tissue is important because of the dependence on these properties of blood flow characteristics in the vascular bed which, in turn, affect the hemodynamic stresses on the vessel wall. The vessel properties also determine the distribution of strain energy density[5] through the vessel wall and thereby may influence permeability of the vascular intima to lipids and proteins. Moreover, as shown before, the structure of the wall in the subendothelial region varies from site to site depending on the history of previous exposure to hemodynamic stresses, thus leading to nonuniform local properties and nonuniform permeability of the vascular interface. Therefore, in this section, we first describe recent work on gross and local mechanical properties of large blood vessels and follow it up with other areas of interest in the study of rheology of the vascular tissue. For a summary of previous work in this area see Bergel (9) and Patel & Vaishnav (82).

## Incremental and Nonlinear Properties

A proper characterization of the mechanical properties of the vascular tissue should take into account various observed properties of the tissue, including capability of undergoing large deformations, incompressibility, viscoelasticity, nonhomogeneity,

[5]Strain energy density in a given configuration is the recoverable energy stored in a unit volume of tissue. It can be visualized easily in a stretched rubber band. In materials for which strain energy density is a unique function of strain, the mechanical properties are completely described by the knowledge of this functional form. Thus, inasmuch as the vascular tissue can be assumed to have a strain energy density function, determination of its functional form is a proper way to characterize its nonlinear elastic behavior. The independent strain variables to be used as arguments for the strain energy function depend on the type of material symmetry exhibited by the material in question.

anisotropy,[6] and nonlinearity of material response. Nonlinear material response can be treated either in the incremental sense, where the response is considered as being linear for small static or dynamic strains in the neighborhood of large strains, or directly through establishment of relations between the state of stress and the state of large deformation and the history thereof. Both approaches are valuable. Since pulsatile blood flow imposes small dynamic pulsatile strains on a state of large deformation corresponding to the mean vascular pressure, the incremental approach describes a very realistic situation and generates incremental material constants in a direct manner; the constants, of course, depend on the particular level of mean deformation under study. The direct nonlinear approach is more general, but at the same time more involved.

Patel et al (83) observed dynamic incremental anisotropic properties of the middle descending thoracic aorta in living dogs. They isolated in situ a segment of the middle descending thoracic aorta and connected it to a reservoir of oxygenated blood which could be raised to a desired height to impress a known mean pressure in the segment. Small sinusoidal pressure at frequencies of 0–5 Hz was superimposed on the mean pressure by means of a fluid-displacement pump. At each state of large strain, two independent states of incremental strain were imposed in succession. The first state was created by sealing off the segment to hold a constant blood volume and then imposing sinusoidal length changes; the second state consisted of holding the segment at a constant length and imposing a sinusoidal volume change. Sinusoidal changes in pressure, force, radius, and length were measured as functions of time at several frequencies. From these data, incremental storage (elastic) and loss (viscous) moduli in the circumferential, longitudinal, and radial direction were computed. In general, the incremental moduli were functions of the initial strains, thus indicating the nonlinear nature of the response of the arterial wall. Within the physiological range of pressure, the longitudinal storage and loss moduli were the largest, and the circumferential loss modulus was the smallest. The loss moduli at 2 Hz were less than 12% of the corresponding storage moduli, indicating a small viscous component relative to its elastic counterpart. The elastic moduli increased markedly from 0–2 Hz and then settled down to a relatively constant value. The authors also observed that the values of longitudinal storage and loss moduli from the in vivo experiments were higher than their in vitro counterparts, and they attributed the difference to the vascular tethering present in vivo. Thus, a method and theory are now available for obtaining dynamic incremental viscoelastic moduli

[6]The following will help in understanding some of the technical terms to appear in the text. Consider an infinitesimally small unit cube of tissue from a hypothetical, homogeneous, cylindrical blood vessel segment with edges in the radial, circumferential, and longitudinal directions, and subject it to equal and opposite normal tensile stresses on the three pairs of faces. If the tissue were *isotropic,* it would undergo equal strains in the directions of the stresses and thus the element would remain cubical. If it were *transversely isotropic* in the plane of the cross section of the blood vessel, it would become a rectangular parallelopiped with equal dimensions in the thickness and circumferential directions. If it were *curvilinearly ortho-tropic,* it would become a rectangular parallelopiped with dimensions unequal in general. For higher degrees of anisotropy, it would remain a parallelopiped but not a rectangular one. That the arterial tissue is at least *orthotropic* has been demonstrated.

for the aortic tissue in the physiological ranges of initial and incremental strains and in the frequency range of prime interest.

In the preceding study, no attempt was made to fit any particular model to the data, although the authors suggested the use of a spring and a dashpot in parallel (Voigt model) for each direction as a conceptual device. On the other hand, Cox (26) and Wesseling et al (109) have used five-parameter models to describe dynamic response of canine and human arteries in the circumferential direction. Cox found that a model consisting of a spring in series with a Voigt element adequately represented data from experiments on femoral arteries of dogs when the fundamental heart frequency was 2 Hz or more, but when the latter was 1 Hz or less, two Voigt elements of different time constants in series with the spring were necessary to represent the data. Wesseling et al applied the model of Westerhof & Noordergraaf (111) to data from human thoracic and abdominal aortas and the iliac, femoral, and carotid arteries for young and old age groups. They compared the ratio of high frequency Young's modulus to the static modulus and found that this ratio decreased for the carotid artery but increased for the iliac and femoral arteries, with increasing age. This ratio, to a certain degree, is a measure of smooth muscle content in the tissue, the more peripheral vessels having a higher percentage of it. For more details on the effect of vascular smooth muscle on vessel rheology, see a recent review by Gow (49).

Scott et al (98) compared the elastic properties of human intracranial arteries and aneurysms, and found the aneurysms considerably less distensible than the major cerebral arteries.

Studies of nonlinear elastic response of arteries have been reported by Doyle & Dobrin (31), Simon et al (99), and Vaishnav et al (104, 105). The first work, on canine carotid arteries, shows that the vessels are indeed anisotropic in their unstressed state. The second treats various arteries as transversely isotropic in the plane of the arterial cross section. In both these works segment lengths were varied, but only to evaluate the parametric dependence of the material constants in the transverse directions. The studies of Vaishnav et al on middle descending thoracic aorta are more general in that an arterial segment is treated therein as curvilinearly orthotropic. The authors evaluated the tissue constants by simultaneous variations in the longitudinal and circumferential directions. In the following discussion of these works, we retain the original authors' symbols for the constitutive parameters in spite of some overlap, as no confusion seems likely to arise thereby.

Doyle & Dobrin found that the circumferential stress, $S_\theta$, was related to the circumferential stretch,[7] $\lambda_\theta$, as

$$S_\theta = A \left[ 1 - (\lambda_0/\lambda_\theta) \right] e^{K\lambda_\theta} \qquad \qquad 5.$$

while the longitudinal stress, $S_z$, depended on $\lambda_\theta$ as

$$S_z = Be^{C\lambda^3_\theta} \qquad \qquad 6.$$

[7]Circumferential stretch (or extension ratio) is the ratio of the length of a circumferential tissue fiber in the deformed state to its length in the undeformed state. A similar definition holds for any other direction.

In these equations, $A$, $B$, $C$, and $K$ are tissue constants at a chosen value of the longitudinal stretch and $\lambda_0$ is the value of $\lambda_\theta$ at zero inflation pressure. If one is interested only in the nonlinear stress-strain relation for fixed segment lengths, Equations 5 and 6 should prove useful. The strain energy density, $W$, in an incompressible material can be expressed as a function of two principal[8] stretches $\lambda_\theta$ and $\lambda_z$ only, since $\lambda_r$, the radial stretch, is related to $\lambda_\theta$ and $\lambda_z$ through the incompressibility condition. Thus

$$W = W(\lambda_\theta, \lambda_z) \qquad\qquad 7.$$

represents a general constitutive relation for the arterial tissue. The stresses $S_\theta$ and $S_z$ can be determined, to within an undetermined hydrostatic pressure, in terms of the derivatives of $W$ with respect to $\lambda_\theta$ and $\lambda_z$ and, if the functional form of $W$ is known, $S_\theta$ and $S_z$ can be determined therefrom. Determination of $W$ from the stresses, on the other hand, requires knowledge of $S_\theta$ and $S_z$ as functions of $\lambda_\theta$ and $\lambda_z$ both. Therefore, in the present case, $W$, or the incremental elastic moduli in the $\theta$, $z$, and $r$ directions, cannot be fully determined from Equations 5 and 6 since the functional form of the dependence of $S_\theta$ and $S_z$ on $\lambda_z$ is not known.

Simon et al assumed $W$ to be of the form

$$W = W(I,K) \qquad\qquad 8.$$

where

$$I = \lambda_\theta^2 + \lambda_z^2 + \lambda_r^2 \qquad\qquad 9.$$

and

$$K = \tfrac{1}{2}(\lambda_z^2 - 1) \qquad\qquad 10.$$

Since $\lambda_\theta$, $\lambda_z$, and $\lambda_r$ are symmetrically involved in $I$, dependence on $I$ signifies isotropy. Introduction of $K$ isolates the $z$ direction. Thus, in Equation 10, only $\lambda_\theta$ and $\lambda_r$ are involved symmetrically, which implies assumption of transverse isotropy in the $r\theta$ plane. For a constant $\lambda_z$ the parameter $K$ is also constant and $W$ is a function of $I$ only. The radial and circumferential stresses are then functions of $\partial W/\partial I$, which Simon et al assumed to be of the form

$$\tfrac{\partial W}{\partial I} = C\, e^{k(I - I_0)} \qquad\qquad 11.$$

where $I_0$ is the value of $I$ when the intravascular pressure is zero, and $C$ and $k$ are constants which can be used for the particular experimental value of $K$. These authors performed experiments on several different types of artery and gave values of $C$ and $k$ for typical in vivo values of $K$. They used these values of $C$ and $k$ to evaluate the distribution of radial and circumferential stress through the wall thick-

[8]By requiring $\lambda_\theta$, $\lambda_z$, and $\lambda_r$ to be the principal stretches, we restrict ourselves to states of deformation free of shearing strains when described in the coordinate system oriented along the $\theta$, $z$, and $r$ directions. The vessel segment under an internal pressure and a longitudinal force would undergo such deformation if it were curvilinearly orthotropic in the $\theta$, $z$, and $r$ directions or, less generally, if it were isotropic or transversely isotropic in the $r\theta$, $\theta z$, or $zr$ plane.

ness. As their theory and experiments related to constant values of axial strain, they could not compute the distribution of the longitudinal stress at all and could compute the distribution of $W$ only to within an additive constant.

A more general constitutive relation for the aortic tissue was proposed by Vaishnav et al (104). They considered the tissue to be incompressible and curvilinearly orthotropic (81) and the strain energy density to be a function of direct strains in the radial, circumferential, and longitudinal directions and of the squares of three shearing strains. Under a state of stress corresponding to an intravascular pressure and a longitudinal force only, the shearing strains in an orthotropic material would vanish, and therefore the strain energy density for physiological applications of this type can be considered to be a function only of the three direct strains, of which only two are independent because of the condition of imcompressibility. Strain energy density thus is a function of only two strains. Accordingly, Vaishnav et al recommended using the following polynomial expression for $W$:

$$W = Aa^2 + Bab + Cb^2 + Da^3 + Ea^2b + Fab^2 + Gb^3 \qquad 12.$$

where $a = \frac{1}{2} (\lambda_\theta^2 - 1)$ and $b = \frac{1}{2} (\lambda_z^2 - 1)$ are the Green-St. Venant strains in the circumferential and longitudinal directions, respectively, and $A \ldots G$ are the nonlinear elastic constitutive constants for the tissue. The expression for $W$ given by Equation 12 permits simultaneous independent variations in the circumferential and longitudinal strains. The authors gave the values of the constitutive constants based on in vivo and in vitro experiments on canine middle descending thoracic aorta. Vaishnav et al (105) in a subsequent work obtained the distribution of radial, circumferential, and longitudinal stresses as well as the strain energy density through the wall thickness. They found the magnitudes of all three stresses and $W$ to be the highest at the intimal surface, rapidly decreasing toward the adventitial surface. Since the magnitude of $W$ appears to be relevant to the question of the permeability of the blood-vascular interface, knowledge of its distribution through the wall thickness acquires added significance.

Cheung & Hsiao (23) developed a nonlinearly viscoelastic anisotropic constitutive relation for the blood vessel tissue. They assumed the blood vessel to be encompressible and transversely isotropic but confined their experiments to fixed values of axial stretches. They computed four material relaxation functions of time which could be measured from one experiment, but did not compute the relaxation functions required to describe tissue behavior when longitudinal stretch was also changed.

What is needed now is a nonlinearly viscoelastic constitutive relation for an orthotropic, incompressible arterial tissue. Such a relation should be capable of incorporating simultaneous changes in $\lambda_\theta$ and $\lambda_z$ and should be validated by a carefully performed set of experiments. Ideally, from such a relation one should be able to derive nonlinear elastic response as well as incremental dynamic response. However, such a relation would of necessity be very complicated.

## Microrheological Techniques to Measure Local Mechanical Properties

All of the preceding work is directed toward measuring what may be called gross, average, or effective mechanical properties. To whatever extent tissue can be considered to be homogeneous, these properties would also describe local properties which are indeed of interest from the point of view of tissue failure. However, added impetus has been given to this problem as a result of recent investigations of the pathogenesis of atherosclerosis. For example, the local permeability of the vascular interface appears to be sensitive to the local tissue properties (44).

As a beginning toward characterizing the mechanical properties of the vascular intima and the underlying structures, Gow & Vaishnav (50) have constructed a microindentor which allows them to measure the surface hardness from point to point on the intimal surface. The instrument, which essentially consists of a modified sensitive analytical balance one pan of which is replaced by a weighted rod with a cylindrical microprodder tip, applies forces of 120 mg to the intimal surface of an aortic segment which has been previously removed from the animal, slit longitudinally, stretched to in vivo dimensions in a rack, and backed by a hardened slurry of plaster of Paris. Indentations are continuously measured as the output of a specially designed linear differential transformer. Preliminary results show the indentation to be extremely time dependent, irrespective of the applied force or tip diameter. Thus, mapping of the surface properties has been carried out by recording the indentation at an arbitrarily chosen period of 30 sec following the application of the force. For a prodder with tip diameter of 0.2 mm the average value of the indentation turns out to be about 60 $\mu$ with not much variation from point to point for normal dog aortas. However, the intimal pad areas immediately distal to intercostal flow dividers are in general harder than the adjacent tissue. This, considering their increased collagen content, demonstrates that the technique is indeed sensitive to structural changes in the surface tissue. In atherosclerotic aortas from man, dog, and rabbit, certain areas on the intima with lipid deposition are at least twice as compliant as the areas which are spared. These preliminary data suggest that the technique will be useful in following the changes in the surface properties of arteries in animals with experimental atherosclerosis.

## Other Studies on Tissue Properties

Considerable work has been done on miscellaneous isolated aspects of tissue properties of possible relevance to the major theme of this review. For instance, Kresch & Noordergraaf (61) present a mathematical analysis for determining the shape of a collapsible blood vessel, such as a vein, for a given transmural pressure if the initial shape is known. They assume the wall thickness to be small in comparison with the radius of curvature at all points at all times. They also neglect end effects, longitudinal prestress, inertial forces, viscous losses, and stretching of the wall. Further, they assume wall thickness to be uniform and the tissue to be homogeneous, but not necessarily isotropic. From equilibrium considerations they derive a generalized form of Laplace's law and solve it using a digital computer with cross-sectional shapes displayed on an oscilloscope. They find the cross-sectional shapes to be gratifyingly similar to those obtained by Reddy et al (85) using a radiologic technique.

Next, we consider three recent papers on the subject of aging and the mechanical and histological properties of tissue. Band et al (5) report longitudinal dynamic experiments (1–5 Hz) on rat's thoracic aorta in two groups 6 and 18 months of age. Creep recovery was significantly lower in old rats than in young ones. Differences in real and imaginary parts of the dynamic Young's modulus became significant only in the tests carried out at lengths 1.2 times the in vivo length, in which case the values were higher for the old rats presumably as a result of an increase in collagen with aging. Wolinsky (112) observed the effects of long term hypertension on the thoracic aorta of male rats and found striking increases in elastin and collagen content of the vessel wall. The wall thickness increased progressively with the duration of hypertension. Changes due to aging were qualitatively similar to, but much less pronounced than, those seen with hypertension. The studies of Cannon & Davidson (16) on solubility of tail tendons of rats of various ages revealed that even at 1 month of age all collagen molecules are interlinked, but many of the bonds between the chains are labile in strong salt or weak acid solutions. In the older animals, it appears that there is increased cross-linking with most of the polypeptides linked within and between the molecules. These findings should also have a counterpart in observed mechanical behavior.

## Measurement of Arterial Diameter

Effective estimation of vascular mechanical properties depends heavily on the techniques used to measure the diameter of the blood vessel. Previously, large amounts of data from surgically exposed arteries have been obtained using electrical calipers (8). In more recent years, the intravascular diameter gauge has been developed (3, 60, 84, 86) which permits measurement of vessel diameter in vivo. Attractive as these intravascular gauges are, their influence on passive and active tissue properties will have to be carefully evaluated before they can be accepted as dependable instruments for measurement of diameter.

Perhaps the most significant advances in arterial diameter measurement have been in techniques employing ultrasound whose major advantage is, of course, their ability to record data without surgical intervention. In an early use of an ultrasonic device to measure carotid artery diameter in man, Arndt et al (1) found that the pulsatile excursion of the human carotid artery was much larger than that previously reported by Greenfield et al (51). The average pulsatile diameter excursion was 14% of the mean, which, if correct, implies that intact arteries might be more distensible than surgically exposed ones. However, more recently, Hokanson et al (57) using a more sophisticated phase-locked version of the earlier echo-tracking instrument (56) found that pressure of the probe on the tissues overlying the artery led to increased amplitudes of diameter excursion. On this basis they feel that the previous values for diameter excursions obtained with the earlier ultrasonic devices were large. The new instrument uses the same crystal for transmitting and receiving ultrasonic pulses. It is less sensitive to changes in amplitude and shape of the echo returning from the arterial wall and therefore is easier to use than the former one.

Recently, an esophageal probe has been used by Olson & Shelton (78) for measurement of arterial diameter. They photographed on the oscilloscope the traces of the transmitted and received bursts of ultrasound together with intravascular pressure and claimed a resolution of $\pm$ 40 $\mu$ in the diameter signal. It is interesting that the values of canine aortic wave velocity obtained using this technique were comparable to similar published data from surgically exposed vessels (80).

In summary, we have reviewed some of the recent work on blood vessel rheology. We feel that areas requiring future research are: accurate mapping of surface properties of the aorta and its branches; evaluation of wall properties in areas of complicated geometry such as curvatures, branch sites, and bifurcations; and development of precise noninvasive techniques for measurement of vessel diameter.

## CONCLUDING REMARKS

We have attempted to summarize some of the complexities involved in the study of pathogenesis of atherosclerotic processes and the complex role that hemodynamic factors play in it. We have reviewed some of the recent research and concepts in the field in an effort to spotlight important avenues for future research. It has been shown, for example, that to understand the problem of lipid flux into the arterial wall is to understand the multiplicity of factors affecting local driving forces and local endothelial permeability. The latter, we now know, is sensitive to the adjacent hemodynamic events such as disturbed flow, hydrodynamic shear stress, and hypertension which increases wall stretch. Moreover, local tissue properties, which are shown to be nonuniform through histological as well as microrheological techniques, also play an important role in influencing local permeability. Future progress, we believe, will depend heavily on our ability to measure details of local flow fields and local tissue properties in critical areas of the circulatory system.

Finally, because of the limited nature of this review, many excellent papers could not be included. Some of the more pertinent ones are listed in the bibliography (10, 13, 14, 27, 39, 71, 73, 79).

ACKNOWLEDGMENTS

We dedicate this review to Dr. Donald A. McDonald (1917–1973), who in a short life did so much for hemodynamics. We are grateful to Dr. D. L. Fry for his help and criticism. We thank M. P. Vaishnav, Prof. H. B. Atabek, Dr. V. Ferrans, and Dr. B. Gregory Brown for helpful criticisms; Linda Dawson, Mrs. C. K. Floyd, and Mrs. K. Holcombe for editorial assistance; Mrs. R. Brown, Mrs. E. Costello, and Mr. K. Friedman for typing and preparation of the manuscript; and Mrs. K. Vashaw, Mr. R. Chadha, and Mrs. Z. Parsa for literature search. Courtesy of the American Heart Association Inc. for permission to reproduce Figure 1 is gratefully acknowledged. During the preparation of this review, Dr. Gow was supported by a Research Fellowship of the National Heart Foundation of Australia. Part of this work was performed under NIH Grant HL 15270–01 and NSF Grant GK–39164 to Dr. Vaishnav.

*Literature Cited*

1. Arndt, J. O., Klauske, J., Mersch, F. 1968. The diameter of the intact carotid artery in man and its change with pulse pressure. *Pfluegers Arch.* 301:230–40
2. Attinger, E. O., Ed. 1964. *Pulsatile Blood Flow.* New York:McGraw. 462 pp.
3. Baan, J., Iwazumi, T., Szidon, J. P., Noordergraaf, A. 1971. Intravascular area transducer measuring dynamic local distensibility of the aorta. *J. Appl. Physiol.* 31(3):499–503
4. Baker, D. W. 1970. Pulsed ultrasonic doppler blood-flow sensing. *IEEE Trans. Sonics Ultrasonics* SU-17, 3: 170–85
5. Band, W., Goedhard, W. J. A., Knoop, A. A. 1972. Effects of aging on dynamic viscoelastic properties of the rat's thoracic aorta. *Pfluegers Arch.* 331: 357–64
6. Bergel, D. H., Schultz, D. L. 1971. Arterial elasticity and fluid dynamics. *Progr. Biophys. Mol. Biol.* 22:3–36
7. Bergel, D. H., Ed. 1972. *Cardiovascular Fluid Dynamics.* New York:Academic. Vol. 1, 365 pp., Vol. 2, 398 pp.
8. Bergel, D. H. The measurement of lengths and dimensions. See Ref. 7, 1: 91–114
9. Bergel, D. H. 1972. The properties of blood vessels. In *Biomechanics: Its Foundations and Objectives,* ed. Y. C. Fung et al, 105–139. New Jersey:Prentice-Hall. 641 pp.
10. Betz, E. 1972. Cerebral blood flow: its measurement and regulation. *Physiol. Rev.* 52(3):595–630
11. Bird, R. B., Stewart, W. E., Lightfoot, E. N. 1960. *Transport Phenomena.* New York:Wiley. 780 pp.
12. Brown, B. G., Pierce, J. E., Fry, D. L. 1973. The fate of surgically implanted cyrstalline lipids in the arterial wall of dogs. *Circulation* 48:Suppl. IV, 78 (abstr.)
13. Burns, J. W., Covell, J. W., Myers, R., Ross, J. Jr. 1971. Comparison of directly measured left ventricular wall stress and stress calculated from geometric reference figures. *Circ. Res.* 28: 611–21
14. Burns, J. W., Covell, J. W. 1972. Myocardial oxygen consumption during isotonic and isovolumic contractions in the intact heart. *Am. J. Physiol.* 223(6): 1491–97
15. Burton, A. C. 1972. *Physiology and biophysics of the circulation.* Chicago: Yearb. Med. Publ. 226 pp.
16. Cannon, D. J., Davison, P. F. 1973. Cross-linking and aging in rat tendon collagen. *Exp. Geront.* 8:51–62
17. Cannon, T. M., Greenfield, H. 1972. Adaptibility of computer graphics to studies of atherosclerosis pathogenesis. *J. Assoc. Advan. Med. Instrum.* 6(3): 250–55
18. Carew, T. E. 1971. *Mechano-chemical response of canine aortic endothelium to elevated shear stress in vitro.* PhD thesis. The Cath. Univ. America, Wash. DC. 152 pp.
19. Carew, T. E., Patel, D. J. 1973. Effect of tensile and shear stress on intimal permeability of the left coronary artery in dogs. *Atherosclerosis* 18:179–83
20. Caro, C. G., Fitz-Gerald, J. M., Schroter, R. C. 1971. Atheroma and arterial wall shear. Observation, correlation and proposal of a shear dependent mass transfer mechanism for atherogenesis. *Proc. Roy. Soc. B* 177:109–59
21. Caro, C. G. 1972. Transport of material between blood and wall in arteries. In *Atherogenesis: Initiating Factors.* Ciba Found. Symp. 12 (new series), 127–164. Amsterdam:Assoc. Sci. Publ. 288 pp.
22. Caro, C. G., Nerem, R. M. 1973. Transport of $^{14}C$-4-cholesterol between serum and wall in the perfused dog common carotid artery. *Circ. Res.* 32: 187–205
23. Cheung, J. B., Hsiao, C. C. 1972. Nonlinear anisotropic viscoelastic stresses in blood vessels. *J. Biomech.* 5:607–19
24. Constantinides, P., Robinson, M. 1969. Ultrastructural injury of arterial endothelium: II–Effects of vasoactive amines. *Arch. Pathol.* 88:106–12
25. Constantinides, P. 1973. Opening of endothelial junctions and other endothelial changes caused by catecholamines in arteries. *Fed. Proc.* 32(3):855 (abstr.)
26. Cox, R. H. 1972. A model for the dynamic mechanical properties of arteries. *J. Biomech.* 5:135–52
27. D'Alecy, L. G., Feigl, E. O. 1972. Sympathetic control of cerebral blood flow in dogs. *Circ. Res.* 31:267–83
28. Davids, N., Cheng, R. C. 1972. Transient laminar flow in ducts of arbitrary cross-section by finite element methods. *J. Biomech.* 5:485–99
29. Davids, N., Mani, M. K. 1972. Effects of turbulence on blood flow explored by finite element analysis. *Comput. Biol. Med.* 2:1–9

30. U.S. Dept. HEW. 1971. *Arteriosclerosis: A Report by the National Heart and Lung Institute Task Force on Arteriosclerosis.* Publ. No. (NIH) 72-219, Vol. 2. 365 pp.

31. Doyle, J. M., Dobrin, P. B. 1971. Finite deformation analysis of the relaxed and contracted dog carotid artery. *Microvasc. Res.* 3:400-15

32. Duncan, L. E. Jr., Buck, K., Lynch, A. 1963. Lipoprotein movement through canine aortic wall. *Science* 142:972-73

33. Dunkman, W. B. et al 1972. Clinical and hemodynamic results of intraaortic balloon pumping and surgery for cardiogenic shock. *Circulation* 46:465-77

34. Falsetti, H. L., Kiser, K. M., Francis, G. P., Belmore, E. R. 1972. Sequential velocity development in the ascending and descending aorta of the dog. *Circ. Res.* 31:328-38

35. Ferguson, G. G., Roach, M. R. Flow conditions at bifurcations as determined in glass models, with reference to the focal distribution of vascular lesions. See Ref. 7, 2:141-56

36. Flaherty, J. T., Ferrans, V. J., Pierce, J. E., Carew, T. E., Fry, D. L. 1972. Localizing factors in experimental atherosclerosis. In *Atherosclerosis and Coronary Heart Disease,* eds W. Likoff et al, 540-83. New York:Grune & Stratton. 532 pp.

37. Flaherty, J. T. et al 1972. Endothelial nuclear patterns in the canine arterial tree with particular reference to hemodynamic events. *Circ. Res.* 30:23-33

38. Fox, J. A., Hugh, A. E. 1966. Localization of atheroma: a theory based on boundary layer separation. *Brit. Heart J.* 28:388-99

39. Friedman, W. F. 1972. The intrinsic physiologic properties of the developing heart. *Progr. Cardiovasc. Dis.* 15(1):87-111

40. Fry, D. L. 1968. Acute vascular endothelial changes associated with increased blood velocity gradients. *Circ. Res.* 22:165-97

41. Fry, D. L. 1969. Certain histological and chemical responses of the vascular interface to acutely induced mechanical stress in the aorta of the dog. *Circ. Res.* 24:93-108

42. Fry, D. L. 1969. Certain chemorheologic considerations regarding the blood vascular interface with particular reference to coronary artery disease. *Circulation.* 39, 40:Suppl. IV, 38-59

43. Fry, D. L. 1972. Localizing factors in arteriosclerosis. See Ref. 36, 85-104

44. Fry, D. L. 1973. Responses of the arterial wall to certain physical factors. See Ref. 21, 93-125

45. Fung, Y. C. 1971. Biomechanics: a survey of the blood flow problem. *Advan. Appl. Mech.* 11:65-130

46. Gilbert, D. B., Greenfield, J. C. Jr. 1973. The effect of tensile stretch upon cholesterol uptake in bovine elastin. *Fed. Proc.* 32(3):237 (abstr.)

47. Goldsmith, H. L. 1973. Some rheological aspects of platelet thrombosis. *Can. Med. Assoc. J.* 108:452-53

48. Goldstein, R. J., Adrian, R. J. 1971. Measurement of fluid velocity gradients using laser-doppler techniques. *Rev. Sci. Instrum.* 42(9):1317-20

49. Gow, B. S. 1972. The influence of vascular smooth muscle on the viscoelastic properties of blood vessels. See Ref. 7, 2:65-110

50. Gow, B. S., Vaishnav, R. N. 1973. A micro-indentor for measurement of local rheological properties of vascular tissue. *Assoc. Advan. Med. Instrum. Ann. Meet., 8th* (Abstr.)

51. Greenfield, J. C., Tindall, G. T., Dillon, M. L., Mahaley, M. S. 1964. Mechanics of the human common carotid artery in vivo. *Circ. Res.* 15:240-46

52. Gregg, D. E., Khouri, E. M., Donald, D. E., Lowensohn, H. S., Pasyk, S. 1972. Coronary circulation in the conscious dog with cardiac neural ablation. *Circ. Res.* 31:129-44

53. Gutstein, W. H., Schneck, D. J., Marks, J. O. 1968. In vitro studies of local blood flow disturbance in a region of separation. *J. Atheroscler. Res.* 8:381-88

54. Gutstein, W. H., Farrell, G. A. 1972. Endothelial defects and blood flow disturbance in atherogenesis. *Experientia* 28:1299-1300

55. Histand, M. B., Miller, C. W., McLeod, F. D. 1973. Transcutaneous measurement of blood velocity profiles and flow. *Cardiovasc. Res.* 7(5):703-12

56. Hokanson, D. E., Strandness, D. E. Jr., Miller, C. W. An echo-tracking system for recording arterial wall motion. See Ref. 4, 130-32

57. Hokanson, D. E., Mozersky, D. J., Sumner, D. S., Strandness, D. E. Jr. 1972. A phaselocked echo tracking system for recording arterial diameter changes in vivo. *J. Appl. Physiol.* 32(5):728-33

58. Jørgensen, L., Packham, M. A., Rowsell, H. C., Mustard, J. F. 1972. Deposition of formed elements of blood on the

intima and signs of intimal injury in the aorta of rabbit, pig, and man. *Lab. Invest.* 27(3):341–50

59. Kern, W. H., Dermer, G. B., Lindesmith, G. G. 1972. The intimal proliferation in aortic-coronary saphenous vein grafts. *Am. Heart J.* 84(6):771–77

60. Kolin, A., Culp, G. W. 1971. An intraarterial induction gauge. *IEEE Trans. Biomed. Eng.* BME-18:110–14

61. Kresch, E., Noordergraaf, A. 1972. Cross-sectional shape of collapsible tubes. *Biophys. J.* 12:274–94

62. Lew, H. S. 1971. Low Reynolds number equi-bifurcation flow in a two dimensional channel *J. Biomech.* 4:559–68

63. Lighthill, M. J. 1972. Physiological fluid dynamics: a survey. *J. Fluid Mech.* 52(3):475–97

64. Ling, S. C., Atabek, H. B. 1972. A nonlinear analysis of pulsatile flow in arteries. *J. Fluid Mech.* 55(3):493–511

65. Ling, S. C., Atabek, H. B., Letzing, W. G., Patel, D. J. 1973. Non-linear analysis of aortic flow in living dogs. *Circ. Res.* 33:198–212

66. Lynn, N. S., Fox, V. G., Ross, L. W. 1972. Computation of fluid-dynamical contributions to atherosclerosis at arterial bifurcations. *Biorheology* 9:61–66

67. Maroko, P. R. et al 1972. Effects of intraaortic balloon counterpulsation on the severity of myocardial ischemic injury following acute cornonary occlusion. Counterpulsation and myocardial injury. *Circulation* 45(6):1150–59

68. McDonald, D. A. 1960. *Blood Flow in Arteries.* Baltimore:Williams & Wilkins. 328 pp.

69. McDonald, D. A. 1968. Hemodynamics. *Ann. Rev. Physiol.* 30:525–56

70. Mills, C. J. Measurement of pulsatile flow and flow velocity. See Ref. 7, 1:51–90

71. Milnor, W. R. Pulmonary hemodynamics. See Ref. 7, 2:299–340

72. Morris, R. D., Histand, M. B., Miller, C. W. The resolution of the ultrasound pulsed doppler for blood velocity measurements. *J. Biomech.* In press

73. Moskalenko, Y. E., Kislyakov, Y. Y., Vainshtein, G. B., Zelikson, B. B. 1972. Biophysical aspects of the intracranial circulation. *Am. Heart J.* 83(3):401–14

74. Mueller, H., Ayres, S., Grace, W., Giannelli, S. 1972. External counterpulsation—A non invasive method to protect ischemic myocardium in man. *Circulation* 45, 46 : Suppl. II, 775. (Abstr.)

75. National Committee for Fluid Mechanics Films. 1972. *Illustrated Experiments in Fluid Mechanics.* Cambridge, Mass.: MIT Press. 251 pp.

76. Nerem, R. M., Seed, W. A. 1972. An in vivo study of aortic flow disturbances. *Cardiovasc. Res.* 6:1–14

77. Netusil, M., Spacek, B., Winter, Z., Vrana, M. 1972. Coronary blood flow during intraaortic counterpulsation. *Cor Vasa* 14(2):149–62

78. Olson, R. M., Shelton, D. K. Jr. 1972. A nondestructive technique to measure wall displacement in the thoracic aorta. *J. Appl. Physiol.* 32(1):147–51

79. Parmley, W. W., Chuck, L., Sonnenblick, E. H. 1972. Relation of $V_{max}$ to different models of cardiac muscle. *Circ. Res.* 30:34–43

80. Patel, D. J., Janicki, J. S., Carew, T. E. 1969. Static anisotropic elastic properties of the aorta in living dogs. *Circ. Res.* 25:765–79

81. Patel, D. J., Fry, D. L. 1969. The elastic symmetry of arterial segments in dogs. *Circ. Res.* 24:1–8

82. Patel, D. J., Vaishnav, R. N. The rheology of large blood vessels. See Ref. 7, 2:1–64

83. Patel, D. J., Janicki, J. S., Vaishnav, R. N., Young, J. T. 1973. Dynamic anisotropic viscoelastic properties of the aorta in living dogs. *Circ. Res.* 32:93–107

84. Pieper, H. P., Paul, L. T. 1968. Catheter-tip gauge for measuring blood flow velocity and vessel diameter in dogs. *J. Appl. Physiol.* 24(2):259–61

85. Reddy, R. V., Noordergraaf, A., Moreno, A. H. 1970. In vitro changes of shapes of veins under pressure. *Ann. Conf. Eng. Med. Biol., 23rd* 12:15

86. Reddy, R. V., Iwazumi, T., Moreno, A. H. 1973. A catheter-tip probe for dynamic cross-sectional area measurement. In *Chronically Implanted Cardiovascular Instrumentation,* ed. E. P. McCutcheon, 149–58. New York: Academic. 482 pp.

87. Roach, M. R. 1972. Poststenotic dilatation in arteries. See Ref. 7, 2:111–39

88. Roach, M. R., Scott, S., Ferguson, G. G. 1972. The hemodynamic importance of the geometry of bifurcations in the circle of Willis (glass model studies). *Stroke* 3:255–67

89. Roach, M. R., Cornhill, J. F. 1973. Flow separation: possible effects on vessel wall. *Can. Med. Assoc. J.* 108:452 (Abstr.)

90. Rodbard, S., Johnson, A. C. 1962. Deposition of flowborne materials on vessel walls. *Circ. Res.* 11:664–68
91. Rodbard, S. 1970. Physical factors in arterial sclerosis and stenosis. *Advan. Cardiol.* 4:72–93
92. Rodbard, S., Farbstein, M. 1972. Stress concentrations induced by flow. *Cardiovasc. Res.* 6:562–68
93. Rosen, L. A., Hollis, T. M., Anthony, A. 1973. Endothelial histamine synthesis following shearing stress exposure. *Fed. Proc.* 32(3):855 (abstr.)
94. Rudd, M. J. 1972. Velocity measurements made with a laser dopplermeter on the turbulent pipe flow of a dilute polymer solution. *J. Fluid Mech.* 51(4): 673–85
95. Sako, Y. 1962. Effects of turbulent blood flow and hypertension on experimental atherosclerosis. *JAMA* 179: 36–40
96. Sanders, C. A., Buckley, M. J., Leinbach, R. C., Mundth, E. D., Austen, W. G. 1972. Mechanical circulatory assistance. Current status and experience with combining circulatory assistance, emergency coronary angiography, and acute myocardial revascularization. *Circulation* 45:1292–313
97. Schultz, D. L. Pressure and flow in large arteries. See Ref. 7, 1:287–314
98. Scott, S., Ferguson, G. G., Roach, M. R. 1972. Comparison of the elastic properties of human intracranial arteries and aneurysms. *Can. J. Physiol. Pharmacol.* 50(4):328–32
99. Simon, B. R., Kobayashi, A. S., Strandness, D. E., Wiederhielm, C. A. 1972. Reevaluation of arterial constitutive relations. *Circ. Res.* 30:491–500
100. Stemerman, M. B., Ross, R. 1972. Experimental arteriosclerosis: I. Fibrous plaque formation in primates, an electron microscope study. *J. Exp. Med.* 136(4):769–89

101. Stiles, R. K., Bischoff, K. B., Fry, D. L. 1972. An investigation of the wall shear stress in canine aortic model using an electrochemical technique. *Am. Inst. Chem. Eng. Ann. Meet., 65th,* 92
102. Taylor, M. G. 1972. Hemodynamics. *Ann. Rev. Physiol.* 35:87–116
103. Texon, M. 1972. The hemodynamic basis of atherosclerosis. Further observations: the ostial lesion. *Bull. NY Acad. Med.* 48(5):733–40
104. Vaishnav, R. N., Young, J. T., Janicki, J. S., Patel, D. J. 1972. Nonlinear anisotropic elastic properties of the canine aorta. *Biophys. J.* 12:1008–27
105. Vaishnav, R. N., Young, J. T., Patel, D. J. 1973. Distribution of stresses and strain energy density through the wall thickness in a canine aortic segment. *Circ. Res.* 32:577–83
106. Vatner, S. F. et al 1971. Coronary dynamics in unrestrained conscious baboons. *Am. J. Physiol.* 221:1396–1401
107. Vatner, S. F., Higgins, C. B., Franklin, D., Braunwald, E. 1972. Role of tachycardia in mediating the coronary hemodynamic response to severe exercise. *J. Appl. Physiol.* 32:380–85
108. Wemple, R. R., Mockros, L. F. 1972. Pressure and flow in the systemic arterial system. *J. Biomech.* 5:629–41
109. Wesseling, K. H., Weber, H., deWit, B. 1973. Estimated five component viscoelastic model parameters for human arterial walls. *J. Biomech.* 6:13–24
110. Westerhof, N., Bosman, F., DeVries, C. J., Noordergraaf, A. 1969. Analog studies of the human systemic arterial tree. *J. Biomech.* 2:121–43
111. Westerhof, N., Noordergraaf, A. 1970. Arterial viscoelasticity: a generalized model. *J. Biomech.* 3:357–79
112. Wolinsky, H. 1972. Long-term effects of hypertension on the rat aortic wall and their relation to concurrent aging changes. *Circ. Res.* 30:301–9

# HEART: ELECTROPHYSIOLOGY[1]

*S. Weidmann*

Department of Physiology, University of Berne, Buehlplatz 5, Berne, Switzerland

About a year ago the author distributed a letter to some 400 colleagues, asking them for reprints of recent publications. This method of obtaining the basic information was so successful that it seemed both unavoidable and legitimate to limit the review to those aspects closest to the personal interests of the reviewer. Among the fields which have been almost completely excluded are metabolism, contractility, and drug effects. Furthermore, little emphasis has been placed on the results obtained from hearts in situ.

Several reviews on special aspects of cardiac electrophysiology have appeared. A volume edited by De Mello (20) contains sixteen articles written by specialists in their respective fields. Comparative electrophysiology of the heart is treated by McCann (68, 69). A major part of a "Liber Memorialis" marking the 65th birthday of Dr. Chandler McC. Brooks (50) is devoted to cardiac electrophysiology. The *Proceedings of the 4th International Biophysics Congress* held in Moscow in 1972 make it clear that a theoretical analysis of conduction in various networks has been the main contribution of our Russian colleagues (28). There is a volume on cardiac metabolism containing forty-eight individual contributions (75). To satisfy clinically-minded readers, a large number of recent reviews treat the problem of dysrhythmia (1, 16, 21, 37, 88, 101).

Many would welcome an updated monograph covering the whole field of cardiac electrophysiology as was last published in 1960 by Hoffman & Cranefield (40). Nonexistence of such a text may be taken as an indication that the field as a whole has undergone that seemingly unavoidable process of being split into subspecialities.

## Cardiac Tissue at Rest

Measurements of basic constants such as specific membrane resistance ($R_m$, $\Omega$ cm$^2$), membrane capacity ($C_m$, $\mu$F cm$^{-2}$), and internal specific resistance ($R_i$, $\Omega$ cm) present considerable difficulties. Only in the case of Purkinje fibers and in strands

[1]Supported by Grant 3.758.72 from the Swiss National Science Foundation.

155

of tissue culture cells (62) is it possible to apply the principle of cable analysis. Two approaches are now available to deal with more complicated structures. First, monolayer tissue cultures from rat hearts are suitable for impalement by two micro-electrodes. By an adequate mathematical treatment (47) the experimental results yield values for $R_m$, $C_m$, and $R_i$. Second, a thick-walled extracellular electrode may be used to flow current through such complicated structures as rabbit sino-atrial (SA) node, crista terminalis, and atrial muscle (7, 8). The space constant for monolayer tissue cultures works out to 0.36 mm (47); for SA node it is measured as 0.5 mm (8); for mammalian atrial and ventricular tissue earlier data giving values near 1.0 mm are confirmed. Calculated membrane capacities fall near 1 $\mu$F cm$^{-2}$; those for membrane resistance fall into a range of a few thousand $\Omega$ cm$^2$ (7, 47). Specific membrane capacity of bovine Purkinje fibers has to be corrected from about 10 $\mu$F cm$^{-2}$ (74) to 1 $\mu$F cm$^{-2}$ when it is realized that the current flows across the surface of single cells rather than the outside membrane of multicellular fibers. The same argument increases the value given previously for $R_m$ of Purkinje fibers from 2000 $\Omega$ cm$^2$ to 20,000 $\Omega$ cm$^2$. The conclusion seems unavoidable that the surface membrane of sheep and calf Purkinje cells is less permeable to ions than are the membranes of ventricular muscle of the same species.

$^{24}$Na efflux from bovine Purkinje fibers has been measured using the trick of cooling and rewarming in order to minimize the difficulties arising from a relatively large extracellular space (10, 11). Intracellular Na concentration is estimated at 25 m$M$ and the ratio of Na$^+$ permeability to K$^+$ permeability at rest is 0.2. This value is compatible with the measured resting potential of about $-85$ mV at an extracellular K concentration of 5.4 m$M$.

Na$^+$ extrusion must be looked upon as being an active process since Na$^+$ has to move outward against the electrochemical gradient. Whether Na$^+$ extrusion is electrogenic (i.e. directly contributing to the membrane potential) or coupled to K$^+$ uptake in a 1:1 stoichiometry and thus electroneutral is a more difficult question. Conditions can be found under which Na$^+$ extrusion is certainly electrogenic, but this is not convincing evidence as far as ionic movements under normal conditions are concerned. Blocking active transport in the cold for about 24 hours leads to intracellular Na$^+$ accumulation and K$^+$ depletion. Upon rewarming of cold-stored Purkinje fibers, the resting potential reaches values about 10 mV higher than those measured previous to cooling and higher than the estimated K$^+$ equilibrium potential (38). This can only be explained on the grounds of electrogenic Na$^+$ extrusion. Much larger effects on the membrane potential (a rise of up to $-300$ mV) have previously been reported for cat ventricle (102). The discrepancy with respect to the magnitude of the effect is not easily accounted for, but confidence in the extremely high resting potentials is strengthened by looking at records of action potentials starting from $-300$ mV and even showing an "overshoot" across the zero reference line (103). Experiments with rewarmed guinea pig auricles (30) indicate that the rate of Na$^+$ extrusion is dependent on the extracellular K$^+$ concentration. Electrical driving prevents guinea pig right auricle from becoming inexcitable at 20°C (14). On the other hand, under normal conditions Na$^+$ extrusion is almost insensitive to a change of extracellular K concentration (11). An interaction between Na$^+$ and

$K^+$ movements in opposite directions is suggested by the observation that substitution of extracellular $Na^+$ by choline$^+$ reduces $K^+$ uptake (83).

As a consequence of adrenalectomy the resting potential of rat hearts as measured in situ drops from $-86$ mV to $-68$ mV (94). The rise of plasma potassium from 4.3 to slightly above 7.0 m$M$ and the drop of intracellular potassium from 132 to 126 m$M$ cannot be the only reasons for the low resting potential. This follows from the fact that perfusion of the coronary vessels with Tyrode's solution does not restore normal resting potentials. On the other hand, substitution therapy with various adrenocortical hormones results in an increase of resting potentials to the region of normal values, although plasma potassium (this is difficult to understand) does not fall below 6.0 m$M$.

## The Cardiac Action Potential

Depolarization of the surface membrane and reversal of the potential difference must be the consequence of inward current. Since the cardiac action potential has a long-lasting plateau during which there is an increased driving force for $K^+$ efflux, it seems unavoidable to assume some inward current, however small, to nearly balance the outward current during activity. Evidence has been accumulating that calls for a subdivision of the total inward current of vertebrate hearts into at least two components: (a) rapid and transient inward current, carried by $Na^+$, bringing the membrane potential into the region of inside positivity, and (b) slow and sustained inward current, carried mainly by $Ca^{2+}$ ions, responsible for the plateau of the action potential. It seems convenient and legitimate to treat these two components separately (58, 86, 87, 90, 104).

## The Rapid Inward Current

The characteristics of this current component are not easily analyzed. Any method of voltage clamping becomes highly questionable when records are to be made of strong and short-lasting currents (23). From a theoretical point of view (55) the cable nature of myocardial fibers will forever preclude an ideal "space clamp." However, with an optimal geometry, with a feedback amplifier capable of delivering strong currents, and by taking precautions not to let strong currents flow for more than a few milliseconds (oscillations), the rapid inward current of mammalian myocardium has now been recorded with the possible minimum of artefacts (76). This initial component is switched on and off within about one millisecond, a time corresponding to the upstroke of a monophasic action potential; peak inward currents as obtained by voltage clamping are a continuous function of membrane voltage without a threshold-like response and are of the same order of magnitude as those calculated from the maximal upstroke velocity of a propagating action potential (order of mA cm$^{-2}$). It is reported (without illustrations) that the fast component of the frog auricle has a reversal potential of $+25$ mV (91). One of the necessary checks on the "space clamp" is a voltage recording by means of a second intracellular electrode inserted as far as possible from the voltage-controlling electrode.

The cooling of mammalian Purkinje fibers to 8°C (24) is useful in describing the initial current in terms of activation and inactivation rate constants. With frog atrial muscle, somewhat surprisingly (36), the process of inactivation is about 50 times faster than the process of recovery from inactivation. This finding applies to a given potential level within the subthreshold region to which the membrane is clamped from either more negative or more positive values. An extension of the Hodgkin-Huxley equations describing the kinetics of $Na^+$ inward current (39) is proposed to deal with the observed difference of rate constants (36). When the reavailability of fast $Na^+$ inward current is tested following repolarization from the region of zero mV, time constants of more than 100 msec are obtained (4–7°C). Slowing of reavailability of fast inward current at the end of an action potential is one of the important mechanisms for the protective action of drugs that act like quinidine (22, 36).

## The Slow Inward Current

The slow current component has a relatively low peak value and is switched on and off at much lower rates than the fast component. Under these conditions a meaningful analysis by the voltage clamp method is possible. The slow component is separated from the fast component by either starting all clamp experiments from a holding potential (–50 mV) at which the fast system is inactivated (5, 6), or by blocking the fast system by tetrodotoxin (5, 77). Slow inward current is switched on with a time constant depending on membrane voltage. $\tau$ for "on" is of the order of 20 msec at threshold and decays to small values (difficult to measure) when the potential inside the cell is positive (76). Peak slow inward current is observed near 0 mV (4, 76). Time constants for switching slow current off are also voltage dependent, and much larger than $\tau$ values for "on". They are especially large at +30 mV (plateau region of the ventricular action potential) and decrease to about 60 msec at 0 mV (76). Experimental results diverge with respect to voltage dependence within the region of inside negativity. A further decrease (4), as well as an increase (5), is reported. This issue is of considerable importance in the attempt to account for the repolarization of the "free-running" action potential. It seems essential, therefore, to get additional information concerning this point.

The time course of slow inward current can be described as a consequence of a changing conductance to an ion with an equilibrium potential in the positive voltage range. First, the amplitudes of the so-called tail currents closely parallel the time course of the slow inward current (5). Second, phasic inward current turns into phasic outward current when the voltage is clamped to highly positive potentials (4). Carriers of charge for the slow inward current are $Ca^{2+}$ ions (5, 42, 53, 54, 77, 86). This follows from the effect of varying $[Ca^{2+}]_o$ on the amplitude of the slow current. Within a period of time corresponding to a normal action potential the calcium equilibrium potential is shifted quite appreciably to less positive values (4). This is to be expected on the grounds of the calculated transfer of charge and on the assumption that $[Ca^{2+}]$ in the cell water is extremely low, of the order of $10^{-7}\ M$ at rest. The well known fact that electrical activity is possible in $Ca^{2+}$-free solutions is generally accounted for by assuming that $Na^+$ ions can take the place of $Ca^{2+}$ ions within the "slow system" (87).

Interference with metabolism has long been known to shorten the duration of the cardiac action potential. No universally accepted explanation is at hand. An increase of membrane $K^+$ conductance or a decrease of a (hypothetical) electrogenic $K^+$ uptake during the plateau have been offered as alternative explanations. A third hypothesis is now proposed (29, 41). ATP is known as a chelator for $Ca^{2+}$. Its depletion in the immediate vicinity of the membrane inside the cell might give rise to a higher $Ca^{2+}$ concentration and thus to a decrease of $Ca^{2+}$ inward current. Another explanation which combines an increase of $g_K$ (5) and an increase of $[Ca^{2+}]_i$ is that there is a direct relation between $[Ca^{2+}]_i$ and $g_K$ as in erythrocytes and nerve. In most instances, interference with cardiac metabolism leads to changes that are at best partially reversible. Monolayer cultures of rat heart cells (29, 41) are clearly superior to other preparations for studies on metabolic poisons since even strong effects on the electrical activity are perfectly reversible.

A number of interventions suppress slow inward current (and the duration of the action potential) while leaving the rapid component unaltered. Among them are $Mn^{2+}$ (87, 93), $La^{3+}$ (93), and several drugs such as verapamil and D 600 (53, 54).

The action potential of crustacean (crab) hearts is normally maintained by nervous impulses from the cardiac ganglion. Electrical stimulation of denervated myocardial strips results in graded responses (58). However, in the presence of tetraethylammonium (TEA), 20 m$M$, all-or-nothing activity is recorded which is explained by the depressing action of TEA on $K^+$ permeability (59). The responses so obtained are insensitive to extracellular $Na^+$ but sensitive to $Ca^{2+}$. Therefore, it seems likely that nervous activity originating in the cardiac ganglion enhances $Ca^{2+}$ conductance of crustacean myocardial membranes.

## Possible Causes of Repolarization

For many years two different theories have been proposed for repolarization, either a time-dependent increase of outward current ($K^+$), or a time-dependent decrease of inward current ($Na^+$, $Ca^{2+}$). It is relieving to note (78) that both processes are gradually finding their place, and that one or the other is likely to be of major importance, depending on whether experiments are performed with Purkinje fibers, auricle, or ventricle. A satisfactory reconstruction of the time course of the action potential is not available as yet. One of the important unknowns is the possible contribution of electrogenic pumps in the different phases of the cardiac cycle (see 33–35). Another factor, which might or might not be relevant, is the accumulation or depletion of ions within narrow extracellular spaces. Prolonged depolarization of frog auricular trabeculae is associated with increasing outward current (17), and most probably with accumulation of $K^+$ ions in extracellular clefts (67); this might assist in terminating the individual action potential. On the other hand, the plateau duration of guinea pig papillary muscle is insensitive to extracellular $K^+$ (range 4.8–9.6 m$M$) while action potentials are clearly shortened when the rate of stimulation is increased (85). These latter findings would indicate that $K^+$ accumulation is not even responsible for the shortening of the action potential as observed at high rates of stimulation.

## Calcium Action Potentials and Slow Impulse Propagation

There has been growing interest in this field for two reasons: (*a*) $Ca^{2+}$ has been neglected for too long a time as a carrier of charge, and (*b*) $Ca^{2+}$ action potentials are conducted slowly and may well be the cause of certain kinds of ectopic activity (113).

Clamp depolarization to the region of 0 mV results in a transient inward current. This current is all that is needed to obtain a so-called membrane action potential as soon as the membrane voltage is displaced beyond threshold. In the case of a propagated impulse, local circuit current has to be drawn to change the charge on the membrane capacity. Whether the relatively weak $Ca^{2+}$ inward current is capable of fulfilling the requirements for nondecremental propagation is a quantitative question. Membrane depolarization is known to inactivate the fast component of inward current carried by $Na^+$ in Purkinje fibers. Epinephrine is known to increase $Ca^{2+}$ conductance. Under these conditions (depolarization by 16.2 m$M$ KCl; addition of epinephrine, $10^{-5}$ $M$) the rate of propagation can indeed be decreased by a factor of 100 to values of a few cm $sec^{-1}$ (15, 113). In frog atrial muscle bathed in completely $Na^+$-free solution, propagated contractions are sometimes obtained by increasing the extracellular $Ca^{2+}$ concentration to 83 m$M$ (12). Adding 5 × $10^{-6}$ $M$ epinephrine increases the safety factor for conduction (18). The resting potential of these fibers is slightly increased ($[K]_o = 3$ m$M$), and the overshoot of the action potential is as high as +90 mV. Another way of obtaining propagated $Ca^{2+}$ action potentials is to increase $[Ca^{2+}]_o$ to 16.2 m$M$ and to use $TEA^+$ as a substitute for $Na^+$. TEA possibly reduces $K^+$ permeability (58). Action potentials are then recorded propagating at a rate of 10 cm $sec^{-1}$ along dog Purkinje fibers, and having an overshoot of +20 mV. The size of the overshoot varies by 30 mV per 10-fold change of $[Ca^{2+}]_o$, and the upstroke velocity (normally 4 V $sec^{-1}$) is a linear function of $[Ca^{2+}]_o$ over the range 4.0–16.2 m$M$, indicating that inward current is indeed carried by $Ca^{2+}$ (2).

A decrease of maximal $Na^+$ conductance in the system delivering rapid inward current would be expected to block conduction before slowing it to a few cm $sec^{-1}$ (63). Theoretically, a large increase of inside longitudinal resistance might account for slow conduction along a biological cable (63). In my opinion there is yet another possibility. Two factors may be important: maximal $g_{Ca}$ is small when compared to maximal $g_{Na}$, and $g_{Ca}$ rises much more slowly than $g_{Na}$ (39, eq. 30; 77).

## Pacemaker Activity of the Sino-Atrial Node

The literature up to 1971 has been extensively reviewed (13, 44, 112). Voltage clamp data from the SA node of the frog discloses that inward current during diastole is sensitive to $Mn^{2+}$ and insensitive to tetrodotoxin (TTX) (60), thus strengthening the view that this current is mainly carried by $Ca^{2+}$ ions. While it is generally accepted that a decrease of $K^+$ conductance is the cause of slow diastolic depolarization in

Purkinje fibers, the same assumption is often made for the SA pacemaker (13). Using strips of right atrium, including the nodal area, mounted in a double sucrose gap, a "reversal potential" of membrane current has now been demonstrated (43). This result is consistent with the idea that $K^+$ conductance is large at the end of an action potential and then decreases as a function of time. Unfortunately, the reversal potential cannot be given in absolute units because the method of clamping the SA region is far from ideal.

Perfusion of the isolated nodal artery of the dog heart (45) is a useful method in studying the properties of pacemaker cells. The relatively high resistance of the SA pacemaker to $K^+$ ions (65) depends on adrenergic activity, as shown by the effects of various techniques such as sympathectomy or administration of reserpine or propranolol (108). From the observation of pacemaker shift within the nodal area (65) and from the response of the SA node to invasion by early premature excitations (9), it seems possible to assume that the SA node of rabbit heart (about 2 mm long and 0.5 mm broad) is composed of loosely coupled cells. This view is confirmed by the value of the space constant (0.5 mm) as determined by applying square pulses of current in the phase of diastolic depolarization (8).

Conduction of the nodal action potential to the crista terminalis of rabbit right atrium is mediated by fibers of intermediate electrical properties, called perinodal fibers (100) or follower cells (43). None of the results presented (43, 100) seem to fully exclude the idea that the properties of cells in this region are due to electrotonic interaction between typical nodal cells and typical atrial cells.

One of the major surprises for the present reviewer was a report on cardiac muscle within the anterior leaflet of the mitral valve of dogs (27). There is muscular continuity with the right atrium but not with the ventricle. The impulse from the right atrium is conducted to the valvular muscle with considerable delay occurring at the base of the anterior leaflet. Contractions of the valvular muscle and intracellular action potentials are of the cardiac type.

## The Atrio-Ventricular Node

Mendez & Moe have reviewed the literature on the atrio-ventricular node up to 1972 (73). Spread of excitation through the rabbit AV node is mapped from the result of recording by 200 electrodes (107). During antegrade conduction the major input of the rabbit node comes from the crista terminalis. The major output during retrograde conduction is directed towards the interatrial septum. Deadend pathways are detected by simultaneously pacing the right atrium and the His bundle. Such endings are expected to draw local circuit current during normal conduction and must represent an additional reason for slow conduction through the node. The shape of the monophasic action potential as recorded from a given cell depends on the direction of conduction, which is suggestive of spatial interaction with neighboring cells. This statement applies to the rabbit AV node (114) and to the transitional region between the right atrium and ventricle of the toad (49). Electrotonic interaction has previously been demonstrated for the region between terminal Purkinje fibers and ventricular myocardium (73, 90).

Records from the $N$ region of the rabbit AV node add to the evidence for electrical coupling (114). In the case of antegrade conduction the impulse penetrates the $N$ region with relative ease and undergoes a large delay when propagating to the $NH$ region. In the case of retrograde conduction the major delay occurs when the impulse propagates from the $N$ region into the $NA$ region.

The unanimous opinion is that the weakness of inward current in cells of the $N$ region, which translates itself as a slow rate of rise of the monophasic action potential, is one of the major reasons for slow conduction. Cells of the $N$ region happen to have low resting potentials. It may be asked if hyperpolarization by the flow of current would result in a steeper upstroke. This is indeed observed (93). Increasing the resting potential of cat AV node from $-62$ mV into the region of $-80$ mV greatly affects the upstroke velocity of the action potential, as if a system capable of carrying strong inward current were unmasked at higher resting potentials. Under pathological conditions the junction between terminal Purkinje fibers and myocardium may become the site of considerable AV conduction delay. This is demonstrated for hypertonic solutions (48), prolonged hypoxia (48), high $[K^+]_o$ (73), and premature beats (73).

## Embryonic Development

Reviews by Johnson & Lieberman (46) and by Sperelakis (96) offer a more extensive treatment of this subject. A considerable amount of recent data is available for chick heart, covering embryonic life from 2 to 21 days (hatching).

Resting potentials and overshoots increase appreciably from day 2 to day 12, then reach steady levels of $-70$ mV and $+28$ mV, respectively (98). The impressive rise of membrane voltage during the first days is not connected with corresponding changes of intracellular electrolytes. Thus $[K^+]_i$ stays practically constant during development (98), or even drops (70) from day 2 (167 m$M$) to day 14–18 (117–119 m$M$). $[Na^+]_i$ stays constant at 30–35 m$M$ over this period (70). From electrolyte concentrations and resting potential it is calculated that the ratio $P_{Na}:P_K$ drops from 0.08 at day 3 to 0.01 at days 14–18 (70). This may signify that inward $Na^+$ leak current, and thus active extrusion of $Na^+$, gets smaller as a function of embryonic age. Alternatively, $P_K$ may increase. Activity of $Na^+$, $K^+$-ATPase increases about two-fold between day 6 and day 16, the opposite of what should be expected on the assumption of a fall of $P_{Na}$ (95). On the other hand, there is evidence from electrical data for a decrease of membrane resistance to the flow of $K^+$ (97). Specific $K^+$ permeability seems to increase at the time of vagal innervation, between day 4 and day 6 (81). The results can thus be interpreted by assuming an increasing $K^+$ ion selectivity of the membrane.

There is general agreement that a system of fast inward current is added to a system of slow inward current early in development, between day 4 and day 7 (71, 80, 98). Rhythmical activity is not affected by TTX at day 4 but stops at day 7 when TTX is administered at a concentration of $10^{-6}$ g ml$^{-1}$ (71). In a transitional stage (6 days) TTX ($1 \times 10^{-5}$ $M$) decreases upstroke velocity of the action potential but does not abolish rhythmical activity and has little effect on the size of the overshoot, while at days 12 to 18 a TTX concentration of $1.6 \times 10^{-7}$ $M$ blocks action potential generation (80). Changes of extracellular $Na^+$ concentration have little effect on overshoot at day 6, but a large one at day 18. Overshoot at day 6 is highly $Ca^{2+}$ dependent (80), and this slow component is blocked by $Mn^{2+}$ and $La^{3+}$ (92). The increase of overshoot during development might be the result of a change from a "slow system" ($Ca^{2+}$) to a "fast system" ($Na^+$) at practically constant $[Na]_i$.

Action potential configuration and amplitude of human embryonic hearts between weeks 7 and 12 are similar to those of adult hearts in the corresponding parts (106). Whether a transition from a slow inward current system to a fast system might be detected at earlier stages of development remains an open question.

## Tissue Culture

Monolayer cultures from chick embryonic hearts of any age are only slightly sensitive to TTX (89). This is consistent with the finding that diphenylhydantoin, known to act on the rapid inward current, has no effect on cells in monolayer cultures (97). Sensitivity is partially regained as soon as clusters are formed (89). The following observations (89) lead to the conclusion that the formation of TTX "receptors" depends on protein synthesis: (*a*) clusters do not fall apart in trypsin-containing solution and regain TTX sensitivity when trypsin is removed, (*b*) sensitivity to TTX is not regained if protein synthesis is blocked by cyclohexamide (5 $\mu$g ml$^{-1}$).

With rat heart cells in tissue culture (82), coordination of contraction is improved by epinephrine, supposedly by tighter coupling between cells. An increase of $Ca^{2+}$ inward current, and thus an increase of local circuit current, may be an alternative explanation for improved synchronization.

It is now possible to grow "artificial cables" from cells in tissue culture (84). This preparation is of great promise to cardiac electrophysiology, since the geometry of the cells can be influenced. The core of the cable consists of myoblasts, some cells even resembling avian Purkinje fibers. The outer layer is composed by fibroblasts. These "synthetic stands" have a space constant of the order of 1 mm and a specific membrane capacitance of the order of 1 $\mu$F cm$^{-2}$ (62), values which are close to those of trabecular muscle of adult hearts as quoted in the first section. Their specific membrane resistance is high, of the order of 40,000 $\Omega$ cm$^2$, and there is hardly any systematic error in determining $R_m$ since the membrane time constant ($\tau = C_m \times R_m$), straightforward to measure, is also high (40 msec).

The synthetic strands normally conduct at a rate of 30 cm sec$^{-1}$ (63), but propagation over short distances may slow to values as low as 0.2 cm sec$^{-1}$. Changes of the diameter of the strand are not sufficient to explain the slowing. Reducing simultaneously $g_{Na}$ and $g_K$ of the Hodgkin–Huxley equations causes block long before conduction is slowed to values as experimentally observed. Theoretically, an increase of the internal longitudinal resistance might account for sufficient slowing (63). The specific internal resistance of synthetic strands is 223 $\Omega$ cm (62). It would be interesting to see whether the theoretical relationship between internal resistance and conduction velocity could be experimentally confirmed. Cytochalasin B disrupts synthetic strands into single cells but unfortunately acts on excitable membranes as well (64). Thus conduction velocity is decreased by only 30% when the preparation reaches the state of inexcitability.

## Electro-Mechanical Coupling

Since a number of recent review articles deal specifically with electro-mechanical coupling (4, 56, 86), only the most recent publications on this topic are reviewed here. Depolarization and inward current of $Ca^{2+}$ through the surface membrane is certainly one of the mechanisms resulting in the development of tension. But there are findings which call for the assumption of other mechanisms. Voltage clamping of frog auricular trabeculae, so that intracellular potentials are zero or positive, results in a phasic contraction which, for clamp durations of several hundred msec, is followed by a steady "creep" (61, 109, 110). The initial, phasic component, which depends on $Ca^{2+}$ concentration in the medium, is depressed by $Mn^{2+}$ ions (61) and by a number of drugs supposed to inhibit $Ca^{2+}$ influx (i.e. verapamil and D 600) (53, 54). The height of the contractile response when plotted as a function of clamp voltage is then closely paralleled by the strength of slow inward current. Contractions as well as amplitudes of inward current decrease towards zero when the membrane is clamped into the strongly positive region (61, 109, 110). This is to be expected since $Ca^{2+}$ influx should decrease as the $Ca^{2+}$ equilibrium potential is approached. The creep of the contraction is not affected by $Mn^{2+}$ (61), but is abolished in $Na^+$-free solution (109). It is thus speculated that $Na^+$ influx leads to an increase of $[Na^+]_i$ which in turn releases $Ca^{2+}$ ions from intracellular binding sites (109). After removal of extracellular $Na^+$ (replacement by $Li^+$), relaxation of the phasic component is markedly slowed (31, 109). From this and other findings the hypothesis is advanced that transmembrane $Ca^{2+}$ efflux is enhanced by the entry of $Na^+$ (31, 32, 57, 109).

It is often difficult to decide whether the composition of the bathing medium acts on the strength of contraction by altering the action potential, or whether the effect on contraction is independent of electrical activity. When a small part of the tissue is exposed to the test solution, and the major part is kept in normal Tyrode solution, there will be electrotonic interaction to make the action potential of the membranes within the test compartment follow the voltage changes of the fibers in Tyrode solution. By using this method it has been demonstrated (51) that elevation of $K^+$ concentration per se has a positive inotropic effect on dog ventricular trabeculae, while the application of the same solution to the whole preparation depresses contractility via the well known shortening of the action potential.

## Microstructure and Function

Morphometric data are available for one of the most popular preparations: the Purkinje fiber of the sheep (74). Membrane surface area is about 11.5 times that of a corresponding cylinder. Cells within the fibers are connected by certain specialized structures. Gap junctions (nexuses) occupy as much as 17% of the total cell surface, desmosomes 2.3%, fascia adherens 1.4%. In dog auricle 6% of the membrane area of the intercalated disk is of the nexus type (99) compared to 10–13% in rat ventricle (66). The folding factor of the disk membrane in rat ventricle is 9. Therefore, the treatment of the disk as a straight cross section with nexus properties turns out to be a reasonable approximation. Measurements on rat myocardium suggest (79) that the narrow extracellular space within the disk is a much better candidate for ion accumulation or depletion than are the T-tubules, the surface:volume ratio of the former being 20 times that of the latter.

Electrophysiologists have impatiently been waiting for structural demonstration of direct connections between cardiac cells which would allow the passage of small particles. In continuation of their own work and that of others, McNutt & Weinstein, in a review article (72), estimate aqueous pores to be 15–20 Å in diameter and about 150 Å in length. An independent estimate (66) suggests "more than 10 Å" for the diameter of such pores. From morphometric data, and by making the assumption that $K^+$ ions are the main carriers of charge within the pores, a specific disk resistance is calculated as 0.05 $\Omega$ cm$^2$ (66). This result is compatible with electrical measurements of inside longitudinal resistance (0.25 $\Omega$ cm$^2$, 47) since a large fraction of the electrical value would be left for the resistance of myoplasm between the disks.

In view of the widely used sucrose gap technique it is of considerable importance that ion-free sucrose solution increases internal longitudinal resistance continuously (76) [about 10-fold in 4 hours (52)]. This increase cannot quantitatively be accounted for by loss of $K^+$ ions from the cells (52) and thus is probably the result of uncoupling at the site of the disks. Addition of small quantities of $CaCl_2$ (100 $\mu$mol/liter) slows down the process considerably (52, 76). Thus the advice to voltage clampers: add some calcium to sucrose and collect your electrical data as fast as possible.

It is of importance to know whether or not larger particles, e.g. metabolites, might pass through pores from cell to cell. There is good evidence that the tetraethylammonium$^+$ ion (mol wt 120) as well as the dye Procion yellow$^{3+}$ (mol wt 700) do so (111); an upper limit for molecular diameter has not been determined as yet.

When cardiac muscle is injured it "heals over," preventing spread of depolarization into undamaged tissue (25). By using a laser pulse to damage the membranes it is possible to keep microelectrodes within Purkinje fibers and to record membrane potential and input resistance shortly after damage (19). Purkinje fibers heal over in about one minute (19), frog auricular bundles in about twenty minutes (26). $Ca^{2+}$ ions are necessary for the process of "sealing" (19). In frog auricle $Mg^{2+}$ and $Ba^{2+}$ cannot substitute for $Ca^{2+}$ while $Sr^{2+}$ can (26). The long-standing question of whether healing over may occur anywhere within a cell or only at pre-existing membrane structures seems to be answered (3). Electron micrographs of frog atrium show perfectly normal cells immediately adjacent to damaged cells (uniformly opaque). It is pointed out (3) that no transformation of the specialized membrane structures is detectable between surviving and dying cells. Thus, at present, there seems to be no morphological way of detecting whether a membrane structure is sealed or still an open pathway between inside and outside.

*Literature Cited*

1. Antoni, H. 1971. Electrophysiological mechanisms underlying pharmacological models of cardiac fibrillation. *Naunyn Schmiedebergs Arch. Pharmakol. Exp. Pathol.* 269:177–99
2. Aronson, R. S., Cranefield, P. F. 1973. The electrical activity of canine cardiac Purkinje fibers in sodium-free, calcium-rich solutions. *J. Gen. Physiol.* 61:786–808
3. Baldwin, K. M. 1970. The fine structure and electrophysiology of heart muscle cell injury. *J. Cell Biol.* 46:455–76
4. Bassingthwaighte, J. B., Reuter, H. 1972. Calcium movement and excitation-contraction coupling in cardiac cells. In *Electrical Phenomena in the Heart,* ed. W. C. De Mello, 354–95. New York: Academic
5. Beeler, G. W. Jr., Reuter, H. 1970. Membrane calcium current in ventricular myocardial fibers. *J. Physiol. London* 207:191–209
6. Beeler, G. W., Reuter, H. 1970. The relation between membrane potential, membrane currents and activation of contraction in ventricular myocardial fibers. *J. Physiol. London* 207:211–29
7. Bonke, F. I. M. 1973. Passive electrical properties of atrial fibers of the rabbit heart. *Pfluegers Arch.* 339:1–15
8. Bonke, F. I. M. 1973. Electrotonic spread in the sinoatrial node of the rabbit heart. *Pfluegers Arch.* 339:17–23
9. Bonke, F. I. M., Bouman, L. N., Schopman, F. J. G. 1971. Effect of an early atrial premature beat on activity of the sinoatrial node and atrial rhythm in the rabbit. *Circ. Res.* 29:704–15
10. Bosteels, S., Carmeliet, E. 1972. Estimation of intracellular Na concentration and transmembrane Na flux in cardiac Purkyně fibers. *Pfluegers Arch.* 336:35–47
11. Bosteels, S., Carmeliet, E. 1972. The components of the sodium efflux in cardiac Purkyně fibers. *Pfluegers Arch.* 336:48–59
12. Bozler, E. 1971. Responses and Ca uptake of cardiac muscle in Na-free high-Ca solutions. *Am. J. Physiol.* 221:618–22
13. Brooks, C. McC., Lu, H. H. 1972. *The Sinoatrial Pacemaker of the Heart.* Springfield, Ill: Thomas. 179 pp.
14. Carpenter, R., Vassalle, M. 1972. Restoration of electrical activity of guinea pig atria during hypothermia. Effect of norepinephrine and electrical stimulation on membrane potentials. *Circ. Res.* 31:507–19
15. Cranefield, P. F., Wit, A. L., Hoffman, B. F. 1972. Conduction of the cardiac impulse. III. Characteristics of very slow conduction. *J. Gen. Physiol.* 59:227–46
16. Cranefield, P. F., Wit, A. L., Hoffman, B. F. 1973. Genesis of cardiac arrhythmias. *Circulation* 47:190–204
17. De Hemptinne, A. 1971. Properties of the outward currents in frog atrial muscle. *Pfluegers Arch.* 329:321–31
18. Delahayes, J. F. 1972. Electrical responses of cardiac muscle in Na-free high-Ca solution. *Experientia* 28:1054
19. Délèze, J. 1970. The recovery of resting potential and input resistance in sheep heart injured by knife or LASER. *J. Physiol.* 208:547–62
20. De Mello, W. C., Ed. 1972. *Electrical Phenomena in the Heart.* New York: Academic. 415 pp.
21. Dreifus, L. S., Likoff, W., Eds. 1973. *Cardiac Arrhythmias.* New York: Grune and Stratton
22. Ducouret, P., Massé, Chr., Gargouïl, Y.-M. 1972. Mécanismes d'action d'une substance antiarrythmique étudiée par la méthode du courant et du voltage imposés. *C. R. H. Acad. Sci. Paris Ser. D* 275:607–9
23. Dudel, J. 1972. Excitation process in heart cells. See Ref. 20, 111–32
24. Dudel, J., Rüdel, R. 1970. Voltage and time dependence of excitatory sodium current in cooled Purkinje fibers. *Pfluegers Arch.* 315:136–58
25. Engelmann, T. W. 1877. Vergleichende Untersuchungen zur Lehre von der Muskel—und Nervenelektricität. *Pfluegers Arch.* 15:116–48
26. Escobar, I., De Mello, W. C., Pérez, B. 1972. Healing over and muscle contraction in toad hearts. *Circ. Res.* 31:389–96
27. Fenoglio, J. J. Jr., Pham, T. D., Wit, A. L., Bassett, A. L., Wagner, B. M. 1972. Canine mitral complex. Ultrastructure and electromechanical properties. *Circ. Res.* 31:417–30
28. Gelfand, I. M., Gurfinkel, V. S., Fomin, S. V., Tsetlin, M. L. 1971. *Models of Structural–Functional Organization of Certain Biological Systems.* Cambridge, Mass.: MIT Press. 405 pp.
29. Girardier, L. 1971/72. Dynamic energy partition in cultured heart cells. *Cardiology* 56:88–92
30. Glitsch, H. G. 1969. Membrane potential of guinea pig auricles after hypothermia. *Pfluegers Arch.* 307:29–46

31. Goto, M., Kimoto, Y., Saito, M., Wada, Y. 1972. Tension fall after contraction of bullfrog atrial muscle examined with the voltage clamp technique. *Jap. J. Physiol.* 22:637–50
32. Goto, M., Kimoto, Y., Suetsugu, Y. 1972. Membrane currents responsible for contraction and relaxation of the bullfrog ventricle. *Jap. J. Physiol.* 22: 315–31
33. Haas, H. G. 1972. Active ion transport in heart muscle. See Ref. 20, 163–89
34. Haas, H. G., Hantsch, F., Otter, H. P., Siegel, G. 1967. Untersuchungen zum Problem des aktiven K- und Na-Transports am Myokard. *Pfluegers Arch.* 294:144–68
35. Haas, H. G., Kern, R., Einwächter, H. M. 1970. Electrical activity and metabolism in cardiac tissue: An experimental and theoretical study. *J. Membrane Biol.* 3:180–209
36. Haas, H. G., Kern, R., Einwächter, H. M., Tarr, M. 1971. Kinetics of Na inactivation in frog atria. *Pfluegers Arch.* 323:141–57
37. Heistracher, P. 1971. Mechanism of action of antifibrillatory drugs. *Naunyn-Schmiedebergs Arch. Pharmakol. Exp. Pathol.* 269:199–212
38. Hiraoka, M., Hecht, H. H. 1973. Recovery from hypothermia in cardiac Purkinje fibers: Considerations for an electrogenic mechanism. *Pfluegers Arch.* 339:25–36
39. Hodgkin, A. L., Huxley, A. F. 1952. A quantitative description of membrane current and its application to conduction and excitation in nerve. *J. Physiol. London* 117:500–44
40. Hoffman, B. F., Cranefield, P. F. 1960. *Electrophysiology of the Heart.* New York: McGraw. 323 pp.
41. Hyde, A., Cheneval, J.-P., Blondel, B., Girardier, L. 1972. Electrophysiological correlates of energy metabolism in cultured rat heart cells. *J. Physiol. Paris* 64:269–92
42. Imanishi, S. 1971. Calcium-sensitive discharges in canine Purkinje fibers. *Jap. J. Physiol.* 21:443–61
43. Irisawa, H. 1972. Electrical activity of rabbit sino-atrial node as studied by a double sucrose gap method. In *12th International Colloquium Vectocardiographicum,* ed. P. Rijlant, 242–48. Bruxelles: Presses Académiques Européennes
44. James, T. N. 1973. The sinus node as a servomechanism. *Circ. Res.* 32:307–13
45. James, T. N., Nadeau, R. A. 1962. Direct perfusion of the sinus node: Experimental model for pharmacologic and electrophysiologic studies on the heart. *Henry Ford Hosp. Med. Bull.* 10: 21–25
46. Johnson, E. A., Lieberman, M. 1971. Heart: excitation and contraction. *Ann. Rev. Physiol.* 33:479–532
47. Jongsma, H. J., van Rijn, H. E. 1972. Electrotonic spread of current in monolayer cultures of neonatal rat heart cells. *J. Membrane Biol.* 9:341–60
48. Kamiyama, A., Saeki, Y., Sano, T. 1973. Conduction block from Purkinje fiber to ventricular muscle under abnormal conditions. *Jap. Heart J.* 14:71–79
49. Kanno, T. 1970. The heterogenous structure of the specialized tissue in the heart as a factor in atrioventricular conduction delay. *Jap. J. Physiol.* 20:417–33
50. Kao, F. F., Koizumi, K., Vassale, M., Eds. 1971. *Research in Physiology.* A liber memorialis in honor of Professor Chandler McCuskey Brooks. Bologna: Aulo Gaggi. 761 pp.
51. Kavaler, F., Hyman, P. M., Lefkowitz, R. B. 1972. Positive and negative inotropic effects of elevated extracellular potassium level on mammalian ventricular muscle. *J. Gen. Physiol.* 60: 351–65
52. Kléber, A. 1973. Effects of sucrose solution on the longitudinal tissue resistivity of trabecular muscle from mammalian heart. *Pfluegers Arch.* In press
53. Kohlhardt, M., Bauer, B., Krause, H., Fleckenstein, A. 1972. New selective inhibitors of the transmembrane Ca conductivity in mammalian myocardial fibers. Studies with the voltage clamp technique. *Experientia* 28:288–9
54. Kohlhardt, M., Bauer, B., Krause, H., Fleckenstein, A. 1972. Differentiation of the transmembrane Na and Ca channels in mammalian cardiac fibers by the use of specific inhibitors. *Pfluegers Arch.* 335:309–22
55. Kootsey, J. M., Johnson, E. A. 1972. Voltage clamp of cardiac muscle. A theoretical analysis of early currents in the single sucrose gap. *Biophys. J.* 12:1496–1508
56. Langer, G. A. 1973. Heart: excitation-contraction coupling. *Ann. Rev. Physiol.* 35:55–86
57. Langer, G. A. 1972. Myocardial $K^+$ loss and contraction frequency. *J. Mol. Cell. Cardiol.* 4:85–86
58. Lassalle, B., Guilbault, P. 1972. Les Mécanismes ioniques intervenant lors de l'activité électrique du lambeau myocardique de crabe Carcinus meanas. *C. R. H. Acad. Sci. Paris Ser. D* 275: 847–49

59. Lassalle, B., Guilbault, P. 1970. Action des ions potassium (K⁺), sodium (Na⁺), chlore (Cl⁻) et Calcium (Ca²⁺) sur le potentiel de membrane de la fibre striée cardiaque du crabe (Carcinus maenas). *C. R. Soc. Biol.* 164:2552

60. Lenfant, J., Mironneau, J., Aka, J.-K. 1972. Activité répétitive de la fibre sino-auriculaire de grenouille. *J. Physiol. Paris* 64:5–18

61. Léoty, Cl., Raymond, G. 1972. Mechanical activity and ionic currents in frog atrial trabeculae. *Pfluegers Arch.* 334:114–28

62. Lieberman, M. 1973. Electrophysiological studies of a synthetic strand of cardiac muscle. *The Physiologist.* In press

63. Lieberman, M., Kootsey, J. M., Johnson, E. A., Sawanobori, T. 1973. Slow conduction in cardiac muscle. A biophysical model. *Biophys. J.* 13:37–55

64. Lieberman, M., Manasek, F. J., Sawanobori, T., Johnson, E. A. 1973. Cytochalasin B: Its morphological and electrophysiological actions on synthetic strands of cardiac muscle. *Develop. Biol.* 31:380–403

65. Lu, H. H. 1970. Shifts in pacemaker dominance within the sinoatrial region of cat and rabbit hearts resulting from increase of extracellular potassium. *Circ. Res.* 26:339–46

66. Matter, A. 1973. A morphometric study on the nexus of rat cardiac muscle. *J. Cell Biol.* 56:690–6

67. Maughan, D. W. 1973. Some effects of prolonged polarization on membrane currents in bullfrog atrial muscle. *J. Membrane Biol.* 11:331–52

68. McCann, F. V. 1972. Comparative aspects of electrogenesis in myocardial cells. See Ref. 20, 293–322

69. McCann, F. V., Ed. 1969. *Comparative Physiology of the Heart: Current Trends.* Basel: Birkhäuser. 270 pp.

70. McDonald, T. F., De Haan, R. L. 1973. Ion levels and membrane potential in chick heart tissue and cultured cells. *J. Gen. Physiol.* 61:89–109

71. McDonald, T. F., Sachs, H. G., De Haan, R. L. 1972. Development of sensitivity to tetrodotoxin in beating chick embryo hearts, single cells, and aggregates. *Science* 76:1248–50

72. McNutt, N. S., Weinstein, R. S. 1973. Membrane ultrastructure at mammalian intercellular junctions. *Progr. Biophys. Mol. Biol.* 26:45–101

73. Mendez, C., Moe, G. K. 1972. Atrioventricular transmission. See Ref. 20, 263–91

74. Mobley, B. A., Page, E. 1972. The surface area of sheep cardiac Purkinje fibers. *J. Physiol. London* 220:547–63

75. Moret, P., Fejfar, Z., Eds. 1972. *Metabolism of the Hypoxic and Ischaemic Heart. Proc. Joint Symp. Int. Soc. Cardiol. and WHO, Geneva, 1971.* Basel: Karger. 493 pp.

76. New, W., Trautwein, W. 1972. Inward membrane currents in mammalian myocardium. *Pfluegers Arch.* 334:1–23

77. New, W., Trautwein, W. 1972. The ionic nature of slow inward current and its relation to contraction. *Pfluegers Arch.* 334:24–38

78. Noble, D., Tsien, R. W. 1972. The repolarization process of heart cells. See Ref. 20, 133–61

79. Page, E., McCallister, L. P. 1973. Studies on the intercalated disk of rat left ventricular myocardial cells. *J. Ultrastruct. Res.* 43:388–411

80. Pappano, A. J. 1972. Action potentials in chick atria. Increased susceptibility to blockade by tetrodotoxin during embryonic development. *Circ. Res.* 31:379–88

81. Pappano, A. J. 1972. Sodium-dependent depolarization of noninnervated embryonic chick heart by acetylcholine. *J. Pharmacol. Exp. Ther.* 180:340–50

82. Pelkonen, K., Tirri, R. 1972. The adrenergically mediated coordination of contraction in isolated cell groups from rat ventricular myocardium. *Experientia* 28:1040–41

83. Polimeni, P. I. 1971. Choline substitution for extracellular Na in cardiac Purkinje fibers: effects on K fluxes. See Ref. 50, 45–57

84. Purdy, J. E., Lieberman, M., Roggeveen, A. E., Kirk, R. G. 1972. Synthetic strands of cardiac muscle. Formation and ultrastructure. *J. Cell Biol.* 55: 563–78

85. Reiter, M., Stickel, F. J. 1968. Der Einfluss der Kontraktionsfrequenz auf das Aktionspotential des Meerschweinchen-Papillarmuskels. *Naunyn Schmiedebergs Arch. Pharmakol. Exp. Pathol.* 260:342–65

86. Reuter, H. 1973. Divalent cations as charge carriers in excitable membranes. *Progr. Biophys. Mol. Biol.* 26:1–43

87. Rougier, O., Vassort, G., Garnier, D., Gargouil, Y.-M., Coraboeuf, E. 1969. Existence and role of slow inward current during the frog atrial action potential. *Pfluegers Arch.* 308:91–110

88. Rosen, R., Hoffman, B. F. 1973. Mechanisms of action of antiarrhythmic drugs. *Circ. Res.* 32:1–8

89. Sachs, H. G., De Haan, R. L. 1973. Embryonic myocardial cell aggregates: volume and pulsation rate. *Develop. Biol.* 30:233–40

90. Sano, T., Sawanobori, T. 1972. Electrical properties of cells at the Purkinje fiber-myocardial cell region of the mammalian heart. *J. Electrocardiol.* 5:173–83

91. Seyama, I. 1971. Characteristics of transient current in the atrial myocardium of the frog. *J. Physiol. Soc. Jap.* 33:729–30

92. Shigenobu, K., Sperelakis, N. 1972. Calcium current channels induced by catecholamines in chick embryonic hearts whose fast sodium channels are blocked by tetrodotoxin or elevated potassium. *Circ. Res.* 31:932–52

93. Shigeto, N., Irisawa, H. 1972. Slow conduction in the atrioventricular node of the cat: A possible explanation. *Experientia* 28:1442–43

94. Soustre, H. 1972. Electrogénèse cardiaque du rat surrénalectomisé, interprétation en fonction des variations de gradients ioniques et de perméabilités membranaires. *Pfluegers Arch.* 333:111–25

95. Sperelakis, N. 1972. (Na⁺, K⁺)-ATPase activity of embryonic chick heart and skeletal muscles as a function of age. *Biochim. Biophys. Acta* 266:230–37

96. Sperelakis, N. 1972. Electrical properties of embryonic heart cells. See Ref. 20, 1–61

97. Sperelakis, N., Henn, F. A. 1970. Effect of diphenylhydantoin on membrane potentials and Na-K-ATPase of cultured chick heart cells. *Am. J. Physiol.* 118:1224–7

98. Sperelakis, N., Shigenobu, K. 1972. Changes in membrane properties of chick embryonic hearts during development. *J. Gen. Physiol.* 60:430–53

99. Spira, A. W. 1971. The nexus in the intercalated disk of canine heart: Quantitative data for an estimation of resistance. *J. Ultrastruct. Res.* 34:409–25

100. Strauss, H. C., Bigger, J. T. Jr. 1972. Electrophysiological properties of rabbit sinoatrial perinodal fibers. *Circ. Res.* 31:490–506

101. Szekeres, L., Papp, G. J. 1971. *Experimental Cardiac Arrhythmias and Antiarrhythmic Drugs.* Budapest: Akadémiai Kiadó. 448 pp.

102. Tamai, T., Kagiyama, S. 1968. Studies of cat heart muscle during recovery after prolonged hypothermia; Hyperpolarization of cell membranes and its dependence on the sodium pump with electrogenic characteristics. *Circ. Res.* 22:423–433

103. Tamai, T., Kagiyama, S. 1967. Transmembrane potentials of cardiac muscle cells during recovery after prolonged hypothermia (Abstract in Japanese). *J. Physiol. Soc. Jap.* 29:464

104. Tarr, M. 1971. Two inward currents in frog atrial muscle. *J. Gen. Physiol.* 58:523–43

105. Tarr, M., Luckstead, E. F., Jurewicz, P. A., Haas, H. G. 1973. Effect of propranolol on the fast inward sodium current in frog atrial muscle. *J. Pharmacol. Exp. Ther.* 184:599–610

106. Tuganowski, W., Cekański, A. 1971. Electrical activity of a single fibre of the human embryonic heart. *Pfluegers Arch.* 323:21–26

107. Van Capelle, F. J. L., Janse, M. J., Varghese, P. J., Freud, G. E., Mater, C., Durrer, D. 1972. Spread of excitation in the atrioventricular node of isolated rabbit hearts studied by multiple microelectrode recording. *Circ. Res.* 31:602–16

108. Vassalle, M., Greineder, J. K., Stuckey, J. H. 1973. Role of sympathetic nervous system in the sinus node resistance to high potassium. *Circ. Res.* 32:348–55

109. Vassort, G. 1973. Influence of sodium ions on the regulation of frog myocardial contractility. *Pfluegers Arch.* 339:225–40

110. Vassort, G., Rougier, O., Favelier, J. 1971. Influence du potentiel de membrane et des courants transmembranaires sur l'activité contractile des faisceaux sino-auriculaires de la grenouille. *Arch. Int. Physiol. Biochim.* 79:401–6

111. Weingart, R., Imanaga, I., Weidmann, S. 1973. Low resistance pathways between myocardial cells. In *Myocardiology: Recent Advances in Studies on Cardiac Structure and Metabolism.* Baltimore, Md.: Univ. Park Press. In press

112. West, T. C. 1972. Electrophysiology of the sinoatrial node. See Ref. 20, 191–217

113. Wit, A. L., Cranefield, P. F., Hoffman, B. F. 1972. Slow conduction and reentry in the ventricular conducting system. II. Single and sustained circus movement in networks of canine and bovine Purkinje fibers. *Circ. Res.* 30:11–22

114. Zipes, D. P., Mendez, C., Moe, G. K. 1973. Evidence for summation and voltage dependency in rabbit atrioventricular nodal fibers. *Circ. Res.* 32:170–7

# CIRCULATION IN INVERTEBRATES

❖1109

*Arthur W. Martin*[1]

Department of Zoology, University of Washington, Seattle, Washington

## INTRODUCTION

The problems of circulation in invertebrate animals are many and fascinating, but the background of their morphology and physiology may be relatively unfamiliar. Because the number of workers in the field is rather small, I have used the space available to set the background whenever I considered it appropriate, and then incorporated the newer work. Papers on the subject are widely scattered, and I apologize for those works that I have missed in the course of preparing this review.

## MAINTENANCE OF BLOOD COMPOSITION

Only in the lowest members of the vertebrate line is there a failure to regulate the composition of the *milieu interieur* rather narrowly. The case is quite the opposite in many invertebrate groups. Some large ones, like the echinoderms and cephalopod molluscs, are restricted to the seas and either do little to alter the composition of fluids circulating in the body or have a relatively simple system of regulation. Of greater interest in the present context are those animals that, invading intertidal, brackish, or terrestrial environments without adequate provision of impermeable integuments or osmoregulatory organs, have had perforce to expose the body cells to rapid changes in salt concentration. Even nerve processes in some invertebrate animals appear to be exposed directly to blood (106), so that a continuation of function in the presence of huge changes in ionic environment is a triumph of cellular adaptation.

At the cellular level study of the accumulation of amino acids within cells to help meet high blood salt concentrations continues to be a major theme (38) and, for molluscs, the process has been reviewed by Schoffeniels & Gilles (85). Gilles has continued the study of molluscs in this respect (46) and, with Gerard, has extended his observations to crustacea (42). A few of the many other papers in the field are

[1]Supported in part by Grant GB-17539 of the National Science Foundation.

171

merely noted: for coelenterates see (29) and for crustacea see (70). Lin & Cohen (67) have made some effort to examine the possible accumulation through this mechanism of pharmacologically active amino acids. A particular role for taurine continues to be sought, as discussed in a review (5) and a more recent paper (6) by Allen & Garrett.

Related species may show differences in the degree of osmoregulation; these are being actively studied and thus only a few examples can be given. Sutcliffe (91–93), in some amphipod crustaceans, has shown that fresh water populations lose sodium more slowly than brackish water animals, and that intracellular sodium is regulated in the face of large changes in blood sodium. The most marine isopods of a series showed the least hyperosmotic regulation (58). Lockwood (68) has shown in *Gammarus duebeni* that not only changes in blood sodium concentration but variations in body volume may influence the rate of sodium uptake. The mechanisms employed, even in species with overlapping environments, may depend largely upon behavior. Thompson & Pritchard (97) reviewed the previous work illustrating the resistance to fresh water exposure characteristic of the burrowing mudshrimps and then compared the mechanisms of resistance. *Upogebia* maintains an open burrow system which quickly fills with brackish or rain water; thus this genus turns out to be a reasonably good osmoregulator. *Callianassa* burrows freely in the mud, which probably protects it from as rapid a dilution of body salt; it proves to be much more of an osmoconformer. Both genera are fairly resistant to natural periods of dilution of the environment.

There has been a long history of study of neuroendocrine regulation, which in the crustacea was originally directed at the control of the time of molting. The possibility that there is a continuous osmoregulation has been suggested; Kamemoto & Ono (60) have described some encouraging results that have been pursued by Kamemoto & Tullis (61). They are able to obtain from the brains of *Procambarus clarkii* and *Macrobrachium rosenbergii,* but not from the brains of some marine shrimps and crabs, a heat-stable, nondialyzable factor that increases the concentration of chloride in the blood and the rate of uptake of sodium from the medium. Lechenault (65) has suggested that at a much lower level, neurosecretory activity is involved in osmotic regulation of nemertine worms. In *Lineus ruber* and *Lineus viridis,* which quickly gain weight when immersed in diluted sea water but return to original weight within 24 hr, the removal of the cerebral ganglion delays the return to normal to 72 hr and removal of both cerebral ganglion and cerebral organ prevents weight restoration. The effect is thought to be neurohumoral, and is not a consequence of the surgical interference because experimental inversion of the cerebral structures delays the weight recovery only briefly. Kamemoto, Kato & Tucker (59) review the effects of brain removal and reimplantation in earthworms and conclude there is probably a neurosecretory factor that influences salt and water balance. In *Nereis virens,* a volume regulator, they find an increase in the aldehyde-fuchsin positive cells in the brain upon exposure to diluted sea water. But Baskin (10), working with the polychaete *Nereis limnicola,* thinks it unlikely that the unusually large alpha cells, the major component of the infra cerebral gland, have anything to do with the relatively effective osmoregulation of this species.

The transition to land represents an even more difficult step, and two recent symposia have dealt with some of the problems encountered (16, 66). A few matters are touched on in *Adaptations of Intertidal Organisms* (66), but in the symposium on *Terrestrial Adaptations in Crustacea* (16) there are many pertinent papers (for example, 15).

## BLOOD PIGMENTS

No general principle has yet been discovered to account for the distribution of oxygen-carrying pigments through the invertebrate groups, a distribution recently summarized in general by Manwell (71), for annelids by Florkin (37), and for molluscs by the Ghirettis (43, 44). Hemoglobin, perhaps because of its chemical relationship to the cytochromes, appears to have been developed first. Nematode worms of several different species utilize hemoglobin (88). Nemertine worms, suggested to have the first functional circulatory systems (72), use hemoglobin and produce erythrocytes. Brachiopods and annelids, near the stem of the protostomatous line, utilize hemoglobin if any pigment is formed. But arthropods and molluscs, belonging to the same line, commonly use hemocyanin. This is surprising because (*a*) the genetic code for hemoglobin must be almost complete in their chromosomal complement. Some species also synthesize hemoglobin or myoglobin for tissues other than blood. One whole group, the bivalves, either have no pigment or utilize hemoglobin. Also (*b*), hemocyanin does not appear to be as effective in oxygen transport as hemoglobin. The bivalves are relatively inactive animals and thus, for oxygen storage, hemoglobin is the better choice, but it would also appear to be better as the circulating pigment. Redmond (82) has discussed the use of hemocyanin in oxygen transport, and Ghiretti et al (45) have discussed the evolution of chemical structure in hemocyanin. Young (107, 108) has looked for systematic variations in hemocyanin in relation to terrestrialness, but finds the relationship complicated by the problems of dessication and carbon dioxide accumulation.

The hemoglobins still warrant much comparative study. Terwilliger & Koppenheffer (95) compared coelomic cell hemoglobin in a polychaete annelid with the hemoglobin in solution in the blood, and found three hemoglobins present. This is reminiscent of Read's (81) observation of a three-component hemoglobin of the bivalve *Phacoides pectinatus.* Collett & O'Gower (25) report that the hemoglobin of some arcid clams shows some unusual temperature characteristics. Like most hemoglobins, at low temperatures there is a shift of the dissociation curve to the right with increasing temperature; but at high temperatures the curve begins to shift back to the left with increasing temperature. This is interpreted to be a meaningful evolution for adaptation to a transient high-temperature survival, and implies a shift in the Hill coefficient.

## SYSTEMATIC SURVEY OF THE CIRCULATION

### Annelida

We know so little about the circulatory physiology of the annelid worms that Laverack in his monograph (63) on the physiology of earthworms gives only a section of the chapter on respiration to the subject. The publication of a study in 1965 on a giant earthworm of Brazil (53) has not been reviewed previously and may warrant a short account. It was possible in these very large worms (200–500 g body weight) to cannulate the dorsal and ventral blood vessels and to measure the pressures in the worms after recovery from anesthesia in a relatively unrestrained condition. The dorsal vessel develops a very respectable pressure as a result of the sweep of a peristaltic wave, moving forward nearly the entire length of the animal, which returns mixed blood to the lateral hearts. At rest the mean pressure in the dorsal vessel at the level of the first pairs of lateral hearts varied from a diastolic of 14 to a systolic of 24 cm of water at a beat frequency of 6–8 per minute. The systolic pressure in the dorsal vessel rose to 40 cm of water during activity. The beat frequency of the five pairs of lateral hearts was ordinarily higher (average 20/min) than that of the dorsal blood vessel, so that filling of the lateral hearts from the dorsal blood vessel occurred several times during the arrival of each peristaltic wave at the anterior end. The pressure developed in the lateral hearts, therefore, often was greater during this increased filling than during diastole of the dorsal vessel; this phenomenon can be seen in the recordings. At rest the systolic pressure in the ventral vessel of healthy specimens varied from 45–90 cm of water and the diastolic pressure from 30–70 cm of water. When the animals were active the systolic and diastolic pressures could both mount above 100 cm of water. Such high pressures are no doubt needed to accomplish the perfusion of several hundred segments simultaneously. Local vasoconstriction is probably highly developed because the worms could autotomize posterior sections of the body and in doing so did not lose significant amounts of blood.

In a companion paper (54) some measurements of oxygen transport were reported. In both dorsal and ventral vessels the saturation of hemoglobin is, of course, the same. The blood was, on the average, 40% saturated, except that, when a worm was allowed to burrow and expose the skin to wet mud, the mean saturation increased to 73%. The earthworm must operate on a relatively inefficient mixing system. In each somite, part of the blood from the ventral vessel is directed through the skin vessels and presumably approaches saturation; the other part is directed through the visceral vessels and may approach complete unsaturation. The two streams meet again at the dorsal vessel, equilibrate, and the blood is recirculated. The increase in saturation of blood in the dorsal vessel of a worm in a wet burrow may simply reflect a greater volume flow of blood to the skin vessels, but other explanations are possible and untested. Fourtner & Pax (39) have observed the contractile vessels of *Lumbricus terrestris* and, in this smaller worm, find a beat of 11/min in comparison with the 6 beats/min of the large Brazilian worms. The velocity of the peristaltic waves was very nearly the same in the two worms: about 2.4 cm/sec. Experimental analysis on this relatively delicate animal is difficult but should be rewarding in view of the complexity of regulating the blood flow to so many individual somites.

## Arthropods

Of the five classes of modern arthropods only the Crustacea and Arachnida will be considered. There is too little recent work on Onychophorans and Myriapods to warrant consideration, and the Insecta receive separate coverage in the *Annual Review of Entomology*. McCann (75) reviewed the physiology of insect hearts in 1970 and included sections on ultrastructure, electrophysiology, and origin of the heart beat; since these have been better studied in insects than in most invertebrate groups, the subjects will receive little attention here.

CLASS CRUSTACEA   The *Physiology of Crustacea* was published in 1960 and no such detailed treatment as Maynard's chapter on the heart and circulation of Crustacea (73) has appeared in the interval. It will be recalled that the heart beat in all except the Branchiopoda, a large group of fairy shrimps, clam shrimps, and water fleas, is neurogenic in origin. A few pacemaker neurones give rise to a burst of impulses, the heart responds with a brief tetanus, and, ordinarily, diastolic filling is assisted by the recoil of stretched suspensory ligaments. The innervation may be relatively simple and accessible, as in the lobster (7). Regulatory cellular interactions continue to be analyzed (8). The pacemaker neurones may operate endogenously in small groups (26). The participation of a nervous regulatory system is indicated in the papers resulting from the continued interest in the effects of anoxia, or even reduced oxygen tension, on the heart rate. The heart of *Cancer magister* (90) slows in rate and decreases in amplitude either in situ or in vitro as the heart becomes anoxic. The in situ heart, however, makes a rapid recovery when reoxygenated. Larimer (62) had previously shown that bradycardia resulted in a crayfish heart from various degrees of hypoxia, despite a still increasing ventilation rate, and that tachycardia (9) occurred when the heart was exposed to increased carbon dioxide in vitro, though not in vivo. The difference was attributed to reflex regulation of the heart in vivo, and a direct action of carbon dioxide on the neurones of the cardiac ganglion in vitro. Flindt and co-workers (33, 34), using both crayfish and crabs, have described a close correlation between heart rate and oxygen tension over a wide range of tensions, so that in the upper ranges Flindt feels the animals were not anoxic but that receptors were responsible for the effects noted. Failure to obtain bradycardia therefore indicates something about the condition of the animal. Ahsanullah & Newell (3) noted that there was little evidence of bradycardia in the shore crab *Carcinus maenas* even after 6 or 7 hr of aerial exposure. They argue that aerobic metabolism must be effectively maintained and so, in turn, the gills must be sufficiently ventilated. The crabs were not subjected to forced activity so the margin for activity in the air is not known. Other crustaceans seem to have less sensitive regulators. Thompson & Pritchard (96) measured heart rates in a burrowing shrimp that is very resistant to anoxia. Below an oxygen tension of 30 mm of Hg, at about the same point at which the rate of oxygen consumption begins to decline, there was a marked bradycardia.

Since Alexandrowicz (4) described the pericardial organs of decapod crustaceans there has been continuous interest in them as neurohumoral tissues. Terwilliger et al (94) have now localized a cardio-excitatory peptide in sedimentable granules from an homogenate of the pericardial organs and described the solubilization of the material. Berlind & Cooke (12) obtained the release of the neurohormone by electrical stimulation of the crab pericardial organs and assayed for it by means of isolated hearts. They described the role of some divalent cations in the release and subsequent cardiac excitation. The complete picture of the afferent limbs, the CNS control, and the efferent pathways should emerge from continuing these varied approaches to the control of the heart.

Blatchford (14) has recorded several vascular pressures by modern methods using relatively normal specimens of *Carcinus maenas*. Ventricular systole raised intraventricular pressure from 0 cm $H_2O$ to 14 cm $H_2O$; since the pressure then dropped off symmetrically, the heart must spend about equal time in systole and diastole. Synchronous records show that there are coupled changes in pressure in the dorsal pericardium and the lateral pericardium, but these are so out of phase, and the pressures are so different, that the two pericardial chambers are probably separated and behave quite differently. The pressures in the pericardial chambers are sufficient to fill the ventricle, but the means of filling the dorsal pericardium is not clear and the present interpretation is that it participates in some way in the propulsion of the blood. A pressure of about 1 cm of water is maintained across the branchial system, the systolic pulses being very faint on the afferent side at this point, while on the efferent side of the gills there is evidence of some negative pressure indicating that blood is being drawn towards the lateral pericardium.

Redmond's (82) estimate of cardiac output in a lobster, computed from measurements assembled for different species and from several sources, was the best estimate available for any crustacean for a long while. Johansen, Lenfant & Mecklenburg (52) have now made the appropriate measurements on a single species, *Cancer magister*. Ventilation and oxygen extraction were measured directly on unrestrained animals. A mask was molded to the carapace and the excurrent water measured with an electromagnetic flowmeter. The figures obtained were higher than any previous measurements, all of which had been made by an overflow method which probably resulted in increased resistance. Closed chamber respirometry gave satisfactory checks on the values obtained for ventilation.

Blood sampling was by indwelling catheters, again in unrestrained animals. The new and pleasing feature of the result was the high resting arterial $O_2$ tension obtained. Clearly restraint and handling of most invertebrate animals grossly upsets the normal performance of the respiratory system; this is illustrated in this work by a failure of active crabs to arterialize the blood very well. When the appropriate computations are made the cardiac output of the crabs on the average was 29 ml $kg^{-1}$ $min^{-1}$. Redmond's computation, based on low arterial saturations, gave the very high values of 80 ml $kg^{-1}$ $min^{-1}$. The new value is very similar to those of vertebrate animals but is no longer strikingly in excess of them.

SUBCLASS CIRRIPEDIA   Circulation of the highly specialized Cirripedia group of barnacles offers many puzzles. It is generally agreed that most of the orders have no provision for blood circulation, but in the order Thoracica, which includes the largest barnacles, a full-fledged circulatory system is present. An accessory heart, the blood-pump, which is not a homolog of the usual crustacean heart, provides the pressure for circulation of the blood. Cannon (22) published an excellent description of the major vessels of one species of the group and said: "to explain how the blood is forced around the canalicular system just described, I shall assume merely that the muscles of the blood-pump contract periodically, whether regularly or not is of no consequence."

The physiological evidences in support of his assumption have been given in a recent paper (40) that raises as many questions as it resolves. The origin of the beat of the blood-pump has not been ascertained. Presumably it is neurogenic, but it is not necessarily from the cardiac ganglion. The rhythm was regular over at least three hours, and the rate fairly high. It was temperature dependent from a low of about 1 beat/min at 4°C to 40 beats/min at 25°C. High pressures were generated by the system. Pulse pressures up to 70 cm of water were recorded, with mean hemolymph pressures of about 250 cm of water. It is not apparent why such high pressures should be developed, nor is it clear how much of a gradient is produced from the blood-pump, through the peduncular vessel, lateral vessels, and back through the gut parenchyma to the heart. The morphology, again, may provide a guide. Cannon has said that: "the blood flows next to the lateral vessels, the subintestinal vessels, and into the gut parenchyma. The pressure must be considerable, for the lateral vessels would be completely occluded every time the blood-pump contracted." This is an unusual system for a crustacean, and worthy of much further attention.

CLASS ARACHNIDA

*Order Xiphosura*    The heart of *Limulus* continues to interest comparative physiologists. The review by Abbott et al (1) covers the recent developments adequately.

*Order Araneida*    There has been some interest in circulation in spiders, warranted by the advantages offered the investigator. Different groups of spiders have developed different circulatory stratagems. The spiders known popularly as tarantulas use only book lungs and so rely on blood and a pigment to transport oxygen to the tissues. As a result, the hemocyanin level is fairly high, averaging in *Dugesiella hentzi* 7.5% in a blood volume of about 19% of the body weight (89). So, where hemoglobin accounts for nearly 1.2% of the human body, hemocyanin accounts for 1.4% of the weight of this spider. Some spiders utilize both book lungs and a tracheal system, still others possess only a tracheal system. It is to be expected that these latter groups will have less hemocyanin and less blood, but measurements have not yet been made which permit this judgment. The situation is complicated, too, by the practice of using an hydraulic mechanism for the extension of some leg joints. Perhaps this led to the development of the ability of salticid spiders to leap for long distances, studied by Parry & Brown (79, 80).

Bursey & Sherman (20, 21) have described the cardiac ganglion of a tarantula *Eurypelma marxi* and some aspects of its function, which is similar to that of the other arthropods. Sherman & Pax (86, 87) have made pharmacological studies on the excised heart. All of these studies confirm that the heartbeat is neurogenic in origin and they also confirm that acetycholine (ACh) speeds the heart and increases the amplitude of beat, an action potentiated by eserine and reduced by atropine, hexamethonium, and D-tubocurarine. Epinephrine and norepinephrine increase the heart rate and amplitude, while gamma-amino butyric acid (GABA) and 5-hydroxy-tryptamine (5-HT) decrease the heart rate and amplitude. An action of exogenous epinephrine does not, of course, demonstrate that it is produced in the system. In a general review of catecholamines in arthropods, Murdock (77) says that evidence for epinephrine as a transmitter in the group is minimal and subject to doubt, and that norepinephrine is present but that dopamine is the most likely transmitter.

Wilson (102–104) has described many aspects of circulatory physiology in *Heteropoda venatoria*, beginning with a description of the pedicel because of the necessity of moving blood in both directions through this very restricted space between prosoma and opisthosoma. He identified, for the first time, a dorsal cardiac nerve (the cardiac ganglion of Bursey & Sherman) in a spider. Transection of the nerve resulted in a transient phase shift between the two halves of the heart, where initially the anterior half beat regularly while the posterior half beat spasmodically. Complete removal of the nerve did not stop cardiac contractions but they became irregular and poorly coordinated. Since the total number of cells approaches 85 (21) it is quite possible that some nerve cells were left in the heart. The presence of connections to the central nervous system is suspected but unproved morphologically. When the pedicel is cut or severely damaged the heart rate increases, probably due to freeing from prosomal influence. If the pedicel is merely constricted the heartbeat slows, perhaps due to the impediment to blood flow. During a struggle the heart rate declines, but following a struggle the heart rate increases. This is thought to prove the existence of cardio-accelerator nerves.

Certain spiders quickly become exhausted when made to run continuously. Wilson raises the question whether this is due to circulatory and respiratory inefficiency or to imbalance of the hydrostatic system (105). In *Amaurobius ferox* he showed within eight seconds after the beginning of a struggle a volume of blood moved from prosoma to opisthosoma; the imbalance remained during the struggle. At the end of the struggle, within four seconds the heart restored the original distribution of the blood. Also, opisthosomal muscles, by contraction, can move the blood back to the prosoma, but it is thought that the greater strength of the prosomal musculature dominates in this respect and that the collapse is due in part to the reduction in blood volume in the prosoma and in part to the deprivation of oxygen supply resulting from the high pressure in the prosoma that prevents the ingress of oxygenated blood. The development of tracheal systems in some spiders suggests that the supply of oxygen is the critical factor. This idea is supported by the older experiments of Cloudesley-Thompson (24) which show that maximum running speed could be maintained for long periods of time when the spiders were supplied with oxygen, although no details of the methodology were given.

## Mollusca

Many molluscs withdraw into a shell for protection against various vicissitudes. Some are then so idle that they can withstand years of inactivity. Trueman (98) developed a method of recording activity of the heart during such closure; it has thus been possible to study normal responses, and clarify the considerable literature on responses of the heart in vitro. *Mytilus edulis* exposed to air showed depression of the heart rate after three hours, and almost complete suppression of the heartbeat after a somewhat longer exposure. When reimmersed in water the heartbeat picked up promptly and showed an overshoot interpreted as due to oxygen debt. This sequence may be interpreted simply as due to anoxia developing progressively during the closure. Some work of Brand (19, cited in 99) bears out this idea. He cannulated the mantle of *Anodonta* and passed oxygenated sea water through it while the valves were clamped shut. The heartbeat continued as long as the perfusion was continued. In a tropical form, *Isognomon alatus* (99), natural valve closure led to suppression of the heartbeat within five minutes. About two minutes before the valves opened the heartbeat recommenced, showing that preparation for the relaxation of the adductor muscles played a role or at least gave some indication that nervous control may be present. The heartbeat during immersion is normally continuous, though it varied between 15 and 36 beats/min. Even in the sea the heart might stop for two or three hours. Upon observation of the animals it was noted that the valves were closed during this time. Trueman & Lowe suggested that temperature receptors might affect the heart reflexly because of both the rapidity of the rate changes and the difference in the effect of temperature changes when the animal was ventilating as opposed to periods of shell closure.

Lowe & Trueman (69) have continued this kind of analysis in *Mya arenaria* by measuring the water flow with a flow meter probe. When the heart rate and water flow rate were maintained stable the heart rate increased rapidly when the water temperature was increased. If the water temperature was changed at a low rate of water flow, the heart showed less response. It was thought that the heart rate was coupled to the rate of metabolism in some way and that oxygen tension might be the link.

Bayne (11) found in *Mytilus edulis* that he had to deal with two groups: metabolic regulators and metabolic conformers. In either group the ventilation rate and the frequency and amplitude of the heartbeat increased at slightly reduced oxygen tensions. At low oxygen tensions the ventilation rates and heart rates declined, but there might be an increased amplitude of heartbeat. The ventilation:perfusion ratio could be calculated; it decreased with declining oxygen tension in the regulators but remained constant in the conformers. It was suggested that the regulation of oxygen consumption was based upon the control of the ventilation:perfusion ratio, but the differences between individuals responsible for this regulation are not clear.

The mechanism by which control of the heart may be obtained is much better understood. Welsh (100) reviewed his work in this field and, with Hill, prepared the chapter on heart and circulation in *Physiology of the Mollusca* (50) which remains the most complete modern statement. Other comparative papers have also appeared (2, 32, 49, 64). The excitatory transmitter appears to be 5-HT, which is active at very low concentration, is present in the nerve fibers to the ventricle, and may perhaps work through adenyl cyclase and the production of cyclic AMP (27). Irisawa et al (51) and Wilkens & Greenberg (101) have compared the effects of ACh and 5-HT on ionic mechanisms of action and on membrane conductance in molluscan hearts. ACh has long been accepted as the inhibitory transmitter, and molluscan hearts have been widely used as an assay preparation because of their sensitivity to this substance and the reversibility of the effect. Considerable amounts of dopamine have been found in the molluscan nervous system, but the application of dopamine to the heart produces different effects in different molluscs. In *Patella vulgata* a threshold inhibitory concentration of $10^{-9}$ *M* dopamine is about the same as the inhibitory concentration of ACh in this species. Perhaps a particular role, for example a long-acting versus a short-acting cardio-inhibition, may be determined by further study. Nerve fibers are abundant in the auricle, but scarce in the ventricle, of *Archachatina marginata;* it therefore has been suggested that the auricle is controlled neurohumorally and the ventricle by neurosecretion. But since dopamine is active in this heart only at fairly high concentrations, no firm conclusions can yet be drawn (78).

A constant-volume hypothesis holds that in gastropods and lamellibranchs the contraction of the ventricle results in the filling of the auricle, and vice versa. Hill & Welsh (50) comment that this idea needs quantitative testing. Two different approaches have now been used to support the view. Jones (56) cites Trueman's confirmation in bivalves and presents experiments confirming the idea in two gastropods. Individuals of *Patella vulgata* were held in a clamp, usually in air, for strain-gauge measurements of blood pressure. There was a gradient of about 3 cm of water from bulbus aortae to pallial vein to propel blood through the system. During ventricular systole, producing 5 cm of water pressure, the pericardial pressure declined from a level of 2 cm to 0 cm of water, thus exerting a suction pressure to fill the auricle. On one occasion recordings were made while the bulbus aortae was contracting; the record showed a slight negative pressure in the pericardium.

The pressures were larger and the evidences even better for *Helix* (57), in which the ventricular systolic pressure reached 24 cm of water, reducing the pericardial pressure from about 3 to 1 cm water. The diastolic pressure in the auricle is normally about 5 cm, so there is a gradient through the system of 19 cm of water. The auricular systolic pressure barely exceeded the ventricular diastolic pressure; Jones makes the interesting point that, in essence, the ventricle is drawn back over the column of blood rather than the blood being forced along the tubular heart, and a large pressure gradient is thus not to be expected. The analysis confirms the constant-volume hypothesis for these animals.

Civil & Thompson (23) have removed the hearts of *Helix pomatia* and installed them in artificial pericardial sacs in a procedure requiring about 40 min. Successful preparations beat for several hours with apparently normal patterns of contraction. Without the artificial pericardium the behavior appeared much less normal. The pumping rate of the preparation was, of course, a direct function of frequency and stroke volume. The stroke volume could be regulated through the pericardial pressure so that, in effect, a cardiac tamponade could be produced by too great a filling, or a distention of the heart by a reduced pressure. These authors, too, conclude that the constant-volume hypothesis is useful in understanding the function of these molluscan hearts.

### Echinodermata

Two symposium volumes within the last eight years (18, 76) have dealt with various aspects of echinoderm biology, including circulatory physiology. These bring the student reasonably up to date in a field in which little physiological work has been done. An interesting contribution on the respiratory side takes advantage of a long-known (28) specialization in the family *Pterasteridae.* These sea stars brood their young in a nidamental chamber formed by tenting over the dorsal body surface with a supradorsal membrane supported by the crowns of calcium carbonate pillars, the paxillae. But since male animals, too, possess this chamber its origin must have been primarily to serve respiration and its use in brooding is a secondary development. Whereas sea stars in general use dermal branchiae and tube-feet projecting into the seawater for respiratory gas exchange, in *P. tesselatus* the branchiae are covered by the supradorsal membrane. Rodenhouse & Guberlet (83, 84) described how water is drawn into this chamber through spiraculae and expelled through a central osculum. Now Johansen & Petersen (55) have used a thermal water velocity probe to measure ventilation and oxygen electrodes to measure oxygen tension. There was up to 50% oxygen extraction at 10°C from the respiratory water, accounting for at least 90% of the total oxygen uptake. The respiratory rate increased with temperature and with decreased ambient oxygen tension, thus providing compensation and suggesting a control mechanism. The details of the analysis stop at this point. The delivery of up to 15 ml $O_2 \cdot kg^{-1} \cdot hr^{-1}$ to the tissues is accomplished through the coelomic fluid, essentially seawater. The dermal branchiae are thought to expand and retract during each respiratory cycle; this cycle would be effective in mixing oxygenated and deoxygenated blood in what is assumed to be a slow current produced by the beat of cilia lining the coelom. The part played by the haemal gland, or heart, has not been assessed but it must meet the needs of the central core of tissues and assist in general in the distribution of oxygen.

The haemal systems of sea stars and sea urchins are similar. We may add the observations of Boolotian (17) on *Strongylocentrotus purpuratus,* in which the axial gland contracts about 6 times per minute producing a detectable circulation, to the older observations of Gemmill (41) which showed that not only the axial gland but the gastric haemal tufts and the aboral haemal ring all undergo rhythmic contraction.

## Ascidians

The tunic in many of these primitive chordates is clear enough to reveal the beating of the heart. The reversal of the direction of beat at intervals is so striking a phenomenon that it was described very early and has continued to call forth observation and hypothesis. A very small dorsal ganglion (cerebral ganglion) is connected by nerve fibers to various structures, in particular to both ends of the heart. Florey (35) found acetylcholine in the dorsal ganglion and later (36) identified this ester in extracts of the body wall musculature. Its action was not potentiated by eserine but was blocked by atropine as well as *d*-tubocurarine. Ebara (30) has continued his studies on the ascidian heart taking advantage of the structure of the compound ascidian *Perophora orientalis* where a stolon carries blood between the zooids. He isolated one pair of zooids in which blood was observed to be flowing, and stimulated the dorsal ganglion electrically. A slowing of the heart and an alteration of the pattern of reversal was obtained in the zooid stimulated, but, in addition, the heart of the zooid, connected only by the blood stream, also slowed and the time delay was about that for the transmission time of the blood. In this case, however, eserine potentiated the inhibitory action and atropine did not block it, the reverse of Florey's observations on the body musculature. Ebara concludes that there is nervous and humoral transmission from ganglion to heart.

Goddard (47) has described the morphology of the heart of a large solitary ascidian *Pyura praeputialis,* the cells of each long tubular half making about a full spiral turn, on one side clockwise and on the other counterclockwise, until they meet in the middle. Some degree of spiralling of the cells seems to be characteristic of other ascidian hearts. The visible distinction of the two halves made observation easier. As a result of his observations, Goddard favors the hypothesis that fatigue is responsible for reversal since it was the "front" side of the heart that accomplished most of the work of circulation in each cycle of reversal. The estimation of work (48) was made possible by the insertion of catheters after removal of the visceral mass from the stalk. The posterior tunic vessel was immediately tied to prevent further blood loss, and a catheter inserted into the anterior tunic vessel where it originates from the visceral mass and pushed into the posterior aorta. The second, and opposite, catheterization was a needle placed in the cardio-visceral vessel. In a successful experiment pressures of about 30 mm of water were built up in the direction of the beat, primarily by the activity of the adjacent half of the heart. At the opposite end a pressure of about –7 mm of water was measured. When the beat reversed these pressure relationships were essentially inverted; several reversals could be followed in this way.

One theory of heart reversal has held that blood accumulated in the tunic vessels on one side of the stalk until a significant back pressure developed, after which the beat would reverse. Goddard's work does not support such a view. Of two parallel blood circuits, the one through the visceral mass has been known to be complete; blood pumped in at the anterior end returns to the heart at the posterior end, and vice versa. The circuit through the tunic has been thought to be incomplete (13, 31), that is, without capillaries, although there are many anastomosing small vessels in the tunic. Goddard applied the tip of a Pasteur pipette containing a little India ink to the large anterior tunic vessel after removal of the visceral mass and, by a very small pressure, caused the ink to emerge through the opening of the posterior tunic vessel. The reverse flow was as easily accomplished; thus it may be concluded that there is a complete throughway, probably capillary in nature. The advantage conferred by the reversal of the heart is not yet clear and offers a fascinating subject for speculation (cf. Kriebel; and Mislin, 74). The theory that the reversal is due to fatigue is made the more likely if one half of the heart is accomplishing most of the work throughout one half of each cycle.

CIRCULATION IN INVERTEBRATES    183

*Literature Cited*

1. Abbott, B. C., Lang, F., Parnas, I., Parmley, W., Sonnenblick, E. 1969. Physiological and pharmacological properties of *Limulus* heart. In *Comparative Physiology of the Heart: current trends*, ed. F. V. McCann. *Experientia, Suppl.* 15
2. Agarwal, R. A., Ligon, P. J. B., Greenberg, M. J. 1972. The distribution of cardioactive agents among molluscan species and tissues. *Comp. Gen. Pharmacol.* 3:249–60
3. Ahsanullah, M., Newell, R. C. 1971. Factors affecting the heart rate of the shore crab *Carcinas maenas. Comp. Biochem. Physiol. A* 39:277–87
4. Alexandrowicz, J. S. 1953. Nervous organs in the pericardial cavity of the decapod crustacea. *J. Mar. Biol. Assoc. UK* 31:563–80
5. Allen, J. A., Garrett, M. R. 1971. Taurine in marine invertebrates. *Advan. Mar. Biol.* 9:205–53
6. Allen, J. A., Garrett, M. R. 1972. Studies on taurine in the euryhaline bivalve *Mya arenaria. Comp. Biochem. Physiol. A* 41:307–17
7. Anderson, M., Cooke, I. M. 1969. Neuromuscular transmission on the heart of the lobster *Homarus americanus.* See Ref. 1
8. Anderson, M., Cooke, I. M. 1971. Neural activation of the heart of the lobster *Homarus americanus. J. Exp. Biol.* 55:449–68
9. Ashby, E. A., Larimer, J. L. 1964. Cardiac responses of the crayfish, *Procambarus simulans*, to external and internal carbon dioxide stress. *Physiol. Zool.* 37:21–32
10. Baskin, D. G. 1972. Studies on the infracerebral gland of the polychaete annelid *Nereis limnicola*, in relation to reproduction, salinity and regeneration. *Gen. Comp. Endocrinol.* 15:352–60
11. Bayne, B. L. 1971. Ventilation, the heart beat and oxygen uptake by *Mytilus edulis* L. in declining oxygen tension. *Comp. Biochem. Physiol. A* 41:1065–86
12. Berlind, A., Cooke, I. M. 1971. The role of divalent cations in electrically elicited release of a neurohormone from crab pericardial organs. *Gen. Comp. Endocrinol.* 17:60–72
13. Berrill, N. J. 1950. *The Tunicata.* Monogr. 133. London: The Ray Society
14. Blatchford, J. G. 1971. Haemodynamics of *Carcinus maenas* (L.) *Comp. Biochem. Physiol. A* 39:193–202

15. Bliss, D. E. 1968. Transition from water to land in decapod crustaceans. *Am. Zool.* 8:355–92
16. Bliss, D. E., Mantel, L. H., Eds. 1968. Symposium on Terrestrial Adaptations in Crustacea. In *Am. Zool.* 8:309–673
17. Boolootian, R. A. 1964. A primitive heart in the echinoid *Strongylocentrotus purpuratus. Science* 145:173–75
18. Boolootian, R. A., Ed. 1966. *Physiology of Echinodermata.* New York: Interscience
19. Brand, A. R. 1968. *Some adaptations to the burrowing habit in the class bivalvia.* PhD thesis. Univ. Hull, England. (See Ref. 99)
20. Bursey, C. R., Sherman, R. G. 1969. Microscopic anatomy of the cardiac ganglion of the tarantula, *Eurypelma marxi* Simon. *Am. Zool.* 9:586
21. Bursey, C. R., Sherman, R. G. 1970. Spider Cardiac Physiology. I. Structure and function of the cardiac ganglion. *Comp. Gen. Pharmacol.* 1:160–70
22. Cannon, H. G. 1947. On the anatomy of the pedunculate barnacle *Lithotrya. Phil. Trans. Roy. Soc. London B* 233:89–136
23. Civil, G. W., Thompson, T. E. 1972. Experiments with isolated hearts of the gastropod, *Helix pomatia*, in an artificial environment. *J. Exp. Biol.* 56:239–47
24. Cloudesley-Thompson, J. L. 1957. Studies in diurnal rhythm. V. Nocturnal ecology and water-relations of the British cribellate spiders of the genus *Ciniflo* Bl. *J. Linn. Soc. London Zool.* 43:134–52
25. Collett, L. C., O'Gower, A. K. 1972. Molluscan hemoglobins with unusual temperature-dependent characteristics. *Comp. Biochem. Physiol. A* 41:843–50
26. Connor, J. A. 1969. Burst activity and cellular interaction in the pacemaker ganglion of the lobster heart. *J. Exp. Biol.* 50:275–95
27. Cottrell, G. A., Osborne, N. N. 1969. Localization and mode of action of cardioexcitatory agents in molluscan hearts. See Ref. 1
28. Danielssen, D., Koren, J. 1856. Observation sur le developpement des asteries. *Fauna littorae Norvegiae* 2
29. Dumas, R., Ceccaldi, J. J. 1973. Acids amines libres et proteiques chez le siphonophore Forskalia edwardsi. *Comp. Biochem. Physiol. B* 45:43–50
30. Ebara, A. 1971. Physiological relations of the dorsal ganglion to the heart of a

compound ascidian, *Perophora orientalis. Comp. Biochem. Physiol. A* 39: 795–805

31. Endean, R. 1955. Studies of the blood and tests of some Australian ascidians. II. The test of *Pyura stolonifera. Aust J. Freshwater Res.* 6:139–56

32. Evans, T. G., Leake, L. D., Walker, R. J. 1971. The action of cholinergic drugs on the heart beat of the limpet, *Patella vulgata. Comp. Gen. Pharmacol.* 2: 5–14

33. Flindt, R. 1971. Zur abhangigkeit des Herzschlags von $O_2$ Gehalt des Wassers bei *Carcinus maenas. Mar. Biol.* 9: 224–27

34. Flindt, R., Kahrmann, E. G. 1972. Oxygen induced variations of heart rates in crayfish. *Physiol. Zool.* 45: 119–24

35. Florey, E. 1963. Acetylcholine and cholinesterase in tunicates. *Comp. Biochem. Physiol.* 8:327–30

36. Florey, E. 1967. Cholinergic neurons in tunicates: an appraisal of the evidence. *Comp. Biochem. Physiol.* 22:617–27

37. Florkin, M. 1969. *Annelida, Echiura and Sipuncula,* Vol. IV, *Chemical Zoology,* ed. M. Florkin, B. T. Scheer. New York: Academic

38. Florkin, M. 1973. The call of comparative biochemistry. *Comp. Biochem. Physiol. B* 44:1–10

39. Fourtner, C. R., Pax, R. A. 1972. The contractile blood vessels of the earthworm, *Lumbricus terrestris. Comp. Biochem. Physiol. A* 42:627–38

40. Fyhn, H. J., Petersen, J. A., Johansen, K. 1973. Heart activity and high-pressure circulation in *Cirripedia. Science* 180:513–15

41. Gemmill, J. F. 1914. The development and certain points in the adult structure of *Asterias rubens. Phil. Trans. Roy. Soc. London B* 205:213–94

42. Gerard, J. F., Gilles, R. 1972. The free amino-acid pool in *Callinectes sapidus* (R) tissues and its role in the osmotic intracellular regulation. *J. Exp. Mar. Biol. Ecol.* 10:125–36

43. Ghiretti, F., Ghiretti-Magaldi, A. 1972. Respiratory Proteins in Mollusks. *Chem. Zool.,* Vol. III, ed. M. Florkin, B. T. Scheer. New York: Academic

44. Ghiretti, F., Ed. 1968. *Physiology and Biochemistry of Hemocyanins.* New York: Academic

45. Ghiretti, F., Ghiretti-Magaldi, A., Salvato, B. 1972. Some chemical basis for the evolution of hemocyanins. *Proc. Int. Congr. Comp. Physiol.* In press

46. Gilles, R. 1972. Osmoregulation in three molluscs: *Acanthochiton discrepans, Glycymeris glycymeris* and *Mytilus edulis. Biol. Bull.* 142:25–35

47. Goddard, C. K. 1972. Structure of the heart of the ascidian *Pyura praeputialis. Aust. J. Biol. Sci.* 25:645–47

48. Goddard, C. K. 1973. Vascular physiology of the ascidian *Pyura praeputialis. J. Zool. London* 170:271–98

49. Greenberg, M. J. 1970. A comparison of acetylcholine structure-activity relations on the hearts of bivalve molluscs. *Comp. Biochem. Physiol.* 33:259–94

50. Hill, R. B., Welsh, J. H. 1966. Heart, Circulation, and Blood Cells. *Physiology of Mollusca,* ed. K. M. Wilbur, C. M. Yonge, Chap. 4, Vol. II. New York: Academic. 645 pp.

51. Irisawa, H., Wilkens, L. A., Greenberg, M. J. 1973. Increase in membrane conductance by 5-hydroxytryptamine and acetylcholine on the hearts of *Modiolus demissus* and *Mytilus edulis. Comp. Biochem. Physiol. A* 45:653–66

52. Johansen, K., Lenfant, C., Mecklenburg, T. A. 1970. Respiration in the crab, *Cancer magister. Z. Vergl. Physiol.* 70:1–19

53. Johansen, K., Martin, A. W. 1965. Circulation in a giant earthworm, *Glossoscolex giganteus.* I. Contractile processes and pressure gradients in the large blood vessels. *J. Exp. Biol.* 43: 333–47

54. Johansen, K., Martin, A. W. 1965. Circulation in a giant earthworm, *Glossoscolex giganteus.* II. Respiratory properties of the blood and some patterns of gas exchange. *J. Exp. Biol.* 45: 165–72

55. Johansen, K., Petersen, J. A. 1971. Gas exchange and active ventilation in a starfish, *Pteraster tesselatus. Z. Vergl. Physiol.* 71:365–82

56. Jones, H. D. 1970. Hydrostatic pressures within the heart and pericardium of *Patella vulgata* L. *Comp. Biochem. Physiol.* 34:263–72

57. Jones, H. D. 1971. Circulatory pressures in *Helix pomatia* L. *Comp. Biochem. Physiol. A* 39:289–95

58. Jones, M. B. 1972. Osmoregulation in the *Jaera albifrons* group of species. *J. Mar. Biol. Assoc. UK* 52:419–29

59. Kamemoto, F. I., Kato, K. N., Tucker, L. E. 1966. Neurosecretion and salt and water balance in the Annelida and Crustacea. *Am. Zool.* 6:213–19

60. Kamemoto, F. I., Ono, J. K. 1969. Neuroendocrine regulation of salt and

water balance in the crayfish *Procambarus clarkii*. *Comp. Biochem. Physiol.* 29:393–401

61. Kamemoto, F. I., Tullis, R. E. 1972. Hydromineral regulation in decapod crustacea. *Gen. Comp. Endocrinol. Suppl.* 3:299–307

62. Larimer, J. L. 1962. Responses of the crayfish heart during respiratory stress. *Physiol. Zool.* 35:179–86

63. Laverack, M. S. 1963. *The Physiology of Earthworms.* New York: Macmillan

64. Leake, L. D., Evans, T. G., Walker, R. J. 1971. The role of catecholamines and 5-hydroxytryptamine on the heart of *Patella vulgata*. *Comp. Gen. Pharmacol.* 2:151–58

65. Lechenault, H. 1965. Neurosecretion et osmoregulation chez les *Lineidae* (Heteronemertes). *CR Acad. Sci. Paris* 261:4868–91

66. Lent, C. M. 1969. Symposium on Adaptations of Intertidal Organisms. In *Am. Zool.* 9:271–426

67. Lin, S., Cohen, H. P. 1973. Crayfish ventral nerve cord and hemolymph: Content of free amino acids and other metabolites. *Comp. Biochem. Physiol. B* 45:249–63

68. Lockwood, A. P. M. 1970. The involvement of sodium transport in the volume regulation of the amphipod crustacean *Gammarus duebeni*. *J. Exp. Biol.* 53:737–51

69. Lowe, G. A., Trueman, E. R. 1972. The heart and water flow rates of *Mya arenaria* at different metabolic levels. *Comp. Biochem. Physiol. A* 41:487–94

70. Lynch, M. P., Webb, K. L. 1973. Variations in serum constituents of the blue crab, *Callinectes sapidus:* free amino acids and total ninhydrin positive substances. *Comp. Biochem. Physiol. B* 45:407–18

71. Manwell, C. 1964. Chemistry, genetics and function of invertebrate respiratory pigments-configurational changes and allosteric effects. In *Oxygen in the Animal Organism,* ed. F. Dickens, E. Neil. New York: Macmillan

72. Martin, A. W., Johansen, K. 1965. Adaptations of the circulation in invertebrate animals. *Handbook of Physiology, Section 2: Circulation,* Vol. III. Washington D.C.: Am. Physiol. Soc.

73. Maynard, D. M. 1960. Circulation and heart function. *Physiology of Crustacea,* ed. T. H. Waterman, Vol. 1, Chap. 5. New York: Academic. 670 pp.

74. McCann, F. V., Ed. 1969. *Comparative Physiology of the Heart: current trends. Experientia Suppl.* 15:111–34, 192–99

75. McCann, F. V. 1970. The physiology of insect hearts. *Ann. Rev. Entomol.* 15:173–200

76. Millot, N., Ed. 1967. *Echinoderm Biology.* London: Academic

77. Murdock, L. L. 1971. Catecholamines in arthropods: a review. *Comp. Gen. Pharmacol.* 2:254–74

78. Nisbet, R. H., Plummer, J. M. 1969. Functional correlates of fine structure in the heart of *Achatinidae*. In *Comparative Physiology of the Heart: current trends,* ed. F. V. McCann. *Experientia Suppl 15*

79. Parry, D. A., Brown, R. H. J. 1959. The hydraulic mechanism of the spider leg. *J. Exp. Biol.* 36:423–33

80. Parry, D. A., Brown, R. H. J. 1959. The jumping mechanism of salticid spiders. *J. Exp. Biol.* 36:654–65

81. Read, K. R. H. 1965. The characterization of the hemoglobins of the bivalve mollusc *Phacoides pectinatus* (Gmelin). *Comp. Biochem. Physiol.* 15:137–58

82. Redmond, J. R. 1955. The respiratory function of homocyanin in Crustacea. *J. Cell Comp. Physiol.* 46:209–47

83. Redmond, J. R. 1968. The respiratory function of hemocyanin. *Physiology and Biochemistry of Hemocyanin,* ed. F. Ghiretti. New York: Academic

84. Rodenhouse, I. Z., Guberlet, J. E. 1946. The morphology and behavior of the cushion star *Pteraster tesselatus* Ives. *Univ. Wash. Publ. Biol.* 12:21–48

85. Schoffeniels, E., Gilles, R. 1970. Ionoregulation and osmoregulation in mollusks. *Chem. Zool.* 5:199–227

86. Sherman, R. G., Pax, R. A. 1970. Spider cardiac physiology. II. responses of a tarantula heart to cholinergic compounds. *Comp. Gen. Pharmacol.* 1:171–84

87. Sherman, R. G., Pax, R. A. 1970. Spider cardiac physiology. III. Responses of a tarantula heart to certain catecholamines, amino acids, and 5-hydroxytryptamine. *Comp. Gen. Pharmacol.* 1:185–95

88. Smith, M. H. 1969. The pigments of Nematoda and Acanthocephala. *Chem. Zool.* 3:Chap. 10

89. Stewart, D. M., Martin, A. W. 1970. Blood and fluid balance of the common tarantula *Dugesiella hentzi*. *Z. Vergl. Physiol.* 70:223–46

90. Stiffler, D. F., Pritchard, A. W. 1972. A comparison of *in situ* and *in vitro* responses of crustacean hearts to hypoxia. *Biol. Bull.* 143:247–55

91. Sutcliffe, D. W. 1971. Regulation of water and some ions in Gammarids *(Amphipoda)*. I. *Gammarus duebeni* Lilljeborg from brackish water and fresh water. *J. Exp. Biol.* 55:325–44

92. See Ref. 91, II. *Gammarus pulex* (L). 345–55

93. See Ref. 91, III. Three euryhaline species. 357–69

94. Terwilliger, R. C., Terwilliger, N. B., Clay, G. A., Belamarich, F. A. 1970. The subcellular localization of a cardio-excitatory peptide in the pericardial organs of the crab *Cancer borealis. Gen. Comp. Endocrinol.* 15:70–79

95. Terwilliger, R. C., Koppenheffer, T. L. 1973. Coelomic cell hemoglobin of the polychaete annelid *Pista pacifica* Berkeley. *Comp. Biochem. Physiol. B* 45: 557–66

96. Thompson, K. T., Pritchard, A. W. 1969. Respiratory adaptations of two burrowing crustaceans, *Callianassa californiensis* and *Upogebia pugettensis. Biol. Bull.* 136:274–87

97. Thompson, L. C., Pritchard, A. W. 1969. Osmoregulatory capacities of *Callianassa* and *Upogebia* (Crustacea: Thalassinidea) *Biol. Bull.* 136:114–29

98. Trueman, E. R. 1967. Activity and heart rate of bivalve molluscs in their natural habitat. *Nature London* 214: 832–33

99. Trueman, E. R., Lowe, G. A. 1971. The effect of temperature and littoral exposure on the heart rate of a bivalve mollusc, *Isognomon alatus,* in tropical conditions. *Comp. Biochem. Physiol. A* 38:555–64

100. Welsh, J. H. 1971. Neurohumoral regulation and the pharmacology of a molluscan heart. *Comp. Gen. Pharmacol.* 2:423–32

101. Wilkens, L. A., Greenberg, M. J. 1972. Electrophysiological and ionic bases of acetylcholine and 5-hydroxytryptamine action on the heart of a bivalve mollusc, *Modiolus demissus granosissimus. Comp. Biochem. Physiol. A* 45:637–51

102. Wilson, R. S. 1965. The pedicel of the spider *Heteropoda vehatoria. J. Zool.* 147:38–45

103. Wilson, R. S. 1967. The heartbeat of the spider *Heteropoda venatoria. J. Insect Physiol.* 13:1309–26

104. Wilson, R. S. 1970. Some comments on the hydrostatic system of spiders (*Chelicerata, Araneae*). *Z. Morphol. Oekol. Tiere* 68:308–22

105. Wilson, R. S., Bullock, J. 1973. The hydraulic interaction between prosoma and opisthosoma in *Amaurobius ferox* (*Chelicerata, Araneae*). *Z. Morphol. Oekol. Tiere* 74:221–30

106. Witmer, A., Martin, A. W. 1973. The fine structure of the branchial heart appendage of the cephalopod *Octopus dofleini* martini. *Z. Zellforsch. Mikrosk. Anat.* 136: 545–68

107. Young, R. E. 1972. The physiological ecology of haemocyanin in some a selected crabs. I. The characteristics of hemocyanin in a tropical population of the blue crab *Callinectes sapidus* Rathbun. *J. Exp. Mar. Biol. Ecol.* 10: 183–92

108. Young, R. E. 1972. The physiological ecology of haemocyanin in some a selected crabs. II. The characteristics of haemocyanin in relation to terrestrialness. *J. Exp. Mar. Biol. Ecol.* 10:193–206

# FETAL AND NEONATAL CIRCULATION AND RESPIRATION[1]

❖1110

*Abraham M. Rudolph and Michael A. Heymann*[2]

Cardiovascular Research Institute and Departments of Pediatrics and Physiology,
University of California, San Francisco, California

Most of our knowledge of the fetal circulation until 1967 was derived either from
morphologic studies of various mammalian fetuses or from physiologic observations
of cardiovascular function and peripheral circulatory responses in exteriorized fetal
lambs. Many important concepts were derived from these studies, particularly in
regard to the effects of pharmacologic agents and changes in blood gases and pH
on specific circulations. The results of many of these observations have been well
summarized (24, 68). In recent years, several different techniques have been applied
to the study of the heart and circulation in the embryo and fetus. These include 1.
observations of early embryonic hearts and individual embryonic myocardial cells
in tissue culture (84, 88), 2. examination of the responses of isolated papillary
muscles or moderator band strips in tissue baths (13, 37), 3. studies on isolated intact
hearts (31), 4. responses of isolated vessels, such as the ductus arteriosus and
umbilical artery (56, 61), and 5. more recently both acute and chronic studies of the
normal physiology and responses to stress of fetuses in utero (9, 28, 69, 71). As the
latter studies have developed it has become increasingly evident that the exteriorized
fetus undergoes major physiologic changes of the circulation as well as other organ
systems. Both in the lamb (46) and in the previable human fetus (72), umbilical
blood flow falls rapidly initially, and continues to fall during the several hours of
observation after exteriorisation of the fetus, even under apparently ideal circumstances. Since umbilical blood flow represents about 40% of the combined left and
right ventricular outputs, major changes in umbilical flow could markedly alter
cardiac output and its distribution.

Although acute observations of fetuses in utero have provided more meaningful
data than in the exteriorized preparation, it is now evident that many physiologic

[1]Supported by Program Project Grant HE 06285 from the National Heart and Lung
Institute.

[2]Recipient Research Career Development Award HD 35398 from the National Institute of
Child Health and Human Development.

187

functions are influenced by the surgical and anesthetic procedures performed. This has prompted investigators to study the fetus in utero after recovery from the effects of surgery in chronic preparations. A period of 2–5 days has been shown to be necessary for return to normal physiologic function, depending on the extent of the surgical procedures performed. Thus it has been shown that right ventricular output increases by 20–100% in the 3–4 days following thoracotomy with implantation of an electromagnetic flow transducer around the main pulmonary trunk (71). Renal function is modified for as long as 5 days after surgical procedures (42) and adrenal cortical activity is increased for several days (10). Electrocortical activity is disturbed and respiratory and swallowing movements normally seen in the undisturbed fetus are suppressed for several days after surgical intervention (16, 28, 74). Although studies in these chronic preparations provide data which may be considered to represent normal physiologic function more reliably, they may still not be indicative of normal state since there is a relatively high incidence of spontaneous parturition 5–7 days after surgery.

In this review we have considered developmental changes in the structure and function of the myocardium and various peripheral circulations. We have also briefly reviewed the development of respiratory movements and the initiation of respiration after birth.

## THE HEART

### Structural Development

HEART MUSCLE   There are marked structural differences between fetal and adult myocardium (37, 88). Heart muscle cells are smaller in the fetus and the amount of noncontractile mass (nuclei, mitochondria, and surface membranes) is considerably greater; thus the number of myofibrils per unit mass of muscle is much lower in the fetus than in the adult. About 30% of fetal muscle consists of contractile mass as compared to 60% in the adult. In chick embryo ventricle there is a continuous increase in the density of the myofibrils in each individual muscle cell with advancing gestation (1). The developmental process in the myocardium continues after birth, but is quite variable in different species (88). Postnatally in the rat, the muscle cells progressively lose mitotic activity and further development is associated with increasing cell size and a decrease in nuclear density. At birth myocardial cell diameter is 5–6 microns and this increases to 15 microns in the adult heart. The organization of the muscle cells as well as of the myofibrillar elements changes during development. Fetal sarcomeres are not well organized, and are arranged in a more or less random fashion, whereas adult cells have a well organized parallel orientation. In the newborn cat, the myofibrils tend to be arranged peripherally in each cell with a central clear area (12), which appears from studies in the newborn rat to be a collection of glycogen (48). Both in the cat and in the rat, the adult structures are not well established until about three weeks after birth. Ultrastructural studies in cat heart muscle have shown that at birth the muscle cells are markedly interdigitated with short transverse segments of intercalated discs and numerous lateral attachments between the cells. With maturation, the transverse intercalated discs increase and the lateral attachments decrease (12).

CONDUCTION SYSTEM   Developmental changes in the conduction system have also been observed (49). The early fetal sinoatrial node shows greater cellularity, particularly with an increase in the number of pacemaker or P-cells. These gradually decrease in number during gestation and also for several months after birth. The atrioventricular node and His bundle are poorly organized in the fetus with components of conducting elements separated by loose areolar tissue. Numerous connections exist between atrial muscle and the atrioventricular node and bundle of His. The node and bundle are gradually defined, particularly after birth, by the combined process of cell resorption and development of collagen tissue, most prominently towards the left ventricular side of the interventricular septum.

AUTONOMIC NERVOUS DEVELOPMENT   The development of sympathetic innervation to the heart as examined by the monoamine fluorescence staining technique is quite variable in different species. The rabbit and rat, relatively immature at birth, have no demonstrable cardiac sympathetic nerves until about one week after birth (38, 53). However, the newborn guinea pig, which is quite mature, has well developed sympathetic nervous supply almost equivalent to that of the adult (53). Similarly, more detailed studies in the lamb (52) have demonstrated the presence of large numbers of dopamine cells, but no sympathetic nerves, before 0.5 of gestation. In the lamb, myocardial sympathetic nerves are first noted at only about 0.6 of gestation. The pattern of innervation is similar in all species examined. Sympathetic fibers appear initially in the sinoatrial region of the right atrium and progress to the left atrium, then to the bases of the ventricles, to the body of the right ventricle, and finally to the apex of the left ventricle. Innervation of the coronary arteries is always more advanced than that of the surrounding myocardium itself.

The pattern of development of parasympathetic innervation of the heart is less well defined; cholinesterase activity has been demonstrated in neural ganglia in the atrial epicardium and atrioventricular groove of human fetuses as early as about 8–10 weeks of gestation (79). There is an increase in both the extent and density of the epicardial plexus of nerves during development and, by about 16 weeks, nerves are noted in the myocardium and along major coronary arteries. It appears, therefore, that parasympathetic innervation precedes sympathetic innervation in the fetus.

## Biochemical Development

The anatomic observations of late development of sympathetic innervation are in accord with the observations that in the rat uptake and retention of labelled norepinephrine do not reach adult levels until about three weeks after birth (40) and that myocardial norepinephrine content gradually increases from fetal to adult life (37). Furthermore, the enzymes concerned with production of norepinephrine (tyrosine hydroxylase) and catabolism of norephinephrine (monoamine oxidase) are present in somewhat lower concentrations in fetal lamb myocardium than in the adult sheep (37).

Studies of myocardial metabolism in the fetus and newborn heart are quite limited. It has been suggested that myocardial ATP activity is greater in fetal and newborn puppies than in mature dogs (59); however, in fetal and newborn lambs ATP production and ATPase activity were found to be similar to that in adult sheep (83). Myocardial mitochondrial oxygen consumption per kilogram of protein in the presence of ADP was significantly greater in fetal and newborn animals than in the adult. Similarly, oxygen consumption in mitochondria uncoupled by DNP was higher in fetal and newborn myocardium. These findings by Wells et al (83), combined with their observation that cytochrome c oxidase activity was about 60% greater in fetal and newborn mitochondria than in adult mitochondria, suggested that there may be an increase in electron transport in the immature animal. They have further suggested that the age-related differences in mitochondrial oxidative phosphorylation could be related to the relative hypoxemia which is present in the fetus, since increased oxidative activity has been reported in mitochondria isolated from the hearts of cattle raised at high altitude (62).

## Myocardial Function

The performance of isolated muscle strips obtained from fetal, neonatal, and adult animals has been extensively examined. Length-tension and force-velocity relationships of moderator bands obtained from lambs and sheep (37) and of papillary muscle from newborn kittens and adult cats (13) have demonstrated that there are striking differences in resting tension, maximum active tension, and velocity of shortening of immature compared to mature heart muscle. In all studies reported, an attempt was made to normalize the data by correcting for length and cross-sectional area of the muscle strips. Resting or passive tension was higher in fetal lamb moderator bands than in those from the adult at any length along the length-tension curve; the increased slope of the resting tension curve indicated that fetal muscle had a lower compliance; this difference was greater as length was increased to approach L-max. The lower compliance of fetal muscle has been confirmed by measurements of pressure-volume relationships of the ventricular chambers in the intact hearts of fetal lambs and adult sheep (66). The right and left ventricles of hearts obtained within 15 minutes after death were distended with saline to develop pressure-volume curves. The pressure-volume relationships of the two ventricles were similar in the fetus, but after birth, the left ventricle was consistently less compliant than the right. Both the left and right ventricles showed a progressive decrease in stiffness with advancing age. These authors also attempted to examine the influence of possible differences in collagen content on ventricular compliance. It was thought that this was not an important consideration. Although hydroxyproline concentrations were greater in the adult heart, there was no significant difference when the data was corrected for dry weight, suggesting that the measured differences in collagen content were due to the higher water content of fetal muscle. Since the ventricles were less compliant in the immature animals, distention of one ventricle resulted in a more marked apparent decrease in compliance of the opposite ventricle.

At all muscle lengths, fetal muscle strips developed considerably less active tension during isometric contraction than did those of the adult (37). Studies of cat heart after birth indicated that there was a progressive increase in the development of active tension which only reached the adult level by about 32 days (13). Furthermore, the extent of shortening at any level of tension and the velocity of shortening in isotonic afterloaded contractions was impaired both in the fetal and neonatal lamb and neonatal cat as compared with the adult animal. Studies of paired electrical pacing of cat papillary muscle indicated that there was a smaller increase in developed tension in the younger animal (13).

All these observations have raised questions as to the cause of the relative inefficiency of the immature myocardium. Friedman (37) has suggested that it cannot be accounted for by inadequate performance of individual sarcomeres but that it is probably due to the smaller total number of sarcomeres (contractile units) as related to the total muscle mass. However, studies with glycerinated muscle fibers (37) in which the contribution of mitochondria, sarcolemmas, and saroplasmic reticulum is lost, suggested that there may also be some disturbance in the excitation-contraction coupling of the fetal heart.

Studies by Downing (31) of left ventricular performance in anesthetized newborn lambs in which heart rate, blood pressure and venous return could be controlled have confirmed many of the observations made in isolated fetal cardiac muscle. The presence of a Frank-Starling relationship in the newborn heart was documented by the demonstration of an increase in stroke volume produced by an increase in venous return to the left atrium while heart rate was controlled by atrial pacing and aortic mean blood pressure was kept constant. In these studies there was, however, a very narrow range of left ventricular end diastolic pressure over which stroke volume increased. Raising left ventricular end diastolic pressure from 4–12 mm Hg produced about a 100% increase in stroke volume, but stroke volume started to fall with further elevation of pressure above this level. On the basis of these studies, the behavior of the newborn lamb heart would appear to be quite different from that of the adult animal in which a continuing increase in stroke volume occurs with elevation of left ventricular end diastolic pressure to levels of about 25 mm Hg. In the same experimental preparation, Downing studied the effects of increasing afterload on the left ventricle by raising mean aortic pressure while maintaining heart rate. Increasing mean aortic pressure from 50–75 mm Hg had no effect on left ventricular stroke volume, but with a further elevation to 90 mm Hg there was a modest decrease in stroke volume, and with an increase above 90 mm Hg there was a precipitous fall in stroke volume. A similar response occurred in adult animals, but at considerably higher levels of aortic pressure.

Some question may be raised regarding the reliability of these studies in expressing the actual performance of the myocardium in intact unanesthetized animals, particularly since left ventricular stroke volume fell when left ventricular end diastolic pressure was raised above 10–12 mm Hg. One wonders whether the effects of anesthesia and the extensive surgical procedures performed may have had a deleterious effect. Since the quantitative and qualitative effects of anesthesia on the heart could be different in the fetal, newborn, and adult animal, it is not reasonable to assume that one can compare myocardial performance under similar experimental circumstances in each group.

In view of the increasing evidence that the heart and circulation as well as other physiologic functions in the fetus and newborn are markedly influenced by anesthesia and surgical procedures, efforts have been directed to developing models for studying undisturbed, unanesthetized animals. Polyvinyl catheters have been inserted into a hind-limb artery and vein, a forelimb artery and vein, or the carotid artery and jugular vein and into the trachea in fetal lambs for longterm observations in utero (75, 82). More recently, an electromagnetic flow transducer has also been applied around the main pulmonary trunk in fetal lambs of 0.7–0.85 gestation for continuous measurement of right ventricular stroke volume and output (71). In this preparation a catheter or catheter tip pressure transducer has also been inserted directly into the right ventricle. In some animals, two platinum electrodes were positioned on the left atrium or around the left vagus nerve and a small balloon catheter was passed through a femoral artery into the descending aorta (71). All catheters and electrodes were passed through the uterus and the lateral abdominal wall and positioned in a pocket attached to the flank of the ewe. Observations could then be made immediately, but a 3–5 day period of recovery was allowed before actual studies of physiologic performance were made. Continuous observations of fetal heart rate, arterial blood pressure, tracheal pressure, right ventricular pressure, and right ventricular output were made for several hours at a time. A consistent relationship between heart rate and mean right ventricular output was noted in association with spontaneous variations in heart rate. An increase in heart rate was always associated with an increase in right ventricular output, whereas reduction in heart rate was associated with a fall in right ventricular output. The relationship between the heart rate and right ventricular output was also examined during left atrial pacing at various rates and during left vagal stimulation (Figure 1). When heart rate was increased from control levels of 160–180/min to rates of 240–270/min, right ventricular output increased by about 12%. There was no additional increase of right ventricular output with a further increase in heart rate up to rates of 300–315/min, above which there was a rapid fall in right ventricular output. With a decrease in heart rate to about 120/min, produced by vagal stimulation, right ventricular output fell by 20%. The marked fall in right ventricular output when heart rate decreased was accounted for by a lack of any significant increase in right ventricular stroke volume.

The effects of increased afterload on the right ventricle were examined by graded inflation of the balloon inserted into the descending aorta thereby increasing right ventricular systolic pressure from a resting level of 60 mm Hg to a maximum of 80 mm Hg. This increase in pressure produced a fall both in right ventricular output and heart rate. When the fall in heart rate was eliminated either by left atrial pacing or by blocking the baroreflex with atropine, the fall in right ventricular output persisted, since there was a reduction in stroke volume which was maintained throughout the period of balloon inflation.

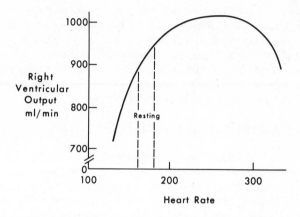

*Figure 1*  Effect on right ventricular output of increasing or decreasing heart rate from the resting level in a fetal lamb of 0.8 gestation [Reproduced from (71)]

The effects of increasing preload on right ventricular output were examined by rapid infusion of warmed saline (20–30 ml/kg fetal weight per min) into the fetal jugular vein. Right ventricular end diastolic pressure, corrected by subtraction of tracheal or intra-amniotic pressure, increased from 8–10 mm Hg at rest to levels of 25–30 mm Hg within two minutes. Right ventricular output increased only 15–20% in striking contrast with the 3- to 4-fold increase found in adult animals. These findings, in unanesthetized fetal lambs, of the limited ability of the myocardium to maintain stroke volume in response to increasing afterload, or of increasing stroke volume in response to an increase in preload, support the observations in isolated cardiac muscle strips.

It is thus evident that the fetal heart behaves very much like an adult heart at the upper limits of its ventricular function curve and that the Frank-Starling relationship would therefore not be an effective mechanism of regulation of cardiac output. In the adult animal the Frank-Starling mechanism serves the important function of providing a balance between the outputs of the left and the right ventricles. In the fetus, however, since the two ventricles effectively function in parallel, the Frank-Starling mechanism would not be of particular importance. In view of this limited ability for increasing stroke volume, fetal cardiac output is regulated predominantly by changes in heart rate.

## Responses to Hypoxia and Acidemia

In the anesthetized newborn lamb, as in the adult sheep, hypoxia produced by ventilation with low oxygen gas mixtures resulted in tachycardia (31). An increase in heart rate also occurred when fetal hypoxia was produced in anesthetized sheep by lowering the concentration of inspired oxygen (26). However, the unanesthetized lamb consistently developed bradycardia with systematic arterial hypertension when $Po_2$ was lowered by similar means (23).

Downing et al have shown that left ventricular myocardial function in newborn lambs is not depressed by hypoxia until arterial saturation falls below 25% (33). Similarly a reduction in arterial pH to levels of 6.8 and less had little influence on left ventricular function. However, a combination of hypoxia and acidemia produced marked depression of myocardial performance. Norepinephrine increased left ventricular myocardial function in the newborn lamb and this response was not depressed by acidemia, even of fairly severe degree.

## CARDIAC OUTPUT AND ITS DISTRIBUTION

The fetal circulation differs from the adult in that the flow of blood from the right and left ventricles is not in series. Whereas in the adult the outputs of the two ventricles are normally quite similar, there may be great differences in the output of each ventricle in the fetus. Also, blood from both ventricles is distributed to many systemic organs and the placenta. It has thus become convenient to consider cardiac output in the fetus as the combined output of the two ventricles. In previous studies of exteriorized fetal lambs, combined ventricular output measured by either the Fick method (30), indicator dilution curves (57), or electromagnetic flow transducers (5) ranged between 235 and 360 ml/kg fetal weight per min. The proportion of combined ventricular output ejected by the right ventricle in those studies varied between 45–58%. Recent studies using radionuclide labelled microspheres in fetal lambs of 0.8–1.0 gestation in utero after 3–5 days recovery from surgery, showed higher levels of combined ventricular output (490 ml/kg fetal weight per min) with the right ventricular output dominant, contributing about 2/3 of the combined output (Figure 2).

The radionuclide labelled microscophere method has also been used to measure the distribution of cardiac output and organ blood flows (69). The percentages of combined ventricular output distributed to various organs in the term fetal lamb were found to be: placenta 41, lungs 7, kidneys 2, myocardium 3.6, brain 3, and gastrointestinal tract 5.5. The remaining 38% was distributed to the fetal body. The actual blood flows based on ml flow per 100 g of organ weight per min were 126 to the lungs, 173 to the kidneys, 291 to the myocardium, 132 to the brain, and 69 to the gastrointestinal tract. The patterns of blood flow and distribution of combined ventricular output were found to vary with fetal gestational age.

The inferior vena caval return provided 69% of combined ventricular output and the superior vena caval 21%. Only minimal amounts of superior vena caval return crossed the foramen ovale, whereas 39% of inferior vena caval return representing 29% of combined ventricular output crossed the foramen ovale into the left atrium. Of the blood ejected by the right ventricle 90% (59% of combined ventricular output) passed across the ductus arteriosus to the descending aorta. The proportions of blood shunted are influenced by changes in pulmonary vascular resistance (Lewis, Heymann & Rudolph unpublished observation). An increase in pulmonary blood flow is associated with a fall in the proportion of inferior vena caval return crossing the foramen ovale.

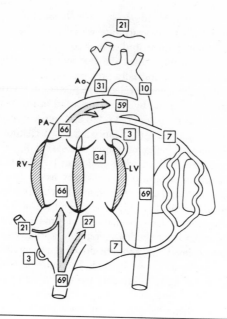

*Figure 2* Percentages of combined ventricular output ejected by left and right ventricles and distributed to the major vascular channels in the fetus.

## CONTROL OF THE CIRCULATION

### Autonomic Nervous Regulation

Cardiovascular function in the adult is influenced in a complex manner by cerebral cortical, hypothalamic, and medullary activity. Little is known regarding the development of autonomic regulation of the circulation in the fetus. Autonomic regulation is dependent on the development of the central nervous components and the efferent pathway and receptors; reflex activity requires establishment of afferent connections as well. Recent observations on fetal lambs have shown that changes in electrocortical activity from slow, high voltage to rapid, low voltage, associated with rapid eye movement sleep were accompanied by irregular respiratory activity and often an increase in heart rate and systemic arterial pressure (28). Other evidence that has corroborated the fact that cerebral cortical activity may influence the circulation has been derived from studies of the effects of injection into fetal lambs of lidocaine in sufficient amounts to produce electrocortical patterns characteristic of epileptiform activity (80). These changes were associated with intermittent episodes of marked fetal hypertension.

Hypothalamic control has been studied directly by stimulation of an electrode inserted by stereotactic techniques into the hypothalamus of fetal lambs from 0.75–0.9 gestation (85). After 3–4 days recovery from surgery, electrode stimulation produced a rise in fetal arterial blood pressure which could be prevented by alpha adrenergic blockade and a rise in heart rate which could be eliminated by beta adrenergic blockade. Although these studies showed that the pathways and connections were developed in the fetus, they did not indicate whether hypothalamic control over the circulation was normally present.

Baroreflex activity has been demonstrated to be present in exteriorized fetal lamb preparations of about 0.6 gestation by observing a fall in the heart rate following an increase in arterial blood pressure (7, 17, 29) and, more directly, by recordings of impulses in the carotid sinus nerve (11). Since it is now well known that anesthesia and other stimuli may modify reflex responses, the sensitivity of the baroreflex in comparison with the unanesthetized adult could not be reliably assessed in those studies. A detailed analysis of baroreflex sensitivity has been performed in fetal lambs from 0.6–1.0 gestation and in newborn lambs in which catheters and an aortic balloon were chronically implanted (75). The magnitude of fall in heart rate, in relationship to blood pressure rise was analyzed in a manner similar to Smyth et al (78). In the younger lambs, a sudden increase in aortic pressure produced by balloon inflation was associated only sporadically with a baroreflex response. When it was elicited, the response was quite limited. The baroreflex sensitivity progressively increased with advancing gestation until term but there was no further change after birth.

Stimulation of arterial chemoreceptors in the fetus produces predominantly cardiovascular responses and massive stimulation is required to produce respiratory movements. It has been suggested since carotid chemoreceptors are primarily concerned with respiration and aortic chemoreceptors are mainly concerned with circulatory regulation, that only aortic chemoreceptors should respond in the fetus. In acute studies of exteriorized fetal lambs, stimulation of aortic chemoreceptors by reduction of fetal arterial $Po_2$ resulted in tachycardia, an increase in arterial blood pressure, and vasoconstriction in the hind limb (25, 26). These responses could be abolished by cutting the aortic nerve or vagus nerve in the neck. In other studies performed with the use of carotid arterial delay loops (41), cardiovascular responses could be produced by stimulating either the aortic or carotid and central chemoreceptors, and the effects of stimulation of the aortic chemoreceptors or carotid and central chemoreceptors could be separated by sodium cyanide or sodium bicarbonate injection. Cardiovascular responses were different; aortic chemoreceptor stimulation produced bradycardia and either mild hypotension or hypertension, whereas carotid or central stimulation usually produced hypertension with either tachycardia or no change in heart rate. Results were quite variable in this study and it is unlikely that reliable observations of chemoreceptor function can be obtained in acute preparations, in view of the variable effects of anesthesia and the influence on chemoreceptor activity of the level of sympathetic activity (11).

Some of the earliest studies performed on fetuses were concerned with the ability of the circulation to respond to neurotransmitter substances (7). Recently, considerable attention has been directed to assessing the development of circulatory responses to sympathetic and parasympathetic stimulation. Heart rate responses to beta sympathetic stimulation occur early in gestational development. Exposure to epinephrine of 12–13 day old chick embryo heart cells in culture resulted in an increase in rate of contraction; this increase was blocked by veratramine and two beta adrenergic blocking agents, nethalide and dichlorisoproterenol, but not by an alpha adrenergic blocker phenoxybenzamine (86).

The intact fetal lamb in utero shows an increase in heart rate with infusion of isoproterenol by 0.4 gestation, the youngest lamb studied (9). The sensitivity of the heart rate response to isoproterenol did not change significantly during advancing gestation, since similar amounts of isoproterenol in relationship to fetal body weight were required to produce an increase in heart rate in fetal lambs from 0.55–1.0 gestation (82). Studies of the sensitivity of other cardiovascular responses to beta adrenergic stimulation are sparse. Coronary circulation dilates in response to beta adrenergic stimulation by 0.4, and the pulmonary circulation by 0.5 gestation.

The response of the myocardium has been studied in detail in isolated cardiac muscle preparations obtained from late gestation fetal lambs (37). Isoproterenol produced an increase in myocardial contractility similar to that found in the adult. An increase in contractility due to norepinephrine was also demonstrated; however, the percentage increase of tension was greater in fetal muscle than in adult muscle strips at similar norepinephrine concentrations. Since increase in tension produced by similar concentrations of isoproterenol was the same in fetal and adult muscle, Friedman (37) suggested that fetal muscle demonstrated hypersensitivity which was explained by absent or delayed development of sympathetic nerve supply.

An increase in left ventricular contractility in response to postganglionic stimulation in the newborn lamb also indicated that the response was well developed by birth (32). Studies of the effects of beta adrenergic stimulation on myocardial performance have recently been performed on the fetal lamb in utero by examining the response of right ventricular output to atrial pacing with and without isoproterenol infusion (71). The greater right ventricular output during isoproterenol infusion at all levels of output suggested that right ventricular myocardial performance was improved by beta adrenergic stimulation.

The response of several vascular structures to alpha adrenergic stimulation has been demonstrated to exist by about 0.5 gestation in fetal lambs (9). Arterial blood pressure increased in response to methoxamine infusion and renal and peripheral vasoconstriction occurred. Sensitivity of the vascular structures to alpha adrenergic stimulation at different stages of development did not change with advancing gestation. Vasoconstriction can also be produced in the pulmonary circulation by 0.5 gestation in fetal lambs by norepinephrine infusion (22). Injection of the parasympathetic neurotransmitter substance, acetylcholine, into fetal lambs in utero produced a fall in heart rate by 0.5 gestation, the youngest animals examined, and there was no significant change of the heart rate response with increase in fetal age (82). The pulmonary vessels are markedly dilated by acetylcholine infusion by 0.5 gestation in fetal lambs (22). The above studies all indicate that alpha and beta adrenergic and parasympathetic receptors are present in many vascular structures at an early gestational age. It is not yet known, however, whether there is a change in the actual numbers of receptors in an individual cell or within an organ during development. Although receptors are present, the role of the autonomic nervous system in affecting normal vasomotor activity, heart rate, and myocardial performance has not been fully examined. The fact that hexamethonium, a ganglionic blocker, produced a fall in heart rate and blood pressure by 0.66 gestation suggested that there was resting sympathetic activity by that age. Since the studies were performed in exteriorized fetuses, it is possible that autonomic stimulation was present because of the type of experimental preparation used (24). In an attempt to avoid these effects, specific autonomic functions were blocked selectively by pharmacologic means in chronic fetal lamb preparations from 0.6–1.0 gestation (82). Parasympathetic blockade with atropine produced a small change in heart rate in young fetuses, but this effect increased markedly by 0.7 gestation. Similarly, alpha adrenergic blockade with phenoxybenzamine or phentolamine resulted in only a small decrease in blood pressure in young fetuses, but a much greater fall after 0.7 gestation. Blockade of beta adrenergic activity with propranolol or practalol produced only small decreases in heart rate up to 0.8 gestation, after which there was a rapid increase in the effect. These studies suggest that there is increasing autonomic nervous control of heart rate and blood pressure with advancing gestation, but that the pattern of development of different autonomic functions is variable. The effects of the autonomic nervous system on the development of other cardiovascular functions are yet to be determined.

The discussion so far presented has been concerned with the general responses of the circulation to autonomic nervous stimulation and blockade. Apart from detailed studies of the lung, relatively little information is available regarding the responses of the circulation in specific organs in the fetus to local environmental changes and to nervous and hormonal influences.

## Responses of Circulation in Individual Organs

CEREBRAL BLOOD FLOW   The changes in cerebral blood flow during fetal development, measured by use of radionuclide labeled microspheres, indicate a marked increase from about 30 ml/100 g brain wet weight per min in the fetus at 0.5 gestation to 130 ml/100 g brain wet weight per min at term (69). There are, however, conflicting data on actual levels of flow near term. Purves & James (64) reported much lower flow in the term fetal lamb of about 15 ml/100 g per min for white matter and 70 ml/100 g per min for gray matter using washout curves with $^{133}$Xenon. In fetal rats, Barker (8) found cerebral blood flow of about 150 ml/100 g per min using $^{131}$Iodine antipyrine. Cerebral blood vessels in the fetal lamb appear to show autoregulation similar to that in adult vessels, suggested by the study using $^{133}$Xenon, in which gray matter blood flow was noted to be constant over a mean arterial pressure ranging from 40–80 mm Hg (64). However, this was not present in the fetal rat (8). Several studies have also shown that a rise in $Pco_2$ or fall in $Po_2$ of the blood perfusing the brain produced an increase in cerebral blood flow (8, 20, 54, 64). There is also conflict in the reported observations of changes in cerebral blood flow after birth. Using electromagnetic flow transducers to measure carotid flow, Lucas et al (54) demonstrated a dramatic fall following clamping of the umbilical cord despite an increase in total cardiac output. Purves & James (64), however, indicated that clamping of the umbilical cord produced an increase in cerebral blood flow and also an increase in cerebral oxygen consumption. Many of the reported results may be questioned in view of the experimental preparation and techniques used. Most of the studies were performed on exteriorized fetuses and, in some, extensive surgical procedures were performed. Measurements of flow with electromagnetic flow transducers on the carotid artery do not exclude flow to extracranial tissues and also do not consider variations in carotid and vertebral arterial contribution to cerebral blood flow. It is also possible that the proportion of intracranial and extracranial flow may vary depending on the preparation. In the Xenon washout studies, it is also possible that a significant contribution of extra-cranial flow to the sagittal sinus may have lowered the calculated measurement of cerebral blood flow. It was also assumed that little superior vena caval blood crossed the foramen ovale; however, the experimental manipulations performed may have induced significant shunting of superior vena caval blood through the foramen ovale, resulting in early recirculation, thus interfering with the measurement. In view of these potential errors, the observations that bilateral vagotomy decreases resting cerebral blood flow in the fetus (64) remain to be confirmed.

THE UMBILICAL CIRCULATION    Previous reviews have demonstrated that the isolated umbilical vessels constrict with an increase in $Po_2$ and dilate when exposed to low $Po_2$. The responses have been of interest since, apart from the small length at the fetal attachment, the umbilical vessels appear to have no nerve supply and there are few vasa vasorum. It has usually been assumed that the vessels close by constriction of the circular muscle. Roach (65) has stressed that circular muscle constriction alone is ineffective in producing closure of the umbilical artery. Constriction of the longitudinal muscle, by shortening the vessel and making the intima protrude into the lumen aids the circular muscle in producing complete closure. In the human umbilical cord, coiling of the vessels normally seen is due to an additional spirally oriented longitudinal muscle bundle which Roach has termed the "coiling muscle." Removal of this muscle uncoils the isolated artery. She has stressed that the circular and longitudinal muscles may respond differently. The circular muscle is readily constricted by an increase in $Po_2$ and relaxed by a decrease in $Po_2$, but the results with changes in blood gases are less consistent with longitudinal muscle. However, the longitudinal muscle responds actively with constriction to stretch. In the human umbilical cord, the coiling muscle is actively constricted by a fall in temperature to about 27°C. These recent observations raise questions regarding previous studies on the responses of the isolated umbilical artery to changes in pH and blood gases and to pharmacologic agents, since they were conducted either with helical muscle strips, umbilical arterial rings, or perfused segments of the vessels in which length was controlled. It would seem that in most of these studies only the circular muscle responses were being examined. Constriction of the umbilical arteries at birth probably results from a combination of changes in temperature and $Po_2$ as well as stretch. Altura et al (2) showed that serotonin, oxytocin, and bradykinin in very low concentrations consistently induced constriction whereas the effects of prostaglandins, acetylcholine, histamine, angiotension, epinephrine, and norepinephrine were erratic. Their studies were all performed on human umbilical vessels in a 95% oxygen environment. The results must be questioned since the vessels were already constricted under these circumstances, and since the responses to pharmacologic agents of umbilical arteries vary with the oxygen environment (34). In the intact fetal-placental unit, umbilical blood flow is about 200 ml/kg fetal weight per min, representing about 40% of the combined ventricular output in the fetal lamb near term (58, 69). It is not influenced by changes in femoral arterial blood gases and most vasoactive agents (24). During fetal hypoxia, with or without acidemia, induced by administering gas mixtures low in oxygen to conscious ewes, umbilical blood flow was maintained, even though fetal cardiac output fell (23). The maintenance of umbilical blood flow was probably related to an increase in fetal arterial blood pressures, since it had been suggested previously that the umbilical circulation does not demonstrate any autoregulation (24). In contrast, controlled hemorrhage in fetal lambs resulted in a marked fall in umbilical blood flow associated with a decrease in cardiac output, presumably since arterial blood pressure also fell (81).

PULMONARY CIRCULATION    The responses of the pulmonary circulation have been extensively studied in exteriorized fetal lambs, but there are few measurements of actual levels of pulmonary blood flow in the fetus in utero. Studies done in utero using radionuclide labeled microspheres have shown that the pulmonary blood flow increased out of proportion to the increase in fetal weight during advancing gestation (69). The blood flow to the lungs represented about 3.5% of the combined ventricular output between 0.4 and 0.7 gestation and this increased to about 7% by term. Pulmonary blood flow increased from about 30–40 ml/100 g lung wet weight per min to about 130 ml/100 g lung wet weight per min over this period. Previous studies in fetal lambs have suggested a linear relationship between pulmonary vascular resistance and the $Po_2$ to which the vessels are exposed (22), but studies in newborn calves (73) indicated that the response was curvilinear and also that an increase in hydrogen ion concentration markedly increased the constrictor response to a fall in $Po_2$. Most observations on the response of the pulmonary circulation to $Po_2$ changes have been concerned with increasing $Po_2$ above the normal fetal level. Studies of exteriorized fetal lambs using cross circulation between twin fetuses demonstrated pulmonary vascular constriction in response to both local changes in $Po_2$ and pH of blood perfusing the lungs, and to a fall of $Po_2$ and pH of systemic arterial blood (19). It was suggested that the pulmonary vascular constrictor response was due to both direct local effects on pulmonary vascular smooth muscle as well as to chemoreflex influences. The reflex responses were not observed in fetal lambs under 0.65 gestation (19). All these studies were subjected to the criticism that they were performed in exteriorized fetuses in which the stress of the experimental preparation may have influenced or modified the responses. The relationship of pulmonary vascular resistance to the fetal pulmonary arterial $Po_2$ was studied in fetal lambs in utero in which pulmonary blood flow, measured by a chronically implanted electromagnetic flow transducer, and pulmonary arterial pressure, could be continuously monitored (70). Fetal pulmonary arterial $Po_2$ was changed without altering pH or $Pco_2$ by administration of various gas mixtures to the conscious ewe.

A curvilinear response over a pulmonary arterial $P_{O_2}$ range of 10–25 torr was demonstrated and the vasoconstrictor response was greater in older lambs.

The fall in pulmonary vascular resistance which occurs at birth has been studied extensively. It had previously been shown by a number of investigators that pulmonary vasodilatation is largely due to the effects of an increase in $P_{O_2}$ associated with ventilation of the lungs. Recently, Gilbert et al (39) have confirmed that rhythmic expansion of the lungs with a gas mixture of 4% $O_2$ and 6% $CO_2$ in nitrogen produced a small decrease in pulmonary vascular resistance. Since this gas mixture produces a $P_{O_2}$, $P_{CO_2}$, and pH environment similar to that of the fetus, they have concluded that physical expansion of the lung with gas in some way decreases pulmonary vascular resistance. When $P_{O_2}$ was also increased, a more dramatic effect was noted.

The fetal pulmonary vessels are very sensitive to various pharmacologic agents being constricted by epinephrine and norepinephrine and dilated by isoproterenol, acetylcholine, histamine, and bradykinin (14, 21, 22, 24, 77). The mechanism by which oxygen dilates pulmonary vessels is still not known. Since bradykinin has been shown to be released into the circulation when fetal lambs were ventilated with oxygen (47) it has been suggested that at least some of the oxygen effects may be associated with the vasodilator effects of released bradykinin.

## DUCTUS ARTERIOSUS

The ductus arteriosus in the fetal lamb carries 59% of combined ventricular output from the main pulmonary trunk to the descending aorta and is thus important in providing umbilical blood flow (45). Little is known about the responses of the ductus arteriosus to various physiologic and pharmacologic influences in the intact fetus in utero. In the exteriorized fetal lamb, high concentrations of epinephrine and norepinephrine have been shown to constrict the ductus arteriosus (15). In exteriorized lambs the ductus arteriosus has also been constricted by increasing fetal arterial $P_{O_2}$ by subjecting the ewe to a hyperbaric oxygen environment (4).

Most observations of the responses of the ductus arteriosus have been made either on isolated perfused vessels or on excised segments suspended in tissue baths. The constriction induced by increasing $P_{O_2}$ in surrounding fluid was reported initially by Kennedy & Clark (51), and subsequently by several other workers. The response to oxygen was confirmed and patterns of response studied in detail in isolated perfused ductuses (56) and in ductal rings (61) obtained from fetal lambs. The response to oxygen is curvilinear and is also related to the fetal gestational age. Ductuses obtained from fetal lambs less than 0.66 gestation showed almost no response to increases in $P_{O_2}$ over 600 torr. With advancing gestation, there was a decrease in level of $P_{O_2}$ required to produce an initial response and the tension developed at any $P_{O_2}$ level was greater as gestational age advanced (Figure 3). The ductus arteriosus of the fetal lamb was most relaxed when the environmental $P_{O_2}$ was about 15–35 torr but constricted when $P_{O_2}$ was decreased below this level to 8–10 torr (61). The mechanism by which oxygen constricts the ductus arteriosus is still not known. It has been suggested by Fay (35) from studies on guinea pig

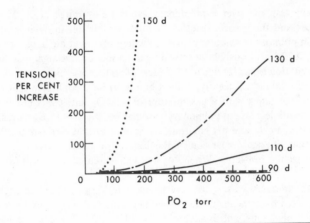

*Figure 3* Percentage increase in tension above baseline produced by increasing the $PO_2$ above resting (35 torr) in the ductus arteriosus of fetal lambs of advancing gestation.

ductuses that an increased rate of oxidative phosphorylation is produced by increasing the availability of oxygen to the terminal component of cytochrome, probably cytochrome $a_3$. On the basis of his studies, the contraction is probably produced by a direct effect of oxygen on the smooth muscle cells.

The possibility that oxygen may constrict the ductus arteriosus by releasing a mediating substance has also been considered. The ductus arteriosus isolated from human fetuses of 10–20 weeks gestation failed to constrict when exposed to oxygen, but did constrict with acetylcholine (55). Aronson et al (3) studied human fetal ductus arteriosus between 10–20 weeks gestation by histochemical means and found no cholinergic nerve fibers or cholinesterase within the wall. However, the ductus arteriosus at term, both in fetal puppies (60) and in fetal lambs (76), has been shown to contain large quantities of cholinesterase and Silva & Ikeda have suggested (76) that this demonstration of cholinesterase indicates the presence of cholinergic nerves. In ductal rings obtained from late gestation fetal lambs, the constrictor response to an increased oxygen environment was completely reversed by high concentrations of atropine (61). It is therefore possible that changes in $O_2$ environment could relate to a mechanism providing the local release of acetylcholine.

The increase in arterial $Po_2$ after birth is probably not the only mechanism responsible for closure of the ductus arteriosus. In newborn guinea pigs exposed to a low oxygen environment (36) and in infants with congenital heart disease with markedly reduced arterial $Po_2$ (67), closure after birth may be delayed but the ductus arteriosus does close in spite of a consistently lower than normal $Po_2$. It is well known that 5-hydroxytryptamine, bradykinin, acetylcholine, and norepineph-rine produce constriction of the ductus arteriosus, but the role of these substances in the normal closing process has not been fully assessed. It has been suggested that the increase in bradykinin concentration that occurs at the time of birth may contribute to closure of the ductus arteriosus (47).

Postnatal closure is related not only to muscular contraction, but also to a necrotic process which occurs within the subintimal layers and it has been suggested that this is due to interference with nutritional supply (36).

## INITIATION OF BREATHING

Recent observations on chronically instrumented fetal lambs have demonstrated that fetal respiratory movements are present from about 0.66 gestation (28). These movements were also observed in fetal lambs at 0.27 gestation delivered into a warm saline bath (28) and appeared to become deeper and more rapid with advancing gestation. Continuous observations over long periods have shown that these rapid, irregular respiratory movements are present for 30–50% of the time. They occur at a frequency of about 80–100/min and are not associated with much change of chest volume, only 2–4 ml of tracheal fluid moving backwards and forwards during respiration. Occasionally, a more prolonged expiratory grunt led to the net outward flow of small volumes of fluid. Mild degrees of hypoxia and manipulation of the fetus suppressed these movements; however, over the normal physiologic range of pH and blood gases there was apparently no change in respiratory activity. Simultaneous measurement of electrocortical activity, eye movements and respiratory motion have shown a close relationship between respiratory activity and electrocortical activity. The change from the slow, high voltage electrocorticogram seen in the awake animal or during nonrapid eye movement sleep, to an electrocorticogram showing fast, low voltage activity suggestive of rapid eye movement sleep, was associated with respiratory activity.

The possibility that initiation of breathing after birth is related to changes in arterial pH, $P_{CO_2}$, or $P_{O_2}$ affecting the peripheral and central chemoreceptors has been investigated predominantly in fetal lambs. It was first suggested that gradual increases in $P_{CO_2}$ or decreases in $P_{O_2}$ of fetal arterial blood did not stimulate ventilatory activity, but that rapid changes, produced by infusion of hypoxemic or acidemic blood into the carotid artery, produced sustained ventilation (6, 43, 44). It was also suggested by Pagtakhan et al (63) that there is an interaction between changes of $P_{O_2}$ and $P_{CO_2}$ in their effect on initiating ventilation. They could not confirm Harned's observations that a rapid change of blood gas was necessary. Woodrum et al (87) perfused the carotid artery unilaterally or bilaterally with carotid loop preparations in late gestation fetal lambs. Changes in $P_{O_2}$ of the perfusing blood produced ventilatory responses but there was a time delay of about 9 seconds. This delay was even greater (29 seconds) after an increase in $P_{CO_2}$. Their studies and also observations of the ventilatory response produced by injection of sodium cyanide into the carotid artery (27, 41) all suggest that the fetal chemoreceptors are relatively insensitive to blood gas and pH changes in regard to ventilatory responses. The rather prolonged delay in the response and the relative insensitivity of chemoreceptors suggest that changing blood gases is not a predominant mechanism involved in the initiation of breathing after birth. Fetal respiration can be stimulated by cooling of the skin in the exposed fetus or by stimulation with cold water in utero (41). Ventilation is also initiated by tactile stimuli. It has been suggested that increased sensory impulses from the periphery enhance the sensitivity of the respiratory centers and that this is the mechanism responsible for maintenance of the rhythmicity of these centers (18). Biscoe et al demonstrated a rapid increase in the sensitivity of the carotid chemoreceptor responsiveness to blood gas changes after birth and hypothesized that this resulted, at least in part, from increased cervical sympathetic activity (11). Once established, regular respiration can be reflexly inhibited. A recent study has demonstrated the importance of inhibitory reflexes in producing apnea in newborn animals (50); these may be related to stimulation of taste receptors, arising from the posterior pharynx of fetal and newborn lambs.

*Literature Cited*

1. Adams, M. H., Barry, W. H., Harrison, D. C. 1972. Changes in inotropic responsiveness with increasing age of chick embryo ventricle. *Circulation* 46:II–36
2. Altura, B. M., Malaviya, D., Reich, C. F., Orkin, L. R. 1972. Effects of vasoactive agents on isolated human umbilical arteries and veins. *Am. J. Physiol.* 222:345
3. Aronson, S., Gennser, G., Owman, C. H., Sjoberg, N. O. 1970. Innervation and contractile response of the human ductus arteriosus. *Eur. J. Pharmacol.* 11:178
4. Assali, N. S., Kirschbaum, T. M., Dilts, P. V. Jr. 1968. Effects of hyperbaric oxygen on uteroplacental and fetal circulation. *Circ. Res.* 22:573
5. Assali, N. S., Morris, J. A., Beck, R. 1965. Cardiovascular haemodynamics in the fetal lamb before and after lung expansion. *Am. J. Physiol.* 208:122
6. Avery, M. E., Chernick, V., Young, M. 1965. Fetal respiratory movements in response to rapid changes of $CO_2$ in the carotid artery. *J. Appl. Physiol.* 20:225
7. Barcroft, J., Barron, D. H. 1945. Blood pressure and pulse rate in the fetal sheep. *J. Exp. Biol.* 22:63
8. Barker, J. N. 1966. Fetal and neonatal cerebral blood flow. *Am. J. Physiol.* 210:897
9. Barrett, C. T., Heymann, M. A., Rudolph, A. M. 1972. Alpha and beta adrenergic function in fetal sheep. *Am. J. Obstet. Gynecol.* 112:1114
10. Bassett, J. M., Thorburn, G. D. 1969. Foetal plasma corticosteroids and the initiation of parturition in sheep. *J. Endocrinol.* 44:285
11. Biscoe, T. J., Purves, M. J., Sampson, S. R. 1969. Types of nervous activity which may be recorded from the carotid sinus nerve in the sheep fetus. *J. Physiol. London* 202:1
12. Bishop, S. P. 1972. Myocardial cell growth and intercalated disc structure in normal and overloaded neonatal canine myocardium. *Circulation* 46:II–4
13. Boerth, R. C. 1972. Postnatal development of myocardial contractile function in the cat. *Circulation* 46:II–36
14. Born, G. V. R., Dawes, G. S., Mott, J. C. 1955. The viability of premature lambs. *J. Physiol. London* 130:191
15. Born, G. V. R., Dawes, G. S., Mott, J. C., Rennick, B. R. 1956. The constriction of the ductus arteriosus caused by oxygen and by asphyxia in newborn lambs. *J. Physiol. London* 132:304
16. Bradley, R. M., Mistretta, C. M. 1972. Swallowing in fetal sheep. *Science* 179:1016
17. Brinkman, C. R. III, Ladner, C., Weston, P., Assali, N. S. 1969. Baroreceptor functions in the fetal lamb. *Am. J. Physiol.* 217:1346
18. Burns, B. D. 1963. The central control of respiratory movements. *Brit. Med. Bull.* 19:7
19. Campbell, A. G. M., Cockburn, F., Dawes, G. S., Milligan, J. E. 1967. Pulmonary vasoconstriction in asphyxia during cross-circulation between twin foetal lambs. *J. Physiol. London* 192:111
20. Campbell, A. G. M., Dawes, G. S., Fishman, A. P., Hyman, A. I. 1967. Regional redistribution of blood flow in the mature fetal lamb. *Circ. Res.* 21:229
21. Campbell, A. G. M., Dawes, G. S., Fishman, A. P., Hyman, A. I., Perks, A. M. 1968. Release of a bradykinin-like pulmonary vasodilator substance in foetal and new-born lambs. *J. Physiol. London* 195:83
22. Cassin, S., Dawes, G. S., Ross, B. B. 1964. Pulmonary blood flow and vascular resistance in immature foetal lambs. *J. Physiol. London* 171:80
23. Cohn, H. E., Sacks, E. J., Heymann, M. A., Rudolph, A. M. 1972. Cardiovascular responses to hypoxemia and acidemia in unanesthetised fetal lambs. *Pediat. Res.* 6:342

24. Dawes, G. S. 1968. *Foetal and Neonatal Physiology.* Chicago: Yearb. Med. 247 pp.

25. Dawes, G. S. 1969. Foetal blood gas autonomy. *Foetal Autonomy, Ciba Foundation Symposium,* ed. G. E. W. Wolstenholme, M. O'Conner, p. 162. London: Churchill. 326 pp.

26. Dawes, G. S. et al 1969. Hypoxaemia and aortic chemoreceptor function in foetal lambs. *J. Physiol. London* 201:105

27. Dawes, G. S. et al 1969. Cyanide stimulation of the systemic arterial chemoreceptors in fetal lambs. *J. Physiol. London* 201:117

28. Dawes, G. S., Fox, H. E., Leduc, B. M., Liggins, G. C., Richards, R. T. 1971. Respiratory movements and rapid eye movement sleep in the foetal lamb. *J. Physiol. London* 220:119

29. Dawes, G. S., Mott, J. C., Rennick, B. R. 1956. Some effects of adrenaline, noradrenaline and acetylcholine on the foetal circulation in the lamb. *J. Physiol. London* 134:139

30. Dawes, G. S., Mott, J. C., Widdicombe, J. G. 1954. The foetal circulation in the lamb. *J. Physiol. London* 125:563

31. Downing, S. E. 1970. Metabolic and reflex influences on cardiac function in the newborn. *Pathophysiology of Congenital Heart Disease,* ed. F. H. Adams, H. J. C. Swan, E. V. Hall, p. 59. Los Angeles: Univ. Calif. Press. 446 pp.

32. Downing, S. E., Talner, N. S., Campbell, A. G. M., Halloran, K. H., Wax, H. B. 1969. Influence of sympathetic nerve stimulation on ventricular function in the newborn lamb. *Circ. Res.* 25:417

33. Downing, S. E., Talner, N. S., Gardner, T. H. 1966. Influence of arterial oxygen tension and pH on cardiac function in the newborn lamb. *Am. J. Physiol.* 211:1203

34. Eltherington, L. G., Stoff, J., Hughes, T., Melmon, K. L. 1968. Constriction of human umbilical arteries. *Circ. Res.* 22:747

35. Fay, F. S. 1971. Guinea pig ductus arteriosus. I. Cellular and metabolic basis for oxygen sensitivity. *Am. J. Physiol.* 221:470

36. Fay, F. S., Cooke, P. H. 1972. Guinea pig ductus arteriosus. II. Irreversible closure after birth. *Am. J. Physiol.* 222:841

37. Friedman, W. F. 1973. The intrinsic physiologic properties of the developing heart. *Neonatal Heart Disease,* ed. W. F. Friedman, M. Lesch, E. M. Sonnenblick, p. 21. New York: Grune & Stratton. 229 pp.

38. Friedman, W. F., Pool, P. E., Jacobowitz, D., Seagren, S. C., Braunwald, E. 1968. Sympathetic innervation of the developing rabbit heart. *Circ. Res.* 23:25

39. Gilbert, R. D., Hessler, J. R., Eitzman, D. V., Cassin, S. 1972. Site of pulmonary vascular resistance in fetal goats. *J. Appl. Physiol.* 32:47

40. Glowinski, J., Axelrod, J., Kopin, I., Wurtman, R. 1964. Physiological disposition of $H^3$—norepinephrine in the developing rat. *J. Pharmacol. Exp. Ther.* 146:48

41. Goodlin, R. C., Rudolph, A. M. 1972. Factors associated with initiation of breathing. *Proceedings of the International Symposium on Physiological Biochemistry of the Fetus,* ed. A. A. Hodari, F. G. Mariona, p. 294. Springfield: Thomas

42. Gresham, E. L., Rankin, J. H. G., Makowski, E. L., Meschia, G., Battaglia, F. C. 1972. An evaluation of fetal renal function in a chronic sheep preparation. *J. Clin. Invest.* 51:149

43. Harned, H. S. Jr., MacKinney, L. G., Berryhill, W. S. Jr., Holmes, C. K. 1966. Effects of hypoxia and acidity on the initiation of breathing in the fetal lamb at term. *Am. J. Dis. Child.* 112:334

44. Harned, H. S. Jr., Rowshan, G., MacKinney, L. G., Sugioka, K. 1964. Relationships of $P_{O_2}$, $P_{CO_2}$, and pH to onset of breathing of the term lamb as studied by a flow-through cuvette electrode assembly. *Pediatrics* 33:672

45. Heymann, M. A., Creasy, R. K., Rudolph, A. M. 1973. Quantitation of blood flow pattern in the foetal lamb in utero. *Foetal and Neonatal Physiology: Proceedings of the Sir Joseph Barcroft Centenary Symposium,* p. 129. Cambridge: Cambridge Univ. Press. 641 pp.

46. Heymann, M. A., Rudolph, A. M. 1967. Effect of exteriorization of the sheep fetus on its cardiovascular function. *Circ. Res.* 21:741

47. Heymann, M. A., Rudolph, A. M., Nies, A. S., Melmon, K. L. 1969. Bradykinin production associated with oxygenation of the fetal lamb. *Circ. Res.* 25:521

48. Hopkins, S. F. Jr., McCutcheon, E. P., Wekstein, D. R. 1973. Postnatal changes in rat ventricular function. *Circ. Res.* 32:685

49. James, T. N. 1970. Cardiac conduction system; fetal and postnatal development. *Am. J. Cardiol.* 25:213

50. Johnson, P., Robinson, J. S., Salisbury, D. 1973. The onset and control of breathing after birth. *Foetal and Neonatal Physiology: Proceedings of the Sir Joseph Barcroft Centenary Symposium,* p. 217. Cambridge: Cambridge Univ. Press. 641 pp.

51. Kennedy, J. A., Clark, S. L. 1942. Observations on the physiological reactions of

the ductus arteriosus. *Am. J. Physiol.* 136:140

52. Lebowitz, E. A., Novick, J. S., Rudolph, A. M. 1972. Development of myocardial sympathetic innervation in the fetal lamb. *Pediat. Res.* 6:887

53. Lipp, J. A., Rudolph, A. M. 1972. Sympathetic nerve development in the rat and guinea-pig heart. *Biol. Neonate* 21:76

54. Lucas, W., Kirschbaum, T., Assali, N. S. 1966. Cephalic circulation and oxygen consumption before and after birth. *Am. J. Physiol.* 210:287

55. McMurphy, D. M., Boreus, L. O. 1971. Studies on the pharmacology of the perfused human fetal ductus arteriosus. *Am. J. Obstet. Gynecol.* 109:937

56. McMurphy, D. M., Heymann, M. A., Rudolph, A. M., Melmon, K. L. 1972. Developmental changes in constriction of the ductus arteriosus: Responses to oxygen and vasoactive substances in the isolated ductus arteriosus of the fetal lamb. *Pediat. Res.* 6:231

57. Mahon, W. A., Goodwin, J. W., Paul, W. M. 1966. Measurement of individual ventricular outputs in the fetal lamb by a dye dilution technique. *Circ. Res.* 19:191

58. Meschia, G., Cotter, J. R., Makowski, E. L., Barron, D. H. 1967. Simultaneous measurement of uterine and umbilical blood flows and oxygen uptakes. *Quart. J. Exp. Physiol.* 52:1

59. Miller, W. W., Gilliland, K. 1972. Developmental differences in canine myocardial adenosine triphosphatase activity. *Circulation* 46:11

60. Molnar, J. J., Mesel, E., Golinko, R. J., Rudolph, A. M. 1962. Structure, histochemistry and physiology of ductus arteriosus in the dog. *J. Histochem. Cytochem.* 10:667

61. Oberhansli-Weiss, I., Heymann, M. A., Rudolph, A. M., Melmon, K. L. 1972. The pattern and mechanisms of response to oxygen of the ductus arteriosus and umbilical artery. *Pediat. Res.* 6:693

62. Ou, L. C., Tenney, S. M. 1970. Properties of mitochondria from hearts of cattle acclimatized to high altitude. *Resp. Physiol.* 8:151

63. Pagtakhan, R. D., Faridy, E. E., Chernick, V. 1971. Interaction between arterial $Po_2$ and $Pco_2$ in the initiation of respiration in sheep. *J. Appl. Physiol.* 30:382

64. Purves, M. J., James, I. M. 1969. Observations on the control of cerebral blood flow in the sheep fetus and newborn lamb. *Circ. Res.* 25:651

65. Roach, M. R. 1973. A biophysical look at the relationship of structure and function in the umbilical artery. *Foetal and Neonatal Physiology: Proceedings of the Sir Joseph Barcroft Centenary Symposium,* p. 141. Cambridge: Cambridge Univ. Press. 641 pp.

66. Romero, T., Covell, J., Friedman, W. F. 1972. A comparison of pressure-volume relations of the fetal, newborn, and adult heart. *Am. J. Physiol.* 222:1285

67. Rudolph, A. M. 1970. The changes in the circulation after birth: Their importance in congenital heart disease. *Circulation* 41:343

68. Rudolph, A. M., Heymann, M. A. 1968. The fetal circulation. *Ann. Rev. Med.* 19:195

69. Rudolph, A. M. 1970. Circulatory changes during growth in the fetal lamb. *Circ. Res.* 26:289

70. Rudolph, A. M., Heymann, M. A. 1972. Pulmonary circulation in fetal lambs. *Pediat. Res.* 6:341

71. Rudolph, A. M., Heymann, M. A. 1973. Control of the foetal circulation. *Foetal and Neonatal Physiology: Proceedings of the Sir Joseph Barcroft Centenary Symposium,* p. 89. Cambridge: Cambridge Univ. Press. 641 pp.

72. Rudolph, A. M., Heymann, M. A., Teramo, K. A. W., Barrett, C. T., Raiha, N. C. R. 1971. Studies on the circulation of the previable human fetus. *Pediat. Res.* 5:452

73. Rudolph, A. M., Yuan, S. 1966. Response of the pulmonary vasculature to hypoxia and $H^+$ ion concentration changes. *J. Clin. Invest.* 45:399

74. Scibetta, J. J., Fox, H. E., Chik, L., Rosen, M. G. 1973. On correlating the fetal heart and brain in the sheep. *Am. J. Obstet. Gynecol.* 115:946

75. Shinebourne, E. A., Vapaavuori, E. K., Williams, R. L., Heymann, M. A., Rudolph, A. M. 1972. Development of baroreflex activity in unanesthetized fetal and neonatal lambs. *Circ. Res.* 31:710

76. Silva, D. G., Ikeda, M. 1971. Ultrastructural and acetylcholinesterase studies on the innervation of the ductus arteriosus, pulmonary trunk and aorta of the fetal lamb. *J. Ultrastruct. Res.* 34:358

77. Smith, R. W., Morris, J. A., Assali, N. S., Beck, R. 1964. Effects of chemical mediators on the pulmonary and ductus arteriosus circulation in the fetal lamb. *Am. J. Obstet. Gynecol.* 89:252

78. Smyth, H. S., Sleight, P., Pickering, G. W. 1969. Reflex regulations of arterial pressure during sleep in man. *Circ. Res.* 24:109

79. Taylor, I. M., Smith, R. B. 1971. Cholinesterase activity in the human fetal heart between the 35- and 160-millimeter crown-rump length stages. *J. Histochem. Cytochem.* 19:498

80. Teramo, K. et al. Effects of lidocaine on heart rate, blood pressure and corticogram in the fetal sheep. *Am. J. Obstet. Gynacol.* In press

81. Toubas, P. L., Silverman, N. H., Heymann, M. A., Rudolph, A. M. 1973. Cardiovascular responses to acute hemorrhage in the fetal lamb. *Circulation* 48:iv–38

82. Vapaavuori, E. K., Shinebourne, E. A., Williams, R. L., Heymann, M. A., Rudolph, A. M. 1973. Development of cardiovascular responses to autonomic blockade in intact fetal and neonatal lambs. *Biol. Neonate* 22: 177

83. Wells, R. J., Friedman, W. F., Sobel, B. E. 1972. Increased oxidative metabolism in the fetal and newborn lamb heart. *Am. J. Physiol.* 222:1488

84. Wildenthal, K. 1973. Studies of foetal mouse hearts in organ culture: Metabolic requirements for prolonged function in Vitro and the influence of cardiac maturation on substance utilization. *J. Mol. Cell. Cardiol.* 5:87

85. Williams, R. L., Hof, R. D., Heymann, M. A., Rudolph, A. M. 1972. Cardiovascular effects of hypothalamic stimulation in the chronic fetal lamb preparation. *Circulation* 46:II-5

86. Wollenberger, A. 1964. Rhythmic and arrhythmic contractile activity of single myocardial cells cultured in vitro. *Circ. Res.* 15: Suppl. 2, 184

87. Woodrum, D. E., Parer, J. T., Wennberg, R. P., Hodson, W. A. 1972. Chemoreceptor response in initiation of breathing in the fetal lamb. *J. Appl. Physiol.* 33:120

88. Zak, R. 1973. Cell proliferation during cardiac growth. *Am. J. Cardiol.* 31:211

# LUNG METABOLISM AND BIOCHEMISTRY

❖1111

*Donald F. Tierney*[1]

Respiratory Division, UCLA-Harbor General Hospital, Torrance, California

In terms of phylogeny the lung is a relatively new organ, but it has been in existence longer than have biochemists and physiologists. Why, then, has its metabolism and biochemistry been ignored until recently? Probably the notion that the lung and chest wall were simple bellows and nothing more dominated the thinking of most biological scientists until 1965. Only in the last decade has it been widely appreciated that the extremely complex mechanics of the lung are dependent upon its metabolism, and the exocrine secretion of the lung is vital for survival. In addition, the lung is perhaps ideally positioned and structured to change circulating vasoactive substances and hormones; this metabolic role of the lung may also prove to be vital. The lung becomes essential suddenly at birth; premature birth is commonly associated with an immature lung which is unable to meet its demanding metabolic requirements. Therefore, lung metabolism has been most appreciated by scientists interested in fetal and neonatal development, but it also deserves more attention as a metabolic organ in adults.

This is the first review of lung biochemistry in this publication and several thousand references could be included in a comprehensive review. However, I will focus upon substrate utilization, surfactant metabolism, and the role of the lung in changing circulating substances.

## SUBSTRATE UTILIZATION

Substrate utilization may be uniquely important for the lung. Unlike other organs, interruption of its blood supply may not deprive a ventilated lung of oxygen. Airspace gas normally has a $P_{O_2}$ sufficient to supply oxygen to tissue at a distance of 50 $\mu$m or more from the alveolar wall. Therefore, if a pulmonary artery is occluded, lung infarcts may primarily be due to interruption of a supply of substrates such as glucose, lipids, and amino acids, rather than to oxygen deprivation.

[1]The author was supported by US PHS Research Career Development Award HE 10,637 from the National Heart and Lung Institute.

209

How long can lung tissue survive without a supply of substrates provided by perfusion? Dog lungs survive transplantation only if the lung has been ischemic for less than 6 hr at 37° (84), a result suggesting that some essential substrates may be depleted within 6 hr if $O_2$ is supplied by maintaining the lung inflated with air (90). Oxygen consumption ($\dot{Q}O_2$) of lung tissue slices has not been determined for prolonged periods, but it remains nearly constant for 5 hr, even when substrate is not added to the medium (7). Therefore, it appears that oxidative phosphorylation in lung tissue can continue at a nearly constant rate for several hours without added substrate.

Substrate utilization by several organs has been estimated in vivo by using Fick's principle and many attempts have been made to apply this approach to the lung (31, 66). Most efforts to measure the concentration difference of glucose, lactate, and free fatty acids between mixed venous and arterial blood have failed to find any differences attributable to lung metabolism. However, the great blood flow through the lung could overwhelm a significant substrate utilization by lung tissue.

To illustrate the problem, O'Neil[2] and I assumed from in vitro studies that the glucose consumption by human lung tissue in vivo is 6 $\mu$ mole per gram per hour. Therefore, a 1000 g human lung would consume 100 $\mu$ mole of glucose per minute. If the cardiac output were 5 liters/min, the difference of glucose concentration between arterial and venous blood would be 20 $\mu$ mole per liter, or 0.36 mg per 100 ml. This predicted arterial-venous difference of glucose is considerably less than the reproducibility of glucose determination reported by Harris and associates (31), who measured glucose concentrations in paired samples of blood drawn from the same vein over a 2 min period and found a mean difference of 147 $\pm$ 87 $\mu M$; similar calculations can be made for lactate, and one must conclude that attempts to measure substrate utilization by the normal lung in vivo have not succeeded largely because the arterial-venous differences for the substrates are too small to be measured with the methods used.

Since these efforts have not been fruitful, our limited information stems from studies of lung tissue in vitro in a variety of tissue preparations including lung mitochondria, homogenates, minces, tissue slices, and isolated perfused lungs.

Reiss was among the first investigators to use lung mitochondria (64, 65), and he discussed some of the problems with their preparation. For instance, the lung consists of many cell types and the low yield of mitochondria may represent only those cells most easily fragmented by homogenization. Reiss concluded that lung mitochondria as prepared with his method can oxidize glucose but not fatty acids, and he proposed that the lung may be glucose dependent for energy supply in a manner similar to the brain. His conclusions are not supported by the results obtained with slices and minces, which have shown that lung tissue can oxidize fatty acids (71, 91).

Lung homogenates have rarely been used since Barron and associates (7) noted a very low $\dot{Q}O_2$ for homogenates when compared with tissue slices. They attributed

[2]John J. O'Neil, Ph.D., Respiratory Division, UCLA–Harbor General Hospital, Torrance, California.

this low value to a release of nucleosidases when the cell membranes were ruptured. More recently, Ryan & Smith (68, 69) have nicely demonstrated that the outer surface of the endothelial cells in lung contain ATPase and 5'-nucleotidase. The great activity of these enzymes in the intact lung would destroy circulating adenine nucleotides in the plasma, but presumably not the adenine nucleotides within the cell. Homogenization would, of course, expose the cellular nucleotides to these enzymes, and the markedly different metabolic activity of lung homogenates and tissue slices may relate in part to release of such enzymes from the endothelial surface.

Most of our information regarding substrate utilization by the lung stems from the use of tissue slices, which also may differ from the lung in vivo. Lung slices have been prepared by methods developed for other organs, but the lung may require special techniques. Some investigators used the wet weight of lung slices after bathing the lung in an aqueous solution; unlike other tissues, this weight may not represent the true mass of lung tissue since the lung with its airspaces has some characteristics of a sponge. Lung slices have been cut with different techniques and at different thicknesses, but Levy & Harvey (46) have reported that lung slices 300 $\mu$ thick have a 30% lower $\dot{Q}_{O_2}$ than slices cut 1000 $\mu$ thick. The airspaces of the lung fill with the incubation medium, and the diffusion distances may be relatively small compared to the thickness of the slice. Lung is also a relatively fragile tissue and small fragments break loose while it is being shaken in a flask (O'Neil & Tierney, unpublished observations). Consequently, if the slices are removed at the end of an incubation and analyzed for metabolic products, they do not represent the total mass of tissue placed in the flask. Finally, Scholz & Rhoades (76) have reported that lung tissue in 0.9% NaCl solution is remarkably sensitive to chilling to temperatures often used in preparing slices.

In addition to these technical problems, there are several general objections to the use of tissue slices. Krebs (44) has noted that ketogenesis in liver slices is strikingly less than in the isolated perfused liver. He and his associates reported that slicing the liver led to a 50% fall of ATP, and after 10 min incubation 72% of the original quantity of ATP had been lost. They observed similar effects for other tissues and concluded that the use of slices in metabolic studies has limited value. Although such observations should lead to caution when interpreting data from tissue slices and might encourage the use of the isolated lung, O'Neil and I found no significant differences between tissue slices and the isolated perfused rat lung when we compared glucose consumption, lactate production, or $^{14}CO_2$ production from $1\text{-}^{14}C\text{-}$glucose, $6\text{-}^{14}C\text{-}$glucose, or $1\text{-}^{14}C\text{-}$palmitate (58).

The isolated perfused lung has been used sparingly for studies of substrate metabolism (48, 58), probably because it is so time-consuming and because pulmonary edema develops readily. Nevertheless, there is considerable interest in its use since perfusion and ventilation can be controlled and it thus may not have the disadvantages of tissue slices. For instance, the effect of ventilation with various air pollutants can be determined with the isolated perfused lung, and metabolism may be related to the ventilation or perfusion. Longmore et al (48) used the isolated perfused rat lung to study the effects of $CO_2$ concentration upon phospholipid metabolism and found that glucose incorporation into phosphatidylcholine increased by as much as 50% when high concentrations of $CO_2$ were used.

Oxygen consumption and utilization of glucose, lipids, and amino acids have all been studied with tissue; a separate discussion of each follows.

## Oxygen Consumption

The $\dot{Q}o_2$ of intact lungs (20, 88) has been reported to be lower than the $\dot{Q}o_2$ of tissue slices. Faridy & Naimark (20) reported that the $\dot{Q}o_2$ of the isolated lung increases by as much as 50% when the lung is distended. However, the $\dot{Q}o_2$ observed for the distended dog lung was about three units, whereas Krebs had reported (43) that slices of the dog lung had a $\dot{Q}o_2$ about five units (units for $\dot{Q}o_2$ are $\mu l$ $O_2$ per hour per mg dry weight). This major discrepancy between estimates of $\dot{Q}o_2$ by these two preparations illustrates the problems of selecting the best method to study lung metabolism. Does the higher $\dot{Q}o_2$ of the tissue slice or the lower $\dot{Q}o_2$ of the isolated lung most nearly represent in vivo metabolism? For other major organs, this problem could probably be answered by using the Fick principle to estimate $\dot{Q}o_2$ in vivo. However, the quantity of oxygen consumed by the normal lung is miniscule when compared with the amount of oxygen in the airspaces and blood. The accuracy of measuring the quantity of oxygen entering and leaving the lung is not sufficient to estimate oxygen consumption of the lung in vivo.

## Glucose Utilization

Tissue slices and perfused lungs consume large quantities of glucose, but the glucose stores in the adult lung are small (90). Although lung function has not yet been shown to be glucose dependent, glucose does play several important roles in the lung and any of these may become critical after a significant period of glucose deprivation.

Glucose utilization by the lung has been judged by incubating tissue with radiolabeled glucose and determining the subsequent distribution of the label in metabolic products. Yeager & Massaro (92) used rabbit lung slices and reported that about 30% of the glucose consumed appeared in lactic acid, about 20% in $CO_2$, 4% in lipid, 0.4% in nucleic acid, and 1.4% in protein. In addition, several investigators have used 1-[14]C and 6-[14]C glucose and noted that the lung has an active pentose pathway (71, 91).

The channeling of glucose consumption toward lactate production is of unknown significance to lung function, but it occurs in slices even when the $Po_2$ is high and at lactate levels that may be greatly in excess of those found in plasma under normal conditions (79). Since the lung has a very high $Po_2$, many physiologists may be concerned about such reports of lactate production. Net lactate consumption was not reported in the publications I read for this review, although there were at least eight reports that lung tissue produces lactate. The ATP produced through glycolysis with lactate production must be small when compared to the ATP produced by oxidative phosphorylation, but some cells may depend upon glycolysis for their energy needs. Lactate production generally is associated with hypoxia, but other tissues, including the papillary tip of the kidney (45), may depend upon glycolysis for a source of ATP even when the $Po_2$ is high. Possibly the attenuated type I alveolar epithelial cells depend upon glycolysis to supply ATP in the relatively great interval between mitochondria.

The pentose pathway for glucose oxidation supplies NADPH, which in other tissues is used for synthesis (adipose tissue) or for reducing oxidants (erythrocytes). Massaro et al (51) have demonstrated that this pathway has an important role in protein synthesis by lung slices. However, it may also play a role in producing tolerance to lung injury and in reducing oxidants inhaled by the lung (80). The activity of enzymes in this pathway increases in lungs of rats made relatively tolerant to oxygen toxicity by prior exposure to oxygen or by injection of $\alpha$-naphthylthiourea (ANTU). Whether this increased enzymatic activity is partially responsible for the relative tolerance to oxygen toxicity in these rats remains to be demonstrated.

Felts suggested (22) that glucose serves another important role by providing the glycerol moiety for phospholipid synthesis. The radiolabel from glucose that is incorporated into lipids is primarily in the glycerol fraction (22, 76) and therefore the contribution of glucose toward fatty acid synthesis is small compared with its contribution to the glycerol component of phospholipids.

## Lipid Utilization

When radiolabeled palmitate bould to albumin is injected intravenously, about 2% of the dose appears in the lung and esterification is nearly complete within 30 min (93). Up to 90% of the radiolabel is in phospholipids and 30% is in the highly surface-active, saturated phosphatidycholine (lecithin) (93), which will be discussed in detail under the section on surfactant.

The capacity of lung tissue to esterify free fatty acids and to incorporate acetate into lipids appears to be relatively great, and it has been assumed that pulmonary metabolism may be oriented toward lipogenesis since it secretes considerable quantities of lipid in the surface active material. However, no quantitative analyses have been reported that include the specific activities of immediate precursors of lipids such as acetyl-CoA in the lung. The rate of utilization of free fatty acids by lung tissue depends upon the concentrations of free fatty acid and of glucose in the medium (71, 91). For such reasons, it is not possible to state the quantity of lipid utilized or synthesized by the lung.

The active lipid metabolism might surprise the casual observer, who finds few cells in the lung giving morphological evidence of active metabolism. However, the type II alveolar cells, long considered to secrete the pulmonary surfactant (40), must be among the titans of lipid metabolism. Darrah & Hedley-Whyte (15) used autoradiography and found the type II cells to be the only ones in lung that were highly labeled following the injection of tritiated palmitate into mice.

Although free fatty acids are rapidly esterified in the lung, there is now ample evidence that lung tissue can also readily oxidize fatty acids (71, 86, 91). In vivo, the fatty acids utilized by lung may be derived from the plasma lipoproteins as well as from the nonesterified free fatty acids (22). In contrast with the limited stores of carbohydrate in the adult lung, the lipids may be sufficient to supply mitochondria with acetyl-CoA for many hours.

## Amino Acids

Protein synthesis by lung tissue is augmented by glucose, probably because the synthesis requires the pentose pathway to supply NADPH (51). Massaro et al reported (51) that about 1–7% of the radiolabeled protein synthesized by lung slices from amino acids was secreted into the medium during a 6 hr period, but the secretion could be blocked by cyanide. The type II cell is also involved in the utilization of amino acids, and Massaro & Massaro have demonstrated by autoradiography (50) that after incubation of leucine-4,5-$^3$H with lung slices, the radioactivity is primarily in the rough endoplasmic reticulum of the type II cell.

## Specific Substrate Utilization by Different Cell Types

The lung contains many different cell types, and the pattern of substrate utilization by the whole lung may mask critical differences in the substrate requirements of specific cells. The alveolar macrophage is the only cell type from the lung that has been studied extensively; its contribution to the total lung metabolism is probably small, since the cumulative mass of the alveolar macrophages is relatively small. The type II alveolar cell is apparently very active in lipid metabolism, as the autoradiographs demonstrate, but we have almost no information regarding substrate utilization by other cell types.

New methods to separate cells from the lung (29) are promising and may eventually lead to answers to questions such as these: (*a*) Which cell type, if any, is dependent upon glycolysis and lactate production for its energy needs? (*b*) Are any cell types dependent upon glucose for oxidative phosphorylation? (*c*) What is the role of the pentose pathway for glucose oxidation in different cell types?

## SURFACTANT METABOLISM

The term "surfactant" refers to a substance which is surface active, i.e. one that will lower the surface tension at an air-liquid interface. The surface tension may be determined by a layer only one molecule thick, and many complex molecules, including lipids, proteins, and other substances in biological fluids, are surfactants since they may lower the surface tension of water to as low as 20 dynes/cm. The phrase "pulmonary surfactant," however, is used to denote the substance responsible for the unusually great surface activity present in mammalian lungs. For brevity, I will use surfactant to mean pulmonary surfactant. The search for such a surfactant began when physiological studies indicated that extremely low surface tensions (i.e. 10 dynes/cm or lower) must be present within the air-filled lung when it is at a low volume. The original and best evidence that justified this search for a highly surface-active material on the alveolar surface was the observation that a lung does not collapse completely when very low distending pressures are present. A soap bubble the size of an alveolus would collapse at considerably higher pressures. Since several diseases, including the respiratory distress syndromes, are associated with increased lung recoil and increased surface forces, there has been a major effort to separate and identify the pulmonary surfactant, to measure it quantitatively and, it is hoped, to determine more precisely its role in disease.

Extracts of mammalian lung have great surface activity, and surface tensions near zero can develop transiently. Valuable concepts have come from many of the earlier studies of the pulmonary surfactant, which were done with extracts obtained by simply mincing lung tissue in saline. However, the saline extracts have major limitations since they cannot be used to quantify the amount of surfactant. Other substances in the tissue and blood may prevent very low surface tensions even in the presence of normal quantities of surfactant (82). Therefore, the most that can safely be concluded with the conventional saline extracts is that a low surface tension indicates the presence of surfactant, but in unknown quantity.

To make a simple extraction technique more nearly quantitative, Clements et al (13) developed a method which permits application of an extract directly to the surface of water. By spreading an alcohol extract of lung on water, surface-active substances remain at the interface and do not enter the liquid below the surface. Clements demonstrated an excellent correlation between the surface area (quantity of surfactant) occupied by the extracted material when the surface tension is at 12 dynes/cm, and the quantity of highly surface-active phospholipid (dipalmitoyl phosphatidylcholine) present in the lung. This technique appears to be satisfactory for normal lungs but it has not been applied to diseased lungs which may contain inhibitors of the surface active material. It is also possible that the extracted surface active lipids are not all derived from the surfactant.

## Chemical Composition of Pulmonary Surfactant

There are several substances within lung tissue that can develop extremely low surface tensions (less than 10 dynes/cm) when spread on an air-liquid interface. Saturated phosphatidylcholine (lecithin), phosphatidyl dimethylethanolamine, sphingomyelin, and perhaps some other phospholipids all have characteristics similar to that of lung extracts. Klaus and associates (39) first suggested that 1,2-dipalmitoyl-3-sn-phosphatidylcholine (DPPC)[3] is an essential component of the pulmonary surfactant. The evidence to support their original suggestion now includes the following:

(a) Of the several surface-active phospholipids present in lavage fluid obtained by washing saline solution in and out of the lung, only DPPC is present in sufficient quantity to make a monomolecular layer over the entire surface (37, 55, 93). Although other phospholipids may also be in the surface film, they cannot completely occupy the huge area of the airspaces.

(b) During fetal development, there are parallel changes of the pressure-volume characteristics of the lung and the content of saturated phosphatidylcholine, especially DPPC. Brumley et al (9) demonstrated that immature fetal lungs inflated with air collapse readily at low distending pressures, but the mature fetal lung is a stable structure which remains inflated at low pressures. These characteristics of mature lungs are attributed to the surfactant and they appear when DPPC increases in quantity.

[3]This substance, DPPC, is a saturated lecithin containing two palmitates. It was previously termed dipalmitoyl lecithin.

(c) Phospholipase C, which cleaves phosphatidylcholine (PC) including DPPC, will raise the minimum surface tension of lung extracts (82) and will considerably alter the pressure-volume characteristics of excised rat lungs. Although this is a relatively nonspecific enzyme that will also attack other phospholipids, these studies indicate that phospholipids are probably important components of the surfactant.

(d) Surface-active lipoprotein isolated from the lung (36, 37) is very rich in DPPC. PC comprises 73–78% of the lipid present in this lipoprotein and 60% of the PC is anenoic, i.e. saturated PC (such as DPPC). This represents a considerable enrichment of saturated PC compared to whole lung tissue.

If DPPC were present only in surfactant and if surfactant were of fixed composition, we could use DPPC for quantitative studies of surfactant metabolism. Unfortunately, we lack evidence that it is uniquely present in surfactant; it is present in other organs (49) and may be a constituent of some cellular membranes. Young & Tierney (93) used radiolabeled palmitate and found evidence that several pools of DPPC exist in rat lungs. Although alternate possibilities exist, the evidence is consistent with the concept that a significant amount of DPPC is extra-surfactant.

Since DPPC is apparently an essential component of the pulmonary surfactant, but not necessarily the only component, multiple efforts have been made to obtain fractions of the lung which contain DPPC and to determine which of these fractions might represent the surfactant. At this juncture, the definition of surfactant again becomes important. When first applied to the lung, the term was used to indicate a substance which could lower the surface tension to extremely low values. It does not necessarily include everything on the "surface" of an airspace which can be removed by lung lavage. For instance, the extracellular material seen on the alveolar surface with electron microscopy may be many molecules deep and only the outer layer may have the surface activity attributed to surfactant.

The surfactant may not have the same composition and structure throughout its biological evolution. It appears from studies by Chevalier & Collet (11) that PC may be synthesized in the endoplasmic reticulum of the type II cell, transferred through the Golgi complex, eventually incorporated into secretory granules (lamellar bodies), secreted onto the surface, and then removed or lost from the airspace by unknown means. The DPPC, which is eventually to be secreted as a component of surfactant, may initially be bound to a transfer substance before it is bound to an apoprotein. The lamellar body is probably composed largely of surfactant but other substances may also be present. After secretion, the composition and structure of surfactant may change since large molecules tend to uncoil when they reach an air-liquid interface and proteins may be denatured. Finally, once the surfactant leaves the surface (via airways, macrophages, lymphatics, or resorption into the epithelium) it may undergo additional changes as it reenters pools of intermediary metabolism. It would not be surprising, therefore, if several surface-active fractions containing DPPC are isolated from lungs.

What criteria should be used to determine whether or not surfactant has been isolated? It is not logical to isolate a substance with a surface tension of 20–40 dynes/cm at body temperature and physiological pH and consider it to be pure surfactant. If we find it necessary from physiological studies to propose a surface tension of 10 dynes/cm in the alveolar surface, we must isolate a fraction which can develop a surface tension of 10 dynes/cm at 37°C or consider the fraction impure.

In the last few years several groups of investigators have expressed doubt that the surface tension in the lung is very low, and have suggested that perhaps the surfactant may not be extremely surface active. I will therefore briefly review the evidence that the surface tension in the lung must be very low and that this should be a criterion for judging whether a fraction is surfactant.

Lungs frozen rapidly with liquid propane have very small alveoli (radii of 40–80 $\mu$m) which can remain open with a distending pressure of 2–3 cm $H_2O$. The surface forces of a bubble the size of an alveolus would require much greater distending pressures if the surface tension were 20–40 dynes/cm and, therefore, a low surface tension (10 dynes/cm) has been considered essential. However, several investigators have suggested other possible explanations: 1. The lung tissue may have a minimum volume to which it returns spontaneously but below which it resists the collapsing force of a high surface tension (10). 2. The alveolar surface may not be a true air-liquid interface but a semisolid gel which resists collapse and cannot be compared to an air-liquid interface (23). Lung tissue can probably resist collapsing forces to some extent and the extracellular material may at times be a gel, but these possibilities do not discount the evidence obtained by pressure-volume studies of excised lungs favoring a surfactant. Rat lungs inflated with 0.9% NaCl solution will retain about 1 ml of solution after deflation. Upon subsequent inflation and deflation with air, it is apparent that the lung still remains inflated at low pressures. This result is consistent with a surface-active material that is free to seek the new air-liquid interface created by the liquid filling of the lung. It appears to deny the possibility of a gel upon the surface that could retain this quantity of water and still be a semisolid. Even more conclusive are the pressure-volume relationships of the air-filled lung after rinsing with a solution containing a nonionic detergent such as Tween-20 (62). Unlike the 0.9% NaCl solution, Tween-20 is surface active and it produces a constant surface tension of approximately 30 dynes/cm. Since about 1 ml of this solution remains in the lung, it is very likely that it displaces the former surface. If the surface tension of the lung were not changed by the Tween-20, we would expect little or no change of the pressure-volume relationships when the lung is subsequently filled with air. However, a marked shift of the pressure-volume curve is apparent after rinsing the lung with Tween-20, and it appears that these observations reject a tissue structure that could resist surface forces due to a surface tension of 30 dynes/cm.

The essential requirement of the surfactant, that it develop surface tensions below 10 dynes/cm at body temperature and physiological pH, has not been met by the great majority of fractions isolated from lung and considered to be surfactant. Several of these isolated lung fractions develop surface tensions below 10 dynes/cm at 22°C but not at 37°C. Very small quantities of impurities such as cholesterol or other lipids can prevent low surface tensions at 37°C but may not at 22°C, and, therefore, many fractions may contain the surfactant but may also contain contaminants that influence the surface activity.

King & Clements (37) list characteristics of the surface-active material that should be considered for any fraction of the lung which may be surfactant. In addition to the requirements of low surface tensions at body temperature, the other most important characteristic is that it be present in sufficient quantity to completely cover the surface of the lung.

DPPC meets both of these requirements, but the surfactant may contain other substances. DPPC is a solid at body temperature and spreads very slowly when placed on an air-water interface. If released onto the alveolar surface as pure DPPC, it probably would not spread at the interface rapidly enough to maintain low surface forces.

Although there is general agreement that the surfactant must contain phospholipids, there is controversy over the protein content. Several laboratories have obtained highly surface-active lipoproteins (19, 23, 37, 41), which remain as intact units despite the use of varying gradient centrifugation and other gentle techniques for separation. Unfortunately, only two of these studies have demonstrated low surface tensions at 37°C (19, 37). In contrast to this evidence that the surfactant is a lipoprotein, several other laboratories have reported that no protein is present in the surface-active fraction (74, 75, 77). These reports have generally considered the surfactant to be primarily phospholipid; none has shown that a low surface tension (10 dynes/cm) would develop at 37°C. Some of these fractions do not develop surface tensions below 12 dynes/cm, and other fractions isolated by the same investigators may develop equally low surface tensions but were not considered to be surfactant. It now seems likely that the lipoprotein was separated into its lipid and protein components by the methods used to extract it, but possibly the surfactant was isolated at different stages of its evolution.

King & Clements in a meticulous and detailed report (36–38) have isolated, by differential centrifugation, surface-active lipoproteins that will develop surface tensions below 10 dynes/cm at 37°C and are present in sufficient quantities to cover the entire alveolar surface. They suggest that some of the constituents of their surface-active lipoproteins may be essential for the adsorption of DPPC onto the surface. For instance, protein and lipids which are more readily dissolved or suspended in aqueous phases may transfer the DPPC and contribute to its spreading. Saturated phosphatidylcholine (primarily DPPC) amounts to about 40% of the total mass of their lipoprotein fractions.

These surface-active lipoproteins isolated by King & Clements meet the physiological requirements of the surfactant, but, unfortunately, the procedure is very time consuming. It is hoped such methods will lead to answers for such questions as the following: (a) To what extent is the surfactant reduced in neonatal and adult respiratory distress syndromes, and to what extent is it abnormal, inhibited, or inactivated? (b) What is the metabolic pathway for synthesis of the protein and of the lipid constituents of the surfactant? (c) Is the protein component of the surfactant present in excess quantities in the lungs of patients with alveolar proteinosis? (d) What are the immunological characteristics of the surfactant?

## Surfactant Synthesis

Since the exact character of the surfactant has not been defined and its isolation has not been possible until recently, we know very little about its synthesis as a unit. However, there has been much interest in the synthesis and secretion of phospholipids, especially DPPC.

There are two basic routes for the synthesis of phosphatidylcholine (PC). The major difference between them is in the use of pre-formed choline instead of the addition of individual methyl groups to form the choline component. The first pathway (CDP choline reaction) uses cytidine diphosphate choline and 1,2-diacylglycerol to form PC. When PC is catabolized, the choline may be salvaged to be reused by the tissue.

The second basic route (methyl transferase reaction) for phosphatidylcholine synthesis adds three methyl groups independently to phosphatidylethanolamine. The phosphatidylethanolamine is synthesized indirectly from phosphatidic acid and cytidine nucleotides, primarily in the endoplasmic reticulum.

Morgan and associates (55) found evidence that about 5% of the phospholipid in lung may be an intermediate between phosphatidylethanolamine and PC in the methyl transferase pathway. This intermediate has had two methyl groups added to the phosphatidylethanolamine and is termed phosphatidyldimethylethanolamine (PDME). Morgan has also extracted from the lung an enzyme system (N-methyl-transferase) which can transfer methyl groups to phosphatidylethanolamine (54). Finally, he observed very similar fatty acid compositions in PDME and saturated PC. These observations suggest that a major route for synthesis of DPPC may be through methylation of phosphatidylethanolamine.

To compare the relative rates of synthesis by the two pathways, several investigators have studied the incorporation of radiolabeled methyl donors (i.e. methionine or S-adenosylmethionine) and radiolabeled choline into PC. Weinhold (89) reported that the incorporation of methyl groups into phospholipids of rat lung slices from methionine was low, but was highest in the 19-day fetal rat lung (6.3 nmole $g^{-1}$ $hr^{-1}$) and lowest (4.4–4.9 nmole $g^{-1}$ $hr^{-1}$) in the mature rat lung. In contrast, he reported that the incorporation of radiolabeled choline increased from 30 nmole $g^{-1}$ $hr^{-1}$ at 19 days of gestation to 189 and 185 nmole $g^{-1}$ $hr^{-1}$ in the 22-day fetal rat lung and in the adult rat lung. The use of radiolabeled choline requires the formation of CDP choline which may be a rate-limiting step. Nevertheless, the results indicate that PC synthesis in the lung is dominated by the first pathway (CDP choline pathway).

Morgan (54) and Wolfe et al (91) have also concluded that the contribution of the methylation route to total PC synthesis is relatively small, but Morgan suggested that its contribution to DPPC synthesis may be significant. Possible support for this view that the DPPC in surfactant is synthesized by methylation of phosphatidylethanolamine is a report by Scarpelli that $^{14}$C-palmitate given intravenously appears first in phosphatidylethanolamine of the fetal lamb's tracheal fluid and later in phosphatidylcholine (73). In addition, DiAugustine (18) noted a more rapid incorporation of $^{14}$C-oleate into PDME; his evidence would support Morgan's suggestion that PDME may be selectively saturated. However, DiAugustine did not find evidence that PDME was a precursor of phosphatidylcholine, and he concluded that PDME was probably a biosynthetic product rather than an intermediate.

Most of these studies have relied upon thin layer chromatography to separate and identify PDME. Pfleger and associates (61) have reported that the fraction of lipids in the lung lavage that has generally been considered PDME is probably phosphatidylglycerol. These two lipids have very similar chromatographic characteristics and some of the studies will need to be reviewed with Pfleger's report in mind. If investigators have been studying phosphatidylglycerol, but considered it PDME, their conclusions may be in error.

Considerable interest in surfactant synthesis has been stimulated by Gluck and associates (24–28), who suggested that saturated PC may have a different fatty acid composition if it is synthesized by the methylation route rather than through direct incorporation of choline. In a series of reports, these investigators suggested that the methylation pathway synthesizes palmitoyl-myristoyl PC which may replace DPPC in surfactant, espeically in the newborn infant. Thus, myristate could replace one palmitate of DPPC. These investigators proposed that the methylation pathway dominates the synthesis of surface active PC in the human fetus before 35–37 weeks of gestation and, therefore, this pathway and its production of palmitoyl-myristoyl PC may be essential to survival if the infant is born prematurely. Furthermore, this methylation pathway is sensitive to conditions such as acidosis or hypothermia which could suppress the synthesis of surfactant and predispose the prematurely born infant to the respiratory distress syndrome.

This postulate of Gluck's is based upon the following evidence: (a) Fluid aspirated from airways of infants contains a possible intermediate of the methylation route (PDME) as early as 22–24 weeks gestation, and the primary fatty acid structure was palmitate in the $\alpha$ and myristate in the $\beta$ position. (b) The fatty acid composition of PDME was very similar to the fatty acid composition of saturated PC in the fluid so aspirated. (c) Infants without the respiratory distress syndrome had greater percentages of palmitate in the $\beta$ position of PC but not in PDME. (d) Infants with the respiratory distress syndrome had lost both PDME and PC; those infants who died of the respiratory distress syndrome also lacked PDME in the material obtained by saline lavage of the lungs. An infant's condition seemed to be associated with the loss of PDME and of myristic acid in the $\beta$ carbon of PC. In partial support of this postulate is Morgan's observation (54) that N-methyl transferase activity in the fetal lamb lung tripled during the last third of gestation, and then declined just before term. However, Morgan did not report the relationship of the N-methyl transferase to myristate in the $\beta$ position.

Although this concept has received considerable attention, several questions remain:

(a) Does the PC which contains $\alpha$ palmitate–$\beta$ myristate meet the conditions for surfactant? In particular, is this PC able to lower the surface tension below 10 dynes/cm at 37°C? The surface tension studies reported by Gluck (25) were done with a threefold excess of acetone-precipitated PC at room temperature, and the low surface tension may have been related to DPPC in this fraction.

(*b*) Does the presence of myristate in the $\beta$ position necessarily depend upon the activity of the methylation pathway? The CDP choline pathway has not been shown to exclude myristate from the $\beta$ position.

(*c*) Is the substance with the chromatographic characteristic of PDME a single substance throughout gestation, or could it, for instance, contain phosphatidylglycerol at some stages (61)?

In addition to the two basic pathways other routes of PC synthesis are known. Abe, Akino & Ohno (1) have evidence that other pathways must also be present in lung tissue and they suggest that DPPC may be synthesized by transacylation of two molecules of lysolecithin.

## Surfactant Secretion

Surfactant secretion has been studied primarily by use of radiolabeled palmitate and other precursors of DPPC, but radiolabeled amino acids have been used to follow the protein component. Klaus et al (40) suggested that the lamellar bodies of the type II alveolar epithelial cells contained the surfactant and were destined to be secreted onto the alveolar surface. Although some reports suggested that these lamellar bodies were ingested, it is now apparent that they are formed within the cell. Numerous investigators have reported electron micrographs of lamellar bodies that appeared to be leaving the cell and spreading over the surface. Askin & Kuhn (5) found fine structural differences between the cell surface at the site of these disrupted lamellar bodies and provided evidence that the cell was not in the process of ingesting them. They also noted that [3]H-palmitate labeled the lamellar bodies of rat lungs. Two studies have used autoradiography to show that other radiolabeled substances injected into animals appear in the lamellar bodies after a delay of about 1–2 hr. Massaro & Massaro (50) incubated the amino acid leucine-4,5-[3]H with rat lung slices and used morphometric methods to determine the location of [3]H. Lungs removed 4 min after the addition of leucine showed 70% of the grains from type II cells to be above the rough endoplasmic reticulum and 10% to be over the lamellar bodies. By 40 min after the injection the relationship had changed so that 56% of the grains were over the rough endoplasmic reticulum and 29% over the lamellar bodies, an apparent transfer of the radioactivity to the lamellar bodies. Chevalier & Collett (11) reported similar studies with the mouse, but they used three potential precursors of the surfactant: choline-[3]H, leucine-[3]H, and galactose-[3]H. These three precursors should have a relatively high specificity for the phosphatidylcholine, protein, and carbohydrate components of the surfactant. Between 30 and 120 min after injection of any of the three precursors, the number of grains over the lamellar bodies increased relative to the number of grains elsewhere. Therefore, the evidence now appears to be overwhelming that these lamellar bodies are produced by type II cells rather than ingested.

Recently Page-Roberts (59) has prepared a fraction from rat lung that is rich in lamellar bodies. This fraction has a high ratio of phospholipid to protein and it is surface active; these characteristics are consistent with the concept that these lamellar bodies contain the surfactant.

More direct evidence as to which cells secrete surfactant could be obtained if the cells in lungs could be separated and isolated as individual cell types. Gould and associates (29) tackled the difficult task of separating cells from the lungs. Previously, small quantities of cells had been removed from lungs; however, these may not have been representative samples but rather those cells that were most easily removed. Gould collected a high proportion of cells from the rabbit lung and it is very likely that specific cell types will be isolated in the near future. A preliminary report by Kikkawa & Yoneda (35) indicates that they have isolated a relatively pure fraction of type II cells.

The lung is a vital secretory organ and the dynamic character of its extracellular surface has been documented. This extracellular material can be removed by lung lavage (rinsing the airspaces with saline). Pawlowski et al (60) injected $^3$H-palmitate dissolved into alcohol into dogs and then removed lungs at intervals during the next 6 hr. They extracted their surface-active fraction from both the lavage material and from the residual lung. Their results suggested an extremely rapid half-life of the material in the residual lung (about 5 hr) and the specific activity of phosphatidyl-choline in the lavage material did not reach that in the residual lung. Therefore, they did not observe a simple precursor-product type of relationship in which initially the precursor (residual lung surfactant) has a higher specific activity than the product (secreted surfactant) but subsequently the specific activity of the product should exceed that of the precursor. They estimated that the DPPC in the fraction obtained from lung lavage was 3.6% of the whole lung DPPC. Only 5.0% of the whole lung DPPC was present in the surface-active fraction they obtained from the residual lung. This quantity of DPPC in their surface-active fraction would not be sufficient to form a layer on the surface of the lung that could decrease the surface tension to 10 dynes/cm. It appears, therefore, that their extraction may not have yielded all of the surfactant, but perhaps the specific activity was representative of the surfactant.

Tierney, Clements & Trahan (81) injected radiolabeled palmitate and glucose and followed the half-life of radioactivity in rat lung PC. The saturated (anenoic), monoenoic, and dienoic PCs had a radioactive half-life of approximately 14 hr, but the polyenoic PC, which contained arachidonate, had a longer half-life of about 20 hr. The radioactive half-lives in the glycerol (derived from glucose) and fatty acid moieties were similar, which suggested that extensive deacylation and reacylation did not occur. Young & Tierney (93) conducted similar studies with rats, but they also determined the specific activity of DPPC in the lung lavage material. They reported that: (a) The decreasing specific activity of DPPC in lung tissue did not follow a single exponential relationship as one would predict if a single tissue pool of DPPC existed. (b) Specific activities of DPPC in the lung tissue and lavage fluid did not demonstrate a simple precursor-product type of relationship since the DPPC in the lavage fluid had a higher specific activity at 8 hr but not at 48 and 72 hr after the injection. The loss of radioactivity from DPPC in the whole lung is rapid initially (i.e. 8 hr half-life), but much slower after 48 hr (i.e. 54 hr half-life). Although several possibilities exist, the results suggest that DPPC in the lung may not be limited to the surfactant, but may also be present in other cell components. These results complicate attempts to measure surfactant quantitatively since quantitative determination of DPPC in the lung may not reflect the quantity of surfactant.

Once secreted onto the surface of the lung, how is the surfactant lost? There are several possibilities, which include: (a) passage up the airways and out of the lung, (b) removal or metabolism by the alveolar macrophages, (c) re-entry into the alveolar epithelium where it may be utilized or transported to the circulating blood, and (d) passage through the lymphatics and out of the lung. Surprisingly, there are almost no data to support any of these over the others. It has been suggested that alveolar proteinosis is a disease due to inadequate removal of surfactant from the lung (63) but the primary lesion in this disease has not been described.

Loss of functional surfactant from the surfaces of excised rat (52) and dog lungs (21) apparently is accelerated by ventilation with large tidal volumes. This conclusion is based upon a shift of the pressure-volume relationships toward a higher pressure at any given volume after the ventilation. Subsequent incubation of the lung at 37° reverses the changes; the investigators have concluded that surfactant upon alveolar surfaces was depleted by the large changes in surface area associated with the ventilation but that additional surfactant was secreted during the incubation. This rapid increase of surface forces during ventilation of excised lungs is not likely to be due to removal by macrophages or reabsorption into epithelium; it seems more likely that ventilation inactivates surfactant or forces it up the airways.

## Surfactant and Lung Maturation

The most exciting application of surfactant biochemistry to clinical medicine relates to the developing mammalian lung. Ten to fifteen years ago, research in this field could be considered basic and a relatively small group of investigators was studying the composition of lung surfactant and its quantitative changes during fetal development. Now, however, these concepts are applied by obstetricians and pediatricians who wish to anticipate the development of the respiratory distress syndrome in the newborn infant. It may also be possible in the next few years to increase surfactant production in the premature infant by accelerating lung maturation with hormones.

The mammalian lung undergoes changes late in gestation that are essential if the newborn infant is to survive. Brumley and associates (9) thoroughly documented the changes of morphology, saturated PC, and pressure-volume curves during maturation of the fetal lamb lung. Saturated PC increases severalfold as the pressure-volume curve of the lung changes to one of increased stability. Thus, these biochemical and mechanical evaluations of surfactant correlate very well.

The trigger for lung maturation has been related, at least in part, to the effect of steroids upon the fetal lung. Liggins (47) observed that hydrocortisone infusion into the fetal lamb led to premature delivery, but perhaps more significant was his observation that these prematurely born lambs were viable at an earlier gestational age than if they had not received the steroids.

This early maturation following steroid injections has been explored by Avery and her associates. DeLemos et al (16) and Kotas & Avery (42) reported that injections of hydrocortisone and 9-fluoroprednisolone acetate produced early lung maturation in the lamb and rabbit fetus as reflected in the surface tension of lung extracts and pressure-volume curves. Wang et al (87) and Motoyama et al (56) attributed these effects in the fetal rabbits to accelerated changes of the alveolar epithelium.

Ballard & Ballard (6) have associated this dramatic maturation of the lung by steroids with the presence of many receptors for steroids. These receptors are present in the fetal lung in greater quantity per unit mass than in any other organ studied; they bind the steroid and probably transport it to active sites within the cell.

Currently the major clinical application of surfactant biochemistry is to estimate lung maturity by determination of surfactant in amniotic fluid and so predict the respiratory distress syndrome. After considerable controversy regarding the source of amniotic fluid, a series of papers demonstrated that the lung is a major source (2, 3, 24, 73). Adams & Fujiwara (3) reported that the immature lamb (fetal age of 120 days) lacked surface activity in the tracheal fluid, whereas the mature fetus had detectable surfactant in the tracheal fluid. They noted, however, that amniotic fluid lacked this surface activity. It appears now that the surfactant enters the amniotic fluid of the mature fetus, but its surface activity is not readily detected. A specific biochemical test for surfactant rather than an estimate of surface activity may have led to an earlier appreciation of the use of amniotic fluid to determine lung maturity.

Predicting the respiratory distress syndrome of the newborn is now a practical clinical science largely developed by Gluck and associates (24). Infant mortality and the respiratory distress syndrome are closely related to lung immaturity and probably to inadequate surfactant secretion. Gluck capitalized on the observation that during maturation the lung has little change of sphingomyelin content but a great change of saturated PC. He concentrated these two phospholipids by use of cold acetone, which dissolves most lipids but not sphingomyelin or saturated PC, and assumed that the lecithin and sphingomyelin in the amniotic fluid would be determined largely by the secretion of surfactant from the lung. Early in gestation, the lecithin/sphingomyelin (L/S) ratio in the lung and in amniotic fluid is low, and if a ratio of 1.5 or lower is present in amniotic fluid within 24 hr of birth, a high incidence of respiratory distress occurs. In contrast, when the L/S ratio is above 2.0, a low incidence of respiratory distress occurs. Measurements on amniotic fluid can therefore be used to predict the respiratory distress syndrome if the fetus is delivered within the next 24 hr. These observations also suggest that lung immaturity with inadequate secretion of saturated PC may be necessary for the respiratory distress syndrome to develop.

Although this L/S test for immaturity is reliable, it requires several hours to extract the lipids and separate lecithin and sphingomyelin. Clements (12) designed a simpler and more direct test for surfactant in the amniotic fluid. This test can be done at the bedside and relies upon the stability of bubbles formed with surfactant. Amniotic fluid is shaken with a foam breaker (alcohol) and the presence or absence of foam is noted after 15 min. To be stable in the alcohol solution, a bubble must have a surface tension lower than that of the solution. Few substances can develop such a low surface tension, and the test is thus relatively specific. In a clinical trial, this test was also shown to be valuable in predicting the respiratory distress syndrome (12).

## METABOLISM OF CIRCULATING SUBSTANCES

If an engineer were to design an organ which would rapidly change the concentrations of blood-borne substances, he might arrange that the entire cardiac output flow through it and come in contact with a large surface area. The lung meets these requirements since it receives the entire cardiac output and has a huge capillary surface area. This ensures contact between the endothelial surface of the lung and blood-borne substances each time they circulate through the body. In recent years, the lung has been shown to change many circulating substances; some become biologically active, some become inactive, and some may be stored and later released. This newly-discovered function of the lung may turn out to be a very important one although to date most reports have dealt with the normal lung and no diseases have been found to be related to failure of this function of the lung. However, methods are now available to study the possible effects of lung injury upon this newly recognized function.

Many of the advances in this field were made using highly sensitive biological assays and in vitro preparations. Although some physiologists may feel uncomfortable using information obtained from an isolated lung perfused with a balanced salt solution rather than a protein-containing solution, the investigators have been imaginative, dramatic advances have been made, and many observations have been confirmed by subsequent investigations done in vivo.

The function of the pulmonary endothelium now appears to be much more than a simple physical barrier to large molecules. These structurally simple cells dominate the metabolism of some substances that have great potential for disrupting the normal condition of the body.

Due largely to the pioneering efforts of Vane and associates, the lung's vital role in regulating the concentrations of vasoactive substances in blood has been recognized. In 1968, Vane reviewed this field and presented an excellent discussion of the methods and concepts of bioassay (83). The advances made by studying vasoactive substances have been particularly rapid, probably because the biological assays are so sensitive. Only a few nonvasoactive substances are known to be altered on passage through the lung. Many hormones and other compounds may also be affected by the lung, but investigations are often handicapped by inadequate or time-consuming tests for their activity. Lipoproteins are attacked by lipoprotein lipase, an enzyme which is activated by heparin and may be on the surface of the endothelial cell. The effect of the lung on other circulating substances such as steroids, endotoxin, and insulin is just now being investigated. This review considers only vasoactive substances.

### Vasoactive Substances

Vane (83) has categorized the vasoactive substances that are metabolized while circulating through the lung as amines (acetylcholine, 5-hydroxytryptamine, catecholamines), peptides (bradykinin, angiotensins, vasopressin), and prostaglandins. Acetylcholine is attacked by cholinesterase in the blood and the potential of the lung to destroy acetylcholine is probably rarely utilized. The half-life of acetylcholine in blood is less than 2 sec.

5-HYDROXYTRYPTAMINE    To a large extent the lung maintains the low blood concentrations of 5-hydroxytryptamine (5HT) and this role may be clinically important since 5HT apparently produces: (*a*) symptoms of carcinoid tumors, (*b*) the dumping syndrome after gastrectomy, (*c*) airway constriction after pulmonary emboli, and (*d*) platelet aggregation. Recently, Gruby et al (30) have suggested that any condition that might disrupt the normal metabolic function of the lung may promote platelet aggregation and possibly deep vein thrombosis if 5HT is not cleared from the blood.

The 5HT is initially removed from the blood by a process which may be a $Na^+$-dependent carrier system (34). Strum & Junod (78) demonstrated with autoradiography that the pulmonary endothelial cells of the isolated rat lung are the major sites for removal and storage of 5HT. Prior to their study, platelets, mast cells, and nerve endings were considered candidates for this role.

Do monoamine oxidase inhibitors influence the uptake of 5HT by the lung? Strum & Junod (78) found a marked effect due to imipramine ($10^{-4}$ $M$) upon the radioactivity that remained in the rat lung after perfusion with a medium containing 5HT-$^3$H. In contrast, Gruby et al (30) added another monoamine oxidase inhibitor (nialamide, 30–40 ng/ml) and found no change in the disappearance of 5HT from the perfusate of isolated guinea pig lungs. They concluded, however, that although the monoamine oxidase inhibitor had no effect upon the initial uptake by the lungs, the 5HT metabolism to 5-hydroxyindole acetic acid was markedly affected.

CATECHOLAMINES    Epinephrine (83) and isoproterenol (8) are not affected by passage through the pulmonary circulation. However, about 30% of norepinephrine disappears during passage through the lungs (83).

PEPTIDES    The angiotensin and bradykinin are class favorites for investigators interested in this general field and their fate has been extensively studied.

Ng & Vane (57) were the first investigators to report that a very high proportion of the decapeptide, angiotensin I, is converted to the octapeptide, angiotensin II, by a single passage through the lung. The loss of two amino acids from angiotensin I has been attributed to a "converting enzyme." Ryan, Smith & Niemeyer (70) have gathered data which strongly support the concept that circulating angiotensin I is metabolized by enzymes on the luminal surface of pulmonary endothelial cells. By using $^{14}$C-angiotensin I and blue dextran (a large molecule which flows through the vascular bed without leaving the vessels), they demonstrated that angiotensin I was converted to angiotensin II within the time required for the perfusate to pass through the lungs. The volume of distribution of the radioactive angiotensin is not greater than that of dextran and the mean transit times are identical. Therefore, the angiotensin when compared to dextran is not delayed within the isolated rat lung although it is converted from angiotensin I to angiotensin II. These investigators (68) also prepared a plasma membrane fraction of lung and reported that sufficient converting enzyme activity may be present on the endothelial surface to meet the requirements for in vivo conversion of angiotensin I during a single passage through the lung.

The activity of angiotensin-converting enzyme has been estimated using several different methods (14, 17, 33). Cushman & Cheung (14) used a spectrophotometric assay to measure the production of hippuric acid from hippuryl-L-leucine and assumed that the converting enzyme split histidyl leucine from this compound in the same fashion that it does from angiotensin I. They noted four classes of inhibitors of this enzyme from rabbit lungs: chelators, sulfhydryl compounds, heavy metal ions, and peptides. Bradykinin and a bradykinin-potentiating pentapeptide were the most effective inhibitors. This interrelationship of kininase activity and angiotensin-converting enzyme activity extends to the cleavage of C-terminal phenylalanylarginine from bradykinin. However, bradykininase activity appears to be different from the activity of the angiotensin-converting enzyme (72).

Depierre & Roth (17) have reported that the activity of converting enzyme varies considerably in the lungs of ten different species. In general, the activity is greatest in the pellet obtained after homogenizing and centrifuging and therefore it is not primarily a cytoplasmic enzyme, except in the rat and mouse lung in which considerable activity is present in both fractions. The presence of this enzyme in the pellet is consistent with the views of several investigators that this enzyme is firmly fixed to the membranes of the endothelial cells. Angiotensin-converting enzyme has relatively little specificity and a more general term, dipeptidylcarboxypeptidase, has been used to describe its activity. It can cleave other substances, including insulin, which has been reported to be partially removed by passage through the pulmonary circulation (67).

Bradykinin is another important vasoactive peptide which is attacked by enzymes in the lung. Isolated lungs of guinea pigs, rats, and dogs, perfused with Krebs bicarbonate solution, inactivated 95–99% of the bradykinin perfused through the lung (4). Bradykinin inactivation is due to enzymatic degradation which can be inhibited by several compounds including peptides from the venom of *Bothrops jaraca* (4). These peptides potentiate the effect of bradykinin, presumably by decreasing its destruction.

Do toxic levels of bradykinin ever develop secondary to failure of the lung to inactivate this polypeptide? The fetus, and possibly the adult during cardiopulmonary bypass, might be considered candidates for inadequate removal of bradykinin, since the systemic blood is largely shunted away from the lungs. There is no evidence that this shunting produces an abnormal bradykinin concentration; however, bradykinin has been shown to play a fascinating role in the newly born animal. Heymann et al (32) have demonstrated increased concentrations of bradykinin in the fetal lamb when the arterial $Po_2$ rises to levels normally obtained shortly after birth. They have proposed that bradykinin is produced from kininogen in the lungs. Since bradykinin constricts the ductus arteriosus and dilates the pulmonary vascular bed, it would act to decrease the shunting of blood and should increase the arterial $Po_2$.

PROSTAGLANDINS    This group of hormones has such diverse actions that it sometimes seems one could attribute almost any condition upon activation of inactivation of one prostaglandin or another. Different prostaglandins may act in opposing directions; for instance, prostaglandins $F_2\alpha$ increases pulmonary vascular resistance whereas prostaglandin $E_2$ decreases it. Some prostaglandins appear to produce bronchoconstriction whereas others produce bronchodilation.

Prostaglandins which originate in the intestine or spleen are largely removed by the liver. However, if prostaglandins pass the liver, or originate elsewhere, the lung can remove about 95% of prostaglandins E and F that pass through it (83). Prostaglandins $A_1$ and $A_2$ appear unchanged by passage through dog lungs (53).

The destruction of prostaglandins in the lung has been attributed to the enzyme prostaglandin 15-hydroxydehydrogenase. In contrast with the angiotensin-converting enzyme, prostaglandin 15-hydroxydehydrogenase is found in the soluble fraction obtained after homogenizing and centrifuging swine lung. Presumably, prostaglandin must be intracellular for this dehydrogenase to be effective. Ryan & Smith (69) found the transit time of prostaglandin $F_2\alpha$ through the pulmonary circulation to be longer than that of dextran, which suggests a delay due to entry of this prostaglandin into cells. Vonkeman, Nugteren & Van Dorp (85) reported that prostaglandins $A_1$ and $A_2$ are destroyed by prostaglandin 15-hydroxydehydrogenase. If these prostaglandins are not altered by passage through the lung (53) it appears likely that they do not enter the cells which contain this enzyme.

ADENINE NUCLEOTIDES    Ryan & Smith (69) have emphasized the potential significance of the lung in shock. For instance, after trauma, vasodilators such as adenine nucleotides might be released by muscle injury and contribute to the hypotension. However, these nucleotides are normally removed by passage through the lungs. ATP is degraded to adenosine and AMP by enzymes on or very close to the luminal surface of the pulmonary endothelium.

These same investigators (68) have succeeded in preparing a fraction from lung which is rich in pinocytotic vesicles and the plasma membrane of lung; their method depends upon the presence of 5'-nucleotidase in the vesicles. This major advance has led to more specific studies of the action of the endothelial cell surface upon substances which are in the circulation.

*Literature Cited*

1. Abe, M., Akino. T., Ohrfo, K. 1973. On the metabolism of lecithin in lung and liver of fetal rabbits. *Tohoku J. Exp. Med.* 109:163–72
2. Adams, F. H., Desilets, D. T., Towers, B. 1967. Control of flow of fetal lung fluid at the laryngeal outlet. *Resp. Physiol.* 2: 302–9
3. Adams, F. H., Fujiwara, T. 1963. Surfactant in fetal lamb tracheal fluid. *J. Pediat.* 63:537–42
4. Alabaster, V. A., Bakhle, Y. S. 1972. Converting enzyme and bradykininase in the lung. *Circ. Res.* 30–31 (Suppl. II): 72–84
5. Askin, F. B., Kuhn, C. 1971. The cellular origin of pulmonary surfactant. *Lab. Invest.* 25:260–68
6. Ballard, P. L., Ballard, R. A. 1972. Glucocorticoid receptors and the role of glucocorticoids in fetal lung development. *Proc. Nat. Acad. Sci. USA* 69: 2668–72
7. Barron, E. S. G., Miller, Z. B., Bartlett, G. R. 1947. Studies on biological oxidations. XXI. The metabolism of lung as determined by a study of slices and ground tissue. *J. Biol. Chem.* 171:791–800
8. Boileau, J. C., Campeau, L., Biron, P. 1970. Pulmonary fate of histamine, isoproterenol, physalaemin, and substance

P. *Can. J. Physiol. Pharmacol.* 48: 681–84

9. Brumley, G. W. et al 1967. Correlations of mechanical stability, morphology, pulmonary surfactant, and phospholipid content in the developing lamb lung. *J. Clin. Invest.* 46:863–73

10. Cavagna, G. A., Stemmler, E. J., Du Bois, A. B. 1967. Alveolar resistance to atelectasis. *J. Appl. Physiol.* 22:441–52

11. Chevalier, G., Collet, A. J. 1972. In vivo incorporation of choline-$^3$H, leucine-$^3$H and galactose-$^3$H in alveolar type II pneumocytes in relation to surfactant synthesis. A quantitative radioautographic study in mouse by electron microscopy. *Anat. Rec.* 174:289–310

12. Clements, J. A. et al 1972. Assessment of the risk of the respiratory-distress syndrome by a rapid test for surfactant in amniotic fluid. *N. Engl. J. Med.* 286: 1077–81

13. Clements, J. A., Nellenbogen, J., Trahan, H. J. 1970. Pulmonary surfactant and evolution of the lungs. *Science* 169: 603–4

14. Cushman, D. W., Cheung, H. S. 1971. Concentrations of angiotensin-converting enzyme in tissues of the rat. *Biochim. Biophys. Acta* 250:261–65

15. Darrah, H. K., Hedley-Whyte, J. 1973. Rapid incorporation of palmitate into lung: site and metabolic fate. *J. Appl. Physiol.* 34:205–13

16. DeLemos, R. A., Shermeta, D. W., Knelson, J. H., Kotas, R., Avery, M. E. 1970. Acceleration of appearance of pulmonary surfactant in the fetal lamb by administration of corticosteroids. *Am. Rev. Resp. Dis.* 102:459–61

17. Depierre, D., Roth, M. 1972. Activity of a dipeptidyl carboxypeptidase (angiotensin converting enzyme) in lungs of different animal species. *Experientia* 28: 154–55

18. DiAugustine, R. P. 1971. Lung phospholipids I. In vivo studies of the incorporation of $^{32}$P, (methyl-$^{14}$C) choline, 1-$^{14}$C-palmitic acid and 1-$^{14}$C-oleic acid into phosphatidylethanolamine, phosphatidyl-*n*, *n*-dimethylethanolamine and phosphatidylcholine. *Biochem. Biophys. Res. Commun.* 43:311–17

19. Dickie, K. J., Massaro, G. D., Marshall, V., Massaro, D. 1973. Amino acid incorporation into protein of a surface-active lung fraction. *J. Appl. Physiol.* 34: 606–14

20. Faridy, E. E., Naimark, A. 1971. Effect of distension on metabolism of excised dog lung. *J. Appl. Physiol.* 31:31–37

21. Faridy, E. E., Permutt, S., Riley, R. L. 1966. Effect of ventilation on surface forces in excised dog lungs. *J. Appl. Physiol.* 21:1453–62

22. Felts, J. M. 1964. Biochemistry of the lung. *Health Phys.* 10:973–79

23. Frosolono, M. F., Charms, B. L., Pawlowski, R., Slivka, S. 1970. Isolation, characterization, and surface chemistry of a surface-active fraction from dog lung. *J. Lipid Res.* 11:439–57

24. Gluck, L. et al 1971. Diagnosis of the respiratory distress syndrome by amniocentesis. *Am. J. Obstet. Gynecol.* 109: 440–45

25. Gluck, L., Kulovich, M. V., Eidelman, A. I., Cordero, L., Khazin, A. F. 1972. Biochemical development of surface activity in mammalian lung. IV. Pulmonary lecithin synthesis in the human fetus and newborn and etiology of the respiratory distress syndrome. *Pediat. Res.* 6:81–99

26. Gluck, L., Motoyama, E. K., Smits, H. L., Kulovich, M. V. 1967. The biochemical development of surface activity of mammalian lung. I. The surface-active phospholipids; the separation and distribution of surface-active lecithin in the lung of the developing rabbit fetus. *Pediat. Res.* 1:237–46

27. Gluck, L., Sribney, M., Kulovich, M. V. 1967. The biochemical development of surface activity in mammalian lung. II. The biosynthesis of phospholipids in the lung of the developing rabbit fetus and newborn. *Pediat. Res.* 1:247–65

28. Gluck, L., Landowne, R. A., Kulovich, M. V. 1970. Biochemical development of surface activity in mammalian lung. III. Structural changes in lung lecithin during development of the rabbit fetus and newborn. *Pediat. Res.* 4: 352–64

29. Gould, K. G., Clements, J. A., Jones, A. L., Felts, J. M. 1972. Dispersal of rabbit lung into individual viable cells: A new model for the study of lung metabolism. *Science* 178:1209–10

30. Gruby, L. A., Rowlands, C., Varley, B. Q., Wyllie, J. H. 1971. The fate of 5-hydroxytryptamine in the lungs. *Brit. J. Surg.* 58:525–32

31. Harris, P. et al 1963. Lactate, pyruvate, glucose, and free fatty acid in mixed venous and arterial blood. *J. Appl. Physiol.* 18:933–36

32. Heymann, M. A., Rudolph, A. M., Nies, A. S., Melmon, K. L. 1969. Bradykinin production associated with oxygenation of the fetal lamb. *Circ. Res.* 25:521–34

33. Igic, R., Yeh, H. S. J., Sorrells, K., Erdös, E. G. 1972. Cleavage of active peptides by a lung enzyme. *Experientia* 28:135–36

34. Junod, A. F. 1972. Uptake, metabolism and efflux of $^{14}$C-5-hydroxytryptamine in isolated perfused rat lungs. *J. Pharmacol. Exp. Theor.* 183:341–55

35. Kikkawa, Y., Yoneda, K. 1973. *Isolation of Type II Epithelial Cells from Rat Lung.* Presented at Ann. Meet. Am. Thorac. Soc., NY

36. King, R. J., Clements, J. A. 1972. Surface active materials from dog lung. I. Method of isolation. *Am. J. Physiol.* 223:707–14

37. King, R. J., Clements, J. A. 1972. Surface active materials from dog lung. II. Composition and physiological correlations. *Am. J. Physiol.* 223:715–26

38. King, R. J., Clements, J. A. 1972. Surface active materials from dog lung. III. Thermal analysis. *Am. J. Physiol.* 223: 727–33

39. Klaus, M. H., Clements, J. A., Havel, R. J. 1961. Composition of surface-active material isolated from beef lung. *Proc. Nat. Acad. Sci. USA* 47:1858–59

40. Klaus, M. H., Reiss, O. K., Tooley, W. H., Piel, C., Clements, J. A. 1962. Alveolar epithelial cell mitochondria as source of the surface-active lung lining. *Science* 137:750–52

41. Klein, R. M., Margolis, S. 1968. Purification of pulmonary surfactant by ultracentrifugation. *J. Appl. Physiol.* 25: 654–58

42. Kotas, R. V., Avery, M. E. 1971. Accelerated appearance of pulmonary surfactant in the fetal rabbit. *J. Appl. Physiol.* 30:358–61

43. Krebs, H. A. 1950. Body size and tissue respiration. *Biochim. Biophys. Acta* 4: 249–69

44. Krebs, H. A. 1970. Rate control of the tricarboxylic acid cycle. *Advan. Enzyme Regul.* 8:335–53

45. Lee, J. B., Peter, H. M. 1969. Effect of oxygen tension on glucose metabolism in rabbit kidney cortex and medulla. *Am. J. Physiol.* 217:1464–71

46. Levy, S., Harvey, E. 1974. The effect of tissue slicing on rat lung metabolism. *J. Appl. Physiol.* In press

47. Liggins, G. C. 1969. Premature delivery of fetal lambs infused with glucocorticoids. *J. Endocrinol.* 45:515–23

48. Longmore, W. J., Niethe, C. M., Sprinkle, D. J., Godinez, R. I. 1973. Effect of $CO_2$ concentration on phospholipid metabolism in the isolated perfused rat lung. *J. Lipid Res.* 14:145–51

49. Mason, R. J. 1973. Disaturated lecithin concentration of rabbit tissues. *Am. Rev. Resp. Dis.* 107:678–79

50. Massaro, G. D., Massaro, D. 1972. Granular pneumocytes. Electron microscopic radioautographic evidence of intracellular protein transport. *Am. Rev. Resp. Dis.* 105:927–31

51. Massaro, D., Simon, M. R., Steinkamp, H. 1971. Metabolic factors affecting protein synthesis by lung in vitro. *J. Appl. Physiol.* 30:1–6

52. McClenahan, J. B., Urtnowski, A. 1967. Effect of ventilation on surfactant, and its turnover rate. *J. Appl. Physiol.* 23: 215–20

53. McGiff, J. C., Terragno, N. A., Strand, J. C., Lee, J. B., Lonigro, A. J. 1969. Selective passage of prostaglandins across the lung. *Nature* 223:742–45

54. Morgan, T. E. 1971. Biosynthesis of pulmonary surface-active lipid. *Arch. Int. Med.* 127:401–7

55. Morgan, T. E., Finley, T. N., Fialkow, H. 1965. Comparison of the composition and surface activity of "alveolar" and whole lung lipids in the dog. *Biochim. Biophys. Acta* 106:403–13

56. Motoyama, E. K. et al 1971. Effect of cortisol on the maturation of fetal rabbit lungs. *Pediatrics* 48:547–55

57. Ng, K. F., Vane, J. R. 1968. Fate of angiotensin I in the circulation. *Nature* 218: 144–50

58. O'Neil, J., Tierney, D. F. 1974. Rat lung metabolism: glucose utilization by tissue slices and the isolated perfused lung. *Am. J. Physiol.* In press

59. Page-Roberts, B. A. 1972. Preparation and partial characterization of a lamellar body fraction from rat lung. *Biochim. Biophys. Acta* 260:334–38

60. Pawlowski, R., Frosolono, M. F., Charms, B. L., Przybylski, R. 1971. Intra- and extracellular compartmentalization of the surface-active fraction in dog lung. *J. Lipid Res.* 12:538–44

61. Pfleger, R. C., Henderson, R. F., Waide, J. 1972. Phosphatidyl glycerol—a major component of pulmonary surfactant. *Chem. Phys. Lipids* 9:51–68

62. Radford, E. P. Jr. 1960. Mechanical factors determining alveolar configuration. *Am. Rev. Resp. Dis.* 81:743–44

63. Ramirez-R., J., Harlan, W. R. 1968. Pulmonary alveolar proteinosis. Nature and origin of alveolar lipid. *Am. J. Med.* 45: 502–12

64. Reiss, O. K. 1965. Properties of mitochondrial preparations from rabbit lung. *Med. Thorac.* 22:100–3
65. Reiss, O. K. 1966. Studies of lung metabolism. I. Isolation and properties of subcellular fractions from rabbit lung. *J. Cell Biol.* 30:45–57
66. Rochester, D. F. et al 1973. Arteriovenous differences of lactate and pyruvate across healthy and diseased human lung. *Am. Rev. Resp. Dis.* 107:442–48
67. Rubenstein, A. H., Zwi, S., Miller, K. 1968. Insulin and the lung. *Diabetologia* 4:236–38
68. Ryan, J. W., Smith, U. 1971. A rapid, simple method for isolating pinocytotic vesicles and plasma membrane of lung. *Biochim. Biophys. Acta* 249:177–80
69. Ryan, J. W., Smith, U. 1971. Metabolism of adenosine 5'-monophosphate during circulation through the lungs. *Trans. Assoc. Am. Phys.* 84:297–306
70. Ryan, J. W., Smith, U., Niemeyer, R. S. 1972. Angiotensin I: metabolism by plasma membrane of lung. *Science* 176:64–66
71. Salisbury-Murphy, S., Rubinstein, D., Beck, J. C. 1966. Lipid metabolism in lung slices. *Am. J. Physiol.* 211:988–92
72. Sander, G. E., West, D. W., Huggins, C. G. 1971. Peptide inhibitors of pulmonary angiotensin I converting enzyme. *Biochim. Biophys. Acta* 242:662–67
73. Scarpelli, E. M. 1967. The lung, tracheal fluid, and lipid metabolism of the fetus. *Pediatrics* 40:951–61
74. Scarpelli, E. M., Chang, S. J., Colacicco, G. 1970. A search for the surface-active pulmonary lipoprotein. *Am. Rev. Resp. Dis.* 102:285–89
75. Scarpelli, E. M., Clutario, B. C., Taylor, F. A. 1967. Preliminary identification of the lung surfactant system. *J. Appl. Physiol.* 23:880–86
76. Scholz, R. W., Rhoades, R. A. 1971. Lipid metabolism by rat lung in vitro. Effect of starvation and re-feeding on utilization of (U-$^{14}$C) glucose by lung slice. *Biochem. J.* 124:257–64
77. Steim, J. M., Redding, R. A., Hauck, C. T., Stein, M. 1969. Isolation and characterization of lung surfactant. *Biochem. Biophys. Res. Commun.* 34:434–40
78. Strum, J. M., Junod, A. F. 1972. Radioautographic demonstration of 5-hydroxytryptamine-$^3$H uptake by pulmonary endothelial cells. *J. Cell Biol.* 54:456–67
79. Tierney, D. F. 1971. Lactate metabolism in rat lung tissue. *Arch. Intern. Med.* 127:858–60
80. Tierney, D. F., Ayers, L., Herzog, S., Yang, J. 1973. Pentose pathway and NADPH production: a mechanism which may protect lungs from oxidants. *Am. Rev. Resp. Dis.* 108:In press
81. Tierney, D. F., Clements, J. A., Trahan, H. J. 1967. Rates of replacement of lecithins and alveolar instability in rat lungs. *Am. J. Physiol.* 213:671–76
82. Tierney, D. F., Johnson, R. P. 1965. Altered surface tension of lung extracts and lung mechanics. *J. Appl. Physiol.* 20:1253–60
83. Vane, J. R. 1969. The release and fate of vaso-active hormones in the circulation. *Brit. J. Pharmacol.* 35:209–42
84. Veith, F. J., Koerner, S., Torres, M., Attai, L., Gliedman, M. L. 1969. Functional evaluation of lungs transplanted after varying ischemic intervals and after preservation by mechanical ventricular assistance. *Ann. Thorac. Surg.* 7:446–58
85. Vonkeman, H., Nugteren, D. H., van Dorp, D. A. 1969. The action of prostaglandin 15-hydroxydehydrogenase on various prostaglandins. *Biochim. Biophys. Acta* 187:581–83
86. Wang, M. C., Meng, H. C. 1972. Lipid synthesis by rat lung in vitro. *Lipids* 7:207–11
87. Wang, N. S., Kotas, R. V., Avery, M. E., Thurlbeck, W. M. 1971. Accelerated appearance of osmiophilic bodies in fetal lung following steroid injection. *J. Appl. Physiol.* 30:362–65
88. Weber, K. C., Visscher, M. B. 1969. Metabolism of the isolated canine lung. *Am. J. Physiol.* 217:1044–52
89. Weinhold, P. A. 1968. Biosynthesis of phosphatidyl choline during prenatal development of the rat lung. *J. Lipid Res.* 9:262–66
90. Wichert, P. von 1972. Studies on the metabolism of ischemic rabbit lungs. *J. Thorac. Cardiovasc. Surg.* 63:284–91
91. Wolfe, B. M. J., Anhalt, B., Beck, J. C., Rubinstein, D. 1970. Lipid metabolism in rabbit lungs. *Can. J. Biochem.* 48:170–77
92. Yeager, H. Jr., Massaro, D. 1972. Glucose metabolism and glycoprotein synthesis by lung slices. *J. Appl. Physiol.* 32:477–82
93. Young, S. L., Tierney, D. F. 1972. Dipalmitoyl lecithin secretion and metabolism by the rat lung. *Am. J. Physiol.* 222:1539–44

# THERMORECEPTORS

*Herbert Hensel*

Institute of Physiology, University of Marburg/Lahn, Germany

## INTRODUCTION

Physiology of thermoreception includes various experimental approaches: (*a*) the phenomenological analysis of temperature sensations, (*b*) the measurement of thermal stimuli, and (*c*) the investigation of neural events, mainly by electrophysiological methods. In a wider sense, physiological and behavioral responses belong to this category as well. The connection between these approaches can be symbolized by a triad:

where P is a sensory phenomenon (e.g. temperature sensation), S a physical object (e.g. thermal stimulus), and N an object of neurophysiology (e.g. impulse discharge, thermoregulatory response). Usually the correlation between these is treated as some kind of probability implication (27, 49, 66, 117). The relationship P–S is investigated by "Psychophysics" (or, more precisely, "Phenophysics"), P–N by "Psychophysiology" (or "Phenophysiology"), and S–N by the so-called objective sensory physiology. The latter does not include any thermal sensations but deals only with nonthermal observations.

The concept of thermoreceptors is based originally on human sensory physiology, in particular on the fact that thermal sensations can be elicited from localized spots in the skin. In this respect one can speak of "sensory specificity" (49) of thermoreceptors, which means that a certain neural structure (N) is more or less exclusively correlated with thermal sensations (P), as expressed by the relationship P–N. As a result of neurophysiological methods, thermoreceptors can also be defined in biophysical terms, namely, as neural structures (N) excited only, or preferably, by temperature stimuli (S), as expressed by S–N. This may be called "biophysical specificity." It is obvious that this concept reaches far beyond the realm of conscious temperature sensation. The biophysical definition holds for any thermosensitive structure, irrespective of whether its excitation is correlated with sensations, or whether conscious sensations are difficult to establish, as is the case in animal experiments.

Although both concepts are closely related, they are not identical, the criterion being a quality of sensation (P) in the first case and a quality of stimulus (S) in the second case. A clear distinction between both definitions of specificity is necessary, especially when the relationship between temperature sensation and neural code is concerned. For example, a receptor excited by cooling as well as by menthol might be classified as a specific cold receptor in terms of sensation, but it has at best a relative or selective specificity with respect to the thermal stimulus.

In homeotherms, thermosensors have been found in the skin, the central nervous system, and elsewhere in the body. Furthermore, the existence of thermosensitive structures has been demonstrated in a number of poikilothermic species. Since any biological process is dependent on temperature, it is not easy to decide whether a certain neural tissue can be defined as "thermosensitive." Besides the quantitative amount of the response to local cooling or warming, one must consider the degree of specificity of such a response (119).

## CUTANEOUS THERMORECEPTORS

### Thermal Sensations and Temperature

While the sensory qualities of "warm" and "cold" can easily be discriminated from the spectrum of cutaneous sensations, there is still some discussion about the quality of "heat." Is it a more intense sensation of warmth or a mixture of various qualities? From neurophysiological evidence, it might be argued that "heat" is a quality of its own, its neurophysiological correlate being the activity of particular "heat" fibers which are excited at high skin temperatures beyond the activity range of specific warm fibers (8).

Thermal comfort and discomfort are "pleasant" and "unpleasant" emotional feelings (15, 17, 33, 40, 106) which reflect an integrated state of the thermoregulatory system. This means that not only cutaneous receptors but also thermosensitive structures in deeper parts of the body are involved, most likely in the CNS.

The threshold conditions for warm and cold sensations can be described by the following thermal parameters: ($a$) the absolute temperature $T$ of the skin at the site of the receptors, ($b$) the rate and direction of temperature change ($dT/dt$), and ($c$) the area of stimulation (49, 69, 71). In contrast to these parameters, the direction and slope of the intracutaneous spatial temperature gradient $dT/dx$ is not per se an adequate stimulus for thermoreceptors, as evidenced by sensory physiology as well as by electrophysiological measurements (49).

It is well established that threshold and intensity of thermal sensations are dependent on the area of stimulation. This has been further confirmed by use of equal-intensity contours of thermal sensation. Near the threshold, the stimulus intensity rose by a factor of 10 when the stimulus area was reduced from 20 to 2 cm$^2$, although at high intensities the threshold rose only by a factor of 2 (78, 107, 108). Using the whole body surface, even at constant temperatures the threshold of cold sensation remained above an average skin temperature of 34°C (6, 7).

Starting from adapting temperatures of 34°C, the estimated magnitude of cold sensation turned out to be a linear function of the magnitude of a nearly rectangular cold stimulus over a range of 10°C. Similar results were obtained for rectangular warm stimuli (28). In terms of the so-called psychophysical power law (109), in which the estimated magnitude of temperature sensation $P$ is related to the magnitude of thermal stimulus $\Delta T$ in the form: $P \longrightarrow k \, \Delta T^n$, the exponent was $n = 1$. Applying radiant heat to the frontal area of the subject's body and assessing apparent warmth by magnitude estimation (79) resulted in an exponent of $n = 0.87$ for stimulus durations of 2 to 6 sec, but it rose to 1.04 for durations of 12 sec. The findings suggested the possibility of sensory adaptation during stimulation. Moreover, they are an illustration of the problem that any psychophysical "law" depends on the definition of the stimulus.

## Properties of Cold and Warm Receptors

In biophysical terms, the following general properties are proposed for the definition of cutaneous thermoreceptors: ($a$) a static discharge at constant temperatures $T$, ($b$) a dynamic response to temperature changes $dT/dt$, with either a positive temperature coefficient (warmth receptors) or a negative coefficient (cold receptors), ($c$) no response to mechanical stimuli within reasonable limits of intensity. Irrespective of the initial temperature, warmth receptors respond with an overshoot of their discharge on sudden warming and with a transient inhibition on cooling, whereas cold receptors respond in the opposite direction from that of warmth receptors, temporarily overshooting frequency on cooling and showing transient inhibition on warming. In addition to this dynamic behavior, there are also typical differences in the static frequency curves of both types of cutaneous receptors, the temperature of the maximum discharge being much lower for cold receptors than for warmth receptors (49).

Table 1 shows the occurrence of specific thermoreceptors in various mammals. In the skin of human subjects, cold receptors but no warmth receptors have been identified by electrophysiological methods (49). It seems quite certain from recent experiments in primates (51) and from indirect evidence in humans (115, 126) that warm receptors exist in man and are probably served by unmyelinated C-fibers.

At constant skin temperatures in the normal range, all cutaneous cold receptors exhibit a static discharge with a constant frequency. The temporal sequence of impulses can be more or less regular, or it can consist of periodic bursts of 2 to 10 impulses separated by silent intervals (48, 49, 52, 54, 56–58). Individual cold fibers have various ranges of static activity, the extremes being about 5°C and 43°C. With rising temperature, the static frequency increases, reaches a maximum at temperatures varying between 18° and 34°C for individual fibers, and then decreases again (Figure 1). One cannot, by observing the average static frequency of cold impulses, discriminate between temperatures below and above the maximum, but the burst discharge might carry additional information and thus allow one to differentiate between lower and higher temperatures (56, 57). Moreover, by combination of the static discharges from cold and warmth receptors, unequivocal information is obtained at any temperature.

At higher rates of cooling, the dynamic overshoot of single cold fibers may amount to 300 impulses per second (56), and the ratio of static to dynamic frequencies to 1:30. When equal temperature changes are applied at various adapting temperatures, the dynamic overshoot follows approximately the shape of the static activity curve (56, 70). Some values of dynamic and static activity are given in Table 2.

There is some overlap in the static frequency curves of cold and warmth receptor populations, the curves crossing near 37°C. In contrast to the burst discharge in fibers from cold receptors, the sequence of impulses from warmth receptors is fairly regular (46, 47, 52). In primates there seem to be two populations of warmth receptors, one having a static maximum near 45°C and the other at 40° to 42°C (47). The highest dynamic response of a single fiber from a warmth receptor was 200 impulses per second, that is, 5.5 times higher than the average static maximum. At various adapting temperatures the overshoot caused by equal amounts of dynamic warming follows the general course of the static activity curve (50).

**Table 1**  Specific thermoreceptors in the external skin[a]

| Species | Nerve | Receptive field | Type of receptor |
|---------|-------|-----------------|------------------|
| Man | radial | hairy skin, dorsum of hand | cold |
| Monkey | median, ulnar, saphenous | hairy and glabrous skin, arm and leg | cold |
| | saphenous, radial | hairy skin, dorsum of hand and foot | warm |
| Dog | infra-orbital | hairy and marginal skin | cold |
| | | face | warm |
| Cat | infra-orbital | hairy and marginal skin | cold, warm |
| | saphenous | hairy skin, leg | cold, warm |
| Rat | infra-orbital | hairy and marginal skin, face | cold |
| | saphenous | hairy skin, leg | cold, warm |
| | scrotal | hairy skin, scrotum | cold, warm |

[a]From Hensel (49).

**Table 2**  Properties of cold and warm fiber populations from the nasal area of cats[a]

| Property | Cold fibers | Warm fibers |
|---|---|---|
| Static temperature limits | 5 . . . 43°C | 30 . . . 48°C |
| Maximum static frequency (average) | 9 sec$^{-1}$ | 36 sec$^{-1}$ |
| Temperature of static maximum (average) | 27°C | 46°C |
| Maximum static differential sensitivity (average) | −1 sec$^{-1}$ °C$^{-1}$ | +14 sec$^{-1}$ °C$^{-1}$ |
| Highest dynamic differential sensitivity | −50 sec$^{-1}$ °C$^{-1}$ | +70 sec$^{-1}$ °C$^{-1}$ |
| Highest dynamic frequency | 240 sec$^{-1}$ | 200 sec$^{-1}$ |

[a]Data from Hensel & Kenshalo (52).

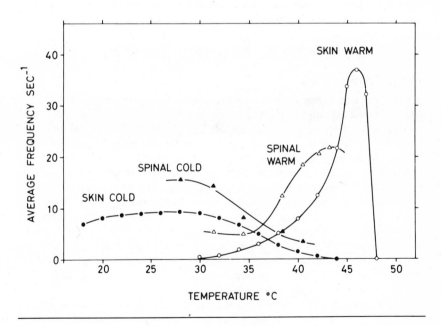

*Figure 1*  Average static frequencies of populations of thermosensors in the cat as a function of temperature. Cutaneous receptors from Hensel & Kenshalo (52), spinal neurons from Simon & Iriki (104). Average values of populations of less than 6 spinal units have been omitted.

The fundamental mechanisms of thermoreceptor excitation are still unknown. A general survey of the effects of temperature on membrane potentials of excitable cells (105) as well as a discussion of the mechanisms of biological temperature reception (57) lead to the conclusion that so far only hypotheses have been put forward. Any model should at least account for (a) the difference between warmth and cold receptors, (b) the static response at constant temperatures, and (c) the dynamic response to temperature changes. A recent model (127, 128) is based on the assumption of temperature-dependent release and inactivation of transmitters coupled with temperature-independent diffusion in various compartments. This model was found to agree well with the properties of cold receptors.

## Ultrastructure of Thermoreceptors

By the direct combination of electrophysiological and electronmicroscopical methods it has now become possible to identify the morphological substrate of cold receptors in the cat's nose (49, 70). In hairy skin, the receptive structures at the site of highly specific cold spots are served by thin myelinated axons dividing into several nonmyelinated terminals within the stratum papillare. The axon terminals are accompanied by unmyelinated Schwann cells as far as the basement membrane of the epidermis. There is a continuous connection between the basement membrane of the epidermis and the nerve terminals. The receptive endings penetrate a few microns deep into the basal epidermal cells and contain numerous mitochondria as well as an axoplasmatic matrix filled with fine filaments and microvesicles (49).

## Bimodal Receptors

A number of nonmyelinated cutaneous fibers in the cat and dog are excited only by intense heating (8). Most of these fibers had thresholds between 46° and 55°C and also responded to strong mechanical stimuli. This receptor population can be distinguished from the group of warmth fibers which are mechanically insensitive and cease to discharge at temperatures between 42° and 47°C.

Another group of cutaneous receptors served by myelinated fibers responds to both mechanical and cold stimulation (49, 56). These "spurious" thermoreceptors are, in fact, slowly adapting mechanoreceptors. In the monkey, their conduction velocities were 30 to 80 m sec$^{-1}$ and thus considerably higher than those of specific thermoreceptors. Furthermore, the mechanosensitive fibers did not exhibit a group discharge pattern on cooling which is a typical property of monkey cold receptors (56). A comparison of fiber activity in the monkey with human cutaneous sensation led to the conclusion that the "spurious" thermoreceptors cannot account for cold sensations but serve a mechanosensitive function (66).

A third population of bimodal fibers was found in the cat's saphenous nerve (80, 82). When a flash of heat radiation was applied to the leg, an increased activity of small myelinated fibers (average conduction velocity 12.4 m sec$^{-1}$) occurred. These fibers had a rather high average threshold around 39°C and were also excited by light tactile stimulation.

## Afferent Pathways

Usually single cold and warmth fibers innervate one peripheral spot in the skin (29, 49, 56, 70) although in a few cases somewhat larger receptive fields have been described (29). In the external skin of dogs, cats, and rats, except the facial region, most specific cold and warmth receptors are served by unmyelinated C fibers while most cold fibers in the infraorbital region of dogs and cats are myelinated (49, 56, 111). The specific cold fibers in the extremities of monkeys are partially myelinated with average conduction velocities in different regions ranging from 6 to 14 m sec$^{-1}$ (29, 51, 56, 89), and partially unmyelinated with a mean conduction velocity of 0.7 m sec$^{-1}$; the warmth fibers are entirely unmyelinated with mean conduction velocities between 0.7 and 1.2 m sec$^{-1}$ (29, 51). The distribution of thermal fibers in man remains to be analyzed; on the basis of available evidence from eletrophysiological recordings (49) and experiments with selective nerve blocking (115, 126) it seems probable that part of the cold fibers are myelinated and that the warmth fibers are unmyelinated.

Ganglion cells in the most superficial layer (Rexed's lamina I) of the dorsal horn of cats are activated by thermal stimulation of the skin (24). Temperature fibers from the trigeminal region terminate predominantly in the nucleus tractus spinalis. Afferent impulses from trigeminal cold receptors have been recorded in the spinal trigeminal nucleus of the cat (34, 90), in the thalamus of cats (71, 75), and in monkeys (90, 91), as well as in the somatosensory cortex of cats (75). In addition to a substantial central convergence of different modalities, especially mechanical and thermal, single neurons in all the nuclear regions may respond specifically to peripheral stimulation by cold. The activity of peripheral cold receptors in response to static and dynamic temperature stimuli can still be clearly recognized in the frequency/temperature curve of single thalamic neurons (91). There are some observations of thalamic units excited by peripheral warming (81). Since the peripheral impulses are likely to be conducted in small myelinated fibers, it is possible that the nerve endings in question are bimodal receptors (82) rather than specific warmth receptors.

## Comparison of Sensory, Behavioral, and Neurophysiological Data

A few direct measurements of afferent impulses from cutaneous thermoreceptors in human subjects (49) prove the existence of specific cold receptors but do not allow the quantitative correlation of the properties of thermoreceptor populations with the data of temperature sensation. In a series of indirect experiments, the activity of populations of cold fibers in monkeys was compared with cold sensation in human subjects (29, 66). The difference limen of sensation for two cooling pulses was found to be a linear function of intensity. Under the assumption that the neural correlate of the difference limen is a certain statistical difference between the average activities of a cold receptor population, the experimental values imply that only cold receptors, and not warmth receptors or slowly adapting mechanoreceptors, can account for human cold discrimination. On the other hand, warmth discrimination cannot be explained on the basis of cold fiber inhibition alone but requires an additional receptor population sensitive to warming. The theory that the sensory qualities of cold and warmth can be ascribed to a dual set of receptors is further supported by the existence of separate cold and warmth spots and by recent experiments with nerve blocking in which selective inhibition of either cold or warmth sensation was achieved (115, 126).

At skin temperatures near 33°C, cold and warmth receptors are continuously active but no conscious temperature sensation is felt. The latter begins when a relatively high number of impulses per unit of time reaches the CNS. This "central threshold" of cold sensation is much higher than that of the mechanoreceptive system, where even a single impulse in a single fiber might elicit a conscious sensation (49) or a neural response (55). When cold stimuli are applied to single cold spots in human subjects, the threshold of conscious sensation corresponds to an impulse frequency of 50 to 80 sec$^{-1}$ of the single fiber (49). Behavioral measurements of the thresholds for thermal stimulation of the cat's face have revealed a temperature sensitivity comparable to that of the human forearm (12, 68).

Afferent impulses from cutaneous thermoreceptors are also a very important input for the system of temperature regulation. It should be emphasized that thermoregulatory reflexes from cold and warmth receptors may be elicited even when no conscious sensations or behavioral responses are present, e.g. during sleep. The significance of thermoreceptors for physiological responses and thermoregulatory behavior lies beyond the scope of this review; it is treated in a number of reviews and monographs (6, 10, 38, 92, 120, 121) as well as in the proceedings of various symposia (11, 16, 41, 116).

## Comparative Aspects

Relatively little is known about thermoreceptor activity in birds (92). Cold receptors in the beak of pigeons increased their static activity from about 0 to 3 impulses/sec when the constant temperature level was lowered from 36 to 20°C. The static discharges of warmth receptors rose from 0 to about 60 sec$^{-1}$ in the temperature range between 20 and 44°C. Both groups of receptors showed very little or no dynamic responses to rapid temperature changes (88). Elasmobranchs, such as rays and sharks, possess the so-called ampullae of Lorenzini. These sense organs respond to cooling in a similar way as found in specific cold receptors in mammals (53, 92). However, it remains an open question whether the ampullae serve as biological thermoreceptors since they respond to mechanical and weak electrical stimulation as well. Elasmobranchs are, in fact, able to detect the bioelectric fields of their prey, and it seems justified to ascribe this function to the ampullae of Lorenzini (67).

Cold receptors have been found on the antennae of cockroaches (*Periplaneta americana*) with about 20 receptors per antenna and rarely more than one per segment (76, 77). They consist of a delicate hair-like structure (sensillum) emerging from a ring-shaped wall. Recordings with microelectrodes have shown that at constant temperatures the cold receptor is continuously active, the average maximum frequency of its discharge being 16 sec$^{-1}$ at temperatures near 28°C (76, 77).

At higher and lower temperatures the steady frequency becomes lower. A dynamic overshoot up to 300 imp sec$^{-1}$ is seen on rapid cooling, while rapid warming is followed by a transient inhibition. Electrophysiological evidence has also been presented for thermosensitive structures in the antennae of migratory locusts (*Locusta migratoria migratorioides*) (118).

## DEEP-BODY THERMOSENSORS OUTSIDE THE CNS

The existence of thermosensors in the deeper tissues of the body has long been postulated. From studies of sweat rates during exercise, the hypothesis was derived that thermoreceptors might be situated in deep leg veins and possibly in the muscle itself (35, 100, 101). Evidence for thermosensitive structures in the veins has been obtained from recordings from afferent nerve fibers serving intact or isolated veins at various blood temperatures (83, 84, 85). There was a static discharge, the frequency of which rose when the constant temperature was set at lower levels, and an overshoot on rapid cooling. An increase in activity was recorded in nerve filaments of the 5th dorsal root in the cat (114) when the femoral vein was perfused with fluid of rising temperature (39–41°C).

Panting could be elicited in the ewe by intra-abdominal heating (95–98), although the temperature of the hypothalamus decreased and that of the spinal cord remained constant. Unilateral section of the splanchnic nerves abolished the response to warming of the ipsilateral side without changing the response on the opposite side (97, 98). It was concluded that the thermoreceptors stimulated lie within the wall of the rumen and intestine, and possibly in the mesenteric veins, the splanchnic nerves being the afferent pathway. The existence of thermosensitive structures within the abdomen was also confirmed by behavioral experiments in the squirrel monkey (1) and by recording of afferent neural activity from the splanchnic nerve in rabbits during intra-abdominal heating (99). A temperature rise above the normal value elicited vasodilatation and respiratory acceleration as well as greater nervous activity, which suggest that the abdomen contains neural structures predominantly sensitive to warming.

## THERMOSENSITIVE STRUCTURES IN THE CNS

### Hypothalamus

On the basis of local thermal probing in unanesthetized homeotherms of various species, the concept developed that thermosensitive neurons are concentrated in the preoptic-anterior hypothalamic (POAH) region. Heating this region activates physiological responses to counteract warming and inhibits responses to counteract cooling, while cooling the hypothalamus causes the opposite effects (9, 10, 13, 14, 38). Another group of responses that can be elicited by local hypothalamic cooling or warming concerns thermal motivation and behavior. When the local hypothalamic temperature in unanesthetized rats (20–22, 25, 26, 86) and monkeys (1, 2, 23, 110) was artificially displaced, the animals showed an operant behavior aiming at a reduction of the thermal deviation.

With microelectrode recordings from the POAH region in rabbits, guinea pigs, cats, and dogs, various types of units have been identified which respond with positive or negative temperature coefficients to local thermal changes. They are mostly designated "warmth-sensitive" and "cold-sensitive" units. In spite of a large amount of data, the results are still difficult to interpret. Is a particular neuron, in fact, a detector of local temperature, an afferent or an efferent interneuron? Is the response a direct effect of temperature or an inhibition of an inhibitory neuron? In contrast to cutaneous thermoreceptors, the central thermosensitive structures have not yet been identified. The problem of recording from an unknown structure with an unknown function is reflected by the vague terminology used in the literature, e.g. "thermoresponsive neurons," "thermosensitive structures," "thermodetectors," and the like. It is widely assumed that changes in neuronal firing induced by thermal stimulation of the POAH region represent correlates of the thermoregulatory responses evoked by this stimulus. But even this assumption can be questioned since thermoresponsive neurons have also been found in the sensorimotor cortex of the cat (4, 5). Nevertheless, the presumption seems reasonable that thermoregulatory responses are being studied when recording activity from thermosensitive neurons in the preoptic area (31, 32).

In the dog, the proportions of insensitive, warmth-sensitive, and cold-sensitive neurons were 60, 30, and 10%, respectively, and the three types appeared to be randomly distributed (31, 44). Some thermosensitive neurons show a linear or continuous relation between firing rate and local temperature over a range of about 8°C, the most sensitive units often responding with an exponential slope, whereas others have nonlinear or discontinuous temperature characteristics (Table 3). These units are thermally insensitive over part of the temperature range, and only above or below a certain threshold do they show a response which is either warmth-sensitive or cold-sensitive. It has been proposed that neurons with linear frequency/temperature characteristics might be primary thermodetectors, while units of the nonlinear type are likely to be interneurons. This view is supported by the fact that these neurons (a) occur in a higher percentage (19, 30, 36, 125), (b) have a lower $Q_{10}$ for their local thermal response (31, 44), and (c) also respond to remote thermal inputs (31, 36, 37, 42, 43, 45). Since only very few linear cold-sensitive responses have been found (19), the existence of primary POAH cold-detectors is still undecided. This is not to say that responses to cooling cannot be obtained from this region, since inhibition of static firing of warmth-detectors could serve this function.

## Midbrain

In rabbits, about 8% of the units in the midbrain reticular formation at the level of the nucleus ruber and pons responded with high sensitivity to local cooling (87). Other units were excited by warming (18, 19). A number of units had bell-shaped frequency/temperature characteristics, the average peak being at 34.5°C for the cold-sensitive cells and 39°C for the warmth-sensitive cells (19).

**Table 3**  Warm-sensitive and cold-sensitive preoptic anterior hypothalamic neurons[a]

| TEMPERATURE RESPONSE | SPECIES STUDIED | ESTIMATED INPUT | OUTPUT |
|---|---|---|---|
| [plot] po | Dog, Rabbit Cat | $T_{po}$ | $+\bar{a}T_{po}$ |
| [plot] po | Dog, Rabbit Cat | $+T_{po}-F_o$ | $+a(+\Delta T_{po})$ |
| [plot] po | Cat, Rabbit Dog | $+F_o+(+\Delta T_{po})$ | $F_o+[a(+\Delta T_{po})]$ |
| [plot] po, mb | Rabbit | $+F_o+(+\Delta T_{po})+(+\Delta T_{mb})$ | $F_o+[a(+\Delta T_{po})+b(+\Delta T_{mb})]$ |
| [plot] po, sc | Rabbit | $+F_o+(+\Delta T_{po})+(+\Delta T_{sc})$ | $F_o+[a(+\Delta T_{po})+c(+\Delta T_{sc})]$ |
| [plot] po, s | Cat | $+F_o+(+\Delta T_{po})+(+\Delta T_s)$ | $F_o+[a(+\Delta T_{po})+d(+\Delta T_s)]$ |
| [plot] po, sc | Rabbit | $+F_o+(+\Delta T_{po})-(+\Delta T_{sc})$ | $F_o+[a(+\Delta T_{po})-c(+\Delta T_{sc})]$ |
| [plot] po, mb | Rabbit | $+F_o+(+\Delta T_{po})+(-\Delta T_{mb})$ | $F_o+[a(+\Delta T_{po})+(-b(-\Delta T_{mb}))]$ |
| [plot] po, mb | Rabbit | $+T_{po}+(-\Delta T_{mb})$ | $-\bar{a}T_{po}+[-b(-\Delta T_{mb})]$ |
| [plot] po | Cat, Rabbit Dog | $+F_o-(-\Delta T_{po})$ | $F_o-[+a(-\Delta T_{po})]$ |
| [plot] po, sc | Rabbit | $+F_o-(-\Delta T_{po})-(-\Delta T_{sc})$ | $F_o-[+a(-\Delta T_{po})+c(-\Delta T_{sc})]$ |
| [plot] re | Rabbit | $T_{po}+(+\Delta T_{re})-(-\Delta T_{sc})$ | $-e[+T_{re}(T_{po}+\Delta T_{sc})]$ |
| [plot] po, sc | Rabbit | $+F_o-(-\Delta T_{po})-(+\Delta T_{sc})$ | $F_o-[+a(-\Delta T_{po})+(-c(-\Delta T_{sc}))]$ |
| [plot] po | Dog, Rabbit | $-T_{po}$ | $-\bar{a}T_{po}$ |
| [plot] po | Dog, Rabbit Cat | $-T_{po}+F_o$ | $-a(-\Delta T_{po})$ |
| [plot] po | Cat, Rabbit | $+F_o,+(-\Delta T_{po})$ | $F_o+[-a(-\Delta T_{po})]$ |
| [plot] po, sc | Rabbit | $+F_o,+(-\Delta T_{po}),+(-\Delta T_{sc})$ | $F_o+[-a(-\Delta T_{po})-c(-\Delta T_{sc})]$ |
| [plot] sc, po | Rabbit | $+F_o,+(-\Delta T_{po}),+(+\Delta T_{sc})$ | $F_o+[-a(-\Delta T_{po})+c(+\Delta T_{sc})]$ |
| [plot] po | Dog, Cat Rabbit | $+F_o,-(+\Delta T_{po})$ | $F_o-[-a(+\Delta T_{po})]$ |
| [plot] po, sc | Rabbit | $+F_o,-(+\Delta T_{po}),-(+\Delta T_{sc})$ | $F_o-[-a(+\Delta T_{po})-c(+\Delta T_{sc})]$ |
| [plot] po, mb | Rabbit | $+F_o,-(+\Delta T_{po}),-(+\Delta T_{mb})$ | $F_o+[-a(+\Delta T_{po})-b(+\Delta T_{mb})]$ |
| [plot] po, mb | Rabbit | $+F_o,+(-\Delta T_{po}),+(-\Delta T_{mb})$ | $F_o+[-a(-\Delta T_{po})-b(-\Delta T_{mb})]$ |

[a]Temperature response: schematic plot of the firing rate (x-axis) as a function of temperature (y-axis), po, preoptic; mb, midbrain; sc, spinal cord; s, skin; re, rectal. Estimated input and output of the neuron: a, b, c, d, e represent temperature coefficients for the output of the stimulated area. $(+\Delta T)$ or $(-\Delta T)$ correspond to temperatures above or below the normal temperature range. Fo, constant input or output insensitive to temperature. From Guieu & Hardy (37).

The physiological significance of these units is not certain. Warming and cooling of the midbrain in the unanesthetized rabbit (18, 39) as well as in the squirrel monkey (*Saimiri sciureus*) (3) elicited thermoregulatory responses but not so effectively as did thermal stimulation of the POAH region. There appear to be no thermosensitive structures in the medulla oblongata that are involved in temperature regulation. Local thermal stimulation of this area causes just the opposite effect on heart and respiratory rate to that seen when stimulating the hypothalamus (112, 113).

## Spinal Cord

In the last few years it has become evident that any thermoregulatory response brought about by hypothalamic temperature changes can also be produced by local heating or cooling of the spinal cord in unanesthetized animals. Such responses have been observed in dogs (62, 63, 65), cats (72), rabbits (61, 73, 74, 102), guinea pigs (14), pigs (59, 60), oxen (64), and pigeons (93, 94). In unanesthetized dogs, spinal cord and hypothalamus represent basically equivalent core sensors of temperature, as seen from the linear relationship between their local temperature and the responses to heating or cooling (62, 63, 65). Similar results have been found in the pigeon (94).

Shivering in guinea pigs could be suppressed by warming a segment ($C_5$ to $T_2$) of the spinal cord (14). Through extirpation experiments and electrophysiological recordings, an ascending pathway was established from the thermosensitive cervicothoracic area via the spinothalamic tract to the posterior hypothalamus. Single warmth-sensitive neurons were found in the cord, showing a linear relationship between discharge frequency and temperature, but no cold-sensitive units were seen (122–124).

Single unit activity was recorded from the spinal cord in cats at the level of $C_2$ to $C_4$ (103, 104). A group of cold-sensitive units showed a roughly proportional negative relation between static discharge rate and vertebral canal temperature in the range between 30° and 40°C, and a group of warmth-sensitive cells exhibited a positive temperature coefficient in the range of 36° to 42°C, the average slope of the static frequency/temperature curve being $-2.2 \ sec^{-1} \ °C^{-1}$ and $+3.9 \ sec^{-1} \ °C^{-1}$, respectively (Figure 1). These values are in the same range as found for thermosensitive POAH neurons in the dog and for cutaneous cold and warm receptors. Part of the units exhibited dynamic responses to temperature changes, in addition to these static responses. The site of the thermosensitive cells is not known; it may be assumed that they are located within, or at least close to, the spinal cord. As determined by micromarking, their ascending spinal impulses are conducted in the spinothalamic tract (102).

*Literature Cited*

1. Adair, E. R. 1971. Evaluation of some controller inputs to behavioral temperature regulation. *Int. J. Biometeorol.* 15:121–28
2. Adair, E. R., Casby, J. U., Stolwijk, J. A. J. 1970. Behavioral temperature regulation in the squirrel monkey: changes induced by shifts in hypothalamic temperature. *J. Comp. Physiol. Psychol.* 72:17–27
3. Adair, E. R., Stitt, J. T. 1971. Behavioral temperature regulation in the squirrel monkey: effects of midbrain temperature displacements. *J. Physiol. Paris* 63:191–94
4. Barker, J. L., Carpenter, D. O. 1970. Thermosensitivity of neurons in the sensorimotor cortex of the cat. *Science* 169:597–98
5. Barker, J. L., Carpenter, D. O. 1971. Neuronal thermosensitivity. *Science* 172:1361–62
6. Benzinger, T. H. 1969. Heat regulation: Homeostasis of central temperature in man. *Physiol. Rev.* 49:671–759
7. Benzinger, T. H. 1970. Peripheral cold reception, sensory mechanisms of behavioral and autonomic thermostasis. See Ref. 41, 831–55
8. Bessou, P., Perl, E. R. 1969. Response of cutaneous sensory units with unmyelinated fibres to noxious stimuli. *J. Neurophysiol.* 32:1025–43
9. Bligh, J. 1972. Neuronal models of mammalian temperature regulation. *Essays on Temperature Regulation,* ed. J. Bligh, R. E. Moore, 105–20. Amsterdam, London: North-Holland
10. Bligh, J., Hensel, H. 1973. Modern theories on location and function of the thermoregulatory centres in mammals including man. *Progress in Human Biometeorology, Progress in Biometeorology,* ed. S. W. Tromp. Amsterdam: Swets & Zeitlinger. In press
11. Bligh, J., Moore, R. E. 1972. *Essays on Temperature Regulation.* Amsterdam, London: North-Holland
12. Brearley, E. A., Kenshalo, D. R. 1970. Behavioral measurements of the sensitivity of cat's upper lip to warm and cool stimuli. *J. Comp. Physiol. Psychol.* 70:1–4
13. Brück, K., Schwennicke, H. P. 1971. Interaction of superficial and hypothalamic thermosensitive structures in the control of non-shivering thermogenesis. *Int. J. Biometeorol.* 15:156–61
14. Brück, K., Wünnenberg, W. 1970. "Meshed" control of two effector systems: nonshivering and shivering thermogenesis. See Ref. 41, 562–80
15. Cabanac, M. 1969. Plaisir ou déplaisir de la sensation thermique et homeothermie. *Physiol. Behav.* 4:359–64
16. Cabanac, M. 1971. Symposium international de thermorégulation comportementale. *J. Physiol. Paris* 63:189–472
17. Cabanac, M. 1972. Thermoregulatory behavior. *Essays on Temperature Regulation,* ed. J. Bligh, R. E. Moore, 19–32. Amsterdam, London: North-Holland
18. Cabanac, M., Hardy, J. D. 1969. Réponses unitaires et thermorégulatrices lors de réchauffements et réfroidissements localisés de la région préoptique et du mésecéphale chez le lapin. *J. Physiol. Paris* 61:331–47
19. Cabanac, M., Stolwijk, J. A. J., Hardy, J. D. 1968. Effect of temperature and pyrogens on single-unit activity in the rabbit's brain stem. *J. Appl. Physiol.* 24:645–52
20. Carlisle, H. J. 1968. Peripheral thermal stimulation and thermoregulatory behavior. *J. Comp. Physiol. Psychol.* 66:507–10
21. Carlisle, H. J. 1968. Initiation of behavioral responding for heat in a cold environment. *Physiol. Behav.* 3:827–30
22. Carlisle, H. J. 1970. Thermal reinforcement and temperature regulation. *Animal Psychophysics: The Design and Conduct of Sensory Experiments,* ed. W. C. Stebbins, 211–29. New York: Appleton
23. Carlisle, H. J. 1971. Behavioral temperature regulation in cynomolgus and pigtailed macaques (I). *J. Physiol. Paris* 63:226–28
24. Christensen, B. N., Perl, E. R. 1970. Spinal neurons specifically excited by noxious or thermal stimuli: marginal zone of the dorsal horn. *J. Neurophysiol.* 33:293–307
25. Corbit, J. D. 1969. Behavioral regulation of hypothalamic temperature. *Science* 166:256–58
26. Corbit, J. D. 1970. Behavioral regulation of body temperature. See Ref. 41, 777–801
27. Darian-Smith, I. 1969. Somatic sensation. *Ann. Rev. Physiol.* 31:417–50
28. Darian-Smith, I., Dykes, R. W. 1971. Peripheral neural mechanisms of thermal sensation. *Oral-Facial Sensory and Motor Mechanisms,* ed. R. Dubner, Y. Kawamura, 7–22. New York: Appleton
29. Darian-Smith, I., Johnson, K. O., Dykes, R. 1973. "Cold" fiber popula-

tion innervating palmar and digital skin of the monkey: responses to cooling pulses. *J. Neurophysiol.* 36: 325–46

30. Edinger, H. M., Eisenman, J. S. 1970. Thermosensitive neurons in tuberal and posterior hypothalamus of cats. *Am. J. Physiol.* 219:1098–1103

31. Eisenman, J. S. 1972. Unit activity studies of thermoresponsive neurons. *Essays on Temperature Regulation*, ed. J. Bligh, R. E. Moore, 55–69. Amsterdam, London: North-Holland

32. Eisenman, J. S., Edinger, H. M. 1971. Neuronal thermosensitivity. *Science* 172:1360–61

33. Fanger, P. O. 1970. *Thermal Comfort.* Copenhagen: Danish Technical Press

34. Fruhstorfer, H., Hensel, H. 1973. Thermal cutaneous afferents in the cat's trigeminal nucleus. *Naturwissenschaften* 60:209

35. Gisolfi, C., Robinson, S. 1970. Central and peripheral stimuli regulating sweating during intermittent work in men. *J. Appl. Physiol.* 29:761–68

36. Guieu, J. D., Hardy, J. D. 1970. Effects of heating and cooling of the spinal cord on preoptic unit activity. *J. Appl. Physiol.* 29:675–83

37. Guieu, J. D., Hardy, J. D. 1971. Integrative activity of preoptic units I: Response to local and peripheral temperature changes. *J. Physiol. Paris* 63:253–56

38. Hammel, H. T. 1968. Regulation of internal body temperature. *Ann. Rev. Physiol.* 30:641–710

39. Hardy, J. D. 1969. Thermoregulatory responses to temperature changes in the midbrain of the rabbit. *Fed. Proc.* 28: 713

40. Hardy, J. D. 1970. Thermal comfort: Skin temperature and physiological thermoregulation. See Ref. 41, 856–73

41. Hardy, J. D., Gagge, A. P., Stolwijk, J. A. J., Eds. 1970. *Physiological and Behavioral Temperature Regulation.* Springfield, Ill.: Thomas

42. Hellon, R. F. 1970. The stimulation of hypothalamic neurones by changes in ambient temperature. *Pfluegers Arch.* 321:56–66

43. Hellon, R. F. 1970. Hypothalamic neurons responding to changes in hypothalamic and ambient temperature. See Ref. 41, 463–71

44. Hellon, R. F. 1972. Central thermoreceptors and thermoregulation. *Handbook of Sensory Physiology*, Vol. III/1, 161–86. Heidelberg, New York: Springer

45. Hellon, R. F. 1972. Temperature-sensitive neurons in the brain stem: their responses to brain temperature at different ambient temperatures. *Pfluegers Arch.* 335:323–34

46. Hensel, H. 1968. Spezifische Wärmeimpulse aus der Nasenregion der Katze. *Pfluegers Arch.* 302:374–76

47. Hensel, H. 1969. Cutane Wärmerezeptoren bei Primaten. *Pfluegers Arch.* 313:150–52

48. Hensel, H. 1970. Temperature receptors in the skin. See Ref. 41, 442–62

49. Hensel, H. 1973. Cutaneous thermoreceptors. *Handbook of Sensory Physiology*, Vol. II, 79–110. Heidelberg, New York: Springer

50. Hensel, H., Huopaniemi, T. 1969. Static and dynamic properties of warm fibres in the infraorbital nerve. *Pfluegers Arch.* 309:1–10

51. Hensel, H., Iggo, A. 1971. Analysis of cutaneous warm and cold fibres in primates. *Pfluegers Arch.* 329:1–8

52. Hensel, H., Kenshalo, D. R. 1969. Warm receptors in the nasal region of cats. *J. Physiol. London* 204:99–112

53. Hensel, H., Nier, K. 1971. Integrated static activity of the ampullae of Lorenzini after long-term exposure to various temperatures. *Pfluegers Arch.* 323: 279–83

54. Hensel, H., Wurster, R. D. 1970. Static properties of cold receptors in nasal area of cats. *J. Neurophysiol.* 33:271–75

55. Hongo, T., Koike, H. 1968. Large-sized EPSPs evoked from single cutaneous afferents in secondary ascending neurones in cats. *Proceedings of the International Union of Physiological Sciences, Vol. VII,* 592. Washington, DC: Am. Physiol. Soc.

56. Iggo, A. 1969. Cutaneous thermoreceptors in primates and subprimates. *J. Physiol. London* 200:403–30

57. Iggo, A. 1970. The mechanisms of biological temperature reception. See Ref. 41, 391–407

58. Iggo, A., Iggo, B. J. 1971. Impulse coding in primate cutaneous thermoreceptors in dynamic thermal conditions. *J. Physiol. Paris* 63:287–90

59. Ingram, D. L., Legge, K. F. 1971. The influence of deep body temperatures and skin temperatures on peripheral blood flow in the pig. *J. Physiol. London* 215:693–707

60. Ingram, D. L., Legge, K. F. 1972. The influence of deep body temperatures and skin temperatures on respiratory frequency in the pig. *J. Physiol. London* 220:283–96

61. Iriki, M. 1968. Änderung der Haut-durchblutung bei unnarkotisierten Kaninchen durch isolierte Wärmung des Rückenmarks. *Pfluegers Arch.* 299: 295–310

62. Jessen, C., Ludwig, O. 1971. Spinal cord and hypothalamus as core sensors of temperature in the conscious dog. II. Addition of signals. *Pfluegers Arch.* 324:205–16

63. Jessen, C., Mayer, E. Th. 1971. Spinal cord and hypothalamus as core sensors of temperature in the conscious dog. I. Equivalence of responses. *Pfluegers Arch.* 324:189–204

64. Jessen, C., McLean, J. A., Calvert, D. T., Findlay, J. D. 1972. Balanced and unbalanced temperature signals generated in spinal cord of the ox. *Am. J. Physiol.* 222:1343–47

65. Jessen, C., Simon, E. 1971. Spinal cord and hypothalamus as core sensors of temperature in the conscious dog. III. Identity of functions. *Pfluegers Arch.* 324:217–26

66. Johnson, K. O., Darian-Smith, I., La-Motte, C. 1973. Peripheral neural determinants of temperature discrimination in man: A correlative study of responses to cooling skin. *J. Neurophysiol.* 36: 347–70

67. Kalmijn, A. J. 1971. The electric sense of sharks and rays. *J. Exp. Biol.* 55: 371–83

68. Kenshalo, D. R. 1968. Behavioral and electrophysiological responses of cats to thermal stimuli. *The Skin Senses,* ed. D. R. Kenshalo, 400–22. Springfield, Ill.: Thomas

69. Kenshalo, D. R. 1970. Psychophysical studies of temperature sensitivity. *Contributions to Sensory Physiology,* ed. W. D. Neff, 4:19–74. New York: Academic

70. Kenshalo, D. R., Hensel, H., Graziadei, P., Fruhstorfer, H. 1971. On the anatomy, physiology and psychophysics of the cat's temperature sensing system. *Oral-Facial Sensory and Motor Mechanisms,* ed. R. Dubner, Y. Kawamura, 23–45. New York: Appleton

71. Kenshalo, D. R., Holmes, Ch. E., Wood, P. B. 1968. Warm and cool thresholds as a function of rate of stimulus temperature change. *Percept. Psychophys.* 3:81–84

72. Klussmann, F. W. 1969. Der Einfluss der Temperatur auf die afferente und efferente motorische Innervation des Rückenmarks. I. Temperaturabhängigkeit der afferenten und efferenten Spon-tantätigkeit. *Pfluegers Arch.* 305: 295–315

73. Kosaka, M., Simon, E. 1968. Kältetremor wacher, chronisch spinalisierter Kaninchen im Vergleich zum Kältezittern intakter Tiere. *Pfluegers Arch.* 302:333–56

74. Kosaka, M., Simon, E. 1968. Der zentralnervöse spinale Mechanismus des Kältezitterns. *Pfluegers Arch.* 302: 357–73

75. Landgren, S. 1970. Projections from thermoreceptors into the somatosensory system of the cat's brain. See Ref. 41, 454–62

76. Loftus, R. 1968. The response of the antennal cold receptor of Periplaneta americana to rapid temperature changes and to steady temperature. *Z. Vergl. Physiol.* 59:413–55

77. Loftus, R. 1969. Differential thermal components in the response of the antennal cold receptor of Periplaneta americana to slowly changing temperature. *Z. Vergl. Physiol.* 63:415–33

78. Marks, L. E. 1971. Spatial summation in relation to the dynamics of warmth sensation. *Int. J. Biometeorol.* 15: 106–10

79. Marks, L. E., Stevens, J. C. 1968. Perceived warmth and skin temperature as functions of the duration and level of thermal irradiation. *Percept. Psychophys.* 4:220–28

80. Martin, H. F. III, Manning, J. W. 1969. Rapid thermal cutaneous stimulation: peripheral nerve responses. *Brain Res.* 16:524–26

81. Martin, H. F. III, Manning, J. W. 1971. Thalamic 'warming' and 'cooling' units responding to cutaneous stimulation. *Brain Res.* 27:377–81

82. Martin, H. F. III, Manning, J. W. 1972. Response of $A\delta$-fibers of peripheral nerve to warming of cutaneous fields. *Brain Res.* 43:653–56

83. Minut-Sorokhtina, O. P. 1968. The nature of rhythmic activity of cold receptors. *Sechenov J. Physiol. USSR* 54:413–20

84. Minut-Sorokhtina, O. P. 1968–69. The nature of rhythmic activity of cold receptors. *Neurosci. Transl.* 7:615–22

85. Minut-Sorokhtina, O. P. 1972. *Physiology of Thermoreception.* Moscow: Medicina

86. Murgatroyd, D., Hardy, J. D. 1970. Central and peripheral temperatures in behavioral thermoregulation of the rat. See Ref. 41, 874–91

87. Nakayama, T., Hardy, J. D. 1969. Unit responses in the rabbit's brain stem to

changes in brain and cutaneous temperature. *J. Appl. Physiol.* 27:848–57

88. Necker, R. 1972. Response of trigeminal ganglion neurons to thermal stimulation of the beak in pigeons. *J. Comp. Physiol.* 78:307–14

89. Perl, E. R. 1968. Myelinated afferent fibres innervating the primate skin and their response to nocious stimuli. *J. Physiol. London* 197:593–615

90. Poulos, D. A. 1971. Trigeminal temperature mechanisms. *Oral-Facial Sensory and Motor Mechanisms*, ed. R. Dubner, Y. Kawamura, 47–72. New York: Appleton

91. Poulos, D. A., Benjamin, R. M. 1968. Response of thalamic neurons to thermal stimulation of the tongue. *J. Neurophysiol.* 31:28–43

92. Precht, H., Christophersen, J., Hensel, H., Eds. 1973. *Temperature and Life.* Heidelberg, New York: Springer

93. Rautenberg, W. 1969. Die Bedeutung der zentralnervösen Thermosensitivität für die Temperaturregulation der Taube. *Z. Vergl. Physiol.* 62:235–66

94. Rautenberg, W., Necker, R., May, B. 1972. Thermoregulatory responses of the pigeon to changes of the brain and spinal cord temperature. *Pfluegers Arch.* 338:31–42

95. Rawson, R. O., Quick, K. P. 1970. Evidence of deep-body thermoreceptor response to intra-abdominal heating of the ewe. *J. Appl. Physiol.* 28:813–20

96. Rawson, R. O., Quick, K. P. 1971. Thermoregulatory responses to temperature signals from the abdominal viscera of sheep. *J. Physiol. Paris* 63:399–402

97. Rawson, R. O., Quick, K. P. 1971. Unilateral splanchnotomy: its effect on the response to intra-abdominal heating in the ewe. *Pfluegers Arch.* 330:362–65

98. Rawson, R. O., Quick, K. P. 1972. Localization of intra-abdominal thermoreceptors in the ewe. *J. Physiol. London* 222:665–77

99. Riedel, W., Siaplauras, G., Simon, E. 1973. Intra-abdominal thermosensitivity in the rabbit as compared with spinal thermosensitivity. *Pfluegers Arch.* 340:59–70

100. Saltin, B., Gagge, A. P. 1971. Sweating and body temperatures during exercise. *Int. J. Biometeorol.* 15:189–94

101. Saltin, B., Gagge, A. P., Stolwijk, J. A. J. 1968. Muscle temperature during submaximal exercise in man. *J. Appl. Physiol.* 25:679–88

102. Simon, E. 1972. Temperature signals from skin and spinal cord converging on spinothalamic neurons. *Pfluegers Arch.* 337:323–32

103. Simon, E., Iriki, M. 1970. Ascending neurons of the spinal cord activated by cold. *Experientia* 26:620–22

104. Simon, E., Iriki, M. 1971. Sensory transmission of spinal heat and cold sensitivity in ascending spinal neurons. *Pfluegers Arch.* 328:103–20

105. Sperelakis, N. 1970. Effects of temperature on membrane potentials of excitable cells. See Ref. 41, 408–41

106. Stevens, J. C., Adair, E. R., Marks, L. E. 1970. Pain, discomfort, and warmth as functions of thermal intensity. See Ref. 41, 892–904

107. Stevens, J. C., Banks, W. P. 1971. Spatial summation in relation to speed of reaction to radiant stimulation. *Int. J. Biometeorol.* 15:111–14

108. Stevens, J. C., Marks, L. E. 1971. Spatial summation and the dynamics of warmth sensation. *Percept. Psychophys.* 9:391–98

109. Stevens, S. S. 1970. Neural events and the psychophysical law. *Science* 170:1043–50

110. Stitt, J. T., Adair, E. R., Nadel, E. R., Stolwijk, A. J. 1971. The relation between behavior and physiology in the thermoregulatory response of the squirrel monkey. *J. Physiol. Paris* 63:424–27

111. Stolwijk, J. A. J., Wexler, I. 1971. Peripheral nerve activity in response to heating the cat's skin. *J. Physiol. London* 214:377–92

112. Tabatabai, M. 1972. Respiratory and cardiovascular responses resulting from heating the medulla oblongata in cats. *Am. J. Physiol.* 222:1558–64

113. Tabatabai, M. 1972. Respiratory and cardiovascular responses resulting from cooling the medulla oblongata in cats. *Am. J. Physiol.* 223:8–12

114. Thompson, F. J., Barnes, C. D. 1969. Evidence for thermosensitive receptors in the femoral vein. *Fed. Proc.* 28(1):722

115. Torebjörk, H. E., Hállin, R. G. 1972. Activity in C fibres correlated to perception in man. *Cervical Pain*, ed. C. Hirsch, Y. Zotterman, 171–78. Oxford: Pergamon

116. Tromp, S. W., Weihe, W. H., Eds. 1971. Proceedings of volunteered papers of the symposium on temperature regulation. *Int. J. Biometeorol.* 15:101–361

117. Vendrik, A. J. H. 1970. Psychophysics of the thermal sensory system and statistical detection theory. See Ref. 41, 819–30

THERMORECEPTORS 249

118. Waldow, U. 1970. Elektrophysiologische Untersuchungen an Feuchte-, Trocken- und Kälterezeptoren auf der Antenne der Wanderheuschrecke Locusta. *Z. Vergl. Physiol.* 69:249–83
119. Wall, P. D., Dubner, R. 1972. Somatosensory pathways. *Ann. Rev. Physiol.* 34:315–36
120. Whittow, G. C., Ed. 1970. *Invertebrates and Nonmammalian Vertebrates. Comparative Physiology of Thermoregulation,* Vol. I. New York, London: Academic
121. Whittow, G. C., Ed. 1971. *Mammals. Comparative Physiology of Thermoregulation,* Vol. II. New York, London: Academic
122. Wünnenberg, W., Brück, K. 1968. Zur Funktionsweise thermoreceptiver Strukturen im Cervicalmark des Meerschweinchens. *Pfluegers Arch.* 299:1–10
123. Wünnenberg, W., Brück, K. 1968. Single unit activity evoked by thermal stimulation of the cervical spinal cord in the guinea pig. *Nature* 218:1268–69
124. Wünnenberg, W., Brück, K. 1970. Studies on the ascending pathways from the thermosensitive region of the spinal cord. *Pfluegers Arch.* 321:233–41
125. Wünnenberg, W., Hardy, J. D. 1972. Response of single units of the posterior hypothalamus to thermal stimulation. *J. Appl. Physiol.* 33:547–52
126. Zenz, M., Fruhstorfer, H., Nolte, H., Hensel, H. 1973. Dissociated loss of cold and warm sensibility during regional anesthesia. *Pfluegers Arch.* Suppl. 339:171
127. Zerbst, E. 1972. *Analyse der Nachrichtenverarbeitung durch biologische Rezeptoren.* Leipzig: Georg Thieme
128. Zerbst, E., Dittberner, K.-H. 1970. Analytical approach to the excitation mechanisms of thermal cold receptors. *Pfluegers Arch.* 319:R126

# INDUCTIVE FUNCTIONS OF THE NERVOUS SYSTEM

❖1113

*A. J. Harris*

Department of Physiology, University of Otago Medical School, New Zealand

*... All nerves are trophic nerves and ... their trophic influences are not limited to one neurone but are the means of binding nerve-elements together.*

G. H. Parker (298)

*Much is to be said in favour of the view that ... the socalled neuro-fibrillar system is not, as is generally assumed, the impulse-transmitting mechanism, but a system of trophic elements leading from the nucleus of the neurone to its more distant parts and concerned in some way with the metabolism of those parts.*

Parker & Paine (299)

## INTRODUCTION

In addition to their responsibility for the minute to minute control of behavior and homeostasis, nerve cells are important in maintaining the long term stability of structure and function of the nervous system and the cells it innervates. The trophic action of motor nerve cells on skeletal muscles is a well known example of such an activity. Miledi (270) defined trophic actions as due to "an influence of the nerve not mediated by impulses," but it has recently been suggested that only some of the classical trophic effects on skeletal muscle are exerted independently of nerve impulses and/or muscle contraction. For example, direct electrical stimulation of a denervated muscle may reverse the development of denervation hypersensitivity (83, 241). The presence and the function of muscle innervation have a variety of independently exerted long term effects on the motoneurone itself, and on the physiological and anatomical state of the muscle. For example, botulinus toxin affects most of the trophic actions of the nerve except the maintenance of endplate cholinesterase (82), preganglionic cholinergic nerves form functional synapses on frog skeletal muscle but do not induce endplate cholinesterase (223), and adrenergic nerves can prevent denervation fibrillation without forming functional synapses (265). Similarly complex sets of interactions have been described elsewhere in the peripheral and autonomic nervous systems, and within the brain as well.

251

This review is intended to cover all functions of nerve cells that can reasonably be called "long term," so as to include phenomena that fit Miledi's definition of trophic effects; long term effects that are primarily due to nervous activity; and the ways nerve cells are specified so that they form and maintain synaptic connections with a particular class of cells or with particular regions of a tissue. The general term "inductive functions" is used to describe these categories of nervous actions, partly because of its lack of implied mechanism, and partly because it suggests an analogy with the inductive phenomena that occur during embryological development.

A comprehensive survey would obviously be outside the bounds of an *Annual Review* article, therefore the material presented here is necessarily selective. Guth (144) has written a comprehensive review of trophic actions of nerves on muscles, and a number of excellent books concerned with this field have recently been published: in particular, Hughes (190), Gaze (124), and Jacobson (196). Earlier books still relevant include Gutmann & Hnik (153), Gutmann (150), and Cannon & Rosenblueth (53).

## LONG TERM EFFECTS OF INNERVATION: EXAMPLES

### Motor Nerve and Skeletal Muscle

Both the structural and the functional integrity of skeletal muscle depend on the presence and normal function of the motor nerve supply. Denervation leads to general muscle atrophy and to a number of specific and well characterized changes in the expression of the muscle genome. There are at least five different effects on muscle cell membranes. The earliest is a reduction in resting potential, followed by the appearance of a tetrodotoxin (TTX)-resistant action potential mechanism, an increase of acetylcholine (ACh) sensitivity in the extrajunctional regions, spontaneous action potentials arising from the endplate region, and, finally, an increase in the specific membrane resistance. Blockers of RNA or protein synthesis prevent the fall in resting potential, the development of TTX-resistant action potentials, and the development of extrajunctional ACh receptors (140).

The following observations indicate that the nerve plays a role in regulating these parameters in normal muscle. 1. Following denervation the reduced resting potential and the TTX-resistant action potential mechanism spread centrifugally from the old endplate region. 2. The fibrillary potentials arise, at least initially, from endplate regions. 3. The increased ACh sensitivity is first obvious near endplates and near muscle-tendon junctions, although it then develops in a rather uniform way. The time course of distribution of the increase in specific membrane resistance is unclear.

Cutting the nerve at a distance from the muscle delays nerve terminal degeneration, the onset of muscle depolarization, and the development of TTX-resistant action potentials. Clearly, this influence of the nerve does not depend on nerve or muscle activity. During the course of reinnervation of a denervated muscle, spontaneous fibrillary action potentials disappear and ACh sensitivity is withdrawn to the vicinity of the old endplates before nerve-muscle transmission is reestablished. The effects of denervation and reinnervation of muscle, and a list of some of the experiments used to dissect the mechanisms underlying these effects, are given in Table 1.

These effects generally involve a change in the rates and kind of synthesis and degradation of structural, contractile, and membrane proteins. They reflect a change in the expression of the muscle cell genome, not the simple running down or acceleration of a constant set of cell functions.

The first change to follow denervation of mammalian skeletal muscle is a reduction in resting potential (5), seen as soon as two hours after nerve section, well before degeneration of the nerve terminals has occurred. The decrease occurs first at the endplate, but within two days the whole length of each muscle fiber is affected. The fall is considerable, about 8 mV within two hours of denervation, when measured close to an endplate, and about 20 mV when measured at any point in a muscle fiber two days or more following denervation. The mechanism underlying this fall is not known. It is not due to any obvious change in the membrane electrical constants, such as increase in specific membrane resistance, as such changes do not occur until about three days after denervation (5). The reduction in resting potential also occurs well in advance of measurable change in the number or distribution of ACh receptors.

Action potentials in denervated muscles are resistant to TTX, indicating either that some property of the sodium channels or of the membrane near them has changed, or that the channels have been replaced with new molecules with different properties (319). TTX will block action potentials for a day or more following denervation, but after two days action potentials can be induced at old endplate regions in the presence of this drug. Within a week of denervation, action potentials can be induced at any part of a muscle fiber in the presence of TTX. The rate of rise of the action potential is always reduced by TTX, although this reduction is least near the old endplate. The action potentials still depend on the presence of sodium ions in the extracellular medium, and show no obvious sensitivity to calcium levels. Reinnervation of a muscle fiber restores the normal sensitivity to TTX.

Denervated muscles become hypersensitive to ACh, in part because of a reduction in endplate cholinesterase, but principally because of the appearance of ACh receptors outside the synaptic region (14, 266). During development of skeletal muscles, postsynaptic sensitivity increases near the synapse and decreases in the extrasynaptic regions, at a time when spontaneous miniature endplate potentials (min. epp's) can be recorded and before nerve-muscle transmission is established. Eventually this gives rise to the adult situation where the receptors are precisely located in the regions of postsynaptic membrane closely apposed to the presynaptic nerve (79). In the adult, extrajunctional ACh sensitivity is not detectable outside the endplate regions on fast mammalian muscles. However, slow muscles, in particular soleus, have a sensitivity in the extrajunctional membrane about 4 orders of magnitude less than at the endplate (278). In both slow and fast muscles, extrajunctional sensitivity increases in a fairly uniform way after denervation. In particular, the increase in sensitive area is not due simply to a spread of receptors away from the endplate (4, 208).

A recently available, very powerful technique for studying the distribution and turnover of ACh receptors is the use of radioactively labeled toxins from various snake venoms that bind very strongly to the receptor (232). The venoms of elapid snakes, such as *Bungarus multicinctus* (banded krait) or *Naja naja* (cobra), contain

**Table 1** Long term effects of nerves on muscles

| Reference | Experiment | Nerve impulses | Fast axoplasmic transport | Transmitter release | Effect |
|---|---|---|---|---|---|
| 4, 14, 266, 319, 358 | Denervation of muscle | None | | Schwann cell min. epp's in amphibia | Lowered resting potential; TTX-resistant a.p.; Fibrillation; Increased $R_m$; ACh supersensitivity; Atrophy; Loss of junctional AChE |
| 100, 140, 159 | Protein or RNA synthesis blocked; muscle denervated or in organ culture | None | | None | No supersensitivity to ACh; Endplate sensitivity retained |
| 159 | Muscle in organ culture, cut nerve attached (frog) | None | ? | ±Normal min. epp's | ACh supersensitivity appears more quickly than after denervation in vivo; Min. epp's make no difference |
| 88 | Mouse mutant | present, normal | ? | Min. epp's present; Nerve-evoked release reduced or absent | Fibrillation and ACh supersensitivity |
| 201, 365 | Isolated spinal cord-muscle preparation: spinal cord and dorsal roots sectioned | infrequent | ? | Normal min. epp's | Limited spread of ACh sensitivity; No fibrillation; Muscle atrophy |
| 114 | Immobilization of muscle | Frequency reduced | | Normal min. epp's | Enlarged ACh-sensitive area; Atrophy (partial?) |
| 82, 85, 164, 357, 380, 381 | Botulinus poisoned muscle | Normal, ? frequency | ? | Blocked (infrequent, small min. epp's) | Muscle reacts as if denervated, except junctional AChE retained |
| 85, 87, 89 | Botulinus poisoned muscle | Normal, ? frequency | ? | Blocked | After a delay, nerve terminals sprout and form new endplates |
| 184 | β-bungarotoxin treated muscle | Normal, ? frequency | ? | Blocked | Muscle reacts as if denervated |
| 81, 381 | Developing or regenerating nerve poisoned with botulinus toxin | ? | ? | ? (no synapses) | Prevents synapse formation in muscle |
| 374, 375 | Muscles from senile rats or hibernating hamsters | infrequent | ? | Reduced frequency of min. epp's | Enlarged ACh-sensitive area on muscle; No atrophy |
| 323, 324 | Local anesthetic applied to sciatic nerve of rabbit, chronically blocking nerve and muscle activity | Blocked | High doses will block | Normal min. epp's | Slight increase in response to intra-arterial ACh; No fibrillation |
| 241 | Local anesthetic on nerve (rat); Nerve-muscle disuse, except for muscle fibrillation | Blocked | High doses will block | Normal min. epp's | ACh supersensitivity; Muscle fibrillates |

| Ref | Experimental preparation | | | | Effects |
|---|---|---|---|---|---|
| 6 | Vinblastine or colchicine chronically applied to nerve. Nerve-muscle activity normal | Normal, ? frequency | Blocked | Normal | Lowered resting potential; ACh supersensitivity; TTX-resistant a.p.'s; Muscle atrophy |
| 1 | Colchicine or lidocaine on nerve (salamander) | Normal | Blocked | Normal | Neighboring nerves sprout and form supernumary endplates |
| 83, 241 | Electrical stimulation of denervated muscle | | | | Denervation supersensitivity reverts to normal state |
| 79 | Developing nerve-muscle junctions | ? | | ? | Raised ACh sensitivity at nerve-muscle contact, and lowered extrajunctional sensitivity, before transmission has developed |
| 23, 25, 267, 383 | Motor nerve regenerating into skeletal muscle | | | | Fibrillation stops and denervation supersensitivity retracts before nerve-muscle transmission is restored |
| 24 | Autonomic cholinergic nerve made to innervate skeletal muscle (rabbit) | Normal | Normal | Normal | En grappe type synapses formed at old endplates; Many muscle fibers not reinnervated; Junctional AChE induced; Fibrillation stopped only in innervated fibers |
| 222, 223 | Autonomic preganglionic innervation of skeletal muscle (frog) | Normal | Normal | Cholinergic, multicomponent; Many epp's subthreshold | As in mammal, except no AChE induced; Muscle atrophy prevented |
| 265 | Postganglionic adrenergic nerve implanted in denervated skeletal muscle; No histology reported | Normal | Normal | Cholinergic, functional, multicomponent, often subthreshold | Fibrillation stopped; Did not look for subthreshold transmission |
| 106, 108 | Extra "fast" nerve implanted in innervated "slow" mammalian muscle; May have been an extra load on muscle | | | No functional transmission; No indications of synapse formation | Muscle hypertrophy, and speeding of slow muscle contraction |
| 208, 268, 269 | Implantation of extra nerve into damaged innervated skeletal muscle | | | | Damaged region becomes hypersensitive to ACh; Ectopic synapses formed and maintained |
| 109 | Nerve implanted into innervated, botulinum poisoned skeletal muscle | | | No release from original nerve terminals | Extra nerve forms functioning synapses; Old innervation sprouts and eventually recovers function, so that muscle becomes doubly innervated |
| 402 | Cross-union of "fast" nerve to chicken slow muscle | Normal | | Normal | Muscle ultrastructure changed to fast type |
| 5, 166, 275 | Motor nerve sectioned close to and distant from skeletal muscle | | | Normal min. epp's while nerve terminals survive | Nerve terminals maintained longer with longer nerve; Onset of muscle depolarization, appearance of TTX-resistant action potentials, delayed by longer length of cut nerve |

closely related proteins known as α-neurotoxins. These are readily isolated as homogenous preparations, and have a very powerful curare-like action in that they bind to ACh receptors and so prevent their activation by ACh (27, 58, 169, 232, 272, 302).

By applying labeled toxin to muscles, and then dividing the total bound radioactivity by the estimated number of endplates (272), or by using autoradiography to estimate radioactivity of single endplates (56, 101, 169, 313), estimates have been made of the total numbers and the densities of ACh receptors at single endplates. Values of $10^5/\mu m^2$ in frog sartorius muscle (272), $1.3 \times 10^4/\mu m^2$ in rat diaphragm (101), $1.37 \times 10^4/\mu m^2$ in mouse diaphragm (313), and $10^4/\mu m^2$ in *Torpedo* electroplax (271) show close agreement between different laboratories and species, with the exception of the frog where a greater allowance may be needed for extrajunctional receptors when making the calculation. Fambrough & Hartzell (101) comment that the packing density of ACh receptors at endplates is comparable to that of rhodopsin molecules in retinal rod outer segments, where rhodopsin accounts for most of the membrane protein. They suggest that motor endplates and perhaps other postsynaptic membranes may be constructed largely of receptor molecules.

The total number of toxin-binding sites in a muscle increases about 20-fold following denervation (27, 56, 169, 272). Hartzell & Fambrough (169) used iontophoretic and radioautographic techniques to study both the physiological and the molecular basis of denervation supersensitivity to ACh in the rat diaphragm. The number of receptors at endplates was not changed following denervation, while the total number per muscle fiber increased 20-fold in the first two weeks following nerve section. These new receptors were fairly uniformly distributed in the extrajunctional regions. (In both normal and denervated fibers receptor density within a few hundred microns of an endplate was higher than in more distant extrajunctional regions.) Receptor density in extrajunctional regions of normal muscle fibers was less than the limit of detection, $5/\mu m^2$. Two days after denervation extrajunctional receptors were just detectable at $7/\mu m^2$, and their numbers increased linearly with time to reach a peak of $1700/\mu m^2$ at 14 days. The density then declined, reaching, for example, $500/\mu m^2$ 45 days after denervation. Peper & McMahan (305) assayed the distribution of ACh sensitivity on frog muscles with the iontophoretic technique and found that sensitivity fell tenfold within a few microns of a nerve terminal, a result that correlates well with Fambrough & Hartzell's (101) description of the distribution of toxin binding sites on rat muscle, where there was an overall difference of at least 2500:1 between junctional and extrajunctional regions.

The appearance of receptors after denervation depends on the synthesis of both RNA and protein (100, 140) and cannot be accounted for by migration of receptors from endplate regions (169). The change in cell metabolism leading to the incorporation of ACh receptors into denervated muscle membranes has not yet been studied in greater detail, but Hartzell & Fambrough (170) have followed the incorporation of receptors into the membranes of developing muscles in tissue culture. Using the binding of iodine-labeled α-bungarotoxin to define receptors they found a pool of intracellular receptors that was incorporated into cell membranes at a steady rate. Replenishment of the pool depended on protein synthesis, and incorporation into membrane appeared to require ATP. The removal or inactivation of extrajunctional receptors that follows reinnervation has not been studied.

The changes in chemosensitivity that follow denervation are not exclusive to cholinergic synapses. Usherwood (370) studied a locust nerve-muscle synapse whose neurotransmitter is glutamate and found that while glutamate sensitivity in normal preparations was undetectable beyond 10–35 $\mu$m from a junction, denervation was followed by a rise in extrajunctional sensitivity to levels approaching those seen at normal synapses.

Filbrillation, a spontaneous unsynchronized twitching of single muscle fibers, is first seen about two days after denervation of rat muscles (326) and increases in intensity during the first week or so following denervation. Belmar & Eyzaguirre (21) studied fibrillation in the first few days following denervation and found that the spontaneous action potentials causing the fibrillary twitching arise from the old endplate region and propagate outwards from there. Recordings from the endplate region showed action potentials arising from slow-rising prepotentials, while elsewhere in the muscle they had an abrupt rise. At these early times, ACh- or electrically-induced depolarization of the central region of a denervated muscle fiber was effective in increasing the rate of fibrillation, while application away from the endplate zone was not. Two types of fibrillary activity have been described in muscles denervated for longer periods: an irregular firing from fast-rising prepotentials (which may also be seen as subthreshold depolarizations) in the old endplate regions, and a regular firing from slow-rising prepotentials which may be seen throughout the muscle (239, 359). ACh-receptor blocking drugs do not affect the regular firing (21, 359); whether they have an effect on the irregular potentials in the endplate regions is unclear. Mitchell & Silver (279) found that ACh continues to be synthesized and released in the endplate regions long after nerve terminals have degenerated.

The specific membrane resistance ($R_m$) of rat muscle is approximately doubled within a week of denervation (5, 359), principally as the result of a decrease in the potassium conductance in the muscle membrane (213).

The most striking result of skeletal muscle denervation is the rapid and extensive muscle atrophy. The rates of atrophy in different muscles and different species vary considerably; for example, rat limb muscles are reduced to half their original weight within two weeks of denervation (344), while rat diaphragm may undergo a transient hypertrophy during the first three or four weeks after denervation before it finally atrophies (352). The effects of denervation on muscle protein metabolism are summarized by Gutmann (150). In general, denervation decreases the rate of synthesis of muscle proteins and increases the rate of their degradation. Goldberg (135, 136) found the loss of myofibrillar proteins to be greater than the loss of sarcoplasmic proteins. This result contrasted with the effects of work-induced hypertrophy where the rate of protein synthesis increased and the rate of degradation decreased. The decreased degradation was more marked in the case of sarcoplasmic proteins, so that both during atrophy and hypertrophy their relative abundance increased with respect to myofibrillar proteins.

Kohn (214) isolated a proteolytic system from denervated muscle that was active on isolated myofibrils; Schiaffino & Hazlikova (327) concluded that the lysosomes that appear following denervation were not the prime cause of myofibrillar loss, but were secondary to the breakdown of muscle cell components. Besides the breakdown of myofibrils and the appearance of lysosomes, other recently described effects of denervation on muscle cell ultrastructure include fragmentation of mitochondria (274) and increase in the sarcoplasmic reticular system (328).

Denervation of muscles in newborn animals gives rise to only a relative atrophy, in that the muscle still grows but at a reduced rate [reviewed in (150)]. Differentiation of the muscle is impeded and mononucleate myoblasts and nonstriated myotubes persist long after the time when control innervated muscles have become fully striated (99, 328). The increase in muscle length as an animal grows depends on use, as immobilization of a muscle prevents the normal addition of sarcomeres to the ends of the fibers (386). This effect is reversible; after the plaster cast is removed from the limb, the immobilized muscles rapidly grow to match those of the control limb. Immobilization greatly reduces motor activity (113), so that requirements for muscle tension and muscle shortening cannot experimentally be separated with this technique.

The nervous effect on muscle differentiation is also seen during regeneration of muscles in adults. Jirmanova & Thesleff (200) used methylbupivacaine to cause muscle degeneration followed by regeneration. Innervation was required for the regenerating muscle fibers to progress past the myotube stage, although initial regeneration proceded independently of the nerve. If an adult muscle is removed from an animal, minced, and replaced, it will eventually regenerate and show a relatively normal morphology and function (54). Effective regeneration of the muscle is critically dependent on innervation; without the implantation of a nerve, the muscle graft is reduced to connective tissue within 2 or 3 weeks. Denervation of adult muscles does not lead to an obvious dedifferentiation, but there is a tendency for cells to bud, so that satellite cells break off from the multinucleated muscle fibers to form mononucleated myoblasts (177).

Myoblasts grown in tissue culture without nerves or other cell types can develop past the myotube stage to form multinucleated, striated, contractile fibers (394). Differences between tissue cultures and in vivo preparations may in part be explained by the use of the various undefined supplements, such as embryo extracts or placental cord serum, that are necessary for "good" cultures; it is not unlikely that these contain factors that are supplied as a result of innervation in the normal situation. Cultures of small fragments of adult muscle provide a better analogy with in vivo preparations than do myoblast cell cultures. Innervation from small explants of spinal cord greatly improves their ability to regenerate and maintain their functional integrity in culture (308).

## Autonomic Postganglionic Nerves and Effector Cells

The structure and functional capacity of tissues normally innervated by the autonomic nervous system are much less affected by denervation than are those of the skeletal musculature. Even the removal shortly after birth of almost the entire peripheral autonomic nervous system has little obvious effect on the development of autonomic effector organs. Blood vessels, glands, the smooth muscles of the gut, etc, are grossly normal after chemical- (362) or immuno-sympathectomy (350). Presumably, some form of specificity is required to explain the ordering of autonomic nerve fibers in their effector tissues (22), but structural evidence of postsynaptic specialization is rare (369), and the degree of correlation between autonomic varicosities and transmitter release sites quite unknown.

Denervated autonomic effector organs, such as smooth muscles and glands, generally develop supersensitivity to their normal neurotransmitter and sometimes to other substances. On the basis of studies of denervated cat nictitating membrane, Langer and his co-workers (225) have defined two components in the development of supersensitivity to norepinephrine (NE). An early presynaptic supersensitivity, maximal after two days, is correlated with degeneration of the nerve terminals. Following this, postsynaptic supersensitivity develops progressively for several weeks, possibly because of an increased density of NE receptors in a way analogous to skeletal muscle supersensitivity (225). The cat nictitating membrane is not typical of adrenergically innervated effectors, and while the postsynaptic component has been confirmed in this tissue by Haeusler et al (157), but not by Tsai et al (367), it is not seen in denervated cat heart (76), cat spleen (141), rat mesenteric artery (156), or chicken expansor secundariorum (129). The situation in the vas deferens is unclear (34, 207).

### Preganglionic Nerves and Autonomic Ganglion Cells

The normal growth and development of sympathetic ganglion cells is critically dependent on the presence of nerve growth factor (NGF) (238) and, to a lesser extent, on their preganglionic cholinergic nerve supply (37, 361). A variety of studies have shown that synaptic activation of mature ganglion cells induces an increased synthesis of neurotransmitter enzymes such as tyrosine hydroxylase and dopamine-$\beta$-hydroxylase (281, 360).

The development of choline acetylase within the superior cervical ganglion depends on formation by the preganglionic fibers of synapses on the postsynaptic cells. If the ganglion cells are destroyed with anti-NGF or 6–OH–dopamine (36), so that only supporting cells are left within the ganglion and synapses cannot form, choline acetylase activity does not develop. If, on the other hand, the number and size of ganglion cells are increased by treatment with NGF, the choline acetylase content of the ganglion is increased (361), presumably as the result of an increase in the number of synaptic terminals.

An analysis of denervation supersensitivity in the superior cervical ganglion, using the indirect technique of assaying the effect of arterial perfusion with ACh on the frequency of action potentials in the postganglionic trunk, led to the suggestion that supersensitivity in this tissue is due solely to loss of acetylcholinesterase (50). This problem has been studied more directly in a parasympathetic ganglion, using the easily visualized and accessible ganglion cells in the interatrial septum of the frog (78, 163, 219). ACh sensitivity of normal cells, assayed as the depolarizing response to iontophoretic application of ACh, was much greater close to synaptic boutons than at randomly chosen spots. A week or more after denervation, large, fast-rising responses to ACh were recorded from all points on a cell, indicating that ACh sensitivity was no longer restricted to the vicinity of synaptic boutons but was to be found in extrasynaptic regions. Thus the basis of denervation hypersensitivity in this tissue, as in denervated muscle, is the appearance of ACh receptors over the whole cell surface.

The first sign of reinnervation of these cells was the sudden and apparently complete loss of ACh sensitivity; this occurred before any response to stimulation of the preganglionic nerve could be recorded (77). Cells at this stage were quite different from normally innervated cells where a response to iontophoretic application of ACh, albeit small and slow, can be recorded from any point on the cell surface. The next stage was a small subthreshold response to nerve stimulation. Careful mapping of the surface of cells at this stage sometimes revealed a small and discrete sensitive spot. Desensitizing this spot by applying a large pulse of ACh abolished the responses both to iontophoretic application of ACh and to nerve stimulation, indicating that it was the site of a newly formed synaptic bouton. With time, the potency of synaptic transmission increased until full transmission was restored. The ganglion cells in this preparation normally receive their synaptic input from a single presynaptic fiber, but, following reinnervation, cells with as many as seven different inputs were found. Whether the situation reverts to normal long after reinnervation is not clear.

## Afferent Nerves and Sensory Transducers

Some of the clearest evidence for the existence of trophic actions that are independent of electrical activity comes from studies of the role of sensory innervation in inducing and maintaining the differentiation of sensory transducers. Examples include (a) taste buds in the tongue, which degenerate if they are denervated, and which are induced anew from germinative epithelium following reinnervation (146); (b) the retinal cells of urodele amphibia, which degenerate following optic nerve section and can be induced anew from cells of the ciliary margin of the eye (128); (c) muscle spindles, which are induced from skeletal muscle myoblasts by sensory nerves, and fail to develop if the muscle is denervated at a critical time in development (403); and (d) free nerve endings in the skin, which expand their zone of innervation if neighboring fibers are sectioned (384).

## Nerve-Glia Relations

The almost universal association of glial cells with both peripheral and central neurones leads to the attractive assumption that glia are in some way essential for the nutrition of nerve cells. There is little positive evidence for this idea, and nerve cells can grow and function in tissue culture without the presence of glial cells (47, 59, 295). Some signal is continually passing between nerves and their surrounding glia as shown by the involvement of glial cells in the chromatolytic reaction of neurones following axotomy (343) and by the fact that associated Schwann cells undergo mitosis and phagocytose a severed axon, in the well known Wallerian degeneration. This reaction occurs first at the distal synaptic terminals, as though some substance normally supplied by the cell body and transported down the axon was progressively used up (275). Other well documented forms of interaction between nerve and glial cells include the migration of glial cells along growing nerve fibers in embryos and, conversely, the mechanical role of Schwann cells as a directing influence in nerve regeneration (346).

Schwann cells make close contacts with the subsynaptic folds following denervation and nerve terminal degeneration in skeletal muscles of amphibia or snakes (32, 120). In frogs, but not snakes, low frequency spontaneous min. epp's reappear a few days after denervation, apparently due to ACh release from the Schwann cells at the endplates. These definitely are not due to nerve regeneration as shown by their appearance in frog muscles maintained in organ culture in the absence of nerve tissue (159, 165). Such Schwann-muscle contacts occur transiently in the rat, and Schwann-released min. epp's are correspondingly infrequent (273). The functional significance of this phenomenon is not clear. The phenomena in frog and snake provide evidence for the existence of some specificity in the subsynaptic membrane that induces Schwann cells to associate with this particular region of the cell once the nerve terminal has degenerated.

## Regulation of Nerve Cells by Their Periphery

Hughes (190) has comprehensively reviewed the evidence that nerve cell death is an important regulating factor in the normal development of the nervous system. He suggests that the formation of a surplus of nerve cells is followed by the retention of those making appropriate synaptic connections. Hughes' principal evidence is the observations that many more nerve cells form in the embryo than are found in an adult, and that under certain experimental circumstances, such as cutting a nerve trunk at a critical time, a greater number of neurones than normal may survive to maturity; the latter indicates the presence of some form of competition between "successful" cells and their neighbors. Recent evidence for this general hypothesis is the finding that neurones may degenerate in the course of normal development even after they have sent axons towards the periphery (314, 320), indicating that neuronal degeneration is not the result of failure to extend an axon, but rather, perhaps, of failure to form or maintain synaptic connections.

Neurones whose axons have been severed and which have not regenerated either atrophy or degenerate (e.g. 364). Axotomy gives rise to an initial response in nerve cell bodies (chromatolysis) which is fairly constant in different cells and circumstances. Chromatolysis has been particularly well studied and clearly described by Matthews & Raisman (256) as it occurs in neurones in the rat superior cervical ganglion in response to ligation or section of the postganglionic nerves. This preparation has the particular advantage of having been well studied physiologically by workers interested in the phenomena and mechanisms of axoplasmic flow (72).

The classical definition of chromatolysis is a dispersion of Nissl substance, seen in the electron microscope as clumps of granular endoplasmic reticulum. This is followed by involution, a partial autophagocytosis of many cell constituents such as granular endoplasmic reticulum, mitochondria, occasional dense cored vesicles, and so on. At the same time, glial cell protrusions into neuronal cytoplasm are common, suggesting a phagocytotic reaction of the sheath cells, which pinch off and sequestrate small masses of neuronal cytoplasm. The nucleus is displaced to the periphery of the cell with its cytoplasmic side indented, and nuclear chromatin condenses against the nuclear membrane.

The physiological response of superior cervical ganglion cells to ligation of the postganglionic trunk has been extensively studied (72). Dense core vesicles, norepinephrine and its synthetic enzymes, and mitochondria accumulate immediately above the ligation, initially with a linear relation to time, but the accumulation ceases within a day or two. Once accumulation has stopped, a second ligation placed above the first does not provoke a similar reaction, indicating that the cellular synthesis of these components has been drastically decreased (46). If, instead of section or ligation, a nerve crush is used, so as to allow rapid regeneration of the nerve, the fluorescence will again accumulate above a second, higher crush within about two weeks of the lower crush (72), showing that within this time the neurone can restore the cellular machinery for peripheral neurotransmitter synthesis, storage, and secretion.

The time course of these events is well correlated with the results of Matthews & Raisman's (256) survey of fine structural changes in the ganglion cells. Involution is evident within two days of ligation or nerve section, and the process is essentially complete within a week. Correspondingly, the rate of accumulation of catecholamine fluorescence above a nerve section is linear with time for about 48 hrs, and then declines to zero within a week (72). After the initial chromatolytic reaction and involution, the Nissl substance progressively reappears until, after a period of some weeks, an essentially normal situation is restored.

Involution does not represent a net loss of RNA, as is indicated by Watson's (377) observation of increased incorporation of radioactive precursors into nuclear and cytoplasmic RNA within two days of hypoglossal axotomy in mice. Mathews & Raisman suggest that their observations are consistent with autolysis of the cell machinery for producing materials for synthesis and release of neurotransmitter, and the reprogramming of the cell to produce material for axonal regrowth.

Other effects of axotomy include changes in the surface morphology of the neurone and in its relations to other cells. In the superior cervical ganglion, axotomized neurones send out many local sprouts, which are later withdrawn, and the surrounding glial cells increase in number and may wrap around presynaptic processes, making a greater area of contact with the nerve cell (256). Blinzinger & Kreutzberg (39) cut the facial nerve in rats and found that 4 days later many synaptic boutons had been displaced from the somatic and dendritic surfaces of the neurone, and fingers of glial cytoplasm were interposed between the pre- and postsynaptic surfaces. Brown & Pascoe (51) described a failure of synaptic transmission through the superior cervical ganglion following postganglionic axotomy, although impulse conduction in pre- and postganglionic trunks was normal. Sumner & Watson (355) measured a retraction of the dendritic tree of rat motor neurones following axotomy, with a consequent displacement of synaptic terminals.

These changes may reflect the reversion of the neurone to an earlier developmental stage. As mentioned previously, there is good evidence for a gross overproduction of nerve cells during development (190) with a subsequent loss of cells that do not make effective and appropriate synaptic contacts. Watson (382) produces evidence that the withdrawal of synaptic contacts is mediated by the axotomized postsynaptic nerve cell, and is not secondary to glial changes.

Withdrawal and reformation of synaptic contacts in the CNS after axotomy and reestablishment of peripheral synapses add new significance to the attempts by Eccles and his co-workers to change the effectiveness of monosynaptic reflexes in the spinal cord by peripherally cross-innervating antagonistic muscles (93). They found statistically significant changes, reflecting both decreases and increases in synaptic potency (and presumably in the number of synaptic contacts) following cross-unions between some motor nerves, but not with others. This apparent variability was correlated with the observation that plastic changes occurred only when motoneurones and afferent fibers had suffered injury from the cross-innervation operations. Thus a functional interpretation of the reorganization of central synaptic connections following chromatolysis can be made: by partially recreating the embryonic situation, the process allows some central compensation to be made for the formation of inappropriate peripheral connections during regeneration, albeit to a very limited extent. No doubt the process works much more efficiently during embryogenesis.

The simplest explanation of these reactions of nerve cells and their surrounding glia is that they are due to injury, perhaps to the separation of the neuronal soma from the greater part of the nerve cell cytoplasm. In a series of elegant experiments Watson (377, 379–382) has shown that many of the changes are due to the loss of functional contact between the cell and its postsynaptic effector tissue. The central response to peripheral nerve regeneration was distinguished from that due to the reestablishment of peripheral synaptic contacts by implanting the cut hypoglossal nerve into the normally innervated sternomastoid muscle, so that regeneration took place but synapses were not formed (381). The initial response to nerve section, an increase in the dry mass and nucleic acid content of nucleolus and cell body, was followed by a maintained decrease in these parameters to a subnormal level as the nerve terminals became stabilized in the muscle without forming synapses. If the nerve was sectioned again at this time, this response was repeated. If, on the other hand, the normal innervation to the sternomastoid muscle, i.e. the spinal accessory nerve, was sectioned, a reaction of hypoglossal neurones occurred. After a latent period of about eight days, nucleolar and cell body dry mass and nucleic acid content increased, concurrent with the functional establishment of synapses between hypoglossal nerves and sternomastoid muscle fibers.

The experiments demonstrate two sequential changes in the synthesis and turnover of neuronal nucleic acids and proteins, one associated with the necessity to regrow the axon, and the other with the establishment of synaptic transmission. After a nerve crush these would be difficult to distinguish, but by experimentally allowing the completion of axonal regeneration without the formation of synapses, Watson separated them in time and thus demonstrated their independence.

The signal for chromatolysis appears to be the failure of the nerve cell body to receive some substance normally carried up the nerve by fast axoplasmic transport. Pilar & Landmesser (311) found that the effects of axotomy can be mimicked by application of colchicine in a dose adequate to block fast transport but not to affect nerve conduction. Watson (381) has shown further that separate signaling systems are concerned with the response to axotomy per se and with the need of the cell to supply the machinery for the formation and maintenance of functional synapses. Application of botulinus toxin to a normal motor nerve leads to cell body changes identical to those caused by axotomy. However, application of toxin to a supernumerary nerve implanted into an innervated muscle does not invoke such changes, even though axotomy at that time would provoke a cell body reaction. If toxin was applied to the supernumerary nerve, and at the same time normal innervation of the muscle was cut, the cell body reaction and synapse formation to be expected from the implanted nerve were delayed for more than three weeks.

The only known actions of botulinus toxin are to prevent impulse-invoked release of ACh from nerve terminals and to reduce greatly the spontaneous release of transmitter (164), as well as to prevent the formation of nerve-muscle junctions in chick embryos (81). Among the several possible explanations for its action in delaying or preventing synapse formation in rats and chicks are that it acts on the nerve to mimic a signal from muscle that normally prevents hyperinnervation, or that it prevents the nerve from inducing or receiving a signal from muscle that induces and maintains synaptic terminals on its surface. If its effect on both transmitter release and synapse formation is a unitary one, then the first of these alternatives is the most attractive, as developing muscle has been shown to restrict the formation of ectopic nerve-muscle junctions, and to render nontransmitting those that do form (310). Similarly, adult fish eye muscles appear capable of rendering structurally normal but inappropriate synaptic connections nontransmitting (254, 255), again demonstrating that the presence or absence of some signal from muscle can switch synaptic transmission on or off in an all-or-nothing way.

Many anatomical demonstrations have been made of cases where deafferentation gives rise to changes in CNS neurones and even in the second order neurones to which these project. When immature neurons are involved, the effects may be as dramatic as the total loss of the deafferented cells (366), whereas in adults the effects are often subtle (312). Degeneration caused by deafferentation appears to follow the cessation of RNA synthesis (366), and thus is quite different from the chromatolytic response to axotomy. Trumpy (366) gives instances where cells responded to axotomy with a chromatolytic reaction, whereas deafferentation led to their total dissolution within a few days. Pinching & Powell (312) suggest that many of the effects of deafferentation of mature nerve cells are due simply to the loss of electrical activation of the cells. Lux et al (246) have convincingly demonstrated the increased incorporation of labeled amino acids into proteins in electrically activated motoneurones, thus confirming the results of many studies that suggest an association between nerve cell activity and nucleic acid and protein metabolism (41, 378).

## Long Range Actions of Nerve Cells

In classical accounts of embryology, differentiation of primitive ectoderm into neural tissue is said to depend on an inductive signal from underlying mesoderm. The mechanism of induction is still as much a mystery as it was in the 1930s; it is not clear, for example, whether physical contact is required between cells in order to pass the inductive signal, or whether it can work by short range diffusion.

Electrical coupling between cells in both the same and different tissues is widespread in the early chick embryo (337), and dispersed cells from *Xenopus* embryos become electrically coupled within 20 min of reaggregation (338). Gilula et al (132) demonstrated that cells in tissue culture that can form gap junctions with one another are electrically coupled and can pass radioactively labeled metabolites and possibly RNA from one cell to the other.

Many amphibians, especially those with a prolonged larval phase, can regenerate limbs following amputation. This regeneration is dependent in a nonspecific way upon innervation, as an adequate number of motor nerves, sensory nerves, or even diverted spinal cord, will support and permit regeneration. Close contact between nerves and regenerating tissues is not essential, suggesting that a diffusible factor is involved. A long series of experiments by Singer and his associates has established that ACh is not involved in this process.

Lebowitz & Singer (231) found that an extract from the nerve trunks entering a regenerating limb bud increased incorporation of $^{14}$C-leucine into protein in a 48 hr denervated test system; an extract of liver, although less potent, did the same. Thus the growth factor is not exclusive to nerve and could be quite nonspecific, at least in terms of this assay. This possibility is supported by the finding that aneurogenic limbs can regenerate with only a minute fraction of the normal nerve supply (363, 395). Any cells capable of mitosis seem able to dedifferentiate and supply the different cell types required for regeneration (376). The high degree of order during regeneration may be supplied by local factors.

In other situations nerves appear able to exert a trophic effect without forming functional synaptic contacts. Elul et al (97) found that frog slow muscle fibers, when innervated with the nerve to a fast muscle fiber, rapidly lose their characteristic ability to produce a maintained contracture in response to ACh or potassium depolarization. Denervating the muscles for as long as a year does not produce this effect, while crushing the nerve so as to allow rapid regeneration of fast nerve fibers abolishes the maintained contracture in as little as 11 days. The effect appears specific to fast nerve fibers, as crushing the nerve close to its point of entry to the muscle, so that fast and slow nerve fibers have a more equal opportunity for reinnervation, does not abolish maintained contractures.

Maintained contractures were consistently abolished before functional reinnervation had occurred; in the case of the nerve crush, for example, contractures disappeared 11 days after the crush, while contraction in response to nerve stimulation was not seen earlier than 24 days after the crush. A careful electronmicroscopic study failed to reveal obvious synaptic contacts on slow muscle fibers at a time soon after the abolition of maintained contracture, but the authors emphasize the difficulty of distinguishing between Schwann cell and nerve cell processes in the early stages of regeneration. Thus, while it is clear that functional synaptic transmission is not required for the transformation, the necessity for nerve-muscle contact is still an open question. Either way, it is apparent that some nerve-released factor, whether applied diffusely or locally, is responsible for the transformation; this substance obviously is not ACh, as this is released by both slow and fast nerves.

At a much later time, some six weeks or so after initial reinnervation in the case of sciatic nerve crush, the maintained contracture is reestablished, presumably as the result of reinnervation of slow muscle fibers by their appropriate nerve.

Nerves may also alter the characteristics of muscles without making functional synaptic contacts when, in the course of reinnervation, fibrillation stops (23, 383) and ACh sensitivity is withdrawn from extrajunctional areas (25, 267) before nerve-muscle transmission has been reestablished.

Fex and collaborators (106–108) made similar interpretations of the results of experiments where a fast nerve was implanted into the slow soleus muscle of the rat, leaving the original innervation intact so that the implanted nerve did not form recognizable endplates but sent sprouts into the muscle near its point of implantation. This resulted in an increase in muscle weight and fiber diameter, a speeding of slow muscle contraction, and a change in the histochemical staining pattern of the muscle fibers. Guth & Wells (148) suggest that these effects are due to the change in muscle activity following denervation of its antagonist, rather than to any effect of the fast nerve.

Another situation in which nerves have been said to exert a trophic action without synaptic contacts is when adrenergic nerves are implanted into skeletal muscles. Mendez, Arana & Luco (265) found that implantation of the postganglionic trunk from the superior cervical ganglion into the denervated longus capitis muscle of the cat greatly reduced denervation fibrillation, although stimulation of the adrenergic nerve trunk did not produce muscle contraction. Luco & Luco (243) deprived a denervated muscle of its normal sympathetic innervation and found that fibrillary activity was enhanced. Direct application of norepinephrine, or sympathetic stimulation, enhances fibrillary activity. Thus it was concluded that the sympathetic effect of slowing or abolishing fibrillation was due to sympathetic release of some trophic substance. No intracellular recordings and no histological studies were made of this material, and it is not clear to what extent muscles were reinnervated with cholinergic nerves. Even if collateral sprouts were not attracted from neighboring muscles, autonomic cholinergic nerves have been shown to make functional synaptic contacts with skeletal muscle in frogs (222, 223) and rabbits (24), and in both cases to produce subthreshold endplate potentials, which would not have been detected by Mendez et al. This does not explain the enhancement of fibrillation seen by Luco & Luco following removal of the sympathetic innervation of the muscle vasculature.

Harris et al (162) showed that autonomic nerve tumor cells can exert one aspect of the normal trophic process on skeletal muscle cells in tissue culture without making a transmitting synapse. This effect depends on nerve-muscle contact, so that it cannot explain the effect seen by Luco & Luco, for which a diffusible trophic agent must be presumed if indeed it was not due simply to an enhanced blood flow to the muscles. The possible existence of such blood-borne agents is suggested by the finding that frog muscle in organ culture in defined medium without serum (165) will in 8 days develop a higher denervation supersensitivity to ACh than will a muscle denervated in vivo for a period of weeks (159).

Lentz (235, 236) found that junctional folds and endplate cholinesterase on denervated newt muscles in tissue culture were better maintained in the presence of a sensory ganglion or if cyclic AMP and theophylline were added to the medium. He did no control experiments with other tissues, so that the signaling mechanism may not have been specific for nerve, as found by Lebowitz & Singer (231) in the experiments reported above.

## Stability of Synaptic Contacts

A number of interesting questions arise concerning the stability and function of synapses, in particular the extent to which they may, in the course of normal development or as the result of environmental changes, cease to function and perhaps be replaced by contacts from other cells, and the extent to which synaptic potency may alter to adapt to different patterns of use or stages of development.

The potency of synaptic transmission can, in principle, be affected in the following ways: transmitter release may be increased due to an increase in quantal unit size or quantal content; postsynaptic sensitivity may change as a result of an increased availability of receptors or of an increase in the synaptic current due to activation of a single receptor. The firing threshold for postsynaptic action potentials may change, and the input resistance of the postsynaptic cell may change so that it is more easily brought to threshold. All these factors may be altered experimentally; the extent to which they change under normal physiological circumstances is unsettled.

The mean amount of neurotransmitter released in individual quantal packets changes as a short term effect of fatigue but not, so far as is known, for longer periods. Experimentally, the quantal size at cholinergic junctions can be reduced by nerve stimulation in the presence of compounds such as hemicholinium-3 or triethylcholine. Among other actions, these drugs compete with choline for uptake into the nerve terminals so that stores of ACh are depleted without replenishment (33), and the drugs are acetylated in place of choline so that they may be stored and released as false transmitters (172, 173). The relevance of phenomena of this kind to normal physiology or even to diseases such as myasthenia gravis (96) is unclear.

A large presynaptic terminal, such as that at a skeletal muscle endplate, releases much more transmitter in response to a single impulse than does a small terminal such as a synaptic bouton on a nerve cell. Kuno et al (221) studied the variation in potency among different endplates within a muscle and found that the larger the terminal the higher the frequency of spontaneously released min. epp's and the greater the quantal content of the epp. Similar comparisons have been made on Clarke's column neurones in spinal cord (220) where the size of an epsp (excitatory postsynaptic potential) due to unitary stimulation depended on the number of synaptic boutons received by the spinal cord neurone from each afferent nerve fiber.

Muscles from hibernating hamsters (375) and from senile rats (152, 374) have a greatly decreased min. epp frequency, although this is less marked in the relatively more used rat diaphragm muscle than in rat limb muscles or hamster diaphragms. Quantal contents of nerve-induced epp's were not examined, and it will be of interest to see if the correlation seen by Kuno et al (221) in the normal case holds in these special conditions. Muscles from hibernating frogs have low quantal contents and show marked facilitation during repetitive nerve stimulation (249, 296) in contrast to muscles from summer frogs, in which transmission is easily depressed.

Gutmann et al (152) saw no evidence of axonal degeneration near endplates from senile rats, but did not measure the size of the terminals. Tuffery (368) found endplates in the muscles of old cats to be more complex, but not necessarily smaller, than those in young animals. He made no histochemical examination for acetylcholinesterase; this might allow a better comparison of the area of functional contact. He concluded that the principal effect of aging is to increase the workload of muscle fibers, both because of loss of muscle fibers (a 1 year old cat has about 5000 muscle fibers in m. peroneus digiti quinti, while a 19 year old has less than 2000) and because of an increase in body weight. Thus, in order to maintain the contractile strength of the whole muscle, individual muscle fibers increase in diameter with age. The nerves supplying them sprout, so that an endplate comes to be innervated by several terminal branches of the one axon; the actual endplate size does not increase, and may even grow less.

Barker & Ip (17) proposed a continuous process of muscle nerve terminal expansion and degeneration throughout the life of an animal. This hypothesis has been revised by Tuffery (368) who suggests that the degenerating terminals seen in normal muscles are not due for renewal but break down without replacement, possibly leading to total loss of both the terminals and the muscle fibers. Protein synthesis decreases in motoneurones of old animals (198); Gutmann et al (151) suggest that this is correlated with a decline in the trophic function of the neurone, which may thus be primarily responsible for many of these changes. Until more is known about the details of nerve and muscle fiber loss, for example, whether whole motor units are lost at one time and whether these are the smaller units that are used more (175), it will be difficult to separate the effects of age per se from those of use and disuse.

Apart from the work with hibernating or senile animals there are few studies of changes in transmitter output at neuromuscular junctions as a result of use or disuse. Lømo & Rosenthal (241) noted that the frequency of min. epp's did not change with short term (up to 2 weeks) disuse of nerve terminals. While they made some estimates of quantal content in curare-blocked preparations, their data, as presented, give no useful information about the ability of the junctions to maintain transmission during a train of impulses. Robbins & Fischbach (321) produced relative disuse of rat soleus muscles by tenotomy and studied synaptic transmission at various times afterwards. At low frequencies of stimulation (5 or 10 per sec), disused terminals showed less variation in the amplitudes of successive epp's than did controls; at higher frequencies (20 or 40 per sec) variation was greater. Their study provides no evidence for a change in ACh metabolism in nerve terminals for up to 6 weeks of relative disuse; nor does it suggest a change in the efficacy of transmitter release.

The availability of postsynaptic receptors, at least at the neuromuscular junction, does not seem to be a parameter of synaptic transmission that could easily be regulated, as the receptors are present in great excess. Evidence for this is that the response to nerve-released (272) or iontophoretically applied (302) ACh is maintained during the initial binding of α-neurotoxin until a point is reached when the response falls linearly with time. The extrapolation of receptor density against response to iontophoretically applied ACh is linear at low receptor densities, but falls off sharply as the high densities typical of endplates are approached (169). The relative refractoriness to desensitization of junctional as compared to extrajunctional receptors (266) may be related to this point.

The elementary electrical event that results from the interaction of ACh with its receptor has a brief time course, about 1 msec at 20°C in frog muscle (209). The resistance-capacitance properties of nerve or muscle cells make the magnitude of a synaptic potential extremely sensitive to the time-course of the synaptic current (122, 348). McBurney & Gage (260) artificially altered the time course of the endplate current by treatment with alcohols of different chain lengths, with consequent large effects on the depolarization evoked by a single quantum. Katz & Miledi (209) found that the ACh receptors that appeared following denervation produced an elementary event with a longer time course than normal. Thus it is at least possible that nerve and muscle cells can alter their receptivity to synaptic transmission by controlling the duration of the elementary event evoked by receptor activation. They may do this by changing the local environment of receptor molecules in the postsynaptic membrane, in the way that the different alcohols presumably do.

After gross disuse (as opposed to denervation), muscle cells are depolarized and their input resistance increases (49). ACh sensitivity spreads to regions close to the endplate (114, 201). The changes in electrical properties oppose one another functionally: the lowering of muscle resting potentials depresses excitability so that epp's that might normally initiate an action potential fail to do so (258), while the increased input resistance means that a greater depolarization results from a given synaptic current. No evidence has been presented to suggest that alterations in specific membrane resistance are significant in allowing nerve or muscle cells to adapt their firing thresholds under different patterns of use. For example, both low- and high-threshold spinal motoneurones have similar specific membrane resistances; the relatively high input impedence of the low-threshold cells is due to their small size (176).

An all-or-nothing, on or off switching of transmission at structurally normal synapses in primitive vertebrates has been reported by Mark and his collaborators (252-255) and it is suggested that similar processes may occur in the mammalian brain (251). This effect has been most thoroughly studied in the extraocular muscles of goldfish eyes (253). The principle experiment is to denervate two antagonistic muscles and to implant the nerve from one muscle into the other. The nerve sprouts and forms functional synaptic contacts, so that the eye moves inappropriately. Next, the nerve that would normally innervate the muscle is reimplanted and also forms synapses. (Fish eye muscles, unlike mammalian skeletal muscles, are multiply innervated, so that functional innervation does not necessarily mean that all the possible synaptic sites on a muscle fiber are occupied.) Shortly afterwards normal eye movements are restored. Electronmicroscopic examination of the muscle at this time shows no signs of degenerating terminals, so that it is concluded that the "taking over" of the muscle by the correct nerve has led to a shutting off of transmission from the inappropriate nerve terminals, without any anatomical changes in them. The critical control experiment, section of the inappropriate nerve and the demonstration of degenerating terminals, has been done only in one animal. Throughout the series the experimental results are variable, so that while the theory is an appealing one, it is not yet fully validated experimentally.

While there are few other examples of synaptic transmission failing without a concurrent degeneration or disjunction of synapses, studies of developing or regenerating synapses have shown no obvious change in structure to be associated with the onset of transmission (23, 121, 267). Ectopic synapses in developing muscle remain nontransmitting until they degenerate (310). Similarly, no structural changes are associated with the complete block of neuromuscular transmission caused by botulinus toxin (87, 357), a finding which gives rise to the exciting possibility that botulinus toxin acts by activating the control mechanism in cholinergic junctions that switches off transmission in the way Mark describes it in fish. In this case the action of the toxin is not reversible and transmission is restored only after the nontransmitting nerve terminals have sprouted and formed new junctions (84, 87, 89).

There are many physiological examples of a loss of function of inappropriate synapses and their functional replacement by the appropriate nerve terminal. Langley (226) found that partial denervation of the superior cervical ganglion of a cat caused the remaining terminals to form functional synapses on the denervated cells. He deduced this from the physiological effects of stimulating the remaining presynaptic inputs to the ganglion. The development of collateral sprouts has been described anatomically (285, 387) and the physiological effects confirmed (147). At a later time, the cut nerves regenerated and normal function was resumed. It is not known whether the new "correct" synapses physically displaced the incorrect ones, or whether the mechanism is that proposed by Mark for fish eye muscles.

Hubel & Wiesel (188) raised kittens with an artificial squint and found that cells in the visual cortex generally responded to one or the other eye, instead of to both as they do in normal cats. The effect was not due to a dropping out of binocularly driven cells; in fact the authors comment that active cells were "unusually rich" in number. Thus the lack of synchrony between different afferents to a cortical neurone led to a relative loss of efficacy, or failure of development, in one set of afferents. There was no indication that the effect was due to selective loss of cells at the lateral geniculate level, as has been suggested (339) as a causative factor in Hubel & Wiesel's experiments on monocular deprivation of vision. The anatomical correlation of the change in synaptic activation of cortical neurones due to squint is not known, although, arguing from the analogous results of monocular deprivation, the effect is a permanent one (189). Chow & Stewart (60) report some reversal following long periods of forced usage of the deprived eye; these results are consistent with use by the animals of the small number of appropriate pathways remaining in the visual system.

Another well characterized example of the reorganization of functional synapses occurs during the regeneration of retinotectal connections in *Xenopus* following section of the optic nerve. Gaze & Keating (125) found that, sufficiently long after nerve section, a precise point to point projection of the retina to the optic tectum was restored. In a series of animals examined at earlier times, ingrowing optic nerve axons appeared to have formed synaptic connections with the first available tectal cell, so that the final highly ordered pattern arose as the result of competition between more or less appropriate synaptic connections. Again, no structural information is available, and it is not known whether inappropriate synapses degenerate or simply become nontransmitting.

## Regeneration of Nerves to the Periphery

The relative roles of the following factors in the embryological development of peripheral synaptic connections are still unknown: the individual recognition of the endorgan by its appropriate nerve, the arrangement of central nervous synaptic patterns after peripheral connections have been made, and the degeneration of nerve cells that have not made appropriate connections. One way to approach this problem is to denervate endorgans in adult animals and study the degree of specificity in regeneration.

Innervated mammalian skeletal muscle will not normally accept synapses from another nerve (124, 144, 155). This barrier to innervation can be overcome in a number of ways, the most obvious being simply to section the original innervation. Aitken (2) showed that a motor nerve implanted into a normal muscle sprouts and gives rise to nerve fibers that ramify through the muscle without forming endplates. If the original nerve is sectioned in such doubly innervated muscles, the implanted, initially nonfunctional nerve can invoke muscle contraction within as few as 3–6 days (107, 110, 381). Thus the barrier to new innervation is rapidly removed following denervation.

New synapses will be accepted by innervated mammalian skeletal muscles, however, at regions of local damage (269), or following botulinus intoxication (109), or as the result of collateral sprouting following partial denervation (143). In these cases, once double innervation has been induced it is both functionally and structurally maintained.

The near lack of evidence for maladaptive nerve-muscle connections in normal animals indicates that synapse formation is well ordered during development. On the other hand, experimental nerve section in adults provides few signs of specificity in the reformation of nerve-muscle junctions. It may be that the initial polyneuronal innervation of embryonic muscle fibers (15, 318) provides an opportunity for replacement of inappropriate connections during development, which is lacking during nerve regeneration in the adult (250).

The reinnervation of mammalian nerve-muscle junctions is not necessarily completely without specificity. Guth (143) studied the plantaris and soleus muscles in the rat; these muscles receive nerves from spinal roots L4 and L5. He crushed L4, so that all the muscle fibers became innervated by nerves from L5 due to collateral sprouting within the muscle (94). The nerves arising in L4 later regenerated and reinnervated a large proportion of the muscle fibers, perhaps even more than they did originally. Thus many muscle fibers received two endplates, both functional. The evidence seems conclusive, but the finding is not easily reconciled with the dogma that a mammalian skeletal muscle, once innervated, however inappropriately, cannot be innervated by a more appropriate nerve, even if such a nerve can be directed to the muscle. A similar phenomenon occurs when a nerve is implanted into a botulinus poisoned muscle: it forms functional synapses (109) and later the original poisoned terminals sprout and form new junctions on the innervated fibers (87) as if the muscle retained some preference for its own nerve. This may merely reflect the normal tendency for innervation to occur in the center of muscle fibers.

Miledi & Stefani (276) looked for specificity at a fine level by cutting the sciatic nerve in rats and later examining the soleus muscle, which contains purely slow muscle fibers, for evidence of specific reinnervation by slow nerve fibers. It was almost completely reinnervated by fast nerves. As these appear to regenerate more quickly than slow nerve fibers, the result supports the dogma that, once innervated, adult muscle fibers will not accept further innervation; it is not known whether specificity would have been evident if the nerves were given a more equal opportunity to compete for their appropriate muscle fibers. Hoh (185) designed an experiment of this type by cutting the nerves to both soleus and extensor digitorum longus (EDL) muscles in the rat and then excising one or the other muscle. The soleus was reinnervated by both nerves, but the EDL was exclusively reinnervated by its own nerve. Hoh suggests that anatomical factors, such as the respective distances required for growth of the different nerves to the remaining muscle, or the relative rate of regeneration of the smaller diameter soleus nerve fibers, were not important. He found that the soleus nerve formed few synapses even if it actually was implanted into the EDL. Fex & Jirmanova (107) obtained a similar result after implanting the soleus nerve into the fast flexor digitorum longus (FDL) muscle, but suggested that this was due both to the difficulty in implanting the relatively short soleus nerve and to the small number of nerve fibers contained in it. The nerve fibers that innervate soleus differ from those supplying fast muscles in several respects, including their rapid terminal sprouting and formation of new endplates following botulinus intoxication (87), and a greater sensitivity to the effects of tetanus toxin (90).

Experimental reinnervation of denervated amphibian limbs can, in many cases, restore apparently normal function to the limb [reviewed by Gaze (124)]. The specificity of reinnervation appears to be due to initial widespread exploratory activity by regenerating nerves, followed by the maintenance of appropriate contacts. The alternative explanation of this result, that regeneration is random followed by a readjustment of central nervous synapses, is not supported by experimental evidence (124). For example, Grimm (142) exchanged nerves between forearm flexor and extensor muscles in axolotls and found that normal function was restored, as predicted by the myotypic respecification hypothesis of Weiss (385). However, a careful physiological study showed that while the nerves appeared to have been successfully crossed, as judged anatomically or by close electrical stimulation, they in fact contained fibers from the original flexor and extensor nerves, respectively. Thus, the normal innervation had been restored to the muscles, apparently as the result of sprouting and recrossing of nerve fibers between trunks higher up in the limb. There was no evidence of myotypic respecification in the experiments on fish eye muscles mentioned above (253) or in other similar experiments (250).

Further studies of the reinnervation of amphibian muscles have been made by allowing the large and small nerve fibers that normally innervate fast and slow muscle fibers, respectively, to reinnervate muscles with and without a slow fiber component. If fast nerve fibers are presented to a muscle containing both types of muscle fiber, then both slow and twitch muscle fibers are innervated by the fast nerve and some of the properties of the slow muscle fibers are transformed; in particular, they can give action potentials and they lose the slow-graded response to tetanic nerve stimulation or to KCl or ACh depolarization (97, 277, 347). Simultaneous reinnervation of the mixed muscle by both types of nerve allows the retention of the normal properties of the slow-graded muscle fibers (97), although fast as well as slow nerves make synaptic connections with the slow-graded muscle fibers (347), as in a similar preparation in the fowl (25). Slow nerve fibers, although present in the nerves to fast muscles, do not activate contraction (186). In the analogous case in the fowl (25, 182), slow nerves form synapses on fast muscles but give subthreshold endplate potentials.

Denervated skeletal muscle fibers are normally reinnervated at the site of the old endplate. This appears to be due to some special attractiveness of this site, and not to guidance of regenerating nerves down preexisting pathways, as the result holds if the nerve is implanted away from its original point of entry into the muscle or if the intramuscular nerve trunks are stripped from the muscle (3, 182, 262, 267, 381). Junctions can form in regions of muscle that do not normally receive them, so the endplate site is not exclusive (107, 109, 149, 155, 268). Formation of junctions in abnormal places is more frequent when a long time interval has elapsed between denervation and reimplantation of the nerve (154), but it may also occur under well controlled conditions shortly after denervation (107).

The innervated soleus muscle will not accept further innervation (107), but it is possible that denervated mammalian slow-twitch muscle fibers may more readily form new endplates away from the old junctional spots than will fast-twitch fibers. Ectopic endplates have been seen in soleus, which is a purely slow-twitch muscle (107), and in rat and mouse tibialis anterior (155, 325), each containing about 50% slow-twitch muscle fibers (61). In the diaphragm (23, 333) and in sternomastoid (381), nerve implants distant from the old endplate zone found their way back to the old endplates, rather than forming new ones. Even in slow-twitch fibers it is clear that the old endplates retain a special attractiveness, as nerve fibers never grow past them to form ectopic endplates more distally (155).

The slow muscle fibers of the soleus muscle have a low level of ACh sensitivity in the extrajunctional regions (278), as if the contrast between junctional and extrajunctional membrane is not as distinct as in fast muscle fibers. Endplates on slow and fast fibers have characteristically different morphologies (86) and, as mentioned above, they react differently to botulinus and tetanus toxins (87, 90).

Presynaptic terminals of nerves to different effectors have characteristic morphologies; these are preserved following cross-innervation to an inappropriate muscle (92, 182, 223). Hnik et al (182) and Bennett et al (25) crossed nerves between fast and slow muscles in the fowl and found that fast nerves made characteristic en plaque endings on slow muscle fibers, and slow nerves made en grappe endings on fast muscle fibers; in both cases, the result was the reverse of the pattern normally seen in those tissues. The pattern of AChE distribution characteristic of the new nerve could be seen superimposed on the faint remains of the original junctional esterase. Fast muscle fibers in the fowl have a single endplate, while slow fibers have a multiple and distributed innervation (133). Cross-reinnervation of fast muscle by the slow nerve leads to synapse formation only in the region of the old endplate, while fast nerves form multiple synapses on slow muscle fibers, at intervals corresponding to the regular spacing of the original en grappe terminals (25). Mixed reinnervation can give rise to innervation of a slow muscle fiber by both types of nerve, although this situation may be temporary (25, 105, 182).

While it is well established that nerves and effector organs can each induce long term changes in the other, it is less clear to what extent these signals can affect the determination of the differentiated state as opposed to the switching on or off of processes already inherent in the other tissue. One technique applicable to this question is to cross-innervate skeletal muscles with autonomic nerves or autonomic ganglia with motor nerves.

When Landmesser (222, 223) transplanted the frog sartorius muscle to the thorax (so that there was little risk of self-reinnervation) and implanted the vagus nerve into it, the nerve formed functional synaptic connections with the muscle. Vagal fibers ramified through the muscle, forming varicose terminal boutons (quite different from the normal innervation to the muscle) over endplate folds that had previously been contacted by the normal motor innervation. The vagal fibers induced ACh receptors with a greater sensitivity to block by hexamethonium than those on normal muscles, but did not induce acetylcholinesterase (AChE). The ACh receptors that appear following denervation also have properties different from those at normal endplates (26, 104). The conclusion in this case is that the muscle did not alter the properties of the nerve, and the nerve, while able to recognize the muscle and form functional synapses at regions previously defined as synaptic, was able to induce only one change, an alteration of the pharmacology of synaptic ACh receptors. The nerve did not induce junctional cholinesterase or synaptic folds, indicating both that the normal innervation must have specific trophic controls for these components, and that these controls do not rely on the release of ACh. It is interesting in this regard that botulinus toxin, which blocks many of the trophic effects of normal innervation, does not prevent the maintenance of junctional AChE (82, 85, 89, 345, 354).

Several groups have demonstrated the functional innervation of mammalian skeletal muscle by autonomic cholinergic nerves, such as sympathetic preganglionics (180), vagal efferent fibers, [presumably preganglionic (24, 92)], and vagal afferents central to the nodose ganglion (371). Dussardier (92) illustrated the induction of cholinesterase at the vagus-diaphragm muscle junction, showing that in this instance mammalian vagal preganglionics differ from those in the frog (although some mammalian vagal nerve fibers supply striated muscle coating the esophagus). Bennett et al (24) confirmed this and the varicose form of the terminals, and showed that nerve-muscle transmission was possible. McLachlan (personal communication) also implanted skeletal muscle motor nerves into the superior cervical ganglion, and demonstrated the formation of functional synapses. The physiological characteristics of synaptic transmission were those of a motor nerve, as was the structure of the synaptic terminals.

The nictitating membrane of the cat is adrenergically innervated, and consequently has attracted studies of the specificity of innervation. Vera et al (372), Vera & Luco (371), and Lennon et al (233) reinnervated the nictitating membrane with cholinergic autonomic nerves. The muscle contracted on stimulation of the implanted nerve, contraction was inhibited by cholinergic blockers, and the muscle content of specific AChE increased 10-fold (233). The nictitating membrane was not examined for the presence of adrenergic nerve fibers. Thus, all these studies are open to the possible objection that the muscles were reinnervated by extraganglionic adrenergic neurones, and the cholinergic pharmacological responses reflected characteristics of the preganglionic synapses on these nerves. Vera et al (372) saw ganglion cells in the postganglionic trunk, and Matsumura & Koelle (257) successfully innervated the superior cervical ganglion with cholinergic vagal afferent fibers [as used by Vera & Luco (371) to innervate the nictitating membrane] and showed that the nictitating membrane was activated trans-synaptically in this circumstance. Vera et al (372) found that myelinated motor nerve fibers reached the nictitating membrane and formed fine terminal branches on the surface of the smooth muscle fibers. Dibenamine blocked the membrane contraction in response to epinephrine, but not to nerve stimulation. On the other hand, denervation supersensitivity to epinephrine, which is largely due to the loss of adrenergic nerve processes, was abolished, suggesting that adrenergic nerve terminals were present. Accordingly, more experiments are necessary to see if the interpretation of these results can be confirmed, particularly as Ceccarelli et al (55) produced an adrenergic innervation in the nictitating membrane by reinnervating it with preganglionic fibers. They interpret this result as a transformation of properties of cholinergic preganglionic neurones, but it is more likely due to the presence of extraganglionic adrenergic neurones in the postganglionic trunk, and possibly collateral sprouting from ganglion cells lower in the sympathetic chain.

Inductive processes, and specificity in the formation of nerve connections, have been extensively analyzed using sensory nerves (124).

Taste buds in the rat tongue are constantly renewed with a half-life of about 3 days (146, 293). After section of their nerve they rapidly degenerate, and then reappear following reinnervation. There is a recent fine-structural study of this process (119).

Only sensory nerves with a specific gustatory function can induce new tastebuds in the rat tongue. Zalewski (398) found that motor nerves or inappropriate sensory nerves were unable to induce tastebuds, while gustatory nerves, even if diverted from other regions of the tongue, could do so. The ability to differentiate into tastebuds is inherent in tongue germinative epithelial cells, as they can be induced in inappropriate regions of tongue by nerve transplantation.

The inherent regional determination of tongue germinative epithelial cells was further illustrated by Oakley (291, 292), who showed that cross-regenerating nerves between the back and the front of the tongue preserved the original distribution of responsiveness; thus a greater response to salt stimulation was obtained from the front of the tongue and to quinine or saccharine stimulation from the back, regardless of which nerve innervated that region. Thus the nerve did not determine the sensory modality of the receptor. Also, the distribution and number of tastebuds in the different regions of the tongue were preserved, so that the cross-regenerated nerves innervated fewer or a greater number of receptors than usual. It would be useful to have behavioral evidence to confirm the anatomical assumptions underlying these conclusions.

Zalewski extended his studies on the specificity of both nerve and epithelium for the induction of tastebuds by showing that fibers from the central end of the isolated nodose ganglion can exert the trophic effect, and that isolated ganglia can induce tastebuds in tongue epithelium, but not skin, when both tissues are transplanted into the anterior eye chamber (399, 400). An important technical advance has recently been reported by Farbman (102) who managed to induce tastebuds in organ cultures of rat tongue by culturing them with fragments of cranial ganglia IX and X.

The evidence so far obtained from fine-structural studies of the induction of tastebuds is that the process depends on an intimate contact between nerve ending and germinative epithelial cells in the tongue (119). An involvement of the fast transport process in nerve in the trophic effect on tastebuds is suggested by the results of Beidler et al (20) who found that intraperitoneal injection of colchicine into rats led to the disappearance of all tastebuds in the tongue within 20 hrs. The effect was similar to that of denervation, being much faster than could be accounted for by the normal turnover rate of the cells as determined by $^3$H-thymidine incorporation.

Baker & Jacobson (16) rotated a strip of skin running from back to belly of tadpoles, and later examined reflex movements of the adult frog in response to touching the skin graft. Soon after metamorphosis the reflex responses were normal; this situation changed later on, however, so that, for example, touching of skin from the back transplanted to the belly gave rise to reflex movements directed towards the back. The basic question in these experiments is whether nerves connecting with particular regions of skin are thus specified, and then seek out the appropriate central nervous connections, or whether sensory neurones are specified by virtue of the CNS connections, and seek out and maintain contacts with the appropriate region of the skin. The first of these mechanisms applies in the sensory projection of retina to tectum (124, 196), while the second is important in motor nerve reinnervation of skeletal muscle (142). For a misdirected response to occur, the skin grafts had to be larger than 40 mm$^2$ and had to cover a region of overlap between the reflexogenic zones of forelimbs and hindlimbs (16). Baker & Jacobson argue from this that a changeover of central nervous reflex pathways occurs, as this would be most likely to happen when the neurones involved in the reflex were close together in the spinal cord. This, they assume, would be the case when the peripheral reflexogenic fields overlap. This model also helps explain the finding that back to belly reversal was effective, while rostral to caudal skin inversion was ineffective, in invoking inappropriate reflex responses.

## Regeneration of Nerves into the Central Nervous System

The functional reconnection of sensory nerves with their correct positions within the CNS is a process seen only in lower vertebrates. The current state of knowledge concerning regeneration of synapses within the mammalian CNS is reviewed by Guth (145). In brief, most investigations show that a proportion of mammalian nerves will sprout and form new synapses, but in a highly disorganized manner (29, 145). The difference in this regard between higher and lower vertebrates is still largely unexplained, although it seems due to more than the mechanical problems associated with glial scar formation (29).

The now classic example of regeneration of nerves into the CNS is provided by the retinotectal projection of fish and amphibia. In brief summary, retinotectal connections regenerate after section of the optic nerves so that visual function is restored. The connections form so as to project a map of the retina onto the tectum. Thus, if the eye is rotated after nerve section, regeneration occurs in a maladaptive way so that the retinal projection to the tectum is inverted. Two gradients of polarity are established in the retina at an early stage in development; in *Xenopus,* for example, the gradients are established in the early tailbud stage. A mediolateral polarity is established an hour or so before a dorsoventral polarity, so that rotating an eyebud during this brief interval gives rise to a projection in the adult with the mediolateral projection reversed but the dorsoventral projection normal. These experiments are reviewed in great detail by Gaze (124) and Jacobson (196).

The specification of anteroposterior and dorsoventral polarities in the developing retina can occur when the eye has been transplanted to other positions in the body wall (191, 192). The only fine structural change seen to occur at the time of specification is a loss of gap junctions between the cells (80).

A puzzling aspect of retinal positional specification is that it occurs at a time when only a small fraction of the adult number of retinal ganglion cells, in *Xenopus* less than 2%, is present (388). Jacobson (195) suggested that specification occurred at a time just after DNA synthesis in presumptive ganglion cells had ceased; later studies (103, 353) showed that cell division and differentiation into ganglion cells continue during larval life by the addition of cells at the ciliary margin. Jacobson's interpretation of his experimental results implies that specified cells communicate news of this specification to their newly-formed neighbors throughout development. Alternatively, it is possible that specification of germinative cells may also occur, and that this information is conserved in the daughter cells, perhaps in some progressively attentuated way that can give rise to the observed radial gradients.

Gaze & Keating (126) review evidence that the specification of retinal cells is in terms of their positions relative to one another, rather than that the cells are individually labeled in terms of one specific connection locus. Powerful experimental support for this argument comes from the recent experiments of Gaze & Sharma (127), Sharma (335), and Yoon (396, 397) on the retinotectal projection in goldfish. Yoon confirmed the finding (127) that the rostral half tectum of a goldfish acquires an orderly projection from the whole retina following excision of the caudal half tectum. A similar compression of the projection took place when the tectum was sectioned and a tantalum barrier was inserted between rostral and caudal halves, even though the optic nerve was left intact so that innervation remained intact in the rostral half and only the caudal half was denervated. Finally, when the barrier was removed the original projection was restored. This experiment demonstrates that retinotectal connections can reform in the adult goldfish, and that the connections between retinal ganglion cells and optic tectal cells are organized in terms of the relative positions of cells within the range of available tectum, and not in a 1:1 matching of particular individual cells in retina and tectum respectively.

The pattern of use of the eyes does not affect the formation and maintenance of the primary visual projection to the CNS, but maintenance of intratectal projections requires symmetrical stimulation of both eyes during metamorphosis (197).

## Collateral Sprouting

As a general rule, partial denervation of a tissue leads to sprouting in the remaining nerve fibers so that they reinnervate some or all of the denervated cells. The older literature is reviewed by Edds (94). This phenomenon is well known in muscle (143), in sympathetic ganglia (147, 226, 285, 387), in autonomic effector tissues (98), within the central nervous system (240, 282, 316, 351), and in the skin (384).

There are two aspects to the phenomenon: (a) an inhibition of sprouting and hyperinnervation, associated with the normal presence of functional synapses, and (b) the active attraction of innervation by denervated tissues so that the presynaptic fibers in another muscle or in a neighboring or contralateral region of the brain will sprout and send a fiber tract into a region from which they normally are absent. Aguilar et al (1) found that application of colchicine to a salamander nerve influenced its neighbors to sprout and form connections within the peripheral territory of the treated nerve despite its continued function. They suggest that fast axonal transport is required to carry trophic factors to the periphery for maintainance of normal fields of innervation of both muscle and skin. Dunn (91) has shown that the extension of nerve fibers growing out from a sensory ganglion in tissue culture is mutually inhibited by contact among the fibers. His system may provide a model for some of the in vivo phenomena.

Raisman (315) found that local denervation of a small region of the brain provoked collateral sprouting from some of the remaining nerves, giving rise to new synaptic terminals in place of those that degenerated. The new terminals appeared inappropriate with respect to both position and neurotransmitter, as judged by their content of dense core vesicles. These fibers formerly formed synapses only on the dendrites of cells in the medial septal nucleus, but after degeneration of some terminals on the cell body they sprouted to form synapses in an abnormal region of the same cell. The postsynaptic cell must always have had the capacity to form the appropriate receptors on at least a part of its surface, although it is not known if they appeared in the region of new innervation or if the new synapses were capable of transmitting.

Moore et al (282) placed lesions in the same system and later used fluorescence histochemistry to locate adrenergic fibers. They saw a great increase in fluorescent varicosities and suggested that the new terminals seen by Raisman may be adrenergic. A similar increase in the number of fluorescent varicosities is seen in the dorsal nucleus of the lateral geniculate body following unilateral ablation of the visual cortex (351). These authors suggest that evidence for similar processes elsewhere in the brain may be lacking because no suitable technique is available for demonstrating them, rather than because such processes do not occur in other than adrenergic nerves.

The embryological process leading to the spatial separation of different classes of afferents on a cell surface may in part depend on the timing of their arrival at the postsynaptic cell. Gottlieb & Cowan (137) used autoradiography to map the projections of hippocampal neurones onto cells of the dentate gyrus: the earlier the cells were formed, the greater the number of synapses they received from the ipsilateral, rather than the contralateral, hippocampus. They suggested that when the earlier dentate cells formed, only fibers from the hippocampus of the same side were present; later, fibers from the opposite side reached the dentate gyrus so that terminals from both sides competed for the available synaptic sites. The total number of sites on each cell was constant, so that some other mechanism must operate in order to restrict a particular class of afferents to a particular region of the cell surface.

## Cells in Tissue Culture

The obvious technical difficulties involved in studying the development of the nervous system at the cellular level arise from the three-dimensional structure of the brain and from the great variety of cell types and morphologies. R. G. Harrison (168) invented the technique of tissue culture in order to avoid such difficulties and to answer fundamental questions concerning the nature of nerve cells and the mechanism of axon growth. Subsequent work has been based on the promise that tissue culture would give fundamental insights into nervous development, but has mostly failed to yield the promised understanding. Most of the literature is concerned with demonstrating that nerve cells can be kept alive in tissue culture and that they can form functional synapses on one another or on effector cells such as skeletal muscle fibers. So far, little experimental work has been devoted to uncovering the mechanisms that underly the interactions or the various inductive phenomena observed in culture. This situation is changing, and experimental work should become much more common during the next few years, now that materials for tissue culture work are readily available commercially and the techniques are standardized and easily accessible.

Important achievements so far include the demonstrations that ordered cellular relations and some kind of complex electrical activity can develop in small fragments of cultured CNS tissue (52, 64, 391), showing controls for these processes to be intrinsic, and that cultures from a mouse neurological mutant exhibit a derangement in development similar to that which occurs in the mouse (390). DeLong & Sidman (75) have extended this work to the cellular level. They demonstrated the histiotypic reaggregation of dissociated embryonic brain cells associated with a critical stage in their development and showed that cells from the mouse neurological mutant, *reeler*, have a particular deficit in this process. Further work on the age dependence of aggregative behavior is reported by Garber & Moscona (123). Other important findings are that functional synapses will form between cultured fragments of spinal cord and peripheral tissues such as dorsal root ganglia or skeletal muscle (64, 65, 202), that synaptic transmission can develop between nerve and muscle cells cultured in the presence of curare (62, 68, 297), that synaptic structures are seen in cerebral explants exposed to lidocaine to prevent action potentials (280), and that synapses can develop between explants taken from different species (66, 307, 308).

Most of the work quoted above concerns primary explants, small pieces of tissue with some degree of organization present prior to being placed in culture. Disaggregated nerve cells can also be maintained in culture, where they will grow axons and stay alive in the absence of glial cells (47, 59, 237, 295). Nerve cells from disaggregated spinal cords can form functional synapses with one another (67, 112, 304) and with muscle cells (112, 322).

## Clonal Nerve Cell Lines

Primary nerve cell cultures have the disadvantages (a) that they usually contain a mixture of cell types which are sometimes difficult to distinguish from one another; (b) that it is difficult to provide homogeneous material for biochemical analysis; and (c) that they are not reproducible from group to group. Clonal lines offer the opportunity of overcoming some of these problems; a number of clonal lines derived from nerve cell tumors are now available and have been used to study some aspects of synapse formation (160, 162, 349). Results reported in the literature so far have come from the C1300 mouse neuroblastoma (13, 289, 330).

Clonal lines derived from this tumor show many of the properties of normal nerve cells: they grow axons, produce action potentials (289), are sensitive to ACh (161, 288), and synthesize enzymes used in transmitter synthesis (8). When mixed with a cloned line of rat skeletal muscle cells (394) they extend processes and contact the muscle fibers (162). The muscle fibers have a diffuse sensitivity to ACh except at a point of contact with a neuroblastoma process, where the sensitivity is 5–40X greater than in the extrajunctional regions. Properly developed nerve-muscle transmission has not been seen in this system, but the raised sensitivity to ACh at points of contact is seen at developing nerve-muscle junctions both in vivo (79) and in vitro (202). Botulinus toxin prevents the nerve-muscle interaction (A. J. Harris, unpublished results) as it does in vivo (81, 381), although it is not toxic to the cells and does not reverse the interaction once it has occurred. Thus, insofar as it has been tested, the neuroblastoma-muscle system provides a model for one of the processes involved in normal synapse formation (160).

Miledi (267, 269) has noted in muscle a regional association between sensitivity to ACh and ability to accept innervation. The neuroblastoma-muscle system provided an opportunity to see if this relation is causal (349). Nerve and muscle cells were incubated together in the presence of α-neurotoxin from Naja naja, which binds powerfully, specifically, and reversibly to ACh receptors on the muscle (302). After several days' incubation, the formation of new ACh receptors was halted with a protein synthesis blocker; a high concentration of curare was then added to remove the α-neurotoxin by competitive interaction, and thus to unmask receptors that had been synthesised and incorporated into muscle membrane. The receptors were found to be localized to points of neuroblastoma contact. Further, neuroblastoma cells from a clone low in choline acetylase were grown for several generations in the presence of an inhibitor of this enzyme, and then mixed with muscle in the presence of both the inhibitor and the receptor blocker. Even under these conditions, where the nerve cells had no store of ACh and could not synthesize more ACh, and the muscles could not be activated by ACh, nerve-muscle contacts with a localized concentration of ACh receptors were formed. Thus there is no evidence that either ACh release from nerve or the presence of functional ACh receptors on a muscle surface is a necessary precondition for nerve-muscle synapse formation. The ACh receptors could still be associated with some property of the muscle membrane which influences the process by which the ingrowing nerve recognizes the previous endplate sites (223, 267, 381). The availability of a specific agent for preventing the interaction makes it hopeful that the model system will provide more information about the mechanism of the early intercellular reactions that precede synapse formation.

## MECHANISMS OF INDUCTIVE ACTIONS IN NERVE TISSUE

### Nerve Growth Factor

The only well characterised nerve-inducing agent is the nerve growth factor (NGF) isolated from some mouse sarcomas, snake venoms, and adult male mouse submaxillary glands (238, 340).

NGF causes an outgrowth of nerve fibers from sensory and sympathetic ganglion cells, both in culture and in vivo. It appears to be essential for the normal development of these cells, as application of NGF-antiserum to newborn animals causes most sympathetic ganglion cells to degenerate (350). It also induces differentiation of ganglion cells from their stem cells, both in vivo (37) and in vitro (40).

The cellular locus of action of NGF is not known, as it induces a number of different events that are experimentally separable; among these are a general stimulation of RNA and protein synthesis, including microtubule protein (179) and tyrosine hydroxylase (174), and an increase in the rate of neurite extension, which can occur even if RNA synthesis is blocked, but which depends on the maintenance of protein synthesis (300). Recent suggestions that its effects are mediated by cyclic AMP are not supported by Hier et al (179) who found that dibutyryl cyclic AMP will stimulate neurite outgrowth in the absence of protein synthesis, while NGF will not.

Treatment with NGF-antiserum kills only young cells and is ineffective in adult animals. Schucker (332) has made a fine-structural study of cells treated with antiserum and suggests that its effect is to prevent synthesis of ribosomal RNA.

The site or sites of production of NGF and its regulation during development are unknown. While it apparently is not essential for the maintenance of adult sympathetic ganglion cells, they still respond to its action (11); thus it may be effective throughout life. Normal development of sympathetic ganglion cells in vivo depends on their innervation; section of the presynaptic nerves in 4-day-old mice prevents any further increase in the number of ganglion cells or of their content of tyrosine hydroxylase or monamine oxidase (37). Administration of NGF to mice with decentralized ganglia can restore the normal increases in tyrosine hydroxylase and cell numbers, and even raise these well above the normal, but these values are, however, always higher in innervated ganglia treated with NGF. Essentially similar results were obtained from rats by Thoenen et al (361). NGF does not restore the development of monamine oxidase activity, showing that this is separately controlled by nerve terminals (37). Thus, while it is possible that NGF is synaptically released, it cannot account for all the effects of innervation. This distinction between the effects of innervation and of NGF is heightened by the finding that adrenal medullary cells are not affected by NGF (12) even though they depend upon their innervation for normal development (303).

## Axoplasmic Transport

The demonstration that several different nervous inductive processes can be selectively disrupted by halting the fast component of axoplasmic transport (Table 2), without preventing the normal electrical activity of the nerve, makes knowledge of the mechanisms of axoplasmic transport and the nature of the substances transported essential to understanding the nervous inductive processes.

"Axoplasmic flow" is a term originally coined by Weiss and his co-workers to describe the bulk flow of axoplasm in nerve cells from cell body to periphery, at a rate of a few mm per day. Superimposed on this background are a number of more specific transport systems operating both towards and away from the cell body. Several hundred papers describing these processes have been published in the last five years; recent reviews and symposia include Dahlström (72), Lasek (227), Friede & Seitelberger (118), and Lubinska (242).

If radioactive amino acids are taken up by a nerve cell body they may be incorporated into protein, some of which will be transported down the axon at a fast rate. In mammals, this rate is of the order of 400 mm/day (294). Material transported at this fast rate is largely particulate, and the transport mechanism appears to be associated with neurotubules (28, 212, 234). The fast transport is blocked by colchicine or vinblastine, substances that can bind to microtubule protein. Low concentrations of these substances will block the fast transport without causing obvious disruption to microtubules and without irreversibly damaging the neuron as a whole (115, 203, 215, 301). Cytochalasin-B also blocks fast transport, but the significance of this action is not yet understood (69).

The materials carried by the fast transport system have been best characterized in adrenergic neurons (72), where they include both large and small dense core vesicles, with which are associated norepinephrine and some of the enzymes involved in its metabolism (199). Acetylcholinesterase, which is found in both adrenergic and cholinergic nerves, is carried by the fast transport system, but choline acetylase, which is thought to be a soluble enzyme, moves with the slow axoplasmic flow (301). Few of the other protein components carried by the fast transport system have yet been identified.

**Table 2** Effects of blocking fast transport

| Reference | Preparation | Agent | Effect | Control |
|---|---|---|---|---|
| 184 | rat sciatic-nerve | colchicine | ACh supersensitivity and TTX-resistant action potentials in muscle | denervation |
| 183 | rat sciatic nerve | colchicine | no reduction in twitch amplitude in m. gastrocnemius | untreated |
| 6 | rat sciatic nerve | colchicine vinblastine | nerve-muscle transmission retained; Lowered resting potential; TTX-resistant action potentials; Atrophy | denervation |
| 194 | rat spinal cord | colchicine | flaccid paralysis of hind limbs; Schwann cell reaction; Some nerve degeneration later | |
| 331 | cat spinal cord | colchicine | reduction or block of synaptic transmission to motoneurones; Block of axoplasmic flow along dendrites | |
| 1 | salamander somatic nerves | colchicine | collateral sprouting by neighboring fibers | axotomy |
| 187 | adult newt forearm | colchicine | retraction of presynaptic terminals at nerve-muscle junction; Loss of postjunctional folds | |
| 311 | postganglionic trunk from chick ciliary ganglion | colchicine | chromatolysis; Depression of synaptic transmission through ganglion | axotomy |
| 158 | hypothalamus | colchicine | detachment of synaptic terminals from nerve cell soma; Glial reactions | chromatolytic reaction to axotomy |
| 73 | rat superior cervical ganglion | vinblastine | degeneration of postganglionic adrenergic nerve endings | ganglionectomy |
| 71, 306 | intraocular injection in pigeons | colchicine | enlarged synaptic vesicles in optic nerve terminals; depression of synaptic transmission | nerve section |

Other substances said to be transported by the fast system include RNA (44) and gangliosides (116). The physiological role of RNA in peripheral nerve is still controversial. Synaptosomes from cerebral cortex incorporate labeled amino acids into protein (283). Some of this synthesis is clearly due to mitochondria, and this point is not debated. Ramirez et al (317) describe a cell-free synaptosomal membrane system for protein synthesis that shares many of the properties of the mitochondrial system, but is clearly distinct from it. The three proteins which are synthesized are located in the junctional complex; this is the Triton X-100 insoluble material associated with regions of contact between pre- and postsynaptic membrane. The authors state that this system and the mitochondrial system together account for all the protein synthesis in synaptosomes. Other groups propose the existence of a more conventional system (131), but this may reflect the contamination of their preparations with cellular components. Even in Ramirez et al's (317) preparation the synthesis could depend on the presence of the fragment of postjunctional membrane attached to the junctional complex. Whether or not extramitochondrial protein synthesis is a property of normal nerve terminals, there is general agreement that the great majority of nerve terminal proteins are supplied by axoplasmic transport from the cell body; about one-third are carried in the various components of the fast transport system and two-thirds by slow axoplasmic flow (204).

Mitochondria, and their associated enzymes, move at a rather slower rate than other components of fast transport, although they may rely on the same mechanism for movement, i.e. an interaction with neurotubules (203, 206, 212, 301).

A number of glycoproteins are carried from the cell body by fast transport, as demonstrated by movement of labeled aminosugars (95, 117, 205). Other glycoproteins found in nerve terminals are formed from the local glycosylation of proteins (401) by nerve terminal glycoprotein:glycosyl transferases (45).

The rate of fast transport is not regulated by nervous activity (139, 246, 290) or by any other known physiological factor. On the other hand, the amount of material transported is increased by chronic nervous activity as the result of a greater rate of synthesis of the transported substances in the cell body (139, 246, 290). Ochs (294) suggests that a further possible control is present at the point of transfer of transported substances from cell cytoplasm to axonal transport system. Fast transport depends on the local integrity of the transport system, so that local blockage over a few millimeters of nerve prevents passage of material past that point. Blockage can experimentally be induced by interfering with oxidative metabolism (294), by local application of vinblastine or colchicine (95), or by local anesthetics such as procaine or lidocaine (9, 111).

Fast axoplasmic transport carries material both towards and away from the cell body. The most direct evidence for this statement comes from experiments where horseradish peroxidase or Evans blue-labeled albumin was taken up by nerve terminals and transported to the cell bodies (216–218, 228). After local blockage of fast transport by ligation or by blocking metabolism, transported material accumulates both above and below the block (72). Bray et al (48) and Partlow et al (301) present evidence for a reversal of the direction of movement of axoplasmic components when they reach a nerve terminal or an artificial ligation. Kirkpatrick et al (212) and Berlinrood et al (28) filmed particle movements in isolated segments of nerve and saw that while the majority of particles moved towards the nerve terminals, others moved in the opposite direction.

While most studies of the movement of labeled proteins along nerves have indicated that the proteins accumulate in nerve terminals and are not taken up by the postsynaptic cells (42, 43, 206, 329), it has been suggested (138, 287) that this negative result is due to obscuring of a small amount of intercellular transfer by high levels of background radioactivity. The use of $^3$H-proline, which gives much lower background contamination than $^3$H-leucine, indicates that protein may migrate trans-synaptically in fish and mouse visual systems. This interpretation relies on assumptions about the anatomy of the systems used, apart from the possibility of protein degradation and reincorporation of label, so that more work is required before these results can be accepted. If correct, they bear obvious relevance to mechanisms of nerve trophic action. Proteins involved with transmitter packaging and synthesis are released from adrenergic nerves following nerve stimulation. A similar release of proteins, as yet unidentified with respect to function, has been seen following stimulation of the motor nerves to skeletal muscle (286).

## Inductive Actions of Transmitter Substances

The possibility that ACh is the unique trophic factor for the maintenance of skeletal muscle is now conclusively disproved (6, 184, 241, 349). The enzymes tyrosine hydroxylase and dopamine-$\beta$-hydroxylase are induced in sympathetic ganglia as the result of an increase in synaptic stimulation (281, 284, 360), and this effect is prevented by ganglion blocking drugs (284). Activity of these enzymes in cultured ganglia is increased as the result of depolarization with potassium (248, 342) leading to the suggestion that postsynaptic depolarization alone will account for the effects of synaptic transmission. Unfortunately, potassium was added to the cultured ganglia during the first 24–48 hrs of incubation, so that the presynaptic nerve terminals were still present and functional for a part of the experimental period. The concentrations of potassium were adequate to induce synaptic release of ACh (78), so that these experiments cannot be clearly interpreted. Keen & McLean (210) produced a protein synthesis-dependent rise in ganglionic dopamine-$\beta$-hydroxylase by incubating rat superior cervical ganglia with dibutyryl cyclic AMP, indicating that a rise in intracellular 3',5'-cyclic AMP may be the intermediary in the effects of synaptic transmission on neurotransmitter-synthesizing enzymes.

Norepinephrine is involved in protein synthesis-dependent regulation of enzyme activities via its action on $\beta$-receptors in some tissues (74); in such cases its action is mediated by 3',5'-cyclic AMP. ACh will induce tyrosine aminotransferase in liver (35); again, its action appears to rely on some intermediary agent.

A number of reports indicate that nerve cell RNA or protein synthesis can be enhanced by synaptic stimulation, but not by direct electrical stimulation (30, 130, 134, 309). This work is much less convincing than the demonstration of protein synthesis-dependent changes in enzyme activity, as it suffers the technical drawback that possible changes in the specific activity of precursor pools, which may result from electrical or synaptic stimulation, are not assayed. McBride & Klingman (259) found an apparent increase in tissue levels of free amino acids as a result of stimulating isolated superior cervical ganglia from rats. Wilson & Berry (389) concluded that an apparent effect of stimulation on RNA synthesis in an *Aplysia* neuron was due to a change in specific activity of precursor uridine. Lux et al (246) partly overcame the problem of not knowing the specific activity of the precursor pool by intracellular injection of labeled amino acids into spinal motoneurones; they then found that incorporation of label into protein increased as the result of direct electrical stimulation of the cell.

The transmitter analogues 6-hydroxydopamine (362) and 5,6-dihydroxytryptamine (18) are extremely toxic to norepinephrine- and serotonin-containing neurones, respectively, causing degeneration of peripheral nerve varicosities. When these substances are administered to young animals, the effects may be permanent with a total loss of nerve cells (10).

The peripheral terminations of adrenergic neurons may be rather labile, when compared, for example, with somatic nerves. Blocking fast axoplasmic transport leads to their rapid degeneration (73), whereas motor nerve terminals survive two weeks or more of chronic blockage (6). However, the destructive effects of the transmitter analogues appear to be due not to an action on a physiological control process normally affected by norepinephrine or 5-HT, respectively, but to intracellular oxidation of the analogues to form toxic derivatives (362).

## Role of Activity in Maintaining Effector Organs

Many of the changes that follow denervation of an effector may simply be due to disuse, rather than to loss of a long term function of nerve contact. Different techniques have been used to interrupt various aspects of nerve function while leaving synaptic contacts structurally intact, the most informative of these being the use of colchicine or vinblastine to block fast axoplasmic transport without otherwise affecting nerve impulse propagation or causing the transmitter release to drop to subthreshold levels (Table 2). The effect of this treatment is in many ways similar to that of denervation.

A variety of techniques have been used to produce ACh hypersensitivity in skeletal muscle in the presence of an intact nerve (Table 1). Simply cutting the nerve is not normally adequate, as in most systems the nerve terminals degenerate before an increase in sensitivity can be noted. An exception is seen with frog nerve-muscle preparations maintained in organ culture (165), where nerve terminal survival is prolonged and extrajunctional ACh receptors appear in the presence of an intact and functional nerve terminal (159). Tower (365) introduced the technique of isolating the region of spinal cord from which the motor nerves to a particular group of muscles were derived, and so produced long-lasting disuse of a particular muscle. The muscles atrophied, as after denervation, but Johns & Thesleff (201) found that, while extrajunctional ACh sensitivity close to an endplate was increased, there was no generalized hypersensitivity of muscle fibers. It is not certain that nerve impulses are totally absent from such preparations. A similar spreading of endplate sensitivity without generalized supersensitivity is seen in the relatively disused muscles excised from hibernating hamsters (375).

Total disuse of nerve terminals has been produced by the chronic application of local anesthetics or diphtheria toxin to a segment of nerve above the muscle, thus creating a local block of nerve conduction without otherwise interfering with nerve terminal structure or function. Robert & Oester (323, 324) saw neither fibrillation nor an increase of ACh sensitivity in rabbit muscles subjected to nerve conduction block for up to 14 days. Lomo & Rosenthal (241) obtained the opposite result when they applied Robert & Oester's technique to rats; both fibrillation and ACh sensitivity developed with similar time course and to similar degree as after complete denervation. Artificial stimulation of the nerve below the block prevented or reversed the effects of the nerve blockade, as did direct stimulation of denervated muscle.

Albuquerque et al (6) used Robert & Oester's technique to apply vinblastine or colchicine chronically to a segment of sciatic nerve in rats. This treatment produced no obvious muscular paralysis, and action potentials could propagate past the nerve cuff to initiate transmitter release and muscle contraction. The pattern of use of the operated limbs is not described, but, as there was a considerable muscle weight loss, the muscles may not have been naturally activated to any great extent during application of the drug. Membrane depolarization, ACh supersensitivity, and tetrodotoxin-resistant action potentials appeared essentially as after denervation. The authors suggest that a neural factor other than ACh must normally pass down the nerve and maintain the normal state of the muscle. Hofmann & Thesleff (184) had a result similar to that of Albuquerque et al (6) when they injected colchicine into rat sciatic nerve. They obtained the same effect when they blocked transmitter release with β-bungarotoxin (57), and so concluded that either the toxin prevented release of trophic factors from nerve, or trophic factors and muscle activity both are required for the prevention of denervation-like changes. Lomo & Rosenthal's (241) local anesthetic treatment most likely affected fast transport as well as action potential conduction (9, 111). Thus, the results of their experiments, where denervation-like effects were reversed by both direct and indirect stimulation of muscle, are best reconciled with those of Hofmann & Thesleff and Albuquerque et al by assuming that maintenance of the normal state of muscles depends both on muscle contraction and on the application of some nerve-released factor which may also be diffusely present in blood.

A different form of evidence for the participation of the fast transport process in nerve terminal function comes from the relation between the length of a cut nerve and the time of onset of postsynaptic denervation phenomena. In skeletal muscle, for example, the earliest of these phenomena, the local depolarization of the endplate that later spreads laterally to involve the whole muscle fiber, occurs before degenerative changes are seen in the nerve terminal, with a latency that depends on the length of cut nerve (5). Thus the local depolarization clearly does not result from inactivity of the muscle: it may occur in one muscle fiber within two hours of close section of the nerve, but not in another fiber several mm away within the same muscle even six hours after nerve section. The mechanism presumably involves a transport process within the nerve whose components are exhausted at a rate of several cm per day. Harris & Thesleff (166) report a similar effect on the development of

TTX-resistant action potentials. The time a nerve terminal survives following axotomy depends on the length of cut nerve left attached to it (275). This presumably is the result of the exhaustion of components normally supplied to the terminal by fast axoplasmic transport. Paradoxically, terminal survival is prolonged if the transport process is slowed with colchicine or vinblastine (245), perhaps reflecting the supply of a smaller amount of material for a longer time.

The compensatory hypertrophy that follows removal of one of a pair of autonomic effectors seems solely due to the changed pattern of use and not to a more indirect effect of its innervation (19). Similar changes are seen in organs that rely on hormonal or other forms of control.

The pattern of use of CNS synapses during critical periods in their development determines their functional state for the rest of the animal's life (38, 189). Whether changes of a similar nature occur throughout life in other parts of the brain, for example, as the basis of some aspects of memory (251), is a completely open question. So too is the problem of the relation between usage and survival of individual neurones and the cells or tissues they innervate.

### Synapse Formation and Cell Contacts

There is general agreement about the fine-structural details of most of the events seen during the formation of nerve-muscle junctions in embryos (181, 211, 356). Fine unmyelinated axons are present in the muscle at an early stage, even when the muscle is composed mostly of unfused myoblasts. These nerve processes occur in bundles enclosed as a group by a Schwann cell wrapping; the nerves contain neurotubules, neurofilaments, and mitochondria. Where nerves approach muscle cells they contain fewer neurotubules, and both clear and dense core vesicles are present. Slightly later, nerve and muscle are separated by a gap of 1000–3000 Å, with basal lamina material interposed, and both pre- and postsynaptic membrane thickenings can be seen. Kelly & Zacks (211) describe an intermediate event, where nerve and muscle become closely apposed, possibly forming a gap junction. This was looked for, but not seen, in a study of newly formed nerve-muscle junctions in adult muscles by Saito & Zacks (325). Junctions of this kind were observed by Sheffield & Fischman (336) to precede synapse formation in the developing chick retina. They are rarely seen in developing spinal cord in *Xenopus* (171). Fischbach (112) has described electrical coupling between a small proportion of nerve and muscle cells forming synapses in tissue culture.

Once the pre- and postsynaptic thickenings with interposed basal lamina have been formed, further development of the synapse involves enlargement of this area of apposition, together with formation of primary and then secondary synaptic folds. Acetylcholinesterase appears before these folds have formed. The only opportunity for direct transfer of cytoplasmic components between nerve and muscle is during the period of gap junction formation, if indeed this is a normal feature of synapse formation. Any other inductive process must rely on local diffusion between the different cell types. Nerve terminals will take up proteins from the extracellular fluid (216, 217); pinocytotic vesicles are a feature of muscle cell membranes, suggesting that muscles can take up material in a similar way.

The position of the nerve-muscle contact is maintained by extracellular cementing substances; if these are digested with collagenase or proteases the nerve terminal is detached (263). The efficiency with which synaptic contacts are normally maintained is indicated by the fact that junctional complexes survive the strenuous treatments used to form synaptosomes.

The role of the dense core vesicles that are present in developing or regenerating presynaptic terminals (181, 211, 244, 356) is obscure. They may contain trophic substances (244) or catecholamines. Csillik (70) described a band of paraformalde-hyde-induced fluorescence extending across the endplate zone of newborn rat diaphragm muscles, which he suggested was due to 5-HT contained in teloglial cells.

Several nerve processes form synapses within each developing endplate zone. These processes come from different axons, as endplate potentials recorded from muscle fibers in newborn rats or kittens have several components that can be separated by their different thresholds to nerve stimulation (15, 318).

Landmesser & Pilar (224) made a combined physiological and electronmicroscopic investigation of synapse formation in the chick ciliary ganglion. The earliest structurally recognizable stage was a thickening of presumptive pre- and postsynaptic membranes together with the presence of a few vesicles in the presynaptic terminal. The ganglion cells at this early stage had many processes, so that a dense and tangled neuropil was formed. Most of the neuropil was withdrawn once synapses had formed; thus its function may have been to increase the chance that ingrowing fibers could make their appropriate connection. Perisomatic processes on cerebellar Purkinje cells behave in a similar way (7). The ganglion cells made connections with their peripheral effectors before the preganglionic fibers made synapses, suggesting that their specification came from the periphery.

Transmission in the ciliary ganglion is of particular interest because in the adult the ganglionic synapse functions both chemically and electrically. If a brief period of electrical coupling is a common feature of developing synapses, and is perhaps required to induce the pre- and postsynaptic specializations that precede the development of function, then the ciliary ganglion would seem to be aberrant, since this coupling does not disappear at the normal time. In fact, the opposite occurs: chemical transmission is seen before any signs of electrical coupling. Transient electrical coupling at an early stage would not have been detected in this study.

The development of synaptic function in rat cerebellum was studied by Woodward et al (393). Purkinje cells fired spontaneously before synapses had formed on their surface, and the rate of firing could be decreased or increased by iontophoretic application of various neurotransmitter substances, showing that receptors were present before synapses had formed. The distribution of the receptors, either before or after synapse formation, is not known. Synaptic transmission was found at a time when few synapses could be seen and young synapses had very few synaptic vesicles, as in the chick ciliary ganglion (224).

While the gross features of interneuronal connections are constant from animal to animal, evidence is now accumulating for a considerable degree of variability at a fine level. For example, Macagno et al (247) compared different individuals within a clone of *Daphnia* with respect to their nervous systems. They found that individual nerve cells had a constant position and made relatively constant contributions to their synaptic connections with other cells, but the fine details of nerve branching and arrangement of synaptic boutons were variable between animals or between paired symmetrical structures in the same animal. Differences in dendritic branching patterns and connectivity, correlated with different patterns of rearing, have been noted in mammals (63, 373).

## Fields and Gradients

The experiments described above on retinotectal connections in fish and amphibia, and those of Hibbard (178) on the recognition of axial gradients by growing nerve fibers, make it clear that mechanisms for setting up and recognizing two- or three-dimensional coordinate systems must play an important part in the organization of developing neural tissue. The physical nature of these gradients is unknown. An important experimental analysis of possible mechanisms is presented by Lawrence et al (230).

## Derangements in Inductive Processes

Disturbances of inductive processes resulting from application of toxins, from disease, or from genetic lesions offer promise as a means of determining the normal mechanisms of these processes. The usefulness of botulinus toxin as a tool for dissecting nerve-muscle and nerve terminal-neuronal soma relations is noted above; tetanus toxin has some rather similar actions (90, 264).

Many neurological mutants of mice are available and several have apparent lesions in neural inductive processes: *jimpy* is deficient in CNS myelination (392); *reeler* shows a derangement in positioning of granule cells in cerebral cortex and cerebellum (75); *wobbler* appears to have a defect in axoplasmic flow (31); *med* shows a failure in the development and maintenance of neuromuscular junctions (88); and in *staggerer,* granule cells in the cerebellar cortex fail to form recognizable synaptic contacts on Purkinje cell dendritic spines, although they form normal synaptic contacts with basket and stellate cells, and the Purkinje cells receive synapses from other cell types (341). Some forms of muscular dystrophy, in both man (261) and mouse (167, 229), may also primarily be due to a neural lesion. Neurological mutants of *Drosophila* are also being investigated electrophysiologically (193) and by tissue culture (334).

## CONCLUSION

The most important recent advance in this field is the finding that the fast transport component of axoplasmic flow is part of the mechanism by which nerves maintain a number of their trophic actions. The materials carried, their regulation, and the manner in which they affect other cells are still largely unanswered questions.

A second class of mechanism (which in some circumstances may be affected by substances delivered by fast axoplasmic transport) is that of surface contact. Contact phenomena are thought to be important in directing synapse formation and have been shown to have a role in the specific reaggregation of dissociated embryonic brain cells. Recent advances in glycoprotein chemistry may well help progress in this field.

Tissue culture, after a lapse of many years, is rapidly growing in vigor as a research tool for the study of neural development. This progress is greatly aided by recent developments in the techniques of membrane chemistry.

Neurological mutants, particularly of *Drosophila* and mice, are becoming increasingly important as tools for dissecting mechanisms of long term interactions between nerve cells and other tissues. The replication in tissue culture of some of the defective actions is helping in this type of analysis.

ACKNOWLEDGMENTS

I thank my wife, Jocelyn Harris, for constant support during the compilation of this review. Work in the author's laboratory is supported by the New Zealand Medical Research Council.

*Literature Cited*

1. Aguilar, C. E., Bisby, M. A., Diamond, J. 1972. Impulses and the transfer of trophic factors in nerves. *J. Physiol. London* 226:60–61P
2. Aitken, J. T. 1950. Growth of nerve implants in voluntary muscle. *J. Anat.* 84:38–49
3. Aitken, J. T. 1965. Problems of reinnervation of muscle. In *Degeneration pattern in the nervous system*, ed. M. Singer, J. P. Schade. *Progr. Brain Res.* 14:232–62
4. Albuquerque, E. X., McIsaac, R. J. 1970. Fast and slow mammalian muscles after denervation. *Exp. Neurol.* 26:183–202
5. Albuquerque, E. X., Schuh, F. T., Kauffman, F. C. 1971. Early membrane depolarization of the fast mammalian muscle after denervation. *Pfluegers Arch.* 328:36–50
6. Albuquerque, E. X., Warnick, J. E., Tasse, J. R., Sansone, F. M. 1972. Effects of vinblastine and colchicine on neural regulation of the fast and slow skeletal muscles of the rat. *Exp. Neurol.* 37:607–34
7. Altman, J., Anderson, W. J. 1972. Experimental reorganization of the cerebellar cortex. I. Morphological effects of elimination of all microneurons with prolonged X-irradiation started at birth. *J. Comp. Neurol.* 146:355–406
8. Amano, T., Richelson, E., Nirenberg, M. 1972. Neurotransmitter synthesis by

neuroblastoma clones. *Proc. Nat. Acad. Sci. USA* 69:258–63
9. Anderson, K. E., Edström, A. 1973. Effects of nerve blocking agents on fast axonal transport of proteins in frog sciatic nerves *in vitro*. *Brain Res.* 50:125–34
10. Angeletti, P. U., Levi-Montalcini, R. 1970. Sympathetic nerve cell destruction in newborn mammals by 6-hydroxydopamine. *Proc. Nat. Acad. Sci. USA* 65:114–21
11. Angeletti, P. U., Levi-Montalcini, R., Caramia, F. 1971. Ultrastructural changes in sympathetic neurons of newborn and adult mice treated with nerve growth factor. *J. Ultrastruct. Res.* 36:24–36
12. Angeletti, P. U., Levi-Montalcini, R., Kettler, R., Thoenen, H. 1972. Comparative studies on the effect of the nerve growth factor on sympathetic ganglia and adrenal medulla in newborn rats. *Brain Res.* 44:197–206
13. Augusti-Tocco, G., Sato, G. 1969. Establishment of functional clonal lines of neurons from mouse neuroblastoma. *Proc. Nat. Acad. Sci. USA* 64:311–15
14. Axelsson, J., Thesleff, S. 1959. A study of supersensitivity in denervated mammalian skeletal muscle. *J. Physiol. London* 147:178–93
15. Bagust, J., Lewis, D. M., Westerman, R. A. 1973. Polyneuronal innervation of kitten skeletal muscle. *J. Physiol. London* 229:241–55

16. Baker, R. E., Jacobson, M. 1970. Development of reflexes from skin grafts in *Rana pipiens:* Influence of size and position of grafts. *Develop. Biol.* 22: 476–94

17. Barker, D., Ip, M. C. 1966. Sprouting and degeneration of mammalian motor axons in normal and de-afferentated skeletal muscle. *Proc. Roy. Soc. London B* 163:538–54

18. Baumgarten, H. G., Lachenmayer, L., Schlossberger, H. G. 1972. Evidence for a degeneration of indoleamine containing nerve terminals in rat brain, induced by 5,6-dihydroxytryptamine. *Z. Zellforsch. Microsk. Anat.* 125:553–69

19. Bazerque, P. M., Meiss, A., Moroni, M. N. 1971. Autonomous denervation and salivary glands hypertrophy after parathyroidectomy. *Acta Physiol. Latinoam* 21:107–11

20. Beidler, L. M., Nejad, M. S., Smallman, R. L., Tateda, H. 1960. Rat taste cell proliferation. *Fed. Proc.* 19:302 (abstr.)

21. Belmar, J., Eyzaguirre, C. 1966. Pacemaker site of fibrillation potentials in denervated mammalian muscle. *J. Neurophysiol.* 29:425–41

22. Bennett, M. R. 1972. *Autonomic Neuromuscular Transmission.* London: Cambridge. 273 pp.

23. Bennett, M. R., McLachlan, E. M., Taylor, R. S. 1973a. The formation of synapses in reinnervated mammalian striated muscle. *J. Physiol. London.* In press

24. Bennett, M. R., McLachlan, E. M., Taylor, R. S. 1973b. The formation of synapses in mammalian striated muscle reinnervated with autonomic preganglionic nerves. *J. Physiol. London.* In press

25. Bennett, M. R., Pettigrew, A. G., Taylor, R. S. 1973. The formation of synapses in reinnervated and cross-reinnervated adult avian muscle. *J. Physiol. London* 230:In press

26. Beránek, R., Vyskočil, F. 1967. The action of tubocurarine and atropine on the normal and denervated rat diaphragm. *J. Physiol. London* 188:53–66

27. Berg, D. K., Kelly, R. B., Sargent, P. B., Williamson, P., Hall, Z. W. 1972. Binding of α-bungarotoxin to acetylcholine receptors in mammalian muscle. *Proc. Nat. Acad. Sci. USA* 69:147–51

28. Berlinrood, M., McGee-Russell, S. M., Allen, R. D. 1972. Patterns of particle movement in nerve fibres *in vitro*—an analysis by photokymography and microscopy. *J. Cell Sci.* 11:875–86

29. Bernstein, J. J., Bernstein, M. E. 1971. Axonal regeneration and formation of synapses proximal to the site of lesion following hemisection of the rat spinal cord. *Exp. Neurol.* 30:336–51

30. Berry, R. W. 1969. Ribonucleic acid metabolism of a single neuron: correlation with electrical activity. *Science* 166:1021–23

31. Bird, M. T., Shuttleworth, E. Jr., Koestner, A., Reinglass, J. 1971. The wobbler mouse mutant: an animal model of hereditary motor system disease. *Acta Neuropathol.* 19:39–50

32. Birks, R., Katz, B., Miledi, R. 1960. Physiological and structural changes at the amphibian myoneural junction, in the course of nerve degeneration. *J. Physiol. London* 150:145–68

33. Birks, R., MacIntosh, F. C. 1961. Acetylcholine metabolism of a sympathetic ganglion. *Can. J. Biochem. Physiol.* 39:787–827

34. Birmingham, A. T., Paterson, G., Wójcicki, J. 1970. A comparison of the sensitivities of innervated and denervated rat vasa deferentia to agonist drugs. *Brit. J. Pharmacol.* 39:748–54

35. Black, I. B. 1970. Induction of hepatic tyrosine aminotransferase mediated by a cholinergic agent. *Nature* 225:648

36. Black, I. B., Hendry, I. A., Iverson, L. L. 1972. The role of post-synaptic neurones in the biochemical maturation of presynaptic cholinergic nerve terminals in a mouse sympathetic ganglion. *J. Physiol. London* 221:149–59

37. Black, I. B., Hendry, I. A., Iverson, L. L. 1972. Effects of surgical decentralization and nerve growth factor on the maturation of adrenergic neurons in a mouse sympathetic ganglion. *J. Neurochem.* 19:1367–77

38. Blakemore, C., Mitchell, D. E. 1973. Environmental modification of the visual cortex and the neural basis of learning and memory. *Nature* 241:467–68

39. Blinzinger, K., Kreutzberg, G. 1968. Displacement of synaptic terminals from regenerating motoneurons by microglial cells. *Z. Zellforsch. Microsk. Anat.* 85:145–57

40. Blood, L. A. 1972. Some quantitative effects of nerve growth factor on dorsal root ganglia of chick embryos in culture. *J. Anat.* 112:315–28

41. Bocharova, L. S., Borovyagin, V. L., Dyakonova, T. L., Warton, S. S., Veprintsev, B. N. 1972. Ultrastructure and RNA synthesis in a molluscan giant neuron under electrical stimulation. *Brain Res.* 36:371–84

42. Bondy, S. C. 1971. Axonal transport of macromolecules. I. Protein migration in the central nervous system. *Exp. Brain Res.* 13:127–34

43. Bondy, S. C. 1971. Axonal transport of macromolecules. II. Nucleic acid migration in the central nervous system. *Exp. Brain. Res.* 13:135–39

44. Bondy, S. C. 1972. Axonal migration of various ribonucleic acid species along the optic tract of the chick. *J. Neurochem.* 19:1769–76

45. Bosmann, H. B. 1972. Synthesis of glycoproteins in brain: identification purification and properties of glycosyl transferases from purified synaptosomes of guinea pig cerebral cortex. *J. Neurochem.* 19:763–78

46. Boyle, F. C., Gillespie, J. S. 1968. Relationship between the accumulation of noradrenaline and the development of fluorescence above a constriction in cat splenic nerves. *J. Physiol. London* 195:27–28P

47. Bray, D. 1973. Branching patterns of individual sympathetic neurons in culture. *J. Cell Biol.* 56:702–12

48. Bray, J. J., Kon, C. M., Breckenridge, B. McL. 1971. Reversed polarity of rapid axonal transport in chicken motoneurons. *Brain Res.* 33:560–64

49. Brooks, J. E. 1970. Disuse atrophy of muscle. *Arch. Neurol.* 22:27–30

50. Brown, D. A. 1969. Responses of normal and denervated cat superior cervical ganglia to some stimulant compounds. *J. Physiol. London* 201:225–36

51. Brown, G. L., Pascoe, J. E. 1954. The effect of degenerative section of ganglionic axons on transmission through the ganglion. *J. Physiol. London* 123:565–73

52. Bunge, R. P., Bunge, M. B., Peterson, E. R. 1965. An electron microscope study of cultured rat spinal cord. *J. Cell Biol.* 24:163–91

53. Cannon, W. B., Rosenblueth, A. 1949. *The Supersensitivity of Denervated Structures; a Law of Denervation.* New York: Macmillan. 245 pp.

54. Carlson, B. M., Gutmann, E. 1972. Development of contractile properties of minced muscle regenerates in the rat. *Exp. Neurol.* 36:239–49

55. Ceccarelli, B., Clementi, F., Mantegazza, P. 1972. Adrenergic re-innervation of smooth muscle of nictitating membrane by preganglionic sympathetic fibers. *J. Physiol. London* 220:211–27

56. Chang, C. C., Chen, T. F., Chuang, S.-T. 1973. N,O-di and N,N,O-tri [³H] acetyl α-bungarotoxins as specific labelling agents of cholinergic receptors. *Brit. J. Pharmacol.* 47:147–60

57. Chang, C. C., Chen, T. F., Lee, C. Y. 1973. Studies of the presynaptic effect of β-bungarotoxin on neuromuscular transmission. *J. Pharmacol. Exp. Ther.* 184:339–45

58. Chang, C. C., Lee, C. Y. 1966. Electrophysiological study of neuromuscular blocking action of cobra neurotoxin. *Brit. J. Pharmacol. Chemother.* 28:172–81

59. Chen, J. S., Levi-Montalcini, R. 1970. Long-term cultures of dissociated nerve cells from the embryonic nervous system of the cockroach periplaneta americana. *Arch. Ital. Biol.* 108:503–37

60. Chow, K. L., Stewart, D. L. 1972. Reversal of structural and functional effects of long-term visual deprivation in cats. *Exp. Neurol.* 34:409–33

61. Close, R. I. 1972. Dynamic properties of mammalial skeletal muscles. *Physiol. Rev.* 52:129–97

62. Cohen, M. W. 1972. The development of neuromuscular connexions in the presence of D-tubocurarine. *Brain Res.* 41:457–63

63. Cragg, B. G. 1972. Plasticity of synapses. In *The Structure and Function of Nervous Tissue,* ed. G. H. Bourne, 4:1–60. London: Academic

64. Crain, S. M. 1966. Development of "organotypic" bioelectric activities in central nervous tissues during maturation in culture. *Int. Rev. Neurobiol.* 9:1–43

65. Crain, S. M. 1970. Bioelectric interactions between cultured fetal rodent spinal cord and skeletal muscle after innervation *in vitro. J. Exp. Zool.* 173:353–70

66. Crain, S. M., Alfei, L., Peterson, E. R. 1970. Neuromuscular transmission in cultures of adult human and rodent skeletal muscle after innervation *in vitro* by fetal rodent spinal cord. *J. Neurobiol.* 1:471–88

67. Crain, S. M., Bornstein, M. B. 1972. Organotypic bioelectric activity in cultured reaggregates of dissociated rodent brain cells. *Science* 176:182–84

68. Crain, S. M., Peterson, E. R. 1971. Development of paired explants of fetal spinal cord and adult skeletal muscle during chronic exposure to curare and hemicholinium. *In Vitro* 6:373

69. Crooks, R. F., McClure, W. O. 1972. The effect of cytochalasin B on fast axoplasmic transport. *Brain Res.* 45:643–46

70. Csillik, B. 1965. *Functional Structure of the Post-Synaptic Membrane in the Myoneural Junction.* Budapest: Akadémiai Kiadó. 154 pp.

71. Cuénod, M., Sandri, C., Akert, K. 1972. Enlarged synaptic vesicles in optic nerve terminals induced by intraocular injection of colchicine. *Brain Res.* 39: 285–96

72. Dahlström, A. 1971. Axoplasmic transport (with particular respect to adrenergic neurons). *Phil. Trans. Roy. Soc. London B* 261:325–58

73. Dahlström, A., Häggendal, J., Linder, A. 1973. Degeneration contraction after local vinblastine treatment of superior cervical ganglia in the rat. *Eur. J. Pharmacol.* 21:41–45

74. Deguchi, T., Axelrod, J. 1972. Control of circadian change of serotonin N-acetyltransferase activity in the pineal organ by the $\beta$-adrenergic receptor. *Proc. Nat. Acad. Sci. USA* 69:2547–50

75. DeLong, G. R., Sidman, R. L. 1970. Alignment defect of reaggregating cells in cultures of developing brains of reeler mutant mice. *Develop. Biol.* 22:584–600

76. Dempsey, P. J., Cooper, T. 1968. Supersensitivity of the chronically denervated feline heart. *Am. J. Physiol.* 215: 1245–49

77. Dennis, M. J., Harris, A. J. Unpublished results

78. Dennis, M. J., Harris, A. J., Kuffler, S. W. 1971. Synaptic transmission and its duplication by focally applied acetylcholine in parasympathetic neurones in the heart of the frog. *Proc. Roy. Soc. London B* 177:509–39

79. Diamond, J., Miledi, R. 1962. A study of foetal and new-born rat muscle fibres. *J. Physiol. London* 162:393–408

80. Dixon, J., Cronly-Dillon, J. 1973. Quoted by Jacobson, M., Hunt, R. K. 1973. How do nerve fibers locate their "address" in the brain? *Sci. Am.* 228: 26–35

81. Drachman, D. B. 1967. Is acetylcholine the trophic neuromuscular transmitter? *Arch. Neurol.* 17:206–18

82. Drachman, D. B. 1972. Neurotrophic regulation of muscle cholinesterase: effects of botulinum toxin and denervation. *J. Physiol. London* 226:619–27

83. Drachman, D. B., Witzke, F. 1972. Trophic regulation of acetylcholine sensitivity of muscle; effect of electrical stimulation. *Science* 176:514–16

84. Duchen, L. W. 1970. The effects in the mouse of nerve crush and regeneration on the innervation of skeletal muscles paralysed by *Clostridium botulinum* toxin. *J. Pathol.* 102:9–14

85. Duchen, L. W. 1970. Changes in motor innervation and cholinesterase localization induced by botulinum toxin in skeletal muscle of the mouse: differences between fast and slow muscles. *J. Neurol. Neurosurg. Psychiat.* 33:40–54

86. Duchen, L. W. 1971. An electron microscopic comparison of motor end-plates of slow and fast skeletal muscle fibres of the mouse. *J. Neurol. Sci.* 14: 37–45

87. Duchen, L. W. 1971. An electron microscopic study of the changes induced by botulinum toxin in the motor end-plates of slow and fast skeletal muscle fibres of the mouse. *J. Neurol. Sci.* 14: 47–60

88. Duchen, L. W., Stefani, E. 1971. Electrophysiological studies of neuromuscular transmission in hereditary 'motor end-plate disease' of the mouse. *J. Physiol. London* 212:535–48

89. Duchen, L. W., Strich, S. J. 1968. The effects of botulinum toxin on the pattern of innervation of skeletal muscle in the mouse. *Quart. J. Exp. Physiol.* 53: 84–89

90. Duchen, L. W., Tonge, D. A. 1973. The effects of tetanus toxin on neuromuscular transmission and on the morphology of motor end-plates in slow and fast skeletal muscle of the mouse. *J. Physiol. London* 228:157–72

91. Dunn, G. A. 1971. Mutual contact inhibition of extension of chick sensory nerve fibers *in vitro. J. Comp. Neurol.* 143:491–508

92. Dussardier, M. 1960. *Recherches sur le Contrôle Bulbaire de la Motricité Gastrique ches les Ruminants,* Thèse Faculté Sciences Paris, Série A, No. 3491. Paris: Inst. Nat. Recherche Agronomique

93. Eccles, J. C., Eccles, R. M., Shealy, C. N., Willis, W. D. 1962. Experiments utilizing monosynaptic excitatory action on motoneurons for testing hypotheses relating to specificity of neuronal connection. *J. Neurophysiol.* 25:559–80

94. Edds, M. V. 1953. Collateral nerve regeneration. *Quart. Rev. Biol.* 28:260–76

95. Edstrom, A., Mattsson, H. 1972. Rapid axonal transport *in vitro* in the sciatic system of the frog of fucose-, glucosamine- and sulphate-containing material. *J. Neurochem.* 19:1717–29

96. Elmqvist, D., Hofmann, W. W., Kugelberg, J., Quastel, D. M. J. 1964. An electrophysiological investigation of neuromuscular transmission in myas-

thenia gravis. *J. Physiol. London* 174: 417–34

97. Elul, R., Miledi, R., Stefani, E. 1970. Neural control of contracture in slow muscle fibres of the frog. *Acta Physiol. Latinoam* XX:194–226

98. Emmelin, N., Perec, C. 1968. Reinnervation of submaxillary glands after partial postganglionic denervation. *Quart. J. Exp. Physiol.* 53:10–18

99. Engel, W. K., Karpati, G. 1968. Imparied skeletal muscle maturation following neonatal neurectomy. *Develop. Biol.* 17:713–23

100. Fambrough, D. M. 1970. Acetylcholine sensitivity of muscle fiber membranes: mechanism of regulation by motoneurons. *Science* 168:372–73

101. Fambrough, D. M., Hartzell, H. C. 1972. Acetylcholine receptors: number and distribution at neuromuscular junctions in rat diaphragm. *Science* 176: 189–91

102. Farbman, A. I. 1972. Differentiation of taste buds in organ culture. *J. Cell Biol.* 52:489–93

103. Feldman, J. D., Gaze, R. M. 1972. The growth of the retina in *Xenopus laevis:* an autoradiographic study. II. Retinal growth in compound eyes. *J. Embryol. Exp. Morphol.* 27:381–87

104. Feltz, A., Mallart, A. 1971. Ionic permeability changes induced by some cholinergic agonists on normal and denervated frog muscles. *J. Physiol. London* 218:101–16

105. Feng, T. P., Wu, W. Y., Yang, F. Y. 1965. Selective reinnervation of a 'slow' or 'fast' muscle by its original motor supply during regeneration of a mixed nerve. *Sci. Sinica* 14:1717–20

106. Fex, S. 1969. "Trophic" influence of implanted fast nerve on innervated slow muscle. *Physiol. Bohemoslov.* 18:205–8

107. Fex, S., Jirmanová, I. 1969. Innervation by nerve implants of "fast" and "slow" skeletal muscles of the rat. *Acta Physiol. Scand.* 76:257–69

108. Fex, S., Sonesson, B. 1970. Histochemical observations after implantation of a "fast" nerve into an innervated mammalian "slow" skeletal muscle. *Acta Anat.* 77:1–10

109. Fex, S., Sonesson, B., Thesleff, S., Zelená, J. 1966. Nerve implants in botulinum poisoned mammalian muscle. *J. Physiol. London* 184:872–82

110. Fex, S., Thesleff, S. 1967. The time required for innervation of denervated muscles by nerve implants. *Life Sciences* 6:635–39

111. Fink, B. R., Kennedy, R. D., Hendrickson, A. E., Middaugh, M. E. 1972. Lidocaine inhibition of rapid axonal transport. *Anesthesiology* 36:422–32

112. Fischbach, G. D. 1972. Synapse formation between dissociated nerve and muscle cells in low density cell cultures. *Develop. Biol.* 28:407–29

113. Fischbach, G. D., Robbins, N. 1969. Changes in contractile properties of disused soleus muscles. *J. Physiol. London* 201:305–20

114. Fischbach, G. D., Robbins, N. 1971. Effect of chronic disuse of rat soleus neuromuscular junctions on postsynaptic membrane. *J. Neurophysiol.* 34: 562–69

115. Flament-Durand, J., Dustin, P. 1972. Studies on the transport of secretory granules in the magnocellular hypothalamic neurons. I. Action of colchicine on axonal flow and neurotubules in the paraventricular nuclei. *Z. Zellforsch. Microsk. Anat.* 130:440–54

116. Forman, D. S., Ledeen, R. W. 1972. Axonal transport of gangliosides in the goldfish optic nerve. *Science* 177: 630–33

117. Forman, D. S., McEwen, B. S., Grafstein, B. 1971. Rapid transport of radioactivity in goldfish optic nerve following injections of labelled glucosamine. *Brain Res.* 28:119–30

118. Friede, R. L., Seitelberger, F., Eds. 1971. Symposium on pathology of axons and axonal flow. *Acta Neuropathol.* Suppl. V:1–266

119. Fujimoto, S., Murray, R. G. 1970. Fine structure of degeneration and regeneration in denervated rabbit vallate taste buds. *Anat. Rec.* 168:393–414

120. Fukami, Y., Ridge, R. M. A. P. 1971. Electrophysiological and morphological changes at extrafusal endplates in the snake following chronic denervation. *Brain Res.* 29:139–45

121. Furness, J. B., McLean, J. R., Burnstock, G. 1970. Distribution of adrenergic nerves and changes in neuromuscular transmission in the mouse vas deferens during postnatal development. *Develop. Biol.* 21:491–505

122. Gage, P. W., McBurney, R. N. 1972. The generation and spread of current in muscle due to the action of transmitter on receptors. *Proc. Aust. Physiol. Pharmacol. Soc.* 3(2):93

123. Garber, B. B., Moscona, A. A. 1972. Reconstruction of brain tissue from cell suspensions. I. Aggregation patterns of cells dissociated from different regions of the developing brain. *Develop. Biol.* 27:217–34

124. Gaze, R. M. 1970. *The Formation of Nerve Connections.* London: Academic. 288 pp.
125. Gaze, R. M., Keating, M. J. 1970. Further studies on the restoration of the contralateral retinotectal projections following regeneration of the optic nerve in the frog. *Brain Res.* 21:183–95
126. Gaze, R. M., Keating, M. J. 1972. The visual system and "neuronal specificity." *Nature* 237:375–78
127. Gaze, R. M., Sharma, S. C. 1970. Axial differences in the reinnervation of the goldfish optic tectum by regenerating optic nerve fibres. *Exp. Brain Res.* 10: 171–81
128. Gaze, R. M., Watson, W. E. 1968. Cell division and migration in the brain after optic nerve lesions. In *Growth of the Nervous System,* ed. G. E. W. Wolstenholme, M. O'Connor, 53–67. Ciba Foundation Symposium. London: Churchill. 295 pp.
129. Geffen, L. B., Hughes, C. C. 1972. Degeneration of sympathetic nerves *in vitro* and development of smooth muscle supersensitivity to noradrenaline. *J. Physiol. London* 221:71–84
130. Geinismann, Y. Y. 1972. Effects of excitatory and inhibitory synaptic actions on RNA content of spinal motoneurones. *Brain Res.* 44:221–29
131. Gilbert, J. M. 1972. Evidence for protein synthesis in synaptosomal membranes. *J. Biol. Chem.* 247:6541–50
132. Gilula, N. B., Reeves, O. R., Steinbach, A. 1972. Metabolic coupling, ionic coupling and cell contacts. *Nature* 235: 262–65
133. Ginsborg, B. L., Mackay, B. 1961. A histochemical demonstration of two types of motor innervation in avian skeletal muscle. *Bibl. Anat.* 2:174–81
134. Gisiger, V. 1971. Triggering of RNA synthesis by acetylcholine stimulation of the postsynaptic membrane in a mammalian sympathetic ganglion. *Brain Res.* 33:139–46
135. Goldberg, A. L. 1969a. Protein turnover in skeletal muscle. I. Protein catabolism during work-induced hypertrophy and growth induced with growth hormone. *J. Biol. Chem.* 244: 3217–22
136. Goldberg, A. L. 1969b. Protein turnover in skeletal muscle. II. Effects of denervation and cortisone on protein catabolism in skeletal muscle. *J. Biol. Chem.* 244:3223–29
137. Gottlieb, D. I., Cowan, W. M. 1972. Evidence for a temporal factor in the occupation of available synaptic sites during the development of the dentate gyrus. *Brain Res.* 41:452–56
138. Grafstein, B. 1971. Transneuronal transfer of radioactivity in the central nervous system. *Science* 172:177–79
139. Grafstein, B., Murray, M., Ingoglia, N. A. 1972. Protein synthesis and axonal transport in retinal ganglion cells of mice lacking visual receptors. *Brain Res.* 44:37–48
140. Grampp, W., Harris, J. B., Thesleff, S. 1972. Inhibition of denervation changes in skeletal muscle by blockers of protein synthesis. *J. Physiol. London* 221: 743–54
141. Green, R. D., Fleming, W. W. 1968. Analysis of supersensitivity in the isolated spleen of the cat. *J. Pharmacol. Exp. Ther.* 162:254–62
142. Grimm, L. M. 1971. An evaluation of myotypic respecification in axolotls. *J. Exp. Zool.* 178:479–96
143. Guth, L. 1962. Neuromuscular function after regeneration of interrupted nerve fibres into partially denervated muscle. *Exp. Neurol.* 6:129–41
144. Guth, L. 1968. "Trophic" influences of nerve on muscle. *Physiol. Rev.* 48: 645–87
145. Guth, L. 1970. The enigma of central nervous regeneration. *Exp. Neurol.* Suppl. 5:1–43
146. Guth, L. 1971. Degeneration and regeneration of taste buds. *Handbook of Sensory Physiology,* ed. L. M. Beidler, Vol. IV, pt. 2, 63–74. Berlin: Springer-Verlag. 410 pp.
147. Guth, L., Bernstein, J. J. 1961. Selectivity in the re-establishment of synapses in the superior cervical sympathetic ganglion of the cat. *Exp. Neurol.* 4:59–69
148. Guth, L., Wells, J. B. 1972. Physiological and histochemical properties of the soleus muscle after denervation of its antagonists. *Exp. Neurol.* 36:463–71
149. Guth, L., Zalewski, A. A. 1963. Disposition of cholinesterase following implantation of nerve into innervated and denervated muscle. *Exp. Neurol.* 7: 316–26
150. Gutmann, E., Ed. 1962. *The Denervated Muscle.* Prague: Czech Acad. Sci. 486 pp.
151. Gutmann, E., Hanzlíková, V., Jakoubek, B. 1968. Changes in the neuromuscular system during old age. *Exp. Gerontol.* 3:141–46
152. Gutmann, E., Hanzlíková, V., Vyskočil, F. 1971. Age changes in cross striated muscle of the rat. *J. Physiol. London* 219:331–43

153. Gutmann, E., Hnik, P., Eds. 1963. *The Effect of Use and Disuse on Neuromuscular Functions.* Amsterdam: Elsevier. 576 pp.

154. Gutmann, E., Young, J. Z. 1944. The re-innervation of muscle after various periods of atrophy. *J. Anat.* 78:15–43

155. Gwynn, D. G., Aitken, J. T. 1966. The formation of new motor endplates in mammalian skeletal muscle. *J. Anat.* 100:111–26

156. Haeusler, G., Haefely, W. 1970. Pre- and post-junctional supersensitivity of the mesenteric artery preparation from normotensive and hypertensive rats. *Naunyn Schmiedebergs Arch. Pharmakol. Exp. Pathol.* 266:18–33

157. Haeusler, G., Haefely, W., Thoenen, H. 1969. Chemical sympathectomy of the cat with 6-hydroxydopamine. *J. Pharmacol. Exp. Ther.* 170:50–61

158. Hansson, H.-A., Norström, A. 1971. Glial reactions induced by colchicine-treatment of the hypothalamic-neurohypophyseal system. *Z. Zellforsch. Microsk. Anat.* 113:294–310

159. Harris, A. J. 1968. *The Trophic Relations Between Nerves and Muscles.* PhD thesis. Univ. London, London. 213 pp.

160. Harris, A. J. 1973. Role of acetylcholine receptors in synapse formation. In *Synaptic Transmission and Neuronal Interaction,* ed. M. V. L. Bennett, New York: Raven. In press

161. Harris, A. J., Dennis, M. J. 1970. Acetylcholine sensitivity and its distribution on mouse neuroblastoma cells. *Science* 167:1253–55

162. Harris, A. J., Heinemann, S., Schubert, D., Tarakis, H. 1971. Trophic interaction between cloned tissue culture lines of nerve and muscle *Nature* 231:296–301

163. Harris, A. J., Kuffler, S. W., Dennis, M. J. 1971. Differential chemosensitivity of synaptic and extrasynaptic areas on the neuronal surface membrane in parasympathetic neurons of the frog, tested by microapplication of acetylcholine. *Proc. Roy. Soc. London B* 177:541–53

164. Harris, A. J., Miledi, R. 1971. The effect of type D botulinum toxin on frog neuromuscular junctions. *J. Physiol. London* 217:497–515

165. Harris, A. J., Miledi, R. 1972. A study of frog muscle maintained in organ culture. *J. Physiol. London* 221:207–26

166. Harris, J. B., Thesleff, S. 1972. Nerve stump length and membrane changes in denervated skeletal muscle. *Nature New Biol.* 236:60–61

167. Harris, J. B., Wallace, C., Wing, J. 1972. Myelinated nerve fibre counts in the nerves of normal and dystrophic mouse muscle. *J. Neurol. Sci.* 15:245–49

168. Harrison, R. G. 1907. Observations on the living developing nerve fiber. *Anat. Rec.* 1:116–18

169. Hartzell, H. C., Fambrough, D. M. 1972. Acetylcholine receptors. Distribution and extrajunctional density in rat diaphragm after denervation correlated with acetylcholine sensitivity. *J. Gen. Physiol.* 60:248–62

170. Hartzell, H. C., Fambrough, D. M. 1973. Acetylcholine receptor production and incorporation into membranes of developing muscle fibers. *Develop. Biol.* 30:153–65

171. Hayes, B. P., Roberts, A. 1973. Synaptic junction development in the spinal cord of an amphibian embryo: an electron microscope study. *Z. Zellforsch. Microsk. Anat.* 137:251–69

172. Hemsworth, B. A. 1971. The effects of a hemicholinium analogue, HC-15, on neuromuscular transmission. *Eur. J. Pharmacol.* 15:91–100

173. Hemsworth, B. A., Smith, J. C. 1970. The enzymic acetylation of choline analogues. *J. Neurochem.* 17:171–77

174. Hendry, I. A., Iverson, L. L. 1971. Effect of nerve growth factor and its antiserum on tyrosine hydroxylase activity in mouse superior cervical sympathetic ganglion. *Brain Res.* 29:159–62

175. Henneman, E., Somjen, G., Carpenter, D. O. 1965. Functional significance of cell size in spinal motoneurones. *J. Neurophysiol.* 28:560–80

176. Henneman, E., Somjen, G., Carpenter, D. O. 1965. Excitability and inhibitibility of motoneurones of different sizes. *J. Neurophysiol.* 28:599–620

177. Hess, A., Rosner, S. 1970. The satellite cell bud and myoblast in denervated mammalian muscle fibers. *Am. J. Anat.* 129:21–40

178. Hibbard, E. 1965. Orientation and directed growth of Mauthner's cell axons from duplicated vestibular nerve roots. *Exp. Neurol.* 13:289–301

179. Hier, D. B., Arnason, B. G. W., Young, M. 1972. Studies on the mechanism of action of nerve growth factor. *Proc. Nat. Acad. Sci. USA* 69:2268–72

180. Hillarp, N.-A. 1946. Structure of the synapse and the peripheral innervation apparatus of the autonomic nervous system. *Acta Anatomica* Suppl. IV. 153 pp.

181. Hirano, H. 1967. Ultrastructural study of the morphogenesis of the neuromuscular junction in the skeletal muscle of the chick. Z. Zellforsch. Microsk. Anat. 79:198–208

182. Hník, P., Jirmanová, I., Vykličký, L., Zelená, J. 1967. Fast and slow muscles of the chick after nerve cross-union. J. Physiol. London 193:309–25

183. Hofmann, W. W., Struppler, A., Weindl, A., Velho, F. 1973. Neuromuscular transmission with colchicine-treated nerves. Brain Res. 49:208–13

184. Hofmann, W. W., Thesleff, S. 1972. Studies on the trophic influence of nerve on skeletal muscle. Eur. J. Pharmacol. 20:256–60

185. Hoh, J. F. Y. 1969. The problem of selectivity during reinnervation of fast and slow rat skeletal muscles. Aust. J. Exp. Biol. Med. Sci. 47(4):P–17

186. Hoh, J. F. Y. 1971. Selective reinnervation of fast-twitch and slow-graded muscle fibers in the toad. Exp. Neurol. 30:263–76

187. Hsu, L., Lentz, T. L. 1972. Effect of colchicine on the fine structure of the neuromuscular junction. Z. Zellforsch. Microsk. Anat. 135:439–48

188. Hubel, D. H., Wiesel, T. N. 1965. Binocular interaction in striate cortex of kittens reared with artificial squint. J. Neurophysiol. 28:1041–59

189. Hubel, D. H., Wiesel, T. N. 1970. The period of susceptability to the physiological effects of unilateral eye closure in kittens. J. Physiol. London 206:419–36

190. Hughes, A. F. W. 1968. Aspects of Neural Ontogeny. London: Logos. 249 pp.

191. Hunt, R. K., Jacobson, M. 1972. Development and stability of positional information in Xenopus retinal ganglion cells. Proc. Nat. Acad. Sci. USA 69:780–83

192. Hunt, R. K., Jacobson, M. 1972. Specification of positional information in retinal ganglion cells of Xenopus: stability of the specified state. Proc. Nat. Acad. Sci. USA 69:2860–64

193. Ikeda, K., Kaplan, W. D. 1970. Unilaterally patterned neural activity of gynandromorphs, mosaic for a neurological mutant of Drosophila melanogaster. Proc. Nat. Acad. Sci. USA 67:1480–87

194. Jacobs, J. M., Cavanagh, J. B., Chen, F. C.-K. 1972. Spinal subarachnoid injection of colchicine in rats. J. Neurol. Sci. 17:461–80

195. Jacobson, M. 1968. Cessation of DNA synthesis in retinal ganglion cells correlated with the time of specification of

196. Jacobson, M. 1970. Developmental Neurobiology. New York: Holt Rinehart & Winston. 465 pp.

197. Jacobson, M., Hirsch, H. V. B. 1973. Development and maintenance of connectivity in the visual system of the frog. I. The effects of eye rotation and visual deprivation. Brain Res. 49:47–65

198. Jakoubek, B., Gutmann, E., Fischer, J., Babický, A. 1968. Rate of protein renewal in spinal motoneurons of adolescent and old rats. J. Neurochem. 15:633–41

199. Jarrott, B., Geffen, L. B. 1972. Rapid axoplasmic transport of tyrosine hydroxylase in relation to other cytoplasmic constituents. Proc. Nat. Acad. Sci. USA 69:3440–42

200. Jirmanová, I., Thesleff, S. 1972. Ultrastructural study of experimental muscle degeneration and regeneration in the adult rat. Z. Zellforsch. Microsk. Anat. 131:77–97

201. Johns, T. R., Thesleff, S. 1961. Effects of motor inactivation on the chemical sensitivity of skeletal muscle. Acta Physiol. Scand. 51:136–41

202. Kano, M., Shimada, Y. 1971. Innervation and acetylcholine sensitivity of skeletal muscle cells differentiated in vitro from chick embryo. J. Cell Physiol. 78:233–42

203. Karlsson, J.-O., Hansson, H.-A., Sjöstrand, J. 1971. Effect of colchicine on axonal transport and morphology of retinal ganglion cells. Z. Zellforsch. Microsk. Anat. 115:265–83

204. Karlsson, J.-O., Sjöstrand, J. 1971. Transport of microtubular protein in axons of retinal ganglion cells. J. Neurochem. 18:975–82

205. Karlsson, J.-O., Sjöstrand, J. 1971. Rapid intracellular transport of fucose-containing glycoproteins in retinal ganglion cells. J. Neurochem. 18:2209–16

206. Karlsson, J.-O., Sjöstrand, J. 1972. Axonal transport of proteins in retinal ganglion cells. Characterization of the transport to the superior colliculus. Brain Res. 47:185–94

207. Kasuya, Y. et al 1969. Non-specific denervation supersensitivity in the rat vas deferens 'in vitro'. Eur. J. Pharmacol. 8:177–84

208. Katz, B., Miledi, R. 1964. The development of acetylcholine sensitivity in nerve-free segments of skeletal muscle. J. Physiol. London 170:389–96

209. Katz, B., Miledi, R. 1972. The statistical nature of the acetylcholine potential

and its molecular components. *J. Physiol. London* 224:665–99

210. Keen, P., McLean, W. G. 1972. Effect of dibutyryl cyclic-AMP on levels of dopamine-$\beta$-hydroxylase in isolated superior cervical ganglia. *Naunyn Schmiedebergs Arch. Pharmakol. Exp. Pathol.* 275:465–69

211. Kelly, A. M., Zacks, S. I. 1969. The fine structure of motor endplate morphogenesis. *J. Cell Biol.* 42:154–69

212. Kirkpatrick, J. B., Bray, J. J., Palmer, S. M. 1972. Visualization of axoplasmic flow *in vitro* by Normarski microscopy. Comparison to rapid flow of radioactive proteins. *Brain Res.* 43:1–10

213. Klaus, W., Lüllmann, H., Muscholl, E. 1960. Der Kalium-Flux des normalen und denervierten Rattenzwerchfell. *Pfluegers Arch.* 271:761–75

214. Kohn, R. R. 1969. A proteolytic system involving myofibrils and a soluble factor from normal and atrophying muscle. *Lab. Invest.* 20:202–6

215. Kreutzberg, G. W. 1969. Neuronal dynamics and axonal flow. IV. Blockage of intra-axonal enzyme transport by colchicine. *Proc. Nat. Acad. Sci. USA* 62: 722–28

216. Kristensson, K., Olsson, Y. 1971. Uptake and retrograde axonal transport of peroxidase in hypoglossal neurones. Electron microscopical localization in the neuronal perikaryon I. *Acta Neuropathol.* 19:1–9

217. Kristensson, K., Olsson, Y. 1973. Uptake and retrogade axonal transport of protein tracers in hypoglossal neurons. Fate of the tracer and reaction of the nerve cell bodies. *Acta Neuropathol.* 23:43–47

218. Kristensson, K., Sjöstrand, J. 1972. Retrograde transport of protein tracer in the rabbit hypoglossal nerve during regeneration. *Brain Res.* 45:175–82

219. Kuffler, S. W., Dennis, M. J., Harris, A. J. 1971. The development of chemosensitivity in extrasynaptic areas of the neuronal surface after denervation of parasympathetic ganglion cells in the heart of the frog. *Proc. Roy. Soc. London B* 177:555–63

220. Kuno, M., Muñoz-Martinez, E. J., Randić, M. 1973. Synaptic action on Clarke's column neurones in relation to afferent terminal size. *J. Physiol. London* 228:343–60

221. Kuno, M., Turkanis, S. A., Weakly, J. N. 1971. Correlation between nerve terminal size and transmitter release at the neuromuscular junction of the frog. *J. Physiol. London* 213:545–56

222. Landmesser, L. 1971. Contractile and electrical responses of vagus-innervated frog sartorius muscles. *J. Physiol. London* 213:707–25

223. Landmesser, L. 1972. Pharmacological properties, cholinesterase activity and anatomy of nerve-muscle junctions in vagus-innervated frog sartorius. *J. Physiol. London* 220:243–56

224. Landmesser, L., Pilar, G. 1972. The onset and development of transmission in the chick ciliary ganglion. *J. Physiol. London* 222:691–713

225. Langer, S. Z., Draskóczy, P. R., Trendelenburg, U. 1967. Time course of development of supersensitivity to various amines in the nicititating membrane of the pithed cat after denervation or decentralization. *J. Pharmacol. Exp. Ther.* 157:255–73

226. Langley, J. N. 1897. On the regeneration of pre-ganglionic and of post-ganglionic visceral nerve fibres. *J. Physiol. London* 22:215–30

227. Lasek, R. J. 1970. Protein transport in neurons. *Int. Rev. Neurobiol.* 13:289–324

228. LaVail, J. H., LaVail, M. M. 1972. Retrograde axonal transport in the central nervous system. *Science* 176:1416–17

229. Law, P. K., Atwood, H. L. 1972. Nonequivalence of surgical and natural denervation in dystrophic mouse muscles. *Exp. Neurol.* 34:200–9

230. Lawrence, P. A., Crick, F. H. C., Munro, M. 1972. A gradient of positional information in an insect, *Rhodnius. J. Cell Sci.* 11:815–53

231. Lebowitz, P., Singer, M. 1970. Neurotrophic control of protein synthesis in the regenerating limb of the newt, *Triturus. Nature* 225:824–27

232. Lee, C. Y., Tseng, L. F., Chiu, T. H. 1967. Influence of denervation on localization of neurotoxins from Elapid venoms in rat diaphragm. *Nature* 215:1177–78

233. Lennon, A. M., Vera, C. L., Rex, A. L., Luco, J. V. 1967. Cholinesterase activity of the nictitating membrane reinnervated by cholinergic fibers. *J. Neurophysiol.* 30:1523–30

234. Lentz, T. L. 1972. Distribution of leucine-$^3$H during axoplasmic transport within regenerating neurons as determined by electron microscope radioautography. *J. Cell Biol.* 52:719–32

235. Lentz, T. L. 1972. Development of the neuromuscular junction. III. Degeneration of motor end plates after denervation and maintenance *in vitro* by nerve explants. *J. Cell Biol.* 55:93–103

236. Lentz, T. L. 1972. A role of cyclic AMP in a neurotrophic process. *Nature New Biol.* 238:154–55

237. Levi-Montalcini, R., Angeletti, P. U. 1963. Essential role of the nerve growth factor in the survival and maintenance of dissociated sensory and sympathetic embryonic nerve cells *in vitro. Develop. Biol.* 7: 653–59

238. Levi-Montalcini, R., Angeletti, R. H., Angeletti, P. U. 1972. The nerve growth factor. See Ref. 63, 5:1–38

239. Li, C. L., Shy, G. M., Wells, J. 1957. Some properties of mammalian skeletal muscle fibres with particular reference to fibrillation potentials. *J. Physiol. London* 135:522–35

240. Liu, C. N., Chambers, W. W. 1958. Intraspinal sprouting of dorsal root axons. *Arch. Neurol. Psychiat.* 79:46–61

241. Lømo, T., Rosenthal, J. 1972. Control of ACh sensitivity by muscle activity in the rat. *J. Physiol. London* 221:493–513

242. Lubinska, L. 1964. Axoplasmic streaming in regenerating and in normal nerve fibres. *Progr. Brain Res.* 13:1–71

243. Luco, C. F., Luco, J. V. 1971. Sympathetic effects on fibrillary activity of denervated striated muscles. *J. Neurophysiol.* 34:1066–71

244. Lüllmann-Rauch, R. 1971. The regeneration of neuromuscular junctions during spontaneous re-innervation of the rat diaphragm. *Z. Zellforsch. Microsk. Anat.* 121:593–603

245. Lundberg, D. 1972. Effects of colchicine, vinblastine and vincristine on degeneration transmitter release after sympathetic denervation studied in the conscious rat. *Acta Physiol. Scand.* 85: 91–98

246. Lux, H. D., Schubert, P., Kreutzberg, G. W., Globus, A. 1970. Excitation and axonal flow: autoradiographic study on motoneurones intracellularly injected with a $^3$H-amino acid. *Exp. Brain Res.* 10:197–204

247. Macagno, E. R., Lopresti, V., Levinthal, C. 1973. Structure and development of neuronal connections in isogenic organisms: variations and similarities in the optic system of *Daphnia magna. Proc. Nat. Acad. Sci. USA* 70: 57–61

248. Mackay, A. V. P., Iverson, L. L. 1972. Trans-synaptic regulation of tyrosine hydroxylase activity in adrenergic neurones: effect of potassium concentration on cultured sympathetic ganglia. *Naunyn Schmiedebergs Arch. Pharmakol. Exp. Pathol.* 272:225–29

249. Maeno, T. 1969. Analysis of mobilization and demobilization process of neuromuscular transmission in the frog. *J. Neurophysiol.* 32:793–800

250. Mark, R. F. 1969. Matching muscles and motoneurones. A review of some experiments on motor nerve regeneration. *Brain Res.* 14:245–54

251. Mark, R. F. 1970. Chemospecific synaptic repression as a possible memory store. *Nature* 225:178–79

252. Mark, R. F., Marotte, L. R. 1972. The mechanism of selective reinnervation of fish eye muscles. III. Functional, electrophysiological and anatomical analysis of recovery from section of the IIIrd and IVth nerves. *Brain Res.* 46: 131–48

253. Mark, R. F., Marotte, L. R., Mart, P. E. 1972. The mechanism of selective reinnervation of fish eye muscles. IV. Identification of repressed synapses. *Brain Res.* 46:149–57

254. Marotte, L. R., Mark, R. F. 1970. The mechanism of selective reinnervation of fish eye muscle. I. Evidence from muscle function during recovery. *Brain Res.* 19:41–51

255. Marotte, L. R., Mark, R. F. 1970. The mechanism of selective reinnervation of fish eye muscle. II. Evidence from electromicroscopy of nerve endings. *Brain Res.* 19:53–62

256. Matthews, M. R., Raisman, G. 1972. A light and electron microscopic study of the cellular response to axonal injury in the superior cervical ganglion of the rat. *Proc. Roy. Soc. London B* 181:43–79

257. Matsumura, M., Koelle, G. B. 1961. The nature of synaptic transmission in the superior cervical ganglion following reinnervation by the afferent vagus. *J. Pharmacol. Exp. Ther.* 134:28–46

258. McArdle, J. J., Albuquerque, E. X. 1973. A study of the reinnervation of fast and slow mammalian muscles. *J. Gen. Physiol.* 61:1–23

259. McBride, W. J., Klingman, J. D. 1972. The effects of electrical stimulation and ionic alterations on the metabolism of amino acids and proteins in excised superior cervical ganglia of the rat. *J. Neurochem.* 19:865–80

260. McBurney, R. N., Gage, P. W. 1972. Effects of ethanol and octanol on the conductance change caused by a quantum of transmitter. *Proc. Aust. Physiol. Pharmacol. Soc.* 3(2):209

261. McComas, A. J., Sica, R. E. P., Currie, S. 1970. Muscular dystrophy: evidence for a neural factor. *Nature* 226:1263–64

262. McLachlan, E. M., Taylor, R. S., Bennett, M. R. 1972. The site of synapse formation in reinnervated and cross-reinnervated mammalian muscle. *Proc. Aust. Physiol. Pharmacol. Soc.* 3(1):62

263. McMahon, U. J., Spitzer, N. C., Peper, K. 1972. Visual identification of nerve terminals in living isolated skeletal muscle. *Proc. Roy. Soc. London B* 181:421–30

264. Mellanby, J., Thompson, P. A. 1972. The effect of tetanus toxin at the neuromuscular junction in the goldfish. *J. Physiol. London* 224:407–19

265. Mendez, J., Arana, L. C., Luco, J. V. 1970. Antifibrillary effect of adrenergic fibers on denervated striated muscles. *J. Neurophysiol.* 33:882–90

266. Miledi, R. 1960. The acetylcholine sensitivity of frog muscle fibres after complete or partial denervation. *J. Physiol. London* 151:1–23

267. Miledi, R. 1960. Properties of regenerating neuromuscular synapses in the frog. *J. Physiol. London* 154:190–205

268. Miledi, R. 1962. Induced innervation of end-plate free muscle segments. *Nature* 193:281–82

269. Miledi, R. 1963. Formation of extra nerve-muscle junctions in innervated muscle. *Nature* 199:1191–92

270. Miledi, R. 1963. An influence of nerve not mediated by impulses. See Ref. 153, 35–40

271. Miledi, R., Molinoff, P., Potter, L. T. 1971. Isolation of the cholinergic receptor protein of *Torpedo* electric tissue. *Nature* 229:554–57

272. Miledi, R., Potter, L. T. 1971. Acetylcholine receptors in muscle fibres. *Nature* 233:599–603

273. Miledi, R., Slater, C. R. 1968. Electrophysiology and electron-microscopy of rat neuromuscular junctions after nerve degeneration. *Proc. Roy. Soc. London B* 169:289–306

274. Miledi, R., Slater, C. R. 1968. Some mitochondrial changes in denervated muscle. *J. Cell Sci.* 3:49–54

275. Miledi, R., Slater, C. R. 1970. On the degeneration of rat neuro-muscular junctions after nerve section. *J. Physiol. London* 207:507–28

276. Miledi, R., Stefani, E. 1969. Non selective re-innervation of slow and fast muscle fibres in the rat. *Nature* 222:569–71

277. Miledi, R., Stefani, E., Steinbach, A. B. 1971. Induction of the action potential mechanism in slow muscle fibres of the frog. *J. Physiol. London* 217:737–54

278. Miledi, R., Zelená, J. 1966. Sensitivity to acetylcholine in rat slow muscle. *Nature* 210:855–56

279. Mitchell, J. F., Silver, A. 1963. The spontaneous release of acetylcholine from the denervated hemidiaphragm of the rat. *J. Physiol. London* 165:117–29

280. Model, P. G., Bornstein, M. B., Crain, S. M., Pappas, G. D. 1971. An electron microscopic study of the development of synapses in cultured fetal mouse cerebrum continuously exposed to xylocaine. *J. Cell Biol.* 49:362–71

281. Molinoff, P. B., Brimijoin, S., Weinshilboum, R., Axelrod, J. 1970. Neurally mediated increase in dopamine-$\beta$-hydroxylase activity. *Proc. Nat. Acad. Sci. USA* 66:453–58

282. Moore, R. Y., Björklund, A., Stenevi, U. 1971. Plastic changes in the adrenergic innervation of the rat septal area in response to denervation. *Brain Res.* 33:13–35

283. Morgan, I. G., Austin, L. 1968. Synaptosomal protein synthesis in a cell-free system. *J. Neurochem.* 15:41–51

284. Mueller, R. A., Thoenen, H., Axelrod, J. 1970. Inhibition of neuronally induced tyrosine hydroxylase by nicotinic receptor blockade. *Eur. J. Pharmacol.* 10:51–56

285. Murray, J. G., Thompson, J. W. 1957. The occurrence and function of collateral sprouting in the sympathetic nervous system of the cat. *J. Physiol. London* 135:133–62

286. Musick, J., Hubbard, J. I. 1972. Release of protein from mouse motor nerve terminals. *Nature* 237:279–81

287. Neale, J. H., Neale, E. A., Agranoff, B. W. 1972. Radioautography of the optic tectum of the goldfish after intraocular injection of [$^3$H] proline. *Science* 176:407–10

288. Nelson, P. G., Peacock, J. H., Amano, T. 1971. Responses of neuroblastoma cells to iontophoretically applied acetylcholine. *J. Cell Physiol.* 77:353–62

289. Nelson, B., Ruffner, W., Nirenberg, M. 1969. Neuronal tumor cells with excitable membranes grown *in vitro. Proc. Nat. Acad. Sci. USA* 64:1004–10

290. Norström, A., Sjöstrand, J. 1971. Effect of haemorrhage on the rapid axonal transport of neurohypophysial proteins of the rat. *J. Neurochem.* 18:2017–26

291. Oakley, B. 1967. Altered temperature and taste responses from cross-regenerated sensory nerves in the rat's tongue. *J. Physiol. London* 188:353–71

292. Oakley, B. 1970. Reformation of taste buds by crossed sensory nerves in the

rat's tongue. *Acta Physiol. Scand.* 79: 88–94

293. Oakley, B., Benjamin, R. M. 1966. Neural mechanisms of taste. *Physiol. Rev.* 46:173–211

294. Ochs, S. 1972. Fast transport of materials in mammalian nerve fibers. *Science* 176:252–60

295. Okun, L. M. 1972. Isolated dorsal root ganglion neurons in culture: cytological maturation and extension of electrically active processes. *J. Neurobiol.* 3:111–51

296. Otsuka, M., Endo, M., Nonomura, Y. 1962. Presynaptic nature of neuro-muscular depression. *Jap. J. Physiol.* 12: 573–84

297. Pappas, G. D., Peterson, E. R., Masurovsky, E. B., Crain, S. M. 1971. Electron microscopy of the *in vitro* development of mammalian motor end plates. *Ann. NY Acad. Sci.* 183: 33–45

298. Parker, G. H. 1932. On the trophic influence so-called, its rate and nature. *Am. Natur.* 66:147–58

299. Parker, G. H., Paine, V. L. 1934. Progressive nerve degeneration and its rate in the lateral-line nerve of the catfish. *Am. J. Anat..* 54:1–25

300. Partlow, L. M., Larrabee, M. G. 1971. Effects of a nerve-growth factor, embryo age and metabolic inhibitors on growth of fibres and on synthesis of ribonucleic acid and protein in embryonic sympathetic ganglia. *J. Neurochem.* 18:2101–18

301. Partlow, L. M., Ross, C. D., Motwani, R., McDougal, D. B. Jr. 1972. Transport of axonal enzymes in surviving segments of frog sciatic nerve. *J. Gen. Physiol.* 60:388–405

302. Patrick, J., Heinemann, S. F., Lindstrom, J., Schubert, D., Steinbach, J. H. 1972. Appearance of acetylcholine receptors during differentiation of a myogenic cell line. *Proc. Nat. Acad. Sci. USA* 69:2762–66

303. Patrick, R. L., Kirshner, N. 1972. Developmental changes in rat adrenal tyrosine hydroxylase, dopamine-$\beta$-hydroxylase and catecholamine levels: effect of denervation. *Develop. Biol.* 29:204–13

304. Peacock, J. H., Nelson, P. G., Goldstone, M. W. 1973. Electrophysiologic study of cultured neurones dissociated from spinal cords and dorsal root ganglia of fetal mice. *Develop. Biol.* 30: 137–52

305. Peper, K., McMahan, U. J. 1972. Distribution of acetylcholine receptors in the vicinity of nerve terminals on skeletal muscle of the frog. *Proc. Roy. Soc. London B* 181:431–40

306. Perísić, M., Cuénod, M. 1972. Synaptic transmission depressed by colchicine blockade of axoplasmic flow. *Science* 175:1140–42

307. Peterson, E. R., Crain, S. M. 1970. Innervation in cultures of fetal rodent skeletal muscle by organotypic explants of spinal cord from different animals. *Z. Zellforsch. Microsk. Anat.* 106:1–21

308. Peterson, E. R., Crain, S. M. 1972. Regeneration and innervation in cultures of adult mammalian skeletal muscle coupled with fetal rodent spinal cord. *Exp. Neurol.* 36:136–59

309. Peterson, R. P., Kernell, D. 1970. Effects of nerve stimulation on the metabolism of ribonucleic acid in a molluscan giant neurone. *J. Neurochem.* 17:1075–85

310. Pettigrew, A. G., McLachlan, E. M. Bennett, M. R. 1973. The site of synapse formation in reinnervated mammalian striated muscle during post-natal development. *Proc. Aust. Physiol. Pharmacol. Soc.* 4:In press

311. Pilar, G., Landmesser, L. 1972. Axotomy mimicked by localized colchicine application. *Science* 177:1116–18

312. Pinching, A. J., Powell, T. P. S. 1971. Ultrastructural features of transneuronal cell degeneration in the olfactory system. *J. Cell Sci.* 8:253–87

313. Porter, C. W., Chiu, T. H., Wieckowski, J., Barnard, E. A. 1973. Types and locations of cholinergic receptor-like molecules in muscle fibres. *Nature New Biol.* 241:3–7

314. Prestige, M. C., Wilson, M. A. 1972. Loss of axons from ventral roots during development. *Brain Res.* 41:467–70

315. Raisman, G. 1969. Neuronal plasticity in the septal nuclei of the adult rat. *Brain Res.* 14:25–48

316. Raisman, G., Matthews, M. R. 1972. Degeneration and regeneration of synapses. See Ref. 63, 4:61–104

317. Ramirez, G., Levitan, I. B., Mushynski, W. E. 1972. Highly purified synaptosomal membranes from rat brain. Incorporation of amino acids into membrane protein *in vitro. J. Biol. Chem.* 247: 5382–90

318. Redfern, P. A. 1970. Neuromuscular transmission in new-born rats. *J. Physiol. London* 209:701–9

319. Redfern, P., Thesleff, S. 1971. Action potential generation in denervated rat skeletal muscle. II. The action of tetrodotoxin. *Acta Physiol. Scand.* 82: 70–78

320. Reier, P. J., Hughes, A. 1972. Evidence for spontaneous axon degeneration during peripheral nerve maturation. *Am. J. Anat.* 135:147–52

321. Robbins, N., Fischbach, G. D. 1971. Effect of chronic disuse of rat soleus neuromuscular junctions on presynaptic function. *J. Neurophysiol.* 34: 570–78

322. Robbins, N., Yonezawa, T. 1971. Physiological studies during formation and development of rat neuromuscular junctions in tissue culture. *J. Gen. Physiol.* 58:467–81

323. Robert, E. D., Oester, Y. T. 1970. Absence of supersensitivity to acetylcholine in innervated muscle subjected to a prolonged pharmacologic nerve block. *J. Pharmacol. Exp. Ther.* 174:133–40

324. Robert, E. D., Oester, Y. T. 1970. Nerve impulses and trophic effect. *Arch. Neurol.* 22:57–63

325. Saito, A., Zacks, S. I. 1969. Fine structure of neuromuscular junctions after nerve section and implantation of nerve in denervated muscle. *Exp. Mol. Pathol.* 10:256–73

326. Salafsky, B., Bell, J., Prewitt, M. 1968. Development of fibrillation potentials in denervated fast and slow skeletal muscle. *Am. J. Physiol.* 215:637–43

327. Schiaffino, S., Hanzlíková, V. 1972. Studies on the effect of denervation in developing muscle. II. The lysosomal system. *J. Ultrastruct. Res.* 39:1–14

328. Schiaffino, S., Settembrini, P. 1970. Studies on the effect of denervation in developing muscle. I. Differentiation of the sarcotubular system. *Virchows Arch. B* 4:345–56

329. Schonbach, J., Schonbach, C., Cuénod, M. 1971. Rapid phase of axoplasmic flow and synaptic proteins: an electron microscopical autoradiographic study. *J. Comp. Neurol.* 141:485–98

330. Schubert, D., Humphreys, S., Baroni, C., Cohn, M. 1969. *In vitro* differentiation of a mouse neuroblastoma. *Proc. Nat. Acad. Sci. USA* 64:316–23

331. Schubert, P., Kreutzberg, G. W., Lux, H. D. 1972. Neuroplasmic transport in dendrites: effect of colchicine on morphology and physiology of motoneurones in the cat. *Brain Res.* 47:331–43

332. Schucker, F. 1972. Effects of NGF-antiserum in sympathetic neurons during early postnatal development. *Exp. Neurol.* 36:59–78

333. Schukla, P. L., Aitken, J. T. 1963. Formation of motor endplates in denervated voluntary muscles of the rat. *J. Anat.* 97:152–53

334. Seecof, R. L., Teplitz, R. L., Gerson, I., Ikeda, K., Donady, J. J. 1972. Differentiation of neuromuscular junctions in cultures of embryonic *Drosophila* cells. *Proc. Nat. Acad. Sci. USA* 69:566–70

335. Sharma, S. C. 1972. Restoration of the visual projection following tectal lesions in goldfish. *Exp. Neurol.* 35:358–65

336. Sheffield, J. B., Fischman, D. A. 1970. Intercellular junctions in the developing neural retina of the chick embryo. *Z. Zellforsch. Microsk. Anat.* 104:405–18

337. Sheridan, J. D. 1968. Electrophysiological evidence for low-resistance intercellular junctions in the early chick embryo. *J. Cell Biol.* 37:650–59

338. Sheridan, J. D. 1971. Dye movement and low-resistance junctions between reaggregated embryonic cells. *Develop. Biol.* 26:627–36

339. Sherman, S. M., Hoffman, K.-P., Stone, J. 1972. Loss of a specific cell type from dorsal lateral geniculate nucleus in visually deprived cats. *J. Neurophysiol.* 35: 532–41

340. Shooter, E. M., Einstein, E. R. 1971. Proteins of the nervous system. *Ann. Rev. Biochem.* 40:635–52

341. Sidman, R. L. 1972. Cell interactions in developing mammalian central nervous system. *Third Lepetit Colloquim,* ed L. G. Silvestri, 1–13. London: North-Holland. 314 pp.

342. Silberstein, S. D., Brimijoin, S., Molinoff, P. B., Lemberger, L. 1972. Induction of dopamine-β-hydroxylase in rat superior cervical ganglia in organ culture. *J. Neurochem.* 19:919–21

343. Sjöstrand, J. C. 1971. Neuroglial proliferation in the hypoglossal nucleus after nerve injury. *Exp. Neurol.* 30:178–89

344. Solandt, D. Y., Magladery, J. W. 1940. The relation of atrophy to fibrillation in denervated muscle. *Brain* 63:255–63

345. Sonesson, B., Thesleff, S. 1968. Cholinesterase activity after DFP application in botulinum poisoned, surgically denervated or normally innervated rat skeletal muscles. *Life Sciences* 7:411–17

346. Speidel, C. C. 1964. *In vivo* studies of myelinated nerve fibers. *Int. Rev. Cytol.* 16:173–231

347. Stefani, E., Schmidt, H. 1972. Early stage of reinnervation of frog slow muscle fibres. *Pfluegers Arch.* 336:271–75

348. Steinbach, A. B. 1968. A kinetic model for the action of xylocaine on receptors for acetylcholine. *J. Gen. Physiol.* 52: 162–80

349. Steinbach, J. H., Harris, A. J., Patrick, J., Schubert, D., Heinemann, S. 1973. Nerve-muscle interaction *in vitro:* the

role of acetylcholine. *J. Gen. Physiol.* 62:255–70

350. Steiner, G., Schönbaum, E., Eds. 1972. *Immunosympathectomy.* Amsterdam: Elsevier. 253 pp.

351. Stenevi, U., Björklund, A., Moore, R. Y. 1972. Growth of intact central adrenergic axons in the denervated lateral geniculate body. *Exp. Neurol.* 35: 290–99

352. Stewart, D. M., Martin, A. W. 1956. Hypertrophy of the denervated hemidiaphragm. *Am. J. Physiol.* 186: 497–500

353. Straznicky, K., Gaze, R. M. 1971. The growth of the retina in *Xenopus laevis:* an autoradiographic study. *J. Embryol. Exp. Morphol.* 26:67–79

354. Strömblad, B. C. R. 1960. Cholinesterase activity in skeletal muscle after botulinum toxin. *Experientia* 16:458–459

355. Sumner, B. E. H., Watson, W. E. 1971. Retraction and expansion of the dendritic tree of motor neurones of adult rats induced *in vivo. Nature* 233: 273–75

356. Teräväinen, H. 1968. Development of the myoneural junction in the rat. *Z. Zellforsch. Microsk. Anat.* 87:249–65

357. Thesleff, S. 1960. Supersensitivity of skeletal muscle produced by botulinum toxin. *J. Physiol. London* 151:598–607

358. Thesleff, S. 1960. Effects of motor innervation on the chemical sensitivity of skeletal muscle. *Physiol. Rev.* 40: 734–52

359. Thesleff, S. 1963. Spontaneous electrical activity in denervated rat skeletal muscle. See Ref. 153, 41–51

360. Thoenen, H., Mueller, R. A., Axelrod, J. 1969. Trans-synaptic induction of adrenal tyrosine hydroxylase. *J. Pharmacol. Exp. Ther.* 169:249–54

361. Thoenen, H., Saner, A., Kettler, R., Angeletti, P. U. 1972. Nerve growth factor and preganglionic cholinergic nerves; their relative importance to the development of the terminal adrenergic neuron. *Brain Res.* 44:593–602

362. Thoenen, H., Tranzer, J. P. 1968. Chemical sympathectomy by selective destruction of adrenergic nerve endings with 6-hydroxydopamine. *Naunyn Schmiedebergs Arch. Pharmacol. Exp. Pathol.* 261:271–88

363. Thornton, C. S., Thornton, M. T. 1970. Recuperation of regeneration in denervated limbs of *Amblystoma* larvae. *J. Exp. Zool.* 173:293–302

364. Torvik, A., Skjörten, F. 1971. Electron microscopic observations on nerve cell regeneration and degeneration after axon lesions. I. Changes in the nerve cell cytoplasm. *Acta Neuropathol.* 17: 248–64

365. Tower, S. 1939. The reaction of muscle to denervation. *Physiol. Rev.* 19:1–48

366. Trumpy, J. H. 1971. Transneuronal degeneration in the pontine nuclei of the cat. I. Neuronal changes in animals of varying ages. *Ergeb. Anat. Entwicklungsgesch.* 44:1–46

367. Tsai, T. H., Denham, S., McGrath, W. R. 1968. Sensitivity of the isolated nictitating membrane of the cat to norepinephrine and acetylcholine after various procedures and agents. *J. Pharmacol. Exp. Ther.* 164:146–57

368. Tuffery, A. R. 1971. Growth and degeneration of motor end-plates in normal cat hind limb muscles. *J. Anat.* 110: 221–47

369. Uehara, Y., Burnstock, G. 1972. Postsynaptic specialization of smooth muscle at close neuromuscular junctions in the guinea pig sphincter papillae. *J. Cell Biol.* 53:849–53

370. Usherwood, P. N. R. 1962. Glutamate sensitivity of denervated insect muscle fibres. *Nature* 223:411–13

371. Vera, C. L., Luco, J. V. 1967. Reinnervation of smooth and striated muscle by sensory nerve fibers. *J. Neurophysiol.* 30:620–27

372. Vera, C. L., Vial, J. D., Luco, J. V. 1957. Reinnervation of nictitating membrane of the cat by cholinergic fibers. *J. Neurophysiol.* 20:365–73

373. Volkmar, F. R., Greenough, W. T. 1972. Rearing complexity affects branching of dendrites in the visual cortex of the rat. *Science* 176:1445–47

374. Vyskočil, F., Gutmann, E. 1972. Spontaneous transmitter release from nerve endings and contractile properties in the soleus and diaphragm muscles of senile rats. *Experientia* 28:280–281

375. Vyskočil, F., Moravec, J., Janský, L. 1971. Resting state of the myoneural junction in a hibernator. *Brain Res.* 34: 381–84

376. Wallace, H. 1972. The components of regrowing nerves which support the regeneration of irradiated salamander limbs. *J. Embryol. Exp. Morphol.* 28: 419–35

377. Watson, W. E. 1965. An autoradiographic study of the incorporation of nucleic-acid precursors by neurones and glia during nerve regeneration. *J. Physiol. London* 180:741–53

378. Watson, W. E. 1965. An autoradiographic study of the incorporation of

nucleic-acid precursors by neurones and glia during nerve stimulation. *J. Physiol. London* 180:754–65

379. Watson, W. E. 1968. Observations on the nucleolar and total cell body nucleic acid of injured nerve cells. *J. Physiol. London* 196:655–76

380. Watson, W. E. 1969. The response of motor neurones to intramuscular injection of botulinum toxin. *J. Physiol. London* 202:611–30

381. Watson, W. E. 1970. Some metabolic responses of axotomised neurones to contact between their axons and denervated muscle. *J. Physiol. London* 210: 321–43

382. Watson, W. E. 1972. Some quantitative observations upon the responses of neuroglial cells which follow axotomy of adjacent neurones. *J. Physiol. London* 225:415–35

383. Weddell, G., Feinstein, B., Pattle, R. E. 1944. The electrical activity of voluntary muscle in man under normal and pathological conditions. *Brain* 67:178–257

384. Weddell, G., Guttmann, L., Gutmann, E. 1941. The local extension of nerve fibres into denervated areas of skin. *J. Neurol. Psychiat.* 4:206–25

385. Weiss, P. 1955. Special vertebrate organogenesis: Nervous system. *Analysis of Development*, ed. B. H. Willier, P. A. Weiss, V. Hamburger, 346–401. Philadelphia: Saunders. 735 pp.

386. Williams, P. E., Goldspink, G. 1971. Longitudinal growth of striated muscle fibres. *J. Cell Sci.* 9:751–67

387. Williams, T. H., Jew, J. 1970. Collateral nerve sprouts produced experimentally. *Nature* 228:862–64

388. Wilson, M. A. 1971. Optic nerve fibre counts and retinal ganglion cell counts during development of Xenopus Laevis (Daudin). *Quart. J. Exp. Physiol.* 56: 83–91

389. Wilson, D. L., Berry, R. W. 1972. The effect of synaptic stimulation on RNA and protein metabolism in the R2 soma of *Aplysia. J. Neurobiol.* 3:369–79

390. Wolf, M. K. 1970. Anatomy of cultured mouse cerebellum. II. Organotypic migration of granule cells demonstrated by silver impregnation of normal and mutant cultures. *J. Comp. Neurol.* 140: 281–98

391. Wolf, M. K., Dubois-Dalcq, M. 1970. Anatomy of cultured mouse cerebel-

lum. I. Golgi and electron microscopic demonstrations of granule cells, their afferent and efferent snyapses. *J. Comp. Neurol.* 140:261–80

392. Wolf, M. K., Holden, A. B. 1969. Tissue culture analysis of the inherited defect of central nervous system myelination in jimpy mice. *J. Neuropathol. Exp. Neurol.* 28:195–213

393. Woodward, D. J., Hoffer, B. J., Siggins, G. R., Bloom, F. E. 1971. The ontogenetic development of synaptic junctions. Synaptic activation and responsiveness to neurotransmitter substances in rat cerebellar Purkinje cells. *Brain Res.* 34:73–97

394. Yaffe, D. 1968. Retention of differentiation potentialities during prolonged cultivation of myogenic cells. *Proc. Nat. Acad. Sci. USA* 61:477–83

395. Yntema, C. L. 1959. Regeneration in sparsely innervated and aneurogenic forelimbs of *Amblystoma* larvae. *J. Exp. Zool.* 140:101–24

396. Yoon, M. 1971. Reorganization of retinotectal projection following surgical operations on the optic tectum in goldfish. *Exp. Neurol.* 33:395–411

397. Yoon, M. 1972. Reversibility of the reorganization of retinotectal projection in goldfish. *Exp. Neurol.* 35: 565–77

398. Zalewski, A. A. 1969. Combined effects of testosterone and motor, sensory, or gustatory nerve reinnervation on the regeneration of taste buds. *Exp. Neurol.* 24:285–97

399. Zalewski, A. A. 1969. Regeneration of taste buds after reinnervation by peripheral or central sensory fibers of vagal ganglia. *Exp. Neurol.* 25:429–37

400. Zalewski, A. A. 1972. Regeneration of taste buds after transplantation of tongue and ganglia grafts to the anterior chamber of the eye. *Exp. Neurol.* 35: 519–28

401. Zatz, M., Barondes, S. H. 1971. Rapid transport of fucosyl glycoproteins to nerve endings in mouse brain. *J. Neurochem.* 18:1125–33

402. Zelená, J., Jirmanová, I. 1973. Ultrastructure of chicken slow muscle after nerve cross union. *Exp. Neurol.* 38: 272–85

403. Zelená, J., Sobotková, M. 1971. Absence of muscle spindles in regenerated muscles of the rat. *Physiol. Bohemoslov.* 20:433–39

# THE MALE REPRODUCTIVE SYSTEM ❖1114

## W. R. Gomes and N. L. VanDemark

Animal Reproduction Teaching and Research Center, The Ohio State University, Columbus

## INTRODUCTION

This paper marks the first appearance in the *Annual Review of Physiology* of a review devoted exclusively to male reproductive phenomena. Obviously space limitations make it impossible, under the circumstances, to comment on all articles published since the previous review on reproduction. Therefore, specific aspects of male reproduction have been selected for review in an attempt to update areas which appear of current interest in several laboratories. Even within these areas, the bulk of recent literature and space limitations force the use of secondary references for most earlier work, and citation of one or two papers in other cases where three or four would be preferable.

A number of recent reviews are available detailing many aspects of the male reproductive system which could not be covered here. The interested reader is referred to these for coverage of many facets of testicular (121) and epididymal (59) function, sperm transport (8) and testicular morphology (23), endocrinology (31), and pharmacology (64). Pre-1970 literature has been extensively summarized in recent treatises on male reproduction (68, 103, 107).

## FLUID DYNAMICS IN THE TESTIS

In the last 10 to 15 years great strides have been made in understanding the dynamics of the fluids flowing into and out of the testes as a result of the development of adequate micro-methods of measuring blood, lymph, and testicular fluid flow. Since these fluids are responsible for supplying nutrients, hormones, and gases, and removing waste products and secretory products of the testes, it is clearly important that the processes involving these fluids be understood.

Earlier reviews have presented or referred to detailed methods for the measurement of blood flow (113, 142, 143) and have considered factors affecting blood flow and metabolism within the testis, epididymis, and scrotum, and discussed the blood

307

supply to the testis, testicular lymph, and lymphatics, and testicular fluid in the rete testis. Waites (140) has discussed the vascular role in countercurrent heat exchange in his review of temperature regulation in the testis.

## Measurement of Blood Flow

As Setchell (113) has pointed out and documented with several references, one of the striking features of the vascular anatomy of the scrotal testis is the presence of a large number of convolutions in the internal spermatic artery in many species. This coiling of the artery occurs in the pampiniform plexus, just after the artery leaves the inguinal canal, with the convolutions forming a vascular cone. In primates there is only moderate coiling and in man the artery is nearly straight as it approaches the testis.

In the scrotal testis the veins usually arise within the substance of the testis and run either directly to the surface or to a central vein near the mediastinum. The veins then join the pampiniform plexus where they break up into many fine veins (numbering as many as 300 in a ram), which lie closely applied to the coils of the spermatic artery (141).

Within the testis the arteries follow different patterns of coiling on the surface and then descend into the interior portion of the testis, where they break down into arterioles and capillaries. In some cases there are arteriovenous anastomoses as well as capillaries (113).

Many of the techniques available for measuring blood flow cannot be used on reproductive organs because of the small size and slow flow rates of these organs in most species (113). Flowmeters employing electromagnetic or ultrasonic principles can be used for larger animals, but their application is limited. Use of the Fick principle, inert gas clearance rates, and indicator fractionation techniques have greatly enhanced our understanding of blood flow and its control.

Setchell (113) has also described methods of measuring the total venous outflow and of measuring capillary flow. Flowmeters—electromagnetic and ultrasonic devices that can be attached to arteries to measure inflow—present problems because the veins in the pampiniform plexus, if molested in exposing the internal spermatic artery, interfere with normal flow. Local thermal dilution methods also present difficulties because of the complex anatomy of the internal spermatic artery and veins. A diffusion method is described (113) which employs 4-aminoantipyrine as an indicator substance. This compound was originally used to measure uterine blood flow (62). This method also has been used with tritiated water as an indicator. The method is time consuming and there is no way of determining the proportion of the blood which is contributed by the testis itself and that which is contributed by the epididymis. Thus, while total metabolic change and total endocrine change can be determined, appropriate apportionment of these changes to segments of the testis and epididymis cannot be made. Capillary blood flow methods using $^{85}Kr$ and an indicator fractionation technique have also been reviewed in detail by Setchell. Other radioactive substance such as $^{86}Rb$ and 4-($^{131}I$)-iodoantipyrine have been used as isotopes in blood flow techniques in the testis.

Jaffe & Free (65) recently developed a method of measuring blood flow in the testis with a miniature friction flowmeter which operates at flowrates below the range of electronic flow sensors and can be used in arteries of the testis as small as 0.6 mm inside diameter.

The method relies on the measurement of the pressure drop across a small resistance. Using this technique, these investigators found very close agreement with methods using tritiated water and the Ludwig-type stromuhr procedure. The miniature friction flowmeter has been used successfully in monitoring the blood flow in the testis of a conscious rat up to 8 hr during treatment with various vasoactive substances. The method also permits the sampling of arterial-venous blood for analysis.

## Factors Affecting Blood Flow

Using the method just described, Free & Jaffe (41) have reported large increases in testis tissue pressure caused by contractions in the testicular capsule which cause a concomitant increase in testis vein pressure and a small transient decrease in testis blood flow. When the testicular capsule was opened in the anesthetized rat, testis vein and artery pressure and blood flow were unaffected.

Infusion of epinephrine or norepinephrine into the spermatic artery of rats (65) or rams (142) led to a rapid vasoconstriction with a marked decrease in blood flow. The relationship of this finding to physiological events, however, remains obscure, as extensive treatment with large doses of epinephrine was necessary to cause significant changes in testes of rabbits and rats (50). On the other hand, definite relationships have been shown between testis function and crowding, social interaction, or other stresses (50), and adrenal contribution would likely play a role. Related to this is the recent report (136) that ACTH did not affect blood flow through the testis. Unfortunately, these workers (136) employed $^{86}$Rb in an indicator fractionation technique, and the testis is one of three tissues known that partially excludes rubidium (113).

Other agents which can affect blood flow appear to be serotonin and prostaglandins (43), but the role of these compounds in normal in vivo function of the testis remains obscure.

Setchell (113) has reviewed several articles which indicate that the vascular bed of the testis is relatively unresponsive to heat changes, unlike most other organs where similar temperature changes bring increases in blood flow with increased temperatures and decreases with decreased temperatures. He also points out that blood flow to the testis increases following periods of vascular occlusion. Blood flow through the testis is also affected by the posture of the animal. This was found to be true when the scrotum the the ram was raised to the level of the heart, causing a doubling of the blood flow through the testis. Setchell (113) and Gunn & Gould (54) have reviewed, in some detail, the evidence for vascular disruption in the testis as a result of the effects of cadmium salts, which cause an immediate and profound fall in testicular blood flow. Other organs respond with only a slight reduction in blood flow as a result of the effects of cadmium salts.

Johnson & Turner (69) have confirmed the effects of cadmium on blood flow in the testis of the rat showing an increase 1 hr following the administration of cadmium salts, but unlike the findings of Setchell & Waites (118), where the decrease in relative blood flow occurred 3 hr after cadmium injection, Johnson & Turner (69) showed a return to approximately normal blood flow. Zinc pretreatment produced a higher than normal blood flow in the rat testis, and such treated rats were affected only slowly or not at all by cadmium salts. Blood flow in the testis of the domestic fowl was not affected by the administration of cadmium chloride.

Jones (71) has shown that a single X-ray dose applied to the testis (up to 600 rads), which causes a depopulation of the testis, does not affect blood flow rate, but the blood volume per unit weight increases. He has postulated a physiological feedback capable of controlling the blood perfusion in response to the nutritional demands of the tissue. He also suggests that the noncapillary component of the vasculature remains intact.

Joffre & Joffre (66) found that testicular blood flow in the rat is apparently affected by the amount of epididymal fat present when they use the $^{133}$Xenon-clearance method of determining blood flow.

The effects of depopulation of the testis of the rat by X ray and the affects on blood flow are similar to the results found by Bindon & Waites (11) following hypophysectomy. After an initial decline in blood flow from 1 to 10 days after hypophysectomy, testicular and epididymal blood flow returned to levels approximately normal 19 days following the removal. Blood flow exceeded that of intact animals 28 days following hypophysectomy, in spite of the fact that testis and epididymal weights had declined drastically.

## Countercurrent Exchange

The role of the pampiniform plexus in the countercurrent heat exchange has been known for a long time. The extent of the countercurrent exchange of heat and possibly other elements deeper in the testis is not well known. Setchell (113) has cited references indicating that arterial blood below the vascular cone or arterial rete is not different in its general content of oxygen saturation of hemoglobin, $Po_2$, $Pco_2$, pH, glucose, or lactate concentrations. However, there appears to be little or no evidence concerning the possible countercurrent exchange of substances deeper within the testis between the inward bound arteries and the outward bound veins.

One interesting aspect of the blood flow studies conducted by Free & Jaffe (41) is the consistent finding that vasoactive agents are equally effective in altering blood flow whether they are adminsitered into the testicular artery or into the testicular vein at levels that are ineffective peripherally. Studies utilizing cross-circulation of the testes or bypass of the pampiniform plexus suggest that such agents pass from the veins leaving the testis directly to the spermatic artery within the pampiniform plexus (41). Studies by Free et al (42) show that normally occurring compounds (i.e. testosterone) can also "recycle" in the pampiniform plexus. These investigators calculated that the percentage of testosterone transferred from vein to artery by this route was of the order of 15%. A similar countercurrent exchange between vein and artery has been suggested by Barrett et al (5) in the utero-ovarian vein and artery, where tritium-labeled $PGF_{2\alpha}$ infused in the uterine vein of a ewe hastened luteolysis in the ovary, and increased concentrations of the labeled compound could be found in the iliac artery. This type of mechanism, which has been indicated as occurring both near the ovary of the female and in the pampiniform plexus of the male, may be a significant concentrating mechanism in other organs.

## Seminiferous Tubular Fluid

For many years, the secretions of the seminiferous tubules and other tubular portions of the testis were considered primarily as a passive vehicle for carrying spermatozoa from the testis (113). However, due largely to the efforts of Setchell and his co-workers, it has recently been shown that the exocrine secretions likely play a major role in the total process of spermatogenesis (118). This group has used three major techniques to collect the secretions of the testis and measure the amount of secretion. By cannulation of the rete testis, they have demonstrated that the amount of secretion is much greater than had previously been supposed, resulting in a change in the sperm concentration from the rete area of about 1% of the volume to 70% of the volume in the epididymis, as demonstrated by Crabo (25). In addition to the technique of cannulation of the rete testis, a procedure of ligating the efferent ducts and measuring the increase in weight and water content of the ligated testis has given some estimate of the fluid accumulation (114).

A third technique used by these investigators involves use of a fine glass capillary tubing to puncture and sample fluid from an individual seminiferous tubule. This same instrument is used to fill the tubule with colored oil and then later to sample the fluid secreted by the cells lining the seminiferous tubule that breaks up the column of oil. Fluid thus collected is of different composition from that obtained from the rete testis (126).

Setchell (113) has suggested that the seminiferous tubules, each of which connects to the rete testis with both ends of the tubule, are so constructed that there is likely a circulation of fluid from the rete testis through the seminiferous tubule back to the rete testis. In general the testicular fluid is higher than plasma or lymph in its potassium and chloride content and lower in its sodium and bicarbonate levels, and contains no glucose or fructose but generally seems to be high in concentrations of inositol. The protein content is low and the concentrations of most of the free amino acids are lower than in plasma, with the exceptions of glutamic acid, glycine, alanine, aspartic acid, and glutamine. The composition of the rete fluid has been found to differ from the secretions within the tubules. Fluid sampled with the glass capillary directly from the seminiferous tubule contains four times as much potassium as fluid from the rete testis. Also, the concentration of spermatozoa is much higher. The rete area secretes fluid much higher in sodium and chloride and lower in potassium and bicarbonate.

## Factors Influencing Tubular Fluid Secretion

Setchell & Waites (118) believe that fluid secretion is essential for spermatogenesis, but that the reverse is not necessarily required. Although no fluid is secreted in the testis of the prepuberal animal, fluid secretion begins in the testis before the first spermatozoa are shed (114). Mature levels of secretions are reached earlier in age than are the mature sperm-producing levels.

Vitale-Calpe & Burgos (138, 139) have suggested that gonadotropin (LH administration) causes an increased flow of fluid from the testis to the rete testis and that
increased levels of circulating LH hasten the liberation of mature spermatids. However, Setchell and associates (116) were unable to corroborate these findings and
have indicated that LH levels had no effect on the fluid secretion by the testis in the
hamster and rat. Administration of human chorion gonadotropine (HCG) or pregnant mare serum (PMS) for 9 weeks caused a decrease in sperm production but had
little or no effect on the fluid secretion; neither did ovine prolactin or growth
hormone have a signfiicant effect on fluid secretion in the rat (116). Thus, while the
essentiality of gonadotropin in spermatogenesis seems fairly well established, there
still seems to be disagreement concerning the role of these hormones in the secretion
of fluids from the testis.

The effect of local heating of the testis on its spermatogenic and fluid secretion
functions has been investigated. Setchell & Waites (119) found that sperm concentration in the rete testis fluid began dropping between 6 and 10 days following heat
treatment. However, there was no change in fluid secretion per unit weight of testis,
nor was there a change in the concentration of inositol, glycine, or potassium in the
testis fluid. Suoranta (122) showed that localized high temperature treatment of the
testicular capsule resulted in damaged tubules and that the germinal epithelia both
in the area and spreading to the rete testis were damaged beyond repair. This
treatment, as well as the production of microsphere emboli in the intratesticular
arterioles, indicated that the advance of the epithelial degeneration was not related
to the changes seen in the intratesticular blood vessels. Suoranta (122) suggested that
either epithelial or fluid flow changes resulting from the early obstruction of the
affected tubule was responsible for the advance of the degeneration.

Setchell & Brown (115) reported that fluid secretion was reduced by metabolic
alkalosis induced by intravenous infusions of sodium acetate or bicarbonate, but was
unaffected by the infusion of similar amounts of sodium and sodium chloride.
Neither hypotension nor inhibitors of carbonic anhydrase given by mouth had an
effect on fluid secretion. However, acetazolamide injected intravenously and ethox-
yzolamide injected intraperitoneally decreased fluid secretions. VanDemark et al
(127) showed that early release of spermatozoa from the Sertoli cells resulted from
exposing rats to elevated levels of carbon dioxide. These several findings raise the
question as to whether pH may play a role in the release of spermatozoa or in
eliciting hormone release, increased fluid secretion, or other reactions which trigger
the release.

## ENZYME ASSOCIATIONS IN THE TESTIS

In recent years a large number of metabolic changes or alterations in biochemical
constituents have been recorded for testes following treatments which physiologically or pathologically alter testicular function; these changes involve differences in
respiration, protein synthesis, lipid levels and metabolism, and many other properties (68). Some of the changes occurring soon after treatment are likely involved in
the chain of events leading to damage of the germinal cells, but few measurements

have been made prior to the time that histological lesions become evident. Therefore, interpretation of biochemical data depends on the relative proportions of various cell types existing in the testes at the time of sampling, as well as the normality of these cell types. For example, the loss of germinal cells would result in a change from a biochemical pattern mostly reflecting normal germinal cells to a pattern reflecting largely nongerminal cells. The biochemistry of nongerminal cells might also be altered by nondestructive changes in the surviving cells themselves or by changes due to loss of associated cells.

If changes are detected even prior to massive cellular disappearance, it is still difficult to determine which changes represent the primary treatment-induced biochemical lesion, and which result from amplification of changes occurring as a result of that lesion.

If changes caused by treatment are to be differentiated from these secondary changes, if metabolic characteristics of particular cell types in the testis and the role of metabolic changes in cellular division or differentiation are to be elucidated, and if cell types affected by specific treatments are to be delineated more rapidly than can be accomplished by histological techniques, it is necessary to define nonmorphological characteristics of the cells that characterize each cell type. Referring to this as "fingerprinting" the testis, Bishop (12) suggested that the enzyme profiles of the different cell types could be used to identify key stages of spermatogenesis if specific enzymes or specific isoenzymatic forms of enzymes are limited to, or associated with, particular stages. Quantitative data on such enzymes could also serve as functional indicators of spermatogenic activity. Until enzyme-cellular associations become better recognized, examination of the causal relationship of enzymes with specific steps in germ cell differentiations will be impeded.

Until recently, histochemical data were widely used to localize enzymatic activity in the testis. Although such data can often be semiquantitative, the use of histochemistry is limited by the inconsistent degree of staining of lysosomal enzymes, membrane-bound enzymes, and soluble enzymes, and by the inability to distinguish in most cases between different isoenzymes with similar function in the testis. Demonstration of enzymes in tissue homogenates of whole testes from animals with developing or regressing testes is more reproducibly quantitative, and separation or differential quantitation of isoenzymes from the testis (149) permits a more complete enzyme profile. When this profile is completed for tissue preparations containing different cellular populations, "fingerprinting" will become feasible.

Tissues used to relate biochemical parameters to testicular cell types include (a) testes taken during development from aspermatogenesis to complete spermatogenesis, (b) tissues exhibiting degenerative changes in spermatogenesis, (c) preparations from seminiferous tubular and interstitial tissues physically separated from each other, (d) tubular sections separated according to the stage of the spermatogenic cycle, (e) cellular elements from minced tubular preparations separated according to cell type, and (f) combinations of the above.

Testes taken at different ages during puberty can be examined for the cell types existing at each age. In rats, for example, only spermatogonia and Sertoli cells are present in the seminiferous tubule at 10 days of age. In testes from 20-day-old rats, preleptotene and leptotene primary spermatocytes are present; late primary spermatocytes appear at about 25 days of age. At 30 days, cap stage spermatids are present, with elongated spermatids appearing in 40-day-old rats. At 50 days of age, testicular sperm are recognizable in the seminiferous tubular lumen (23, 77, 120, 134). Changes in testis weight and volumetric proportions during this period are largely due to the addition of these cells. Changes in enzyme concentrations are generally assumed, in the absence of evidence to the contrary, to be attributable to relative enzyme contributions of these cells (i.e. if enzyme concentration increases between two periods, the "newest" cell type is considered enzyme rich; if concentration decreases, activity is lacking in the cell type).

Changes in enzyme levels have been examined during loss of germinal cells caused by hypophysectomy (13, 34, 95), allergic aspermatogenesis (12, 73, 74), seasonal decline (12, 57), treatment with aspermatogenic hormones or chemicals, and other deleterious conditions (51). In some cases, biochemical changes can be reexamined during spermatogenic recrudescence following conditions for treatments which are temporary or reversible (52).

The technique first reported by Christensen & Mason (21) to physically separate seminiferous tubules from interstitial elements in the testis permits examination of actual enzyme levels in each portion of the testis. Parvinen & Vanha-Perttula (101) extended the use of this procedure by cutting tubules into fragments representing specific stages of the seminiferous epithelial cycle (23). The stages were identified by differences in light absorption observed using a transillumination technique and verified histologically. Fragments were also subjected to biochemical analysis (101).

Although pure preparations of cell populations have not yet been achieved, a good deal of information has been gained about the biochemistry of testicular cell types following their separation by velocity sedimentation (48, 82, 93) or gel separation (45). An interim step before all normal cells can be separated might be to selectively destroy cells which contaminate a peak, using specific aspermatogenic agents (51, 64), prior to in vitro cell separations (83). Other combinations of the above techniques and the involvement of other procedures, such as tissue culture, as they are improved should result in a more complete enzyme "fingerprint" of the testis.

A number of recent studies on localization characteristics of selected enzymes in testicular cells are summarized in the following pages. For a review of earlier studies, the reader is referred elsewhere (12, 13, 51).

## Acid Phosphatase

Histochemical detection of testicular acid phosphatase has been accomplished many times since the original report of Gomori in 1941 (see 13, 109). Enzyme activity has been located histochemically in virtually all cell types of the testis, and increases during development of spermatogenesis whether measured histochemically (13, 92, 109) or biochemically (92, 109). Examination of subcellular distribution of total enzyme activity generally suggested that most of the activity was lysosomal (74, 92, 110), but significant activity has been found in the soluble fraction (110).

When spermatogenic elements were destroyed by irradiation of rat (56) or mouse (78) testes, by aspermatogenic autoimmunization of guinea pigs (74), by hypophysectomizing rats (34), or by treating rats with estrogen (33), specific activity or concentrations of acid phosphatase generally remained unchanged for a period of 7–10 days, then decreased when the enzyme was assayed biochemically (34, 56, 73, 92), but histochemical staining was generally increased in seminiferous tubules (33, 78, 92). That the rise and fall of acid phosphatase may not be entirely a function of the presence or absence of cells became evident when Blackshaw & Hamilton (16) demonstrated changes in the enzyme within 2 hr of heat treatment of the testes. Studying the histochemical distribution of acid phosphatase during the spermatogenic cycle, Posalaki et al (105) reported that the tubular enzyme activity was associated with different elements of the epithelium in different stages of the cycle.

A good deal of the confusion concerning testicular acid phosphatase localization was alleviated in 1971 when Vanha-Perttula (129) reported that rat testes contain multiple forms of the enzyme (or multiple enzymes catalyzing similar reactions) and outlined their substrate, inhibitor, kinetic, and chromatographic characteristics. During extended studies of the four isoenzymes found following DEAE-cellulose chromatography, enzymes I and II were identified as lysosomal and forms III and IV as soluble enzymes (130). Acid phosphatase I was present in homogenates of total testis tissue but was not found in chromatograms of isolated seminiferous tubules (130); activity of this isoenzyme, based on differential substrate and modifier conditions, decreased slightly between 10 and 30 days of age in rats and was essentially unchanged during cryptorchidism (134). These data suggest an interstitial cell lysosomal location for this form. Although enzyme II was found in small amounts in isolated seminiferous tubules (130), total activity in testicular homogenates (129) and changes during puberty and following cryptorchidism (134) indicate that this isoenzyme is located primarily in interstitial tissue.

Isoenzyme III was as active in seminiferous tubular preparations as in total testis homogenates (BBA), suggesting a tubular location, but activity was essentially unchanged during puberty or following cryptorchidism (134), implicating Sertoli cells and spermatogonia as sources of the enzyme.

Activity of enzyme IV appears limited to the testis, whereas I, II, and III are present in other tissues. The isoenzyme is abundant in the soluble fraction of mature tubules (130) but is not present in testes from 10-day-old rats (134). The rapid increase during puberty and marked fall following cryptorchidism (134) suggested that enzyme IV is associated with more mature germ cells.

To further delineate the cellular associations of enzymes III and IV, Parvinen & Vanha-Perttula (101) isolated tubular fragments corresponding to specific stages of the seminiferous epithelial cycle and examined enzyme levels in these fragments. Acid phosphatase III did not vary markedly in the various stages of the seminiferous cycle, consonant with a location in Sertoli cells or spermatogonia. On the other hand, enzyme IV displayed a gradual increase during Leblond & Clermont's stages I through VII, when maximal numbers of spermatids are present (23), and decreased to minimal levels by stage IX, when testicular sperm have been released. The data suggest that enzyme IV may be produced by relatively less mature germ cells, but is most concentrated in postmeiotic cells.

## Aminopeptidase

Until recently, little has been known of the aminopeptidase content of testes, as histochemical localization of these enzymes is difficult (131) and results in different species are inconsistent (29). Blech (17) measured the hydrolysis of five amino acid substrates by testis tissue and reported an increase in concentration of activity during cryptorchidism. Autoimmune aspermatogenesis in guinea pigs also increased leucine aminopeptidase activity (73).

Using DEAE-cellulose chromatography, Vanha-Perttula demonstrated the presence of four aminopeptidases (131) and four dipeptidyl aminopeptidases (133) in rat testes, though none were unique to this tissue. He characterized the substrate spectra and effects of activators and inhibitors on the four monopeptidyl aminopeptidases (131) and two of the dipeptidyl enzymes (133). Localization studies were also conducted (132, 133).

Aminopeptidases I and II were present in only small amounts in tubules, but quite active in total testis (131). Both were high in prepubertal testes, decreased at 20 and 30 days of age, and increased markedly following cryptorchidism (132). Enzyme I was connected to the mitochondrial-lysosomal particles of the interstitium, and II was membrane localized (131).

Enzymes III and IV were soluble enzymes located mainly in the seminiferous tubules (131). Aminopeptidase III increased markedly during puberty and decreased rapidly following cryptorchidism (132), as one might expect of enzymes located in more mature germ cells. Differences in activity of this enzyme in different stages of the seminiferous cycle (101) support this concept.

Aminopeptidase IV was present in high concentration in immature testes, decreased with age, and increased following cryptorchidism (132), which suggests a spermatogonial or Sertoli cell location.

The two dipeptidyl aminopeptidases studied in detail, I and II, were both lysosomal, as compared to soluble enzyme III and microsomal IV (133). Enzyme I was not present in separated tubules; enzyme II (cathepepsin) was present in tubules but was proportionally greater in interstitial tissue. Neither changed markedly with age or cryptorchidism.

## Carnitine Acetyltransferase

Marquis & Fritz (see 137) reported carnitine acetyltransferase (CAT) increased from low levels in prepuberal rat testes to high adult levels by 35 days, and declined following cryptorchidism. This led Vernon, Go & Fritz (137) to further examine the location of this enzyme in the rat testis. Enzyme levels were minimal in rat testis homogenates until 24 days of age; thereafter, levels increased rapidly, reaching maximal levels in 65- to 150-day-old animals. Carnitine palmitoyltransferase was not elevated during a similar period (137). As might be expected, CAT decreased rapidly following hypophysectomy, reaching prepuberal levels about 35 days after the operation (49). Restoration of enzyme activity was partially accomplished by FSH, LH, or testosterone, but normal levels were achieved only after treatment of hypophysectomized rats with FSH and LH or FSH and testosterone (49).

When spermatogenic cells were separted using the velocity sedimentation technique (48), testes from 7- and 14-day-old rats were found to contain mostly spermatogonia, with a few early primary spermatocytes in the latter group; these cells contained negligible amounts of CAT (137). Cell fractions which contained the greatest proportions of pachytene and diplotene spermatocytes, from 26-day-old or adult rats, also contained the greatest concentrations of CAT; high levels of the enzyme were also present in round spermatids, and significant levels were present in elongated spermatids and sperm cells (49, 137).

## Hexokinase

The high level of glucose utilization by mature spermatogenic elements has led several workers to investigate aspects of testicular hexokinase. Ewing & Schanbacher (39) found initial increases in testicular enzyme activity 2 hr after cryptorchidism in rats and a decline below normal levels 12–48 hr after operation. They did not, however, determine whether multiple forms exist, as in other tissues. Earlier work in *Drosophila* (12) showed a testis isoenzyme of hexokinase, "Hex-t," and work in the rat (120) and guinea pig (104) indicated that a "sperm-type" of a hexokinase might be limited to the testis. This enzyme form has been shown in adult testes from men (120) and rats (19, 120). Recent work from Mexico (120) and in our laboratory (19) confirms the presence of this form and demonstrates that sperm-type hexokinase first appears between 20 and 30 days of age and increases to a maximum before sperm appear in the testes. The two reports differ, however, as to the effects of cryptorchidism on the enzyme. Sosa et al (120) report in their discussion that sperm-type hexokinase disappears following cryptorchidism, but Cheng (19) found only a partial decrease. Furthermore, sperm-type hexokinase could be induced in testes of 20-day-old rats with HCG (19) or in seminal vesicles with testosterone (Cheng, Gomes & VanDemark, unpublished data).

In addition to sperm-type hexokinase, isoenzymes I and II increased with growth of the testis, and hexokinase IV (glucokinase) appeared at 30–40 days of age. Adult patterns of these forms were not dramatically influenced by 28 days of cryptorchidism (19).

## Lactate Dehydrogenase

Probably the most carefully studied testicular enzyme to date has been lactate dehydrogenase (LDH), despite the fact that histochemical studies of LDH in testes with sodium lactate as substrate generally failed to yield interpretable data. Early recognition of testis-specific isoenzymatic form(s) of LDH in some birds and mammals led to extensive studies of the enzyme. Additional research impetus was gained by the discovery that this isoenzyme, called LDH-X, gave a specific histochemical reaction to sodium valerate in rat and mouse testes, but not in other species (12, 13, 149). Characterization of LDH-X and the other five common isoenzymes of LDH has been accomplished (13).

LDH-X is not present in immature testes, but appears as one or more isoenzymes in adult testes from man, mouse, rat, rabbit, dog, guinea pig, ram, bull, pigeon (13), and bat (57). The contribution of LDH-X to total LDH activity in rat testes was

0% at 20 days of age, 27% at 30 days, and 30–37% thereafter (14). LDH-X comprises 80–90% of the total activity in rabbit sperm (13, 149). The testicular isoenzyme first appeared at about 15 days of age in mice and showed developmental patterns similar to those shown for rats (15).

LDH-X isoenzymes were present in testes of adult bats during seasonal spermatogenesis and disappeared when the testes regressed (57). In laboratory mammals, loss of spermatogenesis following cryptorchidism in mice or guinea pigs (13), hypophysectomy in mice (15) or rats (34, 145), or estrogen treatment in rats (33) is accompanied by a precipitous decline in LDH-X, with little change in the other isoenzymes. Loss of spermatogenic cells and LDH-X could be prevented in rats with FSH, LH, and testosterone (32, 145).

It may be concluded that LDH-X is associated with the primary spermatocytes of the testis, probably beginning with pachytene cells, and with all postmeiotic cells. Each attempt to demonstrate increases or decreases in its level without concurrent changes in numbers of these cells (32, 39) has failed.

## Sorbitol Dehydrogenase

Although sorbitol dehydrogenase (SDH) is not limited to testicular tissue, it appears in testes of all species studied from grasshoppers to guinea pigs, cocks to bulls (12). Activity is very low in testes of immature animals and increases rapidly at about 20 days of age in rats (95) and at 4–5 weeks of age in guinea pigs (12), at a time when primary spermatocytes first appear. In both species, and in fowl, SDH concentration continues to increase, reaching adult levels at 60 days in rats and 12 weeks in guinea pigs. Sea urchins undergoing postspawning spermatogenesis demonstrate increased SDH concentrations during spermatogenic activity (12). Rapid depletion of testicular SDH is seen in cryptorchid or autoimmune aspermatogenic guinea pigs (12, 73) and in hypophysectomized rats (95). Hormonal maintenance of testes in hypophysectomized rats (95), histochemical localization in bull testes (94), and fluorescent antibody labeling of SDH in guinea pigs (12) support the localization of SDH in more mature spermatogenic elements.

## Other Enzymes

A number of enzymes which appear to be heterogeneously distributed in the testis seem likely candidates for more extensive studies, but space permits no more than a cursory mention of some of those subjected to recent experimentation.

Males & Turkington (91) confirmed and expanded the early work of Steinberger & Nelson (see 91) which demonstrated the localization of hyaluronidase in more mature cells of the germinal epithelium, and several workers (e.g. 34) have confirmed that β-glucuronidase is concentrated in lysosomes of spermatogonia and Sertoli cells.

Studies designed to elucidate the earliest site of cadmium-induced necrosis in the rat testis led to experiments on the nature of carbonic anhydrase isoenzymes in the testis. Five carbonic anhydrase isoenzymes in testes were identified, including one isoenzyme absent from erythrocytes or kidneys (61). Although a nontubular site was suggested for the $T$ isoenzyme of carbonic anhydrase, further localization has not been carried out.

The observation by Ewing & Schanbacher (39) that phosphofructokinase levels decrease within 8 hr of cryptorchidism in the rat suggests that further study on the localization of this enzyme and its isoenzymatic forms [two appear to be present in testis (125)] may be warranted. Similarly, Free & Payvar (44) reported that pyruvate dehydrogenase decreased significantly 8 hr after translocation of rat testes to the abdomen; enzyme concentration remained at 30–40% of control levels 14–120 days after cryptorchidism was established, suggesting a high specific activity of the enzyme in postmeiotic cells.

With the growing interest in adenosine 3',5'-monophosphate as a "second messenger" of hormone action, the report by Monn, Desautel & Christiansen (96) of seven separate isoenzymes of cyclic nucleotide phosphodiesterase in rabbit and rat tissues may lead to a better understanding of cellular specificity for pituitary or gonadal hormones. Of these isoenzymes, the testes contained two: $c$ and $f$. The $f$ component was present only in the testis, first appearing there coincident with the elongation of spermatids (i.e. 40 days of age in rats) and increasing to adult levels at 50 days of age (96).

Other studies indicate that Sertoli cells are the primary localization of ornithine decarboxylase (89), and spermatogonia and spermatocytes appear to be rich sources of uridine dephosphatase (146). Spermatocytes and spermatids appear to be the location of S-adenosyl-L-methione decarboxylase (89), myoinositol synthesizing enzymes (98), alcohol dehydrogenase (36), and acid proteinase (34). Arylsulfatase, on the other hand, appears localized in spermatids (112).

## HORMONES OF THE SEMINIFEROUS TUBULE

### Androgen Production

The dependence of the spermatogenic processes on androgens has been recognized for some time, but until recently it was generally assumed that these androgens were produced in the Leydig cells surrounding the tubules. This concept was first questioned in 1965, when Christensen & Mason (21) physically separated the seminiferous tubular and interstitial portions of rat testes and incubated each with progresterone-4-$^{14}$C. These workers observed incorporation of label into androgens in both component tissues, with incorporation by interstitial cells exceeding that into tubular androgens by 2.6–9.6 times, suggesting that tubules might be capable of producing 10–25% of the testosterone derived from progesterone in the rat testis. Although specific activity of tubular conversion (i.e. after correction for wet weight) was only 0.6–2.5% that of the much smaller interstitial portion, it is possible that tubular requirements for androgens could be best satisfied by small amounts of locally produced hormone. Others (10, 35, 87) have extended this finding to include pregnenolone as a permissable precursor in humans (87), squirrels (81), and cobras (87), as well as rats (10, 35). Specific activities of steroidogenic enzymes in tubular preparations were 13–34% as high as similar enzymes in interstitial preparations, depending on the enzyme (9, 53, 60) and excepting cholesterol side-chain cleavage enzyme (see below). Disagreement exists concerning the preferred conversion pathway in vitro: Bell, Vinson & Lacy (10) reported that the $\Delta^4$ pathway predominates, whereas Ellis & Van Kampen (35) found that the $\Delta^5$ pathway was preferred by tubular preparations.

The intratubular sites in steroid conversions were studied by Galena & Terner (45), who separated tubular cells on Sephadex G-25 after treating tubules with distilled water to destroy Leydig cells. In subsequent incubations, "round germinal cells" (spermatocytes and early spermatids, according to the authors) proved capable of converting labeled progesterone to androstenedione and testosterone. Conversely, production of aspermatogenesis by heat treatment of rats (81) did not diminish the ability of tubules to convert 21-carbon precursors to androgens, suggesting that Sertoli cells or basal spermatogonia are responsible for the conversion. Furthermore, specific activities of the conversion, if localized in Sertoli cells, for example, could be of the magnitude exhibited by Leydig cells (10). Tubules from X-irradiated rats produced slightly less androgen than controls 20–25 days after treatment (35).

The ability of seminiferous tubules to biosynthesize androgens de novo, however, was cast in serious doubt by the observation of Hall, Irby & de Kretser (58) that tubules were unable to convert cholesterol-$^3$H to androgens, suggesting that side-chain cleavage of the parent molecule was not possible in tubular preparations. Total production of unlabeled testosterone (i.e. from endogenous precursors) following in vitro incubations was one fourth as efficient (ng/mg of tissue) in tubules as in interstitium, according to Lacy et al (81), but only 0.2% as efficient in tubular preparations incubated by van der Vusse, Kalkman & van der Molen, (128). Cooke et al (24), using a similar system, could not demonstrate synthesis of testosterone by tubules in vitro, but inconsistent testosterone synthesis was shown by whole testis preparations.

Since cholesterol is not effectively transported from blood into seminiferous tubules (100), the question arose concerning the amount of exogenous (labeled) cholesterol that might have penetrated the tubule in vitro in the studies by Hall, Irby & de Kretser (58). To determine whether substrate availability was limiting, Wisner & Gomes (unpublished) repeated the experiments of Hall, Irby & de Kretser (58) using tissue homogenates. Comparable results were found, i.e. tubules did not convert cholesterol-$^3$H to measurable testosterone-$^3$H. In examining the same question, Irusta & Wasserman (63) determined whether homogenates and mitochondria of seminiferous tubules from rats could convert cholesterol-$^3$H to pregnenolone-$^3$H. Cleavage of cholesterol was found in both preparations, but quantitative comparisons with interstitial incubations were not made. Bass, Bell & Lacy (7), also using tubular and subcellular preparations, measured the cleavage of isocaproate-$^{14}$C from cholesterol-26-$^{14}$C, as an estimate of side-chain cleavage. Seminiferous tubules exhibited 1.2–6.4% of the specific activity found for interstitium, and tubular mitochondria were 2% as active as interstitial mitochondria in cleaving the side chain from cholesterol (7). Using tissue homogenates or washed mitochondria, and correcting for cleavage rates in a nonsteroidogenic tissue (kidney), we (Wisner & Gomes, unpublished data) found interstitial tissues were 100–1000 times more active (per milligram of protein) than tubular homogenates or mitochondria in cleaving cholesterol. A part of the difference between these two studies may be a result of tubular enzyme loss in the study by Wisner & Gomes, as Bass, Bell & Lacy (7) suggested that the tubular enzyme is particularly labile during tissue preparation; it seems unlikely, however, that this accounts for all of the difference.

Although these studies do not confirm the "zero-activity" finding of Hall, Irby & de Kretser (58), they do point out that cleavage activity in tubules is quite low. Aside from the question of total contribution of tubules, these data may underestimate true cleavage activity in the following cases: 1. seminiferous tubular side-chain cleavage enzyme, unlike the interstitial enzyme, may utilize cholesterol from a subcellular compartment (4) that is unavailable to exogenous (labeled) cholesterol; 2. cholesterol esters, rather than free cholesterol, may normally serve as enzyme substrates (6); 3. conjugated cholesterol (e.g. cholesteryl sulfate) may be utilized (108) in tubular steroidogenic pathways. Until one of these is shown to be the case, one must conclude that de novo synthesis of androgens in seminiferous tubules is at best minimal. This of course does not exclude the conversion of Leydig cell-derived precursors to androgens by seminiferous tubules in vivo.

## Regulation of FSH Levels

Although it is generally agreed that testosterone is the major regulator of LH secretion in the male, the factors controlling circulating levels of FSH remain uncertain. The results of many studies since the early thirties (see 52 for references) suggest that elements within the seminiferous tubule may somehow influence FSH levels in circulation. Extensive studies by Johnsen (67) have indicated a reciprocal relationship between gonadotropin excretion and degree of spermatogenesis in men, but deletion of data from aspermatogenic men or men with severe spermatogenic disruption reduced the correlation to nonsignificant levels. Other workers (28, 40, 102) failed to find a relationship between degree of oligospermia and serum FSH in men, but changes in both FSH and LH have been reported for such men (22, 76).

In those clinical studies which failed to demonstrate a relationship between gonadotropins and degree of spermatogenesis, however, FSH levels have been consistently elevated in cases of azoospermia and lack of complete spermatogenesis (28, 40, 135). In experimental animals increased serum FSH has been reported for cryptorchid rats (1, 2, 123) and for rats treated with antispermatogenic agents (27, 52). In the latter study (52) loss of spermatogenesis, caused by two chemically different compounds, was accompanied by an increase in serum FSH; recovery of spermatogenesis occurred concomitantly with a subsequent decrease in circulating FSH (52). Levels of LH in the above studies were either unaffected or were increased only by the most dramatic antispermatogenic conditions (27).

Two general hypotheses have been formulated to explain the relationship between FSH and spermatogenesis: the "nonutilization" theory and the "inhibin" theory. With regard to the first hypothesis, Heller (see 97) suggested the germinal epithelium metabolized FSH during the action of the hormone on the tissue; if the spermatogenic elements were lost, nonutilization of FSH would lead to increased serum levels and increased urinary excretion. Pituitary FSH changes which occur in aspermatogenic animals (52) presumably could be explained by a short-loop feedback of FSH. On the other hand, the hypothesis cannot explain long-term castration-like changes in the hypophyses of aspermatogenic animals, unless these are due to secondary changes occurring in the Leydig cells. In an experiment conducted to determine whether gonadotropins are changed, or "utilized," in target tissues, Dufau, Catt & Tsuruhara (30) found that human chorionic gonadotropin was not inactivated during binding to testicular receptors; unless FSH behaves differently, these data are difficult to reconcile with a nonutilization hypothesis.

Alternatively, many workers have suggested that the tubule produces a substance, generally referred to as inhibin, that regulates circulating levels of FSH. According to Swerdloff, Jacobs & Odell (123) the depressive action of spermatogenesis on serum FSH first occurs between 35 and 50 days of age in rats; at this time, serum FSH begins to decrease from its highest level (35 days) and continues to decrease until it reaches adult levels at about 63 days of age, when spermatogenesis is complete (123). Inasmuch as the fall in FSH was prevented by cryptorchidism, these workers proposed that an FSH inhibitor is elaborated as sperm are produced (123). Although Kragt & Masken (79) found an increase in rat FSH between 40 and 60 days of age, and although FSH levels do not decline in rams (26) and increase in men (18, 90) during sexual maturation, the inverse relationship between full spermatogenesis and FSH levels appears valid for men (28, 40, 135) as well as for rats (27, 52).

A general lack of information has prevented our concepts concerning actual compound(s) regulating FSH from developing much beyond the level of pure speculation, but the classes of compounds usually included in such speculation include androgens, estrogens, and a nonsterodial inhibin. For a number of years, testicular testosterone was considered sufficiently inhibitory to explain FSH relationships. Since several workers had found that testosterone inhibited FSH, but less efficiently than it inhibited LH (26, 84, 124), a small decrease in testosterone production by aspermatogenic testes could lead to increased FSH with continued depression of LH. A number of workers have indicated decreased testosterone production by aspermatogenic testes (2, 35, 52, 111), but others have shown no consistent effect of arrested spermatogenesis on testosterone levels (135) nor have they recorded increase in testosterone production by cryptorchid testes (38; 86; Gomes, unpublished). Although a single dose of testosterone was ineffective as an inhibitor of FSH in castrate male rats (46, 72), daily treatment reduced FSH and LH equally (47). To alleviate the problem of trying to overcome castration effects in rats, Walsh, Swerdloff & Odell (144) treated intact male rats with the antiandrogen cyproterone to decrease feedback effects of androgens on pituitary gonadotropins; levels of cyproterone which increased serum LH 25–50% had no effect on FSH titers.

Differential effects on various parameters of androgens other than testosterone (20, 124, 148) suggest that one of these compounds may selectively suppress LH in aspermatogenic rats with no effects on FSH. Although $5\alpha$-androstanediol was markedly more effective than testosterone and dihydrotestosterone in depressing LH in castrated male rats, it had no significant effect on FSH levels (148). If a compound such as $5\alpha$-androstanediol were increased at the expense of testosterone in aspermatogenic animals, FSH might be allowed to rise with concomitant suppression of LH. Yamada, Yasue & Matsumoto (147) found a marked difference in metabolism of testosterone to $5\alpha$-androstanediol by testes and seminiferous tubules of immature and mature rats, with the former tenfold more active in this respect. Rivarola, Podesta & Chemes (106) found peak conversion of testosterone to $5\alpha$-adrostanediol by testes and tubules during maturation of spermatogenesis; rats with complete spermatogenesis (60–365 days old) exhibited half the activity of developing rats. Gupta et al (55) found one fifth the $\alpha$-reductase activity in mature testes compared to immature rat testes. Gupta et al (55) also reported a reversion to the prepuberal pattern of testosterone metabolism following irradiation-induced loss of germinal elements. On the other hand, Ewing et al (38) found that the proportion of total androgen not attributable to testosterone in perfusates of rabbit testes decreased following cryptorchidism, but individual compounds were not studied. The production of $5\alpha$-reduced metabolites in the testis, however, may be of minor importance peripherally, since large amounts of these compounds appear to be produced by peripheral conversion of testosterone (3, 75).

Among the several authors who have proposed that the FSH-inhibiting substance from the testis is an estrogen, Johnsen (67) and Lacy (81) have developed the most refined hypothetical models. These propose that the final stages of spermatogenesis somehow increase the ability of the Sertoli cell to produce estrogens which in turn suppress FSH production and/or release. Lacy et al (81) have reported the presence of Sertoli cell estrogens in rats; Longcope, Widrich & Sawin (88) have shown that the human testis secretes estrone and estradiol-$17\beta$; and Kaivola & Johansson (71a) have reported decreased urinary excretion of estrone by men with sperm abnormalities. Kulin & Reiter (80) found a differential effect of estrogen on gonadotropin levels in normal men: FSH was decreased by low dose ethinyl estradiol, but LH was not affected, which lends support to the estrogen feedback hypothesis. To the contrary, however, Kalra et al (72) found that estrogen injections into castrated male rats depressed plasma LH but increased circulating FSH levels, and Naftolin, Ryan & Petro (99) demonstrated that hypothalamic tissues of the rat can convert androgens to estrogens, even though this aromatization step is apparently unnecessary for androgenic activity (124).

Although the above studies document both ends in the hypothetical chain of events necesary to support the hypothesis that inhibin is an estrogen (i.e. the testis can produce estrogens and estrogens can inhibit FSH), the apparent weakness comes in the intermediate links. It is generally recognized that peripheral aromatization of androgens is extensive (88); it has been suggested that this can account for all of the circulating estradiol and most of the estrone in men (85). Unless the testicular contribution of estrogens has been largely underestimated, then, it appears that levels of this hormone secreted into the general circulation would be overwhelmed by hormone from the nongonadal sources. If this were so, changes in testicular estrogen might not be of a magnitude to be recognized at the hypothalamo-pituitary system as other than normal variation.

If inhibin exists, and if it is nonsteroidal in nature, as suggested some forty years ago (see 52 for references), an entirely new approach to the search for inhibin appears necessary. Perhaps a first step in this direction was shown by Setchell & Sirinathsinghji (117), who found antigonadotropic activity in rete testis fluid from rams and boars and suggested that this heat-labile activity might represent inhibin. If this activity were lost in aspermatogenic animals, confirming its inhibin-like properties, rete fluid fractionations should serve to help identify the active compound involved.

Regardless of the nature of the feedback of spermatogenesis on FSH, several factors must be considered in studies on inhibin. Although destruction of the spermatogenic elements in the testis generally results in a selective increase in FSH, this increase never reaches the levels attained after castration, leading several authors to suggest that a second level of control over FSH must exist in the testis. Whether this is testicular androgen (1), a Sertoli cell product (123), or merely the residual production of inhibin, diminished but not destroyed by aspermatogenesis, must be resolved.

Removal of one half of the spermatogenic capacity in the animal, by unilateral cryptorchidism or by unilateral castration, might be expected to increase FSH levels to half those found in bilateral operations, if the inhibin–FSH relationship is quantitative in nature. Although indications of increased FSH in unilaterally castrated rats exist (37, 70), no changes were found in serum FSH following unilateral cryptorchidism (Gomes, unpublished). Furthermore, a minimal degree of complete spermatogenesis may effectively suppress FSH (40), which suggests that inhibin may act in a threshold, or even quantal, fashion in depressing FSH in the male.

*Literature Cited*

1. Altwein, J. E., Gittes, R. F. 1972. Effect of cryptorchidism and castration on FSH and LH levels in the adult rat. *Invest. Urol.* 10:167–70
2. Amatayakul, K., Ryan, R., Uozumi, T., Albert, A. 1971. A reinvestigation of testicular-anterior pituitary relationships in the rat. I. Effects of castration and cryptorchidism. *Endocrinology* 88:872–80
3. Arimasa, N., Kochakian, C. D. 1973. Epitestosterone and 5α-androstane-3α, 17β-diol: the characteristic metabolites of androst-4-ene-3,17-dione produced by mouse kidney *in vitro*. *Endocrinology* 92:72–82
4. Balasubramaniam, S., Mitropoulos, K. A., Myant, N. B. 1973. Evidence for the compartmentation of cholesterol in rat-liver microsomes. *Eur. J. Biochem.* 34:177–83
5. Barrett, S. et al 1971. Initiation of the oestrous cycle in the ewe by infusions of $PGF_{2\alpha}$ to the autotransplanted ovary. *J. Reprod. Fert.* 24:136–37
6. Bartke, A., Musto, N., Caldwell, B. V., Behrman, H. R. 1973. Effects of a cholesterol esterase inhibitor and of prostaglandin $F_{2\alpha}$ on testis cholesterol and on plasma testosterone in mice. *Prostaglandins* 3:97–104
7. Bass, J. J., Bell, J. B. G., Lacy, D. 1973. Side-chain cleavage of (26-$^{14}$C) cholesterol by rat testicular tissues and their subcellular fractions. *J. Endocrinol.* 56:321–22
8. Bedford, J. M. 1972. Sperm transport, capacitation and fertilization. In *Reproductive Biology*, ed. H. Balin, S. Glasser, 338–92. Amsterdam: Excerpta Med.
9. Bell, J. B. G. 1972. Interconversion of testosterone and androstenedione in the human testis: a comparison between the

activities displayed by the interstitium and the seminiferous tubules. *Experientia* 28:212–13

10. Bell, J. B. G., Vinson, G. P., Lacy, D. 1971. Studies on the structure and function of the mammalian testis. III. *In vitro* steroidogenesis by the seminiferous tubules of rat testis. *Proc. Roy. Soc. London B* 176:433–43

11. Bindon, B. M., Waites, G. M. H. 1968. Discrepancy in weight and blood flow of the left and right testis and epididymis of the mouse before and after hypophysectomy. *J. Endocrinol.* 40:385–86

12. Bishop, D. W. 1968. Testicular enzymes as fingerprints in the study of spermatogenesis. In *Reproduction and Sexual Behavior,* ed. M. Diamond, 261–86. Bloomington, Ind.: Indiana Univ. Press

13. Blackshaw, A. W. 1970. Histochemical localization of testicular enzymes. In *The Testis, Vol. 2–Biochemistry,* ed. A. D. Johnson, W. R. Gomes, N. L. VanDemark, 73–123. New York: Academic

14. Blackshaw, A. W., Elkington, J. S. H. 1970. Developmental changes in lactate dehydrogenase isoenzymes in the testis of the immature rat. *J. Reprod. Fert.* 22:69–75

15. Blackshaw, A. W., Elkington, J. S. H. 1970. The effect of age and hypophysectomy on growth and the isoenzymes of lactate dehydrogenase in the mouse testis. *Biol. Reprod.* 2:268–74

16. Blackshaw, A. W., Hamilton, D. 1970. The effect of heat on hydrolytic enzymes and spermatogenesis in the rat testis. *J. Reprod. Fert.* 22:569–71

17. Blech, W. 1968. Zur Biochemie der Hodenatrophie durch einseitigen experimentellen Kryptorchismus. *Acta Biol. Med. Germ.* 21:421–32

18. Blizzard, R. M. et al 1972. Pituitary-gonadal interrelationships in relation to puberty. In *Gonadotropins,* ed. B. B. Saxena, C. G. Beling, H. M. Gandy, 502–23. New York: Wiley-Interscience

19. Cheng, H. C. 1971. *Isoenzymes of hexokinase in rat testes at various developmental and endocrine states.* PhD dissertation. Ohio State Univ., Columbus

20. Chretien, M. 1972. Action comparée de la testostérone, de l'androstanolone et due 3β-androstanediol sur un effecteur: la gland sous-maxillaire de la Souris. *C. R. Acad. Sci. Paris* 274:3428–30

21. Christensen, A. K., Mason, N. R. 1965. Comparative ability of seminiferous tubules and interstitial tissue of rat testes to synthesize androgens from progesterone-4-$^{14}$C *in vitro. Endocrinology* 76:646–56

22. Christiansen, P. 1972. The excretion of FSH and LH in male hypogonadism. See Ref. 18, 609–15

23. Clermont, Y. 1972. Kinetics of spermatogenesis in mammals: seminiferous epithlial cycle and spermatogonial renewal. *Physiol. Rev.* 52:198–236

24. Cooke, B. A., de Jong, F. H., van der Molen, H. J., Rommerts, F. F. G. 1972. Endogenous testosterone concentrations in rat testis interstitial tissue and seminiferous tubules during *in vitro* incubation. *Nature New Biol.* 237:255–56

25. Crabo, B. 1965. Studies on the composition of epididymal content in bulls and boars. *Acta Vet. Scand.* 6:Suppl. 5

26. Crim, L. W., Geschwind, I. I. 1972. Patterns of FSH and LH secretion in the developing ram: influence of castration and replacement therapy with testosterone propionate. *Biol. Reprod.* 7:47–54

27. Debeljuk, L., Arimura, A., Schally, A. V. 1973. Pituitary and serum FSH and LH levels after massive and selective depletion of the germinal epithelium in the rat testis. *Endocrinology* 92:48–54

28. de Kretser, D. M. et al 1972. Hormonal, histological and chromosomal studies in adult males with testicular disorders. *J. Clin. Endocrinol. Metab.* 35:392–401

29. Dey, S. K., Deb, C. 1973. Testicular leucine aminopeptidase in different vertebrates. *Acta Histochem.* 45:71–74

30. Dufau, M. L., Catt, K. J., Tsuruhara, T. 1972. Biological activity of human chorionic gonadotropin released from testis binding-sites. *Proc. Nat. Acad. Sci. USA* 69:2414–16

31. Eik-Nes, K. B. 1971. Production and secretion of testicular steroids. *Recent Progr. Hormone Res.* 27:517–35

32. Elkington, J. S. H., Blackshaw, A. W. Personal communication

33. Elkington, J. S. H., Blackshaw, A. W. 1971. Effect of oestradiol-3,17β-dipropionate on spermatogenesis and lysosomal enzymes in the rat testis. *Aust. J. Biol. Sci.* 24:1263–75

34. Elkington, J. S. H., Blackshaw, A. W., de Jong, B. 1973. The effect of hypophysectomy on testicular hydrolases, lactate dehydrogenase, and spermatogenesis in the rat. *Aust. J. Biol. Sci.* 26:491–503

35. Ellis, L. C., Van Kampen, K. R. 1971. Androgen synthesis and metabolism by rat testicular minced and teased tubular preparations after 450R of whole-body X-irradiation. *Radiat. Res.* 48:146–63

36. Engel, W., Frowein, J., Krone, W., Wolf, U. 1972. Induction of testis alcohol dehydrogenase in prepubertal rats. 1. The effects of human chorion gonadotropine (HCG), theophylline, and dibutyryl cyclic AMP. *Clin. Genet.* 3:34–42

37. England, B. G. 1972. Acute changes in serum LH and FSH concentrations following unilateral and bilateral orchidectomy in rats. *Biol. Reprod.* 7:116

38. Ewing, L. L., Irby, D. C., Johnson, B. H., Chubb, C. 1973. Effect of experimental cryptorchidism for 18 days on androgen secretion by perfused rabbit testes. *Fed. Proc.* 32:298

39. Ewing, L. L., Schanbacher, L. M. 1970. Early effects of experimental cryptorchidism on the activity of selected enzymes in rat testes. *Endocrinology* 87:129–34

40. Franchimont, P. et al 1972. Relationship between spermatogenesis and serum gonadotropin levels in azoospermia and oligospermia. *J. Clin. Endocrinol. Metab.* 34:1003–8

41. Free, M. J., Jaffe, R. A. 1972. Dynamics of circulation in the testis of the conscious rat. *Am. J. Physiol.* 223:241–46

42. Free, M. J., Jaffe, R. A., Jain, S. K., Gomes, W. R. 1973. A testosterone concentrating mechanism in the reproductive organs of the male rat. *Nature New Biol.* 244:24–25

43. Free, M. J., Nguyen Duc Kien 1973. Venous-arterial interactions involving 5-hydroxytryptamine in the pampiniform plexus of the rat. *Proc. Soc. Exp. Biol. Med.* 143:284–88

44. Free, M. J., Payvar, F. 1973. Pyruvate dehydrogenase activity in the normal and cryptorchid rat testis. *Biol. Reprod.* In press

45. Galena, H. J., Terner, C. 1972. Biosynthesis of androgens by isolated spermatocytes and spermatids of rat testis. *Fed. Proc.* 31:295

46. Gay, V. L., Bogdanove, E. M. 1969. Plasma and pituitary LH and FSH in the castrated rat following short-term steroid treatment. *Endocrinology* 84:1132–42

47. Gay, V. L., Denver, N. W. 1971. Effects of testosterone propionate and estradiol benzoate—alone or in combination—on serum LH and FSH in orchidectomized rats. *Endocrinology* 89:161–68

48. Go, V. L. W., Vernon, R. G., Fritz, I. B. 1971. Studies on spermatogenesis in rats. I. Application of the velocity sedimentation technique to an investigation of spermatogenesis. *Can. J. Biochem.* 49:753–60

49. Go, V. L. W., Vernon, R. G., Fritz, I. B. 1971. Studies on spermatogenesis in rats. III. Effect of hormonal treatment on differentiation kinetics of the spermatogenic cycle in regressed hypophysectomized rats. *Can. J. Biochem.* 49:768–75

50. Gomes, W. R. 1970. Metabolic and regulatory hormones influencing testis function. See Ref. 68, 3:67–138

51. Gomes, W. R. 1970. Chemical agents affecting testicular function and male fertility. See Ref. 68, 3:483–554

52. Gomes, W. R., Hall, R. W., Jain, S. K., Boots, L. R. 1973. Serum gonadotropin and testosterone levels during loss and recovery of spermatogenesis in rats. *Endocrinology.* In press

53. Gomes, W. R., Wisner, J. R. 1972. $\Delta^5$-3$\beta$-hydroxysteroid dehydrogenase activity in isolated seminiferous tubules, interstitium and whole testis of an adult rat. *Biol. Reprod.* 7:114

54. Gunn, S. A., Gould, T. C. 1970. Cadmium and other mineral elements. See Ref. 68, 3:377–481

55. Gupta, D., Rager, K., Pfister, G., Vogt, W. 1973. Bioconversion of the androgen precursors by pre- and post-pubertal rat testes with special reference to local irradiation and gonadotropin stimulation. *Steroids* 21:17–23

56. Gupta, G. S., Bawa, S. R. 1971. Phosphatases in testes and epididymides of albino rats after partial body $\gamma$-irradiation *J. Reprod. Fert.* 27:451–54

57. Gutiérrez, M., de Burgos, N. M. G., Burgos, C., Blanco, A. 1972. The sexual cycle of male bats: changes of testicular lactate dehydrogenase isoenzymes *Comp. Biochem. Physiol.* 43:47–52

58. Hall, P. F., Irby, D. C., de Kretser, D. M. 1969. Conversion of cholesterol to androgens by rat testes: comparison of interstitial cells and seminiferous tubules. *Endocrinology* 84:488–96

59. Hamilton, D. W. 1972. The mammalian epididymis. See Ref. 8, 268–337

60. Henry, H., Gomes, W. R. 1972. 17$\beta$-hydroxysteroid dehydrogenase in rat seminiferous tubules. *Fed. Proc.* 31:813

61. Hodgen, G. D., Gomes, W. R., Vandemark, N. L. 1971. A testicular isoenzyme of carbonic anhydrase. *Biol. Reprod.* 4:224–28

62. Huckabee, W. E., Walcott, G. 1960. Determination of organ blood flow using 4-aminoantipyrine. *J. Appl. Physiol.* 15:1139–45

63. Irusta, O., Wasserman, G. F. 1971. Side-chain cleavage of cholesterol by homogenates of isolated seminiferous tubules. *Acta Physiol. Lat. Am.* 21: 260–62

64. Jackson, H. 1973. Chemical methods of male contraception. *Am. Sci.* 61: 188–93

65. Jaffe, R. A., Free, M. J. 1972. A miniature friction flowmeter for use in rat testicular artery and other small vessels. *J. Appl. Physiol.* 32:571–73

66. Joffre, M., Joffre, J. 1971 Débit sanguin testiculaire chez le Rat: mise en évidence sur les courbes de "clearance" du xénon 133 d'une composite liée aux graisses épididymaires. *C. R. Acad. Sci Paris D* 273:496–99

67. Johnsen, S. G. 1972. Studies on the pituitary testicular axis in male hypogonadism, particularly in infertile men with "cryptogenetic" hypospermatogenesis. See Ref. 18, 593–608

68. Johnson, A. D., Gomes, W. R., VanDemark, N. L., Eds. 1970. *The Testis, Vol. 1–Development, Anatomy, Physiology; Vol. 2–Biochemistry; Vol. 3–Influencing Factors.* New York: Academic

69. Johnson, A. D., Turner, P. C. 1972. Early actions of cadmium in the rat and domestic fowl. VI. Testicular and muscle blood flow changes. *Comp. Biochem. Physiol.* 41:451–56

70. Johnson, D. C. 1969. Elevation of plasma gonadotrophins in unilaterally castrated male rats. *J. Endocrinol.* 43: 311–12

71. Jones, T. 1971. Blood flow and volume measurements in the radiation depopulated testis of the rat. *Brit. J. Radiol.* 44:841–49

71a. Kaivola, S., Johansson, C.-J. 1969. Excretion of gonadotrophins (FSH and LH), 17-Ketosteroids and oestrone in men with normal and abnormal spermatogensis. *Ann. Chir. Gynaecol. Fenn.* 58:272–78

72. Kalra, P. S., Fawcett, C. P., Krulich, R., McCann, S. M. 1973. The effects of gonadal steroids on plasma gonadotropins and prolactin in the rat. *Endocrinology* 92:1256–68

73. Katsh, S., Aguirre, A. 1968. Biochemical responses in organs of guinea pigs immunized with aspermatogenic antigen. *Int. Arch. Allergy Appl. Immunol.* 33:141–150

74. Katsh, S., Aguirre, A. R., Katsh, G. F., Willson, J. T. 1970. Lysosomal activity in testes of guinea pigs immunized with aspermatogenic antigen. *Int. Arch. Allergy Appl. Immunol.* 39:496–510

75. Kinouchi, T., Horton, R. 1973. Androstanediol dynamics in man. *Endocrinology* 92:Suppl. A-94

76. Kjessler, B., Wide, L. 1973. Follicle stimulating hormone (FSH) and interstitial cell stimulating hormone (ICSH) in relation to gametic output in 643 males. *Acta Endocrinol.* 72:243–56

77. Knorr, D. W., Vanha-Perttula, T., Lipsett, M. B. 1970. Structure and function of rat testis through pubescence. *Endocrinology* 86:1298–1304

78. Kochar, N. K., Harrison, R. G. 1971. The effect of X-rays on enzymes of the mouse testis. *J. Anat.* 109:39–50

79. Kragt, C. L., Masken, J. F. 1972. Puberty-physiological mechanisms of control. *J. Anim. Sci.* 34 (Suppl. I): 1–15

80. Kulin, H. E., Reiter, E. O. 1972. Gonadotropin suppression by low dose estrogen in men: evidence for differential effects upon FSH and LH. *J. Clin. Endocrinol. Metab.* 35:818–23

81. Lacy, D. et al 1968. The Sertoli cell and spermatogenesis in mammals. *Excerp. Med. Int. Congr.* 184:1019–29

82. Lam, D. M. K., Furrer, R., Bruce, W. R. 1970. The separation, physical characterization and differentiation kinetics of spermatogonial cells of the mouse. *Proc. Nat. Acad. Sci. USA* 65:192–99

83. Lee, I. P., Dixon, R. L. 1972. Effects of Vincristine on spermatogenesis studied by velocity sedimentation cell separation technique and serial mating. *J. Pharmacol. Exp. Ther.* 181:192–99

84. Lee, P. A., Jaffe, R. B., Midgley, A. R. Jr., Kohen, F., Niswender, G. D. 1972. Regulation of human gonadotropins. VIII. Suppression of serum LH and FSH in adult males following exogenous testosterone administration. *J. Clin. Endocrinol. Metab.* 35:636–41

85. Lipsett, M. B. 1968. Leydig cell function: physiology and pathology. *Excerpta Med. Found. Int. Congr.* 184:902–4

86. Lloyd, B. J. 1972. Plasma testosterone and accessory sex glands in normal and cryptorchid rats. *J. Endocrinol.* 54: 285–96

87. Lofts, B. 1972. The Sertoli cell. *Gen. Comp. Endocrinol. Suppl.* 3:636–48

88. Longcope, C., Widrich, W., Sawin, C. T. 1972. The secretion of estrone and estradiol-17β by human testis. *Steroids* 20:439–48

89. MacIndoe, J. H., Turkington, R. W. 1973. Hormonal regulation of spermi-

dine formation during spermatogenesis in the rat. *Endocrinology* 92:595–605

90. McArthur, J. W. 1972. Gonadotropins in relation to sexual maturity. See Ref. 18, 487–501

91. Males, J. L., Turkington, R. W. 1970. Hormonal regulation of hyaluronidase during spermatogenesis in the rat. *J. Biol. Chem.* 245:6329–34

92. Males, J. L., Turkington, R. W. 1971. Hormonal control of lysosomal enzymes during spermatogenesis in the rat. *Endocrinology* 88:579–88

93. Meistrich, M. L. 1972. Separation of mouse spermatogenic cells by velocity sedimentation. *J. Cell. Physiol.* 80:299–312

94. Micucci, M., Rama, F., Castelland, M. A., Germino, N. I. 1971. The histochemical distribution of fructose metabolism enzymes in bovine spermatogenesis. *J. Anat.* 109:209–14

95. Mills, N. C., Means, A. R. 1972. Sorbitol dehydrogenase of rat testis: changes in activity during development, after hypophysectomy and following gonadotrophic hormone administration. *Endocrinology* 91:147–56

96. Monn, E., Desautel, M., Christiansen, R. O. 1972. Highly specific testicular adenosine-3',5'-monophosphate phosphodiesterase associated with sexual maturation. *Endocrinology* 91:716–20

97. Moore, D. J., Roscoe, R. T., Matson, L. J., Heller, C. G. 1962. Increased gonadotropin excretion induced by anti-spermatogenic agents. *Clin. Res.* 10:88

98. Morris, R. N., Collins, A. C. 1971. Biosynthesis of myo-inositol by rat testis following surgically induced cryptorchidism or treatment with triethylenemelamine. *J. Reprod. Fert.* 27:201–10

99. Naftolin, F., Ryan, K. J., Petro, Z. 1972. Aromatization of androstenedione by the anterior hypothalamus of adult male and female rats. *Endocrinology* 90:295–98

100. Parvinen, M., Niemi, M. 1971. Distribution and conversion of exogenous cholesterol and sex steroids in the seminiferous tubules and interstitial tissue of the rat testis. *Steroidologia* 2:129–137

101. Parvinen, M., Vanha-Perttula, T. 1972. Identification and enzyme quantitation of the stages of the seminiferous epithelial wave in the rat. *Anat. Rec.* 174:435–49

102. Paulsen, C. A., Leonard, J. M., de Kretser, D. M., Leach, R. B. 1972. Interrela-

tionship between spermatogenesis and follicle-stimulating hormone levels. See Ref. 18, 628–39

103. Perry, J. S., Ed. 1971. Spermatogenesis and sperm maturation. *J. Reprod. Fert. Suppl.* 13. 97 pp.

104. Pilkis, S. J. 1970. Hormonal control of hexokinase activity in animal tissues. *Biochim. Biophys. Acta* 215:461–76

105. Posalaki, Z., Szabó, D., Bácsi, E., Ökrös, I. 1968. Hydrolytic enzymes during spermatogenesis in rat. An electron microscopic and histochemical study. *J. Histochem. Cytochem.* 16:249–62

106. Rivarola, M. A., Podesta, E. J., Chemes, H. E. 1972. *In vitro* testosterone-$^{14}$C metabolism by rat seminiferous tubules at different stages of development: Formation of 5α-androstandiol at meiosis. *Endocrinology* 91:537–42

107. Rosemberg, E., Paulsen, C. A., Eds. 1970. *Advances in Experimental Medicine and Biology, Vol. 10– The Human Testis.* New York: Plenum. 645 pp.

108. Ruokonen, A., Laatikainen, T., Laitinen, E. A., Vihko, R. 1972. Free and sulfate-conjugated neutral steroids in human testis tissue. *Biochemistry* 11:1411–16

109. Russo, J. 1967. Acid and alkaline phosphatases of the mouse testis at different stages of post-natal development. *Acta Physiol. Lat. Am.* 17:302–8

110. Russo, J. 1970. Subcellular distribution of acid phosphatase in the mouse testis. *Acta Physiol. Lat. Am.* 20:74–76

111. Sananez, R. D., Faillaci, M., Aimar, G., Nowotny, E., Yantorno, C. 1971. Testosterone biosynthesis by normal and autoimmune testes from rabbits. *Hoppe-Seyler's Z. Physiol. Chem.* 352:1465–68

112. Seiguer, A. C., Castro, A. E. 1972. Electron microscopic demonstration of arylsulfatase activity during acrosome formation in the rat. *Biol. Reprod.* 7:31–42

113. Setchell, B. P. 1970. Testicular blood supply, lymphatic drainage and secretion of fluid. See Ref. 68, 1:101–239

114. Setchell, B. P. 1970. The secretion of fluid by the testis of rats, rams and goats with some observations on the effects of age, cryptorchidism and hypophysectomy. *J. Reprod. Fert.* 23:79–86

115. Setchell, B. P., Brown, B. W. 1972. The effect of metabolic alkalosis, hypotension and inhibitors of carbonic anhydrase on fluid secretion by rat testes. *J. Reprod. Fert.* 28:235–40

116. Setchell, B. P., Duggan, M. C., Evans, R. W. 1973. The effects of gonadotrophins on fluid secretion and sperm production by the rat and hamster testis. *J. Endocrinol.* 56:27–36

117. Setchell, B. P., Sirinathsinghji, D. J. 1972. Antigonadotrophic activity in rete testis fluid, a possible "inhibin." *J. Endocrinol.* 53:1x–1xi

118. Setchell, B. P., Waites, G. M. H. 1971. The exocrine secretion of the testis and spermatogenesis. *J. Reprod. Fert. Suppl.* 13:15–28

119. Setchell, B. P., Waites, G. M. H. 1972. The effects of local heating on the flow and composition of rete testis fluid in the rat, with some observations on the effects of age and unilateral castration. *J. Reprod. Fert.* 30:225–33

120. Sosa, A., Altamirano, E., Hernandez, P., Rosado, A. 1972. Developmental patterns of rat testis hexokinase. *Life Sci.* 11:499–510

121. Steinberger, E., Steinberger, A. 1972. Testis: basic and clinical aspects. See Ref. 8, 144–267

122. Suoranta, H. 1971. Tubular damage caused by local thermal injury or microembolization of the rat testis. *Virchows Arch. B* 8:299–308

123. Swerdloff, R. S., Jacobs, H. S., Odell, W. D. 1972. Hypothalamic-pituitary-gonadal interrelationships in the rat during sexual maturation. See Ref. 18, 546–61

124. Swerdloff, R. S., Walsh, P. C., Odell, W. D. 1972. Control of LH and FSH secretion in the male: evidence that aromatization of androgens to estradiol is not required for inhibition of gonadotropin secretion. *Steroids* 20:13–17

125. Tsai, M. Y., Kemp, R. G. 1973. Isozymes of rabbit phosphofructokinase. *J. Biol. Chem.* 248:785–92

126. Tuck, R. R., Setchell, B. P., Waites, G. M. H., Young, J. A. 1970. The composition of fluid collected by micropuncture and catheterization from the seminiferous tubules and rete testis of rats. *Pfluegers Arch.* 318:225–43

127. VanDemark, N. L., Schanbacher, B. D., Gomes, W. R. 1972. Alterations in testes of rats exposed to elevated atmospheric carbon dioxide *J. Reprod. Fert.* 28:457–59

128. van der Vusse, G. J., Kalkman, M. L., van der Molen, H. J. 1973. Endogenous production of steroids by subcellular fractions from total rat testis and from isolated interstitial tissue and seminiferous tubules. *Biochim. Biophys. Acta* 297:79–82

129. Vanha-Perttula, T. 1971. A new type of acid phosphatase from rat testis. *Experientia* 27:42–44

130. Vanha-Perttula, T. 1971. Chromatographic fractionation and characterization of rat testicular acid phosphatases. *Biochim. Biophys. Acta* 227:390–401

131. Vanha-Perttula, T. 1973. Aminopeptidases of rat testis. I. Characterization and fractionation. *J. Reprod. Fert.* 32:33–44

132. Vanha-Perttula, T. 1973. Aminopeptidases of rat testis. II. Effects of puberty, cryptorchidism, and cadmium chloride treatment. *J. Reprod. Fert.* 32:45–54

133. Vanha-Perttula, T. 1973. Aminopeptidases of rat testis. III. Activity of dipeptidyl aminopeptidases I and II in normal and experimental conditions. *J. Reprod. Fert.* 32:55–64

134. Vanha-Perttula, T., Nikkanen, V. 1973. Acid phosphatases of the rat testis in experimental conditions. *Acta Endocrinol.* 72:376–90

135. Van Thiel, D. H., Sherins, R. J., Myers, G. H. Jr., DeVita, V. T. Jr. 1972. Evidence for a specific seminiferous tubular factor affecting follicle-stimulating hormone secretion in man. *J. Clin. Invest.* 51:1009–19

136. Varga, B., Stark, E., Csáki, L., Marton, J. 1969. Effect of ACTH on gonadal blood flow in the golden hamster and the rat. *Gen. Comp. Endocrinol.* 13:468–73

137. Vernon, R. G., Go, V. L. W., Fritz, I. B. 1971. Studies on spermatogenesis in rats. II. Evidence that carnitine acetyltransferase is a marker enzyme for the investigation of germ cell differentiation. *Can. J. Biochem.* 49:761–67

138. Vitale-Calpe, R., Burgos, M. H. 1970. The mechanism of spermiation in the hamster. I. The ultrastructure of spontaneous spermiation. *J. Ultrastruct. Res.* 31:381–93

139. Vitale-Calpe, R., Burgos, M. H. 1970. The mechanism of spermiation in the hamster. II. The ultrastructural effects of coitus and of LH administration. *J. Ultrastruct. Res.* 31:394–406

140. Waites, G. M. H. 1970. Temperature regulation and the testis. See Ref. 68, 1:241–79

141. Waites, G. M. H., Moule, G. R. 1961. Relation of vascular heat exchange to temperature regulation in the testis of the ram. *J. Reprod. Fert.* 2:213–24

142. Waites, G. M. H., Setchell, B. P. 1969. Some physiological aspects of the function of the testis. In *The Gonads,* ed. K. W. McKerns, 649–714. New York: Appleton

143. Waites, G. M. H., Setchell, B. P. 1969. Physiology of the testis, epididymis and scrotum. *Advan. Reprod. Physiol.* 4: 1–63

144. Walsh, P. C., Swerdloff, R. S., Odell, W. D. 1972. Cyproterone: effect on serum gonadotropins in the male. *Endocrinology* 90:1655–59

145. Winer, A. D., Nikitovich-Winer, M. B. 1971. Hormonal effects on the rat gonadal lactate dehydrogenases. *FEBS Lett.* 16:21–29

146. Xuma, M., Turkington, R. W. 1972. Hormonal regulation of uridine diphosphatase during spermiogenesis in the rat. *Endocrinology* 91:415–22

147. Yamada, M., Yasue, S., Matsumoto, K. 1972. Formation of 5α-reduced products from testosterone *in vitro* by germ cells from immature rats. *Acta Endocrinol.* 71:393–408

148. Zanisi, M., Motta, M., Martini, L. 1973. Inhibitory effect of 5α-reduced metabolites of testosterone on gonadotrophin secretion. *J. Endocrinol.* 56: 315–16

149. Zinkham, W. H. 1968. Lactate dehydrogenase isozymes of testis and sperm: biological and biochemical properties and genetic control. *Ann. NY Acad. Sci.* 151:598–610

# ENDOCRINE FUNCTION OF THE PANCREAS[1]

## M. E. Krahl[2]

Department of Physiology, Stanford University, California

The endocrine function of the pancreas is to facilitate storage of foodstuffs by release of insulin following a meal, and to provide a mechanism for mobilization of foodstuffs by release of glucagon during periods of fasting. This review deals with limited aspects of these topics. Specifically, it deals with 1. structure and synthesis of proinsulin and insulin; 2. secretion of insulin; 3. relation of insulin to carbohydrate, fat, and protein storage; 4. mechanism of insulin action; 5. action of glucagon in mobilizing carbohydrate and fat; 6. current views on the etiology of diabetes mellitus.

This review includes the year 1971, which was the fiftieth anniversary of the discovery of insulin. In that year three commemorative symposia were held; the resultant publications have provided an extensive and penetrating set of reviews of the functions of insulin (11, 77, 215). This background, and other reviews (32, 225), permits us to limit attention to the main themes mentioned above. The objective is to provide an entry to the literature, especially that dealing with promising new trends in diabetes research. Emphasis will be on overall physiological function with brief analyses of underlying chemical events.

## STRUCTURE OF PROINSULIN AND INSULIN

### Structure of Proinsulin

Insulin is formed in the $\beta$ cells of the pancreas via the single chain precursor, proinsulin. The proinsulin molecule contains a connecting segment (40, 120) linked at one end through Arg·Lys to the $-NH_2$ terminal glycine $(A_1)$ of the insulin A chain and, at the other end, through Arg·Arg to the carboxyl terminal amino acid of the B chain $(B_{30})$. The conversion of proinsulin to insulin can be accomplished

[1]The literature survey for this review was terminated March 31, 1973. The author regrets that, owing to space limitations, many important publications could not be cited.

[2]Experimental work of the author has been supported in part by grants from the National Institutes of Health (AM-01653 and AM-14086).

with pancreatic trypsin and carboxypeptidase B (120). This reaction is accompanied by liberation of the four basic amino acids from the connecting segment, plus the remainder of the connecting segment [referred to as the connecting peptide (C peptide)]. The C peptides vary in number of amino acids from species to species (40, 120, 190, 231): for human and monkey, there are 31; pig, 29; cow and sheep, 26; and dog, 23.

The antigenic determinants for proinsulin appear to lie in the C peptides rather than the A and B chains of insulin. In porcine proinsulin the major antigenic determinant appears to be the hydrophobic region within the 41–54 amino acid sequence. The C peptides not only have antigenic properties of their own, but cross-react with antibodies to insulin (40). Antibodies against C peptides have been used to assess $\beta$ cell function in human patients (18, 206). In insulin-treated diabetics some proinsulin is bound to large molecular weight material. The evidence indicates that the proinsulin is bound to anti-insulin antibodies (18).

Estimates of insulin-like activity of proinsulin depend on the assay employed. The activity, relative to insulin as 100%, is 3% by inhibition of lipolysis in adipose cells (239), 6% by stimulation of 3–O–methyl glucose penetration into frog muscle (178), 18% by mouse convulsion assay (40), and 45% by cross-reaction to insulin antisera (40). It is estimated that proinsulin and proinsulin-related intermediates may account for 3–6% of the protein in commercial insulin preparations (40). Proinsulin favors glucose uptake in human forearm (69).

## Structure of Insulin A and B Chains

The amino acid sequences for insulin from 19 species have been summarized (221). Two insulins have been found in rat pancreas; they have identical A chains, but the B chains differ. There also appear to be two mouse insulins (29, 164). Guinea pig insulin differs from pig insulin in the position of 18 amino acid residues. Guinea pig insulin, by mouse convulsion assay, has a biological activity of only 2–4 IU/mg (225, 269) as compared to approximately 25 IU/mg for pig or bovine insulin.

The nerve growth factor that exerts a pleiotypic stimulation on developing sympathetic nerves has substantial homologies to insulin and proinsulin with respect to its amino acid sequence (75).

## Structure of Insulin—Three Dimensional

The three-dimensional structure of the insulin molecule has been determined by single crystal X-ray analysis (107). The two chains are compactly arranged with the A chain lying above a central helical region of the B chain.

The A chain residues $A_1$ glycine, $A_5$ glutamine, $A_{19}$ tyrosine, and $A_{21}$ asparagine are on the surface of the molecule. They are invariant and not involved in the aggregation of the molecule. Their deletion affects both the structure and activity of insulin. Substitution of $A_1$ glycine, especially by bulky groups, reduces activity substantially, but it seems to affect the molecular structure to a lesser degree. In proinsulin the connecting peptide appears to cover and mask these residues. Therefore, the A chain terminal residues apparently are important to the activity of the molecule. This cluster may contain the active site (107).

At neutral pH virtually complete dissociation of zinc-insulin hexamer occurs at about 1 $\mu$g/ml, almost 1000 times the concentration of insulin in blood (188). Thus the physiologically active form of insulin in body fluids is considered to be mainly the monomer.

## SECRETION OF INSULIN

In general, insulin secretion is favored by rising or high concentrations of metabolic substrates that are to be stored: glucose, amino acids, and perhaps short-chain fatty acids (260). The major normal stimulus appears to be glucose.

The proposed sequence of events is as follows (137, 199): Proinsulin is synthesized in the endoplasmic reticulum of $\beta$ cells, then transferred to the Golgi complex where proinsulin is converted to insulin. The insulin is enclosed in $\beta$ granules, which either remain free in the cytoplasm or become attached to the microtubular system of $\beta$ cells (184). Glucose initiates entry of calcium (92), which triggers a change in the physical conformation of the microtubules and displacement of the granules to the $\beta$ cell surface where they fuse with the plasma membrane. The granules are released in tandem by emiocytosis. Both insulin and proinsulin are released by isolated islets (209).

The evidence indicates that glucose itself, rather than a metabolite, triggers the release of insulin by stimulating glucoreceptors located on the cell membrane (124, 165). Other carbohydrates (glucosamine, fructose) may influence the glucose receptor (6, 7). In man, glucose produces a marked biphasic response (an early rapid release of insulin followed by a long sustained release) and is the only metabolite that, at physiologic concentrations, stimulates both insulin release and insulin synthesis. Glucose stimulates the overall rate of islet mRNA synthesis, alters the nature of the RNA synthesized, and also stimulates insulin synthesis by a post-transcriptional event (189).

The insulin release that follows exposure of $\beta$ cells to amino acids (67, 68, 186, 260) is most marked with arginine; histidine is inactive. The effect of leucine can be mimicked by a nonmetabolizable analogue, BCH (2-amino-bicyclo-[2,2,1]-heptane-2-carboxylic acid) and that of arginine by GPA (4-amino-1-guanyl piperidine-4-carboxylic acid), leading to the suggestion that the interaction of leucine or arginine with their specific acceptor sites sets off a signal that results in an insulin discharge that is not dependent on metabolism of the amino acid (45). The signal is associated with, though not necessarily dependent on, inward transport of the amino acid or analogue (67, 103). Arginine stimulates mainly the second phase of insulin release, whereas glucose stimulates the first phase (67, 108).

In man, glucose potentiates the insulin secretory response to a protein meal and to infusions of arginine, leucine, and alanine (72). The concurrent plasma glucose level plays a dominant physiologic role by modulating the insulin secretory response to amino acids and other factors (74).

The stimulatory effects of fatty acids and ketones on insulin release in various animals in vivo and in vitro have been extensively reviewed (50, 166, 260).

Both calcium and sodium are required for insulin release from rabbit pancreas in vitro (170). Magnesium blocks the activation of insulin release by calcium or barium (170).

Glucagon, secretin, pancreozymin, and gastrin stimulate insulin release by pancreas in vivo and in vitro (166, 180, 260) by enhancing sensitivity of the $\beta$ cell to glucose (123). This may account for the fact that more insulin is released following an oral glucose load than when the same dose of glucose is given intravenously.

Epinephrine and other agents stimulate insulin release by way of some action of the adenyl cyclase system (26, 203). The epinephrine stimulus the cyclic AMP (cAMP) formation is initiated via the $\beta$ receptors for catecholamines (244). Inhibitors of the phosphodiesterase that destroys cAMP, e.g. caffeine and theophylline, favor insulin release (42). Tolbutamide and chlorpropamide, two oral hypoglycemic agents, have been reported to inhibit phosphodiesterase (28). The role of cAMP in insulin secretion appears to be mainly that of enhancing and modulating the release of insulin in response to glucose (42). Glucagon-stimulated insulin release via the adenyl cyclase system is inhibited during hypoglycemia in man (87).

The question whether circulating insulin exerts a negative feedback on insulin release by $\beta$ cells has been repeatedly examined. Infusion of 1 mU of insulin per ml reduced the insulin output from the uncinate region of dog pancreas by 40% (196).

Inhibitors of insulin release have been extensively investigated. Catecholamines inhibit via $\alpha$ receptors in the $\beta$ cells (244) and inhibitors of monoamine oxidase (4) accentuate catecholamine action. Diazoxide inhibits insulin release both in vivo (94) and in vitro (145); this inhibition is associated with appearance of autophagous lysosomes in the $\beta$ cells (51). Diazoxide also specifically blocks calcium-activated insulin release in vitro (170). Diphenylhydantoin reduces insulin release in man (161). Mannoheptulose blocks the glucose stimulus to insulin release (6) and reduces response to amino acids (158). Inhibitors of aldose reductase produce inhibition of insulin release that is corrected by sorbitol (80). The structure of diabetogenic chemicals has been reviewed (201).

Artificial systems for sensing insulin concentrations and modulating insulin release from implanted depots have been proposed (13, 31).

## INSULIN AND CARBOHYDRATE METABOLISM

There have been extensive new developments in the understanding of regulation by insulin of glycogen synthesis and of gluconeogenesis.

### Insulin and Glycogen Synthase

Glycogen synthase, the enzyme that forms glycogen by addition of glucosyl residues from uridine diphosphoglucose (UDPG) to glycogen primer, exists in two forms. The D form is dependent on glucose-6-phosphate; the I form is not. The conversion of the I to the D form is accompanied by addition of 6 alkali-labile phosphate groups to each monomer of 90,000 molecular weight (139). Each added phosphate appears in the following peptide sequence of rabbit skeletal muscle synthase (D):

$$\left.\begin{array}{c}\text{Lys} \\ \text{Arg}\end{array}\right\} \quad \begin{array}{c}\text{—Glu•Ile. Ser. Val. Arg} \\ | \\ \text{P}\end{array}$$

This sequence is identical to that of the phosphorylated peptide of phosphorylase, but surrounding groups for the two peptides are clearly different in synthase from those in phosphorylase.

The protein kinase (synthase I kinase) that catalyzes the transformation of synthase I to synthase D also exists in two forms, a D form that is dependent on the presence of cyclic AMP (cAMP) for activity, and an I form that is not. The D form of such protein kinases consists of a regulatory subunit, which binds cAMP and a catalytic subunit, the I form. Addition of cAMP liberates the I form of the kinase. This, in turn, leads to phosphorylation of synthase I and shifts the steady state toward the synthase D (inactive) form.

Insulin favors formation of synthase I in a number of tissues (2, 60, 193, 204). This is now provisionally explained by an insulin effect to lower the concentration of cAMP and thus to favor the formation of the cAMP-dependent D (inactive) form of the protein kinase that phosphorylates synthase; this, in turn, allows the synthase to remain in the nonphosphorylated I form. Epinephrine added to the muscle has the opposite effect. There remain problems with this concept owing in part to the difficulty of demonstrating insulin effects on intracellular cAMP concentrations in the absence of added epinephrine or glucagon. An alternate hypothesis has been proposed (139).

## Insulin and Gluconeogenesis

In normal man, a small rise in the hepatic vein glucose concentration reduces hepatic glucose output within 5 min after glucose infusion. In insulin-dependent diabetic patients even much higher glucose concentrations do not reduce hepatic glucose output. This difference has been ascribed to delayed or reduced (37) insulin release from the pancreatic $\beta$ cells. Infusion of glucose does not shut off gluconeogenesis in depancreatized dogs unless insulin is infused concurrently at a suitable dose (251).

Control of gluconeogenesis in liver has long been a knotty problem. Certain principles have emerged.

The first principle is that the activities of rate-limiting glycolytic enzymes are subject to regulation by nucleotides and by inorganic ions (223). This may take the form of allosteric regulation without alteration in the composition of the enzyme molecule (phosphofructokinase); or the structure may be altered by addition or removal of phosphate groups from the protein moiety (phosphorylase and glycogen synthase).

The second principle is that long-chain fatty acids favor reversal of the glycolytic pathway from pyruvate to glucose in liver. (See fat metabolism, below.)

The third principle is that there is an interplay between hormones and substrates in the induction or suppression of key enzymes in the glycolytic cycle (133, 253). Adrenal glucocorticoids increase the concentrations of key enzymes that favor gluconeogenesis; insulin suppresses the formation of the same enzymes. Examples are glucose-6-phosphatase, fructose-1,6-diphosphatase, phosphoenolpyruvate carboxykinase, and pyruvate carboxylase.

The fourth principle is that the balance of insulin versus glucagon and catecholamine concentrations is an important mechanism for rapid regulation of hepatic glucose output (115, 232, 247, 249, 251). Action of catecholamines or glucagon to stimulate gluconeogenesis and related processes in perfused liver can be in part antagonized by insulin. In each case the stimulus by catecholamine is accompanied by a rise in cAMP and the insulin antagonism by a fall in cAMP. Examples are the stimulation of gluconeogenesis, the stimulation of glycogenolysis or activation of phosphorylase, the stimulation of proteolysis, the enhancement of $K^+$ loss, and the induction of phosphoenolpyruvate carboxykinase (65, 187). Liver gluconeogenesis and cAMP levels are increased when insulin is withdrawn from diabetic rats (111); gluconeogenesis and liver phosphoenolpyruvate carboxykinase are elevated in diabetic hamsters (41).

In summary, the short term regulation of gluconeogenesis in normal man or animal models appears to depend on the balance between insulin versus glucagon and/or catecholamines. Gluconeogenesis is elevated when insulin concentration is low and glucagon high. When glucose is fed or infused, the $\beta$ cells release insulin; this suppresses gluconeogenesis via a number of mechanisms, possibly in part by reducing the effective concentration of cAMP at pertinent intracellular loci.

In severe diabetes, gluconeogenesis is unchecked by a carbohydrate meal because insulin released from pancreatic $\beta$ cells is deficient or delayed.

## INSULIN AND FAT METABOLISM

Insulin regulates both lipogenesis and lipolysis. The balance between the two processes is dependent on complex interorgan relationships among specialized tissues.

Insulin deficiency leads to impairment of a number of steps in lipogenesis: decreased entrance of glucose into the glycolytic cycle (133), with consequent reduction in formation of the $\alpha$ glycerophosphate required for triglyceride synthesis; decreased pyruvate dehydrogenase activity, leading to decreased acetyl CoA formation from pyruvate (97, 233); decreased acetyl CoA carboxylase activity (258), with consequent impairment of fatty acid chain initiation; and decreased fatty acid synthetase (138). These defects are repaired by insulin treatment of the diabetic animal.

A direct stimulatory effect of insulin on pyruvate dehydrogenase has been reported (47, 233, 259). In adipose tissue exposed to insulin there is a two- to threefold increase in pyruvic dehydrogenase without any change in activity of pyruvate carboxylase, citrate synthetase, or glutamic dehydrogenase. The insulin effect is said to be due to an increase in the dephospho (active) form of pyruvic dehydrogenase (47, 259).

The surges of insulin secretion that follow high carbohydrate intake have been invoked as a cause of excess formation of triglycerides and very low density lipoproteins (VLDL) in liver (76, 211, 245).

Of particular interest for the problem of obesity is the reported influence of insulin on the hypothalamic satiety center (59, 79). Changes in arterial lipids occur in streptozotocin diabetes (228).

Insulin deficiency also leads to increased lipolysis in adipose tissue and liver. The increased lipolysis results in an augmented supply of fatty acids to the liver and augmented oxidation of fatty acids to ketone bodies there. The release of fatty acids from adipose tissue is increased by lipolytic hormones and by dexamethasone, which suppresses the metabolism of glucose and thereby the re-esterification of free fatty acids (43).

The long chain fatty acids liberated by excess lipolysis in insulin deficiency play a special role in regulating fatty acid synthesis and gluconeogenesis (254). Concentration of palmitoyl CoA in liver rises as the supply of circulating palmitate is increased by high lipolysis in adipose tissue (78). Palmitoyl CoA interrupts the flow of carbons for fatty acid synthesis by inhibiting the pyruvate dehydrogenase complex, the exit of citrate from mitochondria, the acetyl CoA carboxylase reaction, and fatty acid synthetase (78). Concurrently, palmitoyl CoA gives rise to increased intramitochondrial levels of acetyl CoA in liver; increased acetyl CoA in this compartment favors conversion of pyruvate to oxalacetate which is converted to malate; the malate leaves the mitochondria and is converted to phosphoenolpyruvate, which, by reversal of the glycolytic cycle, ultimately gives rise to glucose (78).

A central role in these complex metabolic adjustments is ascribed to the increased lipolysis that occurs in adipose tissue during insulin deficiency. Adipose tissue lipase can exist in an inactive and an active form; the conversion from inactive to active form is accomplished by a phosphoprotein kinase activated by cAMP (48).

Two questions regarding cAMP relations to lipolysis and lipogenesis have been widely examined. The first question is whether the suppression of lipolysis by insulin is completely accounted for by a reduction in cellular cAMP levels. The accumulated results are at present contradictory (66, 250) and require analysis at the subcellular level (121).

The second question concerns the locus of cAMP inhibitory effects on lipogenesis. Lipogenesis is regarded as a highly coordinated set of reaction sequences; cAMP appears to bring about nothing less than a deterioration of the total lipogenic climate of the cell involving all the lipogenic enzyme systems mentioned above (235).

The relation of glucose concentration and other factors to lipid synthesis and lipolysis has been studied in various tissues (19, 71, 113, 126, 177, 240, 243).

## INSULIN AND PROTEIN METABOLISM

In diabetes associated with insulin lack, there is decreased net protein synthesis as evidenced by failure of children or young animals to grow, by negative nitrogen balance, and by reduced protein synthesis in perfused or excised muscle, heart muscle, adipose tissue, and liver. This reduced protein synthesis in tissues of the diabetic can be restored to normal by insulin supplied in vivo or in vitro. Insulin is permissive for anabolic effects of estrogen, testosterone, and growth hormone in rodents (149, 150), and for cortisone stimulation of ventral prostate in hypophysectomized rats (238).

Current experimental analyses of this problem focus on the following steps in protein synthesis.

## Transport and Activation of Amino Acids

There is evidence from the earlier literature (132) and from more recent studies (162, 262) that insulin stimulation of protein synthesis can be divorced from the insulin enhancement of transport of certain amino acids into the cell. The problem is difficult to resolve because of the possible direct coupling of the transfer mechanism to synthetic systems without liberation of intracellular free amino acids (1).

Formation of [$^{14}$C]-leucyl-tRNA or [$^{14}$C]-tyrosyl-tRNA in diaphragm or heart muscle was enhanced by insulin under conditions where the transport of these amino acids was unaffected (58). Activation of amino acids by formation of aminoacyl tRNA derivatives is reported to be nonlimiting for protein synthesis in muscle of diabetic rats (61).

## Translation

The mRNA-directed polymerization of amino acids involves operation of a ribosome cycle in which a 40S ribosomal subunit, messenger RNA, initiating factors, and aminoacyl-tRNA molecules interact with a 60S subunit to form a monomeric ribosome-mRNA complex. Addition of other 40S and 60S subunits in pairs results in formation of polysomes that favor protein synthesis. Activated amino acids are then incorporated into proteins by ribosome-bound and soluble enzymes.

SKELETAL MUSCLE  In muscle from diabetic rats, protein synthesis is impaired; a critical defect appears to lie in the translation step of protein synthesis. Ribosomes prepared from muscle of alloxan-diabetic animals are defective in their capacity to translate mRNA (e.g. polyuridylic acid or mRNA from encephalomyocarditis virus) into the respective protein chains. Diabetic ribosomes are less effective than normal in the formation of the association complex required to initiate protein synthesis; this defect involves the 60S ribosomes (217, 261, 262). The question whether ribosomal-polysomal relations are influenced by the intracellular concentration of amino acids has been raised (176).

Evidence that insulin is concerned with protein chain initiation in psoas muscle (174) has also been obtained by the technique described below for heart muscle.

There is at present no evidence that insulin affects the transcription step in protein synthesis in muscle during short term in vitro incubations. Incorporation of labeled amino acid into skeletal muscle protein is not significantly impaired by actinomycin D (261), which is used to block DNA directed synthesis of mRNA.

HEART MUSCLE  Activity of the protein synthetic pathway in perfused rat hearts was assessed by measurement of incorporation of [$^{14}$C]-phenylalanine into protein, concurrently with measurement of intracellular levels of free amino acids, ribosomal subunits, and polysomes. The rationale for interpretation was as follows: When protein synthesis is low, together with accumulation of ribosomal monomers and subunits, peptide chain initiation is considered to be the rate-limiting step. Also when protein synthesis is low, together with accumulation of nearly all the ribosomal subunits as polysomes, peptide chain elongation is regarded as the major rate-limiting step in protein synthesis (174), as it is also said to be in growth hormone deficiency (130).

In heart muscle from normally fed or fasted rats about 85% of ribosomal RNA was found as polysomes, suggesting that peptide chain elongation was the limiting factor.

As perfusion of the normal heart muscle proceeded over a 180 min period, phenylalanine incorporation into protein fell, the number of polysomes decreased, and the proportion of smaller ribosomal units increased, indicating that a block in peptide chain initiation had developed during perfusion. Addition of insulin to the perfusion fluid prevented development of the block in peptide chain initiation (114).

Besides the stimulus to protein synthesis by its effect on peptide chain initiation, insulin also reduced the rate of protein degradation in heart muscle (174). Insulin inhibition of protein degradation in liver (168, 175) and in adipose cells (171) has also been reported.

LIVER An effect of insulin that is interpreted as an insulin-enhancement of translation has been found with cultured hepatoma cells. When a glucocorticoid is added in vitro, the formation of one specific enzyme, tyrosine amino transferase (TAT), is increased. Addition of insulin during the course of the glucocorticoid stimulation causes a further remarkable increase in this enzyme, reflected by an increase in labeled enzyme precipitated by a specific antibody to TAT. The insulin stimulus is not blocked by actinomycin D, although the glucocorticoid stimulus is (84, 140). The glucocorticoid must act first via the system sensitive to actinomycin D before insulin can enhance the synthesis of TAT. These data are consistent with the suggestion that glucocorticoid stimulates formation of a mRNA with a half-life of 2–3 hr (140) followed by insulin stimulation of a translational event (84, 140). Insulin apparently does not suppress the breakdown of the enzyme (140). There is a defect in polysome formation in liver of diabetic rats (192, 241). Insulin is permissive for stimulation of polysome formation in liver perfused with high concentrations of amino acids (63).

The relation of insulin and other hormones to enzyme synthesis has been reviewed (198, 212).

## Transcription

Support for the view that insulin favors transcription stems largely from two types of experiment: first, suppression of the insulin stimulation of protein synthesis in adipose tissue and liver by actinomycin D, which inhibits DNA-directed RNA formation; second, the finding of increased RNA polymerase activity (224) and increased template activity of liver chromatin (173) in livers of animals injected with insulin.

ADIPOSE TISSUE  Protein synthesis in epididymal adipose tissue of the rat is markedly stimulated by insulin, as measured by incorporation of labeled amino acids (131), labeled amino acid precursors (131), or formation of specific enzymes in vitro (24, 101).

Hexokinase II of adipose tissue behaves as an adaptive enzyme: the tissue level of hexokinase II, as measured by enzyme activity, falls during a 48–72 hr fast; this decrease is reversed by incubation of the tissue in vitro in media containing insulin (24, 101, 102). The insulin effect is obtained in the absence of glucose if pyruvate is supplied as a metabolizable substrate, indicating that the insulin effect on the enzyme level does not depend on increased glucose transport (102).

Double labeling studies with [$^{14}$C]-histidine and [$^3$H]-histidine indicated that insulin promotes a new formation of the protein of hexokinase II (102). The rate of breakdown of hexokinase II protein was unaffected by insulin (102).

The insulin stimulus to hexokinase II formation in isolated adipose tissue, and the incorporation of labeled amino acids into the enzyme protein, are blocked by cycloheximide (102), an inhibitor of protein synthesis, and by actinomycin D, which reduces RNA synthesis under the same conditions by 97% (102). If insulin is allowed to act on the tissue for 8 hr prior to addition of actinomycin D, then the insulin continues to stimulate hexokinase formation to the same degree as before actinomycin D was added. This is apparently due to formation of a mRNA for hexokinase II that has a sufficiently long half-life to support the continued formation of the enzyme (101).

Insulin enhancement of glucose-6-dehydrogenase activity of adipose tissue was also blocked by cycloheximide and actinomycin D (83).

In rats made diabetic 48 hr previously, the levels of phosphofructokinase, glucose-6-phosphate dehydrogenase, and pyruvate kinase were low; they returned to the normal range within 24 hr after injection of insulin (208).

The LDH$_4$ and LDH$_5$ isozymes of lactic dehydrogenase increased in red muscle (soleus) of rats given insulin. Actinomycin D abolished the effect (110).

LIVER  Insulin stimulates incorporation of labeled amino acids into protein (131, 162) and partially suppresses protein breakdown (162, 168, 175) during liver perfusion. In perfused liver, insulin stimulates incorporation of [$^3$H]-orotic acid into nuclear RNA, first into DNA-like RNA, later into ribosomal RNA (183).

In the whole animal (133, 253) insulin has a specific regulatory function of stimulating the formation of hepatic enzymes that favor anabolic events and storage of foodstuffs, and suppressing formation of key hepatic enzymes that are concerned with catabolic events and gluconeogenesis (133, 253, 256).

Glucokinase has been previously found to behave, in the rat, as an adaptive enzyme. Its concentration decreases in fasting or in diabetes and is restored by refeeding or appropriate insulin treatment of the animal. The increase in glucokinase during refeeding requires insulin, as it does not occur when insulin release from the pancreas is reduced by mannoheptulose (191) or when insulin is bound by anti-insulin serum (255). The insulin-dependent restoration of glucokinase during refeeding appears to represent de novo formation of the enzyme protein; this conclusion is based on the finding that a double labeling technique shows that the glucokinase protein becomes labeled more rapidly in the fed rat than in the unfed control and, in fact, more rapidly than other proteins closely comparable to glucokinase in chromatographic and electrophoretic properties (191). The breakdown of labeled glucokinase is not inhibited by insulin under these conditions.

The insulin-dependent restoration of glucokinase during refeeding of starved rats is blocked by cycloheximide (191), lending further support to the concept that insulin stimulates synthesis of glucokinase protein. Since the effect is blocked by actinomycin D, it has been suggested that the insulin effect is related in some manner to the transcription step in formation of mRNA (191).

In an overall sense, the effect of insulin must be remarkably specific to control precisely those enzymes that are critically involved in anabolic actions. This has been interpreted to imply that insulin affects specific gene loci that are designed for this purpose (256).

An important physiologic consideration is that liver enzyme function in the whole animal is subject to regulation by insulin, not only by control of enzyme biosynthesis, but by control of concentration of other molecules that modulate the activity of existing enzyme molecules (253, 255). When insulin is lacking, there is increased lipolysis in adipose tissue and in liver, leading to increased concentrations of free fatty acids, acetyl CoA, and palmitoyl CoA, all of which inhibit specific enzymes that are induced by insulin. This provides a mechanism for rapid control (minutes), as compared with the delayed control (hours or days) that is dependent on alteration of enzyme synthesis. Amylase content of pancreas falls in rats made diabetic by alloxan or streptozotocin, and is restored by administration of insulin to the animal (222).

Insulin stimulates incorporation of proline as proline or hydroxyproline into collagen in cultures of rat bone (213).

## MECHANISM OF INSULIN ACTION

### Background

Major effects of insulin that must be accounted for in a general mechanism of action include (a) an increase in translocation of certain sugars and certain amino acids from extracellular to intracellular phase in skeletal muscle and heart muscle, (b) an increase in accumulation of $K^+$ by muscle and liver and hyperpolarization of muscle membranes, (c) transformation of glycogen synthase from the D to the I form, (d) suppression of lipolysis in adipose tissue, (e) stimulation of protein synthesis in muscle, adipose tissue, and liver, and (f) stimulation of RNA and DNA synthesis. Effects b–e can be accomplished independently of effect a.

Research on insulin action has been characterized by a search for a unitary mechanism that can account for all insulin effects. Such a mechanism was proposed some years ago (131, 236) in the following form: insulin interacts with the cell membrane; this interaction initiates perturbations in membrane structure; these perturbations are propagated to alter biochemical events both at the plasma membrane and within responsive cells in the direction of stimulating anabolic processes and storage of foodstuffs. The concept has recently been further elaborated (104).

## Insulin Receptors in Cell Membranes

There is evidence that the peptide hormone insulin, in contrast to the steroid hormone aldosterone (49, 62), need not enter the cell to produce its metabolic effects; insulin covalently bound to large polysaccharides (5, 17, 52, 56, 230) can mimic the action of insulin under conditions where release of free insulin from the large polysaccharide is not biologically detectable. Indeed, with fetal mammary tissue the insulin-polysaccharide complex is reported to be active in vitro under conditions where free insulin in solution is not (181, 182). The relation of insulin-polysaccharide complexes to the cell membrane has been subjected to critical examination (119).

Specific high affinity acceptors for insulin have been postulated for fat cells and fat cell membranes (54, 98, 129), liver cell membranes (54, 55, 118), lymphocytes (81, 135), and other cells (82, 88, 202).

Some properties reported for insulin receptors are summarized below. The specific receptor system can be saturated with insulin, binding and biological activity both becoming maximal at 20–30 $\mu U$ of insulin per ml. Insulin is not significantly altered during the binding process; disulfide interchange reactions are not involved. Proinsulin binds to fat cell membranes with an affinity 20 times less than that of native insulin. A number of insulin derivatives (e.g. the desalanine, desoctapeptide, and separated A and B chain derivatives) compete with insulin in direct proportion to their biological potency. Somatomedin, which has a number of insulin-like effects, competes with insulin for receptor sites in isolated fat cells, liver membranes, and chondrocytes (105), and inhibits adenyl cyclase activity (234).

A receptor protein that binds [125]I-insulin can be extracted from liver or fat cell membranes with Triton X-100 (55). A water soluble insulin receptor has been obtained from cultures of human lymphocytes (81). In each case, derivatives of insulin compete for binding with [125]I-insulin in proportion to their biological activity.

Insulin binding is decreased by exposure of fat cells or liver cell membranes to trypsin (53, 129). A substantial proportion of the specific binding sites can be lost before the insulin biological response in fat cells dissappears (128, 129); both insulin binding capacity and biological response recover spontaneously when the fat cells are washed free of trypsin after a short exposure, but not after long exposure.

Insulin binding is quantitatively increased by treatment of fat cells or liver cell membranes with phospholipase A or C (but not D), reflecting an increase in total binding capacity; no change in the Km of the receptors for insulin occurs (53).

The validity of the postulates regarding insulin receptors depends heavily on the properties of the [125]I-insulin employed. The labeled insulin must contain less than one atom of [125]I-insulin per insulin monomer, and must be scrupulously purified (53). The use of certain commercial samples of [125]I-insulin has revealed a large number of insulin receptor sites in fat cells that do not exhibit saturation kinetics (53).

Insulin receptors have been defined as those molecules which can recognize insulin with a high degree of specificity and affinity; in addition, these receptors can convey the recognition to other molecules. This, in turn, initiates biologically significant interactions (53). It is apparently possible to interfere not only with the binding of insulin to its receptors in the plasma membrane (see above), but with transmission of information from that locus, and with triggering the final interaction systems. For example, digestion of fat cells with highly purified neuraminidase causes a substantial loss of insulin response with respect to glucose transport or lipolysis without altering the affinity of the specific receptors for insulin (53). Similarly, fat cells from old donor rats are metabolically less responsive to insulin than those from young rats (12). The same is true for fat cells from rats injected with glucocorticoids (12) or made diabetic with streptozotocin (12); in none of these instances is the binding of insulin to receptors altered (12).

## Transmission of the Insulin Signal

The spread of perturbations from the insulin receptor site is postulated to result in alteration of the molecular pattern within the plasma membrane of affected cells (131, 205, 236). These alterations have two experimentally measurable consequences.

First, there is increased transport of glucose and of certain amino acids that does not involve changes in enzyme function. Aspects of these problems have been extensively reviewed (146). Membrane vesicles from insulin-treated adipose cells accumulate glucose more rapidly than membranes from untreated cells (35).

Second, under the influence of insulin there are alterations in activity of membrane-bound enzymes to modulate the release into the cell interior of a product that can act as a "second messenger." This second messenger conveys the insulin signal to intracellular loci where, in turn, the messenger influences other enzymatic processes.

The role of two membrane-bound enzyme systems in transmitting the insulin signal is being investigated. These systems are the adenyl cyclase-cyclic AMP (cAMP) system and the $Mg^{2+}$-activated $(Na^+ + K^+)$-ATPase system.

## Insulin and the Adenyl Cyclase-Cyclic AMP (cAMP) System

The mutually antagonistic effects of insulin and epinephrine (or glucagon) on glycogen synthesis, gluconeogenesis, and lipolysis have been discussed above; each of these processes is substantially altered by cAMP or dibutyryl cAMP.

A principal function of cAMP is to activate protein kinases that catalyse phosphorylation of enzymes.

The lipolytic system of adipose cells is activated by a cAMP-sensitive protein kinase; epinephrine stimulates lipolysis, accompanied by a rise in cAMP. Dibutyryl-cyclic AMP, added to the incubation medium, also enhances lipolysis.

It has been difficult to correlate biological response with cellular cAMP levels because of the high proportion of cAMP bound in inactive form or sequestered in tissues (187). An alternate approach has been to measure insulin effects on adenyl cyclase and on phosphodiesterase.

Experiments on insulin inhibition of adenyl cyclase have been extensively reviewed (250, 252). Such inhibition is difficult to demonstrate unless the cells have been previously exposed to epinephrine, glucagon, ACTH, or other lipolytic agents (136). It is reported that 100 $\mu$U insulin per ml can inhibit the elevated adenyl cyclase activity of a particulate preparation from mouse liver exposed concurrently to glucagon, or the adenyl cyclase activity of fat cell "ghosts" exposed concurrently to norepinephrine (250). Suppressive effects of insulin on adenyl cyclase in rat liver (16) and in human adipose tissue (125) have also been observed.

Insulin effects on the hydrolysis of cAMP by phosphodiesterase have been the subject of debate (57, 154, 250).

## Insulin and the $Mg^{2+}$-Requiring $(Na^+ + K^+)$-ATPase System: Ions as Messengers

The potassium ion has a major influence on membrane potentials and is a regulator of enzyme activity. $Mg^{2+}$ is an activator of many intracellular enzymes. $Ca^{2+}$ acts as a second messenger for muscle contraction when released from the tubular system by electrical stimulation.

Stimulation of $K^+$ transport out of blood plasma and into muscle cells (163, 268) was one of the earliest recognized biochemical effects of insulin. Insulin stimulation of glucose uptake in soleus muscle is dependent on the ion content of the incubation medium (91). Replacement of $Ca^{2+}$, $Mg^{2+}$, or $PO_4^{3-}$ does not affect glucose uptake of mouse adipose cells (142), but omission of $K^+$ or $Na^+$ has complex effects (144).

Insulin accentuates the accumulation of both $Mg^{2+}$ and $K^+$, but not $Ca^{2+}$, in the intracellular compartment of isolated uterine muscle from ovariectomized rat donors (134, 151, 152). The insulin stimulus to both $K^+$ and $Mg^{2+}$ accumulation is blocked by ouabain, an inhibitor of the $Mg^{2+}$-requiring $(Na^+ + K^+)$-ATPase enzyme system that is concerned in $K^+$ and $Na^+$ transport (195). The ATPase ion pump therefore plays a necessary role in the insulin stimulation of the ion translocation.

Insulin stimulates marginally the ATPase activity in a crude membrane fraction from human lymphocytes (95); it has no effect on ATPase extracted from muscle after destruction of the membrane by deoxycholate and freeze-thawing (205).

Ouabain has insulin-like activity with respect to glucose metabolism in fat cells (106, 143), but does not alter 3–O–methyl glucose efflux in soleus muscle (127). Insulin stimulation of sugar transport per se is, therefore, apparently independent of the ATPase system.

These findings have given rise to the proposal that the membrane receptor for insulin occupies a locus close to the $Mg^{2+}$-requiring $(Na^+ + K^+)$-ATPase in the plasma membrane, and activation of the receptor may be capable of modifying ATPase activity. It is further proposed that, as a result of the activation of membrane ATPase by insulin, $Mg^{2+}$ accumulates at critical intracellular loci, there to act as a second messenger to influence intracellular enzyme activities (134, 151, 152). $(Na^+ + K^+)$-ATPase has also been implicated in the calorigenic effect of thyroid hormone (112).

# GLUCAGON

The functions of glucagon with respect to insulin release from $\beta$ cells, gluconeogenesis, and lipolysis, have been discussed in the appropriate sections above.

Glucagon and insulin have opposing actions on glycogenolysis, gluconeogenesis, ureogenesis, and ketogenesis in perfused rat liver. Glycogenolysis and gluconeogenesis are about equally sensitive to glucagon; ureogenesis and ketogenesis are much less so (64, 187).

The metabolic effects of glucagon on liver have been correlated to a substantial degree with stimulation of cAMP formation via the adenyl cyclase system (64, 187). Infusion of glucagon into man causes a rise in plasma cAMP levels (27). The role of fatty acids release from adipose cells under the influence of glucagon in regulating gluconeogenesis in liver has been discussed above.

Glucagon receptors have been found in membrane fractions from pancreatic $\beta$ cells (89) and from adipose cells (15). Glucagon is rapidly inactivated by plasma membranes of rat liver (194).

The physiological significance of glucagon in man (246) and sheep (10) has been explored, particularly with respect to gluconeogenesis (246, 248). The plasma glucagon concentration rises under conditions representing need for gluconeogenesis and vice versa. The plasma insulin:glucagon ratios were found to be 0.4 in starvation, 1.7 on a low carbohydrate diet, 4.4 on a balanced diet, and 29 after a glucose infusion (249). Other studies on glucagon include: immunoreactivity relationships of the glucagon molecule (8), glucagon stimulation of phosphorylation of mitochondrial and lysosomal membranes (267), and glucagon function in induction of deoxyribonucleic acid synthesis in liver (219).

# ETIOLOGICAL FACTORS IN DIABETES

## Major Metabolic Abnormalities of Diabetes

The major abnormalities of diabetes mellitus that have received intense experimental scrutiny include (*a*) glucose intolerance, or perhaps more accurately, inappropriate hyperglycemia in the presence of normal or elevated insulin concentrations; (*b*) ketosis and acidosis; (*c*) failure of growth; (*d*) reduced formation of enzymes for storage of foodstuffs; and (*e*) microangiopathy, including thickened basement membranes of capillaries in muscle and other tissues, abnormalities of renal glomerular capillaries, abnormalities of retinal blood vessels. *a*, *b*, *c*, and *d* can be readily reproduced in animals in which insulin deficiency has been induced experimentally. *e* often occurs in humans before, or even without, demonstrable insulin deficiency. Any reasonably complete theory for development of diabetes must account for these five abnormalities.

## Genetic Factors in Diabetes

At present there is no satisfactory genetic marker for the mutation(s) that result in diabetes. In humans, genetic studies have been based almost exclusively on measurements of inappropriate hyperglycemia. Several excellent reviews have recently appeared (36, 179, 200). The data for humans are inconclusive with respect to a specific genetic pattern associated with diabetes: the simplest current concept is that the diabetic trait in man is transmitted as some form of autosomal recessive, but requires multiple, and poorly understood, additional factors for full expression of the trait. Of the superimposed factors, obesity plays a major role (46). In 274 offspring where both parents were diabetic, 62% of the obese progeny were diabetic versus 45% in the nonobese (117).

In Pima Indians there is a bimodal distribution of glucose tolerance curves that indicates a diabetic and a nondiabetic group (207), but no conclusions regarding the pattern of inheritance can be drawn.

In human subjects, microangiopathy, in the form of capillary basement membrane changes (220), increases with the length of time that carbohydrate intolerance (122) has persisted, and with aging (116, 122).

## Animal Models for Genetic Factors in Diabetes

Genetic factors in diabetes have recently been studied extensively in animal models. Perhaps the most complete information stems from studies on the Chinese hamster. The results suggest that the occurrence of inappropriate hyperglycemia in this species involves a minimum of four gene pairs or alleles, all recessive, of which at least 2 pairs must be homozygous abnormal in order for inappropriate hyperglycemia to occur, and at least 3 pairs must be homozygous abnormal in order for ketosis to occur as well (30, 86).

Genetic patterns of predisposition to inappropriate hyperglycemia for a number of rodents have been summarized (200). The importance of the obesity factor is especially striking in the sand rat. Microangiopathy has been produced in rats rendered chronically diabetic with streptozotocin for periods of six months or longer (159).

## Inhibitory Factors in Diabetes and Prediabetes

Two types of metabolic inhibition are under wide study in man: 1. delay or inhibition of insulin release from the pancreas in response to insulinogenic stimuli (34, 38, 73, 123, 214, 246), 2. inhibition of glucose uptake by tissues (210, 216, 257).

The insulin secretory response pattern in maturity-onset diabetes has been reported to differ in several characteristic ways from that in normal individuals. In response to a glucose tolerance test, the initial peak in plasma insulin levels is often delayed, and the total insulin secretory response may be greater than normal (38, 39, 123, 197).

Current explanations for these diabetic characteristics rest on the postulate that a specific glucose receptor in the islet $\beta$ cells is sensitive to the ambient glucose concentrations and is normally inducible by glucose. In the majority of maturity-onset diabetics, the suggestion is that there is impaired function of the glucose receptor during a glucose tolerance test, so that less insulin is released during the initial phase. The immediate consequence of subnormal release of insulin into portal blood is impairment of net glucose uptake by the liver; this, in turn, leaves more of the glucose to raise the general plasma glucose level. At this higher concentration glucose can activate the glucose receptor in the $\beta$ cell (38, 123). The late insulin release is accentuated at the high glucose concentrations by enteric factors (glucagon, gastrin, pancreozymin, secretin) which themselves are subject to release by high glucose concentrations within the gastrointestinal tract (123).

It has been proposed that the genetically-determined defect in diabetes mellitus in man involves the glucoreceptor mechanism of pancreatic $\beta$ cells (38, 123).

There is no delay in peak insulin release in response to a glucose tolerance test in two strains of genetically hyperglycemic mice, the ob/ob strain (33, 265), or the C57BL/KsJ-db (db/db) strain (200); nor is there a delay in mice made obese by injection of gold thioglucose (33). The insulin secretory patterns for the three types of rats have more in common with human obesity than with human diabetes. It is suggested that these three groups of obese rodents lack an inhibitor of insulin release that may be important in some human diabetics (33). However, there is a defective insulin release mechanism in the diabetic spiny mouse (34).

Evidence for resistance to insulin in maturity-onset diabetes has been reported by Reaven and co-workers (216). The subjects were prepared by infusion of epinephrine (together with propanolol, a blocker of beta adrenergic receptors) to suppress endogenous insulin release. The patients were then given insulin and a glucose load intravenously. Diabetics developed higher plasma glucose levels than did normals, and displayed a lower rate of removal of glucose from plasma at the same glucose and insulin concentrations; this suggests a relative resistance to insulin in these diabetic subjects.

The relation of obesity to hyperglycemia and insulin sensitivity has been studied in various strains of rodents (25, 44, 85, 99, 227, 229, 264, 270), particularly with respect to insulin responsiveness of adipose tissue (90) and diaphragm muscle (85, 90) and, in man, with respect to adipose cell size (141, 226) and total adipose mass (70).

## Anterior Pituitary Factors in Diabetes Mellitus

From the classic work of Young (266) and of Houssay & Anderson (109) it has long been known that the injection of anterior pituitary extracts or of purified growth hormone can, in certain animals, produce permanent diabetes associated with impaired pancreatic $\beta$ cell function. Diabetogenic effects can be obtained in man as well. Injection of a single dose of 10 mg of human growth hormone into normal adult men produced, after 12 hr, an impairment of glucose tolerance and a rise in plasma insulin and free fatty acid concentrations (172). Injection of human growth hormone into African Babinga pygmies did not produce the usual rise in plasma-free fatty acids. The results were considered to be consistent with partial nonresponsiveness to growth hormone or to a factor generated by growth hormone. The defective response to growth hormone is not transmitted as an autosomal or sex-linked trait (167).

Plasma growth hormone levels have been found to be elevated in human juvenile diabetics (96, 100, 237). In some instances the high growth hormone levels were found to be normalized by the institution of good control of blood glucose levels under insulin treatment (100). In another survey among insulin-dependent diabetic patients there was a distinct population characterized by excessive growth hormone secretion and proneness to ketosis, despite adequate diabetic control (39, 96).

In general, plasma growth hormone levels rise in response to insulin-induced hypoglycemia (263). In a careful examination of plasma growth hormone levels in normal humans, the peak values were observed at 4 hr after oral glucose administration (i.e. when glucose levels were falling or subnormal). In a repeat glucose tolerance test 2 hr later, 6 hr after the first, impaired glucose tolerance was observed. The impairment in tolerance was closely correlated with the magnitude of the rise in plasma growth hormone secretion during the falling, or subnormal, glucose levels after the peak of the glucose tolerance curve, suggesting a physiological role for growth hormone in glucose tolerance (263). Rats bearing a growth hormone-producing tumor exhibited elevated insulin and free fatty acid levels in plasma, and insulin resistance in peripheral tissues (3). Repeated injections of growth hormone into beagles produce an X-factor that gives rise to hyperglycemia, insulin resistance, and impairment of the acute growth hormone stimulation of insulin secretion (160).

The mean clearance rate for $^{131}$I-growth hormone in diabetic children has been found to be less than normal, $113.5 \pm 12.6$ ml/min vs $180.4 \pm 14.9$, respectively. In diabetes there may be a defect in the hepatic clearance mechanism for growth hormone (148).

Human chorionic somatomammotropin (HCS), a placental hormone with a high degree of structural homology to human growth hormone (218), has diabetogenic effects as it accumulates in the pregnant woman and when injected into children (9, 93). After oral or intravenous glucose tolerance tests in pregnant women, the peak glucose plasma levels are higher and the rate of fall of plasma glucose is slower than in nonpregnant women (185).

The diabetogenic properties of growth hormone, and the abnormalities in growth hormone levels observed in human diabetes mellitus, have led to intensive efforts to determine whether or not growth hormone or similar substances are related to diabetes.

A large peptide, or protein, has been isolated from urine of diabetic patients (155) and from bovine (157) and human (156) pituitaries. This substance produces impaired glucose tolerance associated with hyperinsulinemia in the dog (156, 157) and inhibits insulin stimulation of glycogen synthase I formation in diaphragm muscle (169).

Two fractions have been prepared from human pituitaries, one containing all the growth-stimulating activity, the other all the lipid-mobilizing activity. Neither fraction was substantially contaminated with the other (242). The tentative molecular weight, estimated by gel filtration, was 16,000 for the growth promoting fraction and 2200 for the lipid mobilizing fraction. The relation of these fractions to $\beta$ lipotropin (14, 147) is not known.

## Growth Hormone Fragments and Etiology of Diabetes

The background for work in this area has been reviewed on the occasion of the 50th anniversary of the discovery of insulin (20, 134). In the late 1960s a fraction was obtained from ovine pituitaries, by extraction at pH 2, that inhibited fatty acid synthesis from acetate by liver slices in vitro (22). This observation has subsequently been followed by investigation in depth in two independent laboratories. In one laboratory a peptide with inhibitory properties similar to that extracted from ovine pituitaries has been isolated after autodigestion of ovine growth hormone (containing pituitary peptidases as impurities) at pH 2.3 (21, 23). In the other laboratory peptides with diabetogenic effects, as measured by elevation of blood sugar levels during a glucose tolerance test and by inhibition of fatty acid synthesis by liver slices in vitro, have been prepared by controlled digestion of sheep or human growth hormone with pepsin (153).

Based on these findings, and the earlier observation that the inhibitory metabolic effects of growth hormone do not appear until some hours after growth hormone administration (131), a working hypothesis regarding the relation of growth hormone to diabetes has been proposed (134). The basic assumption is that growth hormone, with a molecular weight of approximately 20,000 as isolated from the pituitary gland, serves as a macromolecule from which smaller peptides are split off, and that it is these peptide fragments from growth hormone that have diverse and specific physiological effects. From this assumption stem the following concepts relative to the diabetogenicity of growth hormone and its relation to precipitation of overt diabetes mellitus. All these possibilities are subject to experimental test:

(a) The genetic component in diabetes mellitus involves one or more mutations manifested as altered activity in the specific enzymes that form, or destroy, the several metabolically active fragments of pituitary growth hormone.

(b) Excess accumulation of, or sensitivity to, the inhibitory fragment causes impaired glucose uptake by tissues and, most critically, inhibition of the glucose stimulus to insulin release from pancreatic $\beta$ cells. If the genetic defect is fully expressed and the inhibition of glucose uptake by $\beta$ cells is intense, $\beta$ cell function is destroyed early and juvenile diabetes develops. In prediabetics or adult-onset diabetics, where there is a delay in insulin release or release only at elevated glucose concentrations, the effects of obesity and other (unknown) factors are most likely superimposed and exacerbate or ameliorate the influence of the diabetogenic fragment. In juvenile-onset (ketotic) diabetes, the greatly impaired glucose uptake and glycogen synthesis, failure of fat synthesis, and decreased protein (enzyme) synthesis are mainly due to insulin deficiency following $\beta$ cell injury.

(c) Excess accumulation of another fragment with stimulatory effects on collagen synthesis leads to formation of thickened capillary basement membranes and various aspects of microangiopathy. What relationship, if any, the cartilage growth factor (somatomedin) has to collagen synthesis in the vascular system is at present unknown.

ACKNOWLEDGMENTS

The author is indebted to his wife, Dr. Ardis Lostroh, for many valuable suggestions regarding the manuscript.

*Literature Cited*

1. Adamson, L. F., Herington, A. C., Bornstein, J. 1972. Evidence for the selection by the membrane transport system of intracellular or extracellular amino acids for protein synthesis. *Biochim. Biophys. Acta* 282:352–65
2. Adolfsson, S., Isaksson, O., Hjalmarson, A. 1972. Effect of insulin on glycogen synthesis and synthetase enzyme activity in the perfused heart. *Biochim. Biophys. Acta* 279:146–56
3. Åkerblom, H. K., Martin, J. M., Garay, G. L., Moscarello, M. 1972. Growth hormone: experimental hypersomatotropism. II. Metabolic effects in rats bearing the MtT-W15 tumor. *Horm. Metab. Res.* 4:15–21
4. Aleyassine, H., Lee, S. H. 1972. Inhibition of insulin release by substrates and inhibitors of monoamine oxidase. *Am. J. Physiol.* 222:565–69
5. Armstrong, K. J., Noall, M. W., Stouffer, J. E. 1972. Dextran-linked insulin: a soluble high molecular weight derivative with biological activity *in vivo* and *in vitro. Biochem. Biophys. Res. Commun.* 47:354–60
6. Ashcroft, S. J. H., Bassett, J. M., Randle, P. J. 1972. Insulin secretion mechanisms and glucose metabolism in isolated islets. *Diabetes* 21(Suppl. 2): 538–45
7. Ashcroft, S. J. H., Weerasinghe, L. C. C., Bassett, J. M., Randle, P. J. 1972. The pentose cycle and insulin release in mouse pancreatic islets. *Biochem. J.* 126:525–32
8. Assan, R., Slusher, N. 1972. Immunoreactivity relationships of the glucagon molecule and related synthetic peptides. *Diabetes* 21:843–55
9. Baird, J. D. 1969. Some aspects of carbohydrate metabolism in pregnancy with special reference to the energy metabolism and hormonal status of the infant of the diabetic woman and the diabetic effect of pregnancy. *J. Endocrinol.* 44:139–72
10. Bassett, J. M. 1972. Plasma glucagon concentrations in sheep: their regulation and relation to concentrations of insulin and growth hormone. *Aust. J. Biol. Sci.* 25:1277–88
11. Behrens, O. K., Shaw, W. N., Eds. 1972. Proc. Fiftieth Anniv. Insulin Symp., Indianapolis, Indiana, October 18–20, 1971. *Diabetes* 21(Suppl. 2): 385–714
12. Bennett, G. V., Cuatrecasas, P. 1972. Insulin-resistant metabolic states. *Science* 176:175–76

13. Bessman, S. P., Schultz, R. D. 1972. Sugar electrode sensor for the "artificial pancreas." *Horm. Metab. Res.* 4: 413–16
14. Bielmann, P., Chrétien, M., Gattereau, A. 1972. Growth hormone: lipogenic activity of a potent lipolytic hormone. Sheep $\beta$-lipotropin ($\beta$-LPH). II. Further effects of sheep $\beta$-LPH on specificially labeled glucose, and localization of lipogenic active center in the molecule. *Horm. Metab. Res.* 4: 22–25
15. Birnbaumer, L., Pohl, S. L., Rodbell, M., Sundby, F. 1972. The glucagon-sensitive adenylate cyclase system in plasma membranes of rat liver. VII. Hormonal stimulation: reversibility and dependence on concentration of free hormone. *J. Biol. Chem.* 247:2038–43
16. Bitensky, M. W., Gorman, R. E., Neufeld, A. H. 1972. Selective effects of insulin on hepatic epinephrine responsive adenyl cyclase activity. *Endocrinology* 90:1331–35
17. Blatt, L. M., Kim, K. H. 1971. Regulation of hepatic glycogen synthetase. Stimulation of glycogen synthetase in an *in vitro* liver system by insulin bound to sepharose. *J. Biol. Chem.* 246: 4895–98
18. Block, M. B., Mako, M. E., Steiner, D. F., Rubenstein, A. H. 1972. Circulating C-peptide immunoreactivity. Studies in normals and diabetic patients. *Diabetes* 21:1013–26
19. Borensztajn, J., Samols, D. R., Rubenstein, A. H. 1972. Effects of lipoprotein lipase activity in the rat heart and adipose tissue. *Am. J. Physiol.* 223: 1271–75
20. Bornstein, J. 1972. A proposed mechanism of the diabetic action of growth hormone and its relation to the action of insulin. *Isr. J. Med. Sci.* 8(3):407–12
21. Bornstein, J., Armstrong, J. M., Taft, H. P., Ng, F. M., Gould, M. K. 1973. The mechanism of the diabetic effects of pituitary growth hormone. *Postgrad. Med. J.* 49(March Suppl.):219–42
22. Bornstein, J., Krahl, M. E., Marshall, L. B., Gould, M. K., Armstrong, J. M. 1968. Pituitary peptides with direct action on the metabolism of carbohydrates and fatty acids. *Biochim. Biophys. Acta* 156:31–37
23. Bornstein, J., Taylor, W. M., Marshall, L. B., Armstrong, J. M., Gould, M. K. 1969. Mechanism of the diabetogenic action of growth hormone. II. Effect of polypeptides derived from growth hor-

mone on fat metabolism. *Biochim. Biophys. Acta* 192:271–76

24. Borrebaek, B. 1967. Adaptable hexokinase activity in epididymal adipose tissue studied *in vivo* and *in vitro. Biochim. Biophys. Acta* 141:221–30

25. Bray, G. A., York, D. A. 1971. Genetically transmitted obesity in rodents. *Physiol. Rev.* 51:598–646

26. Bressler, R., Cordon, M. V., Brendel, K. 1969. Studies on the role of adenyl cyclase in insulin secretion. *Arch. Intern. Med.* 123:248–51

27. Broadus, A. E. et al 1970. Effects of glucagon on adenosine 3', 5'-monophosphate and guanosine 3',5'-monophosphate in human plasma and urine. *J. Clin. Invest.* 49:2237–45

28. Brooker, R. G., Fischman, M. 1971. Chlorpropamide and tolbutamide inhibition of adenosine 3'5' cyclic monophosphate phosphodiesterase. *Biochem. Biophys. Res. Commun.* 42:824–28

29. Burr, I. M. et al 1971. Insulin of spiny mice (Acomys cahirinus): partial characterization and evidence for two insulins. *Endocrinology* 88:517–21

30. Butler, L., Gerritsen, G. C. 1970. A comparison of the modes of inheritance of diabetes in the Chinese hamster and the KK mouse. *Diabetologia* 6:163–67

31. Cahill, G. F. Jr., Soeldner, J. S., Harris, G. W., Foster, R. O. 1972. Practical developments in diabetes research. *Diabetes* 21(Suppl. 2):703–12

32. Camerini, R. A., Cole, H. S., Eds. 1970. *Early Diabetes. Advan. Metab. Disorders*, March Suppl. 1. 486 pp.

33. Cameron, D. P., Stauffacher, W., Amherdt, M., Orci, L., Renold, A. E. 1973. Kinetics of immunoreactive insulin realease in obese hyperglycemic laboratory rodents. *Endocrinology* 92:257–64

34. Cameron, D. P., Stauffacher, W., Orci, L., Amherdt, M., Renold, A. E. 1972. Defective immunoreactive secretion in the Acomys cahirinus. *Diabetes* 21: 1060–71

35. Carter, J. R., Avruch, J., Martin, D. B. 1972. Glucose transport in plasma membrane vesicles from rat adipose tissue. *J. Biol. Chem.* 247:2682–88

36. Cerasi, E., Luft, R., Eds. 1970. Pathogenesis of diabetes mellitus. *Nobel Symposium No. 13.* New York: Wiley. 354 pp.

37. Cerasi, E., Luft, R. 1972. The prediabetic state, its nature and consequences—a look toward the future. *Diabetes* 21(Suppl. 2):685–94

38. Cerasi, E., Luft, R. 1972. Pathogenesis of diabetes in man. *Isr. J. Med. Sci.* 8:207–23

39. Cerasi, E., Luft, R., Efendic, S. 1972. Decreased sensitivity of the pancreatic beta cells to glucose in prediabetic and diabetic subjects. A glucose dose-response study. *Diabetes* 21:224–34

40. Chance, R. E. 1972. Amino acid sequences of proinsulins and intermediates. *Diabetes* 21(Suppl. 2):461–67

41. Chang, A. Y., Schneider, D. I. 1971. Rate of gluconeogenesis and levels of gluconeogenic enzymes in liver and kidney of diabetic and normal Chinese hamsters. *Biochim. Biophys. Acta* 222: 587–92

42. Charles, A. C., Fanska, R., Schmid, F. G., Forsham, P. H., Grodsky, G. M. 1973. Adenosine 3',5'-monophosphate in pancreatic islets: glucose-induced insulin release. *Science* 179:569–71

43. Chernick, S. S., Clark, C. M. Jr., Gardiner, R. J., Scow, R. O. 1972. Role of lipolytic and glucocorticoid hormones in the development of diabetic ketosis. *Diabetes* 21:946–54

44. Chlouverakis, C. 1972. Insulin resistance in the muscle of obese hyperglycemia mice (obob). Lack of local factors. *Hormones* 3:175–82

45. Christensen, H. N., Cullen, A. M., Harrison, L. I., Fajans, S. S., Pek, S. 1971. Reciprocal transport interactions between amino acids and pancreatic hormones. *Fed. Proc.* 30:200

46. Cohen, A. M., Teitelbaum, A., Saliternik, R. 1972. Genetics and diet as factors in development of diabetes mellitus. *Metabolism* 21:235–40

47. Coore, H. G., Denton, R. M., Martin, B. R., Randle, P. J. 1971. Regulation of adipose-tissue pyruvate dehydrogenase by insulin and other hormones. *Biochem. J.* 125:115–28

48. Corbin, J. D., Reimann, E. M., Walsh, D. A., Krebs, E. G. 1970. Activation of adipose tissue lipase by skeletal muscle cyclic adenosine 3',5'-monophosphate-stimulated protein kinase. *J. Biol. Chem.* 245:4849–51

49. Crabbé, J. 1972. Hormonal influences on transepithelial sodium transport: aldosterone vs insulin. *J. Steroid Biochem.* 3:229–36

50. Crespia, S. R., Greenough, W. B., Steinberg, D. 1972. Effect of sodium linoleate infusion on plasma free fatty acids, glucose, insulin, and ketones in unanesthetized dogs. *Diabetes* 21:1179–84

51. Creutzfeldt, W., Creutzfeldt, C., Frerichs, H., Perings, E., Sickinger, K. 1969. The morphological substrate of the inhibition of insulin secretion by diazoxide. *Horm. Metab. Res.* 1: 53–64

52. Cuatrecasas, P. 1969. Interaction of insulin with the cell membrane: the primary action of insulin. *Proc. Nat. Acad. Sci. USA* 63:450–57

53. Cuatrecasas, P. 1972. The nature of insulin-receptor interactions. See Ref. 77, 137–170

54. Cuatrecasas, P. 1972. The insulin receptor. *Diabetes* 21(Suppl. 2):396–402

55. Cuatrecasas, P. 1972. Properties of the insulin receptor isolated from liver and fat cell membranes. *J. Biol. Chem.* 247:1980–91

56. Cuatrecasas, P. 1973. Biological activity of insulin-sepharose. *Science* 179:1143–44

57. Das, I., Chain, E. B. 1972. An effect of insulin on the adenosine 3',5'-cyclic monophosphate phosphodiesterase activities in the perfused Langendorff and working hearts of normal and diabetic rats. *Biochem. J.* 128:95P

58. Davey, P. J., Manchester, K. L. 1969. Isolation of labelled aminoacyl transfer RNA from muscle. Studies of the entry of labelled amino acids into acyl transfer RNA linkage *in situ* and its control by insulin. *Biochim. Biophys. Acta* 182:85–97

59. Debons, A. F., Krimsky, I., From, A. 1970. A direct action of insulin on the hypothalamic satiety center. *Am. J. Physiol.* 219:938–43

60. Demers, L. M., Gabbe, S. G., Villee, C. A., Greep, R. O. 1972. Effects of insulin on human placental glycogenesis. *Endocrinology* 91:270–75

61. Earl, D. C. N., Hindley, S. T. 1971. The rate-limiting step in protein synthesis *in vivo* and *in vitro* and the distribution of growing peptides between the puromycin-labile and puromycin non-labile-sites on polyribosomes. *Biochem. J.* 122:267–76

62. Edelman, I. S., Fimognari, G. M. 1968. On the biochemical mechanism of action of aldosterone. *Recent Progr. Hormone Res.* 24:1–44

63. Ekren, T., Jervell, K. F., Seglen, P. O. 1971. Insulin and amino acid regulation of polysomes in perfused, diabetic rat liver. *Nature New Biol.* 229:244–45

64. Exton, J. H., Park, C. R. 1972. Interaction of insulin and glucagon in the control of liver metabolism. See Ref. 225

65. Exton, J. H., Lewis, S. B., Ho, R. J., Park, C. R. 1972. The role of cyclic AMP in the control of hepatic glucose production by glucagon and insulin. *Advan. Cyclic Nucleotide Res.* 1:91–102

66. Fain, J. N., Rosenberg, L. 1972. Antilipolytic action of insulin on fat cells. *Diabetes* 21(Suppl. 2):414–25

67. Fajans, S. S. et al 1972. Amino acids and insulin release *in vivo*. *Isr. J. Med. Sci.* 8:233–43

68. Fajans, S. S. et al 1971. Stimulation of insulin release in the dog by a non-metabolizable amino acid. Comparison with leucine and arginine. *J. Clin. Endocrinol. Metab.* 33:35–41

69. Fineberg, S. E., Merimee, T. J. 1970. Proinsulin: metabolic effects on the human forearm. *Science* 167:998–99

70. Flatt, J. P. 1972. Role of the increased adipose tissue mass in the apparent insulin insensitivity of obesity. *Am. J. Clin. Nutrition* 25:1189–92

71. Forsyth, I. A., Strong, C. R., Dils, R. 1972. Interactions of insulin, corticosterone, and prolactin in promoting milk-fat synthesis by mammary explants from pregnant rabbits. *Biochem. J.* 129:929–36

72. Floyd, J. C. Jr. et al 1970. Synergistic effect of certain amino acid pairs upon insulin secretion in man. *Diabetes* 19:102–8

73. Floyd, J. C. Jr., Fajans, S. S., Conn, J. W., Pek, S., Knopf, R. F. See Ref. 32, 113–18

74. Foucan, R. E., Field, J. B. 1972. Effect of control of hyperglycemia on plasma insulin responses to various stimuli in newly diagnosed ketosis-prone diabetic patients. *J. Clin. Endocrinol. Metab.* 35:299–306

75. Frazier, W. A., Angeltti, R. H., Bradshaw, R. A. 1972. Nerve growth factor and insulin. *Science* 176:482–88

76. Frederickson, D. S., Levy, R. I., Lees, R. S. 1967. Fat transport in lipoproteins —an integrated approach to mechanisms and disorders. *N. Engl. J. Med.* 276:273–81

77. Fritz, I. B., Ed. 1972. *Insulin Action.* New York: Academic. 609 pp.

78. Fritz, I. B. 1972. Summary and overview of the integrative aspects of insulin action. See Ref. 77, 571–602

79. Frohman, L. A., Goldman, J. K., Bernardis, L. L. 1972. Studies of insulin sensitivity *in vivo* in weanling rats with hypothalamic obesity. *Metabolism* 21:1133–42

80. Gabbay, K. H., Tze, W. J. 1972. Inhibition of glucose-induced release of insulin by aldose reductase inhibitors. *Proc. Nat. Acad. Sci. USA* 69:1435–39

81. Gavin, J. R. III, Buell, D. N., Roth, J. 1972. Water-soluble receptors from human lymphocytes. *Science* 178:168–69

82. Gavin, J. R. III, Roth, J., Jen, P., Freychet, P. 1972. Insulin receptors in human circulating cells and fibroblasts. *Proc. Nat. Acad. Sci. USA* 69:747-51
83. Geisler, R. W., Hansen, R. J. 1972. Effects of insulin on the adaptation of glucose-6-phosphate dehydrogenase and 6-phosphogluconate dehydrogenase in rat adipose tissue. *Biochim. Biophys. Acta* 279:139-45
84. Gelehrter, T. D., Tomkins, G. M. 1970. Post-transcriptional control of tyrosine aminotransferase synthesis by insulin. *Proc. Nat. Acad. Sci. USA* 66:390-97
85. Genuth, S. M., Przybylski, R. J., Rosenberg, D. M. 1971. Insulin resistance in genetically obese, hyperglycemic mice. *Endocrinology* 88:1230-38
86. Gerritsen, G. C., Needham, L. B., Schmidt, F. L., Dulin, W. E. 1970. Studies on prediction and development of diabetics in the offspring of diabetic Chinese hamsters. *Diabetologia* 6:158-62
87. Goldfine, I. D., Cerasi, E., Luft, R. 1972. Glucagon stimulation of insulin release in man: inhibition during hypoglycemia. *J. Clin. Endocrinol. Metab.* 35:312-14
88. Goldfine, I. D., Gardner, J. D., Neville, D. M. Jr. 1972. Insulin action in isolated rat thymocytes. I. Binding of [125]I-insulin and stimulation of α-amino butyric acid transport. *J. Biol. Chem.* 247:6919-26
89. Goldfine, I. D., Roth, J., Birnbaumer, L. 1972. Glucagon receptors in β-cells. Binding of [125]I-glucagon and activation of adenylate cyclase. *J. Biol. Chem.* 247:1211-18
90. Goldman, J. K., Bernardis, L. L., Frohman, L. A. 1972. Insulin responsiveness *in vitro* of diaphragm and adipose tissue from weanling rats with hypothalamic obesity. *Horm. Metab. Res.* 4:328-30
91. Gould, M. K., Chaudry, I. H. 1970. The action of insulin on glucose uptake by isolated rat soleus muscle. I. Effects of cations. *Biochim. Biophys. Acta* 215:249-57
92. Grodsky, G. M. 1972. A threshold distribution hypothesis for packet storage of insulin. II. Effect of calcium release. *Diabetes* 21(Suppl. 2):584-93
93. Grumbach, M. M., Kaplan, S. L., Sciarra, J. J., Burr, I. M. 1968. Chorionic growth hormone-prolactin (CGP): secretion, disposition, biologic activity in man, and postulated function as the "growth hormone" in the second half of pregnancy. *Ann. NY Acad. Sci.* 148:501-31
94. Gulbenkian, R. A., Ornstein, L., Tabachnick, I. I. A. 1972. The use of diazoxide inhibition of insulin secretion as a tool to investigate insulin stimulation by other agents. *Horm. Metab. Res.* 4:57-58
95. Hadden, J. W., Hadden, E. M., Wilson, E. E., Good, R. A., Coffey, R. G. 1972. Direct action of insulin on plasma membrane ATPase activity in human lymphocytes. *Nature New Biol.* 235:174-77
96. Hagen, T. C., Lawrence, A. M., Kirsteins, L. 1971. Abnormal growth hormone (GH) secretion in ketosis-prone diabetes. *J. Lab. Clin. Med.* 78:993-4
97. Halperin, M. L. 1971. Studies on the conversion of pyruvate into fatty acids in white adipose tissue. Effects of insulin, alloxan-diabetes and starvation. *Biochem. J.* 124:615-22
98. Hammond, J. M., Jarett, L., Mariz, I. K., Daughaday, W. H. 1972. Heterogeneity of insulin receptors on fat cell membranes. *Biochem. Biophys. Res. Commun.* 49:1122-28
99. Han, P. W., Feng, L. Y., Kuo, P. T. 1972. Insulin sensitivity of pair-fed hyperlipidemic, hyperinsulinemic obese-hypothalamic rats. *Am. J. Physiol.* 223:1206-9
100. Hansen, A. P., Mogensen, C. E. 1972. Growth hormone secretion and kidney function during normalization of the metabolic state in newly diagnosed juvenile diabetics. *Horm. Metab. Res.* 4:11-15
101. Hansen, R., Pilkis, S. J., Krahl, M. E. 1967. Properties of adaptive hexokinase isozymes of the rat. *Endocrinology* 81:1397-1404
102. Hansen, R. J., Pilkis, S. J., Krahl, M. E. 1970. Effect of insulin on the synthesis *in vitro* of hexokinase in rat epididymal adipose tissue. *Endocrinology* 86:57-65
103. Hellman, B., Sehlin, J., Taljedal, I. B. 1972. Transport of L-leucine and D-leucine into pancreatic β-cells with reference to the mechanism of amino acid-induced insulin release. *Biochim. Biophys. Acta* 266:436-43
104. Hershko, A., Mamont, P., Shields, R., Tomkins, G. M. 1971. Pleiotypic response. *Nature New Biol.* 232:206-11
105. Hintz, R. L., Clemmons, D. R., Underwood, L. E., Van Wyk, J. J. 1972. Competitive binding of somatomedin to the insulin receptors of adipocytes, chondrocytes, and liver membranes. *Proc. Nat. Acad. Sci. USA* 69:2351-53
106. Ho, R. J., Jeanrenaud, B., Posternak, T., Renold, A. E. 1967. Insulin-like ac-

tion of ouabain. II. Primary antilipolytic effect through inhibition of adenyl cyclase. *Biochim. Biophys. Acta* 144:74–82

107. Hodgkin, D. C. 1972. The structure of insulin. *Diabetes* 21:1131–50

108. Hoshi, M., Shreeve, W. W. 1973. Release and production of insulin by isolated, perfused rat pancreatic islets. *Diabetes* 22:16–24

109. Houssay, B. A., Anderson, E. 1949. Diabetic action of purified anterior pituitary hormones. *Endocrinology* 45:627–28

110. Iljin, V. S., Usatenko, M. S. 1972. Effects of insulin on isozymes of lactate dehydrogenase in rabbit muscles and liver. *Biokhimiya* 37:127–34

111. Ingbretsen, W. R. Jr., Moxley, M. A., Allen, D. O., Wagle, S. R. 1972. Studies on gluconeogenesis, protein synthesis, and cyclic AMP levels in isolated parenchymal cells following insulin withdrawal from alloxan diabetic rats. *Biochem. Biophys. Res. Commun.* 49: 601–7

112. Ismail-Belgi, F., Edelman, I. S. 1971. The mechanism of the calorigenic action of thyroid hormone. Stimulation of Na$^+$ plus K$^+$-activated adenosine triphosphatase activity. *J. Gen. Physiol.* 57:710–22

113. Jacobsson, B., Smith, U. 1972. Effect of cell size on lipolysis and anti-lipolytic action of insulin in human fat cells. *J. Lipid Res.* 13:651–56

114. Jefferson, L. S., Koehler, J. O., Morgan, H. E. 1972. Effect of insulin on protein synthesis in skeletal muscle of an isolated perfused preparation of rat hemicorpus. *Proc. Nat. Acad. Sci. USA* 69:816–20

115. Johnson, M. E. M., Das, N. M., Butcher, F. R., Fain, J. N. 1972. The regulation of gluconeogenesis in isolated rat liver cells by glucagon, insulin, dibutyryl cyclic adenosine monophosphate, and fatty acids. *J. Biol. Chem.* 247:3229–35

116. Jordan, S. W., Perley, M. J. 1972. Microangiopathy in diabetes mellitus and aging. *Arch. Pathol.* 93:261–65

117. Kahn, C. B. et al 1969. Clinical and chemical diabetes in offspring of diabetic couples. *N. Engl. J. Med.* 281: 343–47

118. Kahn, C. R., Neville, D. M. Jr., Roth, J. 1973. Insulin-receptor interaction in the obese-hyperglycemic mouse. A model of insulin resistance. *J. Biol. Chem.* 248:244–50

119. Katzen, H. M., Vlahakes, G. J. 1973. Biological activity of insulin-sepharose? *Science* 179:1142–43

120. Kemmler, W., Peterson, J. D., Rubenstein, A. H., Steiner, D. F. 1972. On the biosynthesis, intracellular transport, and mechanism of conversion of proinsulin to insulin and C-peptide. *Diabetes* 21(Suppl. 2):572–81

121. Khoo, J. C., Jarett, L., Mayer, S. E., Steinberg, D. 1972. Subcellular distribution of, and epinephrine-induced changes in, hormone-sensitive lipase, phosphorylase, and phosphorylase kinase in rat adipocytes. *J. Biol. Chem.* 247:4812–18

122. Kilo, C., Vogler, N., Williamson, J. R. 1972. Muscle capillary basement membrane changes related to aging and to diabetes mellitus. *Diabetes* 21:881–905

123. Kipnis, D. M. 1972. Nutrient regulation of insulin secretion in human subjects. *Diabetes* 21(Suppl. 2):606–16

124. Kipnis, D. M., Permutt, M. A. 1972. Inductive effects of glucose on the insulin secretory and synthetic apparatus of the pancreatic β-cell. *Isr. J. Med. Sci.* 8:224–32

125. Kissebah, A. H., Fraser, T. R. 1972. The *in vitro* $^{14}$C-cyclic AMP production by normal human adipose tissue in response to some hormones and in uncontrolled and controlled diabetic adipose tissue. *Horm. Metab. Res.* 4:72–76

126. Knittle, J. L., Ginsberg-Fellner, F. 1972. Effect of weight reduction on *in vitro* adipose tissue lipolysis and cellularity in obese adolescents and adults. *Diabetes* 21:754–61

127. Kohn, P. G., Clausen, T. 1971. The relationship between the transport of glucose and cations across cell membranes in isolated tissues. VI. The effect of insulin, ouabain, and metabolic inhibitors on the transport of 3-O–methylglucose and glucose in rat soleus muscle. *Biochim. Biophys. Acta* 225:277–90

128. Kono, T. 1972. The insulin receptor of fat cells. The relationship between the binding and physiological effects of insulin. See Ref. 77, 171–204

129. Kono, T., Barham, F. W. 1971. The relation between the insulin-binding capacity of fat cells and the cellular response to insulin. Studies with intact and trypsin-treated cells. *J. Biol. Chem.* 246:6210–16

130. Kostyo, J. L., Rillema, J. A. 1971. *In vitro* effects of growth hormone on the number and activity of ribosomes engaged in protein synthesis in the iso-

lated diaphragm. *Endocrinology* 88:1054–62

131. Krahl, M. E. 1951. The effect of insulin and pituitary hormones on glucose uptake in muscle. *Ann. NY Acad. Sci.* 54:649–70

132. Krahl, M. E. 1961. *The Action of Insulin on Cells.* New York: Academic. 202 pp.

133. Krahl, M. E. 1972. Effects of insulin on synthesis of specific enzymes in various tissues. See Ref. 77, 461–86

134. Krahl, M. E. 1972. Insulin action at the molecular level. Facts and speculations. *Diabetes* 21(Suppl. 2):695–702

135. Krug, U., Krug, F., Cuatrecasas, P. 1972. Emergence of insulin receptors in human lymphocytes during *in vitro* transformation. *Proc. Nat. Acad. Sci. USA* 69:2604–8

136. Kuo, J. F., DeRenzo, E. C. 1969. A comparison of the effects of lipolytic and anti-lipolytic agents on adenosine 3',5'-monophosphate levels in adipose cells as determined by prior labeling with adenine-8-$^{14}$C. *J. Biol. Chem.* 244:2252–60

137. Lacy, P. E. 1972. The secretion of insulin. *Diabetes* 21(Suppl. 2):510

138. Lakshmanan, M. R., Nepokroeff, C. M., Porter, J. W. 1972. Control of the synthesis of fatty-acid synthetase in rat liver by insulin, glucagon, and adenosine 3':5' cyclic monophosphate. *Proc. Nat. Acad. Sci. USA* 69:3516–19

139. Larner, J. 1972. Insulin and glycogen synthase. *Diabetes* 21(Suppl. 2): 428–38

140. Lee, K. L., Reel, J. R., Kenney, F. T. 1970. Regulation of tyrosine α-ketoglutarate transaminase in rat liver. IX. Studies of the mechanisms of hormonal inductions in cultured hepatoma cells. *J. Biol. Chem.* 245:5806–12

141. Leonhardt, W., Hanefeld, M., Schneider, H., Haller, H. 1972. Human adipocyte volumes: maximum size and correlation to weight index in maturity-onset diabetes. *Diabetologia* 8:287–89

142. Letarte, J., Jeanrenaud, B., Renold, A. E. 1969. Ionic effects on glucose transport and metabolism by isolated mouse fat cells incubated with or without insulin. I. Lack of effect of medium $Ca^{2+}$, $Mg^{2+}$ or $PO_4^{3-}$. *Biochim. Biophys. Acta* 183:350–56

143. Letarte, J., Jeanrenaud, B., Renold, A. E. 1969. II. Effect of replacement of $K^+$ and of ouabain. See Ref. 142, 357–65

144. Letarte, J., Renold, A. E. 1969. III.

Effects of replacement of $Na^+$. See Ref. 142, 366–74

145. Levin, S. R., Grodsky, G. M., Hagura, R., Smith, D. F. 1972. Comparison of the inhibitory effects of diphenylhydantoin and diazoxide upon insulin secretion from the isolated, perfused pancreas. *Diabetes* 21:856–62

146. Levine, R. 1966. The action of insulin at the cell membrane. *Am. J. Med.* 40: 691–94

147. Li, C. H., Barnafi, L., Chrétien, M., Chung, D. 1965. Isolation and structure of β-LPH from sheep pituitary glands. *Nature* 208:1093–94

148. Lipman, R. L., Taylor, A. L., Conly, P., Mintz, D. H. 1972. Metabolic clearance rate of growth hormone in juvenile diabetes mellitus. *Diabetes* 21:175–77

149. Lostroh, A. J. 1968. Regulation by testosterone and insulin of citrate secretion in explanted mouse prostates. *Proc. Nat. Acad. Sci. USA* 60:1312–18

150. Lostroh, A. J. 1970. Insulin requirement *in vivo* for estradiol and growth hormone action. *Fed. Proc.* 29:390

151. Lostroh, A. J. 1972. Insulin action: accumulation of $Mg^{++}$, $K^+$ in uterine muscle, and $Mg^{++}$-requiring ($Na^+$ + $K^+$)-ATPase activity. *Excerpta Med. Found. Int. Congr. Ser.* 256:167

152. Lostroh, A. J., Krahl, M. E. 1973. Insulin action. Accumulation *in vitro* of $Mg^{2+}$ and $K^+$ in rat uterus: ion pump activity. *Biochim. Biophys. Acta* 291:260–68

153. Lostroh, A. J., Krahl, M. E., Marshall, L. B. 1973. Diabetogenic peptides of pituitary origin: preparation from sheep or from human growth hormone (GH) by pepsin digestion. *55th Meet. Endocrine Soc. Chicago, June 20–22. Abstr.* A-242

154. Loten, E. G., Sneyd, J. G. T. 1970. An effect of insulin on adipose-tissue adenosine 3':5'-cyclic monophosphate phosphodiesterase. *Biochem. J.* 120:187–93

155. Louis, L. H., Conn, J. W. 1969. A urinary diabetogenic peptide in proteinuric diabetic patients. *Metabolism* 18: 556–63

156. Louis, L. H., Conn, J. W. 1972. Diabetogenic polypeptide from human pituitaries similar to that excreted by proteinuric diabetic patients. *Metabolism* 21:1–9

157. Louis, L. H., Conn, J. W., Appelt, M. M. 1971. Induction of hyperinsulinemia and hyperglycemia in dogs by administration of diabetogenic bovine pituitary peptide. *Metabolism* 20:326–30

158. Lucke, R. C., Kagan, A., Adelman, N., Glick, S. M. 1972. Effect of 2-deoxy-D-glucose and mannoheptulose on the insulin response to amino acids in rabbits. *Diabetes* 21:1–5

159. Luenberger, P., Cameron, D., Stauffacher, W., Renold, A. E., Babel, J. 1971. Ocular lesions in rats rendered chronically diabetic with streptozotocin. *Ophthalmic Res.* 2:189–204

160. Mahler, R. J., Szabo, O. 1970. A postulated mechanism for the insulin synergistic and insulin antagonistic action of growth hormone. See Ref. 32, 147–57

161. Malherbe, R. C., Burrill, K. C., Levin, S. R., Karam, J. H., Forsham, P. H. 1972. Effect of diphenylhydantoin on insulin secretion in man. *N. Engl. J. Med.* 286:339–41

162. Manchester, K. L. 1972. Effect of insulin on protein synthesis. *Diabetes* 21(Suppl. 2):447–52

163. Manery, J. F., Gourley, D. R. H., Fisher, K. C. 1956. The potassium uptake and rate of oxygen consumption of isolated frog skeletal muscle in the presence of insulin and lactate. *Can. J. Biochem. Physiol.* 34:893–902

164. Markussen, J. 1971. Mouse insulins-separation and structure. *Int. J. Protein Res.* 3:149–55

165. Matschinsky, F. M., Landgraf, R., Ellerman, J., Kotler-Brajtburg, J. 1972. Glucoreceptor mechanisms in islets of Langerhans. *Diabetes* 21(Suppl. 2): 555–69

166. Mayhew, D. A., Wright, P. H., Ashmore, J. 1969. Regulation of insulin secretion. *Pharmacol. Rev.* 21:183–212

167. Merimee, T. J., Rimoin, D. L., Cavalli-Sforza, L. L. 1972. Metabolic studies in the African pygmy. *J. Clin. Invest.* 51: 395–401

168. Miller, L. L., Griffin, E. 1972. Direct effects of insulin on amino acid and protein metabolism in the perfused rat liver: Insulin, the hormone essential for positive nitrogen balance. See Ref. 77, 487–508

169. Miller, T. B., Larner, J. 1972. Anti-insulin actions of a bovine pituitary diabetogenic peptide on glycogen synthesis. *Proc. Nat. Acad. Sci. USA* 69: 2774–77

170. Milner, R. D. G., Hales, C. N. 1967. The role of calcium and magnesium in insulin secretion from rabbit pancreas studied *in vitro*. *Diabetologia* 3: 47–49

171. Minemura, T., Lacy, W. W., Crofford, O. B. 1970. Regulation of the transport and metabolism of amino acids in isolated fat cells. *J. Biol. Chem.* 245: 3872–81

172. Mitchell, M. L., Raben, M. S., Ernesti, M. 1970. Use of growth hormone as a diabetic stimulus in man. *Diabetes* 19: 196–99

173. Morgan, C. R., Bonner, J. 1970. Template activity of liver chromatin increased by *in vivo* administration of insulin. *Proc. Nat. Acad. Sci. USA* 65: 1077–80

174. Morgan, H. E. et al 1972. Effect of insulin on protein turnover in heart and skeletal muscle. See Ref. 77, 437–60

175. Mortimore, G. E., Mondon, C. E. 1970. Inhibition by insulin of valine turnover in liver. Evidence for a general control of proteolysis. *J. Biol. Chem.* 245: 2375–83

176. Munro, H. N. 1968. Role of amino acid supply in regulating ribosome function. *Fed. Proc.* 27:1231–37

177. Murthy, V. K., Steiner, G. 1972. Glucose-independent stimulation of lipogenesis by insulin. *Am. J. Physiol.* 222:983–87

178. Narahara, H. T. 1972. Biological activity of proinsulin. See Ref. 77, 63–76

179. Neel, J. V. 1970. The genetics of diabetes mellitus. See Ref. 32, 3–10

180. Oakley, N. W., Harrigan, P., Kissebah, A. H., Kissin, E. A., Adams, P. W. 1972. Factors affecting insulin response to glucagon in man. *Metabolism* 21: 1001–8

181. Oka, T., Topper, Y. J. 1971. Insulin-sepharose and the dynamics of insulin action. *Proc. Nat. Acad. Sci. USA* 68: 2066–68

182. Oka, T., Topper, Y. 1972. Dynamics of insulin action on mammary epithelium. *Nature New Biol.* 239:216–18

183. Oravec, M., Korner, A. 1972. Stimulation of labeling of rat-liver nuclear ribonucleic acid by insulin. *Eur. J. Biochem.* 27:425–30

184. Orci, L., Gabbay, K. H., Malaisse, W. J. 1972. Pancreatic beta-cell web: Its possible role in insulin secretion. *Science* 175:1129–30

185. O'Sullivan, J. B. 1970. Gestational diabetes and its significance. See Ref. 32, 339–44

186. Panten, U., Von Kriegstein, E., Poser, W., Schönborn, J., Hasselblatt, A. 1972. Effects of L-leucine and α-ketoisocaproic acid upon insulin secretion and metabolism of isolated pancreatic islets. *FEBS Lett.* 20:225–28

187. Park, C. R., Lewis, S. B., Exton, J. H. 1972. Relationship of some hepatic ac-

tions of insulin to the intracellular level of cyclic adenylate. *Diabetes* 21(Suppl. 2):439–46

188. Pekar, A. H., Frank, B. H. 1972. Conformation of proinsulin. A comparison of insulin and proinsulin self-association at neutral pH. *Biochemistry* 11: 4013–16

189. Permutt, M. A., Kipnis, D. M. 1972. Insulin biosynthesis. I. On the mechanism of glucose stimulation. *J. Biol. Chem.* 247:1194–99

190. Peterson, J. D., Nehrlich, S., Oyer, P. E., Steiner, D. F. 1972. Determination of the amino acid sequence of the monkey, sheep, and dog proinsulin C-peptides by a semi-micro Edman degradation procedure. *J. Biol. Chem.* 247:4866–71

191. Pilkis, S. J. 1970. Hormonal control of hexokinase activity in animal tissues. *Biochim. Biophys. Acta* 215: 461–76

192. Pilkis, S. J., Korner, A. 1971. Effect of diabetes and insulin treatment on protein synthetic ability of rat liver ribosomes. *Biochim. Biophys. Acta* 247:597–608

193. Piras, M. M., Bindstern, E., Piras, R. 1973. Regulation of glycogen metabolism in the adrenal gland. IV. The effect of insulin on glycogen synthetase, phosphorylase, and related metabolites. *Arch. Biochem. Biophys.* 154: 263–69

194. Pohl, S. L., Kraus, H. M. J., Birnbaumer, L., Rodbell, M. 1972. Inactivation of glucagon by plasma membranes of rat liver. *J. Biol. Chem.* 247:2295–2301

195. Post, R. L., Hegyvary, C., Kume, S. 1972. Activation by adenosine triphosphate in the phosphorylation kinetics of sodium and potassium ion transport adenosine triphosphatase. *J. Biol. Chem.* 247:6530–40

196. Rappaport, A. M. et al 1972. Effects on insulin output and on pancreatic blood flow of exogenous insulin infusion into an *in situ* isolated portion of the pancreas. *Endocrinology* 91:168–76

197. Reaven, G. M., Shen, S. W., Silvers, A., Farquhar, J. W. 1971. Is there a delay in the plasma insulin response of patients with chemical diabetes mellitus. *Diabetes* 20:416–23

198. Rechcigl, M. Jr., Ed. 1971. *Enzyme Synthesis and Degradation in Mammalian Systems.* Baltimore: University Park. 477 pp.

199. Renold, A. E. 1972. The beta cell and its responses: summarizing remarks and some contributions from Geneva. *Diabetes* 21(Suppl. 2):619–31

200. Renold, A. E. et al 1972. Endocrine-metabolic anomalies in rodents with hyperglycemic syndromes of hereditary and/or environmental origin. *Isr. J. Med. Sci.* 8:189–206

201. Rerup, C. C. 1970. Drugs producing diabetes through damage of the insulin secreting cells. *Pharmacol. Rev.* 22: 485–518

202. Robinson, C. A. Jr., Boshell, B. R., Reddy, W. J. 1972. Insulin binding to plasma membranes. *Biochim. Biophys. Acta* 290:84–91

203. Robison, G. A., Butcher, R. W., Sutherland, E. W. 1971. *Cyclic AMP.* New York: Academic. 531 pp.

204. Roch-Norland, A. 1972. Muscle glycogen and glycogen synthetase in normal subjects and in patients with diabetes mellitus. Effect of intravenous glucose and insulin administration. *Scand. J. Clin. Lab. Invest.* 29(Suppl. 125): 1–27

205. Rogus, E., Price, T., Zierler, K. L. 1969. Sodium plus potassium-activated, ouabain-inhibited adenosine triphosphatase from a fraction of rat skeletal muscle, and lack of insulin effect on it. *J. Gen. Physiol.* 54:188–202

206. Rubenstein, A. H., Clark, J. L., Melani, F., Steiner, D. 1969. Secretion of proinsulin C-peptide by pancreatic β-cells and its circulation in blood. *Nature* 224:697–99

207. Rushforth, N. B., Bennett, P. H., Steinberg, A. G., Burch, T. A., Miller, M. 1971. Diabetes in the Pima Indians. Evidence of bimodality in glucose tolerance distributions. *Diabetes* 20:756–65

208. Saggerson, E. D., Greenbaum, A. L. 1969. The effect of dietary and hormonal conditions on the activities of glycolytic enzymes in rat epididymal adipose tissue. *Biochem. J.* 115:405–18

209. Sando, H., Borg, J., Steiner, D. F. 1972. Studies on the secretion of newly synthesized proinsulin and insulin from isolated rat islets of Langerhans. *J. Clin. Invest.* 51:1476–85

210. Santen, A. J., Willis, P. W. III, Fajans, S. S. 1972. Atherosclerosis in diabetes mellitus. *Arch. Int. Med.* 130:833–43

211. Schlierf, G., Raetzer, H. 1972. Diurnal patterns of blood sugar, plasma insulin, free fatty acid and triglyceride levels in normal subjects and in patients with type IV hyperlipoproteinemia and the effect of meal frequency. *Nutr. Metab.* 14:113–26

212. Schimke, R. T., Doyle, D. 1970. Con-

trol of enzyme levels in animal tissues. *Ann. Rev. Biochem.* 39:929–76

213. Schwartz, P. L., Wettenhall, R. E. H., Troedel, M. A., Bornstein, J. 1970. A long-term effect of insulin on collagen synthesis by newborn rat bone *in vitro. Diabetes* 19:465–66

214. Seltzer, H. S. 1970. Evidence that the primary lesion in familial diabetes is an inherited defect of the $\beta$-cell. See Ref. 32, 105–11

215. Shafir, E., Ed. 1972. International Symposium Commemorating the 50th Anniversary of Insulin, Impact of insulin on metabolic pathways. Part I, Lectures. *Isr. J. Med. Sci.* 8:175–494

216. Shen, S. W., Reaven, G. M., Farquhar, J. W. 1970. Comparison of impedance to insulin-mediated glucose uptake in normal subjects and in subjects with latent diabetes. *J. Clin. Invest.* 49: 2151–60

217. Sherton, C. C., Wool, I. G. 1972. Determination of the number of proteins in liver ribosomes and ribosomal subunits by two-dimensional polyacrylamide gel electrophoresis. *J. Biol. Chem.* 247: 4460–67

218. Sherwood, L. M., Handwerger, S., McLaurin, W. D., Lanner, M. 1971. Amino-acid sequence of human placental lactogen. *Nature New Biol.* 233: 59–61

219. Short, J. et al 1972. Induction of deoxyribonucleic acid synthesis in the liver of the intact animal. *J. Biol. Chem.* 247:1757–66

220. Siperstein, M. D., Unger, R. H., Madison, L. L. 1968. Studies of muscle capillary basement membranes in normal subjects, diabetic, and prediabetic patients. *J. Clin. Invest.* 47:1973–99

221. Smith, L. F. 1972. Amino acid sequences of insulins. *Diabetes* 21(Suppl. 2):457–60

222. Sölling, H. D., Unger, K. O. 1972. The role of insulin in the regulation of $\alpha$-amylase synthesis in the rat pancreas. *Eur. J. Clin. Invest.* 2:199–212

223. Stadtman, E. R. 1966. Allosteric regulation of enzyme activity. *Advan. Enzymol.* 28:41–154

224. Steiner, D. F. 1966. Insulin and the regulation of hepatic biosynthetic activity. *Vitam. Horm.* 24:1–61

225. Steiner, D. R., Freinkel, N., Eds. 1972. *Handbook of Physiology: Section 7: Endocrinology. Vol. I: Endocrine Pancreas.* Baltimore: Williams & Wilkins. 731 pp.

226. Stern, J., Batchelor, B. R., Hollander, N., Cohn, C. K., Hirsch, J. 1972. Adipose-cell size and immunoreactive insulin levels in obese and normal weight adults. *Lancet* II:948–49

227. Stern, J., Johnson, P. R., Greenwood, M. R., Zucker, L. M., Hirsch, J. 1972. Insulin resistance and pancreatic insulin release in the genetically obese Zucker rat. *Proc. Soc. Exp. Biol. Med.* 139:66–69

228. Stout, R. W., Buchanan, K. D., Vallance-Owen, J. 1972. Arterial lipid metabolism in relation to blood glucose and plasma insulin in rats with streptozotocin-induced diabetes. *Diabetologia* 8:398–401

229. Strautz, R. L. 1968. Islet implants: Reduction of glucose levels in the hereditary obese mouse. *Endrocinology* 83:975–78

230. Suzuki, F., Daikuhara, Y., Ono, M., Takeda, Y. 1972. Studies on the mode of action of insulin: properties and biological activity of an insulin-dextran complex. *Endocrinology* 90:1220–30

231. Tager, H. S., Steiner, D. F. 1972. Primary structures of the proinsulin connecting peptides from the rat and the horse. *J. Biol. Chem.* 247:7936–40

232. Taunton, O. D., Stifel, F. B., Green, H. L., Herman, R. H. 1972. Rapid reciprocal changes of rat hepatic glycolytic enzymes and fructose-1,6-diphosphatase following glucagon and insulin injection *in vivo. Biochem. Biophys. Res. Commun.* 48:1663–70

233. Taylor, S. I., Mukherjee, C., Jungas, R. L. 1973. Studies on the mechanism of activation of adipose tissue pyruvate dehydrogenase by insulin. *J. Biol. Chem.* 248:73–81

234. Tell, G. P. E., Cuatrecasas, P., Van Wyk, J. J., Hintz, R. L. 1973. Somatomedin inhibition of adenylcyclase activity in subcellular membranes of various tissues. *Science* 180:312–14

235. Tepperman, H. M., Tepperman, J. 1972. Mechanism of inhibition of lipogenesis by 3',5' cyclic AMP. See Ref. 77, 543–70

236. Tepperman, J., Tepperman, H. 1960. Some effects of hormones on cells and cell constitutents. *Pharmacol. Rev.* 12: 301–53

237. Theodorides, C. G., Chance, G. W., Brown, G. A., Williams, J. 1970. Plasma insulin and growth hormone levels in untreated diabetic children. *Arch. Dis. Childhood* 45:70–72

238. Tisell, L. E., Angervall, L. 1972. The growth of the ventral and dorsolateral prostate, the coagulating glands and the seminal vesicles in force-fed hypo-

physectomized castrated adrenalectomized rats injected with cortisone and/or insulin. *Acta Endocrinol.* 71: 179-90

239. Toomey, R. E., Shaw, W. N., Reid, L. R. Jr., Young, W. K. 1970. Comparative study of the effects of porcine proinsulin and insulin on lipolysis and glucose oxidation in rat adipocytes. *Diabetes* 19:209-16

240. Topping, D. L., Mayes, P. A. 1972. The immediate effects of insulin and fructose on the metabolism of the perfused liver. Changes in lipoprotein secretion, fatty acid oxidation and esterification, lipogenesis and carbohydrate metabolism. *Biochem. J.* 126:295-312

241. Tragl, K. H., Reaven, G. M. 1972. Effect of insulin deficiency on hepatic ribosomal aggregation. *Diabetes* 21: 84-88

242. Trygstad, O., Foss, I. 1968. The lipid-mobilizing effect of some pituitary gland preparations. *Acta Endocrinol.* 58:295-317

243. Tulloch, B. R., Dyal, K., Fraser, T. R. 1972. Increased lipid synthesis by liver slices in a superfusion system following raised glucose or insulin concentrations. *Diabetologia* 8:267-73

244. Turtle, J. R., Kipnis, D. M. 1967. An adrenergic receptor mechanism for the control of cyclic 3',5'-adenosine monophosphate synthesis in tissues. *Biochem. Biophys. Res. Commun.* 28:797-802

245. Tzagournis, M., Chiles, R., Herrold, J., Skillman, T. 1972. The role of exogenous insulin in different hyperlipidemic states. *Diabetologia* 8: 215-220

246. Unger, R. H. 1970. The organ of Langerhans in new perspective. *Am. J. Med. Sci.* 260:79-81

247. Unger, R. H. 1971. Glucagon and the insulin/glucagon ratio in diabetes and other catabolic illnesses. *Diabetes* 20: 834-38

248. Unger, R. H. 1971. Glucagon physiology and pathophysiology. *N. Engl. J. Med.* 285:443-49

249. Unger, R. H. 1972. Insulin/glucagon ratio. *Isr. J. Med. Sci.* 8:252-57

250. Vaughn, M. 1972. The role of insulin in regulation of cyclic AMP metabolism. See Ref. 77, 297-318

251. Vranic, M. 1972. Insulin and glucagon: a dual feedback mechanism to control glucose homeostasis. See Ref. 77, 529-42

252. Walaas, O., Walaas, E., Grønnerød, O. 1972. Effect of insulin and epinephrine on cyclic AMP-dependent protein kinase in rat diaphragm. *Isr. J. Med. Sci.* 8:353-57

253. Weber, G. 1972. Integrative action of insulin at the molecular level. *Isr. J. Med. Sci.* 8:325-43

254. Weber, G., Lea, M. A., Stamm, N. B. 1969. Regulation of hepatic carbohydrate metabolism by FFA and acetyl CoA: sequential feedback inhibition. *Lipids* 4:388-96

255. Weber, G. et al 1968. Insulin and glucocorticoids: hepatic mechanism of action at the enzyme level. *Excerpta Med. Found. Int. Congr. Ser.* 184:52-60

256. Weber, G., Singhal, R. L., Srivastava, S. K. 1965. Action of glucocorticoid as inducer and insulin as suppressor of biosynthesis of hepatic gluconeogenic enzymes. *Advan. Enzyme Regul.* 3: 43-75

257. Weisinger, J., Swenson, R. S., Greene, W., Taylor, J. B., Reaven, G. M. 1972. Comparison of the effects of metabolic acidosis and acute uremia on carbohydrate tolerance. *Diabetes* 21: 1109-15

258. Wieland, O. 1965. Diabetic acidosis: Biochemical aspects. *Excerpta Med. Found. Int. Congr. Ser.* 84:533-44

259. Wieland, O. H., Patzelt, C., Löffler, G. 1972. Active and inactive forms of pyruvate dehydrogenase in rat liver. Effect of starvation and refeeding and of insulin treatment on pyruvate-dehydrogenase interconversion. *Eur. J. Biochem.* 26:426-33

260. Williams, R. H., Ensinck, J. W. 1971. Current studies regarding diabetes. *Arch. Intern. Med.* 128:820-31

261. Wool, I. G. et al 1968. Mode of action of insulin in the regulation of protein biosynthesis in muscle. *Recent Progr. Horm. Res.* 24·139-208

262. Wool, I. G., Wettenhall, R. E. H., Kleinbremhaar, H., Abayang, N. 1972. Insulin and the control of protein synthesis in muscle. See Ref. 77, 415-36

263. Yalow, R. S., Goldsmith, S. J., Berson, S. A. 1969. Influence of physiologic fluctuations in plasma growth hormone on glucose tolerance. *Diabetes* 18: 402-8

264. York, D. A., Bray, G. A. 1972. Dependence of hypothalamic obesity on insulin, the pituitary and the adrenal gland. *Endocrinology* 90:885-94

265. York, D. A., Steinke, J., Bray, G. A. 1972. Hyperinsulinemia and insulin resistance in genetically obese rats. *Metabolism* 21:277-84

266. Young, F. G. 1973. Permanent experimental diabetes produced by pituitary (anterior lobe) injections. *Lancet* II:372–74

267. Zahlten, R. N., Hochberg, A. A., Stratman, F. W., Lardy, H. A. 1972. Glucagon-stimulated phosphorylation of mitochondrial and lysosomal membranes of rat liver *in vivo*. *Proc. Nat. Acad. Sci. USA* 69: 800–4

268. Zierler, K. L. 1966. Possible mecha-

nisms of insulin action on membrane potential and ion fluxes. *Am. J. Med.* 40:735–39

269. Zimmerman, A. E., Kells, D. I. C., Yip, C. C. 1972. Physical and biological properties of guinea pig insulin. *Biochem. Biophys. Res. Commun.* 46: 2127–33

270. Zucker, L. M., Antoniades, H. H. 1972. Insulin and obesity in the Zucker genetically obese rat "Fatty." *Endocrinology* 90:1320–30

# CALCIUM AND PHOSPHATE METABOLISM[1,2]

*André B. Borle*

Department of Physiology, University of Pittsburgh School of Medicine,
Pittsburgh, Pennsylvania

Calcium and phosphate homeostasis is controlled by shifts of calcium and phosphate among five different compartments: 1. the extracellular fluids (ECF); 2. the intracellular pool, itself divided into several compartments; 3. the bone and the bone fluids; 4. the intestinal lumen; and 5. the renal tubular fluid. Transport between the various compartments is chiefly regulated by three hormones: parathyroid hormone (PTH), calcitonin (CT), and cholecalciferol (Vitamin $D_3$). This review is not a comprehensive survey of calcium and phosphate metabolism. Many fundamental concepts developed and accepted before 1970 will not be discussed. It is an attempt to underline the new developments which occured in the last four years in several aspects of a very broad field: the metabolism of PTH, CT, and Vitamin D, and their mode of action on the intestine, the kidney, the bone, and at the cellular level. On these subjects, several books and proceedings of international meetings have been published since 1969 (88, 100, 146, 158, 181, 193, 228, 273, 305, 315, 324).

## PARATHYROID HORMONE

Parathyroid hormone plays the principal role in calcium homeostasis. It maintains the concentration of ionized calcium in the extracellular fluids at a constant level and immediately corrects any fall in plasma calcium. PTH also plays a role in bone metabolism, specifically in bone resorption. These two functions of PTH are not to be confused and may have little to do with one another. After parathyroidectomy the plasma calcium falls and plasma phosphate rises. On the other hand, the administration of PTH produces an initial and transient drop in plasma calcium followed by a sustained elevation (22, 215, 245, 250) accompanied by hypophosphatemia.

[1] The writing of this review and the author's research discussed in it were supported by funds from the USPHS Grant AM 07867 from The National Institute of Health.

[2] The survey of literature for this review was concluded in May 1973.

361

## Parathyroid Hormone Chemistry

The chemistry and metabolism of parathyroid hormone (PTH) have been recently reviewed (11, 211). The amino acid composition of human, bovine, and porcine PTH is very similar, comprising 84 residues with a total molecular weight of 9500 (11, 65, 211). Biological activity of PTH resides in the initial 30 residues of the amino terminal (176), and synthetic peptides comprising the first 34 amino acids are biologically active (258). The hormone is synthesized in the parathyroid gland as a prohormone (81, 86, 138, 175) comprising 109 amino acids and with a molecular weight of approximately 12,000 (86, 138). ProPTH reacts with PTH antisera but is biologically half as active as PTH (86). ProPTH may have a hexapeptide attached to its N terminal; this may produce conformational changes or impair binding to the receptors of the target tissues (142). ProPTH undergoes at least two specific cleavages. The first occurs in the parathyroid cells where proPTH is converted to the predominant 84 residue peptide. This conversion may be a point of metabolic control. In the rat, proPTH synthesis is 10 times faster than PTH synthesis; low calcium diet doubles PTH synthesis without affecting proPTH turnover rate (81). This suggests that adaptation to a low calcium diet could be due to an increase in the conversion of proPTH to PTH (81). After the appropriate physiological stimulus, PTH, comprising 84 residues with a molecular weight of 9500, is secreted in the circulation and undergoes a second cleavage, perhaps in the liver (117), into one or more fragments which can be distinguished from the intact hormone by their different immunoreactivity (175, 251). A large hormonal fragment with a molecular weight of 7500 is the predominant peptide in the circulation. This fragment has lost a portion of the N-terminal sequence required for biological activity so that much of the immunoractive PTH detected in plasma may be biologically inactive (139, 259). It has been proposed that the rate of disappearance of the active fragment containing the N-terminal sequence is considerably faster than that of the large inactive molecule containing the carboxyl terminal, so that measurements of PTH by radioimmunoassay may not reflect the concentration of biologically active PTH (139, 159). Finally, both kidney and liver have been shown to contain enzymes able to inactivate PTH (115, 123, 323). Bilateral nephrectomy and partial hepatectomy in the rat result in a significant decrease in the PTH disappearance rate (115).

## Regulation of PTH Synthesis and Secretion

The rate of PTH secretion (0.1–1.0 pmole kg$^{-1}$ body wt min$^{-1}$) is very high compared to the PTH content of the glands (10 pmole kg$^{-1}$ body wt), so that biosynthesis may be the controlling factor in PTH secretion (72). Two secretory phases have been reported: the first occurs early, is insensitive to puromycin, and may reflect secretion of preformed PTH; the other occurs later, is inhibited by puromycin, and may represent PTH synthesis (235). It has been repeatedly shown that the extracellular concentration of ionized calcium regulates parathyroid synthesis and secretion (10, 87, 143, 145, 235, 293, 294, 314). Some in vitro investigations demonstrate an effect of magnesium on PTH synthesis as well (235, 293, 294, 314), while others show no effect of magnesium (87, 145). The concentrations of magnesium used in most of these experiments are 2 to 10 times higher than the physiological plasma concentration of ionized magnesium. There is no evidence that plasma magnesium has any regulatory role in vivo. Increasing extracellular calcium concentration inhibits PTH synthesis, decreases amino acid uptake by the chief cells (72) and their incorporation into PTH (143), and lowers ATP levels of the glands (110). On the other hand, very high concentrations of dibutyryl cyclic AMP and of theophylline stimulate the secretion of PTH in vitro (1, 339). There is an excellent correlation between the release of cyclic AMP and the secretion of PTH in the medium by parathyroid glands incubated in vitro at varying calcium concentrations (1). Adenyl cyclase activity of parathyroid gland homogenates is uniquely sensitive to the concentration of calcium (111). As little as $10^{-7}$ $M$ calcium depresses the adenyl cyclase basal activity and half-maximal inhibition is obtained at $3 \cdot 10^{-6}$ $M$ calcium (111). These results suggest that the effects of calcium on PTH secretion may be mediated by cyclic AMP. Except for the parathyroids, the secretory activity of most endocrine glands is activated by calcium. The unique properties of the parathyroid glands, whose secretion rate is inhibited by calcium, could be due to the fact that its adenyl cyclase is uniquely sensitive and inhibited by extremely low concentrations of calcium (72, 111). Calcitonin also stimulates PTH secretion (111, 235). Since calcitonin may depress intracellular calcium, its action could be explained by a derepression of adenyl cyclase leading to an increased intracellular cyclic AMP concentration and an increased PTH secretion (111).

## CALCITONIN

The physiological role of CT is still not completely clear. Thyroidectomy impairs the ability of an animal to control hypercalcemia. CT may protect the organism from the hypercalcemia which follows calcium absorption (217); it may prevent the rise in plasma phosphate which often accompanies hypercalcemia (306). It may have a role in bone formation and in the protection of skeletal calcium during pregnancy and lactation (191); it may also influence salt and water metabolism and play a role in extracellular volume homeostasis (40). CT may act as a rapidly acting damping factor which suppresses oscillations of plasma calcium above the physiologic levels, while PTH acts primarily as the major controlling factor which sustains the plasma calcium in the physiological range by virtue of its longer half-life and prolonged action, and secondarily to suppress oscillations of the plasma calcium below the physiologic levels (9).

### Calcitonin Chemistry and Metabolism

The chemistry and the metabolism of the calcitonins (CT) obtained from various species have been recently reviewed (6, 72, 260). The hormone is a polypeptide comprising 32 amino acid residues with a molecular weight of approximately 3500. Salmon calcitonin (SCT) is 10 to 100 times more potent than the human and porcine hormone, perhaps because its metabolic clearance from the circulation is 10 times slower than that of other species (140, 260). This may be due to the known structural differences among the various molecules (140, 260). The liver and the kidney may play an important role in the removal and degradation of the hormone from the circulation (118). In contrast to PTH, the basal secretory rate of CT (10 pmole kg$^{-1}$ body weight hr$^{-1}$) is low compared to the hormone content of the thyroid gland, (2 nmole kg$^{-1}$ body weight) (72). After stimulation, CT secretion rate can increase 10- to 100-fold (6, 72). In the pig, CT release is not inhibited by cycloheximide (77); in the chicken, on the other hand, actinomycin and puromycin block CT secretion (346), suggesting that CT turnover in the C cells may vary among different species. An increased extracellular calcium is only one of the possible physiological stimuli for CT secretion (33, 34, 89, 102, 116, 334). Very high concentrations of magnesium, 2 to 10 times physiological, also stimulate CT secretion (8, 33, 74, 297), but magnesium may have little influence on CT in normal conditions (74). Gastrointestinal hormones which share the same C-terminal tetrapeptide amide also stimulate CT secretion: gastrin, pancreozymin-cholecystokinin, enteroglucagon, cerulein, etc (6, 23, 33, 72, 73, 75, 76, 89, 91, 102). Specific stimuli for gastrin secretion, i.e. infusion of meat extracts or 0.14 $M$ NaCl in the stomach, enhance endogenous gastrin release and stimulate CT secretion (73). Infusions of calcium in the GI tract also stimulate CT secretion (89). Furthermore both gastrin and glucagon have been shown to depress plasma calcium, presumably by stimulating CT release (15, 44, 90, 91, 318). Finally adenyl cyclase and cyclic AMP are also implicated in CT release: dibutyryl cyclic AMP or theophylline enhance CT secretion (17, 33, 72, 116, 346) and pancreozymin has been shown to stimulate thyroid adenyl cyclase activity (73).

## VITAMIN D

Within the last three years impressive progress has been made in our understanding of Vitamin D metabolism. It is now accepted that after being absorbed by the intestine or synthesized in the skin, cholecalciferol (D$_3$) is hydroxylated in the liver and converted into 25-hydroxycholecalciferol [25-(OH) D$_3$]. The 25-hydroxylation in the liver requires O$_2$ and is stimulated by reduced pyridine nucleotide (165). 25-(OH) D$_3$ is 2–5 times more potent than Vitamin D$_3$ and, after its administration, it acts more rapidly than D$_3$ on bone and intestine (47, 219). It is the major metabolite circulating in the blood, bound to an $\alpha_2$-globulin (343); however, it is not the ultimate physiological metabolite (150). 1,25-Dihydroxycholecalciferol [1,25-(OH)$_2$D$_3$] is the active form of Vitamin D in intestine and in bone (152, 162, 190, 233, 291). It is 5–10 times more potent than Vitamin D$_3$ (149, 150, 152, 219, 241, 313). The conversion of 25-(OH)D$_3$ to 1,25-(OH)$_2$D$_3$ occurs in the kidney, catalyzed in the mitochondria by the enzyme 25-(OH)D$_3$-1-hydroxylase (119, 134, 231). Like the adrenal 11$\beta$-hydroxylase, this enzyme requires molecular oxygen and NADPH and is inhibited by carbon monoxide (120). The finding that 25-(OH)D$_3$ conversion is inhibited by actinomycin D and cycloheximide (135, 308, 310, 311) is presently disputed (120, 292). Hydroxylase activity is modulated by activation and not by induction (120, 292, 310). The regulation of 25-(OH)D$_3$-1-hydroxylase activity and of the production of 1,25-(OH)D$_3$ is still controversial. The level of extracellular calcium has been implicated (62, 240) and denied (120, 292). Calcitonin has been reported to stimulate (125) and to inhibit (277) 1,25-(OH)$_2$D$_3$ formation.

Parathyroid hormone has been shown to activate the enzyme and to stimulate the conversion to $1,25\text{-}(OH)_2D_3$ by several groups (120, 126, 277), an action mimicked by cyclic AMP (277). However, others found no effect of PTH (292) or even an inhibition of the conversion (124). Finally the conversion of $25\text{-}(OH)_2D_3$ has been shown to be inversely related to the plasma concentrations of inorganic phosphate (309). Low plasma phosphate stimulates $1,25\text{-}(OH)_2D_3$ conversion, while at high plasma phosphate concentrations $25\text{-}(OH)_2D_3$ is converted into an inactive metabolite $24,25\text{-}(OH)_2D_3$ (309). The formation of a new hormone $[1,25\text{-}(OH)_2D_3]$ in the kidney, under the control of a hydroxylase regulated by PTH, by calcium, or by phosphate, constitutes a new endocrine feedback system which may ultimately account for the interdependence of PTH and Vitamin D, for the adaptation of intestinal calcium absorption, and for the pathogeny of some Vitamin D-resistant diseases (62, 141, 277, 309, 341, 343).

## INTESTINE

Calcium transport across the intestine and the effects of Vitamin D on calcium absorption have been the subjects of several recent reviews (14, 16, 99, 105, 106, 239, 329).

### The Active and Passive Steps of Calcium Absorption

Calcium absorption by intestinal cells involves at least two separate steps: calcium uptake on the mucosal side and calcium efflux on the serosal side. At least one of these steps is an active transport process. Several factors have been implicated in intestinal calcium transport: a calcium binding protein, an exchange of calcium for sodium, calcium transport into mitochondria, and the intervention of the enzymes alkaline phosphatase and calcium-sensitive ATPase. According to the latest reports, calcium movement from mucosa to serosa, $J_{ms}$, comprises a saturable term following Michaelis-Menten kinetics at low calcium concentrations and a linear term suggesting simple diffusion at high calcium concentrations (2, 71, 114, 245, 326). There is good agreement between the various measurements of the $K_m$ of the saturable term, $1.0\text{--}2.0$ m$M$ (114, 197, 245, 326, 327), except for a $K_m$ of 24 m$M$ reported in the chick ileum (2). Since mucosal calcium uptake is presumed to be a carrier mediated process, this $K_m$ probably reflects the affinity of the carrier for calcium at the mucosa side (245). The active or passive nature of the calcium uptake step has not yet been established. It has been shown that DNP, iodoacetate, and cyanide greatly reduce the saturable component of calcium influx, and that calcium uptake requires oxygen, suggesting that it is energy dependent (71, 198, 245). On the other hand, in the chick ileum, $N_2$, DNP, and cyanide have no effect on $J_{ms}$, and in Vitamin D-deficient animals the same inhibitors stimulate $J_{ms}$ (2). In the rat jejunum, mucosal calcium uptake seems to be passive: although DNP and $N_2$ inhibit $J_{ms}$, calcium uptake by the tissue is increased severalfold by these inhibitors (114). At low temperature there is no calcium absorption across the jejunum, although calcium uptake is normal (114). Finally, although DNP and KCN inhibit calcium absorption and prevent the establishment of a concentration gradient between the serosa and the mucosa, energy transfer inhibitors such as atractyloside and triethyltin stimulate calcium transport (234). These results suggest that calcium uptake by intestinal cells may include the energy-dependent accumulation of calcium into mitochondria and that it may not be a true reflection of calcium transfer across the mucosal plasma membrane alone. If this were true many apparent contradictions could be explained since mitochondria can use several sources of energy for their accumulation of calcium. The dependence of calcium uptake on energy metabolism may be a function of the substrate available, of the ATP and NADPH levels of the cell, and of the kind of inhibitors which may either block electron transport, uncouple oxidative phosphorylation, block energy transfer, or inhibit calcium efflux out of the cell (2, 234). Calcium efflux out of the cell at the serosal side is usually recognized to be an active transport process or at least coupled to a metabolically dependent process, since calcium has to move against a chemical and an electrical potential gradient. However, recent fundamental information about this particular step of calcium absorption is lacking.

## Role of Calcium and Phosphate

The importance of phosphate in calcium absorption has been studied by many investigators in view of an earlier report showing that phosphate transport is the primary event driving calcium transfer (155). All recent data, however, demonstrate that phosphate is not required for calcium absorption and that phosphate absorption is independent of calcium transport (2, 198, 234, 285, 326). There is general agreement that a low calcium diet (LCD) results in an increased calcium absorption (63, 114, 174, 326, 327). One report demonstrates a decreased $K_m$, no change in $V_{max}$, and no change in membrane potential difference following dietary calcium restriction, indicating an increased affinity of the carrier molecule for calcium (326, 327). Another shows that the conversion of 25-(OH)D$_3$ to 1,25-(OH)$_2$D$_3$ varies with dietary calcium and with the plasma calcium levels; it proposes that LCD tends to depress the plasma calcium, thereby increasing PTH secretion which would favor the conversion of 25-(OH)D$_3$ to 1,25-(OH)$_2$D$_3$ in the kidney (63, 126). The increased 1-25-(OH)$_2$D$_3$ would be responsible for the increased calcium absorption. However, the relation between calcium absorption and plasma calcium may be more complex. In the rat, a linear relationship between calcium absorption and plasma calcium has been observed (83, 84). Calcium absorption is unaffected by dietary phosphate whereas plasma calcium does vary with the $Ca/PO_4$ ratio of the diet: with a high dietary $Ca/PO_4$ ratio the plasma calcium tend to be elevated and parathyroid activity is indirectly shown to be decreased; with a low $Ca/PO_4$ ratio, plasma calcium is normal and parathyroid activity is presumed to be increased. Furthermore a low calcium intake results in a significant decrease in bone weight and ash content, and it appears that magnesium plays an important role in these metabolic interrelations (83, 84). Others found no correlation between calcium absorption and plasma calcium but a good correlation between calcium absorption and the calcium content of the carcass of the rat (174).

## Role of Sodium

The dependence of intestinal calcium transport on the extracellular sodium concentration is still open to question. There is good agreement on one point: calcium uptake at the mucosal side does not require sodium (18, 20, 129, 197, 288). In fact calcium uptake is depressed by sodium and is enhanced if one third of the sodium is replaced by mannitol (18, 20, 197, 288). However, a large reduction in sodium concentration or its total replacement with choline chloride depresses calcium uptake (197, 288). Sodium is not required for the transepithelial transfer of calcium, $J_{ms}$ (129, 234). Actually calcium transport may be enhanced by replacing Na with mannitol up to 30% (197, 288), but further reduction in Na concentration or replacement with choline chloride will depress $J_{ms}$ (71, 197, 288). The effects of ouabain on intestinal calcium transport are also inconsistent. In the rat duodenum and in the goat, ouabain either stimulates calcium transport or has no effect (42, 129, 234). In the chick jejunum, ouabain inhibits calcium uptake even when sodium is shown not to be necessary or even to depress calcium accumulation (18, 20). In the rat ileum, ouabain inhibits calcium transport when applied on the serosal side (2). Thus no definite conclusions can be presently drawn about the role of sodium in calcium absorption.

## Role of Phosphatases

A calcium-sensitive ATPase, located in the intestinal brush border, may play a fundamental role in the cellular uptake of calcium (42, 151, 160, 186, 199, 206, 248, 280). This enzyme requires magnesium, is enhanced by potassium (206), and is unaffected by ouabain (160, 206). There is a convincing correlation between its activity and calcium absorption. Other enzymatic activities also correlate well with intestinal calcium transport, i.e. alkaline phosphatase and pyrophosphatase activity (151, 160, 186, 280); all these enzyme activities may actually represent different measures of a single enzyme (151, 160). Calcium ATPase activity is controlled by Vitamin D and there is a good temporal relationship between Vitamin D-induced calcium transport and Vitamin D-induced enzyme activity (151, 160, 186, 199, 206). However, L-phenylalanine and actinomycin D completely inhibit calcium ATPase, alkaline phosphatase, and pyrophosphatase activity (151, 160), but they do not suppress calcium transport (160, 311). The lack of inhibition by actinomycin D on intestinal calcium transport has recently been challenged (95, 182). Thus, it is still unclear whether a calcium-sensitive ATPase in the brush border is essential for calcium uptake. A calcium-sensitive ATPase located in the basal plasma membrane of intestinal cells has also been studied (42, 248). This enzyme is inhibited by ethacrynic acid but not by ouabain (42, 248); its activity is enhanced by sodium ions (42). In these studies calcium transport is inhibited by ethacrynic acid, is independent from sodium and water transport, and is unaffected by ouabain (42). It has been proposed that this basal membrane Ca ATPase mediates the energy-dependent transport of calcium across the serosal membrane of the intestinal cell (42, 248). The role of sodium in intestinal calcium transport may be to activate this enzyme system inside the cell (42).

## Role of Strontium

The rachitogenic effect of dietary strontium has been known for many years. Strontium is known to inhibit intestinal calcium absorption, to depress plasma calcium concentration, and to promote rachitic bone lesions (97, 98). One explanation is that strontium inhibits the DNA-directed RNA synthesis leading to the formation of a calcium binding protein (CaBP) necessary for calcium transport. However, during recovery from strontium inhibition, the CaBP concentration does not correlate well with the rise in calcium absorption capacity (92, 238). On the other hand, other studies demonstrate that strontium interferes with the renal conversion of 25-$(OH)D_3$ to $1,25\text{-}(OH)_2D_3$ (238). The metabolite $1,25\text{-}(OH)_2D_3$ but not 25-$(OH)D_3$ restores calcium absorption to normal in strontium-fed chicken; the changes in 25-$(OH)D_3$ metabolism in the kidney after strontium administration correlate closely with the changes in intestinal absorption (238). Strontium-induced rickets and hypocalcemia could also derive from a lack in $1,25\text{-}(OH)_2D_3$. The mechanism whereby strontium could alter the renal metabolism of 25-$(OH)D_3$ is unknown.

## Calcium Binding Protein

A calcium binding protein has been found in many different species and in different tissues (330). In mammals, its molecular weight varies between 10,000 and 12,000 and its apparent binding constant lies between $10^{-5}$ and $10^{-6}$ $M^{-1}$ (167). Its role in calcium absorption is still debated. Unquestionably, there is an excellent correlation between CaBP concentration in the intestinal mucosa and the following parameters: (a) the intestinal calcium transport capacity, (b) the changes in calcium absorption as a consequence of adaptation to various calcium and phosphorus intakes (212), (c) the relative absorptive capacity of various regions of the small intestine (170), (d) the increased calcium absorption observed in germ-free rats (280), and (e) the increased calcium transport produced by Vitamin D in D-deficient animals (330, 331). Moreover, in vitro addition of purified CaBP to intestinal sacs in organ culture stimulates calcium uptake and calcium transport (94). In some circumstances, however, correlation is questionable or nonexistent (147). During the egg laying cycle there is no good correlation between CaBP and calcium absorption (19). Actinomycin D inhibits the vitamin D-induced CaBP formation but does not inhibit the normalization of calcium transport (311), although this finding has been very recently challenged (95). Cortisone inhibits calcium absorption but does not affect or even increase CaBP (177, 185). Antiepileptic drugs decrease calcium uptake and the calcium transport capacity while the CaBP concentration is unaffected (70). Finally, the time relationship between CaBP appearance and the rise in calcium transport ability is still debated. The protein has been located at the surface of the microvilli and in the goblet cells of the intestine (316), but this does not necessarily reflect its site of action. Its exact role in calcium transport is completely unknown.

## Role of Vitamin D

It is widely accepted today that $1,25\text{-}(OH)_2D_3$ is the physiologic and metabolically active metabolite controlling intestinal calcium absorption. It is essential for the normal, active transport of calcium in all segments of the small intestine. However, its mode of action is still unknown and all proposed mechanisms are still controversial. There is a time lag of about 7 hr between $1,25\text{-}(OH)_2D_3$ administration and its effect on calcium transport (122, 149, 320). According to some recent reports calcium uptake on the mucosal side is the rate-limiting step which is enhanced and controlled by Vitamin D and its metabolites (2, 198, 344). On the other hand, others believe that the uptake is unaffected and that Vitamin D stimulates the release of calcium from the cell at the serosa both in vivo and in vitro (321, 322). A nonspecific increase in permeability of the mucosal membrane, a hypothesis proposed earlier, is rejected by two recent papers (2, 344). Vitamin D also stimulates phosphate absorption (166, 184); however, the action of Vitamin D on calcium transport is independent from its effect on phosphate (2, 141, 166, 184, 285). Because of the nuclear localization of $1,25\text{-}(OH)_2D_3$ in the intestinal mucosa and of the inhibition of Vitamin D action by actinomycin D, it has been proposed that the active Vitamin D metabolite stimulates the biochemical expression of genetic information (149, 182, 183, 320). However, the genome induction hypothesis has been challenged on the following basis: (a) Vitamin D metabolites are located in the nuclear membrane, not in the chromatine fraction of the nucleus of intestinal cells (80), (b) actinomycin D does not inhibit the rise in intestinal calcium transport induced by $1,25\text{-}(OH)_2D_3$ (311), (c) actinomycin D or cycloheximide inhibits the conversion of $25\text{-}(OH)D_3$ to $1,25\text{-}(OH)_2D_3$ (308).

The above-mentioned findings are critically important, bearing not only on the genome induction theory but also on the role and importance of the calcium binding protein (CaBP) in calcium transport. They deserve further independent confirmation and for the time being only a short communication and unpublished results seem to contradict them (95, 182). According to these reports, actinomycin D inhibits the effects of $1,25\text{-}(OH)_2D_3$ on calcium transport (95). CaBP is believed to be intimately involved in Vitamin D action (94, 96, 192, 331), although its precise function is still unknown. Vitamin $D_3$ and other metabolites can induce the formation of CaBP in intestinal organ cultures (93, 96). An increased incorporation of labeled leucine into CaBP after Vitamin D occurs several hours before calcium transport begins to rise (192). Sometimes the correlation between Vitamin D and CaBP is questionable: in organ culture of intestine, for instance, $1,25\text{-}(OH)_2D_3$ is seven times more potent than $25\text{-}(OH)D_3$ in inducing CaBP formation but has the same potency with regard to calcium uptake (96). It has been proposed that Vitamin D metabolites do not induce a new synthesis of CaBP but trigger the conversion of a precursor protein into CaBP (109). Alkaline phosphatase and Ca-ATPase have also been implicated as possible mediators of Vitamin D action on calcium uptake by mucosal cells (151, 160, 199, 206, 232). These enzymatic activities may represent different measures of a single enzyme which is stimulated by Vitamin D (151, 160). However, in spite of the fact that cycloheximide and L-phenylalanine almost completely inhibit alkaline phosphatase and Ca-ATPase (151, 160, 232), they do not inhibit the stimulation of Vitamin D or of its metabolites on calcium transport (160). Furthermore, phlorizin stimulates Ca-ATPase and alkaline phosphatase activity but inhibits calcium transport (160). Thus it is yet impossible to confirm the validity of the enzyme induction theory. Vitamin D may also induce an alteration of the intestinal microvillar membrane (133, 344), specifically its lipid composition (133). Finally, mitochondria may play a significant role in Vitamin D action. The mitochondrial content, uptake, and exchangeable pool of calcium is depressed in D deficiency and restored after D administration (56, 57, 60, 178, 179). Electron microscopy of small intestine reveals that in Vitamin D deficiency there is a virtually complete disappearance of electron-dense calcium granules from mitochondria, whereas after D administration mitochondria contain numerous and dense calcium granules (286). In vitro addition of CaBP increases the $^{45}Ca$ turnover of isolated mitochondria (144). In this light, it has been proposed that the mitochondria may be the main controller and the regulator of cellular calcium transport (57, 60).

## Hormonal Influences

All recent reports demonstrate an increased calcium absorption after PTH administration (43, 45, 104, 194, 237, 340, 341). However, the effect of PTH is not immediate and depends on the calcium and phosphate of the diet (45, 237, 341). This could indicate that the effects of PTH on calcium absorption may be indirect, perhaps through a possible effect of PTH, calcium, or phosphate on Vitamin D metabolism (126, 309). It has been reported that pharmacological doses of calcitonin increase calcium absorption and calcium balance (136, 159, 236). However, low concentration of calcitonin depresses calcium transport across the small intestine (236). It has also been shown in thyroidectomized rats that neither thyroxin nor calcitonin are necessary for the effect of Vitamin D on calcium absorption (342). Finally it is well known that glucocorticoids diminish the intestinal absorption of calcium. Recent reports confirm this finding and demonstrate that cortisone interferes with intestinal calcium uptake and calcium transport from mucosa to serosa without inhibiting the calcium binding properties of the mucosa and without decreasing the concentration of CaBP (177, 178, 185). It has even been found that the CaBP concentration increases after cortisone administration (177). One report shows that Vitamin D or 25-(OH)D₃ cannot restore the cortisone-induced inhibition of calcium transport (177) while another demonstrates that cortisone does not interfere with the ability of Vitamin D to restore calcium transport in D-deficient animals (185). This inconsistency may be due to the differences in Vitamin D dosage and in the time of administration. Cortisone depresses alkaline phosphatase and Ca-dependent ATP-ase activities which may play a role in calcium absorption (185). Cortisone also induces alteration in mitochondrial function and structure: it depresses calcium uptake, produces a striking enlargement of the mitochondria, and it has been proposed that the cortisone-Vitamin D antagonism may occur at the mitochondrial level (178).

## KIDNEY

### Renal Handling of Calcium and Phosphate

The most recent literature confirms that the bulk of the phosphate reabsorption occurs in the early segment of the proximal tubule (3, 5, 113, 211, 218, 261, 298).

Although one report suggests that some phosphate reabsorption may take place in the distal nephron (5), distal phosphate reabsorption is generally discounted (211, 218, 298). Proximal phosphate transport from lumen to plasma occurs without any significant backflux and there seem to be no exchange of phosphate in the loop of Henle (218). Proximal phosphate reabsorption appears to be closely correlated with that of sodium, calcium, and bicarbonate (121, 261, 263, 279, 299). Saline infusions or most plasma volume expansions increase phosphate, calcium, sodium, and magnesium excretion (121, 261, 299). However, saline infusions have a greater effect on phosphate excretion than on calcium and sodium excretion, presumably because the latter cations can be reabsorbed in the distal tubule (121, 299). Furthermore the phosphaturic effect of a saline infusion seems to require parathyroid hormone since it does not occur in parathyroidectomized animals (121). There is a phosphate $T_m$ which is highly correlated with glomerular filtration rate, GFR, and the ratio $T_m$/GFR is thought to reflect the theoretical maximum reabsorption capacity (36, 39).

It has been proposed that the fasting plasma phosphate concentration in man is largely determined by the activity of tubular phosphate reabsorption (36). One finds no evidence in the recent literature for a secretion of phosphate by any segment of the nephron. Calcium reabsorption occurs in both the proximal and the distal nephron. Calcium reabsorption in the proximal tubule parallels sodium reabsorption (101, 107, 112, 121, 211, 218, 279, 328) except at marked hypercalcemia (112). The ratio of calcium concentration in tubular fluid to that in plasma is constant and close to unity all along the proximal tubule (211). In the distal tubule the ratio is 0.5, suggesting that a large fraction of filtered calcium is reabsorbed either in the pars recta or in the loop of Henle (211). In the proximal tubule, net absorption of calcium involves large bidirectional fluxes. In the ascending limb of the loop of Henle, calcium seems to be actively transported against a chemical gradient with very low backflux (218). In the distal tubule, there is a good correlation between calcium and sodium reabsorption (101, 121, 328). Inhibitors of proximal reabsorption of sodium such as acetazolamide or albumin infusions are only moderately natriuretic and minimally calciuric (101, 113, 279). In contrast, inhibitors acting on the distal nephron, such as ethacrynic acid or saline infusion, produce a marked increase in calcium excretion (101, 112, 279). Because of a good correlation between serum calcium and urinary calcium, it has been proposed that kidney function plays a major role in determining serum calcium (230, 253). However, this suggestion should not be accepted without further data, since in most species only one tenth of the extracellular calcium pool is excreted daily by the kidney. In other species, for instance in the golden hamster, the daily calcium excretion is 12 times larger than the extracellular calcium pool, and in these conditions the kidney plays a major role in the minute to minute maintenance of plasma calcium (35).

## Role of Parathyroid Hormone

The main renal effects of PTH, i.e. increased phosphaturia and decreased calcium clearance, have been confirmed in all recent papers. The hormone binds to a receptor on the kidney cell membrane, stimulates the enzyme adenyl cyclase, and increases the cellular concentration of cyclic AMP (11, 67, 196, 207, 251, 258). Parathyroid extracts, purified preparations, and synthetic peptides are all active in the proximal tubule where they reduce the reabsorption of phosphate (3, 11, 24, 67, 132, 137, 263). The proximal tubular effect of PTH involves the parallel inhibition of sodium, phosphate, and bicarbonate reabsorption (3, 37, 38, 132, 263). The bulk of the phosphate and bicarbonate rejected proximally is excreted in the urine while sodium excretion rises minimally despite the marked proximal inhibition since it is further reabsorbed in the distal nephron. There is no evidence of any distal reabsorption of phosphate. The parallel inhibition of sodium, phosphate, and bicarbonate reabsorption in the proximal tubule, along with an alkaline urine due to an increased loss of bicarbonate, suggests that PTH may depress the normal secretion of $H^+$ ions in the proximal tubule (25, 37, 38, 214, 216, 263, 295). An interrelationship among PTH function, $H^+$ ion homeostasis, and renal tubular acidosis, although unclear in its details, has indeed been reported (25, 213, 214, 216, 295). Micropuncture studies of calcium transport in the proximal tubule of the dog have shown that proximal calcium reabsorption parallels proximal sodium reabsorption (112). Although PTH inhibits proximal sodium reabsorption, the hormone reduces the fractional urinary excretion of both calcium and sodium. This suggests that calcium and sodium must be distally reabsorbed (37, 38, 67, 112). The decreased calcium clearance produced by PTH is probably due to the actions of the hormone on the distal nephron and not on the proximal tubule (37, 38). Thiazide diuretics which act on the distal tubule (131) depress calcium excretion only in presence of PTH (209, 246). Thiazides do not stimulate the parathyroid glands or renal adenyl cyclase but possibly potentiate the effects of PTH on the distal nephron (209).

### Effects of Calcitonin

The effects of CT on renal function have been studied in many species, with physiological as well as pharmacological doses of purified or synthetic peptides from several origins. There is an overwhelming agreement that CT increases the excretion of calcium, phosphate, and sodium (4, 7, 21, 37, 38, 40, 137, 173, 189, 243, 244, 257, 284, 296). CT also increases urine volume and often causes a significant loss of body weight due to water losses (4, 21, 40, 173, 284). The natriuretic effect of CT is different from that of PTH because CT depresses the sodium and chloride reabsorption occurring in the proximal tubule (7, 37, 38, 243) and not the sodium for hydrogen exchange occurring in the distal nephron (37, 38). Although it has been claimed that only pharmacological doses of CT produce natriuresis (103), it has been conclusively shown that physiological doses of purified and synthetic peptides will produce all the effects of pharmacological concentrations of CT (21). The CT-induced phosphaturia is not due to the hypocalcemia (7, 21, 243) and cannot be explained by a stimulation of the parathyroid glands since it can be obtained in thyroparathyroidectomized animals or in hypoparathyroid patients (7, 21, 137, 243, 257, 296). The effect of CT on magnesium excretion is unclear. Some authors report an increased magnesium excretion (137, 243, 296) while others report a drop (4, 21, 173, 257, 337, 338). CT binding to membrane receptors and a stimulation of adenyl cyclase have recently been reported in the outer medulla (204). Nevertheless there is a widespread agreement that CT acts in the proximal tubule by inhibiting the reabsorption of most ions.

## Effects of Vitamin D

It is well known that Vitamin D administration decreases phosphate excretion in normal and D-deficient animals, but it has long been assumed that this was indirectly due to an inhibition of the parathyroid glands. Recent reports demonstrate, however, that the decreased phosphate excretion induced by Vitamin D occurs in normal, Vitamin D-deficient, and thyroparathyroidectomized animals (85, 127, 128, 263, 264). Micropuncture studies show that Vitamin D directly stimulates phosphate reabsorption in the proximal tubule independently from any parathyroid influence (127, 128). Acute clearance studies also show that the active metabolites of Vitamin $D_3$, 25-(OH)$D_3$ and 1,25-(OH)$_2D_3$, increase phosphate, calcium, and sodium reabsorption in the proximal tubule (262, 264). Although 1,25-(OH)$_2D_3$ acts more rapidly than its precursors, it is no more potent than 25-(OH)$D_3$ (262). Finally, a calcium binding protein has been isolated in kidney cortex which may be related to the renal transport of calcium (256, 287, 317) but there is no available evidence that it is regulated by Vitamin D.

# BONE

## Bone and Calcium Homeostasis

Bone plays the major role in the metabolism of calcium. However, many of the crucial questions about the mechanisms by which bone influences calcium homeostasis remain unanswered. There are several areas of controversy, e.g.: 1. Is there a cellular membrane separating the plasma and the ECF from the fluids bathing the bone mineral? 2. What is the relative importance, if any, of osteoclastic bone resorption and of osteocytic osteolysis in calcium homeostasis? 3. Is calcium homeostasis controlled by calcium ion transport without formation or destruction of bone or is it regulated by the well-known processes of bone resorption (osteocytic or osteoclastic) and bone accretion? No clear-cut answer exists to any of these questions and most of them are still based on circumstantial evidence. It has been suggested that the fluids bathing the bone mineral constitute a discrete compartment separated from the blood and ECF by a functional barrier (68, 221, 222, 224). This theory is attractive since it could explain the physiologically well-founded but anatomically ill-defined concept of a bone membrane. The arguments supporting the existence of a functional membrane are as follows: Bone rudiments, tibias, or calvarias, carefully dissected to preserve the integrity of their periosteal and endosteal membranes, are able to control and regulate the calcium concentration of their bathing medium and to restore and maintain a physiological calcium concentration (222, 223). Calcium is transported from bone to medium, without being accompanied by phosphate, by a metabolically dependent process inhibited by iodoacetate (222, 223). Bone mineralization is regulated by a process which depends on metabolism and on the "membrane" integrity; it is markedly increased by metabolic inhibitors, by splitting of the bone, or by destruction of the "membrane" (269, 270); it is independent of the calcium phosphate product of the bathing medium (270). The concentration of potassium in bone is extremely high even though bone cells are few and potassium is excluded from the mineral. Bone potassium does not follow the fluctuations of ECF potassium; it is markedly depressed in hypophysectomized animals and it leaks out of bone when bone is split, metabolically inhibited, or otherwise damaged (68, 221). Thus, destroying the postulated membrane integrity, by splitting the bones or removing the periosteum, prevents the regulation of the medium calcium concentration by the bone rudiments and produces a faster mineralization and a loss of bone potassium (223, 224, 269, 270). Anatomically, the evidence for a tight cellular membrane is not at all conclusive. Tight junctions (zona occludens) are found between osteocytes, between osteocytes and osteoblasts, and between the bodies of osteoblasts (164).[3] These tight junctions could constitute "gap junctions" allowing intercellular communication and intracellular transport subserved by numerous microtubules in osteocytes bodies and microfilaments in the cell processes (164).[3] However, there is no continuous seal between osteoblasts (26, 27, 164),[3] and high molecular weight substances like horseradish peroxidase or thorium oxide easily diffuse in the pericanalicular and perilacunar spaces surrounding the osteocytes (108, 290). In absence of a tight membrane, it has been postulated that because of the enormous lacunar and canalicular surface area, estimated at 1200 m$^2$ (31), the osteocytes could still control the transfer of ions between the calcified bone matrix and the pericapillary space of the harvesian system by influencing the extracellular composition of the pericanalicular and perilacunar "limiting sheath" surrounding the osteocytes (26, 27, 29, 164, 225, 272, 303, 304).

Controversy also exists about the importance of osteoclastes and osteocytes in calcium homeostasis. It is accepted that no temporal correlation exists between the increase in the number osteoclasts induced by PTH and the rise in plasma calcium (41, 325). However, PTH stimulates DNA synthesis in osteoclastes and RNA synthesis in bone in less than 2 hr (41, 300) and calcitonin produces morphological changes in osteoclastes within 15 min (171). Consequently the hyper- and hypocalcemia induced by these hormones are still attributed to changes in osteoclastic activity by some investigators (41, 171). On the other hand, several authors propose that osteocytic osteolysis is responsible for plasma calcium homeostasis (27, 31, 168, 200–203). And indeed morphological changes are seen in osteocytes 30 min to 2 hr after PTH (168, 201) and 5 to 8 min after calcitonin (203). However, the temporal relationship between the cellular changes induced by these hormones and the changes in plasma calcium may not be a valid criterion after all. Quantitative considerations appear to foreclose any significant role for bone formation or bone resorption, whether osteoclastic or osteocytic, in the minute to minute regulation of calcium homeostasis (28, 30, 222, 224, 325). The rates of osteocytic bone formation or resorption are much too slow, and the amount involved much too small, to

[3]M. E. Holtrop, personal communication.

account for any significant change in plasma calcium (28, 30), and so are the rates of osteoblastic bone formation and osteoclastic bone resorption (224).

Thus the third controversy arises: Is calcium homeostasis controlled by cellular transport of calcium ions without involving bone formation or resorption? This theory rests on the following evidence: 1. the rates of accretion and resorption, osteocytic and osteoclastic, are far too small to account for the rapid correction of plasma calcium after a rapid calcium depletion or after a calcium load (57, 224); 2. calcium mobilization from bone occurs without concurrent mobilization of phosphate (222, 223); 3. intact bone rudiments can regulate the calcium concentration of their bathing medium, but not the phosphate concentration (223); 4. the change in plasma calcium specific activity after PTH administration is not paralleled by a change in phosphate specific activity, rendering bone mineral destruction improbable (208); 5. the effect of CT on calcium is not paralleled by an effect on hydroxyproline (333), suggesting that it is independent from bone turnover. Several models of cellular calcium transport in bone have been offered (201, 272, 302–304, 325). However, as long as these important questions are not conclusively settled, it will be difficult to assess whether the hormonal effects on bone reported in the literature are related to calcium homeostasis or to the physiological processes of bone remodeling.

## Effects of Parathyroid Hormone

The effects of PTH on bone are mediated by a stimulation of adenyl cyclase leading to a rise in intracellular cyclic AMP. This has been shown in bone calvaria and in isolated bone cells (12, 78, 153, 156, 157, 254). PTH increases bone resorption and increases the transport of calcium from the bone to its surrounding fluids, two processes which may be totally unrelated (180, 208, 282). One of the early effects of the hormone is an increase influx of calcium into bone cells (226, 249, 252, 282, 283) but calcium efflux from isolated bone cells is also increased (226). An increased lactate production by rat calvaria has been reported 2 min after PTH administration (154) and a cell membrane depolarization 15 min later (205). PTH also increases RNA, DNA, and protein synthesis in osteoclastes (41, 242, 300) and decreases RNA synthesis in osteoblastes (242). Finally PTH stimulates osteocytic bone resorption (168) and within 30 min increases both the number and the density of intramitochondrial calcium granules in all bone cells, a finding which may be related with their transport activity (200–202).

## Effects of Calcitonin

In tissue cultures of bone rudiments calcitonin decreases the transport of calcium from bone to its surrounding fluids (64, 210, 267, 268, 333). In isolated bone cells CT increases calcium influx but appears to depress calcium efflux (148). The effect of CT on the release of isotopic calcium from bone is not paralleled by an effect on labeled hydroxyproline (333), suggesting that the effect of CT on calcium transport may be independent from bone accretion and resorption. Phosphate enhances these effects of CT on bone (333). An escape phenomenon is observed when CT inhibits a PTH-induced calcium mobilization (267, 268, 333). This escape is not apparent when CT affect a spontaneous calcium release. Decreasing the phosphate or the calcium concentration of the fluids bathing the bone rudiments delays the occurrence of the escape phenomenon (333). In addition CT has been shown to increase the membrane potential of osteoclastes (205), to markedly reduce the ruffled borders of osteoclastes where osteoclastic resorption is assumed to occur (32, 163, 171, 345), to inhibit osteocytic bone resorption (32), and to dramatically increase the number and density of intramitochondrial calcium granules in osteocytes and in osteoblastes (203).

## Effects of Vitamin D

It is well known that Vitamin D deficiency produces rickets in bone characterized by wide, undermineralized osteoid borders. Administration of $D_3$ or 25-$(OH)D_3$ increases collagen synthesis and turnover (69), although D deficiency does not prevent the formation of a bone matrix which can attain a normal degree of mineralization (278). Vitamin $D_3$ and its metabolites increase bone mineralization and decrease the width of the osteoid borders (66, 169, 312, 313). In D deficiency, plasma calcium falls and, in vitro, bone is unable to maintain a normal calcium concentration in its bathing fluids (66, 169). Vitamin $D_3$ and its metabolites increase the mobilization of calcium from bone (13, 265–268) and restore normal plasma calcium concentrations (13, 66, 161, 307, 312). There is evidence that 1,25-$(OH)_2D_3$ may be the active physiological metabolite in bone: 1. after administration of labeled cholecalciferol there is a preferential accumulation of 1,25-$(OH)_2D_3$ in bone cell nuclei of rachitic chicks (332); 2. 1,25-$(OH)_2D_3$ is more potent or acts more rapidly than its precursors (66, 266, 307, 312, 313); 3. nephrectomy abolishes bone calcium mobilization as a response to 25-$(OH)D_3$ but not to 1,25-$(OH)_2D_3$ (161); 4. administration of 1,25-$(OH)_2D_3$ tends to produce hypercalcemia presumably because it bypasses the feedback mechanism controlling its formation in the kidney (312). Nevertheless 25-$(OH)D_3$ itself is active since it mobilizes calcium from bone in vitro without being converted to 1,25-$(OH)_2D_3$ (13, 265, 267, 268). The relative potency of these two metabolites varies depending on the parameters used to measure their activity (66, 312). Both PTH and Vitamin D metabolites produce prolonged responses after brief exposures (66, 267, 278), a phenomenon sometimes termed induction. Actinomycin D, mithramycin, cycloheximide, imidazole, cortisol, and colchicine inhibit the 25-$(OH)D_3$-induced calcium mobilization from bone in vitro (13, 265, 267, 268). Cortisol, colchicine, and imidazol also inhibit the PTH-induced calcium mobilization from bone (13, 265, 268). These effects of PTH and of $D_3$ metabolites on calcium mobilization are often additive and they may act synergistically (13, 267). However, the idea that PTH action on bone requires the presence of Vitamin D has been recently challenged (169). Indeed recent data in dogs show that PTH fails to mobilize bone calcium and to restore normal plasma concentrations even in the presence of Vitamin D if rickets is produced by a calcium-deficient diet (169). In these conditions, the plasma concentration of calcium and phosphate is low and the unmineralized osteoid of bone is very wide. The absence of a normally mineralized matrix and not the absence of Vitamin D may be responsible for the inability of PTH to mobilize calcium and raise the plasma calcium concentration (169). On the other hand, since the participation of bone resorption in calcium homeostasis is still debatable, and since the magnitude of the response to PTH depends on the preexisting levels of calcium and phosphate both in vivo and in vitro (251, 267), the failure of PTH to raise plasma calcium in rickets could also be due to the low calcium and phosphate in the plasma and not to the presence of osteoid.

## CELL CALCIUM

Calcium influx across the plasma membrane of isolated cells is a passive process, presumably a carrier-mediated diffusion (50, 54, 57, 60, 187). On the other hand, cellular calcium uptake often involves the active transport of calcium into mitochondria and can be shown to be energy and substrate dependent (82, 255). Calcium efflux from nonexcitable cells is a metabolically dependent process driven by a calcium pump presumably mediated through a Ca-sensitive ATPase (51, 54, 59, 60, 187, 289). In excitable tissues, however, a calcium for sodium exchange diffusion may be responsible for calcium extrusion (46, 130, 281). The cytoplasmic calcium activity is not controlled by the transport of calcium in and out of the cell but rather by the mitochondria which play the role of a buffer system and of a trap for intracellular calcium (48, 54, 57, 59, 60, 188). Intracellular calcium sequestration may also occur in specialized cells involved in calcification or in chorioepithelial membrane transport (172, 227, 301, 319). In target cells, parathyroid hormone stimulates adenyl cyclase and increases the intracellular cyclic AMP concentration (12, 58, 227, 254, 271, 276, 336). In turn, cyclic AMP increases the cytoplasmic free calcium concentration (58, 220, 271, 274, 276) by stimulating the rate of calcium release from mitochondria (57, 58, 60, 61). PTH and cyclic AMP also stimulate calcium influx (52, 53, 58, 79, 227) and calcium efflux (58, 226, 227) into and out of cells and both effects could be secondarily due to the increased cytoplasmic calcium. The increased cellular calcium transport and most of the metabolic effects of PTH can also be accounted for by the rise in intracellular cyclic AMP and in cytoplasmic calcium (57, 60, 274, 276). Calcitonin increases calcium uptake by isolated cells but depresses calcium efflux (49, 148). It has been shown that CT stimulates calcium uptake by mitochondria (57, 203, A. B. Borle, to be published) and indirect evidence suggests that cytoplasmic calcium is depressed (49, 195, 229, 275, 335). It has been proposed that CT lowers cellular calcium transport by stimulating the active transport of calcium into mitochondria, thereby lowering the cytoplasmic calcium activity (57, 60). Others proposed that the drop in cytoplasmic calcium is due to an increased extrusion of calcium since CT has been shown to increase calcium efflux from red blood cells in absence of ATP (247, 274). This contradiction may be only superficial since red blood cells do not have mitochondria and since the active transport of calcium into mitochondria or out of red blood cells may share a common step. Mitochondria may also be involved in the effects of Vitamin D on cellular calcium transport (56, 57, 60, 178, 179, 286). Finally, cellular calcium metabolism is influenced by phosphate (54, 55, 59, 275). The cytoplasmic calcium activity is depressed when ECF phosphate concentration is increased (59,

60, 275). The intracellular actions of phosphate may account for the fact that phosphate inhibits the effect of PTH while it enhances those of CT (60). It remains to be shown which of these effects are specific for certain cell types and which are part of the general physiology of the cell.

## Literature Cited

1. Abe, M., Sherwood, L. M. 1972. Regulation of parathyroid hormone secretion by adenyl cyclase. *Biophys. Biochem. Res. Commun.* 48:396–401
2. Adams, T. H., Norman, A. W. 1970. Studies on the mechanism of action of calciferol. I. Basic parameters of vitamin D-mediated calcium transport. *J. Biol. Chem.* 245:4421–31
3. Agus, Z. S., Puschett, J. B., Senesky, D., Goldberg, M. 1971. Mode of action of parathyroid hormone and cyclic adenosine 3',5'-monophosphate on renal tubular phosphate reabsorption in the dog. *J. Clin. Invest.* 50:617–26
4. Aldred, J. P., Kleszynski, R. R., Bastian, J. W. 1970. Effects of acute administration of porcine and salmon calcitonin on urine electrolyte excretion in rats. *Proc. Soc. Exp. Biol. Med.* 134:1175–80
5. Amiel, C., Kuntziger, H., Richet, G. 1970. Micropuncture study of handling of phosphate by proximal and distal nephron in normal and parathyroidectomized rat. Evidence for distal reabsorption. *Pfluegers Arch.* 317:93–109
6. Anast, C. C., Conaway, H. 1972. Calcitonin. *Clin. Orthop.* 84:207–62
7. Ardaillou, R. et al 1969. Renal excretion of phosphate, calcium and sodium during and after a prolonged thyrocalcitonin infusion in man. *Proc. Soc. Exp. Biol. Med.* 131:56–60
8. Arnaud, C. D. et al 1971. Calcium homeostasis, parathyroid hormone and calcitonin in health and disease. *Recent Advances in Endocrinology,* ed. E. Matter, G. de Brong Mattar, V. H. T. James, 360–72. Amsterdam: Excerpta Med.
9. Arnaud, C. D., Tsao, H. S., Littledike, T. 1970. Calcium homeostasis, parathyroid hormone and calcitonin: preliminary report. *Mayo Clin. Proc.* 45:125–31
10. Au, W. Y. W., Poland, A. P., Stern, P. H., Raisz, L. G. 1970. Hormone synthesis and secretion by rat parathyroid gland in tissue culture. *J. Clin. Invest.* 49:1639–46
11. Aurbach, G. D. et al 1972. Structure, synthesis and mechanism of action of parathyroid hormone. *Recent Progr. Horm. Res.* 28:353–98
12. Aurbach, G. D., Chase, L. R. 1970. Cyclic 3',5'-adenylic acid in bone and the mechanism of action of parathyroid hormone. *Fed. Proc.* 29:1179–82
13. Avery, S. H., Bell, N. H., Stern, P. H. 1971. Inhibition of the hypercalcemic action of vitamin $D_3$ with imidazole. *Endocrinology* 89:951–57
14. Avioli, L. 1972. Intestinal absorption of calcium. *Arch. Intern. Med.* 129:345–55
15. Avioli, L., Birge, S. J., Scott, S., Shieber, W. 1969. Role of the thyroid gland during glucagon induced hypocalcemia in dog. *Am. J. Physiol.* 216:939–45
16. Avioli, L. V., Haddad, J. G. 1973. Vitamin D: current concepts. *Metabolism* 22:507–31
17. Avioli, L. V., Shieber, W., Kipnis, D. M. 1971. Role of glucagon and adrenergic receptors in the thyrocalcitonin release in the dog. *Endocrinology* 88:1337–40
18. Bar, A., Hurwitz, S. 1969. The accumulation of calcium in laying fowl intestine in vitro. *Biochim. Biophys. Acta* 183:591–600
19. Bar, A., Hurwitz, S. 1971. Relationship of calcium binding protein to calcium absorption in the fowl. *Isr. J. Med. Sci.* 7:382–83
20. Bar, A., Hurwitz, S. 1972. In vitro calcium transport in laying fowl intestine: effect of bile preparations. *Comp. Biochem. Physiol.* 41:383–89
21. Barlet, J. P. 1972. Effect of porcine, salmon and human calcitonin on urinary excretion of some electrolytes in sheep. *J. Endocrinol.* 55:153–61
22. Barlet, J. P. 1972. Calcium homeostasis in the normal and thyroidectomized bovine. *Horm. Metab. Res.* 4:300–3
23. Barlet, J. P. 1972. Effet d'une perfusion intraveineuse de gastrine ou d'une excitation vagale sur la calcémie et la phosphatémie du mouton. *CR Acad. Sci. Paris* 274:2220–23
24. Barlet, J. P., Care, A. D. 1972. The influence of parathyroid hormone on urinary excretion of calcium, magnesium

inorganic phosphorus in sheep. *Horm. Metab. Res.* 4:315–16

25. Barzel, U. S. 1971. Parathyroid hormone, blood phosphorus and acid-base metabolism. *Lancet* 1:1329–31
26. Baud, C. A. 1968. Submicroscopic structure and functional aspect of the osteocyte. *Clin. Orthop.* 56:227–36
27. Baud, C. A. 1968. Structure et function des ostéocytes dans les conditions normales et sous l'influence de l'extrait parathyroidien. *Schweiz. Med. Wochenschr.* 98:717–20
28. Baylink, D. J. 1971. Bone formation by osteocytes. *Am. J. Physiol.* 221:669–78
29. Baylink, D. J., Morey, E., Rich, C. 1968. Effect of calcitonin on osteocyte mineral transfer in the rat. *Parathyroid hormone and Thyrocalcitonin (Calcitonin)*, ed. R. V. Talmage, L. Belanger, 196–97. Amsterdam: Excerpta Med.
30. Baylink, D. J., Wergedal, J. 1971. Bone formation and resorption by osteocytes. See Ref. 228, 257–86
31. Bélanger, L. F. 1969. Osteocytic osteolysis. *Calcif. Tissue Res.* 4:1–12
32. Bélanger, L. F., Copp, D. H. 1972. The skeletal effects of prolonged calcitonin administration in birds under various conditions. See Ref. 305, 41–50
33. Bell, N. H. 1970. Effects of glucagon, dibutyryl cyclic 3',5'-adenosine monophosphate, and theophylline on calcitonin secretion in vitro. *J. Clin. Invest.* 49:1368–73
34. Bell, N. H., Stern, P. 1970. Effects of changes in serum calcium on hypocalcemic response to thyrocalcitonin in the rat. *Am. J. Physiol.* 218:64–68
35. Biddulph, D. M., Hirsch, P. F., Cooper, C. W., Munson, P. L. 1970. Effect of thyroparathyroidectomy and parathyroid hormone on urinary excretion of calcium and phosphate in the golden hamster. *Endocrinology* 87:1346–50
36. Bijvoet, O. L. M. 1969. Relation of plasma phosphate concentration to renal tubular reabsorption of phosphate. *Clin. Sci.* 37:23–36
37. Bijvoet, O. L. M., Froeling, G. A. M. 1973. Calcitonin, parathyroid hormone and the kidney. *Clinical Aspect of Metabolic Bone Disease,* ed. B. Frame, Henry Ford Hosp. Int. Symp. 1972. Amsterdam: Excerpta Med. In press
38. Bijvoet, O. L. M., Froeling, G. A. M. 1973. Renal action of parathyroid hormone and calcitonin. *Proc. IV Int. Congr. Endocrinol. Wash. 1972.* Amsterdam: Excerpta Med.

39. Bijvoet, O. L. M., Morgan, B. 1971. The tubular reabsorption of phosphate in man. See Ref. 158, 153–80
40. Bijvoet, O. L. M. et al 1971. Natriuretic effect of calcitonin in man. *N. Engl. J. Med.* 284:681–88
41. Bingham, P. J., Brazell, I. A., Owen, M. 1969. The effect of parathyroid extract on cellular activity and plasma calcium levels in vivo. *J. Endocrinol.* 45:387–400
42. Birge, S. J. Jr., Gilbert, H. R., Avioli, L. V. 1972. Intestinal calcium transport: the role of sodium. *Science* 176:168–70
43. Birge, S. J., Gilbert, H. R. 1972. The influence of parathyroid hormone on intestinal Ca transport. See Ref. 305, 247–48
44. Birge, S. J., Avioli, L. V. 1969. Glucagon-induced hypocalcemia in man. *J. Clin. Endocrinol. Metab.* 29:213–18
45. Birge, S. J., Gilbert, H. R. 1970. Mechanism of action of parathyroid hormone on the intestinal mucosal cell. *Clin. Res.* 18:600
46. Blaustein, M. P., Hodgkin, A. L. 1969. The effect of cyanide on the efflux of calcium from squid axons. *J. Physiol.* 200:497–528
47. Blunt, J. W., DeLuca, H. F. 1969. The synthesis of 25-hydroxycholecalciferol. A biologically active metabolite of vitamin $D_3$. *Biochemistry* 8:671–75
48. Borle, A. B. 1967. Membrane transfer of calcium. *Clin. Orthop.* 52:267–91
49. Borle, A. B. 1969. Effects of thyrocalcitonin on calcium transport in kidney cells. *Endocrinology* 85:194–99
50. Borle, A. B. 1969. Kinetic analyses of calcium movements in Hela cell cultures: I. Calcium Influx. *J. Gen. Physiol.* 53:43–56
51. Borle, A. B. 1969. Kinetic analyses of calcium movements in Hela cell cultures: II. Calcium Efflux. *J. Gen. Physiol.* 53:57–69
52. Borle, A. B. 1970. Kinetic analyses of calcium movements in cell cultures: III. Effects of calcium and parathyroid hormone in kidney cells. *J. Gen. Physiol.* 55:163–86
53. Borle, A. B. 1970. Kinetic analyses of calcium movements in cell cultures: IV. Effects of phosphate and parathyroid hormone in kidney cells. *Endocrinology* 86:1389–93
54. Borle, A. B. 1971. Calcium transport in kidney cells and its regulation. See Ref. 228, 151–74
55. Borle, A. B. 1971. Effet du phosphate sur les movement du calcium en cultures cellulaires. See Ref. 158, 29–45

56. Borle, A. B. 1971. Regulation of Ca transport in intestinal cells by calciferol (D₃). *Endocrinology* 88:A–155

57. Borle, A. B. 1971. Le turn-over du calcium dans l'organisme et les principaux points d'impact hormonaux. See Ref. 181, 5–34

58. Borle, A. B. 1972. Parathyroid hormone and cell calcium. See Ref. 305, 484–91

59. Borle, A. B. 1972. Kinetic analysis of calcium movements in cell cultures: V. Intracellular calcium distribution in kidney cells. *J. Membrane Biol.* 10: 45–66

60. Borle, A. B. 1973. Calcium metabolism at the cellular level. *Fed. Proc.* 32:1944–50

61. Borle, A. B. 1973. *J. Int. Res. Commun. Syst. Med. Sci.* 1(6):9(1–3–1)

62. Boyle, I. T., Gray, R. W., DeLuca, H. F. 1971. Regulation by calcium of in vivo synthesis of 1,25-dihydroxy-cholecalciferol and 21,25-dihydroxy-cholecalciferol. *Proc. Nat. Acad. Sci. USA* 68:2131–34

63. Boyle, I. T., Gray, R. W., Omdahl, J. L., DeLuca, H. F. 1971. The mechanism of adaptation of intestinal calcium absorption to low dietary calcium. *J. Lab. Clin. Med.* 78:813

64. Brand, J. S., Raisz, L. G. 1972. Effects of thyrocalcitonin and phosphate ion on the parathyroid hormone stimulated resorption of bone. *Endocrinology* 90: 479–87

65. Brewer, H. B. et al 1972. Human parathyroid hormone: amino acid sequence of the amino-terminal residue 1–34. *Proc. Nat. Acad. Sci. USA* 69:3585–88

66. Brickman, A. et al 1973. Biologic action of 1,25-dihydroxy-vitamin D₃ in the rachitic dog. *Endocrinology* 92:728–34

67. Butlen, D., Jard, S. 1972. Renal handling of 3',5'-cyclic AMP in the rat. The possible role of luminal 3',5'-cyclic AMP in the tubular reabsorption of phosphate. *Pfluegers Arch.* 331:172–90

68. Canas, F., Terepka, A. R., Neuman, W. F. 1969. Potassium and the milieu intérieur of bone. *Am. J. Physiol.* 217: 117–20

69. Canas, F., Brand, J. S., Neuman, W. F., Terepka, A. R. 1969. Some effects of vitamin D₃ on collagen synthesis in rachitic chick cortical bone. *Am. J. Physiol.* 216:1092–96

70. Caspary, W. F. 1972. Inhibition of intestinal calcium transport by diphenylhydantoin in rat duodenum. *Arch. Pharmacol.* 274:146–53

71. Caspary, W. F. 1972. Evidence for a carrier-mediated, Na+-independent uptake mechanism for calcium in rat duodenum. *Hoppe-Seylers Z. Physiol. Chem.* 353:5–6

72. Care, A. D., Bates, R. F. L. 1972. Control of secretion of parathyroid hormone and calcitonin in mammals and birds. *Gen. Comp. Endocrinol.* Suppl. 3:448–58

73. Care, A. et al 1972. Stimulation of calcitonin secretion by gastro-intestinal hormones. *J. Endocrinol.* 52:27–28

74. Care, A. D., Bell, N. H., Bates, R. F. L. 1971. The effects of hypermagnesaemia on calcitonin secretion in vivo. *J. Endocrinol.* 51:381–86

75. Care, A. D., Bates, R. F. L., Swaminathan, R., Ganguli, P. C. 1971. The role of gastrin as a calcitonin secretagogue. *J. Endocrinol.* 51:735–44

76. Care, A. D. et al 1971. Role of pancreozymin-cholecystokinin and structurally related compounds as calcitonin secretogogues. *Endocrinology* 89: 262–71

77. Care, A. D., Cooper, C. W., Gitelman, H. J. 1969. Effects of cycloheximide on calcitonin release and activity. *Acta Endocrinol.* Suppl. 138, 182

78. Chase, L. R., Aurbach, G. D. 1970. The effect of parathyroid hormone on the concentration of Adenosine 3',5'-monophosphate in skeletal tissue in vitro. *J. Biol. Chem.* 245:1520–24

79. Chausmer, A. B., Sherman, B. S., Wallach, S. 1972. The effect of parathyroid hormone on hepatic cell transport of calcium. *Endocrinology* 90:663–72

80. Chen, T. C., Weber, J. C., DeLuca, H. F. 1970. On the subcellular location of vitamin D metabolites in intestine. *J. Biol. Chem.* 245:3776–80

81. Chu, L. L. H., MacGregor, R. R., Anast, C. S., Hamilton, J. W., Cohn, D. V. 1973. Studies on the biosynthesis of rat parathyroid hormone and proparathyroid hormone: adaptation of the parathyroid gland to dietary restriction of calcium. *Endocrinology.* 93:915–24

82. Cittadini, A., Scarpa, A., Chance, B. 1973. Calcium transport in intact Ascites tumor cells. *Biochim. Biophys. Acta* 291:246–59

83. Clark, I. 1969. Importance of dietary Ca:PO₄ ratios on skeletal Ca, Mg and PO₄ metabolism. *Am. J. Physiol.* 217: 865–70

84. Clark, I. 1969. Metabolic interrelations of calcium magnesium and phosphate. *Am. J. Physiol.* 217:871–78

85. Clark, I., Rivera-Cordero, F. 1971. Effect of parathyroid function on absorption and excretion of calcium, magnesium and phosphate by rats. *Endocrinology* 88:302–8

86. Cohn, D. V. et al 1972. Calcemic Fraction A: Biosynthetic peptide precursor of parathyroid hormone. *Proc. Nat. Acad. Sci. USA* 69:1521–25

87. Cohn, D. V., MacGregor, R. R., Chu, L. L. H., Hamilton, J. W. 1972. Studies on the biosynthesis in vitro of parathyroid hormone and other calcemic polypeptides of the parathyroid gland. See Ref. 305, 173–82

88. Copp, D. H. 1972. Calcitonin. *The Biochemistry and Physiology of Bone,* ed. G. H. Bourne, 2:337–56. New York: Academic

89. Cooper, C. W. et al 1972. Regulation of secretion of thyrocalctonin. See Ref. 305, 128–39

90. Cooper, C. W., Biggerstaff, C. R., Wiseman, C. W., Carlone, M. F. 1972. Hypocalcemic effect of pentagastrin and related gastrointestinal hormonal peptides in the rat. *Endocrinology* 91:1455–61

91. Cooper, C. W., Schwesinger, W. H., Ontjes, D. A., Mahgoub, A. M., Munson, P. L. 1972. Stimulation of secretion of pig thyrocalcitonin by gastrin and related hormonal peptides. *Endocrinology* 91:1079–89

92. Corradino, R. A. 1973. Strontium inhibition of the vitamin D induced calcium binding protein and the intestinal calcium absorptive mechanism. *2nd Int. Conf. Strontium Metab.,* 227–87. Glasgow: Health Safety Lab. USAEC

93. Corradino, R. A., Wasserman, R. H. 1971. Vitamin $D_3$—Induction of calcium binding protein in embryonic chick intestine in vitro. *Science* 172: 731–33

94. Corradino, R. A., Wasserman, R. H. 1971. Stimulation of calcium transport in embryonic chick intestine by incubation in medium containing vitamin D induced calcium-binding protein. *Biophys. Soc. Abstr.* 11, 276a

95. Corradino, R. A. 1973. 1-25 Dihydroxycholecalciferol inhibition of action in organ-cultured intestine by actinomycin D and α-amanitin. *Nature* 243:41–42

96. Corradino, R. A. Embryonic chick intestine in organ culture response to vitamin $D_3$. *Science.* In press

97. Corradino, R. A., Ebel, J. G., Craig, P. H., Taylor, A. N., Wasserman, R. H. 1971. Calcium absorption and the vitamin $D_3$-dependent calcium binding protein. I. Inhibition by dietary strontium. *Calcif. Tissue Res.* 7:81–92

98. Corradino, R. A., Ebel, J. G., Craig, P. H., Taylor, A. N., Wasserman, R. H. 1971. Calcium absorption and the vitamin $D_3$ dependent calcium-binding protein. II. Recovery from dietary strontium inhibition. *Calcif. Tissue Res.* 7:93–102

99. Cramer, C. F. 1972. Aspects of intestinal absorption of calcium, phosphorus and magnesium. *Methods Achiev. Exp. Pathol.* 6:172–92

100. Cuthbert, A. W. 1970. *Calcium and Cellular Function.* New York: St. Martin's. 301 pp.

101. Davis, B. B., Murdaugh, H. V. 1970. Evaluation of interrelationship between calcium and sodium excretion by canine kidney. *Metabolism* 19:439–44

102. Deftos, L. J., Goodman, A. D., Engelman, K., Potts, J. T. Jr. 1971. Supression and stimulation of calcitonin secretion in medullary thyroid carcinoma. *Metabolism* 20:428–31

103. Deftos, L. J., Singer, F. R. 1971. Calcitonin & natriuresis. *N. Engl. J. Med.* 285:463–64

104. Delling, G., Hehrmann, R., Montz, R. 1972. Effect of dibutryl cyclic AMP (DBcAMP) and parathyroid hormone (PTH) on intestinal calcium absorption. *Horm. Metab. Res.* 4:59

105. DeLuca, H. F., Suttie, J. W. 1970. *The Fat Soluble Vitamins.* Madison: Univ. Wisconsin Press. 531 pp.

106. DeLuca, H. F. 1971. The role of vitamin D and its relationship to parathyroid hormone and calcitonin. *Recent Progr. Horm. Res.* 27:479–510

107. DiBona, G. F. 1971. Effect of hypercalcemia on renal tubular sodium handling in the rat. *Am. J. Physiol.* 220:49–53

108. Doty, S. B., Schofield, B. H. 1972. Metabolic and structural changes within osteocytes of rat bone. See Ref. 305, 353–64

109. Drescher, D., DeLuca, H. F. 1971. Possible precursor of vitamin D stimulated calcium binding protein in rats. *Biochemistry* 10:2308–12

110. Dufresne, L. R., Cooper, C. W., Gitelman, H. J. 1972. In vivo supression of parathyroid gland ATP content by hypercalcemia. *Endocrinology* 90: 291–94

111. Dufresne, L. R., Gitelman, H. J. 1972. A possible role of adenyl cyclase in the regulation of parathyroid activity by calcium. See Ref. 305, 202–6

112. Edwards, B. R., Sutton, R. A. L., Dirks, J. H. 1972. Micropuncture study of calcium transport in the proximal renal tubule of the dog. *Clin. Res.* 20:592
113. Eknoyan, G., Suki, W. N., Martinez-Maldonado, M. 1970. Effect of diuretics on urinary excretion of phosphate, calcium and magnesium in thyroparathyroidectomized dogs. *J. Lab. Clin. Med.* 76:257–66
114. Ewe, K. 1972. Calcium transport in rat small intestine in vitro and in vivo. *Arch. Pharmacol.* 273:352–65
115. Fang, V. S., Tashjian, A. H. Jr. 1972. Studies on the role of the liver in the metabolism of parathyroid hormone. I. Effects of partial hepatectomy and incubation of the hormone with tissue homogenate. *Endocrinology* 90:1177–84
116. Feinblatt, J. D., Raisz, L. G. 1971. Secretion of Thyrocalcitonin in organ culture. *Endocrinology* 88:797–804
117. Fischer, J., Oldham, S., Sizemore, G., Arnaud, C. 1972. Calcium-regulated parathyroid hormone peptidase. *Proc. Nat. Acad. Sci. USA* 69:2341–45
118. Foster, G. V. et al 1971. Metabolic fate of human calcitonin in the dog. *Endocrinology 71,* ed. S. Taylor, 71–78. London: Heineman
119. Fraser, D. R., Kodicek, E. 1970. Unique biosynthesis by kidney of a biologically active vitamin D metabolite. *Nature* 228:764–66
120. Fraser, D. R., Kodicek, E. 1973. Regulation of 25-hydroxycholecalciferol-1-hydroxylase activity in kidney by parathyroid hormone. *Nature* 241:163–66
121. Frick, A. 1969. Mechanism of inorganic phosphate diuresis secondary to saline infusions in the rat. Excretion of sodium, inorganic phosphate, and calcium in normal and in parathyroidectomized rats. *Pfluegers Arch.* 313:106–22
122. Frolik, C. A., DeLuca, H. F. 1972. Metabolism of 1,25-dihydroxycholecalciferol in the rat. *J. Clin. Invest.* 51:2900–6
123. Fujita, T., Orimo, H., Ohata, M., Yoshikawa, M., Maruyama, M. 1970. Enzymatic inactivation of parathyroid hormone by rat kidney homogenate. *Endocrinology* 86:42–49
124. Galante, L., Colston, K. W., MacAulay, S., MacIntyre, I. 1972. Effect of parathyroid extract on vitamin D metabolism. *Lancet* 1:985–88
125. Galante, L., Colston, K. W., MacAulay, S., MacIntyre, I. 1972. Effect of cal-

citonin on vitamin D metabolism. *Nature* 238:271–73
126. Garabedian, M., Holick, M. F., DeLuca, H. F., Boyle, I. T. 1972. Control of 25-hydroxycholecalciferol metabolism by parathyroid glands. *Proc. Nat. Acad. Sci. USA* 69:1673–76
127. Gekle, D., Ströder, J., Rostock, D. 1969. The effect of vitamin D on the inorganic phosphate reabsorption in the proximal convolution of the rat kidney. *Klin. Wochenschr.* 21:1177–78
128. Gekle, D., Ströder, J., Rostock, D. 1971. The effect of vitamin D on renal inorganic phosphate reabsorption of normal rats, parathyroidectomized rats, and rats with rickets. *Pediat. Res.* 5:40–52
129. Gibbons, R. A., Sansom, B. F., Sellwood, R. 1972. The passage of calcium and strontium across the gut of the anesthetized goat. *J. Physiol.* 222:397–406
130. Glitsch, H. G., Reuter, H., Scholz, H. 1970. The effect of the internal sodium concentration on calcium fluxes in isolated guinea-pig auricles. *J. Physiol.* 209:25–43
131. Goldberg, M. 1971. Renal tubular sites of action of diuretics. *Renal Pharmacology,* ed. J. W. Fischer, E. J. Carfuny, 99–119. New York: Appleton
132. Goldberg, M., Agus, Z. S., Puschett, J. B., Senesky, D. 1972. Mode of action of parathyroid hormone: micropuncture studies. See Ref. 305, 273–83
133. Goodman, D. B. P., Haussler, M. R., Rasmussen, H. 1972. Vitamin D₃ induced alteration of microvillar membrane lipid composition. *Biochem. Biophys. Res. Commun.* 46:80–86
134. Gray, R., Boyle, I., DeLuca, H. F. 1971. Vitamin D metabolism: the role of kidney tissue. *Science* 172:1232–34
135. Gray, R. W., DeLuca, H. F. 1971. Metabolism of 25-hydroxycholecalciferol and its inhibition by actinomycin D and cycloheximide. *Arch. Biochem. Biophys.* 145:276–89
136. Gruson, M., Cerlaud, M., Miravet, L., Paul, J., Hioco, D. 1970. Action de la calcitonine de porc sur le transfert in vitro du Ca⁴⁵ au niveau du duodénum de rat normal et thyroparathyroidectomisé. *CR Acad. Sci. Natur.* 270:1014–16
137. Haas, H. G., Dambacher, M. G., Guncaga, J., Lauffenburger, T. 1971. Renal effects of calcitonin and parathyroid extract in man: studies in hypoparathyroidism. *J. Clin. Invest.* 50:2689–702

138. Habener, J. F., Kemper, B., Potts, J. T. Jr., Rich, A. 1972. Proparathyroid hormone: biosynthesis by human parathyroid adenomas. *Science* 178:630–33
139. Habener, J. F., Segre, G., Powell, D., Murray, T., Potts, J. T. Jr. 1972. Immunoreactive parathyroid hormone in circulation of man. *Nature New Biol.* 238:152–54
140. Habener, J. F., Singer, F. R., Deftos, L. J., Neer, R. M. 1971. Explanation for unusual potency of salmon calcitonin. *Nature New Biol.* 232:91–92
141. Haddad, J. G., Boisseau, V., Avioli, L. V. 1972. Phosphorus deprivation: the metabolism of vitamin $D_3$ and 25-hydroxycholecalciferol in rats. *J. Nutr.* 102:269–89
142. Hamilton, J. W. et al 1973. Amino-terminal sequence of bone proparathyroid hormone (calcemic fraction A). *Fed. Proc.* 32:269A
143. Hamilton, J. W., Cohn, D. V. 1969. Studies on the biosynthesis in vitro of parathyroid hormone. I. Synthesis of parathyroid hormone by bovine parathyroid gland slices and its control by calcium. *J. Biol. Chem.* 244:5421–29
144. Hamilton, J. W., Holdsworth, E. S. 1970. The release of $Ca^{45}$ from mitochondria of chicken intestinal mucosa by calcium binding protein. *Biochem. Biophys. Res. Commun.* 40:1325–30
145. Hamilton, J. W., Spierto, F. W., MacGregor, R. R., Cohn, D. V. 1971. Studies on the biosynthesis in vitro of parathyroid hormone. II. The effect of calcium and magnesium on synthesis of parathyroid hormone isolated from bovine parathyroid tissue and incubation medium. *J. Biol. Chem.* 246:3224–33
146. Hancox, N. M. 1972. *Biology of Bone.* London: Cambridge Univ. Press. 199 pp.
147. Harmeyer, J., DeLuca, H. F. 1969. Calcium binding protein and calcium absorption after vitamin D administration. *Arch. Biochem. Biophys.* 133:247–54
148. Harell, A., Binderman, I., Rodan, G. A. 1973. The effect of calcium concentration on calcium uptake by bone cells treated with thyrocalcitonin (TCT) hormone. *Endocrinology* 92:550–55
149. Haussler, M. R., Boyce, D. W., Littledike, E. T., Rasmussen, H. 1971. A rapidly acting metabolite of vitamin $D_3$. *Proc. Nat. Acad. Sci. USA* 68:177–81
150. Haussler, M. R., Myrtle, J. F., Norman, A. W. 1968. The association of a metabolite of vitamin $D_3$ with intestinal mucosa chromatin in vivo. *J. Biol. Chem.* 243:4055–64
151. Haussler, M. R., Nagode, L. A., Rasmussen, H. 1970. Induction of intestinal brush border alkaline phosphatase by vitamin D and identity with Ca-ATPase. *Nature* 228:1199–201
152. Haussler, M. R., Rasmussen, H. 1972. The metabolism of vitamin $D_3$ in the chick. *J. Biol. Chem.* 247:2328–35
153. Heersche, J. N. M., Aurbach, G. D. 1972. Cyclic AMP response in bone after prolonged exposure to parathyroid hormone. See Ref. 305, 511–12
154. Hekkelman, J. W. 1971. A study of the metabolism of bone in a perfusion system. *Isr. J. Med. Sci.* 7:351–53
155. Helbock, H. J., Forte, J. G., Saltman, P. 1966. The mechanism of calcium transport by rat intestine. *Biochem. Biophys. Acta* 126:81–93
156. Herrmann-Erlee, M. P. M., Konijn, T. M. 1970. Effect of parathyroid extract on cyclic AMP content of embryonic mouse calvaria. *Nature* 227:177–78
157. Herrmann-Erlee, M. P. M. 1971. Studies on the metabolism of embryonic bone and its modification by parathyroid extract. *Recent Advances in Quantitative Histo and Cytochemistry,* 257–83. Bern: Hans Huber
158. Hioco, D. 1971. *Phosphate et Métabolisme Phosphocalcique.* Paris: Expansion Sci. Fr. 356 pp.
159. Hioco, D., Bordier, P., Miravet, L., Denys, H., Tun-Chot, S. 1969. Prolonged administration of calcitonin in man: biological, isotopic and morphological effects. See Ref. 315, 514–22
160. Holdsworth, E. S. 1970. The effect of vitamin D on enzyme activities in the mucosal cells of the chick small intestine. *J. Membrane Biol.* 3:43–53
161. Holick, M., Garabedian, M., DeLuca, H. 1972. 1,25-Dihydroxycholecalciferol: metabolite of vitamin $D_3$ active on bone in anephric rats. *Science* 176:1146–47
162. Holick, M. F., Schnoes, H. K., DeLuca, H. F. 1971. Identification of 1,25-dihydroxycholecalciferol, a form of vitamin $D_3$ metabolically active in the intestine. *Proc. Nat. Acad. Sci. USA* 68:803–4
163. Holtrop, M. E. 1973. The ultrastructure of osteoclastes during stimulation and inhibition of bone resorption. See Ref. 38. In press
164. Holtrop, M. E., Weinger, J. M. 1972. Ultrastructural evidence for a transport system in bone. See Ref. 305, 365–74

165. Horsting, M., DeLuca, H. F. 1969. In vitro production of 25-hydroxycholecalciferol. *Biochem. Biophys. Res. Commun.* 36:251–56

166. Hurwitz, S., Bar, A. 1972. Site of vitamin D action in chick intestine. *Am. J. Physiol.* 222:761–67

167. Ingersoll, R. J., Wasserman, R. H. 1971. Vitamin D₃ induced calcium binding protein. Binding characteristics, conformational effects and other properties. *J. Biol. Chem.* 246:2808–14

168. Jande, S. 1972. Effects of parathormone on osteocytes and their surrounding bone matrix: an electron microscopic study. *Z. Zellforsch.* 130:463–70

169. Jowsey, J. 1972. Calcium release from the skeletons of rachitic puppies. *J. Clin. Invest.* 51:9–15

170. Kallfelz, F. A., Wasserman, R. H. 1972. Correlation between ⁴⁷Ca absorption and intestinal calcium binding activity in the golden hamster. *Proc. Soc. Exp. Biol. Med.* 139:77–79

171. Kallio, D. M., Garant, P. R., Minkin, C. 1972. Ultrastructural effects of calcitonin on osteoclasts in tissue culture. *J. Ultrastruct. Res.* 39:205–16

172. Kashiwa, H. K. 1970. Calcium phosphate in osteogenic cells. *Clin. Orthop.* 70:200–11

173. Keeler, R., Walker, V., Copp, D. H. 1970. Natriuretic and diuretic effects of calcitonin in rats. *Can. J. Physiol. Pharmacol.* 48:838–41

174. Kemm, J. R. 1972. The effect of previous dietary intake of calcium on calcium absorption in rats. *J. Physiol.* 223:321–32

175. Kemper, B., Habener, J. F., Pott, J. T. Jr., Rich, A. 1972. Proparathyroid hormone: identification of a biosynthetic precursor to parathyroid hormone. *Proc. Nat. Acad. Sci. USA* 69:643–47

176. Keutmann, H. T., Dawson, B. F., Aurbach, G. D., Potts, J. T. Jr. 1972. A biologically active amino-terminal fragment of bovine parathyroid hormone prepared by dilute acid hydrolysis. *Biochemistry* 11:1973–79

177. Kimberg, D. V., Baerg, R. D., Gershon, E., Graudusius, R. T. 1971. Effect of cortisone treatment on the active transport of calcium by the small intestine. *J. Clin. Invest.* 50:1309–21

178. Kimberg, D. V. et al 1969. Effects of vitamin D and steroid hormones on active transport of calcium by intestine. *N. Engl. J. Med.* 280:1396–405

179. Kimmich, G. A., Rasmussen, H. 1969. Regulation of pyruvate carboxylase activity by calcium in intact liver mitochondria. *J. Biol. Chem.* 244:190–99

180. Klein, D. C., Raisz, L. G. 1971. Role of adenosine 3',5'-monophosphate in the hormonal regulation of bone resorption: studies with cultured fetal bone. *Endocrinology* 89:818–26

181. Klotz, H. P. 1971. *Les hormones et le calcium. Problèmes actuels d'endocrinologie et de nutrition,* Série 15. Paris: Expansion Sci. Fr. 358 pp.

182. Kodicek, E. 1972. Recent advances in vitamin D metabolism. See Ref. 193, 305–23

183. Kodicek, E., Lawson, D. E. M., Wilson, P. W. 1970. Biological activity of a polar metabolite of vitamin D₃. *Nature* 228:763–64

184. Kowarski, S., Schachter, D. 1969. Effects of vitamin D on phosphate transport and incorporation into mucosal constituents of rat intestinal mucosa. *J. Biol. Chem.* 244:211–17

185. Krawitt, E. L. 1972. The role of intestinal transport proteins in cortisone-mediated suppression of calcium absorption. *Biochim. Biophys. Acta* 274:179–88

186. Krawitt, E. L. 1972. Correlation between intestinal brush border alkaline phosphatase activity and calcium absorption in dietary calcium restricted rats. *Fed. Proc.* 31:721

187. Lamb, J. F., Lindsay, R. 1971. Effect of Na, metabolic inhibitors and ATP on Ca movements in L cells. *J. Physiol.* 218:691–708

188. Lehninger, A. L. 1970. Mitochondria and calcium transport. *Biochem. J.* 119:129–38

189. Langer, B. 1971. Effets comparés de l'administration d'une dose unique de calcitonine synthétique (de type humain et de type saumon) chez l'homme normal et les sujets atteints de maladie de Paget ou d'hypercalcémie. *Schweiz. Med. Wochenschr.* 101:69–80

190. Lawson, D. E. M., Fraser, D. R., Kodicek, E., Morris, H. R., Williams, D. H. 1971. Identification of 1,25-dihydrocholecalciferol, a new kidney hormone controlling calcium metabolism. *Nature* 230:228–30

191. Lewis, P., Rafferty, B., Shelley, M., Robinson, C. J. 1971. A suggested physiological role of calcitonin: the protection of the skeleton during pregnancy and lactation. *J. Endocrinol.* 49:9–10

192. MacGregor, R. R., Hamilton, J. W., Cohn, D. V. 1970. The induction of cal-

cium binding protein biosynthesis in intestine by vitamin $D_3$. *Biochim. Biophys. Acta* 222:482–90

193. MacIntyre, I. 1972. Calcium metabolism and bone disease. *Clinics in endocrinology and metabolism.* London: Saunders. 328 pp.

194. MacIntyre, I., Robinson, C. J. 1969. Magnesium and the gut experimental and clinical observations. *Ann. NY Acad. Sci.* 162:865–73

195. MacManus, J. P., Whitfield, J. F. 1970. Inhibition by thyrocalcitonin of the mitogenic action of parathyroid hormone, and cyclic 3',5' monophosphate on rat thymocytes. *Endocrinology* 86:934–39

196. Marcus, R., Aurbach, G. D. 1971. Adenyl cyclase from renal cortex. *Biochim. Biophys. Acta* 242:410–21

197. Martin, D. L., DeLuca, H. F. 1969. Influence of sodium on calcium transport by the rat small intestine. *Am. J. Physiol.* 216:1351–59

198. Martin, D. L., DeLuca, H. F. 1969. Calcium transport and the role of vitamin D. *Arch. Biochem. Biophys.* 134:139–48

199. Martin, D. L., Melancon, M. J., DeLuca, H. F. 1969. Vitamin D stimulated calcium-dependent adenosine triphosphatase from brush borders of rat small intestine. *Biochem. Biophys. Res. Commun.* 35:819–23

200. Martin, J. H., Matthews, J. L. 1970. Mitochondrial granules in chondrocytes, osteoblasts and osteocytes: an ultrastructural and microincineration study. *Clin. Orthop.* 68:273–78

201. Matthews, J. L., Martin, J. H. 1971. Intracellular transport of calcium and its relationship to homeostasis and mineralization. *Am. J. Med.* 50:589–97

202. Matthews, J. L., Martin, J. H., Collins, E. J. 1970. Intracellular calcium in epithelial, cartilage and bone cells. *Calcif. Tissue Res.* Suppl. 4:37–38

203. Matthews, J. L., Martin, J. H., Collins, E. J., Kennedy, J. W. III, Powell, E. L. Jr. 1972. Immediate changes in the ultrastructure of bone cells following thyrocalcitonin administration. See Ref. 305, 375–82

204. Marx, S. J., Woodard, C. J., Aurbach, G. D. 1972. Calcitonin receptors of kidney and bone. *Science* 178:999–1001

205. Mears, D. C. 1971. Effects of parathyroid hormone and thyrocalcitonin on the membrane potential of osteoclasts. *Endocrinology* 88:1021–28

206. Melancon, M. J., DeLuca, H. F. 1970. Vitamin D stimulation of calcium-dependent adenosine triphosphatase in chick intestinal brush borders. *Biochemistry* 9:1658–64

207. Melson, G. L., Chase, L. R., Aurbach, G. D. 1970. Parathyroid hormone-sensitive adenyl-cyclase in isolated renal tubules. *Endocrinology* 86:511–18

208. Meyer, R. A., Talmage, R. V. 1972. Effects of parathyroid hormone on bone calcium without concurrent effects on phosphate. See Ref. 305, 416–21

209. Middler, S., Pak, C., Murad, F., Barter, F. 1973. Thiazide diuretics and calcium metabolism. *Metabolism* 22:139–46

210. Minkin, C., Reynold, J. J., Copp, D. H. 1971. Inhibitory effect of salmon and other calcitonins on calcium release from mouse bone in vitro. *Can. J. Physiol. Pharmacol.* 49:263–267

211. Morel, F., Roinel, N., Le Grimellec, C. 1969. Electron probe analysis of tubular fluid composition. *Nephron* 6:350–64

212. Morrissey, R. L., Wasserman, R. H. 1971. Calcium absorption and calcium binding protein in chicks on differing calcium and phosphorus intakes. *Am. J. Physiol.* 220:1509–15

213. Morris, R. C. Jr. 1969. Renal tubular acidosis. *N. Engl. J. Med.* 281:1405–13

214. Morris, R. C. Jr., McSherry, E. 1971. Parathyroid hormone modulation of renal acidification. *J. Clin. Invest.* 50:67a

215. Mueller, W. J., Hall, K. L., Maurer, C. A. Jr., Joshua, I. G. 1973. Plasma calcium and inorganic phosphate response of laying hens to parathyroid hormone. *Endocrinology* 92:853–56

216. Muldowney, F. P., Carroll, D. V., Donohoe, J. F., Freaney, R. 1971. Correction of renal bicarbonate wastage by parathyroidectomy. *Quart. J. Med.* 40:487

217. Munson, P. L. et al 1973. Physiological significance of thyrocalcitonin in mammals. See Ref. 37. In press

218. Murayama, Y., Morel, F., Le Grimellec, C. 1972. Phosphate, calcium and magnesium transfers in proximal tubules and loops of Henle, as measured by single nephron microperfusion experiments in the rat. *Pfluegers Arch.* 333:1–16

219. Myrtle, J. F., Haussler, M. R., Norman, A. W. 1970. Evidence for the biologically active form of cholecalciferol in the intestine. *J. Biol. Chem.* 245:1190–96

220. Nagata, N., Rasmussen, H. 1970. Parathyroid hormone, 3',5'-AMP, Ca++ and renal gluconeogenesis. *Proc. Nat. Acad. Sci. USA* 65:368–74

221. Neuman, W. F. 1969. The milieu interieur of bone: Claude Bernard revisited. *Fed. Proc.* 28:1846–50

222. Neuman, W. F. 1972. The bone blood equilibrium: a possible system for its study in vitro. See Ref. 305, 389–98

223. Neuman, W. F., Mulryan, B. J., Neuman, M. W., Lane, K. 1973. Calcium transport systems in the chick calvaria. *Am. J. Physiol.* 224:600–6

224. Neuman, W. F., Ramp, W. K. 1971. The concept of a bone membrane: some implications. See Ref. 228, 197–206

225. Nichols, G. Jr. 1970. Bone resorption and calcium homeostasis: one process or two? *Calcif. Tissue Res.* 4:61–63

226. Nichols, G. Jr., Hirschmann, P., Rogers, P. 1971. Bone cells, calcification and calcium homeostasis. See Ref. 228, 211–37

227. Nichols, G. Jr., Rogers, P. 1971. Mechanisms for the transfer of calcium into and out of the skeleton. *Pediatrics* 47: 211–28

228. Nichols, G. Jr., Wasserman, R. H. 1971. *Cellular Mechanisms for Calcium Transfer and Homeostasis.* New York: Academic. 513 pp.

229. Nisket, J., Nordin, B. E. C. 1968. Thyrocalcitonin inhibition of bone resorption in tissue culture. *Calcitonin, Proc. Symp. Thyrocalcitonin C Cells,* 230–37. New York: Springer

230. Nordin, B. E. C., Peacock, M. 1969. Role of kidney in regulation of plasma calcium. *Lancet* ii:1280–83

231. Norman, A. W., Midgett, R. J., Myrtle, J. F., Nowicki, H. G. 1971. Studies on calciferol metabolism. I. Production of vitamin D metabolite 4B from 25-OH cholecalciferol by kidney homogenate. *Biochem. Biophys. Res. Commun.* 42: 1082–87

232. Norman, A. W., Mircheff, A. K., Adams, T. H., Spielvogel, A. 1970. Studies on the mechanism of action of calciferol. II. Vitamin D-mediated increase of intestinal brush border alkaline phosphatase activity. *Biochem. Biophys. Acta* 215:348–59

233. Norman, A. W. et al 1971. 1,25-Dihydroxycholecalciferol: identification the proposed active form of vitamin $D_3$ in the intestine. *Science* 173:51–54

234. Ogata, E., Rasmussen, H., Gruden, N. 1971. Basis of action of hormones on calcium absorption. *Intestinal Absorption of Metal Ions, Trace Elements and Radionuclides,* ed. S. C. Skoryna, D. Waldron-Edward, 359–72. New York: Pergamon

235. Oldham, S. B., Fischer, J. A., Capen, C. C., Sizemore, G. W., Arnaud, C. D. 1971. Dynamics of parathyroid hormone secretion in vitro. *Am. J. Med.* 50:650–57

236. Olson, E. B. Jr., DeLuca, H. F., Potts, J. T. Jr. 1972. Calcitonin inhibition of vitamin D induced intestinal calcium absorption. *Endocrinology* 90: 151–57

237. Olson, E. B. Jr., DeLuca, H. F., Potts, J. T. Jr. 1972. The effect of calcitonin and parathyroid hormone on calcium transport of isolated intestine. See Ref. 305, 240–46

238. Omdahl, J. L., DeLuca, H. F. 1972. Rachitogenic activity of dietary strontium. I. inhibition of intestinal calcium absorption and 1,25-dihydroxycholecalciferol synthesis. *J. Biol. Chem.* 247:5520–26

239. Omdahl, J. L., DeLuca, H. F. 1973. Regulation of vitamin D metabolism and function. *Physiol. Rev.* 53:327–72

240. Omdahl, J. L., Gray, R. W., Boyle, I. T., Knutson, J., DeLuca, H. F. 1972. Regulation of metabolism of 25-hydroxycholecalciferol by kidney tissue in vitro by dietary calcium. *Nature New Biol.* 237:63–64

241. Omdahl, J. L., Holick, M., Suda, T., Tanaka, Y., DeLuca, H. F. 1971. Biological activity of 1,25-dihydroxycholecalciferol. *Biochemistry* 10:2935–40

242. Owen, M. 1970. The origin of bone cells. *Int. Rev. Cytol.* 28:213–38

243. Paillard, F., Ardaillou, R., Malendin, H., Fillastre, J. P., Prier, S. 1972. Renal effects on salmon calcitonin in man. *J. Lab. Clin. Med.* 80:200–16

244. Pak, C. Y. C., Ruskin, B., Casper, A. 1970. Renal effects of porcine thyrocalcitonin in the dog. *Endocrinology* 87: 262–70

245. Papworth, D. G., Patrick, G. 1970. The kinetics of influx of calcium and strontium into rat intestine in vitro. *J. Physiol.* 210:999–1020

246. Parfitt, A. 1972. The interactions of thiazide diuretics with parathyroid hormone and vitamin D: studies in patients with hypoparathyroidism. *J. Clin. Invest.* 51:1879–88

247. Parkinson, D. K., Radde, I. C. 1970. Calcitonin action on membrane ATPase, a hypothesis. See Ref. 315, 466–71

248. Parkinson, D. K., Shami, Y., Hanimyan, D., Sheepers, J., Radde, I. C. 1971. $Ca^{2+}$ $Mg^{2+}$-stimulated adenosine triphosphatase (ATPase) in intestinal mucosa: localization of the calcium pump in basal plasma membranes. *Clin. Res.* 19:779

249. Parsons, J. A., Neer, R. M., Potts, J. T. Jr. 1971. Initial fall of plasma calcium after intravenous injection of parathyroid hormone. *Endocrinology* 89: 735–40

250. Parsons, J. A., Robinson, C. J. 1972. The earliest effects of parathyroid hormone and calcitonin on blood-bone calcium distribution. See Ref. 305, 399–406

251. Parsons, J. A., Potts, J. T. Jr. 1972. Physiology and chemistry of parathyroid hormone. See Ref. 193, 33–78

252. Parsons, J. A., Robinson, C. J. 1971. Calcium shift into bone causing transient hypocalcemia after injection of parathyroid hormone. *Nature* 230: 581–82

253. Peacock, M., Robertson, W. G., Nordin, B. E. C. 1969. Relation between serum and urinary calcium with particular reference to parathyroid activity. *Lancet* i:384–88

254. Peck, W. A., Carpenter, J., Messinger, K., DeBra, D. 1973. Cyclic 3',5 adenosine monophosphate in isolated bone cells: response to low concentrations of parathyroid hormone. *Endocrinology* 92:692–97

255. Perdue, J. F. 1971. The isolation and characterization of plasma membranes from cultured cells. III. the adenosine triphosphate-dependent accumulation of $Ca^{2+}$ by chick embryo fibroblasts. *J. Biol. Chem.* 246:6750–59

256. Piazolo, P., Schleyer, M., Franz, H. E. 1971. Isolation and purification of a calcium binding protein from human tissue. *Hoppe-Seyler's Z. Physiol. Chem.* 352:1480–86

257. Nielsen, S. P., Buchanan-Lee, B., Matthews, E. W., Moseley, J. M., Williams, C. C. 1971. Acute effects of synthetic porcine calcitonins on the renal excretion of magnesium, inorganic phosphate, sodium and potassium. *J. Endocrinol.* 51:455–64

258. Potts, J. T. Jr. et al 1971. Synthesis of biologically active N-terminal tetra-triacontapeptide of parathyroid hormone. *Proc. Nat. Acad. Sci. USA* 68:63–67

259. Potts, J. T. Jr. et al 1972. Chemistry of the parathyroid hormones; clinical and physiological implication. See Ref. 305, 152–72

260. Pott, J. T. Jr., Niall, H. D., Deftos, L. J. 1971. Calcitonin. *Current Topics in Experimental Endocrinology,* 1:151–73. New York: Academic

261. Puschett, J. B., Agus, Z. S., Senesky, D., Goldberg, M. 1972. Effect of saline loading and aortic obstruction on proximal phosphate transport. *Am. J. Physiol.* 223:851–57

262. Puschett, J. B. et al 1972. The acute renal tubular effects of 1,25-dihydroxy-cholecalciferol. *Proc. Soc. Exp. Biol. Med.* 141:379–84

263. Puschett, J. B., Goldberg, M. 1969. The relationship between the renal handling of phosphate and bicarbonate in man. *J. Lab. Clin. Med.* 73:956–69

264. Puschett, J. B., Moranz, J., Kurnick, W. S. 1972. Evidence for a direct action of cholecalciferol and 25-hydroxy-cholecalciferol on the renal transport of phosphate, sodium and calcium. *J. Clin. Invest.* 51:373–85

265. Raisz, L. G., Holtrop, M. E., Simmons, H. 1973. Inhibition of bone resorption by colchicine in organ culture. *Endocrinology* 92:556–62

266. Raisz, L. G., Trummel, C. L., Holick, M. F., DeLuca, H. F. 1972. 1,25-dihydroxycholecalciferol, a potent stimulator of bone resorption in tissue culture. *Science* 175:768–69

267. Raisz, L. G., Trummel, C. L., Simmons, H. 1972. Induction of bone resorption in tissue culture: prolonged response after brief exposure to parathyroid hormone or 25-hydroxycholecalciferol. *Endocrinology* 90:744–51

268. Raisz, L. G., Trummel, C. L., Wener, J. A., Simmons, H. 1972. Effect of glucocorticoids on bone resorption in tissue culture. *Endocrinology* 90:961–67

269. Ramp, W. K., Neuman, W. F. 1971. Some factors affecting mineralization of bone in tissue culture. *Am. J. Physiol.* 220:270–73

270. Ramp, W. K., Neuman, W. F. 1973. Bone mineralization in tissue culture, the calcium-phosphate product and ratio. *Calcif. Tissue Res.* 11:171–75

271. Rasmussen, H. 1970. Cell communication, calcium ion, and cyclic adenosine monophosphate. *Science* 170:404–12

272. Rasmussen, H. 1970. Basic aspect of bone function and calcium metabolism. See Ref. 373, 1–8

273. Rasmussen, H. 1970. *Parathyroid Hormone, Thyrocalcitonin and Related Drugs. Int. Encycl. Pharmacol. Ther.,*

ed. G. Peters, Vol. 1, Sec. 51. Oxford: Pergamon. 364 pp.

274. Rasmussen, H. 1971. Ionic and hormonal control of calcium homeostasis. *Am. J. Med.* 50:567–88

275. Rasmussen, H. 1973. Cellular mechanisms of parathyroid hormone action. See Ref. 38. In press

276. Rasmussen, H., Goodman, D. B. P., Tenenhouse, A. 1972. The role of cyclic AMP and calcium in cell activation. *CRC Crit. Rev. Biochem.* 1:95–148

277. Rasmussen, H., Wong, M., Bikle, D., Goodman, D. B. P. 1972. Hormonal control of the renal conversion of 25-hydroxycholecalciferol to 1,25-dihydroxycholecalciferol. *J. Clin. Invest.* 51:2502–04

278. Rasmussen, P. 1970. The action of vitamin D on the degree of mineralization of bone tissue in rats given adequate amounts of calcium and phosphorous in the diet. A microradiographic study. *Brit. J. Nutr.* 24:29–38

279. Rastegar, A., Agus, Z., Connor, T. B., Goldberg, M. 1972. Renal handling of calcium and phosphate during mineralocorticoid "escape" in man. *Kidney* 2:279–86

280. Reddy, B. S. 1972. Studies on the mechanism of calcium and magnesium absorption in germfree rats. *Arch. Biochem. Biophys.* 149:15–21

281. Reuter, H., Seitz, N. 1968. The dependence of calcium efflux from cardiac muscle on temperature and external ion composition. *J. Physiol.* 195:451–70

282. Robertson, W. G., Peacock, M., Atkins, D., Webster, L. A. 1972. The effect of parathyroid hormone on the uptake and release of calcium by bone in tissue culture. *Clin. Sci.* 43:715–18

283. Robinson, C. J., Rafferty, B., Parsons, J. A. 1972. Calcium shift into bone: a calcitonin-resistant primary action of parathyroid hormone, studied in rats. *Clin. Sci.* 42:235–41

284. Sakalo, L. A., Smith, A. J., Smith, R. N. 1971. The effects of porcine calcitonin on renal function in the rabbit. *J. Endocrinol.* 50:485–91

285. Sampson, H. W., Matthews, J. L. 1972. Electron microscope autoradiographic investigation of $^{33}P$ in the intestinal epithelium of rachitic, normal and vitamin D-treated rats. *Calcif. Tissue Res.* 10:58–66

286. Sampson, H. W., Matthews, J. L., Martin, J. H., Kunin, A. S. 1970. An electron microscopic localization of calcium in the small intestine of normal,

rachitic and vitamin D-treated rats. *Calcif. Tissue Res.* 5:305–16

287. Sands, H., Kessler, R. H. 1971. A calcium binding component of dog kidney cortex and its relationship to calcium transport. *Proc. Soc. Exp. Biol. Med.* 137:1267–73

288. Schachter, D., Kowarski, S., Reid, P. 1970. Active transport of calcium by intestine studies with a calcium electrode. See Ref. 100, 108–23

289. Schatzmann, H. J., Vincenzi, F. F. 1969. Calcium movements across the membrane of human red cells. *J. Physiol.* 210:369–95

290. Seliger, W. G. 1970. Tissue fluid movement in compact bone. *Anat. Rec.* 166:247–55

291. Shain, S. A. 1972. In vitro metabolism of 25-hydroxycholecalciferol by chick intestinal and renal cell preparations. Identification of a metabolic product as 1,25-dihydroxycholecalciferol and delineation of its metabolic fate in intestinal cells. *J. Biol. Chem.* 247:4393–403

292. Shain, S. A. 1972. The in vitro metabolism of 25-hydroxycholecalciferol to 1,25-dihydroxycholecalciferol by chick renal tubules. Effect of actinomycin D, puromycin, calcium, and parathyroid hormone. *J. Biol. Chem.* 247:4404–13

293. Sherwood, L. M., Abe, M., Rodman, J. S., Lundberg, W. B. Jr., Targovnik, J. H. 1972. Parathyroid hormone: synthesis storage and secretion. See Ref. 305:183–96

294. Sherwood, L. M., Lundberg, W. B. Jr., Targovnik, J. H., Rodman, J. S., Seyfer, A. 1971. Synthesis and secretion of parathyroid hormone in vitro. *Am. J. Med.* 50:658–69

295. Siddiqui, A. A., Wilson, D. R. 1972. Primary hyperparathyroidism and proximal renal tubular acidosis: report of two cases. *Can. Med. Assoc. J.* 106:654–62

296. Sorensen, O. H., Hindberg, I., Friis, T. 1972. The renal effect of calcitonin in hypoparathyroid patients. *Acta Med. Scand.* 191:103–6

297. Stachura, J., Pearse, A. G. E. 1970. Thyroid C cells in experimental hyper- and hypomagnesaemia. *Virchows Arch. Zellpathol.* 5:173–86

298. Staum, B. B., Hamburger, R. J., Goldberg, H. 1972. Tracer microinjection study of renal tubular phosphate reabsorption in the rat. *J. Clin. Invest.* 51:2271–76

299. Steele, T. H. 1970. Increased urinary phosphate excretion following volume

expansion in normal man. *Metabolism* 19:129–39

300. Steinberg, J., Nichols, G. Jr. 1971. Differential stimulation by parathyroid hormone of bone and kidney ribonucleic acid synthesis. *J. Endocrinol.* 49:493–506

301. Sutfin, L. V., Holtrop, M. E., Oglivie, R. E. 1971. Microanalysis of individual mitochondrial granules with diameters less than 1000 angstroms. *Science* 174:947–49

302. Talmage, R. V. 1969. Calcium homeostasis—calcium transport—parathyroid action. The effects of parathyroid hormone on the movement of calcium between bone and fluid. *Clin. Orthop.* 67:210–23

303. Talmage, R. V. 1971. Morphological and physiological considerations in a new concept of calcium transport in bone. *Am. J. Anat.* 129:467–76

304. Talmage, R. V., Cooper, C. W., Park, H. Z. 1970. Regulation of calcium transport in bone by parathyroid hormone. *Vitamins and Hormones* 38:103–40

305. Talmage, R. V., Munson, P. L. 1972. *Calcium, Parathyroid Hormone and the Calcitonins.* Amsterdam: Excerpta Med. 560 pp.

306. Talmage, R. V., Whitehurst, L. A., Anderson, J. J. B. 1973. Effect of calcitonin and calcium infusion on plasma phosphate. *Endocrinology* 92:792–98

307. Tanaka, Y., DeLuca, H. F. 1971. Bone mineral mobilization activity of 1,25-dihydroxycholecalciferol, a metabolite of vitamin D. *Arch. Biochem. Biophys.* 146:574–78

308. Tanaka, Y., DeLuca, H. F. 1971. Inhibition of the metabolism of 25-hydroxycholecalciferol by actinomycin D and cycloheximide. *Proc. Nat. Acad. Sci. USA* 68:605–8

309. Tanaka, Y., DeLuca, H. F. 1973. The control of 25-hydroxyvitamin D metabolism by inorganic phosphorus. *Arch. Biochem. Biophys.* 154:566–74

310. Tanaka, Y., Chen, T. C., DeLuca, H. F. 1972. Dependence of 25-hydroxycholecalciferol-1-hydroxylase regulation on RNA and protein synthesis. *Arch. Biochem. Biophys.* 152:291–98

311. Tanaka, Y., DeLuca, H. F., Omdahl, J., Holick, M. F. 1971. Mechanism of action of 1,25-dihydroxycholecalciferol on intestinal calcium transport. *Proc. Nat. Acad. Sci. USA* 68:1286–88

312. Tanaka, Y., Frank, H., DeLuca, H. F. 1973. Biological activity of 1,25-dihy-droxyvitamin D in the rat. *Endocrinology* 92:417–22

313. Tanaka, Y., Frank, H., DeLuca, H. F. 1972. Role of 1,25-dihydroxycholecalciferol in calcification of bone and maintenance of serum calcium concentration in the rat. *J. Nutr.* 102:1569–78

314. Targovnik, J. H., Rodman, J. S., Sherwood, L. M. 1971. Regulation of parathyroid hormone secretion in vitro: quantitative aspects of calcium and magnesium ion control. *Endocrinology* 88:1477–82

315. Taylor, S., Foster, G. 1970. *Calcitonin 1969. Proceedings of the Second International Symposium.* New York: Springer. 568 pp.

316. Taylor, A. N., Wasserman, R. 1970. Immunofluorescent localization of vitamin D dependent calcium-binding protein. *J. Histochem. Cytochem.* 18:107–15

317. Taylor, A. N., Wasserman, R. H. 1972. Vitamin D-induced calcium-binding protein: comparative aspects in kidney and intestine. *Am. J. Physiol.* 223:110–14

318. Teitelbaum, S. L., Shieber, W., Moore, K. E. 1972. The effects of acute glucagon stimulation on the parafollicular cells of the dog thyroid. *Cytobios* 5:43–46

319. Terepka, A. R., Coleman, J. R., Gamison, J. C., Spataro, R. F. 1971. Active transcellular transport of calcium by embryonic chick chorioallantoic membrane. See Ref. 228, 371–89

320. Tsai, H. C., Wong, R. G., Norman, A. W. 1972. Studies on calciferol metabolism. IV. Subcellular localization of 1,25 dihydroxy-vitamin $D_3$ in intestinal mucosa and correlation with increased calcium transport. *J. Biol. Chem.* 247:5511–19

321. Urban, E., Schedl, H. P. 1970. Vitamin-D, tissue calcium and calcium transport in in-vivo rat small intestine. *Am. J. Physiol.* 219:944–51

322. Urban, E., Schedl, H. P. 1970. Effect of vitamin D on tissue calcium of rat duodenum. *Scand. J. Gastroenterol.* 5:33–37

323. Vajda, F. J. E., Martin, T. J., Melick, R. A. 1969. Destruction of bovine parathyroid hormone labeled with [131]I by rat kidney tissue in vitro. *Endocrinology* 84:162–64

324. Vaughn, J. M. 1970. *The Physiology of Bone.* Oxford: Clarendon. 325 pp.

325. Vitalli, P. H. 1968. Osteocyte activity. *Clin. Orthop.* 56:213–26

326. Walling, M. W., Rothman, S. S. 1969. Phosphate independent, carrier-mediated active transport of calcium by rat intestine. *Am. J. Physiol.* 217:1144–48

327. Walling, M. W., Rothman, S. S. 1970. Apparent increase in carrier affinity for intestinal calcium transport following dietary calcium restriction. *J. Biol. Chem.* 245:5007–11

328. Walzer, M. 1971. Calcium-sodium interdependence in renal transport. See Ref. 131:21–41

329. Wasserman, R. H., Taylor, A. N. 1969. Some aspect of the intestinal absorption of calcium, with special reference to vitamin D. *Mineral Metabolism,* ed. C. L. Comar, F. Bronner, 3:321–403. New York: Academic

330. Wasserman, R. H., Taylor, A. N. 1973. Physiological significance of the vitamin D-dependent calcium-binding protein. *Triangle, Sandoz Journal of Medical Science.* In press

331. Wasserman, R. H., Corradino, R. A., Taylor, A. N. 1969. Binding proteins from animals with possible transport function. *J. Gen. Physiol.* 54: 114–34

332. Weber, J. C., Pons, V., Kodicek, E. 1971. The localization of 1,25-dihydroxycholecalciferol in bone cell nuclei of rachitic chicks. *Biochem. J.* 125: 147–53

333. Wener, J. A., Gorton, S. J., Raisz, L. G. 1972. Escape from inhibition of resorption in cultures of fetal bone treated with calcitonin and parathyroid hormone. *Endocrinology* 90:752–59

334. West, T. E. T., O'Riordan, J. L. H., Copp, D. H., Bates, R. F. L., Care, A. D. 1973. The effect of hypocalcemia on the secretion of calcitonin. *J. Endocrinol.* 56:463–70

335. Whitfield, J. F., MacManus, J. P., Gillan, D. J. 1971. Inhibition by thyrocalcitonin (calcitonin) of the cyclic AMP-mediated stimulation of thymocyte proliferation by epinephrine. *Horm. Metab. Res.* 3:348

336. Whitfield, J. F., MacManus, J. P., Youdale, T., Franks, D. J. 1971. Roles of calcium and cyclic AMP in the stimulatory action of parathyroid hormone on thymic lymphocyte proliferation. *J. Cell. Physiol.* 78:355

337. Williams, C. C. et al 1971. The renal effects of human and salmon calcitonin in the rat. *Eur. J. Clin. Invest.* 1:395

338. Williams, C. C., Matthews, E. W., Moseley, J. M., MacIntyre, I. 1972. The effects of synthetic human and salmon calcitonins on electrolyte excretion in the rat. *Clin. Sci.* 42:129–37

339. Williams, G. A., Hargis, G. K., Bowser, E. N., Henderson, W. J., Martinez, N. J. 1973. Evidence for a role of adenosine 3',5'-monophosphate in parathyroid hormone release. *Endocrinology* 92: 687–91

340. Wills, M. R., Wortsman, J., Pak, C. Y. C., Bartter, F. C. 1970. The role of parathyroid hormone in the gastro-intestinal absorption of calcium. *Clin. Sci.* 39: 89–94

341. Winter, M., Morava, E., Simon, G., Sos, J. 1970. The role of the parathyroid glands in the absorption of calcium from the small intestine. *J. Endocrinol.* 47:65–72

342. Winter, M., Morava, E., Simon, G. 1970. The role of the thyroid in the intestinal effect of vitamin D on a rachitic rats. *J. Endocrinol.* 48:541–44

343. Winter, M. et al 1972. Some findings on the mechanism of adaptation of the intestine to calcium deficiency. *Brit. J. Nutr.* 28:105–11

344. Wong, R. G., Adams, T. H., Roberts, P. A., Norman, A. W. 1970. Studies on the mechanism of action of calciferol. IV. Interaction of the polyene antibiotic, filipin, with intestinal mucosal membranes from vitamin D-treated and vitamin D-deficient chicks. *Biochim. Biophys. Acta* 219:61–72

345. Zichner, L. 1972. Changes on bone cells in calcitonin treated rats. *Res. Exp. Med.* 157:95

346. Ziegler, R., Delling, G., Pfeiffer, E. F. 1970. The secretion of calcitonin by the perfused ultimobrandrial gland of the hen. See Ref. 315, 301–10

# PROSTAGLANDINS IN REPRODUCTION

❖1117

*B. B. Pharriss and Jane E. Shaw*
ALZA Research, 950 Page Mill Road, Palo Alto, California

## INTRODUCTION

The prostaglandins constitute a group of naturally occurring C-20 unsaturated hydroxy fatty acids. They have a widespread distribution throughout the animal kingdom. Their occurrence, tissue distribution, biosynthesis, metabolism, physiology, and pharmacology have been the subject of many comprehensive reviews and books (47, 82, 88, 89, 96).

The prostaglandins have been proposed as mediators of more physiological responses than any biological substance yet described except cyclic adenosine monophosphate (cAMP); they have been implicated in reproductive processes both in the male and female, being present in most tissues of the reproductive tract. In addition, most tissues associated with reproduction can readily biosynthesize prostaglandins in response to the appropriate stimuli. In reproduction within the female mammal alone, physiological roles of the prostaglandins have been indicated in menstruation, dysmenorrhea, oviduct motility, gamete transport, regression of the corpus luteum, biosynthesis of ovarian steroids, and parturition.

Exploitation of the pharmacological properties of the prostaglandins, such as stimulation of uterine smooth muscle for therapeutic abortion or induction of labor, is hampered by the multiplicity of effects which the compounds exert. This has led to the development of analogues which possess some but not all of the properties of the parent compounds and which have a tendency to be metabolized more slowly. However one of the parent prostaglandin compounds, namely $PGE_2$, has received approval for marketing as an oral medication for induction of labor. In this review we stress the effects of pharmacological responses to prostaglandins in the female reproductive tract, though the implications of endogenous prostaglandins in reproductive processes in both the male and female is a fascinating field of study of current interest to many investigators.

## PHARMACOLOGICAL EFFECTS OF PROSTAGLANDINS ON THE OVARY

*Role of Prostaglandins in the Action of Luteinizing Hormone*

PROGESTERONE SYNTHESIS    It has been known for some years that prostaglandins of the E series can reproduce the stimulatory action of luteinizing hormone (LH) on ovarian progesterone synthesis in vitro in various species (for review, see 82). More evidence, from studies with rats, has indicated a luteotrophic effect of the prostaglandins in vivo (10). Prostaglandins mediate many of their effects in different tissues via changes in the intracellular levels of cAMP, and cAMP, or its more soluble dibutyryl derivative, mimics at least some of the actions of LH on the ovary. This knowledge led to an investigation of the correlation between the effect of prostaglandins on cAMP formation and the observed luteotrophic effect. Prostaglandins, like LH, have been found to stimulate adenyl cyclase activity in ovarian homogenates, ovarian tissue in culture, and the intact ovary (66, 70); the resultant rise in cAMP has been identified with stimulation of progesterone synthesis. Furthermore, theophylline, a compound which increases intracellular cAMP levels by inhibiting phosphodiesterase (the enzyme which metabolizes the nucleotide to inactive 5'AMP), potentiates the effect of both LH and $PGE_2$ on progesterone synthesis. The LH-like effects that followed treatment of ovarian tissue with pharmacological doses of the PGE compounds has been extended to include depletion of ovarian ascorbic acid, ovum maturation, and rupture of the follicle.

Prostaglandin analogues which inhibit the pharmacological actions of the natural prostaglandins are now available; in evaluating these compounds it was determined that 7-oxa-13-prostynoic acid inhibited the action of both $PGE_2$ and LH in promoting steroidogenesis in the mature ovary. Analysis of the data indicated competitive inhibition of both stimulants and led to the suggestion that the prostaglandins endogenous to ovarian tissue may mediate some or all of the actions of LH (67). To evaluate this possibility, numerous experiments have been performed with ovarian tissue of various species. One essential factor to support such a hypothesis would be the demonstration that the prostaglandin content of ovarian tissue changed upon stimulation with LH either as a result of increased uptake from the circulation, decreased metabolism, or increased tissue biosynthesis. Chasalow & Pharriss (20) succeeded in demonstrating the presence of a hormonally sensitive prostaglandin synthetase system in homogenates of rat ovarian tissue. Wilks and his associates have also demonstrated increased formation of $PGF_{2\alpha}$ in monkey ovary during stimulation with LH (98). Much attention has been paid to evaluating the role which prostaglandins may play in mediation of the response to LH by measuring cAMP formation and progesterone synthesis in the presence of previously determined maximally effective doses of LH and prostaglandins. The rationale was that observation of an effect no greater than that observed in the presence of either stimulant alone would indicate that the prostaglandins and LH were likely to be effective via the same receptor. Evidence from such experiments has accumulated both for and against the hypothesis. Thus when using rat (78), mouse (67), or bovine (90) tissue many investigators concur in that their results indicate that maximally effective doses of LH and prostaglandins when added together produce no effect on progesterone synthesis above that attained with the most effective stimulant alone. Conversely, results of other investigators using bovine tissue (70, 86) or rabbit corpus luteum (50) indicate that maximally effective doses of LH and prostaglandins when added together produce greater stimulation of adenyl cyclase than either stimulant alone. These data to date do not provide convincing evidence that the prostaglandins are involved in mediating the effect of LH on ovarian tissue. Furthermore, in porcine granulosa cells and rat ovarian tissue, both Kolena & Channing (66) and Zor and his associates (103) failed to observe an inhibitory effect of 7-oxa-13-prostynoic acid against LH stimulation of cAMP formation.

Thus the balance of evidence would seem to favor the conclusion that prostaglandins are not an essential link in LH activation of cAMP production leading to progesterone synthesis. However, we believe that caution should be exercised in interpreting the above data with respect to the role the endogenous prostaglandins may play in response to stimulation with LH. First, the pharmacological doses of prostaglandins used to elicit a response are far in excess of the concentration endogenous to ovarian tissue. Second, those prostaglandins formed on stimulation with LH are likely to be in the correct juxtaposition relevant to other tissue structures for exertion of their optimal biological effect, which cannot be anticipated and thus mimicked by application of pharmacological concentrations. Third, evaluation of the efficacy of 7-oxa-13-prostynoic acid as an antagonist of prostaglandin action on isolated smooth muscle indicated a requirement for a concentration of the antagonist at some 1000-fold the concentration of the agonist. In their original observations Kuehl and co-workers (67) observed a $K_i$ of $3 \times 10^{-5}$ $M$ for cAMP formation induced by PGE$_2$ ($4 \times 10^{-7}$ $M$); it thus becomes apparent that more potent but specific antagonists of prostaglandin action would be helpful in the above type of study.

Perhaps one of the most important recent observations is that the prostaglandins not only can exert luteotrophic effects in vitro, but luteolytic effects are also manifest under certain conditions. This finding would suggest caution in extrapolation of data based upon measurement of progesterone formation induced by prostaglandins in vitro, for the value obtained may in fact reflect the summation of two opposite effects of the prostaglandins: one leading to progesterone formation via activation of adenyl cyclase and cAMP formation, the other leading to inhibition of progesterone secretion possibly by limiting the availability of cholesterol (in the free form) for pregnenolone formation. The latter possibility arose from the work of Behrman, MacDonald & Greep (9) who demonstrated that in rat ovarian tissue the activities of cholesterol ester synthetase and cholesterol ester esterase are both maintained by prolactin and are effectively inhibited by PGF$_{2\alpha}$. It was speculated that this effect of PGF$_{2\alpha}$ was mediated either via a direct effect on the enzymes or by modifying gonadotropin/receptor interaction. The luteolytic effect of the prostaglandins in vitro has been observed in rat corpus luteum in tissue culture (28); over 24–72 hr, both reduced incorporation of 14-C amino acids into protein and reduced acetate-1-14 C incorporation into progesterone-associated material in the presence of PGF$_{2\alpha}$ was demonstrated. Independently, O'Grady and collaborators (75), using rabbit corpus luteum in tissue culture, demonstrated a 50% reduction in progesterone synthesis by $PGF_{2\alpha}$ over a 6 hr period. Further work is required to determine the precise mechanism of this luteolytic effect. It may be significant that in vitro incubations which demonstrated luteotrophic effects covered a relatively short time interval when compared with the luteolytic effects observed in tissue culture. The latter covered a longer time span during which other factors, excluding adenyl cyclase and cAMP, may become rate limiting in the sequence of events accompanying hormonal stimulation.

Prostaglandins could further interface with LH action by either (a) inhibiting release of LH from the cells of the anterior pituitary, (b) interacting with circulating LH, or (c) modifying the interaction of LH with its receptor at the ovarian level.

Pharriss & Hunter (81) initially observed that the in vivo luteotrophic effects of human chorionic gonadotropin (HCG) and pregnant mare serum (PMS) on the rat ovary can be antagonized by administration of $PGF_{2\alpha}$; these findings were extended to demonstrate that $PGF_{2\alpha}$ effectively inhibited the stimulatory effect of PMS and HCG on ovarian weight gain and ovulation respectively. In the rabbit, where estradiol is an effective luteotrophic agent, a competitive antagonism between estradiol and $PGF_{2\alpha}$ was observed (40, 82). Similarly, for the hamster, where prolactin is the luteotrophic agent, $PGF_{2\alpha}$ effectively terminated pregnancy (49).

The fact that the luteotrophic complex varies from species to species, yet the prostaglandins are not species-specific luteolytic agents, would indicate that if the prostaglandins were effective at the level of the pituitary, they either must totally block trophic hormone release from the anterior pituitary or selectively inhibit the luteotrophic agent characteristic of each species. Furthermore, it has been demonstrated that $PGF_{2\alpha}$ is an effective luteolytic agent in hypophysectomized rats maintained with luteotropin (10).

$PGF_{2\alpha}$ can effectively decrease luteal progesterone in hypophysectomized rats maintained with prolactin (38). These data, together with those obtained by directly measuring pituitary LH content in the rat (78), suggests that prostaglandins do not significantly alter the pituitary content of LH and that the hypothalamus and pituitary are not directly involved in the luteolytic effect of the prostaglandins. The possibility that prostaglandins act initially on the uterus to release a luteolytic substance has been negated by the work of Blatchley & Donovan (14) and Mazer & Hansel (71) who observed a luteolytic effect of $PGF_{2\alpha}$ even in hysterectomized animals. Thus we are left with the possibility either that the prostaglandins interact in vivo with LH at the ovarian receptor level to produce a luteolytic effect, or that the venoconstrictor effect of $PGF_{2\alpha}$ will prove to be the initial cause of luteolysis.

OVUM MATURATION AND OVULATION   Mention was made previously that prostaglandins mimic other actions of LH in the ovary, including ovum maturation and follicular rupture. Normally within the ovary there is no luteinization or meiosis until the time of ovulation, a fact which has been attributed to the presence of an inhibitor in the follicular fluid. In the intact rat, $PGE_2$ can effectively replace LH as an inducer of ovulation. Studies using rat ovarian follicles removed at the time of proestrus and maintained in tissue culture showed that $PGE_2$, like LH, stimulates meiotic division in rat follicles, an effect thought to be mediated via cAMP formation. Indomethacin, an effective inhibitor of prostaglandin biosynthesis in many tissues, did not modify the effect of LH in inducing meiosis (94). On the basis of such experiments, and also the development of refractoriness to LH while prostaglandins were still capable of stimulating cAMP formation, it was concluded that prostaglandins are unlikely to play an obligatory role in mediating the action of LH on ovum maturation. These findings were borne out in in vivo studies which found that in the intact rat, indomethacin effectively blocked follicular rupture but did not inhibit ovum maturation (5). In the rat treated with pentobarbital (to block the preovulatory surge of LH) $PGE_2$ effectively induced ovulation. In the rat treated with both pentobarbital and indomethacin both follicular rupture and ovum maturation were blocked, and addition of LH could not overcome the block of follicular rupture. These results can be interpreted as evidence that $PGE_2$ may play an obligatory role in the action of LH in producing rupture of the follicle. More definitive studies to evaluate the role of the endogenous prostaglandins in the steroid secretion and ovulation response which follows administration of LH to the ovary await careful evaluation of the dynamic aspects of prostaglandin biosynthesis, metabolism, and action. Such studies will undoubtedly utilize (a) the nonsteroidal anti-inflammatory compounds, including indomethacin and aspirin, which effectively reduce prostaglandin biosynthesis in many tissues (95), (b) improved antagonists of prostaglandin action, and (c) more sensitive and specific assays for the endogenous prostaglandins and their metabolites.

## Luteolysis in Nonprimates

In contrast to the luteotrophic effects of the prostaglandins on the corpus luteum in vitro, prostaglandins administered to many animals in vivo have been followed by a decrease in steroidogenesis in the corpus luteum. The functionality of the corpus luteum is essential for the support of pregnancy until the placenta develops sufficiently to produce adequate steroids.

In many mammals an intriguing question for a long time has been what brings the functionality of the corpus luteum to an end so that a new cycle can start. In many species it has been established that the proximity of the uterus to the ovary is a necessity for degeneration of corpus luteum function. Studies to establish this point included hysterectomies, transplantation of the uterus, etc. A search for the mechanism whereby the uterus exerts its inhibitory effect on the functionality of the corpus luteum was undertaken by many investigators. The possibility of a uterine-ovarian portal system has been eliminated, as has use of the lymphatic system or the oviducts for transport of a lytic factor from uterus to ovary.

One thing in common within all species in which the uterus exerts a luteolytic effect is that the ovary and uterus share a common vein, and elegant studies have shown that if one interrupts the venous drainage and separates the uterine and ovarian blood system, then luteal function is maintained. Thus the hypothesis was formulated that if a venoconstrictor substance was released from the uterus, it could, via its contractile effect on the utero-ovarian vein, reduce blood flow through the ovary and thereby initiate luteolysis, possibly as a result of congestion within the ovarian tissue and build-up of unwanted steroid metabolites (82).

VASCULAR EFFECTS OF PROSTAGLANDINS   It had been demonstrated that $PGF_{2\alpha}$, a prostaglandin endogenous to uterine tissue, is an effective venoconstrictor agent (29). Studies with $PGF_{2\alpha}$ in rats were undertaken in an effort to substantiate the hypothesis that a venoconstrictor agent may effect luteolysis. Results were successful in that, when infused intravenously to rats on days 5 and 6 of pseudopregnancy, $PGF_{2\alpha}$ resulted in a decrease in progesterone synthesis and an increase in progesterone metabolite formation. If $PGF_{2\alpha}$ was given on days 1–7 of pseudopregnancy, the normal length of the pseudopregnancy was reduced from $\sim$17 days to 9 days (79). Explanation of the many ways by which $PGF_{2\alpha}$ could exert this luteolytic effect was undertaken:

1. That the hypothalamus/pituitary axis was not involved was construed from the observation that $PGF_{2\alpha}$ was maximally effective at days 5–7 of pregnancy in the rat, a time of peak activity of the corpus luteum. Ergocornine, an agent which blocks the release of prolactin (a luteotrophic factor in the rat), is an effective luteolytic agent much earlier in pregnancy than is $PGF_{2\alpha}$. Furthermore, in the rat, $PGF_{2\alpha}$ can still effect degeneration of the corpus luteum, even in the presence of prolactin.

2. $PGF_{2\alpha}$ effectively contracts uterine myometrium and in this process could potentially elicit release of an agent which subsequently affects the ovary. That this is not likely to be the mechanism of $PGF_{2\alpha}$-induced luteolysis is deduced from the work of Blatchley & Donovan (14) and Mazer & Hansel (71), who demonstrated a luteolytic effect of $PGF_{2\alpha}$ in hysterectomized guinea pigs and hamsters respectively.

3. That the effect of $PGF_{2\alpha}$ was unlikely to be exerted via the pituitary was discussed in a previous section. Results to date strongly suggest that $PGF_{2\alpha}$ operates either by a constrictor effect on the ovarian venous drainage or by a direct lytic effect on the cells of the corpus luteum.

Pharriss and associates (80) cannulated the utero-ovarian vein in rabbits and rats and directly measured a decrease in blood flow during intravenous infusion of $PGF_{2\alpha}$ while general hypertension prevailed. Using a more elegant hydrogen desaturation technique, a selective decrease in ovarian blood flow following administration of $PGF_{2\alpha}$ was detected (39). These results strongly support the concept that congestion of the ovary could follow administration of $PGF_{2\alpha}$, which in turn could account for not only luteolysis, but also for the increased lysosomal fragility which has been observed.

NONVASCULAR EFFECTS OF PROSTAGLANDINS   Results supporting the possibility that $PGF_{2\alpha}$ also exerts a direct luteolytic effect on ovarian tissue come from the studies of Behrman and co-workers (10, 11) who demonstrated that in rats with the uterine vein ligated, prostaglandin administration resulted in a decrease of progesterone secretion without any change in blood flow. Conversely, in the autotransplanted ovary in the ewe, McCracken (72) reported that $PGF_{2\alpha}$ could elicit a decrease in blood flow through the gland which was not associated with changes in release of progesterone.

It is thus conceivable that $PGF_{2\alpha}$ exerts not only a constrictor effect on the ovarian vein, but also produces changes within the ovarian tissue itself. It has been suggested that the latter could result from A-V shunting of the blood with a consequent reduction in capillary flow. However, more recent findings (12, 75) indicate that luteolytic effects of $PGF_{2\alpha}$ are also manifest in tissue cultures of rat and rabbit ovarian tissue respectively, where effects on the vascular system are not likely to be the causal factors.

Additional information implicates the endogenous prostaglandins with control of luteolysis. Thus, in ovine tissue the evidence to date indicates that $PGF_{2\alpha}$ is the physiological uterine luteolytic factor (73). Futhermore, Caldwell made the significant observation that administration of antibodies to $PGF_{2\alpha}$ blocked spontaneous luteolysis in rabbits.

## Luteolysis in Primates

The role of the uterus in regulating the function of the corpus luteum during the normal primate reproductive cycle has not been established. Studies have indicated that in the hysterectomized human female the menstrual cycle persists, suggesting there is no uterine luteolytic factor (24). However, as $PGF_{2\alpha}$ has been so effective in producing luteolysis in numerous species, there has been extensive investigation to establish whether this compound was lytic in primates and humans. Such an effect, if safe, would provide an ideal once-a-month contraceptive.

The original findings of Kirton, Pharriss & Forbes (63) indicated that administration of 30 mg $PGF_{2\alpha}$ subcutaneously twice a day to monkeys was ineffective if administered on days 4–10 or 7–11 of pregnancy. However, when given on days 11–15, a time when the corpus luteum is functioning as the main source of progesterone, $PGF_{2\alpha}$ produced a decrease in progestins and menstruation was precipitated within 48 hr of the first injection. Ovarian blood flow was not measured in these experiments. Similarly, $PGF_{2\alpha}$ has been infused into monkeys after cannulating the ovarian vein for measurement of blood flow and for collection of blood and subsequent estimation of steroid content. Gonadotropins were administered in order to create good luteal tissue, and $PGF_{2\alpha}$ was infused into the ovarian artery at rates varying from 10 pg–50 μg/min. No change in blood flow was observed, but low doses of $PGF_{2\alpha}$ produced a decrease in progesterone secretion while high doses of $PGF_{2\alpha}$ increased progesterone secretion (4).

## Luteolysis in Humans

To date the information gathered from human studies has been consistent but disappointing in that no investigator has succeeded in shortening the luteal phase of the menstrual cycle by administering prostaglandins, though some decrease in progesterone secretion was observed when high concentrations of $PGF_{2\alpha}$ were administered for relatively long periods of time. The results are listed in Table 1, which shows also that $PGF_{2\alpha}$ infusion is almost always accompanied by unwanted intolerable side effects. Thus $PGF_{2\alpha}$ has so far not been demonstrated to be luteolytic

**Table 1** Effect of prostaglandins on luteal phase of the menstrual cycle in humans

| Prostaglandin | $n^a$ | Route | Dose (µg/min) | Duration | Day of Cycle | Progesterone | Luteal Phase | Side Effects | Reference |
|---|---|---|---|---|---|---|---|---|---|
| $PGF_{2\alpha}$ | 6 | iv | 25-46 | 8-14 hr | 4-10, postovulatory | no change | no change | spotting, cramps | (69) |
| $PGF_{2\alpha}$ | 3 | iv | 100 | 8 hr | midluteal | no change | no change | nausea, vomiting, uterine contractions, spotting, incr. temp. | (48) |
| $PGF_{2\alpha}$ | – | iv | 100 | 4 hr | 21 | decreased | – | – | (68) |
| $PGF_{2\alpha}$ | 7 | iv | 12.5-250 | 5-7 hr | late luteal | decreased | no change | cramps, nausea, vomiting, flushing, chest pains, cough, diarrhea | (45) |
| $PGF_{2\alpha}$ | 4 | iv | 8-12 | 8 hr for 2 days | – | no change | no change | – | (100) |
| $PGF_{2\alpha}$ | 2 | iv | 50-100 | 8 hr for 2 days | – | decreased | no change | – | (100) |
| $PGE_2$ | 7 | iv | 10 | 8 hr for 3 days | luteal | variable | no change | uterine contractions | (44) |

$^a$Number of subjects.

in humans if administered either early or late in the luteal phase or in the presence or absence of HCG. In some instances $PGF_{2\alpha}$ produced spotting and cramps, but a normal period always occurred at the predicted time of menstruation. $PGE_2$ did not produce intermenstrual bleeding, but neither did it precipitate premature menstruation. One subject who received $PGE_2$ on days 3, 4, and 5 postovulatory became pregnant during that cycle and successfully carried a normal fetus to term and delivered with no evidence of adverse effects. This isolated finding indicates that $PGE_2$ does not prevent nidation. The use of a prostaglandin-like compound to exert a luteolytic effect and thereby precipitate menstruation remains an intriguing possibility for a novel contraceptive, which will perhaps come to fruition with the availability of prostaglandin analogues that may possess luteolytic activity but little smooth muscle stimulating properties.

## PROSTAGLANDIN-INDUCED TERMINATION OF PREGNANCY

### Abortion

The concept of a drug induced abortion has appeared most attractive since it offers the opportunity of providing a safer, less expensive, less time consuming, more readily available technique than is currently utilized. It has been disappointing in that it has not yet been possible to demonstrate a luteolytic effect of prostaglandins in the human. It has been demonstrated repeatedly, however, that the prostaglandins exert a powerful oxytocic effect associated with interruption of pregnancy at different stages of gestation, depending upon the route and duration of prostaglandin administration.

INTRAVENOUS ADMINISTRATION  Initial reports concerning the ability of prostaglandins to terminate pregnancy prior to term indicated that 50 $\mu g/min$ $PGF_{2\alpha}$ or 5 $\mu g/min$ $PGE_2$ administered intravenously during the first two trimesters of pregnancy caused uterine stimulation, associated with successful abortion, in 26 of 27 patients in less than 18 hr (53, 54). Since that time, investigators in the United States, United Kingdom, and Sweden have produced successful abortions with intravenous administration of prostaglandins (17, 32, 36, 61, 85, 101). Most of these investigators reported the appearance of side effects (which make therapeutically effective concentrations intolerable), including nausea, vomiting, diarrhea, pyrexia, and venous erythema at the site of injection.

To avoid the problems issuing from intravenous therapy for as long as 24 hr, other routes of administration have been explored; these include intrauterine (both extraamniotic and intraamniotic) and intravaginal application.

INTRAVAGINAL ADMINISTRATION  The initial observations of Karim & Sharma (58) indicated that intravaginal application of $PGF_{2\alpha}$ (50 mg) or $PGE_2$ (20 mg) produced uterine contractions which resembled those obtained following intravenous infusion, and if applications were repeated every 2½ hr, abortion eventually occurred. It was considered likely that $PGF_{2\alpha}$ was effective as a result of absorption into the systemic circulation; since side effects were minimal in this study, it was suggested that some prostaglandins may reach the uterus via the cervix. Brenner and associates (15) undertook a study to evaluate intravaginal administration of $PGF_{2\alpha}$ to produce abortion in 36 women between 8 and 17 weeks gestation. They administered $PGF_{2\alpha}$ (50 mg) either every hour or every other hour, as the Tham salt in solution (50 or 200 mg/ml) or in tablet form. In addition, 50 mg was administered in a suppository made from a mixture of triglycerides and fatty acids every 2 hr. Whenever a dosage schedule produced adequate abortion the incidence of side effects was high, independent of the form or route of administration. Similarly, other investigators have reported a high incidence of side effects when monitoring the response of the midpregnant human uterus to vaginal administration of prostaglandin suppositories (8).

EXTRAAMNIOTIC ADMINISTRATION   When prostaglandins are instilled repeatedly via a fine catheter to a plane between the fetal membrane and uterine wall, adequate uterine activity similar to that observed following intravenous administration of the prostaglandins can be achieved, and abortion occurs. The side effects associated with this route of prostaglandin administration are minimal (33, 99). The latter investigators demonstrated that with the intrauterine administration of $PGE_2$ (50–200 $\mu$g) or $PGF_{2\alpha}$ (250–750 $\mu$g) every 1–2 hr, termination of pregnancy was effected in 14 of 15 cases with, in this small study, no difference between patients in the first or second trimester. The time required for abortion ranged from 7½ to 34 hr with a total $PGE_2$ administration ranging from 350–2500 $\mu$g and total $PGF_{2\alpha}$ in two subjects being 3500 $\mu$g and 3800 $\mu$g respectively. This is considerably less material than that required to effect abortion when administered intravenously. In 3 of the 14 cases fragments of the placenta were retained and evacuation of the uterus was subsequently performed. Wiqvist & Bygdeman (99) recorded complete or "partial" abortion in twelve of thirteen patients in the first trimester who were given $PGE_2$ or $PGF_{2\alpha}$. By using a mixture of prostaglandin and radioopaque dye it has been demonstrated that prostaglandins implanted extraamniotically induce a local contraction of the myometrium around the pool of injected fluid, which is then forced upwards between the fetal membranes and uterine wall, establishing surface contact with most of the myometrium and resulting in a generalized stimulation of the whole uterus (102).

Abortion has been attempted in 60 midtrimester patients by continuous extraamniotic infusions of $PGF_{2\alpha}$ or $PGE_2$ (74). In 50 cases, abortion was complete with prostaglandins alone; in the remaining 10 subjects, infusion of oxytocin was used in addition. Embrey extended his investigations to include 83 second trimester patients and achieved 87% success with a mean induction-abortion interval of 22.3 hr (34). Single extraamniotic injection of doses of $PGF_{2\alpha}$ as high as 10 mg have been successfully given for induction of abortion in the first trimester (26, 27). However, these injections were often followed by intense uterine pain and vomiting.

The effectiveness and safety of intermittent extraamniotic administration of prostaglandins make it at present an acceptable method for therapeutic abortion in midtrimester patients, the main inconvenience being the necessity for an indwelling catheter with a potential risk of inducing intrauterine infection.

INTRAAMNIOTIC ADMINISTRATION   In pregnancies of greater than twelve weeks duration it is possible to gain access to the amniotic sac. When hypertonic saline or glucose is used for pregnancy termination, initial withdrawal of amniotic fluid is required. It has been demonstrated that instillation of prostaglandins into the amniotic sac results in strong and frequent uterine contractions, and that under careful supervision it is possible to terminate pregnancy by this method with but a single dose of prostaglandin.

Intraamniotic injection of prostaglandins in the 15th–22nd week of gestation results in a rapid increase in uterine tone and development of strong contractions. Anderson and collaborators investigated the effect of an initial intraamniotic injection of a high dose (40 mg) of $PGF_{2\alpha}$, followed by smaller doses to maintain uterine contractility. In a study with 35 patients abortion was complete in 26 patients, and no difference in the interval from initial injection to abortion was obtained in relation to parity. Significant observations included the finding that there was no change in clotting factors, nor was there any change in plasma prostaglandin levels until some 6 hr following injection, when an increase was detected (1).

Many different dose schedules have been investigated in an attempt to achieve the highest success rate, a short injection-abortion interval, and a low incidence of side effects. In an extensive study utilizing 100 women seeking abortion, six different dose regimens have been followed, starting with intraamniotic injections of 20–40 mg and additional injections (5–40 mg) from 2–18 or 24 hr after the first injection. Of the 100 patients, 65 were aborted completely with intraamniotic $PGF_{2\alpha}$ and 30 others were incompletely aborted. Side effects included vomiting, diarrhea, and an isolated asthmatic attack. There was no significant correlation between time required for abortion and patient age, parity, or gestational age (22). A similar study using 10–25 mg as the initial intraamniotic dose resulted in 17 complete and 1 incomplete abortion in 20 patients (97). There were contractions of the uterus equal to 100 mm Hg pressure just prior to abortion, but a fixed dose of prostaglandin produced an unpredictable response with respect to uterine contraction, indicating that the sensitivity of the uterus may vary considerably among individuals. Intravenous infusion of oxytocin was helpful in completing the abortion if cervical dilation had been achieved.

Toppozada, Bygdeman & Wiqvist administered 10–25 mg $PGF_{2\alpha}$ intraamniotically and reported a correlation between dose and duration of effect. If uterine activity was good, additional injections had no additional stimulatory effect (93).

The conclusion drawn from the above studies is that an initial higher dose of prostaglandin produces the best effect. Furthermore, in comparison with the results obtained following intraamniotic injection of hypertonic saline to effect abortion, there seems little difference between the two methods which respect to the percentage of complete abortions, but prostaglandins offer the possibility of a reduced injection-abortion interval, less bleeding, less likelihood of sepsis, but possibly a greater incidence of vomiting.

Analogues of prostaglandins, which are more slowly metabolized, are now available. These include the 15(S)-15 methyl derivatives of $PGF_{2\alpha}$ in the free acid form; this compound is more potent and possesses a longer duration of effect than $PGF_{2\alpha}$ and has been successfully used for induction of second trimester abortion following intrauterine administration (18, 60). With the use of such analogues it is possible that abortion will be achieved with a single injection, thus negating the use of an indwelling catheter with its risk of infection. Intraamniotic injection of 5 mg 15(S)-15 methyl $PGF_{2\alpha}$ resulted in abortion in 37 of 38 cases with a mean injection-abortion interval of less than 20 hr.

It is well known that the main danger associated with therapeutic abortions lies in the possibility of hemorrhage and infection; these hazards are not removed by use of drugs such as the prostaglandins. For termination during the first trimester, suction curettage remains the method of choice. In the 13th to 14th weeks of gestation the extraamniotic method of prostaglandin administration appears to offer certain advantages over the current procedures, and after 15 weeks or more intraamniotic administration of natural prostaglandins or their analogues compares favorably with the current methods of choice.

## Induction of Labor

INTRAVENOUS ADMINISTRATION The first significant publication describing the use of prostaglandins for the induction of labor at term in humans was published in 1969 (52). Since that time a large number of clinical trials have been carried out to determine the safety and efficacy of prostaglandins administered by various routes to effect induction of labor. These studies have already culminated in the marketing in Europe of an oral $PGE_2$ preparation for labor induction.

One of the most definitive studies for evaluation of the efficacy of intravenous $PGE_2$ and $PGF_{2\alpha}$ for the induction of term labor was performed using a protocol design incorporating a double blind study (2) and an inducibility scoring index (0–13) as described by Bishop (13). This scoring system considers dilation, effacement, station consistency, and position; any patient with a score of 6 or less is considered a "difficult induction." $PGF_{2\alpha}$ (2.5–40.0 $\mu$g/min), $PGE_2$ (0.3–4.8 $\mu$g/min), or oxytocin (1–16 m units/min) were administered intravenously in stepwise gradations to 79 patients, each infusion being no longer than 10 hr. The results indicated that of 79 subjects the success rates for $PGF_{2\alpha}$, $PGE_2$, and oxytocin were 79.6, 89.6, and 85.9% respectively, giving an overall success rate of 79.75%. All patients with a Bishop score of 7 or greater ("easy inductions") were successfully induced no matter which compound was infused. For the patients with a Bishop score of 6 or less there was a good correlation between the effectiveness of $PGF_{2\alpha}$ or oxytocin in inducing labor and the assessment of inducibility of the patient. Thus in patients with a Bishop score of 5–6, 3–4, and 0–1–2, infusion of $PGF_{2\alpha}$ was 93.3%, 56%, and 40% effective respectively. The uterus appeared more sensitive to increased concentration of $PGF_{2\alpha}$ than it did to oxytocin, so attention was paid to careful adjustment of dosage rates to eliminate hypertonus and tachysytolia. Furthermore, uterine sensitivity to oxytocin and prostaglandin alters in a different way during pregnancy. Thus doses of prostaglandins which promote early abortion and induce labor at term differ by about tenfold, while the difference with oxytocin is much greater.

The mean infusion to delivery interval during $PGF_{2\alpha}$ infusion was shorter than during oxytocin infusion. In the difficult induction groups the values averaged 7.77

hr for $PGF_{2\alpha}$ and 9.17 hr for oxytocin. In the easy induction groups the time for delivery was decreased, but again $PGF_{2\alpha}$ offered the advantage over oxytocin of a shorter delivery time (4.5 vs 5.75 hr).

The conclusion of this study was that, with the dosages administered, $PGF_{2\alpha}$ was as effective as oxytocin for inducing labor in patients who had similar cervical characteristics. The compound appeared safe in that it had little effect on fetal heart rate, neonatal condition, or maternal vital signs. Side effects, such as superficial erythema at the site of infusion, nausea, and vomiting, have been reported.

In Africa, using $PGE_2$ (0.5–2.0 μg/min intravenously) Karim (55) reported the successful induction of labor in 90% of 400 patients. Infusing $PGF_{2\alpha}$ (5–10 μg/min intravenously), 93 of 100 patients were successfully induced. The average times for infusion to induction ranged from 7 to 17 hr. These results have been extended to include many more patients giving essentially the same results. A summary of the present status of induction of labor with prostaglandins has been made by Beazley (7).

ORAL ADMINISTRATION   Prostaglandins effectively induce labor at term whether administered orally, intravaginally, extraamniotically, or intraamniotically (59).

$PGF_{2\alpha}$ administered orally in a dose range of 5–25 mg in increasing doses every 2 hr until adequate uterine stimulation is attained, and then repeating that dose every 2 hr, results in effective delivery. $PGE_2$ has been used similarly within the range of 0.5–2.5 mg and effects induction with less side effects than those observed during $PGF_{2\alpha}$ administration. Using such a protocol, Karim & Sharma (56) effectively induced labor in 79 of 80 women who received $PGE_2$ and 16 of 20 women who received $PGF_{2\alpha}$. Other investigators (6, 25) have described the effectiveness of oral prostaglandins but also comment on a fairly high incidence of gastrointestinal disturbances. For this reason, it is generally considered that $PGF_{2\alpha}$ is intolerable in oral form whereas $PGE_2$ is acceptable. The efficacy of $PGE_2$ is enhanced if used together with amniotomy.

It is noteworthy that the prostaglandins have proved effective in both primigravida and multiparous women.

## Mechanism of Action

Prostaglandin-induced abortion during the first trimester of pregnancy could result from a luteolytic, uterotonic, or vascular effect. Numerous investigators have documented that prostaglandin-induced abortion is not preceded by a decrease in progestins, thus making it unlikely that prostaglandins are effective via a luteolytic effect. Thus Hillier & Embrey (46) followed plasma progesterone levels in 20 patients receiving $PGE_2$ or $PGF_{2\alpha}$ intravenously for termination of midtrimester pregnancies. There was no significant diminution in progesterone until after the abortion had occurred. Similarly, when $PGF_{2\alpha}$ is used to induce therapeutic abortion in the early pregnant human female (6–17 weeks gestation), it has been demonstrated that a significant decrease in the progestin levels did not occur until following the abortion; the decrease in plasma progestins was then identical with that which follows surgical evacuation of the uterus (100).

These results suggested that the prostaglandins do not exert a luteolytic effect in the human. Perhaps the most definitive study was that of Speroff and associates who monitored plasma levels of unconjugated estrone, $17\beta$-estradiol, estriol, progesterone, 17 hydroxyprogesterone, HCG, and human chorionic somatomammotropin in patients 7–20 weeks pregnant during infusion of $PGF_{2\alpha}$ for therapeutic abortion (91). A significant decrease in estriol levels preceded a decrease in estradiol levels during the prostaglandin infusion. No significant changes in progesterone were seen prior to the abortion. These authors considered the possibility that the decrease in estriol during prostaglandin infusion reflected changes within the fetus which could have resulted from the hypoxia produced in the fetal-placental unit by the hypertonus resulting from the prostaglandin infusion. The tentative conclusion is that the prostaglandins are effective in inducing abortions by virtue of their ability to stimulate smooth muscle.

It has been a general observation through all the studies concerned with administration of prostaglandins to effect abortion that stimulation of uterine activity is one of the most sensitive responses recorded; however, the magnitude of the contraction appears to vary with different stages of pregnancy. Thus when 20 subjects of 6–8 weeks gestation were infused with $PGF_{2\alpha}$ to effect an abortion, 19 of the subjects aborted concomitant with a good contractile effect on the uterine myometrium, producing pressure as high as 200 mm Hg. Studies with subjects of 9–17 weeks gestation were not so consistent, in that only 8 of 16 subjects were effectively aborted by infusion of $PGF_{2\alpha}$. At this stage of gestation $PGF_{2\alpha}$ did not produce such a strong oxytocic effect, for pressures of only 30–50 mm Hg were recorded; the difference in pressures related to the difference in diameter of the uterus at the different stages of gestation (100).

Examination of the uterine blood vessels after giving X-ray contrast media and 100 $\mu$g $PGE_1$ intravenously revealed no difference in the vascular pattern of the tissue; this suggested that the increase in uterine tone associated with prostaglandin infusion was not likely to result from ischaemia of the tissue.

It has been reported that in 7 women with intrauterine death in the third trimester of pregnancy, intravenous infusion of 500 ml of 10% ethanol over a 60 min period inhibited uterine activity stimulated by infusion of $PGE_2$ or $PGF_{2\alpha}$. Ethanol is considered to be effective by reducing release of oxytocin from the posterior pituitary, so these results could be interpreted as an indication that prostaglandins may stimulate release of oxytocin from the pituitary, and oxytocin may contribute to the uterine stimulation associated with prostaglandin infusion (57). Gillespie (37) measured circulating oxytocin during prostaglandin infusion and obtained direct evidence that prostaglandins could elicit release of oxytocin from the pituitary.

We are left, however, with the knowledge that the ability of prostaglandins to stimulate myometrial activity is undoubtedly the main mechanism whereby the prostaglandins so effectively terminate pregnancy.

The basic biochemical mechanism whereby prostaglandins stimulate uterine smooth muscle is not totally understood at present. Many of the actions of prostaglandins have been identified with changes in the intracellular levels of cAMP.

Harbon & Clauser (42) have demonstrated that $PGE_1$ and $PGE_2$ stimulate adenyl cyclase activity in rat uteri in vitro, indicating that the prostaglandins would increase cAMP in this tissue. It has been reported that PGE compounds increase uterine cAMP in vivo, an effect dependent upon the hormonal state of the animal, prostaglandins being maximally effective in estrous animals (64). However, in both these studies, $PGF_{2\alpha}$ proved ineffective in modifying adenyl cylase/cAMP, yet $PGF_{2\alpha}$ is known to be an effective uterine stimulant. These data, together with those of Robison (84), who has shown that extracellular cAMP actually relaxes uterine smooth muscle, are inconsistent with the concept that prostaglandins stimulate myometrium via stimulation of adenyl cyclase. The experimental evidence to date thus indicates that an alternative mechanism must be involved in the mediation of prostaglandin stimulation of uterine smooth muscle. It is generally accepted that uterine smooth muscle needs calcium for maximal contraction (16), as do skeletal and heart muscle. The role for calcium in the action of prostaglandins has received much attention but has not yet been defined; extracellular calcium is required for manifestation of many of the pharmacological effects of the prostaglandins and it has been postulated that $PGE_1$ can function as a calcium ionophore (62). Carsten (19) has reported that, when using isolated sarcoplasmic reticulum prepared from bovine or human uterine tissue, both $PGE_2$ and $PGF_{2\alpha}$ decrease ATP-dependent calcium binding and increase calcium release from these preparations. It is thus feasible that the prostaglandins could regulate intracellular calcium transport, an effect that may explain their effect on uterine motility.

## PHYSIOLOGICAL IMPLICATIONS OF PROSTAGLANDINS IN THE HUMAN REPRODUCTIVE TRACT

The knowledge that the prostaglandins are found in high concentrations in seminal fluid and that most reproductive tissues can biosynthesize prostaglandins has led to the concept that these endogenous compounds may play a significant role in reproductive physiology.

It has been suggested that prostaglandins may contribute to the normal parturition process in humans (51); this possibility has recently been reinvestigated by Sharma and associates (87), who continuously monitored $PGF_{2\alpha}$ levels in maternal peripheral venous plasma during normal labor. Maximum $PGF_{2\alpha}$ concentration occurred 15–45 sec after the peak in intensity of uterine contraction. Having established that the maternal circulation time from uterus to antecubital vein ranged from 30–55 sec, it was concluded that $PGF_{2\alpha}$ was released into the circulation after onset of a contraction and thus could not be identified as a causative factor for the contraction. Release of prostaglandins from spontaneously contracting myometrium has also been detected in vitro (65).

In addition, prostaglandins have been detected in amniotic fluid in the second trimester of pregnancy (77) and during labor (51). These observations do not as yet support the essentiality of prostaglandins in the process of parturition, but the availability of inhibitors of both prostaglandin biosynthesis and action should aid in elucidating their contribution. $PGF_{2\alpha}$ has been detected in maternal serum during human pregnancy; the amounts vary with the stage of gestation, increasing as pregnancy progresses and peaking during the second trimester. Toward the end of the third trimester, the serum levels approximated those of nonpregnant women (41).

Prostaglandins affect oviduct motility in the human (23). When 100 $\mu$g $PGE_2$ or $PGF_{2\alpha}$ was adminstered intravenously to 8 women uterine contractions were observed, but the different prostaglandins produced different effects on motility of the Fallopian tubes. Thus $PGE_2$ induced relaxation of the tubes, while $PGF_{2\alpha}$ was an effective stimulant. Prostaglandins have also been shown to modify transport in the rabbit (31), though whether these effects on the Fallopian tubes or ovum transport mimic normal physiological processes is not known.

The de novo synthesis of $PGF_{2\alpha}$ in ovarian and uterine tissue from rabbits and monkey has been studied (98). The results indicate that prostaglandin biosynthesis may be under hormonal control, for endogenous levels of $PGF_{2\alpha}$ in monkey ovary were increased by addition of LH. Similarly 17$\beta$-estradiol stimulated prostaglandin biosynthesis in monkey myometrium but had little effect on the endometrial biosynthesis. Studies in the macaca monkey in vivo (3) indicated that administration of estrogen (an effective postovulatory antifertility agent) in the luteal phase of the menstrual cycle resulted in a rapid decline of progesterone levels in the peripheral plasma with a concomitant rise in PGF levels in peripheral plasma, possibly implicating the prostaglandins in this antifertility effect, though more work is needed to elucidate this point.

The human menstruating endometrium produces approximately 1 $\mu$g/g $PGF_{2\alpha}$ during three days of menses (83). It is tempting to speculate that there is some relationship between steroid control of prostaglandin biosynthesis and perhaps control of uterine contractility and/or the process of menstruation.

Use of inhibitors of prostaglandin biosynthesis has led to the suggestion that prostaglandins may play an essential role in the action of certain hormones. We have discussed the evidence pertaining to the role which prostaglandins may play in LH stimulation of ovarian tissue; evidence is also accumulating that prostaglandins may form an essential link in the mechanism whereby the hypothalamic releasing factors elicit release of trophic hormones from the anterior pituitary. Orczyk & Behrman (76) have demonstrated that 9.5 mg/kg twice a day of indomethacin for 56 hr decreased the PGF content of the pituitary and hypothalamus of rats; these effects were associated with inhibition of ovulation which was partially reversed by administration of LH, but not prostaglandin. The inference from these studies was that the endogenous prostaglandins of the hypothalamus or pituitary may be involved in the release of LH prior to ovulation.

With the availability of improved inhibitors of prostaglandin biosynthesis and prostaglandin action, and the development of specific and sensitive techniques to accurately determine the prostaglandin content of tissues during different physiological states, changes in prostaglandin dynamics will undoubtedly be implicated in many physiological processes.

## Male Reproductive Tract

There are few publications describing the effects of prostaglandins on male reproductive processes, although the pharmacological activity identified with the prostaglandins was originally discovered in human semen. The seminal vesicles are the richest source of prostaglandins; the vesicular glands of sheep have been the source of the enzyme utilized for study of the mechanism of biosynthesis of the prostaglandins in vitro. Some 13 different prostaglandins have been identified in human semen, but the smooth muscle stimulating activity is mainly due to $PGE_1$, $PGE_2$, $PGF_{1\alpha}$, and $PGF_{2\alpha}$. Attempts have been made to correlate the prostaglandin content of semen to male fertility but no significant correlation between a low prostaglandin concentration and decreased sperm content, sperm motility, capacitation, morphological abnormalities, or fertility has been described. Addition of exogenous prostaglandins to semen of subfertile males did not result in conception following artificial insemination. Thus the function of the high levels of seminal prostaglandins in primates remains unknown. Seminal prostaglandins may modify adenyl cyclase, an enzyme present in sperm, or the prostaglandins may facilitate the passage of sperm through the female cervix and into the oviduct for fertilization. The content of prostaglandins in semen has been experimentally reduced by administering 2.4 g aspirin daily for 7 days to normal male subjects. There was a significant decrease in both PGE and PGF compounds without any decrease in seminal volume. Unfortunately no fertility study was associated with this experiment (21).

Sturde (92) has reported that cyproterane acetate, an antiandrogen, causes a fourfold increase in seminal prostaglandin content. He suggests that this occurs reflexly through enhancement of gonadotropin secretion resulting in an increase in testicular androgen production. This suggests that prostaglandin synthetase in the human seminal vesicles is sensitive to androgens, providing a situation somewhat analogous to that in the female reproductive tract, inasmuch as $17\beta$-estradiol has been shown to stimulate prostaglandin biosynthesis in the myometrium of the monkey (98).

Intraarterial infusion of $PGE_2$ to the testes of the dog augments testosterone secretion induced by human chorionic gonadotropin or cAMP (30); it was considered that the prostaglandins could be effective by a vascular mechanism. Infusions of prostaglandins into the testes or the testicular artery of the rat have been demonstrated to increase venous pressure and decrease blood flow in the testes of the conscious rat (35). In the halothane anesthetized rat, $PGF_{2\alpha}$ produced a highly significant decrease in blood flow and reduced testosterone secretion. It remains to be determined whether this effect of $PGF_{2\alpha}$ on steroid secretion results from initial changes in blood flow or from a direct effect on the secreting cells (see 88). Thus in the testes as well as the ovary it is possible that initial responses resulting from effects of the prostaglandins on the vasculature confuse the interpretation of the direct effects of prostaglandin on cellular secretion.

Finally, it has been shown that prostaglandins can effectively stimulate the smooth muscle of the rabbit testicular capsule and modify blood flow (43). In comparison with the role of prostaglandins in the female, their role in the male reproductive tract has received little attention; it remains intriguing as to why the male accessory glands have the capacity to biosynthesize such large quantities of such potent compounds.

## SUMMARY

Prostaglandins can modify more than one function within the same tissue. Thus, in the ovary, one can elicit an effect on blood flow and one can also demonstrate either an increase or decrease in steroidogenesis, both in vitro and in vivo, by modifying the conditions of the experiment. Since it has been demonstrated that there is more than one site of action for applied prostaglandins, it becomes essential to stress the importance of using single cell types when concerned with evaluation of the mechanism of prostaglandin action.

Many of the actions of the prostaglandins have been identified with changes in intracellular levels of cAMP, yet their action on uterine smooth muscle has not been identified with such an effect. The action of prostaglandins in stimulating smooth muscle (which appears to be the basis for their effect in terminating pregnancy) is not as yet defined, but has been identified with changes in calcium movements in the uterine tissue.

Elucidation of the precise mechanism of action of prostaglandins in pharmacological doses, together with the availability of new and improved inhibitors of prostaglandin biosynthesis, could lead to the possibility of manipulation and control of the endogenous prostaglandins and thereby to modification of tissue function. Alternatively, the synthesis of improved analogues of the prostaglandins with limited undesirable pharmacological properties should make a significant contribution to therapy within the reproductive field during the next decade.

*Literature Cited*

1. Anderson, G. G., Hobbins, J. C., Rajkovic, V., Speroff, L., Caldwell, B. V. 1972. Midtrimester abortion using intraamniotic prostaglandin $F_{2\alpha}$. *Prostaglandins* 1:147–55
2. Anderson, G. G., Hobbins, J. C., Speroff, L. 1972. Intravenous prostaglandins $E_2$ and $F_{2\alpha}$ for the induction of term labour. *Am. J. Obstet. Gynecol.* 112:382–86
3. Auletta, F. J., Caldwell, B. V., van Wagenen, G., Morris, J. M. 1972. Effects of postovulatory oestrogen on progesterone and prostaglandin F levels in the monkey. *Contraception* 6:411–21
4. Auletta, F. J., Speroff, L., Caldwell, B. V. 1973. Prostaglandin $F_2$ induced steroidogenesis and luteolysis in the primate corpus luteum. *J. Clin. Endocrinol. Metab.* 36:405–7
5. Armstrong, D. T., Grinwich, D. L. 1972. Blockade of spontaneous and LH induced ovulation in rats by indomethacin, an inhibitor of prostaglandin biosynthesis. *Prostaglandins* 1:21–28
6. Barr, W., Naismith, W. C. M. K. 1972. Oral prostaglandins in the induction of labor. *Brit. Med. J.* 2:188–91
7. Beazley, J. M. 1972. In *The Prostaglandins. Clinical Applications in Human Reproduction,* ed. E. M. Southern, 529. New York: Futura
8. Beguin, F., Bygdeman, M., Toppozada, M., Wiqvist, N. 1972. The response of the midpregnant human uterus to vaginal administration of prostaglandin suppositories. *Prostaglandins* 1:397–405
9. Behrman, H. R., MacDonald, G. J., Greep, R. O. 1971. Regulation of ovarian cholesterol esters: evidence for the enzymatic sites of prostaglandin induced loss of corpus luteum function. *Lipids* 6:791–96

10. Behrman, H. R., Yoshinaga, K., Greep, R. O. 1971. Extraluteal effects of prostaglandins. *Ann. NY Acad. Sci.* 180: 426–35

11. Behrman, H. R., Yoshinaga, K., Wyman, H., Greep, R. O. 1971. Effects of prostaglandin on ovarian steroid secretion and biosynthesis during pregnancy. *Am. J. Physiol.* 221:189–93

12. Behrman, H. R., Orczyk, G. P., Greep, R. O. 1972. Effect of synthetic gonadotrophin-releasing hormone (Gn-RH) on ovulation blockade by aspirin and indomethacin. *Prostaglandins* 1: 245–58

13. Bishop, E. H. 1964. Pelvic scoring for elective induction. *Obstet. Gynecol.* 24:266–68

14. Blatchley, F. R., Donovan, B. T. 1969. Luteolytic effect of prostaglandin in the guinea pig. *Nature London* 221: 1065–66

15. Brenner, W. E., Hendricks, C. H., Braaksma, J. T., Fishburne, J. I. Jr., Staurovsky, L. G. 1972. Vaginal administration of prostaglandin $F_{2\alpha}$ for inducing therapeutic abortion. *Prostaglandins* 1:455–67

16. Briggs, A. H., Hannah, H. B. 1965. Calcium magnesium and ATP interaction in glycerinated uterine smooth muscle. In *Muscle, Proc. Symp. Fzc. Med., Univ. Alberta, June 1–4, 1964,* ed. W. M. Paul, E. E. Daniel, E. M. Kay, G. Mounkton, 287–94. New York Pergamon

17. Bygdeman, M., Wiqvist, N. 1971. Early abortion in the human. *Ann. NY Acad. Sci.* 180:473–82

18. Bygdeman, M., Bëguin, F., Toppozada, M., Wiqvist, N. 1972. Intraamniotic administration of prostaglandin $F_{2\alpha}$ for the induction of second trimester abortion. In *Prostaglandins in Fertility Control,* ed. S. Bergström, K. Gréen, B. Samuelson, 2:129–36. Stockholm: W.H.O. Karolinska Institutet

19. Carsten, M. E. 1972. Prostaglandins part in regulating uterine contraction by transport of calcium. *J. Reprod. Med.* 9:277–81

20. Chasalow, F. I., Pharriss, B. B. 1972. Luteinizing hormone stimulation of ovarian prostaglandin biosynthesis. *Prostaglandins* 1:107–17

21. Collier, J. G., Flower, R. T. 1971. Effect of aspirin on human seminal prostaglandins. *Lancet* 2:852–52

22. Corson, S. L., Bolognese, R. J., Merola, J. 1973. Intraamniotic prostaglandin $F_{2\alpha}$ to induce midtrimester abortion. *Am. J. Obstet. Gynecol.* 117:27–34

23. Coutinho, E. M., Maia, H. S. 1971. The contractile response of the human uterus, Fallopian tubes and ovary to prostaglandins in vivo. *Fert. Steril.* 22: 539–43

24. Coyotupa, J., Buster, J., Parlow, A. F., Dignam, W. J. 1972. Normal cyclical patterns of serum gonadotropins and ovarian steroids despite congential absence of the uterus. *J. Clin. Endocrinol. Metabol.* 36:395–96

25. Craft, I. 1972. Amniotomy and oral prostaglandin $E_2$ titration for induction of labor. *Brit. Med. J.* 2:191–94

26. Csapo, A. I., Ruttner, B., Wiest, W. G. 1972. First trimester abortions induced by a single extraovular injection of prostaglandin $F_{2\alpha}$. *Prostaglandins* 1:365–71

27. Csapo, A. I., Mocsary, P., Nagy, T., Kaihola, H. L. 1973. The efficacy and acceptability of the "prostaglandin impact" in inducing complete abortion during the second week after a missed menstrual period. *Prostaglandins* 3: 125–39

28. Demers, L. M., Behrman, H. R., Greep, R. O. 1972. See Ref. 82, 28:73–75

29. Ducharme, D. W., Weeks, J. R., Montgomery, R. G. 1965. Studies on the mechanism of the hypertensive effect of prostaglandin $F_{2\alpha}$. *J. Pharmacol. Exp. Ther.* 160:1–10

30. Eik-Nes, K. B. 1969. Patterns of steroidogenesis in the vertebrate gonad. *Gen. Comp. Endocrinol. Suppl.* 2:87

31. Ellinger, J. V., Kirton, K. T. 1972. Ovum transport in rabbits injected with prostaglandins $E_1$ or $F_{2\alpha}$. *Biol. Reprod.* 7:106

32. Embrey, M. P. 1970. Induction of abortion by prostaglandins $E_1$ and $E_2$. *Brit. Med. J.* 2:258–60

33. Embrey, M. P., Hillier, K. 1971. Therapeutic abortion by intrauterine instillation of prostaglandins. *Brit. Med. J.* 1:588–90

34. Embrey, M. P., Hillier, K., Mahendran, P. 1972. Induction of abortion by extraamniotic administration of prostaglandins $E_2$ and $F_{2\alpha}$. *Brit. Med. J.* 3:146–49

35. Free, M. J., Jaffe, R. A. 1972. Effect of prostaglandins on blood flow and pressure in the testis of the conscious rat. Personal communication

36. Gillespie, A. 1971. Use of prostaglandins for induction of abortion and labor. *Ann. NY Acad. Sci.* 180:524–27

37. Gillespie, A. 1972. Prostaglandinoxytocin enhancement and potentiation and their clinical applications. *Brit. Med. J.* 1:150–52

38. Gutknecht, G. D., Cornette, J. C., Pharriss, B. B. 1969. Antifertility properties of prostaglandin $F_{2\alpha}$. *Biol. Reprod.* 1:367–71

39. Gutknecht, G. D., Duncan, G. W., Wyngarden, L. J. 1970. Effect of prostaglandin $F_{2\alpha}$ on ovarian blood flow in the rabbit as measured by hydrogen desaturation. *Physiologist* 13:214

40. Gutknecht, G. D., Duncan, G. W., Wyngarden, L. J. 1971. Inhibition of prostaglandin $F_{2\alpha}$ or LH-induced luteolysis by 17 β-estradiol. *Biol. Reprod.* 5:87

41. Gutierrez-Cernosek, R. M., Zuckerman, J., Levine, L. 1972. Prostaglandin $F_{2\alpha}$ levels in sera during human pregnancy. *Prostaglandins* 1:331–37

42. Harbon, S., Clauser, H. 1971. Cyclic adenosine 3',5' monophosphate levels in rat myometrium under the influence of epinephrine prostaglandins and oxytocin. Correlations with uterus motility. *Biochem. Biophys. Res. Commun.* 44:1496–1503

43. Hargrove, J. L., Johnson, J. M., Ellis, L. C. 1971. PGE₁ induced inhibition of rabbit testicular contractions in vitro. *Proc. Soc. Exp. Biol. Med.* 136:958

44. Henzl, M. R., Ortega, E., Cortés-Gallegos, V., Tomlinson, R. V., Segre, E. J. 1973. Prostaglandin E₂ and the luteal phase of the menstrual cycle: effects on blood progesterone estradiol, cortisol and growth hormone levels. *J. Clin. Endocrinol. Metab.* 36:784–87

45. Hillier, K., Dutton, A., Corker, C. S., Singer, A., Embrey, M. P. 1972. Plasma steroid and luteinizing hormone levels during prostaglandin $F_{2\alpha}$ administration in the luteal phase of menstrual cycle. *Brit. Med. J.* 4:333–36

46. Hillier, K., Embrey, M. P. 1972. High dose intravenous administration of prostaglandin E₂ and $F_{2\alpha}$ for the termination of midtrimester pregnancies. *J. Obstet. Gynaecol. Brit. Commonw.* 79:14–22

47. Hinman, J. W. 1972. Prostaglandins. *Ann. Rev. Biochem.* 41:161–78

48. Jewelewicz, R., Cantor, B., Dyrenfurth, I., Warren, M. P., Vande Wiele, R. 1972. Intravenous infusion of prostaglandin $F_{2\alpha}$ in the mid-luteal phase of the normal human menstrual cycle. *Prostaglandins* 1:443–51

49. Johnston, J. O., Hunter, K. K. 1970. In vivo interaction of prostaglandin $F_{2\alpha}$ with hamster luteotropic complex. *Abstr. Meet. Soc. Study Reprod., 3rd, Columbus, September 9–11, 1970,* 30

50. Jonsson, H. T. Jr., Shelton, V. L., Baggett, B. 1972. Stimulation of adenyl cyclase by prostaglandin in rabbit corpus luteum. *Biol. Reprod.* 7:197. Abstr.

51. Karim, S. M. M. 1968. Appearance of prostaglandin $F_{2\alpha}$ in human blood during labor. *Brit. Med. J.* 4:618–21

52. Karim, S. M. M., Trussell, R. R., Hillier, K., Patel, R. C. 1969. Induction of labor with prostaglandin $F_{2\alpha}$. *J. Obstet. Gynaecol. Brit. Commonw.* 76:769–82

53. Karim, S. M. M., Filshie, G. M. 1970. Therapeutic abortion using prostaglandin $F_{2\alpha}$. *Lancet* 1:157–59

54. Karim, S. M. M., Filshie, G. M. 1970. Use of prostaglandin E₂ for therapeutic abortion. *Brit. Med. J.* 3:198–200

55. Karim, S. M. M. 1971. Action of prostaglandin in the pregnant woman. *Ann. NY Acad. Sci.* 180:483–98

56. Karim, S. M. M., Sharma, S. D. 1971. Oral administration of prostaglandins for the induction of labor. *Brit. Med. J.* 1:260–62

57. Karim, S. M. M., Sharma, S. D. 1971. The effect of ethyl alcohol on prostaglandins E₂ and $F_{2\alpha}$ induced uterine activity in pregnant women. *J. Obstet. Gynaecol. Brit. Commonw.* 78:251–54

58. Karim, S. M. M., Sharma, S. D. 1971. Therapeutic abortion and induction of labor by the intravaginal administration of prostaglandins E₂ and $F_{2\alpha}$. *J. Obstet. Gynaecol. Brit. Commonw.* 78:294–300

59. Karim, S. M. M. 1972. Prostaglandins and human reproduction: physiological roles and clinical uses of prostaglandins in relation to human reproduction. In *The Prostaglandins Progress in Research,* ed. S. M. M. Karim, 71–164. Oxford: MTP Med. Tech. Publ. Co.

60. Karim, S. M. M., Sharma, S. D. 1972. Termination of second trimester pregnancy with 15 methyl analogues of prostaglandins E₂ and $PGF_{2\alpha}$. *J. Obstet. Gynaecol. Brit. Commonw.* 79:737–43

61. Kaufman, R. G., Greeman, R. K., Mishell, D. R. Jr. 1971. Abortifacient activity of intravenously administered prostaglandins. *Contraception* 3:121–32

62. Kirtland, S. J., Baum, H. 1972. Prostaglandin E₁ may act as a "calcium ionophore." *Nature New Biol.* 236:47–49

63. Kirton, K. T., Pharriss, B. B., Forbes, A. D. 1970. Luteolytic effects of prostaglandin $F_{2\alpha}$ in primates. *Proc. Soc. Exp. Biol. Med.* 133:314–16

64. Kirton, K. T., Gutknecht, G. D., Bergström, K. K., Wyngarden, L. J., Forbes,

A. D. 1972. Prostaglandins and reproduction. See Ref. 7, p. 37

65. Kloeck, F. K., Jung, H. 1973. In vitro release of prostaglandins from the human myometrium under the influence of stretching. *Am. J. Obstet. Gynecol.* 115:1066–69

66. Kolena, J., Channing, C. P. 1972. Stimulatory effects of LH, FSH and prostaglandins upon cyclic 3',5'-AMP levels in porcine granulosa cells. *Endocrinology* 90:1543–50

67. Kuehl, F. A. Jr., Humes, J. L., Tarnoff, J., Cirillo, V. J., Ham, E. A. 1970. Prostaglandin receptor site: evidence for an essential role in the action of luteinizing hormone. *Science* 169:883–86

68. Lehman, F., Peters, F., Breckwoldt, M., Bettendorf, G. 1972. Plasma progesterone levels during infusion of prostaglandin $F_{2\alpha}$ in the human. *Prostaglandins* 1:269–77

69. LeMaire, W. J., Shapiro, A. G. 1972. Prostaglandin $F_{2\alpha}$: its effect on the corpus luteum of the menstrual cycle. *Prostaglandins* 1:259–67

70. Marsh, J. 1971. The effect of prostaglandins on the adenyl cyclase of the bovine corpus luteum. *Ann. NY Acad. Sci.* 180:416–25

71. Mazer, R., Hansel, W. L. 1972. See Ref. 82, 28:63

72. McCracken, J. 1971. Prostaglandin and corpus luteum regression. *Ann. NY Acad. Sci.* 180:456–69

73. McCracken, J. A. et al 1972. Prostaglandin $F_{2\alpha}$ identified as a luteolytic hormone in sheep. *Nature New Biol.* 238:129–34

74. Miller, A. W. F., Calder, A. A., Macnaughton, M. C. 1972. Termination of pregnancy by continuous intrauterine infusion of prostaglandins. *Lancet* 2: 5–7

75. O'Grady, J. P. et al 1972. Inhibition of progesterone synthesis in vitro by prostaglandin $F_{2\alpha}$. *J. Reprod. Fert.* 30: 153–56

76. Orczyk, G. P., Behrmann, H. R. 1972. Ovulation blockade by aspirin or indomethacin. *In vivo* evidence for a role of prostaglandin in gonadotrophin secretion. *Prostaglandins* 1: 3–20

77. Pace Asciak, C., Wolfe, L. S., Gillett, P. G., Kinch, R. A. 1972. Disappearance of prostaglandin $F_{2\alpha}$ from human amniotic fluid after intraamniotic injection. *Prostaglandins* 1:469–71

78. Pharriss, B. B., Wyngarden, L. J., Gutknecht, G. D. 1968. Biological interactions between prostaglandins and

luteotropins in the rat. In *Gonadotropins 1968,* ed. E. Rosenberg, 121–29. Los Altos: Geron-X

79. Pharriss, B. B., Wyngarden, L. J. 1969. The effect of prostaglandin $F_{2\alpha}$ on the progestogen content of ovaries from pseudopregnant rats. *Proc. Soc. Exp. Biol. Med.* 130:92–94

80. Pharriss, B. B., Cornette, J. C., Gutknecht, G. D. 1970. Vascular control of luteal steroidogenesis. *J. Reprod. Fert. Suppl.* 10:97–103

81. Pharriss, B. B., Hunter, K. K. 1971. Interrelationships of prostaglandin $F_{2\alpha}$ and gonadotropins in the immature female rat. *Proc. Soc. Exp. Biol. Med.* 136:503–6

82. Pharriss, B. B., Tillson, S. A., Erickson, R. R. 1972. Prostaglandins in luteal function. *Recent Progr. Horm. Res.* 28:51–89

83. Pickles, V. R., Hall, W. J., Best, F. A., Smith, G. N. 1965. Prostaglandins in endometrium and menstrual fluid from normal and dysmenorrhoeic subjects. *J. Obstet. Gynaecol. Brit. Commonw.* 72:185–92

84. Robison, G. A. 1968. *Proc. Int. Congr. Physiol. Sci., 24th, Washington DC* 6: 165

85. Roth-Brandel, U., Bygdeman, M., Wiqvist, N., Bergström, S. 1970. Prostaglandins for induction of therapeutic abortion. *Lancet* 1:190–91

86. Sellner, R. G., Wickersham, E. W. 1970. Effects of prostaglandins on steroidogenesis. *J. Anim. Sci.* 31:230

87. Sharma, S. C., Hibbard, B. M., Hamlett, J. D., Fitzpatrick, R. J. 1973. Prostaglandin $F_{2\alpha}$ concentrations in peripheral blood during the first stage of normal labour. *Brit. Med. J.* 1:709–11

88. Shaw, J. E., Tillson, S. A. 1973. Interactions between the prostaglandins and steroid hormones. In *Steroids and Pharmacology.* In press

89. Southern, E. H., Ed. See Ref. 7

90. Speroff, L., Ramwell, P. W. 1970. Prostaglandin stimulation of *in vitro* progesterone synthesis. *J. Clin. Endocrinol. Metab.* 30:345–50

91. Speroff, L., Caldwell, B. V., Brock, W. A., Anderson, G. G., Hobbins, J. C. 1972. Hormone levels during prostaglandin $F_{2\alpha}$ infusions for therapeutic abortion. *J. Clin. Endocrinol.* 34: 531–36

92. Sturde, H. C. 1971. The effect of cyproteron therapy on the semen and the sperm prostaglandins production in young men. *Arch. Derm. Forsch.* 241:86

93. Toppozada, M., Bygdeman, M., Wiqvist, N. 1971. Induction of abortion by intraamniotic administration of prostaglandin $F_{2\alpha}$. *Contraception* 4:293-303

94. Tsafriri, A., Lindner, H. R., Zor, U., Lamprecht, S. A. 1972. *In vitro* induction of meiotic division in follicle-enclosed rat oocytes by LH, cyclic AMP and prostaglandin $E_2$. *J. Reprod. Fert.* 31:39-50

95. Vane, J. R. 1971. Inhibition of prostaglandin synthesis as a mechanism of action for aspirin-like drugs. *Nature New Biol.* 231:232-35

96. Weeks, J. R. 1972. Prostaglandins. *Ann. Rev. Pharmacol.* 12:317-36

97. Wentz, A. C., Cushner, I. M., Austin, K., Shams, M. 1972. Intraamniotic administration of prostaglandin $F_{2\alpha}$ for abortion. *Am. J. Obstet. Gynecol.* 113:793-803

98. Wilks, J. W., Forbes, K. K., Norland, J. F. 1972. Synthesis of prostaglandin $F_{2\alpha}$ by the ovary and uterus. *J. Reprod. Med.* 9:271-76

99. Wiqvist, N., Bygdeman, M. 1970. Therapeutic abortion by local administration of prostaglandin. *Lancet* 2:716-17

100. Wiqvist, N., Bygdeman, M., Kirton, K. T. 1971. Nonsteroidal antifertility agents in the female. In *Nobel Symposium 15. Control of Human Fertility,* ed. E. Diczfalusy, U. Borell, p. 137. New York: Wiley

101. Wiqvist, N., Bygdeman, M., Toppozada, M. 1971. Induction of abortion by the intravenous administration of prostaglandin $F_{2\alpha}$. *Acta Obstet. Gynecol. Scand.* 50:381-89

102. Wiqvist, N., Beguin, F., Bygdeman, M., Toppozada, M. 1972. Extra-amniotic administration of prostaglandin for induction of abortion. See Ref. 18, 2:118-25

103. Zor, U. et al 1972. Functional relations between cyclic AMP prostaglandins and luteinizing hormone in rat pituitary and ovary. *Advan. Cyclic Nucl. Res.* 1:503-20

# RELATIONSHIP BETWEEN CARBOHYDRATE AND LIPID METABOLISM AND THE ENERGY BALANCE OF HEART MUSCLE[1]

❖1118

*James R. Neely and Howard E. Morgan*
Department of Physiology, The Milton S. Hershey Medical Center, The Pennsylvania State University, Hershey, Pennsylvania

## INTRODUCTION

Utilization of carbohydrate and fatty acids is strongly influenced by rates of consumption and production of high energy compounds in cardiac muscle. In well-oxygenated hearts, fatty acid has been identified as the preferred substrate by both in vivo and in vitro studies (for review see 146). Availability of fatty acid suppresses glucose utilization by inhibition of several steps in the glycolytic pathway. Since a variety of long- and short-chained fatty substrates are inhibitory and since the effect is abolished in hearts perfused under anaerobic conditions, oxidation of the fatty acid appears to be required for this effect. When energy utilization of well-oxygenated hearts is increased, consumption of fatty acids and/or glucose is accelerated. Under these conditions, fatty acids remain the preferred oxidative substrate.

Availability of oxygen to the heart can be restricted either by lowering or reducing to zero the oxygen tension of the perfusate, thereby inducing hypoxia or anoxia, or by restricting the flow of perfusate containing high oxygen tensions to induce ischemia. In hypoxic or anoxic hearts, fatty acid oxidation is suppressed and glycolysis is stimulated. The acceleration of flux through glycolysis may be as much as 10- to 20-fold. On the other hand, ischemia results in only a transient increase in glycolytic flux that is followed within 3–4 min by inhibition. Fatty acid oxidation is suppressed in ischemic hearts leading to accumulation of long-chained CoA derivatives and increase in triglyceride levels.

[1]Supported by PHS Grants 5R01-HL-13029 and 2R01-HL-13028 and Contract NIH-NHLI-71-2499.

413

The purpose of this article is to identify steps in the pathways of glycolysis and fatty acid oxidation that serve important rate-controlling functions. Effects of cardiac work, hypoxia, anoxia, and ischemia on these reactions are described and an attempt is made to identify regulatory factors responsible for the change in utilization of carbohydrate and fatty acid. Effects of insulin on glucose and glycogen metabolism are mentioned, but, in general, hormonal control of these pathways is not included in the scope of this review. We focus on regulation of the production of acetyl-CoA from glucose and fatty acids. Control of the oxidation of this intermediate through the citric acid cycle is discussed only briefly. The primary purpose of the review is to relate increased energy consumption to accelerated utilization of carbohydrates and fatty acids and to contrast the effects of energy deprivation on glycolysis in anoxic and ischemic hearts.

## METHODS FOR THE STUDY OF REGULATION OF METABOLIC PATHWAYS IN INTACT TISSUES

### Preparations of Heart Muscle Available for Study

Adequate control of substrate and hormone levels, oxygen tension, rates of ventricular pressure development, and coronary flow has been most effectively achieved in isolated perfused hearts (133, 145), frequently of rats. Perfused tissue offers many advantages over heart slices, ventricular or atrial strips, papillary muscles, and homogenates for studies of the regulation of carbohydrate and fatty acid metabolism. In the perfused heart, substrates, hormones, and oxygen are delivered to the cells via an intact capillary circulation. Sufficient tissue is available to simplify measurements of substrate uptake and levels of metabolites. Since cell membranes are intact, regulation of substrate utilization by changes in membrane permeability is retained. In well-oxygenated preparations, ventricular performance is stable for periods in excess of 3 hr. The major limitation of the perfused heart as compared to heart cells in culture (81, 205) involves the period over which experiments are feasible. Although isolated hearts have been maintained for weeks, experiments exceeding several hours are not practical on a large scale. This limitation is not of great importance for studies of most aspects of carbohydrate and lipid metabolism, but does make studies of enzyme induction or of reparative processes difficult.

Isolated hearts are most often perfused by the Langendorff technique (see 143). Modifications of this method allow recirculation of a small volume of perfusate, usually Krebs-Henseleit bicarbonate buffer, from which substrate disappearance can be estimated. In addition, perfusate can be allowed to flow through the heart a single time to provide an unchanged supply of substrate and to prevent accumulation of metabolic products. In these latter experiments glucose utilization and fatty acid oxidation can be estimated by measuring conversion of specifically-tritiated glucose and $^{14}C$-fatty acid to $^3H_2O$ and $^{14}CO_2$. In the Langendorff preparation perfusate is supplied over a range of pressures by retrograde flow down the aorta. Unless special efforts are made to drain the left ventricle, intraventricular pressure increases to levels slightly above the perfusion pressure with each beat. Pressure development depends upon a limited degree of ventricular filling, arising either from the Thebesian circulation or from incompetence of the aortic valve due to use of low viscosity perfusate. Intraventricular pressure development in the Langendorff preparation can be increased by raising perfusion pressure. Increased pressure development is associated with increased oxygen consumption and accelerated utilization of carbohydrate and lipid. Since coronary flow is a linear function of perfusion pressure and ventricular pressure development, these parameters cannot be dissociated in this preparation. Anoxia or hypoxia is induced by exposing the perfusate to gas mixtures containing either zero or reduced oxygen tension.

The major disadvantage of the Langendorff preparation is the inability to vary levels of external cardiac work during perfusion. This difficulty was overcome by development of a working heart apparatus in which both the left atrium and aorta are cannulated (133, 143). Perfusate is supplied to the atrium over a range of left atrial filling pressures and outflow resistance is varied by changing the height of the hydrostatic pressure head against which the heart is required to pump. In this preparation ventricular pressure development is increased either by raising left atrial filling pressure or outflow resistance and results in increased consumption of oxygen, carbohydrates, and fatty substrates. The major advantage of the working heart preparation is the ability to correlate changes in ventricular function with metabolic events. This feature is of particular importance in studies of drug or hormone action or in following the course of ventricular function during anoxia.

As noted above, coronary flow is linearly related to ventricular pressure development in the Langendorff preparation. This also holds true for the working heart model. As a result of this relationship, these preparations are not well-suited for investigation of the effects of ischemia on ventricular function and metabolism. In each case, a reduction in coronary flow was associated with lower levels of ventricular pressure development and energy utilization. Since these changes are parallel, reduced delivery of oxygen is partially compensated for by reduced $O_2$ demand. A preparation suitable for studies of cardiac ischemia was developed by modifying the working heart model (147). Flow of perfusate into the left atrium was maintained, but a ball valve was inserted in the outflow tract, immediately above the aorta. The valve allowed ejection of perfusate during systole, but prevented flow into the coronary ostia during diastole. As a result, aortic diastolic pressure in the area immediately above the aortic valve was reduced from 60 to 20 mm Hg and coronary flow fell by 60%. Initially, peak systolic aortic pressure was maintained despite a reduction in coronary flow. After 4–6 min, however, ventricular failure began and progressively intensified. If a minimal perfusion pressure was not provided, ventricular failure was irreversible after about 30 min. On the other hand, maintenance of a coronary perfusion pressure of 25 mm Hg produced a reduced, but fairly stable, level of ventricular function for at least 1 hr.

The Langendorff, working, and ischemic models of the perfused rat heart allow for detailed studies of the effects of increased ventricular pressure development, cardiac work, hypoxia, anoxia, and ischemia on utilization of carbohydrate and fatty acids. The Langendorff model is easiest to use and is suitable for studies of hormone action, increased ventricular pressure development, and anoxia in situations in which correlation with changes in cardiac work is not required. The working model is needed for studies of the effects of external work on metabolism while the ischemic model allows studies simulating myocardial infarction.

Although the isolated perfused heart is a convenient tool for studies of cardiac metabolism, evaluation of the physiological significance of regulatory mechanisms described in this preparation requires experiments in intact animals. Assessment of metabolic changes in the heart, in vivo, rests upon determinations of A-V differences of substrates and metabolic products, estimation of oxidation of radioactive substrates that are added to the arterial blood, and analysis of metabolite levels in rapidly frozen tissue. Estimation of substrate utilization by measurements of A-V differences is complicated, in some instances, by the small changes that occur, and, in others, by simultaneous utilization and production of the substrate. A-V differences of glucose across the heart are quite small and estimates of the rates of utilization are imprecise (214). Simultaneous uptake and production of substrate is particularly apparent when utilization of fatty acid is calculated (118, 139). The coronary circulation supplies blood both to cardiac muscle and adipose tissue in the epicardial surface and around the major coronary vessels. In some instances, release of free fatty acid (FFA) from adipose tissue and muscle exceeds uptake by the muscle, resulting in higher venous than arterial levels of FFA. Estimation of the rate of uptake and oxidation of [$^{14}$C] fatty acid supplied to the arterial inflow has been used to circumvent these difficulties.

Detection of metabolic changes in abnormal areas of cardiac muscle may be masked if the area is surrounded by larger areas of normal tissue. Resort to biopsy of the affected area for estimation of metabolite levels may allow for detection of abnormal areas in some instances. The major advantage of in vivo studies is the opportunity to explore regulatory mechanisms in a physiological setting that have been defined in isolated hearts.

## Identification of Rate-Controlling Reactions in Carbohydrate and Fatty Acid Metabolism

In general, two approaches have been used for identification of rate-controlling reactions in intact cells (for review see 194). These methods include 1. correlation of levels of metabolites in a pathway with rates of flux through the pathway and 2. detection of reactions whose levels of substrates, products, and cofactors within the tissue are far removed from levels expected from the thermodynamic equilibrium of the reaction. Meaningful conclusions regarding the importance of a reaction in controlling flux through a pathway can be derived by these methods only if the substrates and products are contained within a single compartment of the cell. In this regard, detection of rate-controlling steps in fatty acid oxidation is complicated by compartmentalization of long- and short-chained CoA derivatives between the mitochondrial and cytoplasmic spaces. In these circumstances, increased levels of a substrate within one compartment can mask reduced levels within the other compartment and can lead to incorrect conclusions regarding the rate-controlling function of reactions consuming the substrate.

Correlation of metabolite levels with flux rates allows for detection of "cross-over" points within a pathway (32). For example, acceleration of glycolytic flux in anoxic muscle is usually associated with depletion of the substrates of phosphofructokinase, F-6-P, and ATP, and accumulation of the products, F-1,6-P and ADP. If the metabolite levels of the glycolytic pathway are taken as unity in well-oxygenated tissue, the substrate levels in the anoxic heart fall below 1 while product levels exceed this value. As a result, the metabolite levels are said to "cross-over" the control values at the level of the phosphofructokinase reaction. These findings, in association with an increased glycolytic flux, are interpreted to indicate that the phosphofructokinase reaction is accelerated in anaerobic tissue.

## Studies of Rate-Controlling Enzymes

Enzymatic steps within the pathway of glycolysis or fatty acid oxidation may be identified as rate-controlling as outlined above or may be suggested to be the site of regulation by possessing a number of activators and inhibitors of enzyme activity. It should be emphasized, however, that complex regulation of an enzyme does not establish the physiological role of the catalyst as a regulatory factor.

In studies of the physiological significance of factors controlling an enzymatic activity, it is important to assay activity in the presence of physiological levels of substrates, activators, and inhibitors. For example, the physiological significance of regulation of phosphorylase $b$ by ATP, AMP, and $P_i$ (135) can be understood only if the enzyme is assayed in the presence of relatively high levels of ATP and low levels of AMP and $P_i$. In these circumstances, it is apparent that ATP is strongly inhibitory and that the remaining activity is modulated by changes in AMP and $P_i$.

An additional problem in assessing the significance of regulatory phenomena that are detected in assays of pure enzymes involves use of enzyme concentrations far below those encountered in the cell. For example, citrate synthase is strongly inhibited by ATP when assayed in dilute solution, but the nucleotide is without effect when enzyme concentration is increased to values approximating those in the intact cell (215). Another similar situation is encountered in assessing the physiological significance of the inhibition of adenine nucleotide translocation across the mitochondrial membrane by long-chain acyl-CoA (169, 208). This metabolite is strongly inhibitory when added to mitochondrial suspensions in concentrations near those found in the heart. However, long-chain CoA derivatives are strongly bound to protein, and the mitochondrial concentration in these experiments was far below that encountered in intact cells. Under these circumstances, the ratio of long-chain CoA to mitochondrial protein was much higher than encountered in the cell. These considerations introduce uncertainties in assessing the physiological significance of the regulatory mechanism.

This section has outlined methods for study of regulation of carbohydrate and fatty acid metabolism in heart muscle. Perfusion techniques allow for close control of substrate levels, oxygen supply, and mechanical activity of the heart. Reactions controlling utilization of these substrates can be identified by measurements of metabolites and flux rates. Mechanisms of enzymatic regulation can be investigated using physiological levels of the purified protein, substrates, activators, and inhibitors.

## GENERAL FEATURES OF THE CONTROL OF CARBOHYDRATE UTILIZATION

Utilization of glucose and glycogen by heart muscle is regulated at a number of steps in conversion of these substrates to acetyl-CoA. These steps are described in this section (Figure 1). An increased flux of substrate through a reaction can arise either from a mass action effect due to higher concentrations of one of the substrates or from activation of the enzymatic catalyst. The following reactions have been identified from either cross-over plots or studies of purified enzymes as being subject to

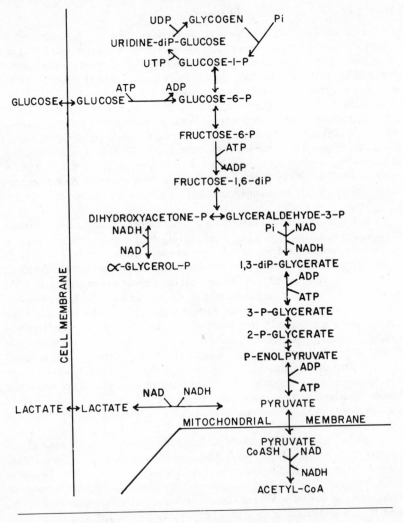

*Figure 1*  Pathway of glucose and glycogen metabolism in the heart.

activation or inhibition: glucose transport, hexokinase, phosphorfructokinase, glyceraldehyde-3-P dehydrogenase, pyruvate kinase, pyruvate dehydrogenase, glycogen synthetase, and glycogen phosphorylase.

## Glucose Transport

Kinetic data on glucose transport through muscle membranes are compatible with the hypothesis that the transport is carrier-mediated, not energy-requiring, and leads to equilibration of sugar concentrations inside and outside the cell (for reveiw see 138). Transport has been studied in greatest detail in erythrocytes. In both muscle and red cells the process has been found to be saturable at increasing sugar concentrations, to be stereospecific, to demonstrate competitive inhibition between pairs of sugars, and to show countertransport. The simple "carrier" model of sugar transport accounts for the kinetic properties of the process in muscle, insofar as these properties have been investigated. In human erythrocytes, more complex models have been proposed, as discussed in recent reviews (114, 138).

Transport regulation is poorly understood on a biochemical basis. A variety of agents are known to accelerate the process in heart muscle, including insulin, growth hormones, epinephrine, anoxia, and increased ventricular pressure development, but the substance that directly modulates the activity of the carrier in these circumstances has not been identified. In each case, kinetic studies have established that the carrier-mediated, stereospecific component of sugar entry, as distinguished from a diffusion component, is the process that is accelerated.

In avian erythrocytes, the rate of transport in anoxic cells is inversely related to cell levels of ATP and directly related to accumulation of low energy compounds (227). If ATP is added to the incubation medium of these cells, however, the nucleotide accelerates transport rate. This effect is contrary to the effect expected if ATP were responsible for the aerobic inhibition of transport. In recent experiments (228), NADH has been found to accelerate transport when added to the incubation medium of these cells. The effect of this nucleotide is consistent with a role as an activator of transport in anaerobic cells.

In several of the studies in heart muscle that we discuss, insulin was added to accelerate transport. After addition of the hormone, intracellular free glucose accumulates and the major rate-controlling step of glucose uptake shifts from transport to glucose phosphorylation. Effects of insulin on transport have been reviewed recently (132).

## Phosphorylation of Glucose

Phosphorylation of glucose by ATP (glucose + MgATP $\longrightarrow$ glucose-6-P + ADP, Mg) is the first step in glycolysis in mammalian cells, including heart muscle. The reaction is catalyzed by hexokinase and is essentially irreversible under physiological conditions; the equilibrium constant at pH 6.0 in the presence of excess $Mg^{2+}$ was found to be 155 (for review see 196). Glucose-6-phosphatase, the enzyme that catalyzes the reverse reactions in liver, is absent from heart muscle.

Hexokinase in mammalian tissues exists in 4 molecular forms (97). Three of these forms, type I, II, and III, are low $K_m$ enzymes that are found in muscle; but type IV, the high $K_m$ glucokinase, is found in liver. Type II hexokinase accounts for more than 50% of total activity in heart muscle; the activity of this form is reduced markedly in hearts from diabetic rats (47, 98). Although the isozymes have different $K_m$ values for glucose and ATP, the physiological implications of a shift in isozyme pattern is unknown. All of the isozymes have a molecular weight of about 95,000 (78).

Mammalian hexokinase is found in both the soluble and mitochondrial fractions of tissue homogenates. Partition between these fractions depends upon the composition of the homogenization medium. When 50 m$M$ tris buffer is used, approximately 30% of the enzyme activity is soluble (55). Inclusion of ions at concentrations simulating those found in the intracellular water increases the proportion of soluble enzyme to about 70% (98). Since the enzyme that is bound to mitochondria is less sensitive to inhibition by glucose-6-P, partition of enzyme between the soluble and mitochondrial fractions is of importance in correlating rates of glucose phosphorylation in intact hearts with the kinetic properties of the enzymatic activity in homogenates. In addition to ionic strength, glucose-6-P, ATP, ADP, and AMP can release enzyme from mitochondria while $Mg^{2+}$ favors rebinding (196). This finding suggests that partitioning of enzyme between the soluble and mitochondrial fractions may vary depending upon rates of glucose metabolism. This possibility was explored by addition of physiological levels of glucose-6-P, nucleotides, and $P_i$ to brain homogenates (181). Variations in the concentrations of these factors, in the physiological range, had only small effects on mitochondrial binding.

The reaction mechanism of hexokinase appears to involve random addition of substrates (181, 196). Release of products is an important factor in the overall rate with release of glucose-6-P following release of MgADP (103). A number of factors regulate the hexokinases of rat heart, including concentrations of ATP, ADP, AMP, and $P_i$ (55). The $K_m$ for glucose averages about 50 $\mu M$ and the $K_m$ for ATP is 0.5 m$M$. The dissociation constant for inhibition, $K_i$, of ATP hydrolysis by glucose-6-P is approximately 0.04 m$M$, while the $K_i$ for inhibition of glucose phosphorylation by glucose-6-P is approximately 0.2 m$M$. Since hearts perfused with buffer containing high perfusate levels of glucose and insulin have intracellular levels of substrates that are 15 to 70 times their $K_m$ values, variation in rate is achieved primarily by enzyme inhibition. The intracellular level of glucose-6-P is the most important factor in determining the rate, accounting for more than 90% of the restraint on glucose phosphorylation. The glucose-6-P inhibition is moderated by tissue levels of ATP (69) and $P_i$ (197). A similar dependence of the rate of glucose phosphorylation on glucose-6-P inhibition was reported earlier in human erythrocytes (195).

Recent studies of Kosow & Rose (104) revealed that the onset of the glucose-6-P inhibition was a biphasic phenomenon. Approximately half of the enzyme was immediately inhibited while restraint of the remaining portion developed with a half-time of 12 or 130 sec for the soluble and bound portions of the enzyme, respectively. The authors suggest that only a portion of the enzyme exists in a form that is immediately inhibited by glucose-6-P and that the delay involves a shift of the remaining enzyme to the inhibition-sensitive form. This property is suggested to allow for rapid build-up of the products ADP and glucose-6-P. ADP signals a burst of $O_2$ consumption while production of fructose-6-P from glucose-6-P provides adequate levels of substrate for activation of phosphofructokinase.

Regulation of hexokinase activity occurs primarily through changes in levels of the product glucose-6-P. Estimations of the rate in intact cells from data obtained with purified enzymes is complicated by the presence of three forms of the enzyme in heart muscle and by binding of the catalyst to mitochondria. Kinetic properties of the various types of hexokinase have not been studied in detail, the extent of mitochondrial binding of hexokinase in intact cells is uncertain, and the changes in kinetic proerties of the bound as compared to soluble enzyme are incompletely explored.

## Phosphofructokinase

Since conversion of glucose-6-P to fructose-6-P, catalyzed by phosphoglucoisomerase, is not an important rate-controlling step in glycolysis, the next site of regulation in the glycolytic pathway is the phosphorfructokinase reaction (fructose-6-P + MgATP $\longrightarrow$ fructose-1,6-diP + MgADP). Regulation at this site was first suggested by Cori (40) in relation to his studies of the effect of work on muscle metabolism. Subsequently, the reaction has been identified as an important rate-controlling step in many cell types, as reviewed recently (15, 120). In the present paper, attention is limited to the physiological role of phosphofructokinase in controlling glycolysis. In this regard, the following factors appear to be of importance: 1. the isozyme of phosphofructokinase that is present, 2. the intracellular pH, and 3. the intracellular concentrations of fructose-6-P, high and low energy phosphates, fructose-1,6-diP, citrate, ammonium ion, and cyclic AMP.

Three isozymes of phosphofructokinase have been identified and labeled A, B, and C (219). Heart and skeletal muscle contain the A isozyme while liver and erythrocytes contain the B form. Other tissues contain both forms and have a complete set of 5 hybrids of the A and B monomers. Brain contains a third monomer, C, which was identified by its lack of reaction to antisera to either the A or B isozymes. The C isozyme has not been purified. Differences in the regulatory behavior of the A and B isozymes have been noted. The B form is sensitive to inhibition by 2,3-diphosphoglycerate, is more sensitive to inhibition by ATP, but less sensitive to inhibition by 3-P-glycerate. The B form is less sensitive to activation by AMP and ADP (100).

Early attempts to purify phosphofructokinase were handicapped by instability of the enzyme. Addition of fructose-1,6-diP stabilized the heart enzyme (120) and led to purification of the protein. The fully active form of phosphofructokinase has a molecular weight of 360,000. Higher molecular weight forms appear which depend on enzyme concentration, pH, and the presence of substrates and modifiers. The specific activity of the more aggregated forms is the same as the form with a molecular weight of 360,000 (1). The enzyme can be dissociated into a relatively inactive dimer at mildly acid pH and can be reassociated at alkaline pH in the presence of fructose-6-P and fructose-1,6-diP (120). In the presence of 6.5 $M$ guanidine HCl, the enzyme appears to dissociate into 6 subunits of approximately 67,000 mol wt each (15). In the studies of Kemp & Krebs (101), one mole of fructose-6-P and three moles of ATP were bound per 90,000 g. Later experiments of Mansour (120) indicated that 3.6 moles of ATP and 1.8 moles of fructose-6-P were bound per 90,000 g.

Intracellular pH would appear to have a large effect on phosphofructokinase activity. Assay of the purified heart enzyme at pH 6.9 revealed a sigmoid relationship between enzyme activity and concentration of fructose-6-P. At this pH, the enzyme is markedly sensitive to allosteric regulation. At pH 8.2, the enzyme exhibits Michaelis-Menten kinetics, has increased activity, and is not subject to regulation (120, 218). The effect of pH is particularly great over the physiological range from pH 6.8 to 7.3.

Allosteric control of phosphofructokinase activity is extensive and provides for large changes in catalytic activity. High and low energy phosphates modify activity. ATP and creatine-P inhibit activity while ADP, AMP, and $P_i$ activate the enzyme. The apparent $K_i$ for ATP varies from 0.08–0.3 m$M$ when fructose-6-P concentrations are in the physiological range. The activators are of special importance since their intracellular levels increase in anoxic or ischemic muscle. Newsholme (150) has pointed out the amplification that is achieved by the combined effects of reduced levels of ATP and creatine-P and increased levels of ADP, AMP, and $P_i$. The amplification mechanism involves adenylate kinase (2 ADP $\rightleftharpoons$ ATP + AMP). Since the equilibrium constant of this enzyme is 0.44, a 15% reduction in ATP levels increases AMP about 5-fold. The effect of this amplification is to markedly increase phosphofructokinase activity with a small fall in ATP.

Fructose-1,6-diP, the product of the reaction, is also a powerful activator. The enzyme binds two moles of this metabolite per 100,000 g (206). One of these sites has a dissociation constant of 0.23 $\mu M$ and the other of 56 $\mu M$. Binding to the low affinity site probably accounts for allosteric regulation at pH 6.9, while binding at the high affinity site affects catalytic activity even at pH 8.2. Removal of fructose-1,6-diP by addition of fructose diphosphatase or aldolase inhibits activity (54). At pH 6.9 this inhibition could be reversed by allosteric activators, while at pH 8.2 only fructose-1,6-diP would overcome the inhibition. The importance of the tight binding of activators is emphasized by the increase in activity that occurs in epinephrine-treated muscle. When phosphofructokinase is extracted from such muscle, it is less sensitive to inhibition by ATP or caffeine (121). This change in behavior is believed to be due to more extensive binding of activators such as fructose-1,6-diP or cyclic-AMP, and not to phosphorylation of the protein.

Citrate inhibits phosphofructokinase and provides a signal coupling oxidation of fatty substrates to glycolysis (120, 177). Citrate is contained within both the mitochondrial and cytoplasmic fractions of the cell. If citrate concentrations in the cytoplasm increase to a greater extent than in the whole heart, compartmentalization of this intermediate could represent an additional mechanism for amplification of phosphofructokinase control (150).

The final substance that may exert a physiologically important control over phosphofructokinase activity in heart muscle is $NH_4^+$. In hearts perfused with buffer lacking insulin, ammonia production is increased approximately 10-fold (131). This increase is inhibited by addition of the hormone. The dissociation constant for binding for $NH_4^+$ to phosphofructokinase is 0.33 m$M$, a value within the physiological range (3). In contrast to other activators, phosphofructokinase exhibits qualitatively the same type of allosteric control in its presence. The increased activity is accounted for by a decreased $K_m$ for ATP and fructose-6-P and an increased $K_i$ for citrate and ATP.

Phosphofructokinase is a major control point in the glycolytic pathway that directs glucose residues into either glycogen or production of pyruvate. The enzyme is subject to a complicated series of controls involving energy levels of the cell, substrate concentration, tricarboxylic acid cycle intermediates, and products of amino acid and nucleotide degradation.

## Glyceraldehyde-3-P Dehydrogenase

Activation of phosphofructokinase leads to accumulation of fructose-1,6-diP and, in some circumstances, to restriction of glycolytic rate by reactions further down the pathway. The next reaction, catalyzed by aldolase, is the conversion of fructose-1,6-diP to dihydroxyacetone phosphate and glyceraldehyde-3-P. Although the mass action ratio of products and substrates of aldolase in the perfused heart is displaced somewhat from equilibrium (232), this displacement has been suggested to be due to binding of dyhydroxyacetone-P to the enzyme rather than to restraint on flux at this step. Similarly, isomerization of the triose phosphates by triose-P isomerase (dihydroxyacetone-P ⇌ D-glyceraldehyde-3-P) is not thought to represent an important regulatory reaction in glycolysis. On the other hand, the ratio of dihydroxyacetone-P/glyceraldehyde-3-P in heart muscle does not reach the equilibrium ratio of 22 (232). Evidence for incomplete equilibration has also been obtained in ascites tumor cells and adipose tissue (196). In the perfused heart, however, the product of the mass action ratios of the aldolase and triose-P isomerase reactions is close to the equilibrium value (232), supporting the contention that these are not important regulatory reactions.

Activation of phosphofructokinase appears to shift the control of glycolytic rate to glyceraldehyde-3-P dehydrogenase in hearts perfused under anoxic or ischemic conditions. Evidence that the dehydrogenase may be rate controlling is based on accumulation of fructose-1,6-diP and triose-P without accumulation of intermediates further down the pathway. Several properties of the enzyme appear to account for this behavior (38, 196). 1. The kinetic constants for all reactants are low. When the enzyme is assayed at low concentrations ($10^{-9}$ $M$) at pH 7.4, the $K_m$ for NAD and glyceraldehyde-3-P is 90 and 2.5 $\mu M$, respectively, while the $K_i$ for NADH and 1,3-diP-glycerate is 0.3 and 1.0 $\mu M$, respectively (71). Since NADH and 1,3-diP-glycerate are competitive with respect to glyceraldehyde-3-P, they may be more effective in setting the intracellular level of glyceraldehyde-3-P than in restricting rate, provided NAD$^+$ is available. On the other hand, the low $K_i$ for NADH compared to the high $K_m$ for NAD indicates that product inhibition may be an important factor in restricting glycolytic rate in cells with impaired ability to reoxidize NADH. 2. The concentration of enzyme is high relative to either the concentration of substrates or products. The high level of enzyme has been proposed to be due to the fact that the pH optimum is about 2 units above the physiological intracellular pH and that the enzyme is inhibited by ATP (39, 64). 3. At pH 7, and in the presence of 1.5 m$M$ P$_i$, the ratio of (NADH) (1,3-diP-glycerate)/(NAD) (glyceraldehyde-3-P) would be expected to be about $10^{-3}$ (196). Since the functional ratio of NADH/NAD may be about $10^{-3}$, approximately equal concentrations of glyceraldehyde-3-P and 1,3-diP-glycerate would be expected. When NADH accumulates, glyceraldehyde-3-P levels would rise.

These factors indicate that glyceraldehyde-3-P dehydrogenase within the cell operates under suboptimal conditions due to the intracellular pH and inhibition by ATP. The rate appears to be controlled by product inhibition. In aerobic cells, the level of 1,3-diP-glycerate is probably the more important inhibitor, while in ischemic or anoxic muscle, NADH would assume the dominant regulatory role.

## Pyruvate Kinase

The next step in the glycolytic pathway that has been suggested to be a regulatory site is pyruvate kinase (P-enolpyruvate + ADP + H$^+$ $\rightleftharpoons$ pyruvate + ATP). The intermediate reactions catalyzed by phosphoglycerate kinase (1,3-diP-glycerate + ADP $\rightleftharpoons$ 3-P-glycerate + ATP), phosphoglycerate mutase (D-2-glycerate $\rightleftharpoons$ P-enolpyruvate + H$_2$O) have not been implicated as regulatory reactions. The finding that the mass action ratio of products and substrates of pyruvate kinase in the perfused heart apparently was displaced from the equilibrium ratio by 2 orders of magnitude suggested that this enzyme might restrict glycolytic rate (232). The apparent displacement was based on whole tissue levels of ADP and ATP and estimates of intracellular pH and free Mg$^{2+}$ concentration. Restriction of the steady state rate of glycolysis at this step has not been demonstrated in heart muscle.

Muscle contains a form of pyruvate kinase that is distinct from the liver enzyme (for review see 99). The muscle enzyme is inhibited by ATP by competition at the ADP site. Inhibition results in accumulation of metabolites preceding this step, including 1,3-diP-glycerate, a powerful inhibitor of glyceraldehyde-3-P dehydrogenase. Recently, the muscle enzyme has been found to be inhibited in an allosteric manner by phenylalanine. Since this inhibition is relieved by alanine that is present in much higher concentration in heart muscle, the physiological significance of this regulatory mechanism is unclear. It should be noted that the muscle enzyme, as contrasted to liver pyruvate kinase, is not inhibited by fructose-1,6-diP.

## Pyruvate Dehydrogenase

Pyruvate produced from glycolysis may be converted to acetyl-CoA, lactate, or alanine in heart muscle. The first two products account for most of the pyruvate. Conversion of pyruvate to lactate as compared to acetyl-CoA is determined by the levels of NADH and acetyl-CoA and the activity of pyruvate dehydrogenase (pyruvate + CoASH + NAD$^+$ $\longrightarrow$ acetyl-CoA + CO$_2$ + NADH + H$^+$).

Pyruvate dehydrogenase is a multienzyme complex consisting of three enzymes that are directly involved in pyruvate metabolism plus two other enzymes involved in modification of pyruvate dehydrogenase activity (for review see 187). The molecular weight of the complex is approximately 4 million. The reactions are catalyzed by the following enzymes.

1. Pyruvate dehydrogenase [pyruvate + TPP (thiamine pyrophosphate) $\longrightarrow$ 1-hydroxyethyl-TPP + $CO_2$].
2. Dihydroxylipoyl transacetylase [(a) 1-hydroxyethyl-TPP + lipoic $acid_{oxid}$ $\longrightarrow$ acetyllipoic $acid_{red}$ + TPP; (b) acetyllipoic $acid_{red}$ + CoASH $\longrightarrow$ acetyl-CoA + lipoic $acid_{red}$].
3. Dihydroxylipoyl dehydrogenase [lipoic $acid_{red}$ + $NAD^+$ $\longrightarrow$ lipoic $acid_{oxid}$ + NADH + $H^+$].
4. Pyruvate dehydrogenase kinase [pyruvate dehydrogenase $a$ + ATP $\longrightarrow$ pyruvate dehydrogenase $b$].
5. Pyruvate dehydrogenase phosphatase [pyruvate dehydrogenase $b$ $\longrightarrow$ pyruvate dehydrogenase $a$ + $P_i$].

The enzymes are linked in the complex by noncovalent bonds. A subcomplex consisting of the transacetylase and dihydroxylipoyl dehydrogenase, a flavoprotein, can be dissociated. The transacetylase has a molecular weight of about 1 million and consists of 24 identical chains, each containing one molecule of covalently-bound lipoic acid. The pyruvate dehydrogenase portion of the complex has a molecular weight of 154,000. The flavoprotein has a molecular weight of 112,000 and contains 2 moles of FAD. The pyruvate dehydrogenase complex appears to be organized to permit efficient interaction of the individual enzymes.

Activity of the pyruvate dehydrogenase complex is subject to regulation by a phosphorylation-dephosphorylation sequence involving pyruvate dehydrogenase kinase and phosphatase. The kinase is tightly bound to the transacetylase portion of the complex, while the phosphatase is loosely attached. In the presence of $Ca^{2+}$ ions the phosphatase is bound tightly (179). The binding is inhibited by EGTA.[2] The site of phosphorylation is a serine residue on the pyruvate dehydrogenase component. Phosphorylation decreases activity while dephosphorylation restores it. Both the kinase and phosphatase are $Mg^{2+}$ dependent, but the phosphatase requires a $Mg^{2+}$ concentration 10 times greater than the kinase for optimal activity. It has been suggested that the kinase and phosphatase are regulated by the intramitochondrial concentration of free $Mg^{2+}$, which is dependent on the ratio of ATP/ADP. Pyruvate protects heart pyruvate dehydrogenase from inactivation by the kinase.

Activity of pyruvate dehydrogenase is inhibited by the products of the reaction, acetyl-CoA, and NADH (185). Initially it was thought that product inhibition accounted for restraint of the enzyme in hearts oxidizing fatty substrates. More recently, Wieland and associates (229, 230) have reported that the enzyme is converted from the active to inactive form in hearts of starved or diabetic rats and that the active form is restored by refeeding and insulin treatment. In fed rats, $\sim$70% of total activity was in the $a$ form, but only 15% was active in hearts of diabetic or starved rats. Similarly, perfusion of rat hearts for 15 min with buffer containing fatty acids or ketone bodies resulted in a fall of the $a$ form from 58 to $\sim$30%. These experiments suggest that the catalytic activity of pyruvate dehydrogenase in the heart is controlled both by product inhibition and interconversion of enzyme forms.

[2]EGTA represents ethylene glycol-bis-($\beta$-aminoethyl ether)-N,N'-tetraacetic acid.

## Enzymes Involved in Turnover of Glycogen

Glycogen synthesis and degradation occur by separate pathways and each pathway is subject to a complicated series of control mechanisms. The enzymes involved and their mechanisms of control have been recently reviewed (61, 77, 112, 222). It is beyond the scope of this article to more than outline the reactions and to indicate the mechanisms of regulation.

GLYCOGEN SYNTHESIS   Three steps are involved in the conversion of glucose-6-P into glycogen. These are catalyzed by phosphoglucomutase (glucose-6-P $\rightleftharpoons$ glucose-1-P), uridyl transferase [UTP + glucose-1-P $\rightleftharpoons$ uridine-diP-glucose (UDPG) + pyrophosphate], and glycogen synthase (UDPG + glycogen$_n$ $\longrightarrow$ glycogen$_{n+1}$ + UDP). Regulation of glycogen synthesis occurs at the synthase step.

Glycogen synthase occurs in two forms: $a$ and $b$. Conversion of one form to the other depends on a phosphorylation-dephosphorylation mechanism. The $a$ form is dephosphorylated. Its affinity for UDPG is increased by glucose-6-P, but the maximal rate of the reaction is unaffected. This form is relatively insensitive to inhibition by ATP and other nucleotides. Synthase $a$ is converted to synthase $b$ by phosphorylation of the protein. This reaction is catalyzed by a cyclic-AMP-dependent protein kinase (222). The $b$ form is essentially inactive in the absence of glucose-6-P and the activation is inhibited by ATP and other nucleotides. Synthase $b$ is reconverted to the $a$ form by synthase phosphatase. Inhibition of the phosphatase by glycogen results in a progressively lower percentage of synthase in the $a$ form as polysaccharide is stored. By this mechanism, glycogen shares in the regulation of its synthesis.

GLYCOGEN BREAKDOWN   Only the phosphorylase reaction is required for conversion of a glucose residue from glycogen to glucose-1-P (glycogen$_{n+1}$ + P$_i$ $\longrightarrow$ glycogen$_n$ + glucose-1-P). Phosphorylase also occurs in two forms, $a$ and $b$. The $a$ form is the phosphorylated form of the enzyme and is active in the absence of AMP. It is converted to the $b$ form by phosphorylase phosphatase. Activity of the $b$ form is dependent upon AMP for activity, and the activity is inhibited by ATP and glucose-6-P. Reconversion to the $a$ form is catalyzed by phosphorylase kinase. Activity of the kinase also is regulated by a phosphorylation-dephosphorylation mechanism and is increased by low levels of Ca$^{2+}$. The cyclic-AMP-dependent protein kinase is responsible for activation of phosphorylase kinase.

In heart muscle, turnover of glycogen is regulated both by hormones and nonhormonal factors. Epinephrine and glucagon activate adenyl cyclase, increase cyclic-AMP levels, and result in conversion of phosphorylase to the $a$ form and synthase to the $b$ form. Insulin increases the fraction of synthase in the $a$ form. The major nonhormonal factors involved in regulating turnover of glycogen are the intracellular levels of 5'-AMP, ATP, glucose-6-P, P$_i$, and glycogen itself.

## INTEGRATED CONTROL OF CARBOHYDRATE METABOLISM

As discussed in the introduction to this paper, studies of the control of carbohydrate utilization in intact tissues depend upon identification of rate-controlling reactions by comparison of the mass action ratios of substrates and products under various conditions with the equilibrium ratio and by cross-over plots. In some instances the levels of metabolites are too low for reliable analysis by existing techniques. In these cases, the contribution of a pair of reactions has been considered together. This situation pertains to the glyceraldehyde-3-P dehydrogenase and phosphoglycerate kinase steps where the level of 1,3-diP-glycerate is usually too low to be measured (232). Additional factors complicating detection of nonequilibrium and rate-controlling reactions are compartmentalization of metabolites of the glycolytic pathway into two or more pools or binding of metabolites to muscle proteins. ATP and ADP are distributed between the cytoplasmic and mitochondrial spaces in heart muscle. In addition, ADP is bound to actin (127). Glucose-6-P in diaphragm muscle has been suggested to be divided into separate compartments for glycogen synthesis and for conversion to pyruvate (6, 110). Since inorganic phosphate binds to muscle proteins (75, 83), the intracellular concentration calculated from whole tissue analyses probably overestimates the concentration available either as a substrate for phosphorylase or glyceraldehyde-3-P dehydrogenase or as an activator of phosphofructokinase and hexokinase. On the other hand, studies of carbohydrate utilization in heart muscle are simplified by the absence of glucose-6-phosphatase, fructosediphosphatase, phosphoenolpyruvate carboxykinase, and pyruvate carboxylase (42, 164). Although the hexosemonophosphate shunt is potentially active in heart muscle (37), the bulk of the carbohydrate appears to be utilized via the main glycolytic pathway.

## Regulation of Carbohydrate Utilization in Well-Oxygenated Hearts

Both in vivo and in the isolated perfused rat heart, fatty substrates are used preferentially to glucose and glycogen (for review, 146). In the heart of man or the unanesthetized dog, 35–75% of oxygen consumption can be accounted for by oxidation of plasma FFA (113, 118, 124, 139). Similarly, in the perfused rat heart 80–100% of oxygen consumption can be accounted for by uptake of short- or long-chain fatty substrates. If an exogenous supply of fatty substrates is not provided, the heart uses endogenous stores of triglyceride in preference to exogenous glucose.

In well-oxygenated hearts that are developing low levels of ventricular pressure, glucose transport is the major restriction to utilization of exogenous glucose and glycogen breakdown is restrainted at the phosphorylase reaction (130, 134). In addition, the mass action ratios of four reactions in the glycolytic pathway are displaced from the equilibrium ratio by 1 order of magnitude or more. These include hexokinase, phosphofructokinase, glyceraldehyde-3-P dehydrogenase, and pyruvate kinase (232).

The rate of glucose transport in well-oxygenated hearts depends upon the levels of insulin bound to the tissue, the sensitivity of transport to stimulation by insulin, and the availability of fatty substrates (for review see 138). Transport is inhibited in hearts of diabetic rats due to low levels of insulin, but, in addition, transport is relatively insensitive to stimulation by insulin (for review see 132). Decreased insulin sensitivity is related to high plasma levels of growth hormone, glucocorticoids, and fatty acids. In hearts of hypophysectomized-diabetic rats the basal transport rate remains low due to insulin deficiency, but sensitivity to stimulation by insulin is restored by removal of the pituitary. Perfusion of rat hearts with buffer containing fatty substrates reduces insulin sensitivity (141), while inhibition of fatty acid oxidation with α-bromopalmitate restores insulin sensitivity of diabetic hearts to normal (26, 183). The inhibitory effect of fatty acid is evident when either entry of glucose or nonmetabolized analogs is measured. Inhibition of transport by fatty acid is sufficient to prevent accumulation of intracellular free glucose despite inhibition of intracellular glucose phosphorylation, except when high levels of insulin are present.

Glycogen breakdown is restrained in the well-oxygenated heart in a number of ways. 1. Phosphorylase is almost entirely in the $b$ form due to low activity of phosphorylase kinase (180). 2. Activity of the $b$ form is restrained by high tissue concentrations of the inhibitors ATP and glucose-6-P, and low concentrations of the activator 5'-AMP (135). 3. The remaining activity of the $b$ form is controlled by tissue levels of inorganic phosphate. Intracellular concentrations of $P_i$ are below the $K_m$ of the inhibited enzyme for this substrate.

The combined effects of fatty acid oxidation are to markedly reduce glucose utilization and to divert most of the substrate that is taken up into glycogen. This effect is particularly apparent in hearts of alloxan diabetic rats. The plasma of these animals contains high levels of FFA and the heart contains increased stores of triglyceride (185). Although glucose uptake by these hearts is markedly restricted (129), the glycogen content of the diabetic heart is twice normal. Increased accumulation of glycogen is explained by a profound inhibition of phosphofructokinase by citrate (177). High levels of citrate accumulate in hearts oxidizing fatty substrates (73, 176). As a result of the inhibition of phosphofructokinase, higher tissue levels of fructose-6-P and glucose-6-P accumulate and shift the pathway of glycogen turnover toward storage of polysaccharide.

Regulation of the portion of the glycolytic pathway between intracellular glucose and acetyl-CoA can be studied more directly by removing the restraint imposed on these reactions by sugar transport. Addition of insulin leads to accumulation of measurable levels of intracellular free glucose and a shift in the control of glycolytic rate to reactions within the cell (62, 130). In these circumstances, the rate of glucose phosphorylation can be expressed as a function of intracellular glucose concentration. As discussed above, the activity of hexokinase is regulated primarily by the intracellular concentration of glucose-6-P. The intracellular level of this intermediate depends upon the activity of phosphofructokinase. Addition of fatty acids to the perfusion medium of isolated hearts restrains glucose phosphorylation due to inhibition of this enzyme (185). Similarly, hearts removed from diabetic rats have a markedly impaired rate of glucose phosphorylation that is associated with high tissue levels of glucose-6-P, fructose-6-P, and ATP, and low levels of fructose-1,6-P (129, 152, 175, 186, 191). Impairment of glucose phosphorylation contributes to the delay in return of blood sugar to normal following administration of large doses of insulin to severely diabetic rats. A period of 4–24 hr is required for return of phosphorylation to normal following insulin treatment (137). Hearts removed from hypophysectomized diabetic rats do not have an impaired rate of glucose phosphorylation, but a block can be induced by treatment of the animal with growth hormone and glucocorticoids (137). Return of inhibition is associated with increased tissue levels of citrate and a cross-over point at the phosphofructokinase reaction (152, 191).

The final site at which fatty acid restrains glycolysis is at the pyruvate dehydrogenase reaction. Acetyl-CoA and NADH, products of the reaction, inhibit the enzyme and lead to conversion of a larger fraction of the pyruvate to lactate (185). Additions of a variety of fatty substrates to the perfusate inhibit pyruvate uptake by the rat heart.

Skeletal muscle also uses fatty acids as a major substrate for oxidative metabolism (28, 84, 85, 118, 182). In patients subjected to a prolonged fast, carbohydrate utilization by skeletal muscle is nil (27). This reduction represents an essential homeostatic mechanism to spare glucose for utilization by the brain and other tissues that are more dependent upon it as a fuel for oxidation. A number of studies have attempted to determine whether preferential utilization of fatty acid in skeletal muscle of fasting or diabetic animals is related to the low plasma levels of insulin and the accompanying slow rates of glucose transport, or whether fatty acids inhibit glycolysis in this tissue as they do in heart muscle (12, 91, 92, 94, 204). A number of factors other than absence of an effect of fatty acid may account for inability to demonstrate these inhibitory effects. 1. Since most of the skeletal muscle preparations that were used were not perfused, access of the fatty acid to the muscle cells cannot be assured. Inhibition of glucose uptake in the diaphragm by ketone bodies has been observed (166, 185). 2. In skeletal muscle, the capacity of glucose phosphorylation is relatively great as compared to the capacity of transport. Even when transport is stimulated by addition of insulin, intracellular free glucose accumulates only if phosphorylation is restrained by a reduction in the incubation temperature (174). 3. Effects of fatty acid on glucose transport in isolated muscle preparations that are contracting have not been investigated. In future studies, it would appear useful to use skeletal muscle preparations from trained rats in which the capacity for fatty acid oxidation is increased (7, 126). This possibility is suggested by the observation that citrate levels increase to a more limited extent in skeletal than heart muscle following fat feeding (4).

To recapitulate, glycolysis in well-oxygenated heart muscle is retrained at the level of glucose transport, hexokinase, phosphofructokinase, and pyruvate dehydrogenase. Factors involved in this restraint are tissue levels of insulin and triglycerides and the availability of fatty substrates in the perfusate.

## Effects of Increased ATP Consumption on Carbohydrate Utilization

An increase in ATP and $O_2$ consumption in heart muscle accompanies increased ventricular pressure development or increased heart rate. An increase in pressure development arises either from an increased end-diastolic volume due to higher atrial filling pressure or higher resistance in the aortic outflow tract (133, 143, 159). In addition, increased utilization of ATP and $O_2$ is induced by addition of inotropic agents such as epinephrine or glucagon (13, 63, 188). In some instances, particularly in epinephrine-treated hearts, the demand for oxygen exceeds the supply (63). In these cases, the effects of increased ATP utilization is complicated by effects of insufficient $O_2$ supply.

When hearts are perfused with substrate-free buffer, increased demand for oxidative substate results in rapid utilization of endogenous stores of triglyceride and glycogen (45, 141). Decreased tissue concentrations of glucose-6-P, together with increased levels of inorganic phosphate, account for an accelerated rate of glycogen breakdown by phosphorylase $b$ (47, 148). Conversion of phosphoyrlase $b$ to $a$ is not a prominent component of the effect. Although ATP utilization is increased, tissue levels of ATP were unaffected by the increase in ventricular pressure development until depletion of polysaccharide was nearly complete.

When glucose is present in the perfusate, an increase in ventricular pressure development accelerates glucose uptake and oxidation (44, 133). This effect is accounted for by more rapid rates of both glucose transport and phosphorylation (133, 142, 144, 163). Acceleration of transport involves an increase in maximal transport rate and can be demonstrated with glucose and the nonmetabolized analogs, L-arabinose and 3-O-methylglucose. The biochemical mechanism by which increased pressure development is transduced into faster transport is unknown. Although an increase in ventricular pressure development makes transport more sensitive to the stimulatory effects of insulin (133), the hormone is not required for the effect on transport since an increase in work by hearts of diabetic rats raised glucose uptake to normal (30).

Although transport is accelerated in hearts that develop higher levels of ventricular pressure, measurable levels of intracellular free glucose do not accumulate (144), indicating that glucose phosphorylation accelerates in concert with glucose transport. Similarly, a 4-fold increase in the rate of flux through phosphofructokinase is accompanied by an increase in fructose-1,6-P but not in glucose-6-P, indicating that phosphofructokinase is accelerated along with transport and hexokinase (142, 148, 163). Factors accounting for the activation of phosphofructokinase in hearts developing increased ventricular pressure are the subject of controversy. Opie et al (163) reported that ATP, creatine-P, and citrate concentrations fell while ADP, AMP, and $P_i$ increased in hearts developing higher levels of ventricular pressure. Although the changes could account for activation of phosphofructokinase, they were not observed in the earlier work of Neely et al (141) or in later experiments (142) in which an attempt was made to reproduce Opie's results. It is our opinion that factors accounting for activation of phosphofructokinase in hearts developing increased rates of ventricular pressure remain to be defined. In support of this opinion, increased work did not reduce high energy phosphates in a rat heart-lung preparation (125).

Provision of both palmitate and glucose to hearts developing higher levels of ventricular pressure results in preferential use of the fatty acid (141). Similarly, acetate is used in preference to glucose when this pair of substrates is supplied (142). Preferential utilization of fatty acid involves inhibition of phosphofructokinase, phosphorylase, and glucose transport. Inhibition of phosphofructokinase is accounted for by higher tissue levels of citrate and creatine-P (148) and leads to higher concentrations of glucose-6-P. Slower rates of glycogen utilization are accounted for by inhibition of phosphorylase $b$ and activation of glycogen synthetase by glucose-6-P. The 6- to 8-fold acceleration of glucose transport, resulting from increased ventricular pressure development in hearts that are provided only glucose, is completely inhibited by inclusion of fatty acid in the perfusate (141). The inhibitory effect also is seen when transport of 3-O-methylglucose is measured. A variety of fatty substrates, including acetate and $\beta$-hydroxybutyrate, as well as palmitate, are inhibitory. When hearts are perfused under anaerobic conditions, the inhibitory effects of fatty acid on glucose transport do not occur. These observations indicate that oxidation of fatty acid is required for the effect of this substrate.

Exposure of the heart to epinephrine or glucagon increases the force and frequency of contraction and results in increased utilization of oxygen and glucose (107, 175, 231). Accelerated uptake of glucose persists after the period of rapid glycogenolysis has passed and results in a large increase in lactate production. Inhibition of the inotropic effect of epinephrine with dichloroisoproterenol abolishes the glycogenolytic effect of epinephrine and partially inhibits the stimulation of glucose uptake. The rapid phase of glycogenolysis in glucagon- or epinephrine-treated hearts is associated with conversion of a large fraction of phosphorylase to the $a$ form and with increased tissue content of cyclic AMP (41, 192, 233). Faster rates of glycolysis involves activation of glucose transport and phosphorylation and phosphofructokinase (233). Epinephrine increases tissue levels of AMP, ADP, creatine, and inorganic phosphate while the level of ATP falls. These changes account for activation of phosphofructokinase. During the period of maximal phosphofructokinase activity, the major restriction of glycolysis is shifted to glyceraldehyde-3-P dehydrogenase (233).

Increased ATP utilization that is associated with increased ventricular pressure development accelerates glucose uptake and glycogenolysis unless fatty substrates are supplied to the heart. Faster rates of carbohydrate utilization involves activation of glucose transport, hexokinase, phosphofructokinase, and phosphorylase $b$. The activities of hexokinase and phosphorylase $b$ are controlled by intracellular levels of glucose-6-P. Factors regulating glucose transport and phosphofructokinase in these experiments remain to be defined. If the need for oxygen exceeds its delivery, the heart may become relatively hypoxic, as indicated by depletion of high energy phosphates and accumulation of low energy products.

## Effects of Decreased ATP Production on Carbohydrate Utilization

The most common cause of decreased ATP production in heart muscle is restriction of oxygen supply. Reduced oxygen availability results from decreased or zero oxygen tension in the perfusate (hypoxia or anoxia) or from decreased flow of well-oxygenated perfusate through the coronary vessels (ischemia). In some experimental situations, ischemia is defined as reduction of blood flow to zero (108, 236), but in pathological situations in man, minimal flow often remains (95). In many earlier studies hypoxia and anoxia were investigated as models of ischemic damage to the heart. As will be discussed, however, hypoxia and anoxia markedly accelerate consumption of glucose and glycogen while ischemia inhibits utilization of these substrates. In future work, these conditions must be clearly distinguished.

In the Langendorff or working heart preparations, hypoxia and anoxia are induced by perfusing the tissue with buffer containing reduced or zero oxygen tensions (136, 151, 234). Coronary flow in these preparations is directly related to the perfusion pressure which is maintained by a peristaltic pump. In order to investigate the effects of ischemia, modifications of the working heart technique were introduced, as discussed earlier in this paper, which allow for dissociation of aortic and coronary flow (147). These models have the advantage that perfusion of the entire heart can be reduced in a controlled fashion. Rates of glucose and glycogen consumption can be determined and levels of metabolites within the pathway can be measured.

Other models of ischemia that have been studied include transection of the aorta (108, 236) and ligation of major coronary vessels (20). Aortic transection results in an abrupt and total cessation of coronary flow and allows for investigation of factors regulating consumption of glycogen stores. This model does not provide for investigation of utilization of exogenous glucose or release of metabolic products from the heart. Ligation or constriction of major coronary vessels most closely simulates myocardial ischemia in man, but mechanisms of control of ischemic muscle are difficult to investigate. The problems arise from inclusion of ischemic muscle within a mass of normal muscle which performs more work as a result of the occlusion.

Perfusion of hearts with a buffer containing glucose and gassed with $N_2:CO_2$ results in a 10- to 20-fold increase in glucose uptake and a rapid rate of glycogen breakdown. Acceleration of glucose transport, hexokinase, phosphorylase, and phosphofructokinase accounts for the increase in flux (41, 136, 151, 175, 191, 234). Reactions in the glycolytic pathway beyond phosphofructokinase accelerate in response to higher levels of substrate. The increase in catalytic activity of these reactions can be accounted for on the basis of the properties of the purified enzyme, with the exception of membrane transport (55, 135, 177). As noted above, however, anoxia stimulates the carrier-mediated component of sugar entry. Acceleration of phosphofructokinase is accounted for by increased intracellular levels of activators of the enzyme, ADP, AMP, and $P_i$, and decreased levels of the inhibitors, ATP and creatine-P. Increased activity leads to depletion of fructose-6-P and accumulation of fructose-1,6-P, another activator of the enzyme. Acceleration of hexokinase results from decreased levels of glucose-6-P, a powerful inhibitor, together with increased levels of $P_i$, a competitive inhibitor of the glucose-6-P inhibition. Activation of phosphorylase involves conversion of a portion of the enzyme to the $a$ form and increased activity of phosphorylase $b$ (41, 236). Conversion to the $a$ form is partially blocked by depletion of endogenous stores of catecholamines or by addition of $\beta$-adrenergic blocking agents (236). The catecholamine-dependent portion of phosphorylase $b$ to $a$ conversion correlates with increased tissue levels of cyclic AMP and increased activity of phosphorylase kinase (105). The activity of phosphorylase $b$ is increased by higher tissue levels of AMP and $P_i$, an activator and substrate of the enzyme, respectively, and decreased levels of ATP and glucose-6-P, inhibitors of the enzyme (135).

Although glycolytic flux is accelerated in anoxic hearts, the increase in rate generates only about 10–15% of the ATP that is formed in well-oxygenated tissue (79, 93, 108). In the anaerobic heart, ATP consumption decreases as a result of ventricular failure which occurs when only about 20% of the ATP is depleted. Failure has been suggested to result from a fall in intracellular pH which interferes with uptake and release of $Ca^{2+}$ from the sarcoplasmic reticulum (140), or from failure of $Ca^{2+}$ to bind to the contractile proteins (96).

The failure of glycolytic flux to increase sufficiently to supply optimal levels of ATP is due to restraint at the glyceraldehyde-3-P dehydrogenase step (234). Restriction of flux through this step could be accounted for by high tissue levels of NADH or 1,3-diphosphoglycerate, powerful product inhibitors of the enzyme. As noted above, levels of 1,3-diphosphoglycerate are below the level of detection in extracts of muscle. Since the levels of 3-P-glycerate and 2-P-glycerate are not increased in anaerobic muscle, it is likely that the level of 1,3-diphosphoglycerate is also unchanged by the shift to an anaerobic environment. If this is the case, intracellular levels of NADH would represent the major restraint on glyceraldehyde-3-P dehydrogenase. Intracellular NADH levels reflect the availability of hydrogen acceptors, such as dihydroxyacetone phosphate and pyruvate, and the rapidity with which the reduced products, $\alpha$-glycerol phosphate and lactate, are released from the cell. High levels of $\alpha$-glycerol phosphate accumulate in anoxic muscle, presumably as a result of low membrane permeability. Lactate efflux is more rapid, but intracellular levels of this product increase 2- to 3-fold in anaerobic hearts (199). It would appear that the glycolytic rate could be enhanced in anaerobic muscle if washout of lactate could be accelerated or if substrate levels of another hydrogen acceptor were provided. Deterioration of mechanical function is delayed in these hearts if increased concentrations of glucose and/or insulin are provided or if the heart contains more glycogen (86, 88, 202, 223, 224).

In contrast to the sustained increase in glycolytic flux in anaerobic mucle, induction of ischemia results in a transient increase in glycolytic flux which is followed by inhibition (199). Inhibition of glycolysis occurs even through intracellular levels of ADP, AMP, and $P_i$ are increased.

The transient acceleration of glycolytic flux principally involves consumption of the glycogen stores (199, 236). In the aortic transection model, acceleration of glycolysis is associated with conversion of phosphorylase *b* to *a* with increased tissue levels of cyclic AMP (237). Comparable measurements are not available at present for the ischemic rat heart. During this phase of increased glycolytic flux, levels of glycose-6-P and fructose-6-P increase in hearts perfused in the absence of insulin. When glycolysis is accelerated by addition of the hormone, control levels of the hexose monophosphates are raised and their intracellular levels are unchanged during the transient acceleration of glycolysis induced by ischemia. In both the presence and absence of insulin, intracellular levels of fructose-1,6-P, glyceraldehyde-3-P, and dihydroxyacetone-P are increased, indicating activation of phosphofructokinase. This activation can be accounted for by higher tissue levels of ADP, AMP, and $P_i$ and reduced levels of ATP and creatine-P.

As the reduction in blood flow is maintained, the glycolytic rate falls below that seen in well-oxygenated hearts and is about one tenth the rate encountered with anoxia (199). Inhibition of the glycolytic rate is not overcome by addition of insulin to the perfusate. In this circumstance, the rate-controlling step appears to be glyceraldehyde-3-P dehydrogenase (unpublished observations). This conclusion is based on the presence of high levels of glyceraldehyde-3-P, low levels of the metabolites beyond this step, and an impaired rate of glycolysis. Restraint at this step appears to involve high levels of NADH. In the ischemic muscle, lactate accumulation is more marked than in anaerobic hearts. Along with the accumulation of lactate, $\alpha$-glycerol phosphate levels increase about 10-fold above control values. Increased accumulation of lactate in ischemic as compared to anaerobic muscle is poorly understood, but involves impaired extracellular washout of this product due to reduction in coronary flow, the effect of pH on levels of undissociated lactate (89), and, possibly, the effects of ischemia on the membrane transfer of lactate. Interventions to improve glycolytic rate in ischemic muscle should be directed toward accelerating release of lactate from the muscle or toward provision of other hydrogen acceptors for reoxidization of NADH.

A number of factors could be suggested to account for the marked difference in glycolytic rate in ischemic as compared to anoxic muscle. Increased accumulation of lactate in the ischemic muscle could decrease intracellular pH more markedly than in anoxic muscle. Decreased extracellular pH decreases glycolytic rate in the isolated rat heart, while increased pH accelerates glycolysis (50, 160, 203). Phosphofructokinase is partially sensitive to pH in the physiological range (218). Estimation of intracellular pH from the distribution of dimethadione (29), however, indicates that intracellular pH decreases only slightly in ischemic muscle while the extracellular pH falls by about 0.6 pH units (unpublished observations).

A second explanation for the difference between anoxia and ischemia may involve the effect of a slow washout of lactate on the intracellular level of NADH. In this case, glycolytic rate would be controlled by removal of the reduced product of glycolysis. If ischemia is less severe, glycolytic rate could increase and finally approach that seen in anaerobic muscle (20, 46, 162). Inhibition of glycolysis in ischemic muscle most likely involves changes in both intracellular pH and lactate concentrations. It should be noted that glucose can be toxic to cells if reoxidation of NADH does not occur. Under these circumstances, ATP is consumed for production of fructose-1,6-diP without achieving ATP synthesis. The effect is apparent in rapidly glycolyzing cells, such as those of tumors, and forms the basis for the antitumor action of compounds such as oxamic acid (76). These considerations should be kept in mind when attempts are made to restrict damage to ischemic muscle by provision of high glucose levels and insulin.

## GENERAL FEATURES OF THE CONTROL OF FATTY ACID AND LIPID METABOLISM

The heart is capable of utilizing both albumin-bound free fatty acids and complex lipids from the blood. The pathways of fatty acid metabolism in cardiac muscle are illustrated in Figure 2. The first step in this pathway is the uptake of fatty acids from plasma proteins. This process appears to occur by passive diffusion of fatty acids from binding sites on plasma proteins to binding sites on the cell surface proteins. A soluble cytosolic protein which binds fatty acids has been described and may function in distributing fatty acids within the cells (157). Plasma triglycerides are hydrolyzed to fatty acids and glycerol before utilization can occur. This process is catalyzed by lipoprotein lipase that is located on the capillary endothelium. There is some evidence that plasma glycerides may be taken up intact or as partial glyc-

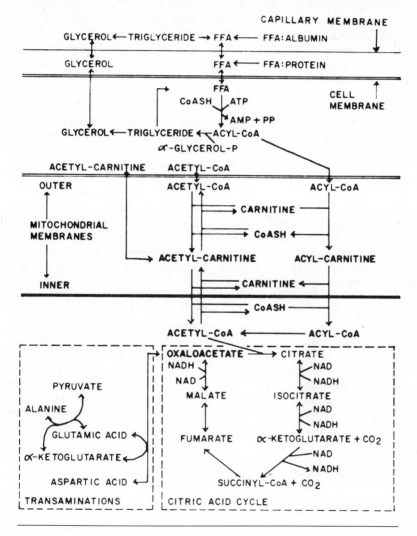

*Figure 2*  Pathway of fatty acid metabolism in the heart.

erides, especially following myocardial injury from toxic doses of catecholamines (190). Inside the cells, fatty acids are activated to fatty acyl-CoA before further metabolism can occur. Activation is catalyzed by a group of enzymes known as acyl-CoA synthetases. The activated fatty acid can either be esterified to triglycerides and phospholipids or oxidized to $CO_2$ and $H_2O$. Acyl-CoA hydrolases are also present that can break down acyl-CoA to fatty acid and CoASH. Tissue lipids can be hydrolyzed to fatty acids and glycerol. Hydrolysis of triglycerides occurs in a stepwise manner with removal of one fatty acid at a time. The process is catalyzed by a series of lipases and the triglyceride lipase appears to be under hormonal control. The fatty acids released from tissue lipids can be reactivated and oxidized.

In heart muscle, oxidation of long-chain fatty acids is completely dependent on the presence of carnitine. The acyl unit from acyl-CoA is transferred to carnitine by carnitine-acyl CoA transferases that are located between the inner and outer mitochondrial membranes. The acyl unit is translocated through the inner mitochondrial membrane and transferred to CoASH inside the mitochondrial matrix by a second carnitine-acyl CoA transferase located on the inner membrane. Carnitine and its acyl derivatives are located exclusively in the cytosolic compartment, whereas CoASH and its acyl derivatives are compartmentalized in both the cytosol and mitochondrial matrix. The inner membrane does not appear to be permeable to either CoASH, carnitine, or their acyl derivatives.

Intramitochondrial acyl-CoA is oxidized to acetyl-CoA by the $\beta$-oxidation system. The acetyl-CoA that is produced is oxidized by the citric acid cycle or transferred to cytosolic carnitine and CoASH by carnitine-acetyl CoA transferases similar to the long-chain acyl transferases.

A number of reviews on fatty acid metabolism have been published. For detailed discussions of many aspects of this subject, the reader is referred to these references (14, 22, 23, 57, 65, 146, 161, 221).

## Rate-Controlling Reactions in Fatty Acid Metabolism

The rate-controlling steps in fatty acid metabolism have not been as well established as they have for carbohydrate metabolism. The rate of utilization is dependent on both the plasma concentration of fatty acids and on the energy demands of the tissue. The availability of plasma fatty acids, as well as alternative substrates, may control the rate of utilization. In addition, lipoprotein lipase appears to be under hormonal control and its activity varies with the nutritional and hormonal status of the animal (193). At any plasma concentration, however, the rate of fatty acid utilization from the plasma or from tissue lipids depends on the energy requirements of the tissue.

The intracellular steps that limit utilization of fatty acid will be discussed in the following sections on individual enzyme systems. However, it is important to point out that the steps that have been reported to limit utilization by isolated mitochondria may be different than those that function in the intact tissue. Many of the conclusions about rate-controlling steps have been derived from studies of the capacity of enzyme systems, i.e. acyl-CoA synthesis or acyl transfer and $\beta$-oxidation, in isolated mitochondria. As pointed out by Bremer & Wajtozak (22), the in vitro capacity of an enzyme system gives little indication of its role as a rate-controlling reaction in vivo. Some of the problems encountered in studying regulation of fatty acid utilization, as mentioned earlier in this review, include the fact that long-chain fatty acids and long-chain acyl-CoA and acyl-carnitine derivatives are only slightly soluble in water, form micelles (241), and bind extensively to soluble and membrane proteins (171). Many of the mitochondrial studies have been conducted with dilute solutions of mitochondria and in some cases without added proteins (22). Therefore, the ratio of long-chain fatty substrates to protein was very different from the ratio in the intact cell. Consequently, concentrations of substrates that have been found to give maximal rates of utilization with isolated mitochondria cannot be expected to behave similarly in the in vivo condition. On the other hand, studies with intact tissue involve measurements of the whole cell content of metabolic intermediates. Reliable methods for distinguishing between cytosolic and mitochondrial matrix metabolites have not been developed. The concentration of unbound fatty acids in the cell has not been measured due to uncertainties of fatty acid binding to proteins in the interstitial and intracellular compartments. In intact cells, one is forced to deal with minimal or maximal possible levels of substrates rather than with concentration of the unbound substrate.

## Mass Action Effect of Increased Plasma Fatty Acids

The rate of fatty acid utilization depends to a large extent on the fatty acid:albumin molar ratio in the plasma (58, 161, 213). With an increase in this ratio, fatty acids bind to sites with less affinity and the rate of uptake by the cells is increased. The rate of uptake is not a linear function of plasma concentration, however, and at high concentrations, cellular binding sites and the capacity of the cells to metabolize fatty acids is saturated. With isolated perfused rat hearts developing low levels of ventricular pressure, a concentration of about 0.5 m$M$ palmitate bound to 3% albumin gives maximal rates of uptake (165). Since this is a higher fatty acid:albumin ratio than is normally found in vivo, the rate of uptake in intact animals could be expected to vary with the plasma concentration up to about 0.8 m$M$ palmitate. With increased cardiac work and increased ATP consumption, a higher fatty acid:albumin ratio was required to saturate uptake.

## Hydrolysis and Uptake of Plasma Lipids

This reaction (plasma triglycerides $\longrightarrow$ glycerol + 3 fatty acids) occurs on the capillary endothelium prior to uptake of glyceride fatty acid by the heart (193). It is catalyzed by lipoprotein lipase (clearing factor lipase), 80% of which is associated with the capillary endothelium and is released with heparin. Activity of clearing factor lipase in adipose tissue is high in fed animals when triglyceride fatty acid is taken up for storage. This activity is decreased in fasted or diabetic animals when mobilization of adipose tissue lipid is rapid. Insulin induces a rise in the activity, and epinephrine, ACTH, growth hormone, and thyroid-stimulating hormone decrease the activity. Although the hormonal effects on lipoprotein lipase are opposite to those on the tissue hormone-sensitive triglyceride lipase, both effects appear to be mediated through changes in cyclic AMP. In heart muscle, as contrasted to adipose tissue, the activity of lipoprotein lipase increases after a 10–24 hr fast and during diabetes in association with accelerated triglyceride oxidation (17). This activity also increased in heart following epinephrine treatment (119) and exercise (154).

## Fatty Acid Activation

This general reaction (ATP+fatty acid+CoASH $\rightleftharpoons$ acyl-CoA+AMP+PP$_i$)[1] accounts for activation of fatty acids in all mammalian tissues (221). It requires $Mg^{2+}$ and is stimulated by other cations, especially $K^+$. The overall reaction is reversible and involves formation of an enzyme-bound acyl adenylate intermediate (9). The acyl-CoA synthetases that catalyze this general reaction appear to have a broad range of specificity with respect to the fatty acid substrate. Enzymes specific for short, medium, and long-chain fatty acids have been described (2, 10, 22, 65, 221). Acetyl-CoA synthetase is found in all tissues and this enzyme also activates propionate. Enzymes that activate butyrate and propionate but not acetate (butyryl-CoA synthetase) are present in heart mitochondria. The medium-chain fatty acids are activated by octanoyl-CoA synthetase. Longer chain acids, $C_{12}$ to $C_{22}$ both saturated and unsaturated, are activated by palmityl-CoA synthetase, so named because its activity is greatest with palmitate as substrate. At the present time it is not clear whether these activities represent a single enzyme for each group of fatty acids or complexes of different enzymes with greater substrate specificity.

Most of the acyl-CoA synthetases require ATP, but about 3% of the activity in liver is GTP-dependent (117, 170, 198). This latter activity does not appear to be present in heart (23). The GTP-specific enzyme activates short, medium, and long-chain fatty acids. Kinetic studies with partially purified long-chain acyl-CoA synthetase indicate that the $K_m$ values for the forward reaction are 42, 4650, and 50 $\mu M$ for palmitate, ATP, and CoASH, respectively (8). For the reverse reaction, the $K_m$ values were 2600, 630, and 890 $\mu M$ for palmityl-CoA, AMP, and PP$_i$, respectively. In homogenates of heart muscle the $K_m$ for CoASH was about 30 $\mu M$ (unpublished observations).

The intracellular distribution of activating enzymes varies somewhat from tissue to tissue. In heart muscle, butyryl-CoA synthetase appears to be located in the mitochondrial matrix, whereas acetyl-CoA synthetase is distributed about equally between matrix and cytosol (10). Medium-chain fatty acids appear to be activated exclusively in the mitochondrial matrix (2), which probably accounts for the fact that mitochondrial oxidation of these fatty acids does not depend on the presence of carnitine (65). Palmityl-CoA synthetase activity in heart muscle is located exclusively on the sarcoplasmic reticulum and outer mitochondrial membrane (23, 49, 65).

Physiological regulation of acyl-CoA synthetases by factors other than availability of substrates (fatty acid or CoASH) has not been clearly established. The total activity in various tissues is greater than that required to support the highest rates of fatty acid oxidation and conversion to tissue lipids (22, 167). In vivo, however, regulation of enzyme activity could make this step rate-controlling. Regulation of palmityl-CoA synthetase by a soluble protein in a manner analogous to regulation of phosphorylase by protein kinase has been proposed (60). Addition of a protein fraction from the supernatant of various tissues was found to activate the microsomal enzyme from liver. Since a high palmitate:albumin molar ratio (6:1) was used in these studies, the effect of the protein fraction could have been to bind fatty acids and palmityl-CoA and to prevent inhibition of the enzyme by these substances. In more recent studies, addition of the supernatant protein fraction did not stimulate synthetase activity (8, 116).

The ATP-dependent enzyme is inhibited by several factors, including $\alpha$-bromopalmitate, high concentrations of erucate, and atractyloside (5, 168, 171, 173, 210). Palmityl-CoA inhibits the liver enzyme by increasing the $K_m$ for CoASH; this inhibition can be reversed by addition of more CoASH (168). Palmityl-CoA synthetase activity in heart muscle is inhibited by long-chain acyl-CoA, and this inhibition can be relieved by addition of albumin (unpublished observations). Product inhibition of fatty acid activation may have a physiological role in regulating rates of fatty acid utilization in intact hearts. High concentrations of palmitate (0.5–1.2 m$M$ bound to 3% albumin) result in accumulation of long-chain acyl-CoA and acetyl-CoA and greatly reduced levels of CoASH in isolated rat hearts (165). It was proposed that fatty acid activation was limited under these conditions by low levels of CoASH. An increase in the $K_m$ of the enzyme for CoASH caused by accumulation of palmityl-CoA would amplify the effect of low CoASH levels. In support of this, acceleration of fatty acid activation by increased cardiac work was associated with higher tissue levels of CoASH and reduced levels of acyl-CoA.

AMP inhibits palmityl-CoA synthetase activity (5, 172), but accelerates activation and oxidation of short- and medium-chain acids, ketone bodies, and citric acid cycle intermediates (56). As pointed out in studies of the AMP inhibition of palmityl-CoA synthetase, high levels of AMP are generally associated with activation of energy-generating pathways. Inhibition of fatty acid activation by AMP would be contrary to this effect. It must be considered, however, that tissue levels of AMP in heart muscle rarely, if ever, increase in well-oxygenated hearts, but increased levels are associated with conditions in which fatty acid oxidation is impaired, i.e. ischemia, hypoxia, or anoxia. Adenosine also inhibits the enzyme (48). Therefore, inhibition of fatty acid activation by AMP and adenosine in oxygen-deficient hearts may have an energy-sparing effect and may limit the undesirable accumulation of long-chain acyl-CoA derivatives in the tissue.

## Triglyceride Homeostasis

Tissue lipids appear to be in a dynamic state at all times. The steady-state levels of tissue triglycerides depend on the relative rates of esterification and lipolysis. Esterification exceeds the rate of lipolysis under some conditions (excess availability of fatty acids and under anoxic or ischemic conditions) and net synthesis of triglycerides occurs. Triglycerides can serve as a source of substrate for energy metabolism in hearts deprived of exogenous fatty acid (45, 52, 158). The rate of lipolysis is accelerated by increased cardiac work or treatment of the tissue with catecholamines (35, 45, 106, 141). Under these conditions, the rate of lipolysis exceeds esterification and the tissue levels of triglycerides decrease.

ESTERIFICATION

 (*a*) acyl-CoA + α-glycerol-P ⟶ 1-acylglycerol-3-P (lyso-phosphatidic acid) + CoASH

 (*b*) 1-acylglycerol-3-P + acyl-CoA ⟶ 1-2-diacylglycerol-3-P (phosphatidic acid) + CoASH

 (*c*) 1-2-diacylglycerol-3-P ⟶ 1-2-diglyceride + $P_i$

 (*d*) 1-2-diglyceride + acetyl-CoA ⟶ triglyceride + CoASH

Acylation of glycerol-3-P occurs in a stepwise manner with addition of one acyl group at a time from long-chain acyl-CoA. Addition of each acyl group appears to be catalyzed by separate enzymes (128). The first acylation is catalyzed by glycerol-3-P acyltransferase, and when saturated acyl-CoA substrates are used it is specific for position one on glycerol-3-P. Monoacylglycerol-3-P acyltransferase catalyzes acylation of the second position forming phosphatidic acid. Lyso-phosphatidic acid and phosphatidic acid have been isolated during liver microsomal and mitochondrial synthesis of complex lipids (200). Phosphatidic acid is an intermediate in the synthesis of both phospholipids and triglycerides. Phosphatidic acid phosphatase catalyzes formation of 1,2-diglyceride. A diglyceride acyl-transferase adds the third acyl group to form triglyceride. These esterification enzymes are found in microsomal, mitochondrial, and lysosomal fractions of cell homogenates.

 Little is known about the regulation of lipid synthesis in heart muscle. Exogenous $^{14}C$-fatty acids are rapidly incorporated into triglycerides (216). Tissue levels of neutral lipids are higher in hearts from diabetic or fasted animals and can be elevated by perfusion of isolated hearts with buffer containing palmitate (141, 185). These increases are associated with higher tissue levels of fatty acid and fatty acyl-CoA (72, 165). The amount of lipid, the rate of fatty acid conversion to trigylcerides, and the tissue levels of fatty acyl-CoA are increased in ischemic and anoxic myocardium (57, 149, 201). These data imply that the rate of esterification depends on the availability of fatty acid, the rate of fatty acid oxidation, and the tissue levels of acyl-CoA. On the other hand, no correlation could be demonstrated between tissue levels of acyl-CoA and rates of esterification in adipose tissue (51) or liver (200). The activity of palmityl-CoA synthetase in liver mitochondria was some 5–6 times higher than that of glycerol-3-P acyltransferase, suggesting that the activity of the latter enzyme was rate-limiting for triglyceride synthesis (200). If this situation pertains to heart, the increase in neutral lipids that occurs with increased availability or decreased oxidation of fatty acids may not be related solely to higher levels of fatty acyl-CoA. It is of interest that isolated hearts perfused with palmitate utilized endogenous triglycerides at a slower rate and have a lower lipase activity than hearts perfused with glucose (43), indicating that decreased lipolysis may account for much of the net increase in tissue lipids.

 Much of the increase in neutral lipids that occurs during oxygen deficiency or exposure to high levels of fatty acids may be related to availability of glycerol-3-P. Tissue levels of glycerol-3-P increase in anoxic (234) and ischemic (unpublished observations) hearts. Increased triglyceride formation in diabetic hearts and in isolated hearts perfused with fatty acid may also be related to increased production of glycerol-3-P (53, 72). Heart muscle contains very little glycerol kinase activity

(153). Since $^{14}$C-glucose is incorporated into glyceride glycerol but not to glyceride fatty acid (53, 122), glycolysis appears to be the source of glycerol-3-P for glyceride synthesis.

LIPOLYSIS
   (a) Triglyceride $\longrightarrow$ diglyceride + fatty acid
   (b) Diglyceride $\longrightarrow$ monoglyceride + fatty acid
   (c) Monoglyceride $\longrightarrow$ fatty acid + glycerol

Triglycerides are sequentially hydrolyzed to fatty acids and glycerol. Removal of the first fatty acid by triglyceride lipase is rate-limiting (52). For this reason, most of the neutral lipid present in heart muscle is triglyceride; the ratio being 13:0.1:0.6 for tri-, di-, and monoglycerides, respectively.

Regulation of lipase activity in heart appears to be similar in many respects to that of the adipose tissue enzyme (35). The rate of lipolysis, as measured by glycerol release, is accelerated in hearts removed from diabetic or fasted animals and subsequently perfused in vitro (72, 185), and is stimulated by catecholamines in association with elevated tissue levels of cyclic AMP (35). Unlike the adipose tissue system, however, insulin does not block the rise in cyclic AMP and the increase in glycerol release induced by isoproterenol (35). The mechanism of the accelerated glyceride utilization that is associated with increased cardiac work in isolated hearts perfused without exogenous fatty acid may involve decreased tissue levels of fatty acid and fatty acyl-CoA (165). Since fatty acids are inhibitory to lipase activity (43), increased lipolysis may result from a faster removal of product.

## Acyl Transfer and Translocation and the Function of Carnitine

   1. acyl-CoA$_{out}$ + carnitine$_{out}$ $\rightleftharpoons$ acyl-carnitine$_{out}$ + CoASH$_{out}$
   2. acyl-carnitine$_{out}$ + CoASH$_{in}$ $\rightleftharpoons$ acyl-CoA$_{in}$ + carnitine$_{out}$

These general reactions account for the transfer of long-, medium-, and short-chain acyl units between acyl-CoA and acyl-carnitine in the extramitochondrial compartment (reaction 1) and between cytosolic acyl-carnitine and CoASH within the mitochondrial matrix (reaction 2) (65, 67). "In" and "out" in the above reactions refer to the space within the inner mitochondrial membrane and the combined intermembrane space and cytosol, respectively. These reactions are catalyzed by carnitine-acyl CoA transferases. Transferase systems that are specific for long-chain (carnitine-palmityl CoA transferase), medium-chain (carnitine-octanoyl CoA transferase), and short-chain fatty acids (carnitine-acetyl CoA transferase) have been described (65, 212).

Fatty acids that are activated in the extramitochondrial space, regardless of chain length, apparently cannot penetrate the inner mitochondrial membrane without first being transferred from acyl-CoA to carnitine by reaction 1 above (22, 65). Short- and medium-chain fatty acids can be activated within the matrix by the acyl-CoA synthetases located within this space and their subsequent oxidation is carnitine independent (23, 65). However, oxidation of long-chain fatty acids by heart muscle is completely dependent on the presence of carnitine. A second transferase enzyme is located on or within the inner mitochondrial membrane (66, 80, 90, 156, 220) and, in some manner, this enzyme transfers the acyl group from acyl carnitine across the membrane and reforms acyl-CoA inside the mitochondrial matrix. As originally proposed by Fritz & Yue (67), the acyl-carnitine derivatives penetrate the inner membrane and transfer of the acyl unit occurred within the matrix space. However, it is now thought that the inner membrane is impermeable to CoASH, acetyl-CoA, carnitine, acetyl-carnitine, and possibly to long-chain acyl-CoA and carnitine derivatives (24, 80).

Yates & Garland (239, 240) modified Fritz's original model to allow for the membrane location of transferase II and for a permeability barrier to both CoASH and carnitine. The model now includes a bimodal distribution of carnitine-acyl CoA transferase with one activity located either on the outer mitochondrial membrane or between the inner and outer membranes (transferase I). Transferase II is more closely associated with the inner membrane and catalyzes the anisotropic translocation of acyl units from cytosolic acyl-carnitine to matrix CoASH without the acyl-carnitine molecule actually penetrating the inner membrane. Two transferase activities with somewhat different properties have been isolated (25, 34, 225). Recently, data has been presented which indicate that long-chain acyl-carnitine does in fact penetrate mitochondrial membranes and that penetration occurs along a hydrogen ion concentration gradient (115). Since free carnitine does not readily penetrate biological membranes, acyl transfer within the mitochondrial matrix would, however, require a mechanism for transporting carnitine back into the cytosol.

The transferase reactions are freely reversible and, based on the measured ratios of substrates and products, are maintained at or near their equilibrium positions in intact tissues (22). The equilibrium constants in the direction of acyl-carnitine synthesis is 0.45 for carnitine-palmityl CoA transferase (155). The equilibrium constant toward acetyl-CoA synthesis is 0.6 for carnitine-acetyl CoA transferase (68). The reported $K_m$ values for the various substrates of carnitine-palmityl CoA transferase range from 5.5 to 45 $\mu M$ for CoASH, 10 to 30 $\mu M$ for palmityl-CoA, 45 to 2100 $\mu M$ carnitine, and 40 to 140 $\mu M$ for palmityl carnitine (21, 102).

Synthesis of palmityl-carnitine was reported to be rate-limiting for fatty acid oxidation in liver mitochondria (207) but more recent studies have shown that either the capacity to translocate acyl units or the rate of β-oxidation limits the maximum rate of oxidation by isolated mitochondria (22, 167). Mitochondria from heart muscle have the highest capacity to oxidize acyl-carnitine of any tissue studied (16); Fritz (65) concluded that synthesis of palmityl-carnitine was rate-limiting for fatty acid oxidation in muscle mitochondria. However, in isolated perfused hearts the rate of acetyl-CoA oxidation through the citric acid cycle limited the rate of fatty acid utilization at low levels of ATP utilization (142, 165). When oxidative phosphorylation and fatty acid oxidation were stimulated by increased cardiac work, the tissue levels of fatty acyl-carnitine increased in association with decreased levels of fatty acyl-CoA and acetyl-CoA, indicating that oxidation of acyl-carnitine limited maximal rates of fatty acid utilization at fast rates of ATP consumption. Acyl translocation and transfer to matrix CoASH, rather than β-oxidation, appeared to be the

limiting step. This conclusion was based on the observation that oxidation of octano-
ate, which can bypass the carnitine-dependent translocation step, maintained high
tissue levels of acetyl-CoA.

Physiological regulation of long-chain acyl transferases has not been clearly established. Carnitine-palmityl CoA transferase is inhibited by all of its substrates (22,
65). Palmityl-CoA inhibits by increasing the $K_m$ for carnitine; this inhibition may
function in vivo to divert acyl units from oxidation to synthesis of triglyceride.
Accumulation of palmityl-CoA and inhibition of acyl-CoA synthetase could also
function to limit fatty acid activation.

## β-Oxidation

1. Acyl-CoA $+$ FAD$^+$ $\rightleftharpoons$ $\alpha$-$\beta$-unsaturated acyl-CoA $+$ FADH$_2$
2. $\alpha$-$\beta$ unsaturated acyl-CoA $+$ H$_2$O $\rightleftharpoons$ $\beta$-hydroxyacyl-CoA
3. $\beta$-hydroxyacyl-CoA $+$ NAD$^+$ $\rightleftharpoons$ $\beta$-ketoacyl-CoA $+$ NADH $+$ H$^+$
4. $\beta$-ketoacyl-CoA $+$ CoASH $\rightleftharpoons$ acyl-CoA ($-2$ carbons) $+$ acetyl-CoA

These four reactions account for the stepwise degradation of fatty acyl-CoAs to
acetyl-CoA by the $\beta$-oxidation system (221). The enzymes that catalyze these
reactions are located in the mitochondrial matrix in close association with the inner
membrane (11). In mammalian cells, fatty acids appear to be degraded exclusively
by the $\beta$-oxidation system (92). The above reactions are catalyzed by acyl-CoA
dehydrogenases, enoyl-CoA hydrase, $\beta$-hydroxyacyl-CoA dehydrogenase, and thiolase, respectively. Fatty acyl-CoAs with chain lengths from $C_4$ to $C_{20}$ are readily
oxidized by this system. Of the acyl-CoA dehydrogenases, enzymes specific for
short-, medium-, and long-chain acyl-CoAs have been isolated (221). Free acyl-CoA
intermediates apparently do occur during oxidation of long-chain acyl-CoAs, and
under specific conditions shorter chain intermediates have been isolated (217). In
isolated mitochrondria, $\beta$-hydroxyacyl-CoA can be made to accumulate when the
NADH/NAD ratio is high (22). This intermediate can also be transferred to carnitine with accumulation of $\beta$-hydroxyacyl-carnitine.

Regulation of $\beta$-oxidation in intact cells appears to occur through variations in
the levels of substrates (acyl-CoA, NAD$^+$, and FAD$^+$) (22). Although the thiolase
reaction is reversible, the equilibrium constant is greatly in favor of acetyl-CoA
formation (221), suggesting that accumulation of acetyl-CoA would not have a large
influence on the overall rate of $\beta$-oxidation except through reduced levels of matrix
CoASH. The rate of $\beta$-oxidation is geared to flux through the citric acid cycle and
to the rate of oxidative phosphorylation. The maximum rate is achieved with an
energy charge of 0.65 (92). A high NADH/NAD ratio inhibits the $\beta$-hydroxyacyl-
CoA dehydrogenase and, based on the appearance of $\beta$-hydroxyacyl-carnitine, $\beta$-
hydroxyacyl-CoA accumulates (22). The presence of succinate inhibits the overall
rate of $\beta$-oxidation in isolated mitochondria apparently by competing for FAD$^+$,
although some decrease in fatty acyl-CoA does occur. A reduction in mitochondrial
acyl-CoA by high levels of carnitine or by binding of extramitochondrial acyl-
carnitine to albumin shifts the transferase reaction toward formation of acyl-carnitine and lowers the rate of $\beta$-oxidation. Similarly, lower levels of long-chain

acyl-CoA and reduced rates of oxidation followed addition of 4-pentenoic acid, whose CoA derivative is oxidized only slowly and accumulates in the mitochondria (70).

In isolated rat hearts perfused with high levels of palmitate, the rate of $\beta$-oxidation is geared directly to the rate of oxidative phosphorylation and may be limited at low rates of energy use by the concerted action of high NADH/NAD ratios and the accumulation of acetyl-CoA (146). With increased oxidative phosphorylation as a result of elevated cardiac work, the NADH/NAD ratio decreased, flux through the citric acid cycle increased, and $\beta$-oxidation accelerated. Since succinate inhibited $\beta$-oxidation in isolated mitochondria by competing for available FAD$^+$ and CoASH (22), it is of interest that the level of succinyl-CoA decreased as the concentration of palmitate was raised in hearts performing low levels of work, and more of the total CoASH was shifted to formation of long-chain acyl-CoA and acetyl-CoA (146). With increased cardiac work and acceleration of the citric acid cycle and $\beta$-oxidation, the reverse shift occurred and the levels of succinyl-CoA increased. These observations indicate that the concentration of succinyl-CoA per se does not greatly influence the rate of either $\beta$-oxidation or the activity of citrate synthetase (211) in intact tissue. The level of succinyl-CoA appears to be determined by the rate of oxidative phosphorylation, the tissue level of acetyl-CoA, and flux through the first portions of the citric acid cycle.

## Acetyl Transfer and Translocation

Transfer of acetyl units between CoASH and carnitine and translocation between the mitochondrial matrix and cytosol occurs by a two-enzyme system similar to that for long-chain acyl units (see section on acyl transfer above). Carnitine acetyl-CoA transferases have been characterized in heart muscle (65, 68, 123). This enzyme system, like the long-chain acyl transferase, appears to function at or near its equilibrium position under most conditions (165, 178). Palmityl-CoA inhibits acetyl transferase by competing with carnitine (33). In the perfused rat heart, the mass-action ratio for these enzymes is shifted toward synthesis of acetyl-CoA when the concentration of exogenous palmitate is high (165). This effect is associated with higher levels of fatty acyl-CoA and possibly results from acyl-CoA inhibition of acetyl transferases. The shift could function to limit $\beta$-oxidation by increasing acetyl-CoA and decreasing CoASH in the mitochondrial matrix.

Since acetate does not represent a major physiological fuel and since a large fraction of the total acetyl-CoA synthetase activity is located in the mitochondrial matrix, the physiological function of carnitine-acetyl CoA transferase is not clear. The activity of this enzyme system is high in tissue with large oxidative capacity (23, 65). It has been proposed that one function of acetyl translocation may be storage of excess high energy acetyl units produced by $\beta$-oxidation as acetyl-carnitine and acetyl-CoA in the cytosol (178). Rapid transfer of acetyl units from the cytosolic compartment would buffer large changes in matrix acetyl-CoA. A more recent proposal suggests that this enzyme system may function to couple the rates of cytosolic fatty acid activation and acyl transfer to the rate of oxidation (165). By this mechanism, excess acetyl units produced in the mitochondrial matrix would be transferred to cytosolic carnitine and CoASH. The lower levels of these substrates in the cytosol could limit fatty acid activation and acyl transfer. With increased oxidative phosphorylation and increased utilization of acetyl-CoA by the citric acid cycle, acetyl units could be rapidly transferred back into the matrix making more CoASH and carnitine available in the cytosol.

# INTEGRATED CONTROL OF FATTY ACID METABOLISM

## Increased Availability of Fatty Acids

The in vivo control of fatty acid metabolism by the heart encompasses regulation of plasma levels of fatty acids, triglycerides, and other substrates by extramyocardial tissues as well as local control of specific enzyme systems involved in myocardial fatty acid utilization. As indicated previously, the rate of fatty acid uptake depends to a large extent on the fatty acid:albumin molar ratio, and within physiological concentrations, the rate of uptake is directly proportional to the level of plasma fatty acid (165). Also, the increased activity of lipoprotein lipase makes more fatty acid available from plasma glycerides for uptake by the heart when fatty acid is mobilized from adipose tissue. Much of the control of myocardial fatty acid utilization is, therefore, exerted by whole body regulation of fatty acid mobilization and synthesis in adipose tissue and liver (193). Thus, in the postabsorptive state, in diabetes or fasting when plasma levels of insulin are low and fatty acid mobilization is rapid, the rate of fatty acid uptake, oxidation, and storage by heart muscle is increased.

In the presence of a high fatty acid:albumin ratio, the rate of acetyl-CoA utilization through the citric acid cycle limits fatty acid oxidation and the tissue levels of acetyl-CoA, acetyl-carnitine, acyl-CoA, and acyl-carnitine increase, while the levels of free CoASH and carnitine decrease (165). Tissue lipids also increased in hearts perfused with high concentrations of palmitate (43, 141). Unlike liver and adipose tissue, cardiac muscle normally accumulates relatively little triglycerides even when excess fatty acids are available. The restricted accumulation of tissue lipids and the limited rate of fatty acid uptake at high perfusate concentrations of fatty acid may be due to 1. control of the activating enzymes by low levels of CoASH and perhaps by increased levels of acyl-CoA and 2. control of $\beta$-oxidation by low levels of CoASH and high levels of NADH (146, 165). Flux through the citric acid cycle is known to be geared to oxidative phosphorylation by changes in the levels of high energy phosphates and NADH (74, 111, 184). Both the level of high energy phosphates and the NADH:NAD ratio increase in hearts oxidizing palmitate as compared to those oxidizing glucose (146). With saturating levels of exogenous palmitate, flux through the citric acid cycle is limited by the dehydrogenase reactions and the level of acetyl-CoA increases about 10-fold. This rise in acetyl-CoA is accompanied by a 50% increase in fatty acyl-CoA, an 8-fold increase in acetyl-carnitine, and a 3-fold increase in acyl-carnitine. Since acetyl-carnitine is located in the cytosol and is in equilibrium with both the cytosolic and matrix pools of acetyl-CoA through the carnitine-acetyl CoA transferase system, the rise in acetyl-carnitine probably indicates that much of the increase in acetyl-CoA occurred in the cytosol. An associated decrease in succinyl-CoA indicates that matrix CoASH is preferentially converted to acetyl-CoA. The levels of both CoASH and carnitine decrease to values below those found to give optimal rates of fatty acid activation and acyl transfer in tissue homogenates (22, 65, 165).

Collectively, these data are interpreted to indicate that limited flux through the citric acid cycle resulted in higher levels of acetyl-CoA and lower levels of CoASH in both the cytosol and mitochondrial matrix. These changes function as a feedback control to limit fatty acid activation in the cytosol and $\beta$-oxidation in the matrix. The low levels of carnitine may also limit fatty acyl transfer, suggesting that the small increase in fatty acyl-CoA occurs in the cytosol. If so, fatty acyl-CoA inhibition of acyl-CoA synthetase activity associated with lower levels of CoASH could account for the limited rate of fatty acid uptake.

## Effects of Fatty Acid Utilization on Production of Inhibitors of Glycolysis

Limited flux through the citric acid cycle in hearts oxidizing fatty acids accounts for increased production of inhibitors of glycolysis (19, 185) and preferential oxidation of fatty acids. Production of acetyl-CoA from fatty acids is associated with production of excess NADH both from $\beta$-oxidation and the citric acid cycle. Since oxidative phosphorylation utilizes NADH only in responses to ATP hydrolysis, the NADH/NAD$^+$ ratio increases and the rates of dehydrogenase reactions, principally isocitric dehydrogenase and a $\beta$-ketoglutarate dehydrogenase (111, 146, 184), are geared to the rate of oxidative phosphorylation. With limited flux through the dehydrogenases and continued production of acetyl-CoA, the rate of citrate and isocitrate synthesis exceeds flux through the rest of the cycle and the levels of these metabolites increase (19, 185). This so-called "unspanning" (184) of the cycle results in lower levels of oxaloacetate which then limits the rate of citrate synthesis and leads to accumulation of acetyl-CoA. Since lower perfusate levels of fatty acid are required to cause accumulation of citrate than of acetyl-CoA, inhibition of the citric acid cycle by high NADH is more marked than inhibition of $\beta$-oxidation (146, 165). The extra carbon involved in accumulation of citrate and isocitrate comes from a shift in the aspartate-oxaloacetate transamination reaction (19). However, only a limited amount of aspartate is available, and with limited production of oxaloacetate from within the cycle, citrate synthesis and oxidation of acetyl-CoA are ultimately controlled by the rate of oxaloacetate formation. As discussed earlier, this mechanism accounts for preferential utilization of fatty acids by inhibition of phosphofructokinase due to higher levels of citrate, inhibition of pyruvate oxidation by increased NADH and acetyl-CoA, and inhibition of glucose transport by as yet unknown factors. It also should be noted that control of the citric acid cycle via coupling to oxidative phosphorylation simultaneously results in regulation of fatty acid and carbohydrate utilization. As noted above, fatty acid oxidation is controlled at the fatty acid activation and $\beta$-oxidation steps by low levels of CoASH.

## Effects of Increased ATP Utilization

Increasing the rate of energy utilization by raising the level of cardiac work accelerated the rate of palmitate uptake and oxidation (44, 141, 165). The sequence of events in the effect of work on fatty acid uptake appears to be increased oxidative phosphorylation, lower levels of NADH, and acceleration of the citric acid cycle (146, 165). With increased flux through the cycle, tissue levels of acetyl-CoA, fatty acyl-CoA, and acetyl-carnitine decrease while the levels of CoASH, carnitine, and fatty acyl-carnitine increase. These changes are associated with lower levels of tissue fatty acids, faster rates of fatty acid oxidation, activation, and uptake. In addition, the reversed flux of acetyl units from the cytosol into the matrix is initiated by increased utilization of acetyl-CoA through the citric acid cycle and leads to elevated levels of cytosolic CoASH and carnitine. These changes increase rates of fatty acid activation and acyl transfer to carnitine, lead to higher levels of fatty acyl-carnitine, and lower levels of tissue fatty acid and accelerated fatty acid uptake. With increased oxidative phosphorylation, the rate of fatty acid oxidation appears to be limited by acyl translocation from acyl-carnitine across the inner mitochondrial membrane (165).

When low levels of exogenous palmitate are present, an increase in CoASH with increased cardiac work cannot account for stimulation of fatty acid activation and uptake. In these hearts, however, there is a small decrease in fatty acyl-CoA. The extent to which this decrease could contribute to activation of acyl-CoA synthetase is unknown. If it is assumed that much of the tissue acyl-CoA is bound to proteins and that the observed decrease occurs in the cytosolic compartment, the decrease in the unbound concentration would be large and could account for a faster rate of fatty acid activation.

Certain other substrates when present in the blood in sufficiently high concentrations can decrease the rate of uptake and oxidation of fatty acids. Pyruvate and ketone bodies have been reported to reduce oxidation (14, 59). The mechanism of this effect is not clear, but may be related to the ability of these substrates to compete for available pools of CoASH and $NAD^+$. Glucose does not decrease the rate of palmitate uptake, indicating that sufficient quantities of pyruvate cannot be produced by glycolysis (161). The presence of high concentrations of pyruvate increase $C^{14}$-palmitate conversion to tissue lipids (59). This observation indicates that pyruvate competes more effectively for matrix CoASH than for cytosolic CoASH and leads to inhibition of $\beta$-oxidation. Erucic acid, an ingredient of margarine in some countries, inhibits fatty acid oxidation and results in increased conversion of fatty acids to triglycerides in heart muscle (36).

Endogenous triglycerides can serve as a source of fatty acids for energy metabolism, whereas phospholipids appear to function primarily as structural lipids and contribute little, if any, fatty acids for energy metabolism. Utilization of tissue lipid is evident in hearts perfused without exogenous substrate or with glucose (44, 52, 141, 158). High levels of tissue triglycerides accumulate in hearts following injury from toxic doses of norepinephrine (190). This increase in tissue lipid only occurs when exogenous lipid is present and is not related to high tissue levels of fatty acids. However, fatty acid oxidation is decreased under these conditions, and, although tissue levels of fatty acyl-CoA were not measured, these levels may have been elevated.

Accelerated rates of triglyceride utilization occur in hearts treated with isoproterenol (35) and in hearts performing increased cardiac work if exogenous fatty acids are not present (43, 141). The contribution of endogenous lipids to energy metabolism is also increased in hearts perfused with glucose and acetate when the work load is raised (142). The effect of catecholamines on triglyceride utilization appears to be mediated by higher levels of cyclic-AMP and activation of the tissue lipase. The effect of increased cardiac work is associated with lower tissue levels of fatty acids and fatty acyl-CoA (165). Thus accelerated utilization of tissue lipid with increased cardiac work may result from lower levels of the products of lipolysis.

## Fatty Acid Metabolism in Oxygen Deficiency

With a decrease in oxygen supply, oxidation of fatty acids by the heart sharply declines (57, 161, 201). Fatty acid uptake is either reduced or remains unchanged, but a large fraction is converted to tissue lipids. In association with the reduced rate of fatty acid oxidation in ischemic rat hearts, the tissue levels of fatty acyl-CoA increases 3-fold (149) and $\alpha$-glycerol-P increases by more than 15-fold (unpublished observation). Increased levels of both substrates for glyceride synthesis may account for the accelerated conversion of fatty acid to tissue lipids. The rate of fatty acid synthesis in the heart is normally slow, but under hypoxic conditions conversion of $^{14}$C-acetate to long-chain fatty acids is increased (82, 226). The rate of fatty acid synthesis is directly proportional to lactate production (82), indicating that lipid synthesis is related to the availability of reducing equivalents.

Other than the inability to synthesize ATP, the metabolic and functional consequences of reduced fatty acid oxidation in hypoxic or ischemic hearts are currently a controversial subject. The presence of high levels of fatty acids has been reported to decrease myocardial contractility (87) and to increase arrhythmias (109), but these observations have been disputed (189). Fatty acids have been reported to be uncouplers of oxidative phosphorylation (18) and to increase oxygen consumption by the heart (31). However, oxygen consumption is increased by only about 13% in isolated rat hearts perfused with 1.2 m$M$ palmitate bound to 3% albumin, as compared to hearts perfused with glucose alone (165). This is the theoretical increase that would be expected from a shift from oxidation of glucose with a P/O ratio of 3.2 to oxidation of fatty acid with a P/O ratio of 2.8; that is, for the same rate of synthesis of ATP or its energetic equivalents, more oxygen must be consumed when fatty acids are substrates.

High levels of fatty acids and fatty acyl-CoA derivatives are known to inhibit many enzymes in a nonspecific manner (171). In addition, fatty acyl-CoAs inhibit some enzymes in a specific fashion. Inhibition of fatty acyl-CoA synthetase by palmityl-CoA was mentioned earlier, and inhibition of adenine nucleotide transferase by fatty acids and several acyl-CoA derivatives has been reported (169, 208, 235). It was suggested that inhibition of nucleotide translocation by acyl-CoAs may have a function in regulation of cardiac metabolism (209). In aerobic hearts perfused with high levels of palmitate, tissue levels of fatty acyl-CoA increased only about 50% (165). This lack of acyl-CoA accumulation results from preferential conversion of available cytosolic CoASH to acetyl-CoA. Acetyl-CoA is not an inhibitor of adenine nucleotide transferase (169). Therefore, rapid conversion of long-chain acyl-CoAs to acetyl-CoA and transfer to the acetyl units to cytosolic CoASH may represent an important protective function of the carnitine-acetyl-CoA transferase in heart muscle. In ischemic hearts, however, the reduction in fatty acid oxidation is accompanied by lower tissue levels of acetyl-carnitine and acetyl-CoA (149), presumably due to inhibition of $\beta$-oxidation, and by increased levels of fatty acyl-CoA and fatty acyl-carnitine. In addition, the carnitine-acyl-CoA transferase activity of mitochondria isolated from chronically ischemic myocardium is greatly reduced and some reduction is seen even after 30 min of ischemia (238).

## SUMMARY

Utilization of carbohydrate and lipid in heart muscle is closely coupled to the energy needs of the heart. When the substrates are present together, fatty acid is used in preference to glucose. Inhibition of glycolysis is accounted for by inhibition of glucose transport, hexokinase, phosphofructokinase, and pyruvate dehydrogenase. Addition of high levels of insulin can overcome the transport block, but inhibition of intracellular glucose metabolism remains. Increased ventricular pressure development accelerates glucose transport, hexokinase, and phosphofructokinase if only the sugar is provided as exogenous substrate. When fatty acid is also present, it remains the preferred substrate. Restriction of oxygen availability by reduction of perfusate oxygen tension to zero markedly accelerates glucose and glycogen utilization. On the other hand, restriction of oxygen availability by reduction of coronary flow inhibits glycolysis. In both cases, levels of fructose-1,6-P are increased, but in the ischemic tissue, disposal of this intermediate is restrained at the glyceraldehyde-3-P dehydrogenase step, probably as a result of high levels of NADH. In the ischemic muscle, high levels of lactate accumulate, suggesting that reoxidation of NADH may be limited by transport of reducing equivalents out of the heart.

The rate of fatty acid uptake and oxidation by aerobic heart muscle is controlled primarily by 1. availability of exogenous fatty acid, 2. the rate of acetyl-CoA oxidation by the citric acid cycle at low rates of energy utilization, and 3. the rate of acyl translocation across the inner mitochondrial membrane at high rates of energy utilization. The presence of a high activity of carnitine-acetyl-CoA transferase appears to have an important function in coupling rates of fatty acid activation and acyl transfer to the rate of oxidative phosphorylation and utilization of acetyl-CoA by the citric acid cycle. The rate of flux through the dehydrogenase reaction of the citric acid cycle ultimately determines the rates of oxidation of both carbohydrate and fatty substrates and adjusts the rate of utilization of each substrate to the availability of the other.

Endogenous triglycerides can be used for energy metabolism. The rate of utilization depends on availability of exogenous fatty acid, the presence of hormones such as catecholamines and insulin, and on the level of cardiac work. The biochemical mechanisms that control the rates of synthesis and lipolysis are poorly understood.

Fatty acid metabolism in hypoxic and ischemic hearts is characterized by reduced rates of oxidation and uptake, higher levels of fatty acyl-CoA and $\alpha$-glycerol phosphate, and increased conversion of fatty acids to tissue lipids. Tissue levels of acetyl-CoA and acetyl-carnitine decrease while levels of CoASH, carnitine, fatty acyl-CoA, and fatty acyl-carnitine increase. Higher tissue levels of fatty acids, fatty acyl-CoA, and fatty acyl-carnitine may be detrimental to myocardial metabolism and function. This point, however, requires further investigation.

*Literature Cited*

1. Aaronson, R. P., Frieden, C. 1972. Rabbit muscle phosphofructokinase: studies on the polymerization. *J. Biol. Chem.* 247:7502–9

2. Aas, M., Bremer, J. 1968. Short-chain fatty acid activation in rat liver. A new assay procedure for the enzymes and studies on their intracellular localization. *Biochim. Biophys. Acta* 164:157–66

3. Abrahams, S. L., Younathan, E. S. 1971. Modulation of the kinetic properties of phosphofructokinase by ammonium ions. *J. Biol. Chem.* 246:2464–67

4. Adrouny, G. A. 1969. Differential patterns of glycogen metabolism in cardiac and skeletal muscles. *Am. J. Physiol.* 217:686–93

5. Alexandre, A., Rossi, C. R., Sartorelli, L., Siliprandi, N. 1969. The action of atractyloside and AMP on long-chain fatty acid oxidation and on the ATP-dependent fatty acid thiokinase. *FEBS Lett.* 3:279–82

6. Antony, G. J., Srinivasan, I., Williams, H. R., Landau, B. R. 1969. Studies on the existence of a pathway in liver and muscle for the conversion of glucose into glycogen without glucose-6-phosphate as an intermediate. *Biochem. J.* 111:453–59

7. Baldwin, K. M., Klinkerfuss, G. H., Terjung, R. L., Mole, P. A., Holloszy, J. O. 1972. Respiratory capacity of white, red, and intermediate muscle: adaptative response to exercise. *Am. J. Physiol.* 222:373–78

8. Bar-Tana, J., Rose, G., Shapiro, B. 1971. The purification and properties of microsomal palmitoyl-coenzyme A synthetase. *Biochem. J.* 122:353–62

9. Bar-Tana, J., Rose, G., Shapiro, B. 1972. Microsomal palmitoyl coenzyme A synthetase from rat liver. *Biochem. J.* 129:1101–7

10. Barth, C., Sladek, M., Decker, K. 1971. The subcellular distribution of short-chain fatty acyl-CoA synthetase activity in rat tissues. *Biochim. Biophys. Acta* 248:23–33

11. Beattie, D. S. 1968. The submitochondrial distribution of the fatty acid oxidizing system in rat liver mitochondria. *Biochem. Biophys. Res. Commun.* 30:57–62

12. Beatty, C. H., Bocek, R. M. 1971. Interrelation of carbohydrate and palmitate metabolism in skeletal muscle. *Am. J. Physiol.* 220:1928–34

13. Bianco, J. A. et al 1971. Effects of glucagon on myocardial oxygen consumption and potassium balance. *Am. J. Physiol.* 221:626–31

14. Bing, R. J. 1965. Cardiac metabolism. *Physiol. Rev.* 45:171–213

15. Bloxham, D. P., Lardy, H. A. 1973. Phosphofructokinase. *Enzymes* 8:239–78

16. Bode, C., Klingenberg, M. 1964. Carnitine and fatty acid oxidation in mitochondria of various organs. *Biochim. Biophys. Acta* 84:93–95

17. Borensztajn, J., Robinson, D. S. 1970. The effects of fasting on the utilization of chylomicron triglyceride fatty acids in relation to clearing factor lipase (lipoprotein lipase) releasable by heparin in the perfused rat heart. *J. Lipid Res.* 11:111–17

18. Borst, P., Loos, J. A., Christ, E. J., Slater, E. C. 1962. Uncoupling activity of long-chain fatty acids. *Biochim. Biophys. Acta* 62:509–18

19. Bowman, R. H. 1966. Effects of diabetes, fatty acids, and ketone bodies on tricarboxylic acid cycle metabolism in the perfused rat heart. *J. Biol. Chem.* 241:3041–48

20. Brachfeld, N., Scheuer, J. 1967. Metabolism of glucose by the ischemic dog heart. *Am. J. Physiol.* 212:603–06

21. Bremer, J., Norum, K. R. 1967. The mechanism of substrate inhibition of palmityl coenzyme A:carnitine palmityltransferase by palmityl coenzyme A. *J. Biol. Chem.* 242:1744–48

22. Bremer, J., Wojtczak, A. B. 1972. Factors controlling the rate of fatty acid β-oxidation in rat liver mitochondria. *Biochim. Biophys. Acta* 280:515–30

23. Bressler, R. 1970. Physiological-chemical aspects of fatty acid oxidation. In *Lipid Metabolism*, ed. S. J. Wakil, 49–75. New York: Academic

24. Brosnan, J. T., Fritz, I. B. 1971. The permeability of mitochondria to carnitine and acetyl carnitine. *Biochem. J.* 125:94P

25. Brosnan, J. T., Fritz, I. B. 1971. The oxidation of fatty-acyl derivatives by mitochondria from bovine fetal and calf hearts. *Can. J. Biochem.* 49:1296–1300

26. Burges, R. A., Butt, W. D., Baggaley, A. 1968. Some effects of α-bromopalmitate, an inhibitor of fatty acid oxidation, on carbohydrate metabolism in the rat. *Biochem. J.* 109:38P–39P

27. Cahill, G. F. Jr., Marliss, E. B., Aoki, T. T. 1970. Fat and nitrogen metabo-

lism in fasting man. In *Adipose Tissue*, ed. R. Levine, E. F. Pfeiffer, 181–85. New York: Academic

28. Carlson, L. A., Ekelund, L. G., Fröberg, S. O. 1971. Concentration of triglycerides, phospholipids and glycogen in skeletal muscle and of free fatty acids and $\beta$-hydroxybutyric acid in blood in response to exercise. *Eur. J. Clin. Invest.* 1:248–54

29. Carter, N. W. 1972. Intracellular pH. *Kidney Int.* 1:341–46

30. Chain, E. B., Mansford, K. R. L., Opie, L. H. 1969. Effects of insulin on the pattern of glucose metabolism in the perfused working and Langendorff heart of normal and insulin-deficient rats. *Biochem. J.* 115:537–46

31. Challoner, D., Steinberg, D. 1966. Effect of free fatty acid on the oxygen consumption of perfused rat heart. *Am. J. Physiol.* 210:280–86

32. Chance, B., Williams, G. R. 1956. The respiratory chain and oxidative phosphorylation. *Advan. Enzymol.* 17:65–134

33. Chase, J. F. A. 1967. The substrate specificity of carnitine acetyltransferase. *Biochem. J.* 104:510–18

34. Chase, J. F. A., Tubbs, P. K. 1972. Specific inhibition of mitochondrial fatty acid oxidation by $\alpha$-bromopalmitate and its coenzyme A and carnitine esters. *Biochem. J.* 129:55–65

35. Christian, D. R., Kilsheimer, G. S., Pettett, G., Paradise, R., Ashmore, J. 1969. Regulation of lipolysis in cardiac muscle: a system similar to the hormone-sensitive lipase of adipose tissue. *Advan. Enzyme Regul.* 7:71–81

36. Christophersen, B. O., Bremer, J. 1972. Erucic acid - an inhibitor of fatty acid oxidation in the heart. *Biochim. Biophys. Acta* 280:506–14

37. Clark, M. G., Williams, J. F., Kolos, G., Hickie, J. B. 1972. The role of the pentose phosphate pathway in myocardial hypertrophy. *Int. J. Biochem.* 3:629–36

38. Colowick, S. P., van Eys, J., Park, J. H. 1965. Dehydrogenation. In *Comprehensive Biochemistry*, ed. M. Florkin, E. H. Stotz, 14:1–98. Amsterdam: Elsevier

39. Constantinides, S. M., Deal, W. C. Jr. 1969. Reversible dissociation of tetrameric rabbit muscle glyceraldehyde-3-phosphate dehydrogenase into dimers or monomers by adenosine triphosphate. *J. Biol. Chem.* 244:5695–5702

40. Cori, C. F. 1942. Phosphorylation of carbohydrates. In *Symposium on Respiratory Enzymes*, 175–89. Madison: Univ. Wisconsin Press

41. Cornblath, M., Randle, P. J., Parmeggiani, A., Morgan, H. E. 1963. Regulation of glycogenolysis in muscle: effects of glucagon and anoxia on lactate production, glycogen content, and phosphorylase activity in the perfused rat heart. *J. Biol. Chem.* 2338:1592–97

42. Crabtreè, B., Higgins, S. J., Newsholme, E. A. 1972. The activities of pyruvate carboxylase, phosphoenolpyruvate carboxylase and fructose diphosphatase in muscles from vertebrates and invertebrates. *Biochem. J.* 130:391–96

43. Crass, M. F. III. 1972. Exogenous substrate effects on endogenous lipid metabolism in the working rat heart. *Biochim. Biophys. Acta* 280:71–81

44. Crass, M. F. III, McCaskill, E. S., Shipp, J. C. 1969. Effects of pressure development on glucose and palmitate metabolism in perfused heart. *Am. J. Physiol.* 216:1569–76

45. Crass, M. J. III, McCaskill, E. S., Shipp, J. C., Murthy, V. K. 1971. Metabolism of endogenous lipids in cardiac muscle: effect of pressure development. *Am. J. Physiol.* 220:428–35

46. Danforth, W. H., Naegle, S., Bing, R. J. 1960. Effect of ischemia and reoxygenation on glycolytic reactions and adenosine triphosphate in heart muscle. *Circ. Res.* 8:965–71

47. Das, I. 1973. Effects of heart work and insulin on glycogen metabolism in the perfused rat heart. *Am. J. Physiol.* 224:7–12

48. De Jong, J. W., Hülsmann, W. C. 1970. Effects of Nagarse, adenosine and hexokinase on palmitate activation and oxidation. *Biochim. Biophys. Acta* 210:499–501

49. De Jong, J. W., Hülsmann, W. C. 1970. A comparative study of palmitoyl CoA synthetase activity in rat liver, heart and gut mitochondrial and microsomal preparations. *Biochim. Biophys. Acta* 197:127–35

50. Delcher, H. K., Shipp, J. C. 1966. The effect of pH, $PCO_2$, and bicarbonate on metabolism of glucose by perfused rat heart. *Biochim. Biophys. Acta* 121:250–60

51. Denton, R. M. Halperin, M. L. 1968. The control of fatty acid and triglyceride synthesis in rat epididymal adipose tissue. Role of coenzyme A derivatives, citrate and L-glycerol-3-phosphate. *Biochem. J.* 110:27–28

52. Denton, R. M., Randle, P. J. 1967. Concentrations of glycerides and phospholipids in rat heart and gastrocnemius muscles. Effects of alloxan diabetes and perfusion. *Biochem. J.* 104:416–22

53. Denton, R. M., Randle, P. J. 1967. Measurement of flow of carbon atoms from glucose and glycogen glucose to glyceride glycerol and glycerol in rat heart and epididymal adipose tissue. *Biochem. J.* 104:423–34

54. El-Badry, A. M., Ontani, A., Mansour, T. E. 1973. Studies on heart phosphofructokinase. Role of fructose diphosphate in enzyme activity. *J. Biol. Chem.* 248:557–63

55. England, P. J., Randle, P. J. 1967. Effectors of rat-heart hexokinases and the control of rates of glucose phosphorylation in the perfused rat heart. *Biochem. J.* 105:907–20

56. Erwin, V. G., Anderson, A. D., Eide, G. J. 1971. Enhancement of fatty acid oxidation and medium-chain fatty acyl coenzyme A synthetase by adenine nucleotides in rat heart homogenates. *J. Pharm. Sci.* 60:77–81

57. Evans, J. R. 1964. Importance of fatty acid in myocardial metabolism. *Circ. Res.* 14, 15, Suppl. 2:96–106

58. Evans, J. R. 1964. Cellular transport of long chain fatty acids. *Can. J. Biochem.* 42:955–69

59. Evans, J. R., Opie, L. H., Renold, A. E. 1963. Pyruvate metabolism in the perfused rat heart. *Am. J. Physiol.* 205:971–76

60. Farstad, M. 1967. A palmityl-CoA synthetase stimulating factor of particle free supernatants. *Biochim. Biophys. Acta* 146:272–83

61. Fischer, E. H., Heilmeyer, L. M. G. Jr., Haschke, R. H. 1971. Phosphorylase and the control of glycogen degradation. *Curr. Top. Cell. Regul.* 4:211–51

62. Fisher, R. B., Lindsay, D. B. 1956. The action of insulin on the penetration of sugars into the perfused heart. *J. Physiol.* 131:526–41

63. Fisher, R. B., Williamson, J. R. 1961. The effects of insulin, adrenaline and nutrients on the oxygen uptake of the perfused rat heart. *J. Physiol.* 158:102–12

64. Francis, S. H., Meriwether, B. P., Park, J. H. 1971. Interaction between adenine nucleotides and 3-phosphoglyceraldehyde dehydrogenase. II. A study of the mechanism of catalysis and metabolic control of the multifunctional enzyme. *J. Biol. Chem.* 246:5433–41

65. Fritz, I. B. 1968. The metabolic consequences of the effects of carnitine on long-chain fatty acid oxidation. In *Cellular Compartmentalization and Control of Fatty Acid Metabolism,* 39–63. Oslo: Universitetsforlaget

66. Fritz, I. B., Marquis, N. R. 1965. The role of acyl carnitine esters and carnitine palmityltransferase in the transport of fatty acyl groups across mitochondrial membranes. *Proc. Nat. Acad. Sci. USA* 54:1226–33

67. Fritz, I. B., Yue, K. T. N. 1963. Long-chain carnitine acyltransferase and the role of acylcarnitine derivatives in the catalytic increase of fatty acid oxidation induced by carnitine. *J. Lipid Res.* 4:279–88

68. Fritz, I. B., Yue, K. T. N. 1964. Effects of carnitine on acetyl-CoA oxidation by heart muscle mitochondria. *Am. J. Physiol.* 206:531–35

69. Fromm, H. J., Zewe, V. 1962. Kinetic studies of the brain hexokinase reaction. *J. Biol. Chem.* 237:1661–67

70. Fukami, M. H., Williamson, J. R. 1971. On the mechanism of inhibition of fatty acid oxidation by 4-pentonoic acid in rat liver mitochondria. *J. Biol. Chem.* 246: 1206–12

71. Furfine, C. S., Velick, S. F. 1965. The acyl-enzyme intermediate and the kinetic mechanism of the glyceraldehyde-3-phosphate dehydrogenase reaction. *J. Biol. Chem.* 240:844–55

72. Garland, P. B., Randle, P. J. 1970. Regulation of glucose uptake by muscle. X. Effects of alloxan-diabetes, starvation, hypophysectomy and adrenalectomy, and of fatty acid, ketone bodies and pyruvate, on the glycerol output and concentrations of free fatty acids, long-chain fatty acyl-coenzyme A, glycerol phosphate and citrate-cycle intermediates in rat heart and diaphragm muscles. *Biochem. J.* 93:678–87

73. Garland, P. B., Randle, P. J., Newsholme, E. A. 1963. Citrate as an intermediary in the inhibition of phosphofructokinase in rat heart muscle by fatty acids, ketone bodies, pyruvate, diabetes and starvation. *Nature* 200:169–70

74. Garland, P. B., Shepherd, D., Nicholls, D. G., Ontko, J. 1968. Energy-dependent control of the tricarboxylic acid cycle by fatty acid oxidation in rat liver mitochondria. *Advan. Enzyme Regul.* 6:3–30

75. Gergely, J., Maruyama, K. 1960. The binding of inorganic phosphate to

myosin in the presence of adenosine triphosphate. *J. Biol. Chem.* 235: 3174–76

76. Goldberg, E. B., Nitowsky, H. M., Colowick, S. P. 1965. The role of glycolysis in the growth of tumor cells. IV. The basis of glucose toxicity in oxamate-treated, cultured cells. *J. Biol. Chem.* 240:2791–96

77. Graves, D. J., Wang, J. H. 1972. α-Glucan phosphorylases - chemical and physical basis of catalysis and regulation. *Enzymes* 7:435–82

78. Grossbard, L., Schimke, R. T. 1966. Multiple hexokinases of rat tissues. Purification and comparison of soluble forms. *J. Biol. Chem.* 241:3546–60

79. Gudbjarnason, S. 1971. Acute alteration in energetics of ischemic heart muscle. *Cardiology* 56:232–44

80. Haddock, B. H., Yates, D. W., Garland, P. B. 1970. The localization of some coenzyme A-dependent enzymes in rat liver mitochondria. *Biochem. J.* 119:565–73

81. Harary, I., Farley, B. 1963. *In vitro* studies on single beating rat heart cells. I. Growth and organization. *Exp. Cell Res.* 29:451–65

82. Harris, P., Gloster, J. 1971. The effects of acute hypoxia on lipid synthesis in the rat heart. *Cardiology* 56: 43–47

83. Hasselbach, W. 1957. Die Bindung von adenosindiphosphat von anorganischem phosphat und von erdalkalien an die strukturproteine des muskels. *Biochim. Biophys. Acta* 25:562–78

84. Havel, R. J., Carlson, L. A., Ekelund, L. G., Holmgren, A. 1964. Turnover rate and oxidation of different free fatty acids in man during exercise. *J. Appl. Physiol.* 19:613–18

85. Havel, R. J., Naimark, A., Borchgrevink, C. F. 1963. Turnover rate and oxidation of free fatty acids of blood plasma in man during exercise: Studies during continuous infusion of palmitate-$^{14}$C. *J. Clin. Invest.* 42:1054–63

86. Hearse, D. J., Chain, E. B. 1972. The role of glucose in the survival and recovery of the anoxic isolated perfused rat heart. *Biochem. J.* 128:1125–33

87. Henderson, A. H., Most, A. S., Parmley, W. W., Gorlin, R., Sonnenblick, E. H. 1970. Depression of myocardial contractility in rats by free fatty acids during hypoxia. *Circ. Res.* 26:439–49

88. Hewitt, R. L., Lolley, D. M., Adrouny, G. A., Drapanas, T. 1973. Protective effect of myocardial glycogen on cardiac function during anoxia. *Surgery* 73: 444–53

89. Hohorst, H. J., Arese, P., Bartels, H., Stratmann, D., Talke, H. 1965. L(+) lactic acid and the steady state of cellular red/ox-systems. *Ann. NY Acad. Sci.* 119:974–94

90. Hoppel, C. W., Tomec, R. J. 1972. Carnitine palmityl transferase. Location of two enzymic activities in rat liver mitochondria. *J. Biol. Chem.* 247:832–41

91. Houghton, C. R., Ruderman, N. B. 1970. Acetoacetate as a fuel for perfused rat skeletal muscle. *Biochem. J.* 121:15P–16P

92. Huxtable, R. J., Wakil, S. J. 1971. Comparative mitochondrial oxidation of fatty acids. *Biochim. Biophys. Acta* 239:168–77

93. Isselhard, W., Merguet, H., Aengenvoort, J. 1965. Vergleich des herzstoffwechsels bei verschiedenen methoden des künstlichen herzstillstandes. *Pfleugers Arch.* 286:336–71

94. Jefferson, L. S., Koehler, J. O., Morgan, H. E. 1972. Effect of insulin on protein synthesis in skeletal muscle of an isolated perfused preparation of rat hemicorpus. *Proc. Nat. Acad. Sci. USA* 69:816–20

95. Jennings, R. B. 1969. Early phase of myocardial ischemic injury and infarction. *Am. J. Cardiol.* 24:753–65

96. Katz, A. M., Hecht, H. H. 1969. The early "pump" failure of the ischemic heart. *Am. J. Med.* 47:479–502

97. Katzen, H. M. 1967. The multiple forms of mammalian hexokinase and their significance to the action of insulin. *Advan. Enzyme Regul.* 5:335–56

98. Katzen, H. M., Soderman, D. D., Wiley, C. E. 1970. Multiple forms of hexokinase. *J. Biol. Chem.* 245:4081–96

99. Kayne, F. J. 1973. Pyruvate kinase. *Enzymes* 8:353–82

100. Kemp, R. G. 1971. Rabbit liver phosphofructokinase. Comparison of some properties with those of muscle phosphofructokinase. *J. Biol. Chem.* 246: 245–52

101. Kemp, R. G., Krebs, E. G. 1967. Binding of metabolites by phosphofructokinase. *Biochemistry* 6:423–34

102. Kopec, B., Fritz, I. B. 1971. Properties of a purified carnitine palmitoyltransferase, and evidence for the existence of other carnitine acyltransferases. *Can. J. Biochem.* 49:941–48

103. Kosow, D. P., Rose, I. A. 1970. Product inhibition of the hexokinases. *J. Biol. Chem.* 245:198–204

104. Kosow, D. P., Rose, I. A. 1972. Origin of the delayed feedback control of glucose utilization in ascites tumor cells.

*Biochem. Biophys. Res. Commun.* 48: 376–83

105. Krause, E. G., Wollenberger, A. 1967. Uber die aktivierung der phosphorylase-b-kinase im akut ischamischen myokard. *Acta Biol. Med. Ger.* 19: 381–93

106. Kreisberg, R. A. 1966. Effects of epinephrine on myocardial triglyceride and free fatty acid utilization. *Am. J. Physiol.* 210:385–89

107. Kreisberg, R. A., Williamson, J. R. 1964. Metabolic effects of glucagon in the perfused rat heart. *Am. J. Physiol.* 207:721–27

108. Kubler, W., Spieckermann, P. G. 1970. Regulation of glycolysis in the ischemic and the anoxic myocardium. *J. Mol. Cell. Cardiol.* 1:351–77

109. Kurien, V. A., Oliver, M. F. 1971. The role of free fatty acids in the production of ventricular arrhythmias after acute coronary artery occlusion. *Eur. J. Clin. Invest.* 1:225–41

110. Landau, B. R., Sims, E. A. H. 1967. On the existence of two separate pools of glucose-6-phosphate in rat diaphragm. *J. Biol. Chem.* 252:163–72

111. LaNoue, K. F., Nicklas, W. J., Williamson, J. R. 1970. Control of citric acid cycle activity in rat heart mitochondria. *J. Biol. Chem.* 245:102–11

112. Larner, J., Villar-Palasi, C. 1971. Glycogen synthase and its control. *Curr. Top. Cell. Regul.* 3:195–236

113. Lassers, B. W., Kaijser, L., Carlson, L. A. 1972. Myocardial lipid and carbohydrate metabolism in healthy fasting man at rest: Studies during infusion of $^3$H-palmitate. *Eur. J. Clin. Invest.* 2: 348–58

114. LeFevre, P. G. 1972. Transport of carbohydrates by animal cells. In *Metabolic Pathways*, 6:385–454. New York: Academic. 3rd ed.

115. Levitsky, D. O., Skulachen, V. P. 1972. Carnitine: the carrier transporting fatty acyls into mitochondria by means of an electrochemical gradient of $H^+$. *Biochim. Biophys. Acta* 275:33–50

116. Lippel, K. 1971. Regulation of rat liver acyl-CoA synthetase activity. *Biochim. Biophys. Acta* 239:384–92

117. Lippel, K., Beattie, D. S. 1970. The submitochondrial distribution of acid: CoA ligase (AMP) and acid:CoA ligase (GDP) in rat liver mitochondria. *Biochim. Biophys. Acta* 218:227–32

118. Little, J. R., Goto, M., Spitzer, J. J. 1970. Effect of ketones on metabolism of fatty acid by dog myocardium and

skeletal muscle *in vivo. Am. J. Physiol.* 219:1458–63

119. Mallov, S., Alousi, A. A. 1969. In vitro effect of epinephrine on lipase activity of heart. *Am. J. Physiol.* 216:794–99

120. Mansour, T. E. 1972. Phosphofructokinase. *Curr. Top. Cell. Regul.* 5:1–46

121. Mansour, T. E. 1972. Phosphofructokinase activity in skeletal muscle extracts following administration of epinephrine. *J. Biol. Chem.* 247:6059–66

122. Marinetti, G. V., Griffith, M., Smith, T. 1962. The incorporation of [1-$^{14}$C] glycerol, [1-$^{14}$C] acetate and DL-[3-$^{14}$C] serine into the lipids of rat-heart and liver homogenates. *Biochim. Biophys. Acta* 57:543–54

123. Marquis, N. R., Fritz, I. B. 1965. The distribution of carnitine, acetylcarnitine and carnitine acetyl transferase in rat tissue. *J. Biol. Chem.* 240:2193–96

124. Miller, H. I., Yum, K. Y., Durham, B. X. 1971. Myocardial free fatty acid in unanesthetized dogs at rest and during exercise. *Am. J. Physiol.* 220:589–96

125. Minelli, R., Casella, C. 1967. Influence of load and work on the high energy phosphates content in the myocardium. *Pfleugers Arch.* 295:119–26

126. Mole, P. A., Oscai, L. B., Holloszy, J. O. 1971. Adaptations of muscle to exercise: increase in levels of palmityl CoA synthetase, carnitine palmityl transferase, and palmityl CoA dehydrogenase, and in the capacity to oxidize fatty acids. *J. Clin. Invest.* 50:2323–30

127. Mommaerts, W. F. H. M. 1952. The molecular transformation of actin. III. The participation of nucleotides. *J. Biol. Chem.* 198:469–75

128. Monroy, G., Kelker, H. C., Pullman, M. E. 1973. Partial purification and properties of an acyl coenzyme A:sn-glycerol 3-phosphate acyltransferase from rat liver mitochondria. *J. Biol. Chem.* 248:2845–52

129. Morgan, H. E., Cadenas, E., Regen, D. M., Park, C. R. 1961. Regulation of glucose uptake in muscle. II. Rate-limiting steps and effects of insulin and anoxia in heart muscle from diabetic rats. *J. Biol. Chem.* 236:262–72

130. Morgan, H. E., Henderson, M. J., Regen, D. M., Park, C. R. 1961. Regulation of glucose uptake in muscle. I. The effects of insulin and anoxia on glucose transport and phosphorylation in the isolated perfused heart of normal rats. *J. Biol. Chem.* 236:253–61

131. Morgan, H. E. et al 1972. Effect of insulin on protein turnover in heart and skeletal muscle. In *Insulin Action*, ed.

I. B. Fritz, 437–59. New York: Academic

132. Morgan, H. E., Neely, J. R. 1972. Insulin and membrane transport. In *Handbook of Physiology*, ed. D. F. Steiner, N. Freinkel, 323–331. Washington: Am. Physiol. Soc.

133. Morgan, H. E., Neely, J. R., Wood, R. E., Liebecq, C., Liebermeister, H., Park, C. R. 1965. Factors affecting glucose transport in heart muscle and erythrocytes. *Fed. Proc.* 24:1040–45

134. Morgan, H. E., Parmeggiani, A. 1964. Regulation of glycogenolysis in muscle. II. Control of glycogen phosphorylase reaction in isolated perfused heart. *J. Biol. Chem.* 239:2435–39

135. Morgan, H. E., Parmeggiani, A. 1964. Regulation of glycogenolysis in muscle. III. Control of glycogen phosphorylase activity. *J. Biol. Chem.* 239:2440–45

136. Morgan, H. E., Randle, P. J., Regen, D. M. 1959. Regulation of glucose uptake by muscle. 3. The effects of insulin, anoxia, salicylate and 2:4-dinitrophenol on membrane transport and intracellular phosphorylation of glucose in the isolated rat heart. *Biochem. J.* 73: 573–79

137. Morgan, H. E., Regen, D. M., Henderson, M. J., Sawyer, T. K., Park, C. R. 1961. Regulation of glucose uptake in muscle. VI. Effects of hypophysectomy, adrenalectomy, growth hormone, hydrocortisone, and insulin on glucose transport and phosphorylation in the perfused rat heart. *J. Biol. Chem.* 236: 2162–68

138. Morgan, H. E., Whitfield, C. F. Regulation of sugar transport in eukaryotic cells. *Curr. Top. Membranes Transp.* In press

139. Most, A. S., Brachfeld, N., Gorlin, R., Wahren, J. 1969. Free fatty acid metabolism of the human heart at rest. *J. Clin. Invest.* 48:1177–88

140. Nakamura, Y., Schwartz, A. 1972. The influence of hydrogen ion concentration on calcium binding and release by skeletal muscle sarcoplasmic reticulum. *J. Gen. Physiol.* 59:22–30

141. Neely, J. R., Bowman, R. H., Morgan, H. E. 1969. Effects of ventricular pressure development and palmitate on glucose transport. *Am. J. Physiol.* 216:804–11

142. Neely, J. R., Denton, R. M., England, P. J., Randle, P. J. 1972. The effects of increased heart work on the tricarboxylate cycle and its interactions with glycolysis in perfused rat heart. *Biochem. J.* 128:147–59

143. Neely, J. R., Liebermeister, H., Battersby, E. J., Morgan, H. E. 1967. Effect of pressure development on oxygen consumption by isolated rat heart. *Am. J. Physiol.* 212:804–14

144. Neely, J. R., Liebermeister, H., Morgan, H. E. 1967. Effect of pressure development on membrane transport of glucose in rat heart. *Am. J. Physiol.* 212:815–22

145. Neely, J. R., Rovetto, M. J. Techniques for perfusing isolated rat hearts. In *Hormones and Cyclic Nucleotides: Methods in Enzymology*, ed. B. W. O'Malley, J. G. Hardman. In press

146. Neely, J. R., Rovetto, M. J., Oram, J. F. 1972. Myocardial utilization of carbohydrate and lipids. *Progr. Cardiovasc. Dis.* 15:289–329

147. Neely, J. R., Rovetto, M. J., Whitmer, J. T., Morgan, H. E. 1973. Effects of ischemia on ventricular function and metabolism in the isolated working rat heart. *Am. J. Physiol.* 225:651–58

148. Neely, J. R., Whitfield, C. F., Morgan, H. E. 1970. Regulation of glycogenolysis in hearts: effects of pressure development, glucose and FFA. *Am. J. Physiol.* 219:1083–88

149. Neely, J. R., Whitmer, J. T., Rovetto, M. J. 1973. Inhibition of glycolysis and fatty acid utilization in hearts during ischemic perfusion. *Myocardiology* (abstr.) Vols. 5, 6. In press

150. Newsholme, E. A. 1971/72. The regulation of phosphofructokinase in muscle. *Cardiology* 56:22–34

151. Newsholme, E. A., Randle, P. J. 1961. Regulation of glucose uptake by muscle. 5. Effects of anoxia, insulin, adrenaline and prolonged starving on concentrations of hexose phosphates in isolated rat diaphragm and perfused rat heart. *Biochem. J.* 80:655–62

152. Newsholme, E. A., Randle, P. J. 1964. Regulation of glucose uptake by muscle. 7. Effects of fatty acids, ketone bodies and pyruvate, and of alloxan diabetes, hypophysectomy, and adrenalectomy, on the concentrations of hexose phosphates, nucleotides and inorganic phosphate in the perfused rat heart. *Biochem. J.* 93:641–51

153. Newsholme, E. A., Taylor, K. 1969. Glycerol kinase activities in muscles from vertebrates and invertebrates. *Biochem. J.* 112:465–73

154. Nikkila, E. A., Torsti, P., Penttila, O. 1963. The effect of exercise on lipoprotein lipase activity of rat heart, adipose tissue and skeletal muscle. *Metabolism* 12:863–65

155. Norum, K. R. 1964. Palmityl-CoA:carnitine palmityl transferase. Purification from calf liver mitochondria and some properties of the enzyme. *Biochim. Biophys. Acta* 89:95–108
156. Norum, K. R., Bremer, J. 1967. The localization of acyl coenzyme A-carnitine acyltransferases in rat liver cells. *J. Biol. Chem.* 242:407–11
157. Ockner, R. K., Manning, J. A., Poppenhausen, R. B., Ho, W. K. L. 1972. A binding protein for fatty acids in cytosol of intestinal mucosa, liver, myocardium, and other tissues. *Science* 177: 56–58
158. Olson, R. E., Hoeschen, R. J. 1967. Utilization of endogenous lipid by the isolated perfused rat heart. *Biochem. J.* 103:796–801
159. Opie, L. H. 1965. Coronary flow rate and perfusion pressure as determinates of mechanical function and oxidative metabolism of isolated perfused rat heart. *J. Physiol.* 180:529–41
160. Opie, L. H. 1965. Effect of extracellular pH on function and metabolism of isolated perfused rat heart. *Am. J. Physiol.* 209:1075–80
161. Opie, L. H. 1968. Metabolism of the heart in health and disease. *Am. Heart J.* 76:685–98
162. Opie, L. H. 1972. Metabolic response during impending myocardial infarction. *Circulation* 45:483–89
163. Opie, L. H., Mansford, K. R. L., Owen, P. 1971. Effects of increased heart work on glycolysis and adenine nucleotides in the perfused heart of normal and diabetic rats. *Biochem. J.* 124:475–90
164. Opie, L. H., Newsholme, E. A. 1967. The activities of fructose-1,6-diphosphatase, phosphofructokinase and phosphoenolpyruvate carboxykinase in white muscle and red muscle. *Biochem. J.* 103:391–99
165. Oram, J. F., Bennetch, S. L., Neely, J. R. 1973. Regulation of fatty acid utilization in isolated perfused rat hearts. *J. Biol. Chem.* 248:5299–5309
166. Ottaway, J. H. 1960/61. The effects of growth hormone and ketone bodies on carbohydrate metabolism in diaphragm from normal and hypophysectomized rats. *J. Endocrinol.* 20–21:443–51
167. Pande, S. V. 1971. On rate-controlling factors of long chain fatty acid oxidation. *J. Biol. Chem.* 246:5384–90
168. Pande, S. V. 1973. Reversal by CoA of palmityl-CoA inhibition of long chain acyl-CoA synthetase activity. *Biochim. Biophys. Acta* 306:15–20
169. Pande, S. V., Blanchaer, M. C. 1971.

170. Pande, S. V., Mead, J. F. 1968. Distribution of long-chain fatty acid-activating enzymes in rat tissues. *Biochim. Biophys. Acta* 152:636–38
171. Pande, S. V., Mead, J. F. 1968. Inhibition of enzyme activities by free fatty acids. *J. Biol. Chem.* 243:6180–85
172. Pande, S. V., Mead, J. F. 1968. Long chain fatty acid activation in subcellular preparations from rat liver. *J. Biol. Chem.* 243:352–61
173. Pande, S. V., Siddiqui, A. W., Gattereau, A. 1971. Inhibition of long-chain fatty acid activation by α-bromopalmitate and phytanate. *Biochim. Biophys. Acta* 248:156–66
174. Park, C. R., Bornstein, J., Post, R. L. 1955. Effect of insulin on free glucose content of rat diaphragm in vitro. *Am. J. Physiol.* 182:12–16
175. Park, C. R. et al 1961. The regulation of glucose uptake in muscle as studied in the isolated perfused rat heart. *Rec. Progr. Horm. Res.* 17:493–538
176. Parmeggiani, A., Bowman, R. H. 1963. Regulation of phosphofructokinase activity by citrate in normal and diabetic muscle. *Biochem. Biophys. Res. Commun.* 12:268–73
177. Passonneau, J. V., Lowry, O. H. 1963. P-fructokinase and the control of the citric acid cycle. *Biochem. Biophys. Res. Commun.* 13:372–79
178. Pearson, D. J., Tubbs, P. K. 1967. Carnitine and derivatives in rat tissues. *Biochem. J.* 105:953–63
179. Pettit, F. H., Roche, T. E., Reed, L. J. 1972. Function of calcium ions in pyruvate dehydrogenase phosphatase activity. *Biochem. Biophys. Res. Commun.* 49:563–71
180. Posner, J. B., Stern, R., Krebs, E. G. 1965. Effects of electrical stimulation and epinephrine on muscle phosphorylase, phosphorylase *b* kinase and adenosine 3'-5'-phosphate. *J. Biol. Chem.* 240:982–85
181. Purich, D. L., Fromm, H. J. 1971. The kinetics and regulation of rat brain hexokinase. *J. Biol. Chem.* 246:3456–63
182. Rabinowitz, D., Zierler, K. L. 1962. Role of free fatty acids in forearm metabolism in man, quantitated by use of insulin. *J. Clin. Invest.* 41:2191–97
183. Randle, P. J. 1969. Apparent reversal of insulin resistance in cardiac muscle in alloxan-diabetes by 2-bromostearate. *Nature* 221:771

184. Randle, P. J., England, P. J., Denton, R. M. 1970. Control of the tricarboxylate cycle and its interactions with glycolysis during acetate utilization in rat heart. *Biochem. J.* 117:677-95

185. Randle, P. J. et al 1966. Interaction of metabolism and the physiological role of insulin. *Rec. Progr. Horm. Res.* 22:1-44

186. Randle, P. J., Newsholme, E. A., Garland, P. B. 1964. Regulation of glucose uptake by muscle. 8. Effects of fatty acid, ketone bodies and pyruvate, and of alloxan diabetes and starvation, on the uptake and metabolic fate of glucose in rat heart and diaphragm muscle. *Biochem. J.* 93:652-65

187. Reed, L. J. 1969. Pyruvate dehydrogenase complex. *Curr. Top. Cell. Regul.* 233-51

188. Regan, T. J., Lehan, P. H., Henneman, D. H., Behar, A., Hellems, H. K. 1964. Myocardial metabolic and contractile response to glucagon and epinephrine. *J. Lab. Clin. Med.* 63:638-47

189. Regan, T. J., Markov, A., Oldewurtel, H. A., Burke, W. M. 1970. Myocardial metabolism and function during ischaemia: response to L-noradrenaline. *Cardiovasc. Res.* 4:334-42

190. Regan, T. J., Passannante, A. J., Oldewurtel, H. A., Burke, W. M., Ettinger, P. O. 1972. Cardiac metabolism of triglyceride, acetate, and oleate in early L-norepinephrine injury. *J. Appl. Physiol.* 33:325-30

191. Regen, D. M., Davis, W. W., Morgan, H. E., Park, C. R. 1964. The regulation of hexokinase and phosphofructokinase activity in heart muscle. *J. Biol. Chem.* 239:43-49

192. Robinson, G. A., Butcher, R. W., Oye, I., Morgan, H. E., Sutherland, E. W. 1965. The effect of epinephrine on adenosine 3'-5'-phosphate levels in the isolated perfused rat heart. *Mol. Pharmacol.* 1:168-77

193. Robinson, D. S., Wing, D. R. 1970. Regulation of adipose tissue clearing factor lipase activity. See Ref 27, 41-45

194. Rolleston, F. S. 1972. A theoretical background to the use of measured concentrations of intermediates in the study of intermediary metabolism. *Curr. Top. Cell. Regul.* 5:47-75

195. Rose, I. A., O'Connell, E. L. 1964. The role of glucose-6-phosphate in the regulation of glucose metabolism in human erythrocytes. *J. Biol. Chem.* 239:12-17

196. Rose, I. A., Rose, Z. B. 1969. Glycolysis: Regulation and mechanisms of the enzymes. See Ref. 38, 17:93-161

197. Rose, I. A., Warms, J. V. B., O'Connell, E. L. 1964. The role of inorganic phosphate in stimulating the glucose utilization of human red cells. *Biochem. Biophys. Res. Commun.* 15:33-37

198. Rossi, C. R., Galzigna, L., Alexandre, A., Gibson, D. M. 1967. Oxidation of long chain fatty acids by rat liver. *J. Biol. Chem.* 242:2102-10

199. Rovetto, M. J., Whitmer, J. T., Neely, J. R. 1973. Comparison of the effects of anoxia and whole heart ischemia on carbohydrate utilization in isolated, working rat heart. *Circ. Res.* 32:699-711

200. Sánchez, M., Nicholls, D. G., Brindley, D. N. 1973. The relationship between palmitoyl-coenzyme A synthetase activity and esterification of sn-glycerol 3-phosphate in rat liver mitochondria. *Biochem. J.* 132:697-706

201. Scheuer, J., Brachfeld, N. 1966. Myocardial uptake and fractional distribution of palmitate-1-$C^{14}$ by the ischemic dog heart. *Metabolism* 15:945-54

202. Scheuer, J., Stezoski, S. W. 1970. Protective role of increased myocardial glycogen stores in cardiac anoxia in the rat. *Circ. Res.* 27:835-49

203. Scheuer, J., Stezoski, S. W. 1972. The effect of alkalosis upon the mechanical and metabolic response of the rat heart to hypoxia. *J. Mol. Cell. Cardiol.* 4:599-610

204. Schonfeld, G., Kipnis, D. M. 1968. Effects of fatty acids on carbohydrate and fatty acid metabolism of rat diaphragm. *Am. J. Physiol.* 215:513-22

205. Seraydarian, M. W., Sato, E., Harary, I. 1970. In vitro studies of beating heart cells in culture. XIII. The effect of 1-fluoro-2,4-dinitrobenzene. *Arch. Biochem. Biophys.* 138:233-38

206. Setlow, B., Mansour, T. E. 1972. Studies on heart phosphofructokinase. Binding of cyclic adenosine 3',5'-monophosphate, adenosine monophosphate, and of hexose phosphates to the enzyme. *Biochemistry* 11:1478-86

207. Shepherd, D., Yates, D. W., Garland, P. B. 1966. The rate-limiting step in the oxidation of palmitate or palmitoyl-coenzyme A by rat liver mitochondria. *Biochem. J.* 98:3C

208. Shug, A., Lerner, E., Elson, E., Shrago, E. 1971. The inhibition of adenine nucleotide translocase activity by oleoyl CoA and its reversal in rat liver mitochondria. *Biochem. Biophys. Res. Commun.* 43:557-63

209. Shug, A. L., Shrago, E. 1973. A proposed mechanism for fatty acid

effects on energy metabolism of the heart. *J. Lab. Clin. Med.* 81:214–18

210. Skrede, S., Bremer, J. 1970. The compartmentation of CoA and fatty acid acivating enzymes in rat liver mitochondria. *Eur. J. Biochem.* 14: 465–72

211. Smith, C. M., Williamson, J. R. 1971. Inhibition of citrate synthase by succinyl-CoA and other metabolites. *FEBS Lett.* 18:35–38

212. Solberg, H. E. 1972. Different carnitine acyltransferases in calf liver. *Biochim. Biophys. Acta* 280:422–33

213. Spector, A. A., Steinberg, D., Tanaka, A. 1965. Uptake of free fatty acids by Ehrlich ascites tumor cells. *J. Biol. Chem.* 240:1032–44

214. Spitzer, J. J., Spitzer, J. A. 1972. Myocardial metabolism in dogs during hemorrhagic shock. *Am. J. Physiol.* 222:101–5

215. Srere, P. A. 1972. The citrate enzymes: Their structures, mechanisms, and biological functions. *Curr. Top. Cell. Regul.* 5:229–83

216. Stein, O., Stein, Y. 1968. Lipid synthesis, intracellular transport and storage. *J. Cell Biol.* 36:63–77

217. Stewart, H. B., Tubbs, P. K., Stanley, K. K. 1973. Intermediates in fatty acid oxidation. *Biochem. J.* 132:61–76

218. Trivedi, B., Danforth, W. H. 1966. Effect of pH on the kinetics of frog muscle phosphofructokinase. *J. Biol. Chem.* 241:4110–14.

219. Tsai, M. Y., Kemp, R. G. 1973. Isozymes of rabbit phosphofructokinase. Electrophoretic and immunochemical studies. *J. Biol. Chem.* 248:785–92

220. Van Tol, A., Hülsmann, W. C. 1969. The localization of palmitoyl-CoA:carnitine palmitoyltransferase in rat liver. *Biochim. Biophys. Acta* 189:342–53

221. Wakil, S. J. 1970. Fatty acid metabolism. See Ref. 23, 1–49

222. Walsh, D. A., Krebs, E. G. 1973. Protein kinases. *Enzymes* 8, pt. A:555–81

223. Weissler, A. M., Altschuld, R. A., Gibb, L. E., Pollack, M. E., Kruger, F. A. 1973. Effect of insulin on the performance and metabolism of the anoxic isolated perfused rat heart. *Circ. Res.* 32:108–16

224. Weissler, A. M. et al 1968. Role of anaerobic metabolism in the preservation of functional capacity and structure of anoxic myocardium. *J. Clin. Invest.* 47:403–16

225. West, D. W., Chase, J. F. A., Tubbs, P. K. 1971. The separation and properties of two forms of carnitine palmitoyl-

transferase from ox liver mitochondria. *Biochem. Biophys. Res. Commun.* 42: 912–18

226. Whereat, A. F., Orishimo, M. W., Nelson, J., Phillips, S. J. 1969. The location of different synthetic systems for fatty acids in inner and outer mitochondrial membranes from rabbit heart. *J. Biol. Chem.* 244:6498–6506

227. Whitfield, C. F., Morgan, H. E. 1973. Effect of anoxia on sugar transport in avian erythrocytes. *Biochem. Biophys. Acta* 307:181–96

228. Whitfield, C. F., Morgan, H. E. 1973. Effects of exogenous nucleotides on sugar transport in avian erythrocytes. *Fed. Proc.* 32:287 Abstr.

229. Wieland, O., Funcke, H. G. V., Loffler, G. 1971. Interconversion of pyruvate dehydrogenase in rat heart muscle upon perfusion with fatty acids or ketone bodies. *FEBS Lett.* 15:295–98

230. Wieland, O., Siess, E., Schulze-Wethmar, F. H., Funcke, H. G. V., Winton, B. 1971. Active and inactive forms of pyruvate dehydrogenase in rat heart and kidney: Effects of diabetes, fasting, and refeeding on pyruvate dehydrogenase interconversion. *Arch. Biochem. Biophys.* 143:593–601

231. Williamson, J. R. 1964. Metabolic effects of epinephrine in the isolated perfused rat heart. 1. Dissociation of the glycogenolytic from the metabolic stimulatory effect. *J. Biol. Chem.* 239: 2721–29

232. Williamson, J. R. 1965. Glycolytic control mechanisms. I. Inhibition of glycolysis by acetate and pyruvate in the isolated perfused rat heart. *J. Biol. Chem.* 240:2308–21

233. Williamson, J. R. 1966. Metabolic effects of epinephrine in the perfused rat heart. II. Control steps of glucose and glycogen metabolism. *Mol. Pharmacol.* 2:206–20

234. Williamson, J. R. 1966. Glycolytic control mechanisms. II. Kinetics of intermediate changes during the aerobic-anoxic transition in perfused rat heart. *J. Biol. Chem.* 241:5026–36

235. Wojtczak, L., Zaluska, H. 1967. The inhibition of translocation of adenine nucleotides through mitochondrial membranes by oleate. *Biochem. Biophys. Res. Commun.* 28:76–81

236. Wollenberger, A., Krause, E. G. 1968. Metabolic control characteristics of the acutely ischemic myocardium. *Am. J. Cardiol.* 22:349–59

237. Wollenberger, A., Krause, E. G., Heier, G. 1969. Stimulation of 3'5'-cyclic

AMP formation in dog myocardium following arrest of blood flow. *Biochem. Biophys. Res. Commun.* 36:664–70

238. Wood, J. M., Sordahl, L. A., Lewis, R. M., Schwartz, A. 1973. Effect of chronic myocardial ischemia on the activity of carnitine palmitylcoenzyme A transferase of isolated canine heart mitochondria. *Circ. Res.* 32:340–47

239. Yates, D. W., Garland, P. B. 1966. The partial latency and intramitochondrial distribution of carnitine palmitoyl-

transferase (E.C.2.3.1.–), and the CoA and carnitine permeable space of rat liver mitochondria. *Biochem. Biophys. Res. Commun.* 23:460–65

240. Yates, D. W., Garland, P. B. 1970. Carnitine palmitoyltransferase activities (E.C.2.3.1.–) of rat liver mitochondria. *Biochem. J.* 119:547–52

241. Zahler, W. L., Barden, R. E., Cleland, W. W. 1968. Some physical properties of palmityl-coenzyme A micelles. *Biochim. Biophys. Acta* 164:1–11

# STRIATED MUSCLE

❖1119

*Franklin Fuchs*[1]

Department of Physiology, University of Pittsburgh School of Medicine,
Pittsburgh, Pennsylvania

## INTRODUCTION

In undertaking a review of striated muscle in 1973 some perspective is gained from the realization that exactly 20 years have passed since the publication of two papers which provided the initial groundwork for the principal themes that now dominate this subject. One was a short paper by Hanson & Huxley (97), in which they suggested that the two major contractile proteins, actin and myosin, are organized into two sets of parallel, interdigitating filaments. The other was an electron microscope study by Bennett & Porter (19) showing the presence of a tubular network, the sarcoplasmic reticulum, within the interfibrillar space of skeletal muscle. Needless to say, the sliding filament model has been established as the fundamental contractile system in all striated muscles (and probably in smooth muscle as well) and the sarcoplasmic reticulum-transverse tubule system, together with the calcium ion, has been shown to provide the connecting link between excitation and the contractile response.

The parallel lines of investigation growing out of these initial efforts have led to the formulation of a reasonably coherent outline of the contraction-relaxation cycle that is supported by a great deal of experimental evidence and that seems to be generally accepted by most investigators. Briefly, force generation is believed to result from the cyclic attachment and detachment of cross-bridges projecting from the thick (myosin) filaments and interacting with the thin (actin) filaments in such a way as to draw them toward the center of the sarcomere. Cross-bridge activity is energetically coupled to the splitting of ATP catalyzed by the cross-bridges themselves and is regulated by the $Ca^{2+}$ concentration in the sarcoplasm. The sarcoplasmic reticulum (SR) membranes contain an ATP-dependent $Ca^{2+}$ pump which maintains the sarcoplasmic $Ca^{2+}$ concentration in resting muscle at a level ($<10^{-7}$ $M$) below that needed for activation of cross-bridge interaction. Upon

[1] Supported by grants from the National Institutes of Health (AM10551) and American Heart Association (69-804).

stimulation an electrical signal is transmitted along the transverse tubules (T-tubule) to the terminal cisternae of the SR, thereby causing a rapid release of $Ca^{2+}$ and an elevation of sarcoplasmic $Ca^{2+}$ concentration to $\sim 10^{-5}$ $M$. Cross-bridge attachment is promoted by the binding of $Ca^{2+}$ to the thin filaments. The activating effect of $Ca^{2+}$ is mediated by two proteins, tropomyosin and troponin, bound to the thin filaments. In the resting state cross-bridge attachment is inhibited by these two proteins and this inhibition is overcome only when $Ca^{2+}$ binds to the troponin. During the relaxation phase $Ca^{2+}$ is reaccumulated within the SR, and the cross-bridges detach from the thin filament.

This rather bare outline of an extremely complex phenomenon provides us with a framework for stating those problems that must yet be solved before we can claim to have a satisfactory understanding of muscle function. What is the nature of the signal transmitted along the T-tubule, and how does this signal induce a release of $Ca^{2+}$ from the SR? How does $Ca^{2+}$ activate the contractile apparatus? Once released, how is $Ca^{2+}$ reaccumulated by the SR? What is the molecular basis of cross-bridge activity, and how is this activity coupled to ATP hydrolysis? How is the energy output of muscle regulated? What are the biochemical and morphological bases of the functional properties of the many different types of striated muscle?

During the period covered by this review significant progress has been made toward obtaining answers to all of these questions. However, given the realities of time, space, and editorial policy, a detailed consideration of each of these problems is clearly out of the question. Therefore, I have chosen to discuss only three areas, namely $Ca^{2+}$ release mechanisms, cross-bridge activity, and $Ca^{2+}$ activation. This choice was dictated by personal interest as well as a feeling that recent research in these areas has been especially rewarding in terms of our ability to relate the mechanical behavior of living muscle to specific intracellular events. Even with this restricted coverage the massive amount of recent literature necessitates the omission of many noteworthy papers from consideration. Attention will be focused mainly on studies of vertebrate skeletal muscle, although reference will be made to investigations of cardiac muscle and invertebrate striated muscle where these may illuminate some fundamental problem common to all forms of striated muscle.

The omission of so many important topics from this review is made somewhat easier by the knowledge that these topics have been very thoroughly discussed elsewhere. Since the last review of striated muscle in this series, that of Sandow (187) in 1970, we have been inundated with an extraordinary number of monographs, symposia, and reviews, covering virtually every aspect of muscle biology. Indeed, the reviewer who makes a conscientious effort to assimilate all of this material runs a serious risk of losing touch with the similarly growing stream of research papers which appear each week in the journals.

Among recent books, mention should be made of Zachar's comprehensive, graduate-level textbook of skeletal muscle physiology (226) and Tonomura's monograph (207) on muscle contraction and cation transport, written mainly from the perspective of his own extensive contributions to these fields. At the introductory level, Smith's book (194), with its main emphasis on comparative ultrastructure, should prove to be quite useful. Although not directly pertinent to the present discussion, special mention should be made of Needham's monumental treatise (162) on the historical development of muscle physiology and biochemistry. Combining impressive historical scholarship with her own expertise as a muscle biochemist, Needham has shown how the effort to understand muscle movement during the past 2000 years has played a central role in the evolution of modern biology.

Most important of recent symposia is the Cold Spring Harbor Symposium on the mechanism of muscle contraction (150), held in June 1972. This volume provides the most extensive source of information now available on the biochemistry and biophysics of the contractile mechanism and, even taking into account the rapid pace of new discoveries, it should be a major reference work for some years to come. A symposium sponsored by The Society of General Physiologists (175) contains valuable reviews of a variety of aspects of muscle function.

Muscle biologists will welcome the appearance of a second edition, in four volumes, of *The Structure and Function of Muscle,* edited by Bourne. The first volume (27) has been published as of this writing and additional volumes will presumably be available by the time this review appears in print. A new addition to the literature on muscle is a serial publication based on invited lectures delivered at the Institute for Muscle Biology in Madison (39). The ten contributions to the first volume deal with diverse areas of muscle biology ranging from enzymology and energetics to pathology and developmental biology.

Reviews of contractile protein biochemistry and the molecular basis of contraction have been written by Dreizen (55), Taylor (203), Harrington (99), Lowy (139), and Tonomura & Oosawa (208). The mechanism of $Ca^{2+}$ transport by the SR is discussed in great detail by Martonosi (145, 146) and Inesi (123). The energetics of muscle function has been reviewed by Woledge (222), Abbott & Howarth (1), Maréchal (143a), and Mommaerts (156), and the application of irreversible thermodynamics to muscle is discussed by Caplan (34). For a critical appraisal of recent theories of muscle contraction see McClare (148, 149). Close (42) has written a very valuable survey of the dynamic properties of mammalian skeletal muscle. The Croonian Lectures of A. F. Huxley (114) and H. E. Huxley (119) have now been published and both investigators have provided us with clearly written summaries of their own monumental contributions.

For more detailed discussions of specific muscle proteins and myofilament structure the reader can consult reviews by Lowey (138), Oosawa & Kasai (168), Ooi & Fujime-Higashi (167), and Pepe (172, 173), as well as an interesting collection of reviews on muscle biochemistry edited by Laki (135). Reviews by Baker (11) and Reuter (180) of $Ca^{2+}$ movement across excitable membranes contain much of interest to muscle physiologists.

Most of the important recent developments in cardiac muscle physiology have been covered in articles published in the three previous volumes of the *Annual Review of Physiology* (127, 136, 182). Also of interest are several symposia devoted to cardiac muscle (4, 51, 100, 151), as well as a general account of cardiac muscle mechanics by Blinks & Jewell (25).

Those in need of methodological guidance in muscle research should find the first volume of *Methods in Pharmacology* (191) to be quite helpful.

## CALCIUM RELEASE MECHANISMS

One of the most important developments of the past two decades has been the discovery that the T-tubule–SR system is the morphological pathway of excitation-contraction coupling in most forms of striated muscle, and that the translocation of $Ca^{2+}$ from the SR to the myofibrils is the connecting link between excitation and contraction. Although many important details have been filled in, the mechanism by which the surface action potential causes a release of internal $Ca^{2+}$ remains an unsolved problem.

### T-Tubule Transmission

Since the classical local stimulation experiments of Huxley & Taylor (115) it has been recognized that the T-tubule is the probable pathway for inward spread of excitation in striated muscle. That it is the only pathway in vertebrate twitch muscle fibers has been proven beyond any reasonable doubt by experiments with muscle fibers in which the T-tubules were disrupted by pretreatment with hypertonic glycerol (112, 132). In such fibers the excitation mechanism is intact but the mechanical response is eliminated. Further studies with such "detubulated" fibers have provided valuable information about excitation-contraction coupling.

Since the T-tubule is essentially an invagination of the surface membrane, an electrical connection between the two is indicated. As to the nature of this connection, earlier theoretical considerations (73) indicated that on the basis of passive cable properties of the T-tubule a simple electrotonic spread from the surface action potential would be sufficient to activate even the innermost myofibrils. However, the experiments of Adrian, Costantin & Peachey (3) showed that the effectiveness of such a mechanism would be marginal at best, and more recent work has provided much evidence that inward transmission is through a $Na^+$-dependent regenerative response, presumably akin to the surface action potential.

The experiments of González-Serratos (88), reported earlier in a preliminary form and discussed by Sandow (187) in his 1970 review, have now been published in full. In these experiments single frog fibers were embedded in gelatin and subjected to longitudinal compression until the myofibrils took on a wavy appearance. Contractile response was indicated by the straightening of the myofibrils following electrical stimulation. From the time course of straightening, as measured by high speed ciné micrography, the velocity of T-tubule transmission could be determined. In a single twitch, fibril straightening was observed throughout the fiber cross section, regardless of fiber diameter. The velocity of inward transmission was estimated to be about 7 cm $sec^{-1}$ at 20°C, with a $Q_{10}$ of 2.13. The latter value was considered to be more characteristic of a regenerative signal than a passive electrotonic system.

Costantin (44) studied radial spread of activation as a function of membrane potential under voltage clamp conditions. When the membrane potential was clamped at values just 1–2 mV less than threshold there was a uniform myofibril shortening throughout the fiber cross section. From the effects on this response of $Na^+$ removal or application of tetrodotoxin it was concluded that activation must depend on a $Na^+$-dependent regenerative signal.

Support for this conclusion has come from the work of Bezanilla et al (20). These workers reasoned that if T-tubule transmission is electrotonic, the extent of radial activation should be a function of action potential magnitude (external $Na^+$ concentration), whereas if the transmission process is regenerative, activation should be independent of action potential magnitude provided there is enough $Na^+$ to support an action potential. The data obtained were clearly consistent with the second alternative. Thus a single frog fiber immersed in a low $Na^+$-Ringer solution developed the same isometric tetanus tension as a fiber in normal Ringer's solution but exhibited a more rapid decay of tension with prolonged stimulation. The authors assume that the tension decay was due to a more rapid depletion of $Na^+$ in the T-tubule with a resultant failure of inward transmission. This assumption was confirmed by direct microscopic observation showing that the fall in tension coincided with the appearance under isotonic conditions of wavy fibrils in the core of the fiber.

The essential role of T-tubule $Na^+$ was demonstrated very nicely by Caputo & Dipolo (37) who measured the speed of recovery of twitch tension of single frog fibers upon transfer from $Na^+$-free Ringer to 47 m$M$ $Na^+$-Ringer. An appreciable delay could be caused by the addition to the Ringer's solutions of 15% dextran, a procedure designed to increase the viscosity of the fluid in the T-tubule. The delay could be accounted for by the reduced rate of diffusion of $Na^+$ re-entering the T-tubule.

Delays in T-tubule diffusion might also obscure the true time course of the $K^+$ contracture response, as suggested by Costantin (45). He observed that with single frog fibers the response to elevated $K^+$ at room temperature was an initial tension spike lasting about a second, followed by a reduced but prolonged tension plateau lasting for several seconds. At low temperature the initial phase was prolonged so that the two phases were no longer distinguishable, an effect presumably due to the delayed relaxation at lower temperature. Costantin presents reasonable arguments in support of the view that the initial spike is due to an immediate depolarization of the surface membrane with resultant electrotonic spread into the T-tubule, whereas the slower response is dependent upon diffusion of $K^+$ into the T-tubule. The dextran treatment described above should provide a test of this hypothesis.

A different approach to T-tubule function is that of Vaughan, Howell & Eisenberg (213). These workers measured the capacitance of intact frog fibers and obtained a value of about 6 $\mu$F cm$^{-2}$, in confirmation of earlier results. With progressive reduction of the ionic strength of the bathing solution the capacitance fell to a limiting value of about 2 $\mu$F cm$^{-2}$. If the T-tubules were disrupted by immersion in 400 m$M$ glycerol-Ringer solution, followed by return to normal Ringer, the membrane capacitance was 2 $\mu$F cm$^{-2}$ and was not affected by reduction in ionic strength. Thus the portion of the total capacitance sensitive to ionic strength is assigned to the T-tubule. The effects of ionic strength on capacitance are explained in terms of a model in which the tubule (or mouth of the tubule) constitutes a resistance in series with the T-tubule capacitance, hence the effects of ionic strength on total capacitance. From the standpoint of T-tubule transmission, the important point to note is that in low ionic strength Ringer, normal twitches could be recorded despite the reduced current flow in the T-tubule. This result would argue in favor of a regenerative type of signal in the T-tubule (however, see 2 for a critical discussion of the above model).

Flitney (74) published an electron microscope study which forces us to revise many of our ideas about the T-tubule system of frog slow (tonic) muscle. With glutaraldehyde fixation and radioactive albumin as a marker, a more extensive T-tubule system was found than was previously believed to exist. It was estimated to be about 0.2% of the fiber volume, in contrast to about 0.5% in twitch fibers. These tubules form diadic and triadic junctions with the sarcoplasmic reticulum, but the contact area was estimated to be about 5–10 times smaller than in twitch fibers. From both morphological and physiological data it seems that the T-tubules form a more diffuse three-dimensional network in slow fibers. It should be noted that the hypertonic glycerol treatment did not prevent radioactive albumin from entering the T-tubules, thus indicating that slow muscle is resistant to T-tubule disruption. This observation is pertinent to an earlier report of Stefani & Steinbach (198) stating that hypertonic glycerol treatment did not affect the contractile response of frog slow muscle. This paper has been cited as evidence that the T-tubules of slow fibers do not play a major role in excitation-contraction coupling, rather the $Ca^{2+}$ flux across the surface membrane is the important factor. However, such a conclusion is obviously premature in the absence of explicit morphological evidence that the T-tubules were actually disrupted. In fact, a very different conclusion emerges from a recent paper by Nasledov et al (161). These investigators reported that if glycerol treatment is performed with single fibers rather than fiber bundles there is a disruption of the T-tubule and a loss of mechanical response; evidently the rate of glycerol removal is a critical factor (see also 112). This result indicates that the T-tubule is absolutely essential for excitation-contraction coupling in tonic as well as phasic muscle and that internal rather than external $Ca^{2+}$ is the activator.

The T-tubules of cardiac muscle have also proven to be refractory to glycerol treatment. In a comparative study of frog skeletal muscle and mammalian ventricular muscle Niemeyer & Girardier (163) found that glycerol concentrations as high as 1 $M$ had no noticeable effects on cardiac muscle other than some reduction in force development while the muscle was immersed in the glycerol. The reasons for this difference are not clear, but the authors mention two morphological features that may be relevant: 1. the basement membrane of cardiac muscle extends into the T-tubule, and 2. the cardiac T-tubule is much shorter and wider than its skeletal counterpart.

Oddly enough, hypertonic glycerol treatment of atrial muscle can cause a temporary, and in some cases permanent, reduction in contractile strength (188, 200). Since this type of muscle is essentially devoid of T-tubules the possibility must be considered that glycerol treatment can have effects on structures other than the T-tubules. Ultrastructural studies of such preparations showed considerable damage to both SR and mitochondria, but the relation between these changes and the mechanical effects has not been worked out.

## T-Tubule and $Ca^{2+}$ Release

While there is now some fairly solid information about the signal conveyed along the T-tubule, the link between this signal and $Ca^{2+}$ release from the SR remains

rather obscure. Two general mechanisms have been considered in the recent literature. In the one case a direct electrical coupling between the T-tubule and SR
membranes has been suggested, with SR $Ca^{2+}$ permeability assumed to be voltage
dependent. As an alternative there is the possibility of a chemical linkage between
the two membranes in which $Ca^{2+}$ itself might play a role in triggering the release
of SR $Ca^{2+}$.

Whatever the mechanism, its morphological locus must be the junction between
the T-tubule and the terminal cisternae of the SR, the triadic junction. The fine
structure of this region has been described in great detail in a series of papers by
Franzini-Armstrong (79–82). She has shown that the structure of the T-tubule–SR
junction is quite unlike that of any of the known low-resistance junctions found
elsewhere. The two membranes are separated by a sizeable gap ($\sim$120 Å). At about
300 Å intervals the SR sends out projections or "feet" which come to within 50
Å of the T-tubule membrane and are joined to it by an amorphous material of
unknown composition. These junctional feet cover about 30% of the T-tubule
membrane but they constitute only about 3% of the SR surface. In a study made
with "skinned" fibers, Franzini-Armstrong (80) showed that most of the junctional
gap is accessible to ferritin molecules (diameter 100 Å) and therefore must be in
direct continuity with the sarcoplasm. The junctional feet are considered to be the
only possible pathway of current flow between the SR and T-tubule since current
flowing through the rest of the T-tubule membrane would escape into the sarcoplasm. Franzini-Armstrong (79) concludes that on morphological grounds one
cannot decide whether coupling is through ionic current flow via the junctional feet
or chemical transmission across the junctional gap.

Other lines of evidence suggest that aqueous channels between the T-tubule and
SR do exist. It will be recalled that frog muscle fibers exhibit an anomalous osmotic
behavior (57) that can be explained by assuming that part of the extracellular space
lies within the fiber. A similar conclusion has been reached on the basis of $Na^+$ efflux
data (see 227 for review). The size of this compartment was estimated to be about
15% of the fiber volume, a figure in remarkably good agreement with the fractional
volume occupied by SR as estimated from electron micrographs (171). In 1969 Birks
& Davey (23) provided more direct electron microscopic evidence by showing that
hypertonic sucrose caused a swelling of the SR of frog muscle, an observation
difficult to explain without assuming an entry of sucrose into the SR lumen. Earlier
work of Freygang et al (83) indicated that hypertonic swelling was confined to the
T-tubules, but in a more recent, carefully controlled study, Birks & Davey (24)
confirmed their earlier findings and showed that the discrepancy between the two
groups could be attributed to differences in fixation techniques.

Two recent morphological studies make further claim for the extracellular nature
of the SR. Rubio & Sperelakis (183) found that horseradish peroxidase, an extracellular marker, penetrated into the T-tubules and terminal cisternae of frog SR. Since
the marker was not seen in the sarcoplasm the route of entry was considered to be
the triadic junction. There was only limited penetration of peroxidase into the
longitudinal reticulum. Penetration of peroxidase into the SR was enhanced in
hypertonic solutions. The authors suggest that there are openings between the
T-tubule and SR through which the peroxidase can move, and that penetration is

increased in hypertonic solution because of a general increase in dimensions of the internal membrane systems. They interpret their data as being consistent with a direct electrical coupling between T-tubule and SR. Kulczycky & Mainwood (134) confirmed that hypertonic sucrose causes swelling of the SR and they also observed penetration of horseradish peroxidase into the T-tubule, SR, and, to some extent, the longitudinal reticulum. An intriguing observation reported in this paper is that the movement of the marker into the longitudinal reticulum was considerably enhanced in the presence of $10^{-5}$ $M$ ouabain. The authors offer some speculation about an ouabain-sensitive fluid flow from longitudinal reticulum to terminal cistern which could counter diffusion in the opposite direction. There is some histochemical evidence of a $Na^+,K^+$–ATPase in the SR membrane (75). This finding may have some bearing on Winegrad's (220) observation of intratubular $Ca^{2+}$ movement from longitudinal reticulum to the terminal cisternae.

While a variety of experimental approaches point to a direct continuity between T-tubule and SR lumen, some questions must still be cleared up before such a concept can be accepted. The careful study of Eisenberg & Eisenberg (63) in 1968 did not reveal any penetration of horseradish peroxidase into the SR. Rubio & Sperelakis (183) attribute this discrepancy to differences in experimental protocol, but explicit evidence in support of this explanation has yet to be presented. In view of the electron microscopic evidence that the SR swells in hypertonic sucrose, an explanation is required for Duggan & Martonosi's (56) discovery that isolated SR vesicles are quite permeable to sucrose. Both electron microscopy and tissue fractionation techniques have their share of hidden artifacts, so it is not certain which set of experiments is a more accurate reflection of the physiological situation. Conceivably, some membrane component which determines permeability properties is washed out during vesicle preparation. Or, expanding on a suggestion of Martonosi (146), it is possible that sucrose permeability is localized to a specific site (junctional feet?) which in the intact cell is joined to the T-tubule. The junctional feet would be the most likely site of aqueous channels between the SR and T-tubule, but such an assignment cannot be made on the basis of the existing evidence.

With regard to a possible electrical coupling between the T-tubule and SR, earlier studies (46, 47) showed that skinned fibers could respond mechanically to electrical stimulation. This response was attributed to a depolarization of internal membranes and resultant $Ca^{2+}$ release. Since skinned fibers must contain elements of both SR and T-tubules, the site of depolarization cannot be localized. The electrical excitability of the T-tubule is strongly indicated, but at present there is no unequivocal evidence of an electrical potential across the SR membrane or of a propogated electrical signal in these membranes.

## Regenerative $Ca^{2+}$ Release

An idea which has been gaining some favor of late is that the release of $Ca^{2+}$ by the SR is a regenerative process in which $Ca^{2+}$ itself promotes the release of $Ca^{2+}$. Bianchi & co-workers (21, 22) appear to have first suggested several years ago that there is a pool of "trigger" $Ca^{2+}$, probably in the T-tubule, which enters the cell during excitation and causes the release of SR $Ca^{2+}$. It is clear that there is an inward flux of $Ca^{2+}$ associated with the action potential in a variety of excitable cells (180), and in cardiac muscle this influx appears to play an important role in excitation-contraction coupling (136, 180). In twitch type skeletal muscle fibers the amount of $Ca^{2+}$ which enters the cell with each action potential is not nearly enough to activate the myofilaments (180), but that does not preclude its having an essential role at some other point in the excitation-contraction coupling process.

Evidence for a regenerative $Ca^{2+}$ release was initially provided in two papers published in 1970. Endo, Tanaka & Ogawa (70) showed that in skinned fibers the release of $Ca^{2+}$ from the SR induced by caffeine was potentiated by $Ca^{2+}$ itself. Ford & Podolsky (76) observed that a concentration of free $Ca^{2+}$ which caused a delayed rise in tension in a skinned frog fiber could cause a rapid development of tension if the SR of the fiber was first preloaded with $Ca^{2+}$. They argued that this rapid response was due to a $Ca^{2+}$-induced release of $Ca^{2+}$ from internal stores in close proximity to the myofilaments.

In a more recent series of papers, Ford & Podolsky (77, 78) painstakingly measured the uptake of $^{45}Ca^{2+}$ by the SR of skinned fiber segments immersed in solutions containing a $Ca^{2+}$ concentration just above the contraction threshold. They showed that the delay in the onset of contraction could be accounted for by a sufficiently rapid accumulation of $Ca^{2+}$ by the SR to keep the $Ca^{2+}$ concentration in the region of the myofilaments below threshold. However, instead of a simple monotonic force development that might be expected if the delay was a function of SR filling, they often observed abrupt tension spikes suggestive of an unloading of SR $Ca^{2+}$. This hypothesis was verified by direct measurement of $^{45}Ca^{2+}$ efflux under conditions that produced tension spikes. Fabiato & Fabiato (72) have also furnished evidence of regenerative $Ca^{2+}$ release in cardiac muscle fragments.

The question must be raised as to whether the hypothesis of regenerative $Ca^{2+}$ release is compatible with the electromechanical coupling properties of striated muscle. If free $Ca^{2+}$ induces a release of stored $Ca^{2+}$ in a simple positive feedback manner, then the naive expectation would be that $Ca^{2+}$ release should be an all or nothing response. The available evidence indicates just the opposite. It is well known that $K^+$ contracture tension can be graded as the membrane potential is reduced from threshold to saturation level (110). Gradation of contraction in voltage-clamped frog fibers has been demonstrated by Costantin & Taylor (48). Taylor, Preiser & Sandow (205) have confirmed and expanded earlier work indicating that $Ca^{2+}$ release from the SR is closely related to the shape of the action potential. These workers studied the effect of Type B potentiators ($Zn^{2+}$, eserine) on electromechanical coupling properties of frog muscle. It will be recalled that the Type B potentiators enhance twitch tension through a prolongation of the action potential, rather than a reduction in mechanical threshold as appears to be the case with Type A potentiators ($NO_3^-$, $Br^-$). In short, this study showed that the rate of tension development in a twitch is a function of the rate of depolarization, whereas the magnitude of developed tension is determined by the delay in repolarization of the membrane. Thus $Ca^{2+}$ release appears to be coupled to membrane potential during both the early and late phases of the action potential. Recent studies by Caputo (36) of the relation between $K^+$ contracture tension and potential (see below) also show that $Ca^{2+}$ release is under continuous membrane control. These conclusions seem difficult to reconcile with a simple regenerative release mechanism. If there is a regenerative increase in SR $Ca^{2+}$ permeability, more complex controls, perhaps inactivation processes (11), must be built into it.

The pathway for entrance of the postulated trigger $Ca^{2+}$ into the cell is not clear, but the electromechanical uncoupling in "detubulated" fibers would argue for the T-tubule as the locus of trigger $Ca^{2+}$ entry, as first suggested by Bianchi (21, 22). Unfortunately data are not yet available comparing the $Ca^{2+}$ entry per impulse per unit surface area in normal and detubulated fibers. Resting $Ca^{2+}$ efflux does not seem to be significantly altered by T-tubule disruption (211). If the membrane were homogeneous with respect to $Ca^{2+}$ permeability one might expect that prolonged stimulation of detubulated fibers would allow enough $Ca^{2+}$ to enter the fiber to trigger a release of $Ca^{2+}$ from the SR, if this is indeed the physiological mechanism of $Ca^{2+}$ release.

The hypothesis that either surface or T-tubule $Ca^{2+}$ plays an essential role in SR $Ca^{2+}$ release has been strongly challenged by Armstrong, Bezanilla & Horowicz (7). These workers immersed single frog semitendinosus fibers in a $Ca^{2+}$-free Ringer solution containing 1 m$M$ ethylene glycol-bis-($\beta$-aminoethyl ether)-N,N'-tetraacetic acid (EGTA), a $Ca^{2+}$-chelating agent. They observed that these fibers responded with normal twitches for 20–25 minutes when stimulated once every 10 seconds. Free $Ca^{2+}$ concentration at the surface and in the T-tubules was calculated to be less than $10^{-8}$ $M$. Microelectrode measurements showed that the ultimate decline in tension in the presence of EGTA was due to the gradual depolarization of the membrane to a level at which the $Na^+$ conductance mechanism was inactivated. These results seem to eliminate any role for superficial $Ca^{2+}$ in SR $Ca^{2+}$ release. However, the possibility still exists that there is some $Ca^{2+}$ tightly bound to the membrane which is not readily removed by EGTA and which is released into the sarcoplasm or at the triadic junction during excitation.

Hagiwara, Henkart & Kidikoro (95) have demonstrated by electron microscopy the existence of a specific accumulation of $La^{3+}$ at the SR–surface membrane junction of the myotomal muscle of amphioxus. In this particular muscle the fibers are lamellar sheets only 1–2 $\mu$m thick. They lack T-tubules and the SR forms a direct contact with the surface membrane, which presumably serves the same function as the triadic junction in frog muscle. Assuming that $La^{3+}$ is a marker for membrane $Ca^{2+}$ binding sites, this observation is consistent with the presence of tightly bound $Ca^{2+}$ in the space between SR and surface membrane (or T-tubule).

Schneider & Chandler (189) have carried out an important study with voltage-clamped frog fibers under conditions where $Na^+$ and $K^+$ conductances were eliminated (immersion in tetrodotoxin, tetraethylammonium Cl, RbCl). They showed that a depolarizing voltage caused a small transient outward current that reversed itself when the membrane potential was restored to its original value. These currents were attributed to charged structures within the membrane that move in response to change in potential. Schneider & Chandler speculate that the junctional feet may be the locus of this current flow and that this current might be a means of communication between T-tubule and SR. Further studies of this phenomenon will be awaited with great interest.

## Mechanical Effects on $Ca^{2+}$ Release

One of the more interesting recent developments is the discovery that the $Ca^{2+}$ release mechanism not only determines the mechanical response but is in turn influenced by the mechanical state of the muscle. Taylor & Rüdel (206) first showed by ciné micrography that in single frog fibers undergoing isotonic shortening from initial sarcomere lengths of 2.0–2.2 $\mu$m, the myofibrils remained straight throughout the fiber until sarcomere length 1.6 $\mu$m, at which point the fibrils in the core of the fiber took on a wavy appearance. The authors suggested that there was a failure of excitation-contraction coupling at short sarcomere lengths, an interpretation which received support from their observation that the fibrils remained straight if the shortening took place in the presence of 1.5 m$M$ caffeine. Regardless of initial length the waviness of the fibrils always appeared at sarcomere length 1.6 $\mu$m. In a second paper Rüdel & Taylor (184) examined the effects of caffeine on the isometric length-force relationship. Caffeine had only a slight effect on the plateau region of the curve, but caused a marked increase in force development on the ascending part. At a sarcomere length of 1.3 $\mu$m, where in a normal fiber tetanic force development is zero, stimulation in the presence of caffeine caused the fiber to generate as much as 35% of maximum force. Assuming that caffeine acts by facilitating $Ca^{2+}$ release from the SR, it appears as if the amount of $Ca^{2+}$ normally released at short sarcomere lengths is not sufficient to saturate the myofilaments.

This conclusion receives further support from the work of Schoenberg & Podolsky (190). In this study skinned fibers of varying sarcomere length were stimulated to generate force by the addition of ATP and $Ca^{2+}$. At sarcomere lengths of 1 $\mu$m these fibers could develop as much as 50% of maximal force provided optimal concentrations of $Ca^{2+}$ were present. Thus the slope of the ascending limb of the length-force curve is probably determined by a combination of a distorted filament lattice and reduced activation. The appearance of wavy fibrils in the core of the fiber, as observed by Taylor & Rüdel (206), is consistent with a failure of T-tubule transmission at short sarcomere lengths, but other possibilities have not been ruled out.

The discovery that $Ca^{2+}$ release is influenced by mechanical state provides a new way of looking at a number of mechanical properties of muscle which have never been satisfactorily explained. For example, it is well known that active state duration increases with increase in muscle length and that an isotonic twitch is terminated sooner than an isometric twitch. These phenomena have been explored in greater detail by Edman & Kiessling (62) in a careful study of active state development and decay as a function of sarcomere length and motion in single frog muscle fibers. The rate of active state development was found to be independent of sarcomere length. However, active state duration increased almost linearly as sarcomere length was increased from 1.7–2.8 $\mu$m. The authors explain this finding in terms of the following model: the amount of $Ca^{2+}$ released from the SR is a function of sarcomere length. Since in the length range studied the amount released is assumed to be more than enough to saturate the myofilament binding sites, the rate of active state development will be independent of sarcomere length. However, if more $Ca^{2+}$ is released at longer lengths than at shorter lengths more time will be needed for its removal from the sarcoplasm, hence the prolongation of active state. The authors emphasize the distinction, not always made explicit, between short sarcomere length and shortening per se. They showed that quick release from any given sarcomere length during an isometric twitch causes an immediate reduction in active state intensity which is proportional to the amount of shortening.

Related experiments were performed by Briden & Alpert (31) in an attempt to find out whether shortening caused a reduction in active state intensity, or deactivation, independent of sarcomere length. They devised a method of active state measurement in which shortening was restricted to the plateau region of the length-force curve, where filament overlap is independent of sarcomere length. Their data clearly show a reduction of active state intensity with isotonic shortening and quick release.

Thus we have two separate phenomena which may or may not be related: 1. increase in active state duration with increase in sarcomere length, and 2. deactivation with shortening independent of sarcomere length. With regard to the first it should be noted that Edman & Kiessling (62) did their measurements at sarcomere lengths greater than that at which Taylor & Rüdel (206) observed buckling of the myofibrils, so it is not clear that the results of these two groups are related. Nor is there any evidence that $Ca^{2+}$ release from the SR is greater at longer sarcomere lengths. In fact, in a brief report several years ago Sopis & Winegrad (195) stated that $^{45}Ca^{2+}$ efflux from stimulated frog muscle is actually three times greater at rest length than at 160% rest length. An alternative to the Edman-Kiessling hypothesis, for which there is some evidence, is that at longer sarcomere lengths the myofilaments bind $Ca^{2+}$ more tightly, thus providing increased competition for the SR $Ca^{2+}$ pump. The deactivation with shortening might also be related to changes in myofilament $Ca^{2+}$ binding (a point also considered by Edman & Kiessling). Therefore, both subjects will be taken up again in the discussion of $Ca^{2+}$ activation.

## Intracellular $Ca^{2+}$ Movement

Ashley & Ridgeway (10), working with the $Ca^{2+}$-sensitive photoprotein aequorin, provided the most direct evidence of a transient rise in sarcoplasmic $Ca^{2+}$ concentration immediately following membrane depolarization. In the giant barnacle muscle fibers used by these workers it is likely that much of the $Ca^{2+}$ came from the extracellular space or surface membrane. These fibers have a very extensive system of membrane invaginations, or clefts, whereas the SR, according to a recent study (113), occupies only about 0.5% of the fiber volume, or about 1/30 of the fractional SR volume of frog twitch fibers.

In the case of amphibian and mammalian twitch fibers the activator $Ca^{2+}$ is believed to be released from the terminal cisternae of the SR. Aside from the fact that this $Ca^{2+}$ activates contraction by binding to troponin, the details of its intracellular transport during the entire cycle are not clear. Winegrad (220) has obtained evidence of a rather complex cycle of $Ca^{2+}$ movement rather than simple exchange between SR and sarcoplasm. On the basis of radioautographic localization of $Ca^{2+}$ in frog toe muscle fixed at various times during and after a brief tetanus, he concluded that $Ca^{2+}$ is cycled through the following morphological pathway: terminal cisternae to thin filaments during activation, accumulation by the longitudinal reticulum, and then transport through the reticulum back to the terminal cisternae. The latter step had a half-time at room temperature of 9 sec and a $Q_{10}$ of 1.7. Since both the rate of muscle relaxation and the rate of $Ca^{2+}$ uptake by isolated SR vesicles have a $Q_{10}$ of about 3 it was inferred that it is the accumulation of $Ca^{2+}$ by the longitudinal reticulum which requires ATP and which is directly responsible for relaxation. The molecular mechanism of the ATP-dependent $Ca^{2+}$ uptake by isolated SR is discussed in great detail elsewhere (145, 146).

Although the detailed conclusions of Winegrad may be subject to further modification, this study does introduce the important idea that the SR is differentiated into "release" sites (terminal cistern) and "relaxation" sites (longitudinal reticulum). If it is assumed that an accumulation of $Ca^{2+}$ at relaxation sites during a tetanus will retard the rate of $Ca^{2+}$ removal from the sarcoplasm, then it might be possible to account in a simple way for the transient prolongation of active state and twitch potentiation which follows a tetanus. Connolly, Gough & Winegrad (43) showed that certain features of the twitches recorded immediately after a brief tetanus (50/sec for 5 sec) could be accounted for in this manner, but, as pointed out by Winegrad (220), the temporal relationship between intracellular $Ca^{2+}$ movement and the classical post-tetanic twitch potentiation does not allow such a simple interpretation. Thus in a recent study by Hanson & Persson (98) the increase in active state duration and the twitch potentiation following a tetanus (10/sec for 60 sec) persisted for about 30 min, a period presumably much longer than that needed for recycling of $Ca^{2+}$.

Caputo (35, 36) has published two papers containing some extremely interesting observations on $K^+$ contracture in single frog semitendinosus fibers. Recall that in twitch fibers $K^+$ contracture is followed by spontaneous relaxation in a matter of seconds and a subsequent period of "repriming," or recovery of contractile ability, which at room temperature is over in less than a minute. Thus prior to repriming a second contracture response cannot be elicited even if the membrane has been allowed to repolarize. With respect to the present discussion, the most important observation in Caputo's first paper is that the repriming period was about 6 times as long at 3°C as it was at 20°C. Caputo attributes repriming to an energy-dependent translocation of $Ca^{2+}$ from relaxation sites to the terminal cisternae—presumably the same process observed by Winegrad (220). This movement is greatly prolonged at low temperature. The duration of the contracture was also much longer (30–40 sec) at 3°C and in the second paper Caputo took advantage of this "slow motion" contracture to study the effects of rapid change in membrane potential applied at various times during the contracture (through alteration of external $K^+$ concentration). Contracture could be terminated at any time by rapidly substituting normal Ringer's solution (2.5 m$M$ $K^+$) for the 190 m$M$ $K^+$ used to elicit the contracture. This finding provides further support for the conclusion (see above) that SR $Ca^{2+}$ release is under continuous surface membrane control. If the high $K^+$ solution was reapplied at any time after the interruption of the contracture the fiber immediately redeveloped tension to the level which existed when the contracture was interrupted and it relaxed with the time course as the normal contracture.

These interrupted contractures had some puzzling properties. First, there was no evidence of repriming during the period of interruption, that is, repriming could only follow spontaneous relaxation, not artificially induced relaxation. Second, the tension-time integral was the same for normal and interrupted contractures. The latter observation suggested to Caputo that with depolarization the SR releases some fixed quantity of $Ca^{2+}$ and that the efflux of $Ca^{2+}$ out of the SR takes place throughout the contracture period. With rapid repolarization $Ca^{2+}$ release is abruptly terminated and relaxation presumably ensues as a consequence of $Ca^{2+}$ uptake by the longitudinal reticulum. The failure to observe repriming during the period of interruption is strange, particularly if one tries to explain repriming in terms of intratubular movement of $Ca^{2+}$ from longitudinal reticulum to terminal cistern. One would expect that the $Ca^{2+}$ removed from the sarcoplasm during repolarization would be transported to the terminal cisternae and released again during the second depolarization. Evidently repriming cannot take place until the entire fixed "packet" of $Ca^{2+}$ has been discharged from the terminal cistern.

Caputo (36) proposed a model in which depolarization causes an initial rapid release of $Ca^{2+}$ followed by a slow, time-dependent and temperature-dependent inactivation. Inactivation of $Ca^{2+}$ conductance has been described in excitable membranes and, as Baker (11) suggests, it is possible that a similar mechanism may be at work in the $Ca^{2+}$ release system of muscle. The need for repolarization as an essential step in repriming would be consistent with an inactivation process. Winegrad (220) observed that 30 seconds following a $K^+$ contracture the terminal cisternae had refilled with $Ca^{2+}$ and the muscle was relaxed with the membrane still in the depolarized state. This finding fits in with Caputo's conclusion that repriming requires both intratubular transport of $Ca^{2+}$ back to the release sites and repolarization. How the phenomena described by Caputo relate to the usual twitch or tetanus type of contraction remains to be determined. Obviously, the kinetics of relaxation after a twitch or tetanus, even at low temperature, is very different from that seen in contractures. Nevertheless, further studies with this preparation may be very rewarding.

Further evidence for the existence of an intracellular compartment which can remove $Ca^{2+}$ from the sarcoplasm but not release it comes from studies of $^{45}Ca^{2+}$ efflux from crab and barnacle muscle fibers reported by Ashley, Caldwell & Lowe (9). Among a number of interesting observations in this paper is the finding that concentrations of $K^+$ (or caffeine) which were below contraction threshold did cause an increased efflux of $^{45}Ca^{2+}$, indicative of $Ca^{2+}$ release into the sarcoplasm. However, this treatment rendered the fibers refractory to further stimulation with higher $K^+$ concentrations. The authors interpret this observation as indicating an intracellular movement of $Ca^{2+}$ to a site from which it cannot be immediately mobilized. In the same vein, Vos & Frank (215) showed that brief exposure (10–30 sec) of frog muscles to subthreshold $K^+$ concentrations caused a potentiation of the contracture tension elicited by the further addition of $K^+$ to a concentration just above threshold. With longer exposure (2 min) potentiation disappeared and the contracture response fell below the control level. This result could also be explained by a slow translocation of $Ca^{2+}$ from release sites to relaxation sites.

## Effects of Hypertonic Solutions

It has been recognized for many years that hypertonic sucrose or NaCl solutions inhibit the contractile response but leave the excitation mechanism intact. Hence hypertonicity has become a familiar method of producing a dissociation of excitation and contraction. Recent studies suggest that the effects of hypertonicity are more complex than originally thought.

Beginning with the observation of Hill (108) in 1968 it has been well documented that hypertonicity by itself causes an increase in tension which appears to be a true contracture response caused by release of internal $Ca^{2+}$ (89, 124). Yamada (223) published an interesting study of resting heat production in hypertonic media. With 2.5–3.0 $N$ hypertonic Ringer, heat production increaded 10–20-fold. This heat production was $O_2$ dependent and inhibited by procaine, thus suggesting that it was due to an increase in the internal cycling of $Ca^{2+}$. Homsher & Briggs (111) and Isaacson (124) have demonstrated that hypertonic solutions stimulate $^{45}Ca^{2+}$ efflux. Two puzzling observations are reported in Yamada's paper. First, the effect of hypertonicity on heat production was not altered by T-tubule disruption with hypertonic glycerol. Second, the increased heat production was only slightly attenuated in muscles depolarized by $K^+$. Hence hypertonicity must bypass the normal T-tubule-triad pathway in effecting $Ca^{2+}$ release.

In this latter respect the effects of hypertonicity are similar to those of caffeine. This parallelism has been emphasized in a recent paper by Lännergren & Noth (137). These workers carried out their experiments with single frog semitendinosus fibers, thereby eliminating the diffusion problems which may have caused the quantitative differences among earlier workers (89). They found that a moderate increase in tonicity (1.75 $N$) caused a small, sustained rise in tension. With higher tonicity (2.25–3.0 $N$) there was, superimposed on the sustained response, a phasic contracture which developed about one-third maximal tetanus tension. Like the classical caffeine contracture, this response was not influenced by membrane potential or external $Ca^{2+}$ concentration and was blocked by 0.1–0.5 m$M$ tetracaine.

Since the inhibiting effects of hypertonicity were the same whether tension was elicited by caffeine, $K^+$ depolarization, or electrical stimulation, Gordon & Godt (89) argued that the primary effect of hypertonicity was on the myofilaments, supposedly as a consequence of an increased sarcoplasmic ionic strength. Lännergren & Noth (137) showed that in the tonicity range 2.25–3.0 $N$ the amplitude of the phasic hypertonic contracture was about the same as that produced by caffeine or $K^+$ at the same tonicity. On this basis they conclude that the limitation on tension development in hypertonic solution is set by the contractile system. Hypertonic contracture tension is about a third of tetanic tension, not because of lesser $Ca^{2+}$ release but because of the limited capability of the contractile system in hypertonic solution. .

Thus it seems that hypertonicity has a dual effect on muscle: 1. inhibition of the contractile system, as proposed by Gordon & Godt (see also 154), and 2. stimulation of $Ca^{2+}$ release from the SR. It should be noted that the small, tonic increase in tension caused by lower tonicities was not inhibited by tetracaine. Hence it probably has a different origin than the phasic contracture and may represent, according to Lännergren & Noth, an increase in the "filamentary resting tension" described by Hill (109). These conclusions could have some bearing on the interpretations given to experiments involving perturbation of muscles treated with hypertonic solution. See, for example, the observations of Rubio & Speralakis (183) on muscles pre-treated with hypertonic solution, then challenged with caffeine.

## Latency Relaxation

The brief relaxation which just precedes contraction in twitch muscles, first observed more than 50 years ago (see 186 for review of earlier literature), has been thought to reflect some fundamental aspect of the activation process. However, only with the newer knowledge of excitation-contraction coupling has it been possible to discuss it in terms of specific intracellular mechanisms.

An attractive explanation of the latency relaxation has been recently proposed by Mulieri (158), this being an extension of a hypothesis put forward several years ago by Sandow (186). The main features of this hypothesis are that 1. part of the resting tension of a muscle is borne by the SR, and 2. this tension is diminished as $Ca^{2+}$ is released from the SR. It is implicit in this hypothesis that the mechanical latent period should be a function of the time it takes for $Ca^{2+}$ to diffuse from the terminal cisternae to the overlap region of the A band. In experiments with single fibers, Mulieri (158) showed that both the magnitude of the latency relaxation $(R)$ and the interval between the stimulus and the beginning of positive tension development $(L)$ increased as the sarcomere length was increased from 2.1–2.8 $\mu$m. In the sarcomere length range 2.8–3.2 $\mu$m the interval $L$ continued to increase but $R$ reached a plateau value. The increase in $L$ is as predicted. To explain the increase in $R$ with increase in sarcomere length up to 2.8 $\mu$m it must be assumed that the latency relaxation is masked by the rapid onset of positive tension development at shorter sarcomere lengths. At sarcomere lengths greater than 2.8 the $Ca^{2+}$ diffusion time is considered to be sufficiently long so that the full development of latency relaxation is recorded. What is more difficult to explain is the observation that $R$ became smaller again as the sarcomere length was increased from 3.2 to 3.7 $\mu$m. Mulieri proposes that this decline is due to an impairment in $Ca^{2+}$ release as a result of mechanical distortion of the terminal cisternae (see 195).

As Sandow (186) has emphasized, this hypothesis leans very heavily on the morphological arrangement of the SR and, therefore, comparative studies should be useful in testing its validity. Unfortunately, there does not appear to have been much effort made in carrying out this recommendation. It remains to be established whether the latency relaxation is solely a property of muscles with a longitudinal SR. Since the terminal cisternae of mammalian skeletal muscle lie directly adjacent to the overlap zones, one would not expect to see the same dependency of mechanical latency on sarcomere length. Some data published by Norris (165) more than a dozen years ago indicated that there may indeed be a positive relation between latent period and muscle length in rat muscle. This problem should certainly be reexamined with more sensitive recording methods.

The significance of the Sandow-Mulieri hypothesis lies not just in its explanation of latency relaxation but in the fact that the magnitude of the latency relaxation is thought to reflect the amount of $Ca^{2+}$ released by the terminal cisternae, whereas the mechanical latent period is a function of the speed of $Ca^{2+}$ movement from terminal cisternae to overlap zone. As pointed out by Mulieri, if this hypothesis is confirmed investigators may have a useful technique for monitoring intracellular $Ca^{2+}$ movements. For a different view of latency relaxation see Hill (108) and discussion by Sandow (187).

## CROSS-BRIDGE MECHANISMS

It is now generally accepted that the sliding of myosin and actin filaments past each other is energetically coupled to the hydrolysis of ATP by the heavy meromyosin segments which form the movable cross-bridges that project from the surface of the myosin filament. In the presence of $Mg^{2+}$ and a low concentration of $Ca^{2+}$ the hydrolysis of ATP by the cross-bridges is activated by actin. The connection between the actin-activated ATP hydrolysis and cross-bridge movement is the major problem to be solved in the effort to provide a molecular description of the chemomechanical transduction process.

For many years the biochemical and ultrastructural approaches to contraction were pursued along more or less separate pathways with only occasional points of contact among workers in the different disciplines. This situation has changed dramatically in recent years. Concurrent developments in actomyosin enzymology and ultrastructural techniques have reached a stage where kinetically defined steps in ATP hydrolysis can be tentatively related to specific phases in the cross-bridge cycle. A detailed discussion of contractile protein biochemistry is beyond the scope of this review and is, in any case, unnecessary in view of the abundance of excellent, up to date reviews already available (see Introduction). Attention will be focused only on those biochemical studies which have a direct bearing on cross-bridge movement and force generation.

### X-ray Diffraction Studies

Certain basic features of myofilament structure and cross-bridge activity were established prior to the period covered by this review and will be referred to only briefly here. The organization of the myosin filament is governed by the self-aggregating properties of the light meromyosin (LMM) "tails" which form the backbone of the filament and the solubility of the globular heavy meromyosin (HMM) "heads" which stick out into the sarcoplasm and form the surface projections seen in the electron microscope (116). The arrangement of the cross-bridges has been deduced by Huxley & Brown (122) on the basis of X-ray diffraction patterns. They derived a model in which the cross-bridges are arranged in pairs pointing in opposite directions. The pairs are spaced 143 Å apart and each pair is rotated 120° relative to its neighbor. Thus the bridges describe a helix with a subunit repeat of 143° and a helical repeat of 3 X 143 Å, or 429 Å.

The earlier X-ray diffraction studies of resting, contracting, and rigor muscle (117, 122), discussed by Sandow (187) in his 1970 review, led to two fundamental results which provided a strong foundation for the sliding filament–moving cross-bridge model. For the methodological and conceptual background the reader should consult the relevant papers and reviews of H. E. Huxley (117–122). First, from the meridional X-ray patterns it was established that in electrically-stimulated muscle the fundamental backbone spacings of the myosin filament are unchanged from the resting state, but there is an increased disorder in the helical array of cross-bridges. This finding was consistent with an asynchronous, axial movement of cross-bridges in the activated state. Second, on the basis of changes in the intensity of equatorial reflections it was determined that in the rigor state there was a transfer of mass from the myosin filament to the actin filament, a finding strongly suggestive of an attachment of the globular HMM heads to the actin.

The latter conclusion has been confirmed and extended in Rome's (181) more recent X-ray diffraction study of glycerinated rabbit psoas muscle. She has shown that in the presence of a "relaxing" solution (ATP + EGTA) there is a change in the relative intensities of equatorial reflections indicative of a movement of material from the actin to myosin filaments. This phenomenon is associated with the transition of the muscle from rigor to the relaxed, or highly distensible, state. Since ATP, in the absence of $Ca^{2+}$, is known to dissociate actin from myosin in vitro, Rome's results provide further evidence for a direct linkage between actin and myosin in rigor muscle.

Much recent literature has been addressed to the problem of myosin-to-actin filament distance and its mechanistic implications. Earlier X-ray studies had shown that the myofibril lattice volume of relaxed frog muscle was constant over a wide range of sarcomere lengths and did not change significantly during contraction (67). Constant-volume behavior has since been demonstrated in other preparations (5, 181) and appears to be an inherent property of contractile systems. For a discussion of the physicochemical basis of constant-volume behavior see the recent paper by Matsubara & Elliott (147) and references cited therein.

From the standpoint of the sliding filament system, the main problem has arisen from the variation in actin-to-myosin distance as sarcomere length is changed. Surface-to-surface distance between actin and myosin has been estimated (in toad muscle) to range from about 50 Å at sarcomere length 3.5 $\mu$m to 130 Å at sarcomere length 1.8 $\mu$m (67). This variability in interfilament spacing has been the primary inspiration for a number of theories of contraction (67a and references therein) based on the principle that longitudinal force arises from repulsive forces between filaments rather than a "pulling" of cross-bridges. However, the arguments in favor of these theories have lost much of their impact with the introduction of the concept of a flexible cross-bridge which can extend from the myosin filament in accordance with the interfilament distance. According to the recent work of Schoenberg & Podolsky (190), mentioned above, cross-bridge attachment must be able to occur even at sarcomere lengths so short (1 $\mu$m) that the filament lattice is grossly distorted.

As to the molecular basis of cross-bridge flexibility, the evidence is largely indirect, being based on considerations of myosin structure. In the cross-bridge model of H. E. Huxley (118) the part of the myosin rod that is sensitive to tryptic digestion and that denotes the connecting region between HMM and LMM segments is conceived to be a flexible "hinge" which allows the HMM to rotate outward from the myosin filament backbone. The HMM can be cleaved into two fragments, subfragment-1 (S-1) which forms the globular terminus of the myosin molecule and carries the ATPase and actin-combining properties of myosin, and subfragment-2 (S-2), a highly $\alpha$–helical rod which is the connecting link between S-1 and LMM (see 120 for review). Since S-2, like S-1, is soluble at physiological ionic strength, it would tend to move easily away from the filament backbone. In the Huxley model a second hinge region is located at the junction of S-1 and S-2 and it is the rotation of S-1 relative to S-2 (with actin linked to S-1) which is assumed to provide the power stroke of the cross-bridge cycle. Thus rotation around the S-2–LMM hinge brings the S-1 into close proximity to actin and rotation of S-1 generates the force. According to Burke, Himmelfarb & Harrington (33) the trypsin-sensitive region of myosin undergoes a helix-coil transition much more readily than adjacent sections of myosin and could therefore be a region of high flexibility. The distance from the postulated S-2–LMM hinge to the S-1 segment, some 400–500 Å, is easily compatible with any range of filament separations that can conceivably occur. Thus on structural grounds the argument that the angle between S-2 and the filament backbone varies with sarcomere length seems quite plausible [see also the results of antibody staining experiments, reviewed by Pepe in (172)]. However, direct evidence of a conformational transition at the HMM–LMM boundary during contraction is still lacking.

Among the most interesting of recent developments arising from X-ray diffraction studies is the discovery that the motion of the cross-bridges in activated muscle may not necessarily be dependent on the presence of actin (121). In frog semitendinosus muscles stretched to sarcomere lengths (3.6–4.5 $\mu$m) at which no filament overlap would be expected, electrical stimulation caused changes in the meridional X-ray reflections indicating a very substantial axial movement of cross-bridges. Also reported in the same paper is the observation that cross-bridge movement, even at rest length, persists for several seconds after the cessation of stimulation. These observations raise some perplexing questions about the function of the $Ca^{2+}$-activating system and the relation of cross-bridge movement to tension development. Current views assign the $Ca^{2+}$-binding sites exclusively to troponin (on the actin filament), yet it appears that the myosin filament can "sense" a rise in intracellular $Ca^{2+}$ concentration even if the troponin binding sites are totally removed from the vicinity of the cross-bridges. The possibility has been raised (128) that $Ca^{2+}$ might bind to both actin and myosin filaments, but at present there is no evidence that $Ca^{2+}$ can bind to myosin under physiological conditions; the available data indicate quite the contrary (see later discussion).

Huxley (121) suggests that cross-bridge movement may be a cooperative response which could be initiated by just a few overlapping filaments that still exist at long sarcomere lengths. Once a few cross-bridges are set in motion the effect would be transmitted to other cross-bridges which are outside of the overlap zone. Such a phenomenon is invoked as a possible explanation of the slow tension development often seen in frog fibers stretched to sarcomere lengths greater than 3.6 $\mu$m (90). Thus, in these terms, cross-bridge movement is still actin-dependent but those cross-bridges outside the overlap zone are in communication with the overlapped cross-bridges through myosin-myosin interactions which are propagated long distances through the myosin filament. Further studies of this phenomenon should certainly prove to be of great interest.

Significant structural changes in the actin filaments of activated frog muscle have also been detected by X-ray methods. However, these are more relevant to the problem of $Ca^{2+}$ activation of contraction and will be considered in that context.

Much recent X-ray diffraction work has been carried out with fibrillar insect flight muscle, especially that of the giant water bug, *Lethocerus*. Aside from the more ordered filament lattice in insect flight muscle, this preparation has certain properties which make it very useful for structural studies. Unlike vertebrate muscle, in the presence of ATP and $Ca^{2+}$ the actomyosin system of this muscle is in a state of "static $Ca^{2+}$ activation" (152) in which ATPase activity and tension are only slightly enhanced. Active tension development with a high rate of ATP splitting is evoked by oscillatory changes in length at a frequency corresponding to the resonant frequency of the thorax-wing system of the insect. This myogenic oscillation is an intrinsic property of the contractile system which can be demonstrated in glycerol-extracted preparations (see 178 for recent review). Thus one can study in glycerinated bundles the structural correlates of four different states: rigor (no ATP), relaxation (ATP), static $Ca^{2+}$ activation (ATP + $Ca^{2+}$), and work-producing oscillation (ATP + $Ca^{2+}$ + stretch).

While the generality of the results obtained with this preparation may be questioned by some, it should be noted that similar myogenic oscillatory behavior has been demonstrated under appropriate conditions in glycerinated preparations of mammalian skeletal (185) and cardiac muscle (199). As Pringle (178) points out, stretch activation seems to be a general property of muscle which has undergone a more exaggerated development in insect flight muscle. The basic lessons learned from this rather specialized muscle are likely to be applicable in at least a qualitative sense to other striated muscles.

Recent work by Miller & Tregear (152, 153) and Armitage et al (6) can be summarized as follows: in the resting state the cross-bridges are, on the average, oriented perpendicular to the myosin filament and detached from actin, while in rigor the cross-bridges move out from the myosin filament and attach to the actin filament, in which position they lie at an angle of about 45°, pointing toward the center of the A band. These results confirm earlier X-ray and electron-optical observations of Reedy, Holmes & Tregear (179) and they also fit in well with the observations of Huxley (116) and Moore et al (157) that HMM and S-1 attach to isolated actin filaments in an angled position. With static $Ca^{2+}$ activation the cross-bridges move out toward the actin filament but, for the most part, do not attach to them. Attachment and large scale axial movement of cross-bridges occur with stretch-induced tension development. In both static $Ca^{2+}$ activation and stretch activation it was calculated that only about 15% of the cross-bridges had actually moved toward the actin filament. It appears that even with maximal activity only a small fraction of the cross-bridges are actually linked to actin at any given instant. Another implication of this work is that the movement of the cross-bridges out toward the actin depends only on the binding of $Ca^{2+}$ to troponin, not ATP hydrolysis and tension development. Whether the same holds true for vertebrate muscle has not yet been determined. Unfortunately, the stiffness of insect flight muscle prevents any study of the effect of filament overlap on the above phenomena.

An interesting problem raised by these findings is how stretching the muscle promotes the attachment of cross-bridges to actin. Lowy (139) has suggested that in the state of static $Ca^{2+}$ activation a small fraction of the cross-bridges are already attached, as indicated by the small increase in ATPase activity and tension. Traction on these attached bridges could, through myosin-myosin interactions propogated along the filaments, cause other cross-bridges to attach to actin and go through their force-generating cycles. This explanation bears some resemblance to H. E. Huxley's (121) hypothesis to explain the movement of cross-bridges which are not overlapped by actin. Earlier studies by D. K. Hill (108) suggested that even in relaxed vertebrate muscle a low level of cross-bridge attachment always occurs. The existence of some degree of continuity between the two sets of filaments provides a possible pathway for mechanical feedback effects on chemical reactions at the cross-bridges.

## Biochemical Indicators of Cross-Bridge Activity

X-ray diffraction patterns of intact muscle, at present resolving power, give information about relatively large-scale changes in cross-bridge orientation but do not provide much information about the orientation or reactivity of chemical groups involved in cross-link formation. Consequently there is a real need for other biochemical and biophysical techniques which can be applied to intact muscle fibers in order to furnish a complementary picture of cross-bridge activity. These results could then be related to the phases of the activity cycle which have been defined by ultrastructural techniques. I will consider here only two recent approaches in this direction which look promising.

Dos Remedios, Millikan & Morales (52) have devised a method for making rapid measurements of the polarization of fluorescence emitted by single muscle fibers when the tryptophan residues are excited by plane polarized light oriented perpendicular to the fiber axis. The rationale behind this approach is discussed in an earlier paper by Aronson & Morales (8). With both glycerol-extracted psoas fibers and single frog fibers, fluorescence polarization was maximal in the relaxed state and minimal in rigor. Myosin contains 50% of the tryptophan residues of the myofibril and accounts for 70% of the total fluorescence. Citing data showing that about 70% of the myosin tryptophan residues are in the S-1 segment, Dos Remedios et al (52) concluded that the signals they record are due to changes in S-1 orientation. Their data can be tentatively correlated with the ultrastructural observations (179) showing that in relaxed muscle the cross-bridges (S-1?) project outward from the myosin filament (maximum fluorescence polarization) while in rigor they lie at an angle pointing toward the center of the A band (minimum polarization). During active force development the polarization had intermediate values. This finding is consistent with other evidence (152) cited above, indicating that only a fraction of the cross-bridges are actually connected to actin filaments during force development.

Bárány and associates (14–16) have adopted a more biochemical approach which derives from earlier work by this group (13) showing that dinitrophenylation of myosin with radioactive 1-fluoro-2,4-dinitrobenzene ($^3$H-FDNB) was decreased in the presence of MgATP or actin. Similar differences were observed with in vivo labeling of myosin extracted from resting and stimulated frog muscle. In later work the sulfhydryl reagent, N-ethylmaleimide (NEM) was found to give more satisfactory results (16). Incorporation of $^{14}$C-NEM into myosin extracted from stimulated muscles was about 17% less than that found in myosin from resting muscles. By means of proteolytic degradation of the myosin it could be shown that the difference was due entirely to changes in reactivity of sulfhydryl groups located on the S-1 moiety. Although the evidence does not seem conclusive, Bárány et al (14–16) are inclined to believe that the altered reactivity is due to a conformational change in S-1 rather than a simple blocking of the amino acid residues by actin. It is of interest that this effect disappeared in muscles stretched to lengths at which tension could not be developed (15). Considering this finding in conjunction with X-ray diffraction data on stretched muscle (see above) it appears that the observed effect must be dependent on the formation of actin-myosin links rather than cross-bridge movement per se. The attractiveness of this approach lies in the fact that regions of the cross-bridge involved in conformational changes or protein-protein interactions can be covalently labeled and subsequently identified by chemical isolation.

## ATP Hydrolysis and Cross-Bridge Movement

One of the more notable recent achievements in the molecular physiology of muscle has been the formulation of relatively simple kinetic schemes of ATP hydrolysis which can be directly related, at least in a tentative way, to specific phases of the cross-bridge cycle. This development has depended upon the application of elegant rapid kinetic methods to the study of the acto-HMM ATPase system, especially by Taylor and co-workers (141, and references cited therein). The original papers, as well as reviews by Taylor (203) and Taylor & Lymn (204), should be consulted for the experimental and conceptual foundations of this work.

The basic features of the acto-HMM ATPase reaction, as summarized by Lymn & Taylor (141), are as follows:

1. Addition of ATP to a solution of acto-HMM leads to dissociation of the acto-HMM and hydrolysis of ATP. Since the rate of dissociation is at least 10 times greater than the rate of hydrolysis the hydrolysis must take place on free HMM rather than on the acto-HMM complex.

2. The rate-limiting step in the hydrolysis of ATP by free HMM is the dissociation of hydrolytic products from myosin, that is $M \cdot ADP \cdot P \longrightarrow M + ADP + P$.

3. The rate of dissociation of the myosin-product complex is markedly increased by the binding of actin to myosin. If this is the rate-limiting reaction in steady-state ATP hydrolysis then the actin activation of myosin ATPase can be simply attributed to an acceleration $M \cdot ADP \cdot P$ dissociation.

Lymn & Taylor (141) have pointed out that the simplest cross-bridge cycle conceivable must consist of at least four steps, as follows: 1. dissociation of the cross-bridge from the actin filament, 2. movement of the cross-bridge, 3. reattachment of the cross-bridge to actin, and 4. movement of the attached cross-bridge back to its original position. This last step is responsible for the sliding of the filaments and force development.

Taking into account both the kinetic and the X-ray diffraction data, it would seem reasonable to suppose that the dissociation of the cross-bridges from actin is caused by the binding of ATP to HMM and that at the moment of ATP binding the cross-bridges are in the tilted orientation, pointing toward the center of the A band (rigor configuration). Following dissociation of the cross-bridge the ATP is rapidly cleaved and the cross-bridge moves to the perpendicular orientation where it exists as the M·ADP·P complex. If the combining site of an actin monomer is in close proximity it will bind to the cross-bridge, displace the products, and the cross-bridge will then move back into the tilted orientation, pulling the actin filament along with it. It should be noted that the combination of actin with the cross-bridge and the power stroke of the cross-bridge are assumed to be exergonic processes. Energy is needed not for the development of force but for returning the free cross-bridge to the position in which it can once again combine with actin.

The role of $Ca^{2+}$ in ATP hydrolysis was considered in a later report by Koretz, Hunt & Taylor (131). It appears that the main effect of $Ca^{2+}$ is an acceleration of the actin-induced dissociation of the myosin-product complex. This effect of actin is inhibited by the tropomyosin-troponin complex unless $Ca^{2+}$ is bound to the troponin.

The authors of the above scheme have been careful to point out (141, 204) that the kinetic mechanism which emerges from their experiments is the simplest one that can be accommodated to the cross-bridge cycle as currently visualized. As such, it is probably an oversimplification and will have to be modified as more biochemical and structural information becomes available. Certain features of this scheme have been confirmed experimentally whereas in other cases inconsistencies have arisen.

One of the predictions of the Lymn-Taylor cycle is that in the relaxed state, with a low rate of interaction between actin and myosin, the great majority of cross-bridges should exist as the M·ADP·P complex. Marston & Tregear (144) have found that in glycerinated fibers relaxed in ATP-EGTA solution the major bound nucleotide is ADP, most of which is bound to myosin. This finding is taken as strong evidence that the detached cross-bridge is indeed a myosin-product complex.

To relate cross-bridge orientation to the kinetic sequence, Mannherz et al (143) have employed an ATP analog, $\alpha,\beta$-methylene ATP (APCPP). This analog causes a dissociation of actomyosin, as evidenced by the increased distensibility of glycerinated muscle in its presence, but its hydrolysis is not activated by actin. Moreover, the initial hydrolytic cleavage, M·ATP⟶M·ADP·P, proceeds about 1000 times faster in the case of the ATP than APCPP. Therefore APCPP should cause dissociation of the cross-bridges from the actin filament, but because of its slow hydrolysis a large number of cross-bridges should remain in the same position they occupied at the moment of detachment. X-ray diffraction studies with glycerinated insect flight muscle showed that in the presence of APCPP most of the cross-bridges were in the tilted configuration characteristic of rigor (but detached from the actin filaments) whereas with the more rapidly hydrolyzed ATP (+ EGTA) the average position of the cross-bridges was perpendicular to the myosin filament axis. Since in the presence of ATP (relaxed state) the cross-bridges are presumably in the M·ADP·P form, these results provide strong evidence that the movement of the detached cross-bridge from the tilted to the perpendicular position is coupled to ATP hydrolysis, in accord with the Lymn-Taylor scheme.

On the other hand, a different picture is obtained with another ATP analog, $\beta$, $\gamma$-imino-ATP (APPNP), a competitive inhibitor of actomyosin ATPase which, according to Yount et al (225), causes dissociation of rabbit actomyosin in solution but is not hydrolyzed by it. Barrington Leigh et al (17) reported that the X-ray diffraction pattern of glycerinated insect flight muscle treated with APPNP indicated that the cross-bridges were in the perpendicular orientation as in muscle relaxed with ATP-EGTA solution. The stiffness of the fibers was only slightly affected by APPNP, showing that most of the cross-bridges were still attached to the actin filaments. The interpretation of Barrington Leigh et al (17) is that APPNP caused the cross-bridges to move from the tilted to the perpendicular orientation while still connected to the actin filaments, essentially a reversal of the power stroke. There is indirect evidence that pyrophosphate may have a similar effect (18, 133). Thus it appears that under certain circumstances, at least in insect flight muscle, the cross-bridge can be induced to move from the tilted to the perpendicular orientation without phosphate bond hydrolysis [see Lymn & Huxley (140) for somewhat more complex effects of APPNP on glycerinated rabbit psoas muscle]. Further studies with a variety of analogs should provide valuable information about the biochemical basis of cross-bridge movement.

With regard to the Lymn-Taylor scheme, the main point of contention among the kineticists is the identify of the rate-limiting step in steady-state ATP hydrolysis. The conclusion that product dissociation is rate limiting has been questioned by Trentham et al (210) and Malik & Martonosi (142). Using rapid kinetic methods, these workers have obtained evidence that rate limitation is set at some intermediate stage between hydrolytic cleavage and product dissociation.

The reaction sequence proposed by Trentham et al (210) can be written as ATP + M $\rightleftharpoons$ M·ATP $\rightleftharpoons$ M$^*$ADP·P $\rightleftharpoons$ M·ADP·P $\longrightarrow$ M + ADP + P where M$^*$ ADP·P is an intermediate myosin-product complex which undergoes a conformational transition to the final myosin-product complex, the rate of this transition determining the overall reaction rate.

Malik & Martonosi (142) have emphasized the possible importance of temperature as a determinant of the kinetic properties of myosin. In their hands, product dissociation from rabbit HMM was rate-limiting at low temperature (6°C), whereas at higher temperature (23°C) product dissociation was considerably faster than the rate of steady-state ATP hydrolysis. Thus caution must be exercised in extrapolating from in vitro experiments with isolated proteins to the intact mammalian filament lattice at 37°C.

This question is of physiological importance in that the location of the rate-limiting step in ATP hydrolysis places certain constraints on the way in which the cross-bridge cycle operates. This point is brought out in a very interesting study by Eisenberg, Dobkin & Kielley (64). Using steady-state kinetic analysis and ultracentrifugation, these workers arrived at the surprising conclusion that under conditions of maximal actin activation of HMM ATPase about 60% of the HMM was present as free HMM. They postulate that at some stage in the reaction there is a rather long-lasting "refractory state" during which the HMM cannot react with actin. In a second communication, Eisenberg & Kielley (66) draw a provocative connection between this finding and the X-ray evidence (152) that in a muscle developing tension less than half of the cross-bridges are actually linked to actin at any given instant. They argue that if product dissociation were truly rate-limiting then with maximal activation more than 90% of the cross-bridges should be linked to actin. If the notion that actin must combine with the M·ADP·P complex is to be retained, it would seem reasonable to suppose that the rate of formation of this complex must be slow relative to its rate of breakdown. In structural terms this might mean that following the power stroke of the cross-bridge there is a rapid dissociation of the bridge from the actin filament, induced by ATP, followed by a relatively slow movement of the cross-bridge back to the perpendicular orientation in which it can once again combine with actin.

It now seems quite firmly·established that the HMM does undergo a conformational transition during ATP hydrolysis. Electron spin resonance spectra measurements by Seidel & Gergely (192) showed that ATP caused a conformational change in myosin which persisted throughout the period of ATP hydrolysis, after which the spectrum became identical to that seen upon the addition of ADP. Since the myosin exists during steady-state hydrolysis mainly as a myosin-product complex, it was concluded that the conformation of the myosin-product complex formed via ATP hydrolysis must be different from that formed simply by the addition of products. The same conclusion was arrived at by Werber, Szent-Györgyi & Fasman (218) on the basis of tryptophan fluorescence measurements of HMM. In addition, the latter group (see also 193) showed that the conformational change in question was dependent upon the hydrolysis of ATP rather than its binding. Thus these results are consistent with the existence of a transitional myosin-product intermediate as postulated by Trentham et al (210). It would be tempting to relate this conformational change to the transition of the cross-bridge from the tilted to the perpendicular orientation, but such a relation is still in the speculative realm. As Taylor & Lymn (204) point out, the links between biochemical reactions and cross-bridge properties are still rather tenuous, and choices between alternative mechanisms cannot be made on the basis of the available data.

The reader should be reminded of the existence of a large amount of important literature dealing with the duplex nature of the enzymatic sites of myosin (two S-1 per HMM), cooperative interactions between S-1 moieties, and the role of the low-molecular weight subunits of myosin. Discussion of these subjects is omitted, mainly because the information so far obtained has not yet been well integrated into our current picture of cross-bridge activity. For references and discussion see (55, 138, 203).

## CALCIUM ACTIVATION

We now recognize, mainly as a result of the efforts of Ebashi and associates (see 59, 60 for review of earlier work), that the requirement for $Ca^{2+}$ as an activator of contraction is conferred by two proteins bound to the actin filaments, tropomyosin and troponin. In the absence of these two proteins, purified actomyosin preparations hydrolyze ATP and superprecipitate in the absence of $Ca^{2+}$. The demonstration that troponin is the $Ca^{2+}$ receptor (61, 86, 224) has led to the concept that control of the contractile system is mediated through the thin filament. The basic problem to be solved is how the binding of $Ca^{2+}$ to the thin filament modulates the activity of cross-bridges projecting from the thick filament. Further complexities have been introduced by the discovery that troponin is a complex of at least three functionally distinct proteins. Hence the $Ca^{2+}$ control of cross-bridge activity must involve complex pathways of intermolecular communication.

### Troponin

Following an initial period of conflicting results and confusing nomenclature there now seems to be agreement (53, 54, 58, 92, 93) that troponin is a complex of three proteins. The nomenclature introduced by the Gergely group (94) seems to be gaining acceptance and will be used in this discussion. The troponin complex is made up of an inhibitory component (TN-I, mol wt 24,000) which prevents actin-myosin interaction, a $Ca^{2+}$ binding component (TN-C, mol wt 18,000), and a component which combines with tropomyosin (TN-T, mol wt 37,000).

It now appears that the preparation originally termed troponin B by Hartshorne & Mueller (104) is a mixture of TN-T and TN-I (93). This preparation, with tropomyosin, produces optimum inhibition of actin-myosin interaction in the presence of ATP and $Mg^{2+}$. This inhibition cannot be reversed by $Ca^{2+}$ unless TN-C is also present. The major disagreement still remaining in the literature concerns the role of the 37,000 mol wt component, TN-T. Greaser & Gergely (93), Ebashi (58), and Drabikowski et al (54) have concluded that it is an essential component of the $Ca^{2+}$-sensitizing complex whereas Wilkinson et al (219) and Murray & Kay (159) reported that full $Ca^{2+}$-sensitizing activity could be obtained with just TN-I and TN-C. The reasons for this discrepancy are not clear. Unfortunately, the various laboratories use highly individualized preparative procedures which make direct comparison of results difficult. Also, the most common assay system is "desensitized" actomyosin, that is, actomyosin which has been subjected to low-ionic strength extraction to remove the tropomyosin-troponin complex. As Greaser & Gergely (93) point out, if the TN-T was not completely removed during extraction then failure to demonstrate its activity may only mean that it was already present as a contaminant in the assay system. TN-T binds very strongly to tropomyosin (93) and has been postulated to serve as a connecting link between that protein and the other components of the troponin complex (54, 93). From the existing data it appears very probable that it is an integral component of the $Ca^{2+}$-activating system.

The troponin complex contains equimolar amounts of TN-I, TN-C, and TN-T. This conclusion follows from ultracentrifugation measurements (103) showing that the particle weight of troponin (88,000) is very close to the sum of the molecular weights of its constituents.

Troponin binds two moles $Ca^{2+}$ per mole troponin with an affinity constant of 1–2 $\times 10^6 \; M^{-1}$ (86, 93). If it is assumed that TN-C is the only $Ca^{2+}$-binding moiety then two $Ca^{2+}$-binding sites on each TN-C molecule are implied. Oddly enough, purified TN-C binds only one mole $Ca^{2+}$ per mole TN-C, the affinity constant being the same as that of the $Ca^{2+}$-troponin affinity constant (93, 94). It seems that with the formation of the troponin complex a second binding site appears whose location cannot be established from the available data. Greaser et al (94) have shown that it is TN-I that, in combination with TN-C, induces the second binding site. Since purified TN-I is devoid of $Ca^{2+}$ binding activity it would seem reasonable to suppose that the second site appears on TN-C. On the other hand, Hartshorne & Pyun (105) observed that troponin B (TN-I + TN-T), only slightly contaminated with TN-C, bound more $Ca^{2+}$ than could be accounted for by binding to the contaminant, thus raising the possibility that TN-I might become a $Ca^{2+}$-binding protein in the presence of TN-C. It seems clear that $Ca^{2+}$-binding by the intact regulatory system is a function of cooperative interactions which remain to be worked out. A second class of lower affinity $Ca^{2+}$-binding sites ($K \sim 10^5 \; M^{-1}$) has also been detected in preparations of troponin and TN-C (105) and there is evidence (216) that super-precipitation requires the binding of $Ca^{2+}$ to both classes of sites.

The $Ca^{2+}$-binding sites of troponin are not completely specific for $Ca^{2+}$. Other divalent cations which can bind, given in order of affinity are $Cd^{2+}$, $Sr^{2+}$, $Mn^{2+}$, and $Pb^{2+}$ (85). Selectivity seems to be on the basis of size, with cations of ionic radius of 1 Å ($Ca^{2+}$, $Cd^{2+}$) being most favored. $Sr^{2+}$ is clearly an activator of contraction (61) and there is suggestive evidence (102) that $Cd^{2+}$, but not $Mn^{2+}$, can also activate actomyosin ATPase and superprecipitation. Further study of the physicochemical differences between active and inactive metal-troponin complexes may provide insight into the initial molecular alteration which triggers contraction.

### Biochemical Studies of Troponin Action

Kinetic studies (65, 170) show quite conclusively that the troponin-tropomyosin complex inhibits the actin-activated myosin ATPase through a blockage of the activating sites on the actin filament. Spudich & Watt (197) found that inhibition of actin activation was maximal when the troponin-tropomyosin-actin monomer molar ratio was 1:1:7. This ratio agrees closely with the molar ratio of these proteins in native thin filaments as deduced from chemical and structural data (60). Thus the kinetic studies lend support to the idea that $Ca^{2+}$ switches on the contractile apparatus by removing the inhibition exercised by the troponin-tropomyosin complex.

However, other data indicate that this view of $Ca^{2+}$-binding may be an oversimplification. From studies of the temperature dependence of actomyosin ATPase in the presence and absence of various regulatory proteins, and the analysis of Arrhenius plots, Hartshorne et al (101) showed that the $Ca^{2+}$–TN-C complex modified, directly or indirectly, the ATPase site of myosin. It was evident in this study, as well as in earlier works (65) that the ATPase activity of highly purified actomyosin was always less than that of the $Ca^{2+}$-activated natural actomyosin (tropomyosin and troponin present). It is not obvious why they should be different if the $Ca^{2+}$-binding reaction was functioning as a simple passive switch mechanism. Rather, it seems that the $Ca^{2+}$-troponin complex is an activator of the actomyosin ATPase. Stewart & Levy (199a) arrived at a similar conclusion on the basis of somewhat different evidence.

From the molar ratio of the relaxing protein complex to actin monomers, 1:7, it is reasonable to suppose that the binding of $Ca^{2+}$ to each troponin receptor "turns on" seven G-actin subunits. According to the presently accepted model of thin filament structure (see later discussion), tropomyosin, a rod-shaped molecule about 400 Å long, lies in the grooves of the actin double helix, each tropomyosin being in contact with seven actin monomers. Troponin is distributed along the thin filament, bound to tropomyosin, at 400 Å intervals. On the basis of this model the $Ca^{2+}$-binding signal must be transmitted to actin via the troponin complex and tropomyosin. Using the spin labeling technique, Tonomura, Watanabe & Morales (209) first showed that the binding of $Ca^{2+}$ to reconstituted thin filaments caused conformational changes in both tropomyosin and actin, as would be predicted from the model.

However, beyond this fundamental observation, relatively little has been learned about the molecular consequences of $Ca^{2+}$ binding. $Ca^{2+}$ has been shown to increase the $\alpha$-helical content of TN-C (160, 212) and reduce the sulfhydryl reactivity of the troponin complex (84). The sulfhydryl groups in question are probably on TN-I; sulfhydryl reactivity of purified TN-C is not altered by $Ca^{2+}$ (84) and TN-T is completely devoid of cysteine (93). According to Perry et al (174), in the presence of $Ca^{2+}$ a mixture of TN-I and TN-C migrated as a single band during electrophoresis in polyacrylamide gels containing 6 $M$ urea, but there was separation into two bands in the presence of EGTA. This observation suggests that $Ca^{2+}$ promotes stronger bonding between TN-C and TN-I.

A new and possibly significant line of inquiry was opened by the discovery that troponin is phosphorylated in the presence of ATP, $Mg^{2+}$, and phosphorylase kinase (177, 201). The phosphorylated protein could be dephosphorylated by phosphorylase phosphatase (71). There is disagreement as to whether the phosphorylation takes place on the TN-I (201) or TN-T (177). It will be of interest to find out whether the $Ca^{2+}$-binding or $Ca^{2+}$-sensitizing properties of troponin are affected by phosphorylation.

An important paper by Bremel & Weber (30) presents new insights into the mode of interaction among myosin, actin, and the regulatory proteins. On the basis of enzymatic analysis these workers showed that the formation of a critical number of actin-myosin links ("rigor complexes") has a non-$Ca^{2+}$-dependent, cooperative effect on adjacent, unbound actin monomers, causing them to assume an orientation in which they can activate myosin ATPase. Thus if we consider a functional thin filament unit of one troponin, one tropomyosin, and seven actin monomers, the formation of, say, four rigor complexes would "turn on" the remaining three actin monomers so that all seven actins would combine with myosin. Under conditions of low ATP concentration (only partial dissociation of actomyosin) the number of rigor complexes is so high that the entire thin filament is "turned on" even in the absence of $Ca^{2+}$. This model would account for the well-documented observation (217) that $Ca^{2+}$ is not required for ATP hydrolysis and superprecipitation if the ATP concentration is sufficiently low. At physiological ATP concentrations the number of rigor complexes existing at any given moment would be far below the level required for the cooperative "turning on" of the functional unit, a condition which can be reversed only by the binding of $Ca^{2+}$ to the troponin. On the basis of the work of Tonomura et al (209), it is very probable that this effect is transmitted to the actin monomers through the tropomyosin, and Bremel, Murray & Weber (29) have in fact shown that it is tropomyosin, specifically, which imposes cooperative properties on the actin chain. Highly purified actin does not exhibit the cooperativity described above.

Another interesting finding of Bremel & Weber (30) is that the properties of troponin are influenced by the formation of rigor complexes. In reconstituted thin filaments the affinity of $Ca^{2+}$ for the low affinity binding sites of troponin was markedly increased when myosin combined with actin. Thus the formation of rigor complexes induces cooperative interactions among actin monomers and between actin and troponin. If the "force-generating complexes" formed under physiological conditions $(ATP + Ca^{2+})$ are the same as the rigor complexes formed in the presence of low ATP, as Bremel and Weber are inclined to believe, then this effect on troponin might have some interesting physiological consequences (see later discussion).

Although the regulation of myosin ATPase activity is mediated physiologically through the thin filament, it is now recognized that myosin itself plays a role, at least in a conformational sense. If certain sulfhydryl groups of myosin were reacted with reagents such as NEM, the troponin-tropomyosin complex no longer inhibited the actin-myosin interaction in the absence of $Ca^{2+}$ (50). That is, with sulfhydryl modification the myosin assumed a conformation in which it could no longer distinguish between the "on" and "off" configurations of the actin filament. Whether myosin might undergo such transitions in situ is an interesting question about which nothing is known.

## Structural Aspects of $Ca^{2+}$ Activation

The realization that $Ca^{2+}$ control of muscular activity is mediated through the thin filament has lent special urgency to the need for a detailed picture of thin filament structure, particularly with regard to the spatial relations between the regulatory proteins, tropomyosin and troponin, and actin.

It has been recognized for more than a decade (see 120 for recent review) that the thin filament is formed from a double helical chain of actin monomers, with a subunit repeat of 55 Å and a helical periodicity of about 370 Å. Tropomyosin is a rod-shaped molecule, about 400 Å long and 20 Å in diameter, which lies in the groove of the actin double helix (60, 120). Several years ago Ohtsuki et al (166) suggested, on the basis of antibody staining of isolated thin filaments, that troponin was distributed periodically at intervals of about 400 Å along the thin filament. In the model of thin filament organization proposed by Ebashi et al (60) the tropomyosin molecules are linked end-to-end in the grooves of the actin double helix with troponin attached to tropomyosin at ~400 Å intervals. A 400 Å thin filament periodicity had been observed in electron micrographs (38, 169) and was evident as a meridional X-ray reflection arising from the thin filaments of living muscle (122). More recently, Hanson (96) has shown that in actin paracrystals of specified composition the 400 Å spacing could be observed only when tropomyosin and troponin were present together. It was absent from actin and actin-tropomyosin paracrystals. These observations constitute strong evidence that troponin is responsible for the 400 Å thin filament periodicity. The location and nature of the attachment between troponin and tropomyosin remains to be determined. The actin monomer is 55 Å in diameter and if the $Ca^{2+}$-binding sites are ~400 Å apart the dimensions are clearly consistent with the assumption that each troponin "controls" seven actins (see above).

Spudich, Huxley & Finch (196) have presented a very detailed picture of the organization of reconstituted thin filaments, based on optical diffraction patterns of electron micrographs and three-dimensional reconstruction (157). They have confirmed the essential features of the Ebashi model. A significant new finding was that the tropomyosin was slightly off the center line of the groove of the helix. Each tropomyosin strand is aligned with a single actin strand and presumably controls the activity of that strand.

X-ray diffraction studies of living frog muscle by Vibert et al (214), Haselgrove (106), and Huxley (121) have provided evidence for a movement of tropomyosin associated with activation. From changes in intensity of thin filament reflections it was determined that during activation the tropomyosin rod moves slightly toward the center line of the groove. The extent of movement was calculated by Haselgrove (106) to be about 15 Å. Although more work is needed, the picture that seems to be emerging is as follows: in resting muscle the tropomyosin rods lie toward the edge of the thin filament groove, each one being in contact with seven actin monomers. In this position the tropomyosin blocks the actin sites which react with the cross-bridges. With the binding of $Ca^{2+}$ to troponin, the tropomyosin rods are drawn toward the center of the groove, thus allowing actin to bind to myosin and activate ATP splitting.

An important point established by Vibert et al (214) is that the change in thin filament configuration with activation is independent of filament overlap. Hence the movement of tropomyosin must be due strictly to $Ca^{2+}$ binding, not to cross-link formation.

Another approach to thin filament structure and function comes from the studies of Ishiwata & Fujime (125) on the quasielastic scattering of laser light by reconstituted thin filaments. For the theory behind this approach see Fujime & Ishiwata (87) and references therein. In brief, this technique measures the spontaneous fluctuations of long chain polymers immersed in a liquid medium. Thus the rigidity of polymer chains can be assessed under a variety of experimental conditions. Purified F-actin filaments were found to be highly flexible, whereas the binding of tropomyosin to the filaments rendered them more rigid. This observation suggests an increased ordering of the actin subunits by tropomyosin and is probably related to the role of tropomyosin in imposing cooperative properties on actin (see above).

Rigidity was increased even further by the addition of tropomyosin-troponin complex in the absence of $Ca^{2+}$. However, in the completely reconstituted filament the rigidity was reduced significantly by the addition of micromolar concentrations of $Ca^{2+}$. The authors suggest that the probability of actin-myosin linkage formation may be related to the amplitude of spontaneous bending movements of the actin strand. This amplitude would be minimal in the absence of $Ca^{2+}$.

## $Ca^{2+}$ and the Force-Velocity Relation

According to the sliding filament model, force generation is a function of the relative number of links formed between actin and the myosin cross-bridges. On the other hand, the velocity of shortening against a given load must depend on the rate of cross-bridge cycling which, in turn, is related to the rate of ATP hydrolysis. Bárány (12) has established a convincing relationship between the intrinsic speed of a muscle and the rate of ATP hydrolysis by the actomyosin of that muscle.

The binding of $Ca^{2+}$ to troponin facilitates cross-bridge attachment through mechanisms already considered. If this is the only consequence of $Ca^{2+}$-binding then maximal shortening velocity should be independent of $Ca^{2+}$ concentration. The study of Podolsky & Teichholz (176) with skinned frog fibers exposed to varying $Ca^{2+}$ concentrations suggested that this was indeed the case. This finding led them to conclude that the $Ca^{2+}$–troponin interaction is a simple on-off switch that controls the number of cross-bridges that can attach but does not affect their kinetic properties. This conclusion has not been supported by the work of other investigators.

Julian (128) studied the effects of buffered $Ca^{2+}$ solutions on the force-velocity properties of single frog fibers briefly treated with glycerol and a detergent to destroy all membrane systems. Both maximal force development and maximal velocity of shortening varied with $Ca^{2+}$ concentration, whereas the hyperbolic shape of the force-velocity curve was unaffected. Wise, Rondinone & Briggs (221) obtained similar results with glycerinated rabbit psoas fibers. In both papers the discrepancy with respect to the findings of Podolsky and Teichholz seems to be adequately explained in terms of differences in experimental design.

Brutsaert, Claes & Goethals (32) showed that the maximal shortening velocity of cardiac muscle was a function of the extracellular $Ca^{2+}$ concentration. Also relevant in this regard is the observation of Blinks et al (26) that caffeine caused a symmetrical shift away from the origin of the force-velocity curve of cardiac muscle. In view of the strong evidence that caffeine raises the intracellular $Ca^{2+}$ concentration, this finding can be taken as further support for the conclusion that $Ca^{2+}$ controls both force development and shortening velocity.

Thus there is compelling evidence, from a variety of preparations, that $Ca^{2+}$ enhances myosin cross-bridge turnover in addition to making more actin sites available for combination with myosin. A satisfactory model to account for this dual action of $Ca^{2+}$ is still lacking. Julian (128) has considered the possibility that $Ca^{2+}$ has a direct effect on myosin in addition to its effects on the actin filament. His experiments were carried out under conditions in which the free $Mg^{2+}$ concentration was very low; hence, there might have been $Ca^{2+}$ bound to myosin (49). The true intracellular free $Mg^{2+}$ concentration is still not known, but there is some indirect evidence (59) that it may be quite low (<0.1 m$M$). However, this cannot be an explanation of the experimental results, as Wise et al (221) arrived at the same conclusion as Julian, despite the fact that in their experiments the free $Mg^{2+}$ concentration (3–4 m$M$) was about three orders of magnitude greater than the free $Ca^{2+}$ concentration ($10^{-6}$–$10^{-5}$ $M$). There seems to be unanimous agreement (86, 130, 202) that under these circumstances $Ca^{2+}$ does not bind to vertebrate myosin. Thus there is no reason for postulating two $Ca^{2+}$ signals, one to each filament (see 121, for a discussion of this point in connection with the actin-independent cross-bridge movement). Of greater likelihood is a unitary mechanism in which cross-bridge kinetics is somehow controlled by the number of actin monomers "switched on" when the $Ca^{2+}$ binds to troponin. Solution to this problem will require a detailed study of the effects of $Ca^{2+}$ on the various rate constants in the hydrolytic scheme (see above).

## $Ca^{2+}$ Activation and Mechanical State

Endo (68) has made the extremely interesting observation that the sensitivity of skinned fibers to $Ca^{2+}$ is increased at longer sarcomere lengths. That is, a $Ca^{2+}$ concentration that was below the contraction threshold at sarcomere length 2.0–2.3 $\mu$m could elicit a significant force development if the fiber were stretched to sarcomere length 3.0–3.3 $\mu$m. Because this phenomenon could be demonstrated after destruction of the SR with a detergent, it must be an intrinsic property of the myofilaments rather than a result of increased $Ca^{2+}$ release. From the available data it cannot be decided whether the increase in sarcomere length causes an increase in the affinity of troponin for $Ca^{2+}$ or some change in the regulatory protein complex that produces a greater "amplification" of the $Ca^{2+}$-binding signal. The simplest assumption would be that $Ca^{2+}$ binds more tightly to troponin; possibly the reduced distance between the filaments as the sarcomere is stretched influences the properties of the $Ca^{2+}$-binding sites, as has been shown to occur when the cross-bridges attach directly to actin (see above).

The functional consequences of this finding were discussed briefly in another communication by Endo (69). It has been demonstrated (see above) that activation is prolonged as sarcomere length is increased in both skeletal (62) and cardiac (164) muscle. Edman & Kiessling (62) hypothesized that more $Ca^{2+}$ is released from the SR at longer sarcomere lengths. However, an alternative hypothesis, for which Endo's experiments provide some support, would be that $Ca^{2+}$ is bound more tightly to the thin filaments at longer sarcomere lengths, and therefore reaccumulation of $Ca^{2+}$ by the SR would be slightly delayed.

The recent study of Close (41) is of interest in this regard. He showed that in many frog sartorius muscles the twitch tension (measured at 20°C) was maximal at sarcomere length 2.8 $\mu$m, while tetanus tension was always maximal at sarcomere length 2.1 $\mu$m, the length corresponding to maximal cross-bridge overlap (91). The fact that the twitch tension–sarcomere length relationship can deviate so markedly from the predictions of the sliding filament theory might be explained by supposing that in certain circumstances the amount of $Ca^{2+}$ released from the SR is less than the amount needed to saturate all of the $Ca^{2+}$-binding sites. Under such conditions it is conceivable that an increase in length could actually potentiate twitch tension by causing a greater $Ca^{2+}$-troponin binding affinity. There is much evidence, reviewed elsewhere by Close (42), that in mammalian muscle at physiological temperatures and in amphibian muscle at room temperature the activation in a single twitch is submaximal. It remains to be determined why some sartorius muscles had a maximal twitch tension at sarcomere length 2.1 $\mu$m and others had maximal tension at 2.8 $\mu$m; perhaps $Ca^{2+}$ release can be variable in the same muscle under uniform experimental conditions. The laser diffraction study of Cleworth & Edman (40) suggested that even among individual sarcomeres in the same fiber, the level of activation could vary in a way that did not correlate with sarcomere length or any other known morphological feature. Further correlations of mechanical behavior, morphology, and electrophysiological properties of single fibers may shed some light on this problem.

Other examples can be found where the mechanical behavior of muscle does not conform to the straightforward predictions of the sliding filament theory [see, for example, D. K. Hill's study of temperature effects (109)]. If the $Ca^{2+}$ sensitivity of the contractile system is a function of sarcomere length, then such deviations could well be expected in situations where the intracellular $Ca^{2+}$ concentration is less than that needed for saturation of the $Ca^{2+}$-binding sites.

Reference has already been made to the work of Bremel & Weber (30) showing that attachment of myosin to actin increases the $Ca^{2+}$ affinity to troponin. These experiments were performed under conditions of low ATP concentration where a high proportion of such "rigor complexes" are formed. At physiological ATP concentrations, few actin-myosin links would form unless $Ca^{2+}$ binds to troponin. It would be reasonable to assume that the "force-generating complexes" formed by $Ca^{2+}$ activation would be of the same nature as the rigor complexes. Thus the greater the number of attached cross-bridges, the higher the overall affinity between $Ca^{2+}$ and the myofilament binding sites. According to A. F. Huxley's (113a) theory of cross-bridge action the average number of attached cross-bridges is maximal under isometric conditions and becomes progressively smaller at higher shortening velocities. Experimental verification of this point has been reported by Huxley (114). Specifically, the ability of an actively contracting muscle to resist a load was found to be considerably diminished if the load was applied abruptly during a period of rapid isotonic shortening. If resistance to a stretching force depends on the number of attached cross-bridges, then this number must be reduced under isotonic conditions.

If the affinity between $Ca^{2+}$ and troponin is a function of the number of attached cross-bridges, then the duration of activation should be related to tension, as has already been demonstrated by A. V. Hill (107). The fact that an isotonic twitch is terminated earlier than an isometric twitch (126) could be explained as follows: in the isometric state the average number of actin-myosin links being formed per unit time is greater than in an isotonic twitch, hence the overall affinity between $Ca^{2+}$ and troponin is greater. Therefore, under isometric conditions it should take longer for the SR to reaccumulate the $Ca^{2+}$ released in response to the stimulus.

This concept was mentioned briefly by Edman & Kiessling (62) and put in a more explicit form by Kaufmann, Bayer & Harnasch (129) in a study of the effects of shortening on activation in cardiac muscle. The latter workers showed that if an isometrically contracting papillary muscle were suddenly released and re-extended, the redeveloped tension was less than it was at that time in the undisturbed twitch, even if the release took place very early following the stimulus. This deactivation with shortening was described earlier by Brady (28) in cardiac muscle and is presumably the same phenomenon recently studied in skeletal muscle by Edman & Kiessling (62) and Briden & Alpert (31). Kaufmann et al (129) propose a feedback system in which the amount of $Ca^{2+}$ bound to the filaments is controlled by the velocity with which the filaments slide past each other. Upon isotonic release a large fraction of the cross-bridges would detach and $Ca^{2+}$-troponin affinity would be reduced. The $Ca^{2+}$ released by the filaments would be taken up by the SR and, upon re-extension of the muscle, less $Ca^{2+}$ would be bound to troponin, thus accounting for the reduced tension. In support of this hypothesis Kaufmann et al (129) showed that the deactivation effect could be diminished by elevating the extracellular $Ca^{2+}$ concentration or accentuated by bathing the muscle in verapamil, a drug known to inhibit transmembrane $Ca^{2+}$ influx.

These experiments are not definitive tests of the hypothesis but the results nevertheless suggest that further study along these lines may provide important insights into the intrinsic control mechanisms of the contractile system. In his essay on the Fenn effect, Mommaerts (155) pointed out that the contractile system must have a way of "sensing" the force on it and adjusting the level of activation accordingly. In view of what we are now beginning to learn about the cooperative interactions among the myofibrillar proteins, it would seem that the tropomyosin-troponin-$Ca^{2+}$ system might be a good candidate for this sensing mechanism.

ACKNOWLEDGMENTS

I am indebted to Drs. John Howell and David Hartshorne for many helpful discussions and to Ms. Donna Hill for assistance in the preparation of the manuscript.

*Literature Cited*

1. Abbott, B. C., Howarth, J. V. 1973. Heat studies in excitable tissues. *Physiol. Rev.* 53:120–58
2. Adrian, R. H., Almers, W. 1973. Measurement of membrane capacity in skeletal muscle. *Nature New Biol.* 242:62–64
3. Adrian, R. H., Costantin, L. L., Peachey, L. D. 1969. Radial spread of contraction in frog muscle fibres. *J. Physiol.* 204:231–57
4. Alpert, N. R., Ed. 1971. *Cardiac Hypertrophy.* New York: Academic. 641 pp.
5. April, E. W., Brandt, P. W., Elliott, G. F. 1971. The myofilament lattice: studies on isolated fibers. I. The constancy of the unit-cell volume with variation in sarcomere length in a lattice in which the thin-to-thick myofilament ratio is 6:1. *J. Cell Biol.* 51: 72–82
6. Armitage, P., Miller, A., Rodger, C. D., Tregear, R. T. 1972. The structure and function of insect muscle. *Cold Spring Harbor Symp. Quant. Biol.* 37: 379–87
7. Armstrong, C. M., Bezanilla, F. M., Horowicz, P. 1972. Twitches in the presence of ethylene glycol bis ($\beta$-aminoethyl ether)-N,N'-tetraacetic acid. *Biochim. Biophys. Acta* 267:605–8
8. Aronson, J. F., Morales, M. F. 1969. Polarization of tryptophan fluorescence in muscle. *Biochemistry* 8:4517–22
9. Ashley, C. C., Caldwell, P. C., Lowe, A. G. 1972. The efflux of calcium from single crab and barnacle muscle fibres. *J. Physiol.* 223:735–55
10. Ashley, C. C., Ridgway, E. B. 1970. On the relationships between membrane potential, calcium transient and tension in single barnacle muscle fibers. *J. Physiol.* 209:105–30

11. Baker, P. F. 1972. Transport and metabolism of calcium ion in nerve. *Progr. Biophys. Mol. Biol.* 24:177–223

12. Bárány, M. 1967. ATPase activity of myosin correlated with speed of muscle shortening. *J. Gen. Physiol.* 50:197–216

13. Bárány, M., Bailin, G., Bárány, K. 1969. Reaction of myosin with 1-fluoro-2,4-dinitribenzene at low ionic strength. *J. Biol. Chem.* 244:648–57

14. Bárány, M., Bárány, K. 1970. Change in the reactivity of myosin during muscle contraction. *J. Biol. Chem.* 245: 2717–21

15. Bárány, M., Bárány, K. 1972. A proposal for the mechanism of contraction in intact frog muscle. *Cold Spring Harbor Symp. Quant. Biol.* 37:157–67

16. Bárány, M., Bárány, K., Gaetjens, E. 1971. Change in the reactivity of the head part of myosin during contraction of frog muscle. *J. Biol. Chem.* 246:3241–49

17. Leigh, J. B. et al 1972. Effects of ATP analogs on the low-angle X-ray diffraction pattern of insect flight muscle. *Cold Spring Harbor Symp. Quant. Biol.* 37:443–47

18. Beinbrech, G., Kuhn, H. J., Rüegg, J. C. 1972. Electron microscope and optical diffraction studies on glycerol-extracted insect flight muscle fibres relaxed by pyrophosphate. *Experientia* 28:511–13

19. Bennett, H. S., Porter, K. R. 1953. An electron microscope study of sectioned breast muscle of the domestic fowl. *Am. J. Anat.* 93:61–105

20. Bezanilla, F., Caputo, C., Gonzalez-Serratos, H., Venosa, R. A. 1972. Sodium dependence of the inward spread of activation in isolated twitch muscle fibers of the frog. *J. Physiol.* 223:507–23

21. Bianchi, C. P. 1968. Pharmacological actions on excitation-contraction coupling in striated muscle. *Fed. Proc.* 27: 126–31

22. Bianchi, C. P., Bolton, T. C. 1967. Action of local anesthetics on coupling systems in muscle. *J. Pharmacol. Exp. Ther.* 157:388–405

23. Birks, R. I., Davey, D. F. 1969. Osmotic responses demonstrating the extracellular character of the sarcoplasmic reticulum. *J. Physiol.* 202: 171–88

24. Birks, R. I., Davey, D. F. 1972. An analysis of volume changes in the T-tubes of frog skeletal muscle exposed to sucrose. *J. Physiol.* 222:95–111

25. Blinks, J. R., Jewell, B. R. 1972. The meaning and measurement of myocardial contractility. In *Casdiovascular Fluid Dynamics,* ed. D. H. Bergel, Vol. 1. New York: Academic

26. Blinks, J. R., Olson, C. B., Jewell, B. R., Braveny, P. 1972. Influence of caffeine and other methylxanthines on mechanical properties of isolated mammalian heart muscle. *Circ. Res.* 30:367–92

27. Bourne, G. H., Ed. 1972. *The Structure and Function of Muscle,* Vol. 1, pt. 1. New York: Academic. 2nd ed.

28. Brady, A. J. 1966. Onset of contractility in cardiac muscle. *J. Physiol.* 184: 560–80

29. Bremel, R. D., Murray, J. M., Weber, A. 1972. Manifestations of cooperative behavior in the regulated actin filament during actin-activated ATP hydrolysis in the presence of calcium. *Cold Spring Harbor Symp. Quant. Biol.* 37:267–75

30. Bremel, R. D., Weber, A. 1972. Cooperation within actin filament in vertebrate skeletal muscle. *Nature New Biol.* 238: 97–101

31. Briden, K. L., Alpert, N. R. 1972. The effect of shortening on the time course of active state decay. *J. Gen. Physiol.* 60:202–20

32. Brutsaert, D. L., Claes, V. A., Goethals, M. A. 1973. Effect of calcium on the force-velocity-length relations of heart muscle of the cat. *Circ. Res.* 32: 385–92

33. Burke, M., Himmelfarb, S., Harrington, W. F. 1973. Studies on the "hinge" region of myosin. *Biochemistry* 12: 701–10

34. Caplan, S. R. 1971. Nonequilibrium thermodynamics and its application to bioenergetics. *Curr. Top. Bioenerg.* 4: 1–79

35. Caputo, C. 1972. The effect of low temperature on the excitation-contraction coupling phenomena of frog single muscle fibres. *J. Physiol.* 223:461–82

36. Caputo, C. 1972. The time course of potassium contractures of single muscle fibres. *J. Physiol.* 223:483–505

37. Caputo, C., Dipolo, R. 1973. Ionic diffusion delays in the transverse tubules of frog twitch muscle fibres. *J. Physiol.* 229:547–57

38. Carlsen, F., Knappeis, G. G., Buchthal, F. 1961. Ultrastructure of the resting and contracted striated muscle at different degrees of stretch. *J. Biochem. Biophys. Cytol.* 11:95–117

39. Cassens, R. G., Ed. 1972. *Muscle Biology,* Vol. 1. New York: Dekker

40. Cleworth, D. R., Edman, K. A. P. 1972. Changes in sarcomere length during isometric tension development in frog skeletal muscle. *J. Physiol.* 227:1–17

41. Close, R. I. 1972. The relations between sarcomere length and characteristics of isometric twitch contractions of frog sartorius muscle. *J. Physiol.* 220: 745–62

42. Close, R. I. 1972. Dynamic properties of mammalian skeletal muscles. *Physiol. Rev.* 52:129–97

43. Connally, R., Gough, W., Winegrad, S. 1971. Characteristics of the isometric twitch of skeletal muscle immediately after a tetanus. *J. Gen. Physiol.* 57:697–709

44. Costantin, L. L. 1970. The role of sodium current in the radial spread of contraction in frog muscle fibers. *J. Gen. Physiol.* 55:703–15

45. Costantin, L. L. 1971. Biphasic potassium contractures in frog muscle fibers. *J. Gen. Physiol.* 58:117–30

46. Costantin, L. L., Podolsky, R. J. 1966. Evidence for depolarization of the internal membrane system in activation of frog semitendinosus muscle. *Nature* 210:483–86

47. Costantin, L. L., Podolsky, R. J. 1967. Depolarization of the internal membrane system in the activation of frog skeletal muscle. *J. Gen. Physiol.* 50: 1101–24

48. Costantin, L. L., Taylor, S. R. 1973. Graded activation in frog muscle fibers. *J. Gen. Physiol.* 61:424–43

49. Dancker, P. 1970 The binding of calcium and magnesium to actomyosin and its modification by natural tropomyosin. *Pfluegers Arch.* 315:198–211

50. Daniel, J. L., Hartshorne, D. J. 1972. Sulfhydryl groups of natural actomyosin essential for the $Ca^{2+}$-sensitive response: location and properties. *Biochim. Biophys. Acta* 278:567–76

51. DeMello, W. C., Ed. 1972. *Electrical Phenomena in the Heart.* New York: Academic. 415 pp.

52. Dos Remedios, C. G., Millikan, R. G. C., Morales, M. F. 1972. Polarization of tryptophan fluorescence from single striated muscle fibers. *J. Gen. Physiol.* 59:103–20

53. Drabikowski, W., Dabrowska, R., Barylko, B. 1971. Separation and characterization of the constituents of troponin. *FEBS Lett.* 12:148–52

54. Drabikowski, W., Nowak, E., Barylko, B., Dabrowska, R. 1972. Troponin—its

55. Dreizen, P. 1971. Structure and function of myofibrillar contractile proteins. *Ann. Rev. Med.* 22:365–90

56. Duggan, P. F., Martonosi, A. 1970. Sarcoplasmic reticulum IX. The permeability of sarcoplasmic reticulum membranes. *J. Gen. Physiol.* 56: 147–67

57. Dydynska, M., Wilkie, D. R. 1963. The osmotic properties of striated muscle fibres in hypertonic solutions. *J. Physiol.* 169:312–29

58. Ebashi, S. 1972. Separation of tropinin into its three components. *J. Biochem. Tokyo* 72:787–90

59. Ebashi, S., Endo, M. 1968. Calcium ion and muscle contraction. *Progr. Biophys. Mol. Biol.* 18:123–83

60. Ebashi, S., Endo, M., Ohtsuki, I. 1969. Control of muscle contraction. *Quart. Rev. Biophys.* 2:351–84

61. Ebashi, S., Kodama, A., Ebashi, F. 1968. Troponin. I. Preparation and physiological function. *J. Biochem. Tokyo* 64:465–77

62. Edman, K. A. P., Kiessling, A. 1971. The time course of the active state in relation to sarcomere length and movement studied in single skeletal muscle fibres of the frog. *Acta Physiol. Scand.* 81:182–96

63. Eisenberg, B., Eisenberg, R. S. 1968. Selective disruption of the sarcotubular system in frog sartorius muscle. *J. Cell Biol.* 39:451–67

64. Eisenberg, E., Dobkin, L., Kielley, W. W. 1972. Heavy meromyosin: evidence for a refractory state unable to bind to actin in the presence of ATP. *Proc. Nat. Acad. Sci. USA* 69:667–71

65. Eisenberg, E., Kielley, W. W. 1970. Native tropomyosin: effect on the interaction of actin with heavy meromyosin and subfragment-1. *Biochem. Biophys. Res. Commun.* 40:50–56

66. Eisenberg, E., Kielley, W. W. 1972. Evidence for a refractory state of heavy meromyosin and subfragment-1 unable to bind to actin in the presence of ATP. *Cold Spring Harbor Symp. Quant. Biol.* 37:145–52

67. Elliott, G. F. 1967. Variations of the contractile apparatus in smooth and striated muscles. X-ray diffraction studies at rest and in contraction. *J. Gen. Physiol.* 50:171–84

67a. Elliott, G. F., Rome, E. M., Spencer, M. 1970. A type of contraction hypothesis applicable to all muscles. *Nature* 226: 417–20

68. Endo, M. 1972. Stretch-induced increase in activation of skinned muscle fibers by calcium. *Nature New Biol.* 237:211–13

69. Endo, M. 1972. Length dependence of activation of skinned muscle fibers by calcium. *Cold Spring Harbor Symp. Quant. Biol.* 37:505–9

70. Endo, M., Tanaka, M., Ogawa, Y. 1970. Calcium induced release of calcium from the sarcoplasmic reticulum of skinned skeletal muscle fibres. *Nature* 228:34–26

71. England, P. J., Stull, J. T., Krebs, E. G. 1972. Dephosphorylation of the inhibitor component of troponin by phosphyrylase phosphatase. *J. Biol. Chem.* 247:5275–77

72. Fabiato, A., Fabiato, F. 1972. Excitation-contraction coupling of isolated cardiac fibers with disrupted or closed sarcolemmas. *Circ. Res.* 31:293–307

73. Falk, G. 1968. Predicted delays in the activation of the contractile system. *Biophys. J.* 8:608–25

74. Flitney, F. W. 1971. The volume of the T-system and its association with the sarcoplasmic reticulum in slow muscle fibres of the frog. *J. Physiol.* 217: 243–57

75. Forbes, M. S., Sperelakis, N. 1972. (Na+, K+)-ATPase activity in tubular systems of mouse cardiac and skeletal muscles. *Z. Zellforsch.* 134:1–11

76. Ford, L. E., Podolsky, R. J. 1970. Regenerative calcium release within muscle cells. *Science* 167:58–59

77. Ford, L. E., Podolsky, R. J. 1972. Calcium uptake and force development by skinned muscle fibres in EGTA buffered solutions. *J. Physiol.* 223:1–19

78. Ford, L. E., Podolsky, R. J. 1972. Intracellular calcium movements in skinned muscle fibres. *J. Physiol.* 223: 21–33

79. Franzini-Armstrong, C. 1970. Studies of the triad. I. Structure of the junction in frog twitch fibers. *J. Cell Biol.* 47: 488–99

80. Franzini-Armstrong, C. 1971. Studies of the triad. II. Penetration of tracers into the junctional gap. *J. Cell Biol.* 49: 196–203

81. Franzini-Armstrong, C. 1972. Studies of the triad. III. Structure of the junction in fast twitch fibers. *Tissue Cell* 4:469–78

82. Franzini-Armstrong, C. 1973. Studies of the triad. IV. Structure of the junc-

tion in frog slow fibers. *J. Cell Biol.* 56:120–28

83. Freygang, W. H., Goldstein, D. A., Hellam, D. C., Peachey, L. D. 1964. The relation between the late afterpotential and the size of the transverse tubular system of frog muscle. *J. Gen. Physiol.* 48:235–63

84. Fuchs, F. 1971. The effect of $Ca^{2+}$ on the sulfhydryl reactivity of tropinin: evidence for a $Ca^{2+}$-induced conformational change. *Biochim. Biophys. Acta* 226:453–58

85. Fuchs, F. 1971. Ion exchange properties of the calcium receptor site of troponin. *Biochim. Biophys. Acta* 245:221–29

86. Fuchs, F., Briggs, F. N. 1968. The site of calcium binding in relation to the activation of myofibrillar contraction. *J. Gen. Physiol.* 51:655–76

87. Fujime, S., Ishiwata, S. 1971. Dynamic study of F-actin by quasielastic scattering of laser light. *J. Mol. Biol.* 52: 251–65

88. Gonzalez-Serratos, H. 1971. Inward spread of activation in vertebrate muscle fibres. *J. Physiol.* 212:777–99

89. Gordon, A. M., Godt, R. E. 1970. Some effects of hypertonic solutions on contraction and excitation-contraction coupling in frog skeletal muscles. *J. Gen. Physiol.* 55:254–75

90. Gordon, A. M., Huxley, A. F., Julian, F. J. 1966. Tension development in highly stretched vertebrate muscle fibres. *J. Physiol.* 184:143–69

91. Gordon, A. M., Huxley, A. F., Julian, F. J. 1966. The variation in isometric tension with sarcomere length in vertebrate muscle fibres. *J. Physiol.* 184: 170–92

92. Greaser, M. L., Gergely, J. 1971. Reconstitution of troponin activity from three protein components. *J. Biol. Chem.* 246:4226–33

93. Greaser, M. L., Gergely, J. 1973. Purification and properties of the components of troponin. *J. Biol. Chem.* 248: 2125–33

94. Greaser, M. L., Yamaguchi, M., Brekke, C., Potter, J., Gergely, J. 1972. Troponin subunits and their interactions. *Cold Spring Harbor Symp. Quant. Biol.* 37:235–44

95. Hagiwara, S., Henkart, M. P., Kidikoro, Y. 1971. Excitation-contraction coupling in amphioxus muscle cells. *J. Physiol.* 219:233–51

96. Hanson, J. 1973. Evidence from electron microscope studies on actin paracrystals concerning the origin of the

cross-striation in the thin filaments of vertebrate skeletal muscle. *Proc. Roy. Soc. London B* 183:39–58

97. Hanson, J., Huxley, H. E. 1953. Structural basis of the cross-striations in muscle. *Nature* 172:530–32

98. Hanson, J., Persson, A. 1971. Changes in the action potential and contraction of isolated frog muscle after repetitive stimulation. *Acta Physiol. Scand.* 81: 340–48

99. Harrington, W. F. 1972. Muscle proteins and muscle contraction. In *Current Topics in Biochemistry*, ed. C. B. Anfinsen, R. F. Goldberger, A. N. Schechter, 135–85. New York: Academic. 255 pp.

100. Harris, P., Opie, L., Eds. 1971. *Calcium and the Heart.* New York: Academic. 198 pp.

101. Hartshorne, D. J., Barns, E. M., Parker, L., Fuchs, F. 1972. The effect of temperature on actomyosin. *Biochim. Biophys. Acta* 267:190–202

102. Hartshorne, D. J., Boucher, L. J. 1972. Calcium and the control of muscle activity. In *Hibernation and Hypothermia: Perspectives and Challenges*, ed. F. E. South, J. P. Hannon, J. R. Willis, E. T. Pengelley, N. R. Alpert, 357–71. Amsterdam: Elsevier

103. Hartshorne, D. J., Dreizen, P. 1972. Studies on the subunit composition of troponin. *Cold Spring Harbor Symp. Quant. Biol.* 37:225–34

104. Hartshorne, D. J., Mueller, H. 1968. Fractionation of troponin into two distinct proteins. *Biochem. Biophys. Res. Commun.* 31:647–53

105. Hartshorne, D. J., Pyun, H. Y. 1971. Calcium binding by the troponin complex, and the purification and properties of troponin A. *Biochim. Biophys. Acta* 229:698–711

106. Haselgrove, J. C. 1972. X-ray evidence for a conformational change in actin-containing filaments of vertebrate striated muscle. *Cold Spring Harbor Symp. Quant. Biol.* 37:341–52

107. Hill, A. V. 1964. The effect of tension in prolonging the active state in a twitch. *Proc. Roy. Soc. London B* 159:589–95

108. Hill, D. K. 1968. Tension due to interaction between the sliding filaments in resting striated muscle. The effect of stimulation. *J. Physiol.* 199:637–84

109. Hill, D. K. 1970. The effect of temperature in the range 0–35°C on the resting tension of frog's muscle. *J. Physiol.* 208:725–39

110. Hodgkin, A. L., Horowicz, P. 1960. Potassium contractures in single muscle fibers. *J. Physiol.* 153:386–403

111. Homsher, E., Briggs, F. N. 1968. Effects of hypertonicity on calcium fluxes in frog sartorius muscles. *Fed. Proc.* 27:375

112. Howell, J. N. 1969. A lesion of the transverse tubules of skeletal muscle. *J. Physiol.* 201:515–33

113. Hoyle, G., McNeill, P. A., Selverston, A. I. 1973. Ultrastructure of barnacle giant muscle fibers. *J. Cell Biol.* 56: 74–91

113a. Huxley, A. F. 1957. Muscle structure and theories of contraction. *Progr. Biophys. Biophys. Chem.* 7:255–318

114. Huxley, A. F. 1971. The activation of striated muscle and its mechanical response. *Proc. Roy. Soc. London B* 178: 1–27

115. Huxley, A. F., Taylor, R. E. 1958. Local activation of striated muscle fibres. *J. Physiol.* 144:426–41

116. Huxley, H. E. 1963. Electron microscope studies on the structure of natural and synthetic protein filaments from striated muscle. *J. Mol. Biol.* 7:281–308

117. Huxley, H. E. 1968. Structural difference between resting and rigor muscle; evidence from intensity changes in the low-angle equatorial X-ray diagram. *J. Mol. Biol.* 37:507–20

118. Huxley, H. E. 1969. The mechanism of muscle contraction. *Science* 164: 1356–66

119. Huxley, H. E. 1971. The structural basis of muscle contraction. *Proc. Roy. Soc. London B* 178:131–49

120. Huxley, H. E. 1972. Molecular basis of contraction in cross-striated muscles See Ref. 27, 301–87

121. Huxley, H. E. 1972. Structural changes in the actin- and myosin-containing filaments during contraction. *Cold Spring Harbor Symp. Quant. Biol.* 37: 361–76

122. Huxley, H. E., Brown, W. 1967. The low-angle X-ray diagram of vertebrate striated muscle and its behavior during contraction and rigor. *J. Mol. Biol.* 30: 383–434

123. Inesi, G. 1972. Active transport of calcium ion in sarcoplasmic membranes. *Ann. Rev. Biophys. Bioeng.* 1:191–210

124. Isaacson, A. 1969. Caffeine-induced contractures and related calcium movements of muscle in hypertonic media. *Experientia* 25:1263–65

125. Ishiwata, S., Fujime, S. 1972. Effect of calcium ions on the flexibility of reconstituted thin filaments of muscle studied

by quasielastic scattering of laser light. *J. Mol. Biol.* 68:511–22

126. Jewell, B. R., Wilkie, D. R. 1960. The mechanical properties of relaxing muscle. *J. Physiol.* 152:30–47

127. Johnson, E. A., Lieberman, M. 1971. Heart: excitation and contraction. *Ann. Rev. Physiol.* 33:479–532

128. Julian, F. J. 1971. The effect of calcium on the force-velocity relation of briefly glycerinated frog muscle fibres. *J. Physiol.* 218:117–45

129. Kaufmann, R. L., Bayer, R. M., Harnasch, C. 1972. Autoregulation of contractility in the myocardial cell. *Pfluegers Arch.* 332:96–116

130. Kendrick-Jones, J., Lehman, W., Szent-Györgyi, A. G. 1970 Regulation in molluscan muscles. *J. Mol. Biol.* 54:313–26

131. Koretz, J. F., Hunt, T., Taylor, E. W. 1972. Studies on the mechanism of myosin and actomyosin ATPase. *Cold Spring Harbor Symp. Quant. Biol.* 37: 179–84

132. Krolenko, S. A. 1969. Change in the T-system of muscle fibers under the influence of the influx and efflux of glycerol. *Nature* 221:966–68

133. Kuhn, H. J., Schröder, H., Rüegg, J. C. 1972. Force generation in glycerinated insect-flight muscles without ATP. *Experientia* 28:510–11

134. Kulczycky, S., Mainwood, G. W. 1972. Evidence for a functional connection between the sarcoplasmic reticulum and the extracellular space in frog sartorius muscle. *Can. J. Physiol. Pharmacol.* 50:87–98

135. Laki, K., Ed. 1971. *Contractile Proteins and Muscle.* New York: Dekker

136. Langer, G. A. 1973. Heart: excitation-contraction coupling. *Ann. Rev. Physiol.* 35:55–86

137. Lännergren, J., Noth, J. 1973. Tension in isolated frog muscle fibers induced by hypertonic solution. *J. Gen. Physiol.* 61:158–75

138. Lowey, S. 1971. Myosin: molecule and filament. In *Subunits in Biological Systems,* ed. S. Timasheff, G. D. Fasman, Pt. A, 201–59. New York: Dekker

139. Lowy, J. 1972. X-ray diffraction studies of striated and smooth muscles. *Boll. Zool.* 39:119–38

140. Lymn, R. W., Huxley, H. E. 1972. X-ray diagrams from skeletal muscle in the presence of ATP analogs. *Cold Spring Harbor Symp. Quant. Biol.* 37: 449–53

141. Lymn, R., Taylor, E. W. 1971. Mechanism of adenosine triphosphate hydrolysis by actomyosin. *Biochemistry* 10:4617–24

142. Malik, M. N., Martonosi, A. 1972. The regulation of the rate of ATP hydrolysis by H meromyosin. *Arch. Biochem. Biophys.* 152:243–57

143. Mannherz, H. G., Leigh, J. B., Holmes, K. C., Rosenbaum, G. 1973. Indentification of the transitory complex myosin-ATP by the use of α, β-methylene-ATP. *Nature New Biol.* 241: 226–29

143a. Maréchal, G. 1972. Les sources d'energie immediate de la contraction musculaire. *J. Physiol. Paris* 65:5A–50A

144. Marston, S. B., Tregear, R. T. 1972. Evidence for a complex between myosin and ADP in relaxed muscle fibres. *Nature New Biol.* 235:23–24

145. Martonosi, A. 1971. The structure and function of sarcoplasmic reticulum membranes. In *Biomembranes,* ed L. Manson, Vol. I, 191–256. New York: Plenum

146. Martonosi, A. 1972. Biochemical and clinical aspects of sarcoplasmic reticulum function. In *Current Topics in Membranes and Transport,* ed. F. Bronner, A. Kleinzeller, Vol. III, 83–197. New York: Academic

147. Matsubara, I., Elliott, G. F. 1972. X-ray diffraction studies on skinned single fibres of frog skeletal muscle. *J. Mol. Biol.* 72:657–69

148. McClare, C. W. F. 1971. Chemical machines, Maxwell's demon and living organisms. *J. Theor. Biol.* 30:1–34

149. McClare, C. W. F. 1972. A "molecular energy" muscle model. *J. Theor. Biol.* 35:569–95

150. Cold Spring Harbor Laboratory. 1972. The mechanism of muscle contraction. *Cold Spring Harbor Symp. Quant. Biol.,* Vol. 37

151. Meijler, F. L., Brutsaert, D. L., Eds. 1971. Contractile behavior of heart muscle. *Cardiovasc. Res. Suppl.* 1:1–119

152. Miller, A., Tregear, R. T. 1970. Evidence concerning cross-bridge attachment during muscle contraction. *Nature* 226:1060–61

153. Miller, A., Tregear, R. T. 1971. X-ray studies on the structure and function of vertebrate and invertebrate muscle. See Ref. 175, 205–28

154. Miyamoto, M., Hubbard, J. I. 1972. On the inhibition of muscle contraction caused by exposure to hypertonic solutions. *J. Gen. Physiol.* 59: 689–700

155. Mommaerts, W. F. H. M. 1970. What is the Fenn effect? *Naturwissenschaften* 57:326–30

156. Mommaerts, W. F. H. M. 1972. Energetics of contraction. In *Muscle Biology*, ed. R. G. Cassens, Vol. 1, 1–12. New York: Dekker

157. Moore, P. B., Huxley, H. E., DeRosier, D. J. 1970. Three dimensional reconstruction of F-actin, thin filaments and decorated thin filaments. *J. Mol. Biol.* 50:279–95

158. Mulieri, L. A. 1972. The dependence of latency relaxation on sarcomere length and other characteristics of isolated muscle fibres. *J. Physiol.* 223:333–54

159. Murray, A. C., Kay, C. M. 1971. Separation and characterization of the inhibitory factor of the troponin system. *Biochem. Biophys. Res. Commun.* 44:237–44

160. Murray, A. C., Kay, C. M. 1972. Hydrodynamic and optical properties of troponin A. Demonstration of a conformational change upon binding calcium ion. *Biochemistry* 11:2622–27

161. Nasledov, G. A., Mandelstam, J. E., Radzjukewich, T. L. 1972. A study of excitation-contraction coupling in frog tonic muscle fibers of *Rana temporaria*. *Experientia* 28:1305–6

162. Needham, D. M. 1971. *Machina Carnis*. Cambridge: Cambridge Univ. Press

163. Niemeyer, G., Forssman, W. G. 1971. Comparison of glycerol treatment in frog skeletal muscle and mammalian heart. *J. Cell Biol.* 50:288–99

164. Nilsson, E. 1972. Influence of muscle length on the mechanical parameters of myocardial contraction. *Acta Physiol. Scand.* 85:1–23

165. Norris, F. H. 1961. Active state plateau and latency in mammalian striated muscle. *Am. J. Physiol.* 201:403–7

166. Ohtsuki, I., Masaki, T., Nonomura, Y., Ebashi, S. 1967. Periodic distribution of troponin along the thin filament. *J. Biochem. Tokyo* 61:817–19

167. Ooi, T., Fujime-Higashi, S. 1971. Structure of tropomyosin and its crystal. In *Advances in Biophysics*, ed. M. Kotani, 2:113–53. Baltimore: University Park

168. Oosawa, F., Kasai, M. 1971. Actin. See Ref. 138, 261–322

169. Page, S. G., Huxley, H. E. 1963. Filament lengths in striated muscle. *J. Cell Biol.* 19:369–90

170. Parker, L., Pyun, H. Y., Hartshorne, D. J. 1970. The inhibition of the adenosine triphosphatase activity of subfragment 1-actin complex by troponin plus tropomyosin, troponin B plus tropomyosin and troponin B. *Biochem. Biophys. Acta* 223:453–456

171. Peachey, L. D. 1965. The sarcoplasmic reticulum and transverse tubules of the frog's sartorius. *J. Cell Biol.* 25:209–31

172. Pepe, F. 1971. Structure of the myosin filament of striated muscle. *Progr. Biophys. Mol. Biol.* 22:75–96

173. Pepe, F. 1971. Structural components of the striated muscle fibril. See Ref. 138, 323–53

174. Perry, S. V., Cole, H. A., Head, J. F., Wilson, F. J. 1972. Localization and mode of action of the inhibitory protein component of the troponin complex. *Cold Spring Harbor Symp. Quant. Biol.* 37:251–62

175. Podolsky, R. J., Ed. 1971. *Contractility of Muscle Cells and Related Processes*. Englewood Cliffs, New Jersey: Prentice-Hall

176. Podolsky, R. J., Teichholz, L. E. 1970. The relation between calcium and contraction kinetics in skinned muscle fibres. *J. Physiol.* 211:19–35

177. Pratje, E., Heilmeyer, L. M. G. 1972. Phosphorylation of rabbit muscle troponin and actin by a 3',5'-c-AMP-dependent protein kinase. *FEBS Lett.* 27:89–93

178. Pringle, J. W. S. 1972. Arthropod muscle. See Ref. 27, 491–541

179. Reedy, M. K., Holmes, K. C., Tregear, R. T. 1965. Induced changes in orientation of the cross-bridges of glycerinated insect flight muscle *Nature* 207:1276–80

180. Reuter, H. 1973. Divalent cations as charge carriers in excitable membranes. *Progr. Biophys. Mol. Biol.* 26:1–43

181. Rome, E. 1972. Relaxation of glycerinated muscle: low-angle X-ray diffraction studies. *J. Mol. Biol.* 65:331–45

182. Ross, J. Jr., Sobel, B. E. 1972. Regulation of cardiac contraction. *Ann. Rev. Physiol.* 34:47–88

183. Rubio, R., Sperelakis, N. 1972. Penetration of horseradish peroxidase in the terminal cisternae of frog skeletal muscle fibers and blockade of caffeine contracture by $Ca^{++}$ depletion. *Z. Zellforsch.* 124:57–71

184. Rüdel, R., Taylor, S. R. 1971. Striated muscle fibers: facilitation of contraction at short lengths by caffeine. *Science* 172:387–88

185. Rüegg, J. C., Steiger, G. J., Schadler, M. 1970. Mechanical activation of the contractile system in skeletal muscle. *Pfluegers Arch.* 319:139–45

186. Sandow, A. 1966. Latency relaxation: a brief analytical review. *Med. Coll. Va. Quart.* 2:82–89
187. Sandow, A. 1970. Skeletal muscle. *Ann. Rev. Physiol.* 32:87–138
188. Schmidt, E., Wilkes, A. B., Holland, W. C. 1972. Effects of various glycerol or urea concentrations and incubation times on atrial contractions and ultrastructure. *J. Mol. Cell Cardiol.* 4:113–20
189. Schneider, M. F., Chandler, W. K. 1973. Voltage dependent charge movement in skeletal muscle: a possible step in excitation-concentration coupling. *Nature* 242:244–46
190. Shoenberg, M., Podolsky, R. J. 1972. Length-force relation of calcium activated muscle fibers. *Science* 176:52–54
191. Schwartz, A., Ed. 1971. *Methods in Pharmacology,* Vol. 1. New York: Appleton
192. Seidel, J. C., Gergely, J. 1971. The conformation of myosin during the steady state of ATP hydrolysis: studies with myosin spin labeled at the $S_1$ thiol groups. *Biochem. Biophys. Res. Commun.* 44:826–30
193. Seidel, J. C., Gergely, J. 1972. Investigation of the conformational changes in spin-labeled myosin: implications for the molecular mechanism of muscle contraction. *Cold Spring Harbor Symp. Quant. Biol.* 37:187–93
194. Smith, D. S. 1972. *Muscle.* New York: Academic
195. Sopis, J., Winegrad, S. 1967. The effect of stretch on $^{45}Ca$ efflux and on sarcoplasmic reticulum in frog skeletal muscle. *Fed. Proc.* 26:597
196. Spudich, J. A., Huxley, H. E., Finch, J. T. 1972. Regulation of skeletal muscle contraction. II. Structural studies of the interaction of the tropomyosin-troponin complex with actin. *J. Mol. Biol.* 72:619–32
197. Spudich, J. A., Watt, S. 1971. The regulation of skeletal muscle contraction. I. Biochemical studies of the interaction of the tropomyosin-troponin complex with actin and the proteolytic fragments of myosin. *J. Biol. Chem.* 246:4866–71
198. Stefani, E., Steinbach, A. 1968. Persistence of excitation-contraction coupling in slow muscle fibres after a treatment that destroys transverse tubules in twitch fibres. *Nature* 218:681–82
199. Steiger, G. J. 1971. Stretch activation and myogenic oscillation of isolated contractile structures of heart muscle. *Pfluegers Arch.* 330:347–61

199a. Stewart, J. M., Levy, A. M. 1970. The role of the calcium-troponin-tropomyosin complex in the activation of contraction. *J. Biol. Chem.* 245:5764–72
200. Strosberg, A. M., Katzung, B. G., Lee, J. C. 1972. Glycerol removal treatment of guinea pig cardiac muscle. *J. Mol. Cell. Cardiol.* 4:39–48
201. Stull, J. T., Brostom, C. O., Krebs, E. G. 1972. Phosphorylation of the inhibitor component of troponin by phosphorylase kinase. *J. Biol. Chem.* 247:5272–74
202. Sugden, E. A., Nihei, T. 1969. The effects of calcium and magnesium ions on the adenosine triphosphatase and inosine triphosphatase activities of myosin A. *Biochem. J.* 113:821–27
203. Taylor, E. W. 1972. Chemistry of muscle contraction. *Ann. Rev. Biochem.* 41:577–616
204. Taylor, E. W., Lymn, R. W. 1972. Enzyme kinetics and the mechanisms of muscle contraction. See Ref. 156, 47–69
205. Taylor, S. R., Preiser, H., Sandow, A. 1972. Action potential parameters affecting excitation-contraction coupling. *J. Gen. Physiol.* 59:421–36
206. Taylor, S. R., Rüdel, R. 1970. Striated muscle fibers: inactivation of contraction induced by shortening. *Science* 167:882–84
207. Tonomura, Y. 1972. *Muscle Proteins, Muscle Contraction, and Cation Transport.* Baltimore: University Park. 350 pp.
208. Tonomura, Y., Oosawa, F. 1972. Molecular mechanism of contraction. *Ann. Rev. Biophys. Bioeng.* 1:159–90
209. Tonomura, Y., Watanabe, S., Morales, M. 1969. Conformational changes in the molecular control of muscle contraction. *Biochemistry* 8:2171–76
210. Trentham, D. R., Bardsley, R. G., Eccleston, J. F., Weeds, A. G. 1972. Elementary processes of the magnesium ion-dependent adenosine triphosphatase activity of heavy meromyosin. *Biochem. J.* 126:635–44
211. Van Der Kloot, W. G. 1968. The effect of disruption of the T-tubules on calcium efflux from frog skeletal muscle. *Comp. Biochem. Physiol.* 26:377–79
212. Van Eerd, J.-P., Kawasaki, Y. 1972. $Ca^{++}$ induced conformational changes in the $Ca^{++}$ binding component of troponin. *Biochem. Biophys. Res. Commun.* 47:859–65
213. Vaughan, P. C., Howell, J. N., Eisenberg, R. S. 1972. The capacitance of

skeletal muscle fibers in solutions of low ionic strength. *J. Gen. Physiol.* 59: 347–59

214. Vibert, P. J., Haselgrove, J. C., Lowy, J., Poulsen, F. R. 1972. Structural changes in actin-containing filaments of muscle. *J. Mol. Biol.* 71:757–67

215. Vos, E. C., Frank, G. B. 1972. The threshold for potassium-induced contractures of frog skeletal muscle. Potentiation of potassium-induced contractures by pre-exposure to subthreshold potassium concentrations. *Can. J. Physiol. Pharmacol.* 50:37–44

216. Weber, A., Bremel, R. D. 1971. Regulation of contraction and relaxation in the myofibril. See Ref. 175, 37–53

217. Weber, A., Herz, R. 1963. The binding of calcium to actomyosin systems in relation to their biological activity. *J. Biol. Chem.* 238:599–605

218. Werber, M. M., Szent-Györgyi, A. G., Fasman, G. D. 1972 Fluorescence studies on heavy meromyosin-substrate interaction. *Biochemistry* 11:2872–83

219. Wilkinson, J. M., Perry, S. V., Cole, H. A., Trayer, I. P. 1972. The regulatory proteins of the myofibril. Separation and biological activity of the components of inhibitory factor preparations. *Biochem. J.* 127: 215–28

220. Winegrad, S. 1970. The intracellular site of calcium activation of contraction in frog skeletal muscle. *J. Gen. Physiol.* 55:77–88

221. Wise, R., Rondinone, J. F., Briggs, F. N. 1971. Effect of calcium on force-velocity characteristics of glycerinated skeletal muscle. *Am. J. Physiol.* 221: 973–79

222. Woledge, R. C. 1971. Heat production and chemical change in muscle *Progr. Biophys. Mol. Biol.* 22:37–74

223. Yamada, K. 1970. The increase in the rate of heat production of frog's skeletal muscle caused by hypertonic solutions. *J. Physiol.* 208:49–64

224. Yasui, B., Fuchs, F., Briggs, F. N. 1968. The role of the sulfhydryl groups of tropomyosin and troponin in the calcium control of actomyosin contractility. *J. Biol. Chem.* 243:735–742

225. Yount, R. G., Ojala, D., Babcock, D. 1971. Interaction of P-N-P and P-C-P analogs of adenosine triphosphate with heavy meromyosin, myosin, and actomyosin. *Biochemistry* 10:2490–95

226. Zachar, J. 1971. *Electrogenesis and Contractility in Skeletal Muscle Cells.* Baltimore: University Park

227. Zierler, K. 1972. Sodium flux and distribution in skeletal muscle. *Scand. J. Clin. Lab. Invest.* 29:343–40

# SMOOTH MUSCLE[1]

♦1120

*C. Ladd Prosser*

Department of Physiology and Biophysics, University of Illinois, Urbana, Illinois

Smooth muscle is distinguished from striated muscle by lack of regular transverse alignment of thick and thin filaments and by absence of a system of T-tubules. In smooth muscle, coupling between cell membrane and contractile elements is more direct than in striated, and fiber diameters are consequently much smaller. This review concentrates on visceral smooth muscles of the unitary type, that is, those showing myogenic rhythmicity. In these, conduction is from fiber to fiber, they may be stimulated by quick stretch, and autonomic nerves have a modulating but not triggering action. Vascular smooth muscle will not be much considered. No attempt is made to cite all recent papers, and emphasis is on publications of the past three years. During this period two symposium volumes (41, 44), a monograph on autonomic neuromuscular transmission (22), and a review of gastrointestinal motility (32) have appeared.

Smooth muscle is receiving increasing attention in many laboratories; it is becoming evident that no two muscles are identical and that corresponding muscles in different species may differ in properties. At present, considerable disagreement exists regarding structure, electrical and mechanical activities, and the cellular action of neural and hormonal regulators. This review can reconcile only a few of these disagreements.

## ULTRASTRUCTURE

Earlier views of the structure of smooth muscle fibers have been deceptively simple; vertebrate unitary muscle must be considered as a recent evolutionary development, certainly not as a primitive muscle. The surface membrane of most smooth muscle fibers contains rows of pinocytotic vesicles (caveolae) 500–800 Å in diameter (900 Å center to center in scanning electron micrographs) (225). Whether all of these vesicles open to the extracellular space (ECS) or not is uncertain. In any case, they increase the surface area immensely and make estimates of ECS and membrane area difficult. Lanthanum and ferritin may be trapped in the caveolae and are not readily washed out. One suggestion has been that these vesicles serve the excitatory function

[1]Preparation of this review has been aided by USPH Grant AM 12768.

of T-tubules; however, the vesicles are not apposed to an internal sarcoplasmic reticular (SR) system and they do not occur opposite nexal regions (198). A second suggestion is that the vesicles are concerned with absorption of ions and metabolites. Another possibility is that they are areas of active ion pumps, especially since mitochondria often occur near them; histochemical staining shows a concentration of Ca-ATPase around them (150).

Another important membrane feature of smooth muscle is the nexus or gap junction, a region of close apposition of adjacent cells. These junctions are apparently very labile in living muscle and may pull apart in hypertonic solutions and then reform (80). They are abundant in unitary muscles (e.g. amnion) where conduction is from cell to cell, and are rare or absent from multiunit muscles (e.g. nictitating membrane). Electrical resistance betwen cells is lower than the input resistance of one cell, and the fact that strips of smooth muscle show electrical continuity in a sucrose gap is proof of the presence of low-resistance paths (166). The distribution of nexuses and the effects of hypertonic solutions on both electrical and structural properties, along with similarities to other tissues, are taken as evidence that these regions may be the areas of low resistance. Nexuses are much less abundant in intestinal longitudinal muscle than in circular muscle, yet some figures designed to show absence of nexuses do in fact show their presence (110). Longitudinal muscle shows electrical couplings, as indicated by electrotonic spread (136) and continuity in a sucrose gap (221). Intestinal fibers transplanted to the anterior chamber of the eye show nexuses when they grow together in a sheet (186). Differences in ease of demonstration of nexuses in various tissues reflect differences in both degree of electrical coupling and the lability of nexal connections during fixation.

In addition to nexuses, membrane thickenings resembling desmosomes and protrusions of one cell into an adjacent cell are noted (87). Bands of nonspecific cholinesterase have been described crossing many fibers (107). Various smooth muscles show postsynaptic structures, dense regions of postsynaptic membranes apposed to nerve varicosities (215).

Descriptions of the internal structure of smooth muscle fibers vary according to the state of the muscle when it is fixed and the fixative used. It is difficult, if not impossible, to fix smooth muscle in a fully relaxed state for electron microscopy. Glycerination damages smooth muscle, so this treatment cannot be used as it is with striated muscle. Whether or not a sarcoplasmic reticular system occurs in smooth muscle has been debated. Rows of small vesicles, which are probably an SR, have been found under "good" fixation and both rough and smooth SR have been identified (79). Some phasic smooth muscles, such as taenia, portal vein, and mesenteric artery, show few SR vesicles, 1.8–2% of cell volume, whereas more tonic muscles, such as pulmonary artery and aorta, have 5% SR; turtle oviduct is intermediate at 3% (199). The SR in uterine muscle (myometrium) increases during estrogen treatment and in pregnancy (198). It has been suggested, by comparison with skeletal muscles, that these vesicles are regions of calcium storage and release. Muscles with much SR maintain contractile response to stimulation, as by acetylcholine, whereas in those with little SR the response is lost rapidly.

Most earlier electron micrographs of smooth muscle showed thin filaments (50–80 Å) but no thick filaments, although myosin could be extracted. In recent studies of muscles fixed in an extended state, thick filaments appear (150 Å) (78, 133, 183). X-ray diffraction measurements show 144 Å meridional reflections, presumably corresponding to thick filaments (154). Frequently the thin filaments are arranged in a rosette around a thick filament with a thin to thick ratio of about 15:1 (78). It is assumed that the thick filments are myosin and, in some published figures, a halo around the thick filaments suggests some condensation of thin elements. Ease in demonstration of thick filaments differs according to muscle and conditions of fixation. Both sizes of filament have been distinguished in freeze-etched material (112).

Cross-bridges between thick and thin filaments have rarely been seen, but arrowhead structures have been formed between thin filaments and heavy meromyosin extracted from smooth muscle (137). Models of interdigitating thick and thin filaments have been drawn (111). Negative staining of gizzard in the presence of Ca, Mg, and ATP before fixation, or fixation in the cold or when stretched, favors thick filament retention (89, 189, 190).

There have been several recent reports of a third or intermediate filament (approximately 100 Å) (182). These have been especially observed in embryo chick gizzard grown in tissue culture, cultured intestinal muscle, and taenia (54). Similar 100 Å filaments occur in endothelial and other cell types; they may have a supporting function.

Many electron micrographs of smooth muscles show dense bodies of unknown function. It was suggested earlier that these may be analogous to Z-substance of striated muscle, but this was not established by chemical extraction. Some figures show the 100 Å filaments converging on the dense bodies as if they were points of attachment. Others show the thin filaments attaching to the cell membrane. Claims that the dense bodies are artifacts (194) seem unjustified, and evidence from antibody staining shows them to contain α-actinin (185).

A series of papers from Lowy's laboratory reported ribbon filaments 150 Å thick and 1000 Å in sections, and many μm long with repeat periods of 56 and 391 Å in dispersed extracts (154, 196). In other laboratories, ribbon filaments in preparations fixed under physiological conditions have not been observed; however, ribbons can be obtained on fixation in a hypertonic solution or after treatment at low temperature. It is suggested that ribbons can be obtained only in cells which are shrunken in hypertonic solution (197). In high potassium and hypo-osmotic solutions, the extracellular space decreases and cell volume increases as the cells swell. In swollen cells the caveolar vesicles disappear, and filament structure is lost (126). It seems clear that the appearance of filaments in smooth muscle depends on the tonicity and temperature of fixation.

Smooth muscles, particularly the stomach of the toad *Bufo marinus,* have been dissociated into separate fibers by mild proteolysis (10). These fibers contract in response to electrical or acetylcholine stimulation. The contractions are extreme and fibers show spiral folding, which is particularly evident in polarized microscopy.

Measurements of these isolated fibers suggest a volume change during contraction (73).

Many questions regarding the structure of smooth muscle fibers remain unanswered. It is agreed that thin filaments are actin. Whether the thick filaments are myosin only and how or whether cross-bridges occur are unknown. The composition and function of the intermediate filaments remain to be learned. The nature and function of the dense bodies are being debated. How tension is developed and maintained in smooth muscles, and how its filaments connect to each other and at their terminals can only be speculated on at present. Similarly, the structural basis for coupling between the short fibers in a sheet of muscle is uncertain. Smooth muscle is remarkably labile in that structures are readily lost under conditions commonly used for fixation of other muscles. It is possible that some structures such as nexuses and caveolae may come and go normally according to functional state; the same may be true for aggregation of myosin into thick filaments. Perhaps too much effort has been devoted to fitting ultrastructure of smooth muscle into the pattern established for striated muscle.

## ION CONCENTRATIONS, RESTING FLUXES, RESTING POTENTIALS

Analyses of smooth muscles for ions show much variation according to prior treatment. Dissection invariably causes extensive injury, especially to surface cells, and this effect may spread inward due to the low resistance nexuses. Potassium leaks out of damaged cells and sodium is gained. The most consistent analyses, also the most useful preparations for experimentation, are obtained after soaking strips of muscle for 1–3 hours in aerated balanced saline at 37°C. Table 1 summarizes recent analytical data; other tables of analysis are given in (41).

Estimates of extracellular space (ECS) vary with the marker agent used but average values of about 35 ml/100 $g_{ww}$ are used. Interpretation of ECS is complicated by the degree of openness of the surface vesicles. In general, intracellular sodium is higher and potassium lower than in skeletal muscle. Intracellular chloride is much higher than in skeletal muscle. One limitation in calculating specific permeabilities from ion fluxes is the uncertainty of surface area involved.

Table 2 gives recent calculated equilibrium potentials; other tables are in reference (141). In general, $E_K$ values are as much as 50–80 percent more negative than the resting potential $(E_m)$, and $E_{Cl}$ is much less negative than in skeletal muscle, i.e. $E_m$ is more negative than $E_{Cl}$. Resting potentials as a function of log $K_o$ deviate from Nernst relations because of realtively high permeabilities to Na and Cl and partly because of an electrogenic Na-K pump (1, 141).

Resting fluxes are usually measured by efflux of tracers and are given in half-times or in rate constants ($k = 0.693/t_{1/2}$). Relatively few measurements of both influx and efflux of the same ion are available. Efflux curves for Na, K, or Cl have been commonly analyzed for convenience in terms of two or three exponential functions (37, 38, 58, 59, 100). A strip of smooth muscle consists of many cells, not all in the same state or geometric combination relative to the bathing medium, and efflux curves for such a complex system represent statistical averages. Identification of the efflux rate constants with specific compartments is speculative, but the fastest time-constant presumably corresponds to the extracellular compartment. A second fraction is slowly exchangeable and, for some ions, probably corresponds to surface-bound ions. A third compartment is very slowly exchangeable and presumably corresponds to internally bound ions in equilibrium with free internal ions. Compartmental analyses have been made for taenia (100) and uterine myometrium (114).

Permeability contants ($P$) have been calculated from flux and membrane potential data. Several limitations to each method make such calculations questionable for smooth muscles. Also, a possible contribution of exchange diffusion is neglected in

Table 1  Ion concentrations (m$M$/kg$_{ww}$ or m$M$/kg cell water)

| Muscle (Ref.) | Na total | Na intracell. | K total | K intracell. | Cl total | Cl intracell. | Ca total | Mg total | Extracell. space (% vol.) |
|---|---|---|---|---|---|---|---|---|---|
| Guinea pig (G.P.) taenia coli | | | | | | | | | |
| (141) | 62.9 | | 86.4 | | | | | | 35.1 |
| (58) | 57 | 28 | 83 | 158 | 71 | 57 | | | |
| (60) | 63 | 31 | 81 | 165 | 81 | 71 | | | 35 |
| (100) | | 35 | | 100 | | 55 | | | 34 |
| (126) | 62 | | 88 | | 64 | | | | 35 |
| (37) | 66 | 42 | 62.9 | | | | | | 33 |
| (9) | 80 | | 74 | | | | 3.2 | 4.8 | |
| (148) | 71 | | | | | | 3.1 | | |
| (155) | | | | | | | 2.6 | | |
| G.P. Ileum | | | | | | | | | |
| (220) | 60.4 | | 111.7 | | | | | | |
| Cat intestinal muscle circular | | | | | | | | | |
| (176) | 60 | | 102 | | | | 1.4 | 6.2 | |
| G.P. Uterus | | | | | | | | | |
| (217) | 60.4 | | 112 | | | | 2.2 | | |
| Vas deferens | | | | | | | | | |
| (58) | 57 | 28 | 82.5 | 158 | 71 | 57 | | | 31 |
| Portal vein | | | | | | | | | |
| (108) | 60 | 45 | 102 | 138 | 100 | 86 | | | 49 |

one way flux measurements. The intracellular concentrations of K and Na obtained by analyses are higher than those obtained by extrapolation from efflux curves. For example, values found by analysis and by extrapolation, respectively, were: $Na_i$ in taenia, 19 and 13.5 m$M$; $Na_i$ in vas deferens, 28 and 20.2 m$M$; $Cl_i$ in vas deferens, 57 and 50 m$M$; and $K_o$ in taenia, 2.92 and 2.44 m$M$ (59, 62).

Calculations of permeability constants from resting membrane potentials and transmembrane ion gradients are of dubious validity. This results from marked effects of different potassium concentrations on membrane conductance and a large Na-K pump contribution to resting potentials. Thus Na and K permeabilities cannot be assumed to be entirely passive. Because of the active pumps, Na efflux and K influx measurements cannot be used for calculations of $P$ values. Values of resting potential calculated by the Goldman equation, using $P$ values obtained by flux measurements, are significantly less than measured membrane potentials ($E_m$). For

**Table 2**  Efflux constants

| Muscle (Ref.) | Na $T_{1/2}$(min) | Na $K$(min$^{-1}$) | K $T_{1/2}$(min) | K $K$(min$^{-1}$) | Cl $T_{1/2}$(min) | Cl $K$(min$^{-1}$) | Ca $T_{1/2}$(min) |
|---|---|---|---|---|---|---|---|
| Taenia | | | | | | | |
| (140) | | | 50 | | | | |
| (148) | | | | | | | 0.4, 4.0 |
| (61) | | .24 | | .01 | | .07 | |
| (100) | | | 2.50 | | | | |
| (37) | .72 | .96 | .57 | 1.2 | | | |
|  | 2.3 | .29 | 3.3 | .21 | | | |
|  | 19.5 | .035 | 64.7 | .01 | | | |
| (188) | | | | | | | <3 |
|  | | | | | | | 3 |
|  | | | | | | | 31 |
| Ileum | | | | | | | |
| (222) | 1 | | 1.8 | | | | |
|  | 4.4 | | 19.2 | | | | |
| (155) | | | | | | | 1 |
|  | | | | | | | 4.5 |
|  | | | | | | | 25 |
| Uterus | | | | | | | |
| (114) | | | 9 | | | | |
|  | | | 81.4 | | | | |
| Vas deferens | | | | | | | |
| (58) | 3 | | 111 | | | | |

example, the calculated RP for taenia was –35 mV as compared with –51 mV measured (60).

Calculations of permeability ratios and equilibrium potentials for ions depend on the particular model which is assumed. One model for taenia coli assumes that the slow efflux represents uniform transmembrane fluxes for Na, K, and Cl and that the fast and middle fluxes are diffusion limited. Another model assumes that slow and middle fluxes for K and Cl are transmembrane, that the fast and middle fluxes of Na are diffusion limited, that slow Na flux is transmembrane, and further that all fluxes are based on a normal distribution of populations of fibers about a mean. Each of these models has experimental support. The two models yield for normal Krebs solution and for hypertonic Krebs (2X) values as follows (37):

|  | normal Krebs | | hypertonic Krebs | |
|---|---|---|---|---|
| Volume/area | 1.07 | | 0.573 | |
| Measured $E_m$ | –50 mV | | –60 mV | |
| | | | | |
| model | I | II | I | II |
| $P_{Na}/P_K$ | 0.0098 | 0.0092 | 0.0082 | 0.0074 |
| $P_{Cl}/P_K$ | 0.66 | 0.96 | 0.58 | 0.53 |
| calculated $E_m$ (mV) | –57 | –41 | 076 | –54 |
| calculated $R_m$ ($k$ ohm/cm$^2$) | 72.2 | 41.6 | 74 | 47.9 |

Despite the limitations on calculating precise permeability constants for smooth muscle from flux and potential measurements, a few comparisons with skeletal muscle are possible. In general, $P_{Na}/P_K$ is higher for smooth muscles, 0.19 in taenia. $P_{Cl}/P_K$ in taenia is higher (0.65) (59), (0.4) (168) than in nerve and lower than in frog sartorius.

High Cl permeability is indicated by higher slopes of $E_m$ versus log $K_o$ when impermeant ions are used than when with permeant ions, such as Cl, are used. Several smooth muscles, particularly rat aorta, swell in saline solutions high in KCl but not when ethanesulfate is substituted for part of the NaCl (126). Replacement

**Table 3** Resting membrane potential and calculated equilibrium potentials (mV) (selected recent data)

| Muscle (Ref.) | $E_m$ | $E_{Na}$ | $E_K$ | $E_{Cl}$ |
|---|---|---|---|---|
| Taenia | | | | |
| (65) | –57 | +39 | –92 | –19 |
| (64) | | +52 | –89 | –24 |
| Vas deferens | | | | |
| (63) | –57 | +42 | –88 | –23 |

of Cl by $NO_3$ slightly increases K efflux but replacement of Cl by a less permeant anion markedly reduces K efflux and also reduces K influx (60). High $P_{Cl}$ is indicated by a reduced slope of $E_m$ for a tenfold change in $K_o$, i.e. shunting by Cl. For example, in taenia the slope of $E_m$ vs log $K_o$ is 38 mV in KCl, 40 in $K_2SO_4$, and 47 mV in K ethanesulfate (140). The interactions beweeen K and Cl with respect to reciprocal permeabilities are complex. In taenia, Cl accounts for 40% of the resting conductance (168) and $P_{Cl}$ is three times as high in K free solution than in normal Krebs (60).

One way of measuring conductances is to estimate membrane resistance ($R_m$) from the magnitude of electrotonic potentials as measured by an intracellular electrode in a bridge circuit. This method gives approximate values which are useful for comparison of effects of different ions. In a hypertonic solution, $R_m$ increases slightly (36, 38) and in low $K_o$ with a permeant anion $G_m$ and $P_K$ increase, but with a nonpermeant anion no such change occurs (60). On transfer from zero $K_o$ to different levels of K in the medium, an initial decrease in membrane resistance occurs followed by a marked rise in resistance; the initial decline is small or lacking and the increase in $R_m$ may be relatively more in high $K_m$ compared to what it is in physiological concentrations. After a period in zero K, the $P_{Cl}$ increases, then when K is readmitted a marked increase in $P_K$ occurs in the presence of permeant anions. High $P_K$ thus short-circuits the Na-K pump in high K concentration range. Also in taenia, membrane resistance decreases, i.e. conductance ($G_m$) increases with a rise in temperature from 17–37°C, and the temperature effect is enhanced in low $Cl_o$; cooling decreases both $G_K$ and $G_{Cl}$ (39). Calcium depolarizes more at low than at high temperature and it has been suggested that Ca may control Na permeability at the outer membrane while K may control it at the inner surface (38, 40).

In summary, measurements of efflux of Na, K, and Cl, of membrane resistance, and of membrane potentials have been used together with uncertain estimates of intracellular ion concentrations and estimates of surface areas to calculate ion permeabilities. Complex interionic actions are indicated, compartmental localization is uncertain. High Na and Cl permeabilities, and an active Na-K pump, make conclusions based on passive properties very uncertain. Certainly, predictions such as have been made for squid axons are impossible.

The effects of calcium are multiple and more complex than those of univalent ions. Some of the membrane effects result from modification by Ca of the permeabilities of other ions, particularly K and Na, and some are electrical actions of Ca per se. Smooth muscle membranes are polarized (made more negative) when $Ca_o$ is increased and are depolarized on decreasing $Ca_o$ down to about half of their normal level; further decrease has little effect (141, 152). In low Ca and Mg, taenia shows a decrease in ECS and increased K influx (100), and depolarization by high $K_o$ is less in high than in low $Ca_o$ (140). High $Ca_o$ increases $P_K$, and in high $Ca_o$, the linear part of the $E_m/K_o$ curve is extended to lower values of $K_o$. The ratio $P_{Na}/P_K$ for cat intestinal muscle is lower in high calcium and higher in low calcium. High $Ca_o$ hyperpolarizes taenia and increases $G_m$, effects antagonized by Na; hence Ca controls permeability to Na and K (38). Longitudinal muscle of guinea pig ileum loses potassium in either low Ca or low Na because the flux constant for K efflux increases

(220). The K content of taenia fell from 72 to 13 m$M$/kg$_{ww}$ when Ca and Mg were omitted from the medium (100).

Calcium washout curves have been interpreted as indicating three compartments. The fastest represents extracellular Ca. The second probably represents Ca-binding at cell and vesicle membranes. It is estimated that there are 10 meq of fixed anionic sites per kg of cells (102). Ca and Mg compete for membrane sites; in taenia the anionic sites have more affinity for $Ca^{2+}$ than for $Mg^{2+}$ (101, 200). Uranyl ion also competes with Ca for anionic sites and can be visualized by electron microscopy (225). Uranyl binding is reversed by cations in the series Ca $\simeq$ Mg $\gg$ K $>$ Na (102). More Mg is taken up in zero K than in high K, and two anionic binding sites have been postulated, one for both divalent and univalent cations, the other for Ca and Mg only.

The third compartment is intracellular. A small part of this is slowly, but measurably, exchangeable, while another part is so slowly exchangeable it is undetected in usual times of washout (223). Calcium influx into smooth muscle is increased by stimulating agents which depolarize. Contractions may make use of Ca which enters from ECS and intracellular and membrane stores; the relative importance of these two sources varies according to the muscle. Acetylcholine increases Ca influx into the muscle of toad stomach (176, 177). Mitochrondrial and microsomal cell fractions of myometrium bind Ca by an ATP-dependent mechanism (15, 56).

An interesting method of assaying the intracellular Ca which has been used only with smooth muscles is based on displacement of extracellular Ca by lathanum (218). $La^{3+}$ at 50 $\mu M$ increases Ca content of taenia and initiates contraction; at 2 m$M$, La inhibits Ca influx and increases K depolarization (67). Lanthanum displaces extracellular Ca, blocks Ca influx, and inhibits contraction by preventing Ca entry. Analysis of a muscle after washing with La provides a measure of total cellular calcium (216).

## ION PUMPS

The preceding discussion deals primarily with passive fluxes; it fails to consider exchange diffusion which may be significant. Further complication of the picture of ion distribution comes from evidence for active Na-K and Ca pumps, possibly also a Cl pump. Freshly dissected smooth muscles, as well as those stored in the cold, lose K, gain Na, and reestablish normal gradients within a few hours in Krebs solution at 37°C. This restoration is blocked by ouabain or zero K (52, 57, 61). Calculations of $E_m$ made on the basis of measured ion concentrations and permeabilities give a computed $E_m$ some 10–15 mV less negative than the measured $E_m$ (64). As $K_o$ is reduced, the $E_m$ of cat intestinal muscle goes through a maximum negative value at about one-fourth the normal $K_o$; this maximum negativity is absent in ouabain or at 22°C (72). In several different visceral muscles, reduction in $K_o$ to zero depolarizes by approximately 10 mV below normal $E_m$. After readmission of K a hyperpolarization occurs which may drive $E_m$ as negative as –90 mV, i.e. more negative than $E_K$ (211). Ouabain at $10^{-6}$ $M$ acts like zero K in depolarizing. The hyperpolarization following readmission of K is abolished by ouabain or by substituting Li for Na; the hyperpolarization is not due to a decrease in $G_K$ since membrane resistance increases only slightly (58, 59). In zero K, smooth muscle cells lose K and gain Na; when K is readmitted to the medium, $Na^+$ is pumped out, the membrane is hyperpolarized, and K is taken up unless ouabain is present or the temperature is low. Ouabain in normal Krebs depolarizes slightly and in intestinal muscle it increases spontaneous spike frequency; later it decreases the amplitude of spikes and blocks them. In taenia at 12–17°C the internal concentration of potassium decreases and that of sodium increases (180). After K depletion, followed by return to normal Krebs solution, the uptake of K and extrusion of Na are related to $E_m$. At high $K_o$ the $E_m$ curve closely follows the Nernst relation because $G_K$ is increased and the pump component diminished; $K_o$ at two to four times normal stimulates the pump less than it does at physiological concentrations.

A variety of measurements have led two laboratories to conclude that taenia pumps Na and K at a ratio of 3:2 (38, 64). In Krebs solution the pump accounts for 15–20 mV of potential and the calculated pump current is 0.8 $\mu A/cm^2$ (61, 64).

An unusual property of the Na-K pump in smooth muscle (at least in taenia) is that it is stimulated by Li. Ouabain depolarizes in the presence of Li, and Li cannot substitute for Na in being pumped, but can substitute for K in activating Na efflux and reduce the amount of Na which enters by exchange diffusion (61–63). High $Na_o$ inhibits the pump and $Li_o$ stimulates it.

The longitudinal ileal muscle of the guinea pig was kept in normal Krebs at 22°C for loading with Na and loss of K. It was then transferred to 35°C for varying times and then into zero K Krebs; for a short period in normal Krebs at 35°C (high remaining $Na_i$) depolarization by zero K was much higher than after a long time (low $Na_i$). When K was readmitted after the depolarization in zero K, twice as much hyperpolarization occurred when the $Na_i$ was high. In low $Cl_o$, membrane resistance increased and the hyperpolarization on readmission of K was enhanced. It is concluded that the pump is stimulated by $Na_i$ and by $K_o$ and that it is attenuated by a decrease in $R_m$ and enhanced by an increase in $R_m$ (30, 31).

The uterine muscle of the rat shows Na-K pump properties much like those of taenia and ileum. In zero K the cells become loaded with Na. On readmission of K, hyperpolarization occurs and Na is extruded unless ouabain is present (205, 206). Rb and Cs as well as K can activate the Na pumping (207). The membrane pump is inhibited by metabolic inhibitors IAA and DNP and only a small amount of ATP is needed, as indicated by the K:ATP ratio of 46–51 (179). Extracts of myometrial cells show a membrane ATPase which in the presence of Mg is stimulated by Na and inhibited by ouabain and Ca. Microsomes (presumably from intracellular SR) have Na-activated ATPase which is also antagonized by ouabain (3).

In guinea pig bladder the $E_m/K_o$ curve has a slope of 31 mV at 30°C and of 24 mV at 12.5°C; readmission of K after soaking in zero K causes hyperpolarization to –65 mV, less in cold solution than in warm (139). In portal vein, either low temperature or zero K depolarizes the muscle. Tris cannot substitute for Na in becoming accumulated in zero K when the saline is isotonic, but Tris can substitute if the saline is made hypertonic (143). Smooth muscle of the capsule of cat spleen contracts to norepinephrine. The response remains after transfer to a K-free medium but disappears on subsequent return to normal K and then returns in zero K (34). It is postulated that hyperpolarization by the stimulated pump may reduce the response to NE. In the rabbit detrusor muscle, contraction occurs in K-free medium, and relaxation on K replacement, presumably by a sequence of depolarization and hyperpolarization (165).

It maybe concluded then, that probably all visceral smooth muscles have a Na-K pump which contributes to the deviation of the resting potential from strict Nernst relations in low K.

The low concentration of intracellular calcium in smooth muscle was previously noted. Even in those muscles with the most SR, the amount of bound Ca is less than in striated muscle. It has been postulated, by analogy with squid axons, that there may be active extrusion of Ca. In taenia, in high $Ca_o$ or low $Na_o$ the electrotonic potential decreases due to high $Ca_i$ and a resulting decrease in $R_m$; $P_K$ may be increased by high $Ca_i$ and decreased by an outward Ca pump (209). Internal calcium increases under conditions when $Na_i$ decreases and a Na–Ca exchange which is dependent on ATP has been postulated (66, 67). In rat uterus the intracellular calcium concentration amounts to 1 m$M$ exchangeable, and 0.45 m$M$ relatively inexchangeable, whereas the intracellular concentration predicted from the potential gradient would be 67 m$M$. Also, $Ca_i$ increases when metabolism is poisoned by IAA or DNP, hence an active outward Ca pump is indicated (217). Direct evidence for a Ca pump at the cell membrane is lacking; active binding of $Ca^{2+}$ by particulates will be mentioned below.

A Cl$^-$ pump in smooth muscle has also been postulated. $E_{Cl}$ is 30 mV less negative than $E_m$, hence a relatively high $Cl_i$ is maintained against a steep electrochemical gradient. Efflux of Cl$^-$ is increased in zero K and a Na-K coupled Cl pump has been suggested (59).

It is concluded that several visceral smooth muscles have active Na-K pumps which contribute significantly to the resting potential in the physiological K range. Firm evidence for other transmembrane pumps is lacking, but a Ca pump is probably present.

## IONIC BASIS OF ELECTRICAL ACTIVITY

Smooth muscles show electrical spikes which are conducted from cell to cell and which trigger contractions; many smooth muscles also show one or more types of slow potentials (178). Many unitary smooth muscles are spontaneously active electrically. Conduction in a sheet of fibers has been established as electrical and via low-resistance connections, but conduction appears to require the interaction of many cells in parallel. A bundle of fibers constitutes a three-dimensional network of short cells, and models indicate the differences between electrical properties of the network and a cylindrical cable (22).

Space and time constants for smooth muscles vary according to method of measurement (22, 144, 207a). Some space constants measured intracellularly as a spread of electrotonic potentials from an extracellularly applied pulse are as follows, in mm: guinea pig rectum 0.81 (142), portal vein 0.5–0.6 (143, 119), taenia coli 1.5 (207a), vas deferens 2.1, cat circular intestinal muscle 1.1, and longitudinal 0.94 (136). The apparent space contants are thus several cell lengths. Time constants measured by extracellular (including pressure) polarization are, in msec: guinea pig rectum 84 (142), portal vein 330 (143), taenia coli 100 (207a), cat circular 133, and longitudinal 92 (136). Time constants measured by intracellular polarization are, in msec: taenia 2–10, vas deferens 1.5–3.5 (207a), cat circular 20–30, and longitudinal 10 (136). Thus the time constants with intracellular polarization are shorter than with extracellular pulses. Because of the attenuation at each end of a spindle-shaped cell, current distribution around a centrally located electrode is uneven. Every smooth muscle cell presumably has low resistance contacts with 6 other cells in any cross section; hence there are many parallel pathways which are cross connected. The surface area of a single cell can only be approximated; therefore, calculation of specific membrane resistance and capacity are of dubious validity. Because of the interconnections, resistance and capacity of single cells may not be meaningful in terms of cable properties.

Identification of ionic mechanisms of spikes and slow electrical activity is ideally attempted by measurements of ionic currents under voltage clamping. The small size of the cells and the electrical interconnections between cells preclude use of intracellular current and voltage electrodes. The most satisfactory method is by double sucrose gap with narrow node width. The limitations of this method, due to uncertainty of current distribution and difficulty of holding all cells of a node under uniform clamp, have been discussed for short-fibered muscles (125). It is difficult to obtain quantitative data for fast current changes; however measurements of slow currents and comparative observations by the double sucrose gap under different treatments are useful.

Another method is measurement of membrane resistance by pulses applied during electrical events. Such measurements are difficult because the long time-constants of smooth muscle membranes often prevent pulses from reaching a steady state. Most conclusions therefore, are based on measuring the effects of ion replacement upon amplitude, rates of rise and fall, and duration of electrical events.

The spikes of visceral smooth muscles are insensitive to TTX and are more sensitive to replacement of $Ca_o$ than of $Na_o$. In taenia transferred to a Ca-free medium, there is slight depolarization and decrease in membrane resistance; no spikes occur and contractions fail (147). Reduction of $Na_o$ to less than 30 m$M$ has no effect on spike characteristics or propagation of the action potential but reduction of $Ca_o$ to 0.1 m$M$ decreases spike height with a slope of 22 mV per 10-fold change in $Ca_o$ (40). The current of the rising phase of a spike is due mainly to Ca influx (21). Both electrical and mechanical activity of taenia are lost within ten minutes in zero Ca and in three minutes if EGTA is added. Replacement of Ca by Mg abolishes spikes without depolarization and without a decrease in membrane resistance (48). The compound D-600 (verapamil) inhibits all spikes and calcium influx in various smooth muscles (149). $Mn^{2+}$ blocks most smooth muscle spikes. In a muscle depolarized by high K, entry of Ca is blocked by D-600. Lanthanum has high affinity for extracellular binding sites and blocks all uptake of Ca, whereas D-600 inhibits only the entry of the trigger Ca associated with spiking (160). When taenia was voltage clamped by step functions in a sucrose gap, reversal from inward to outward current occurred at +5 mV, Mn reduced the inward Ca current, and the inward current was abolished in a Ca-free medium (116, 138).

High $Ca_o$ hyperpolarizes and increases membrane conductance, spike height, and rate of rise of spike (40). In longitudinal and circular muscle of duodenum, high Ca increases spontaneous spiking and amplitude of spikes. The enhancement is antagonized by Mn and Co (152). In taenia, strontium can replace Ca for spiking without effect on the resting potential (141). Mn cannot replace Ca but Ba can convert spikes to plateaus, particularly in low $Ca_o$ (47).

The nature of the falling phase of spikes is uncertain. In stomach muscle, TEA has no effect but in Na-free medium, TEA decreases the rate of fall possibly by slowing an increase in $G_K$ (120). In myometrium, spikes show an undershoot which is abolished by high $K_o$, hence it may result from an increase in $G_K$; Ca is needed for triggered spikes, Na for the pacemaker potential (1).

Effects of calcium are more pronounced but sodium also has effects on smooth muscle spikes; there is some antagonism between sodium and calcium. When, with taenia, sucrose is substituted for NaCl, spike amplitude increases, rate of rise increases, slight hyperpolarization occurs, spontaneous activity eventually stops, but spikes can be triggered; if Ca is decreased at the same time as the decrease in Na, nearly normal spikes remain (38). In cat intestine, both circular and longitudinal muscle spikes show no change over a 2–3-fold range of $Ca_o$ if Na is also changed to keep the ratio $[Na]^2/[Ca]$ constant (72).

In taenia the effect of reducing $Ca_o$ is greater in high Na; after loss of spikes in low Ca, a reduction in $Na_o$ leads to recovery. Hence there is some antagonism between Na and Ca (40). Na is needed for recovery from K contracture but the contraction phase requires $Ca_o$; therefore $Na_o$ decreases the permeability to $Ca^{2+}$ (130). In a Ca-free medium with 0.5 m$M$ Mg, some spiking occurs. This is dependent on Na; in normal $Ca_o$ with excess $Na_o$ the overshoot is increased. Hence, there can be some Na current which normally is not overbalanced by Ca current (47). It is not known whether the effect of Na is on the release of membrane-bound Ca or is an allosteric type action on the Ca channel.

In estrogen dominated uterine smooth muscle of the rat, the rate of rise of spikes increases with increased $Na_o$, and is more in a high Ca than in a low Ca medium (158). In voltage clamping the transient inward current decreases and the reversal potential is more negative in a Na-free medium (Tris or DDA substituted) than normally. Neither Ca nor Na alone can support spikes; La, Mn, or Co reduce or abolish the inward current and TTX has no effect. It is suggested that uterine muscle may have a single conductance channel requiring both Na and Ca (4, 5). Calcium shifts the V/I curve along the voltage axis indicating membrane stabilization and decrease in $P_{Na}$. Voltage clamping indicates that the outward current is carried by $K^+$ (164).

The ureter of many species shows a rapid rise which is spike-like followed by a prolongation of depolarization as a plateau in rat and cat, and as oscillations in guinea pig. In low $Ca_o$ the oscillations of guinea pig ureter decrease but the plateau remains; in high $Ca_o$ the oscillations become spikes. In guinea pig ureter the prolonged plateau disappears in zero Na but repetitive spiking continues. Hence the plateau may represent high Na conductance, the spikes Ca inward current, both controlled by Ca level in the membrane (147). In cat ureter both spike height and rate of rise increase in proportion to $Ca_o$. The slope of the Ca effect is greater in the presence than in the absence of $Na_o$. In a Na-free medium the spike decreases but it reappears if calcium is increased (134, 135). Thus, for both uterus and ureter some cooperativity occurs between Ca and Na in spike production.

In guinea pig vas deferens, reduction of $Na_o$ below 30 m$M$ had no effect on spikes, but decrease in $Ca_o$ to 0.1 m$M$ abolished spikes, with a voltage/log $Ca_o$ slope of 22 mV. When both Na and Ca were varied proportionately, resting potential remained constant but spike amplitude was reduced according to the Ca concentration; therefore in this muscle the inward current appears to be carried exclusively be $Ca^{2+}$ (21).

Toad bladder contracts on cooling, and if NaCl is substituted by sucrose, the tension developed is proportional to the amount of Na substituted and is regulated by Ca (187).

Since calcium ions are necessary for contraction in all smooth muscles and it is probable that a steady state exists between membrane and intracellular Ca, it is postulated that an influx of calcium during the spike is a trigger for release of internal calcium for contraction (160). In the absence of a T-tubule system the Ca spikes permit a more direct coupling than occurs in striated muscle; this direct connection between membrane spikes and contraction is the reason why smooth muscle fibers are, of necessity, small in diameter. Smooth muscles vary in the importance of Na channels and it is not clear, where synergism between Na and Ca occurs, whether (a) the Na is influencing Ca release, (b) there are parallel channels, or (c) both ions interact with a common carrier molecule. The nature of the repolarization phase is unclear; efflux of K is indicated in some muscles but Ca binding may also bring about repolarization.

In addition to spikes (and plateaus in ureter), visceral smooth muscles show several kinds of slow electrical events about which there is confusion as to terminology and mechanism. The first of these are prepotentials or pacemaker potentials. In uterus, some fibers (driver fibers) show prepotentials at the base of spikes while others (followers) lack the prepotentials. In cat intestinal muscles, prepotentials may precede spikes and, like the spikes, they depend on $Ca_o$ (152). In bladder (75) and at the pelvic end of the ureter (134) prepotentials precede spikes. Frequently in taenia and longitudinal intestinal muscle (rabbit) spikes occur in bursts, each spike preceded by a prepotential and showing an undershoot below the prepotential peak.

A type of spontaneous rhythmic wave which occurs in longitudinal muscle of some species has been called "basic electrical rhythm" from in vivo studies, and "pacesetter potential" and "slow waves" from in vivo observations. These waves are prominent in cat, rabbit, dog, and man but may be absent from guinea pig; they set the frequency of segmental movement and have highest frequency at the cephalad end of the bowel and lowest at the caudal end. The frequency in dog is 18/min anteriorly and 13/min posteriorly in the small bowel (13). Slow waves are generated in longitudinal muscle of small intestine; they do not trigger contractions in the absence of spikes. They pass to circular muscle passively via thin connecting muscle strands and bring the membranes of each layer up to threshold for spiking. Spikes occur at the peak of slow waves and frequently a prepotential appears ahead of a spike on the top of a slow wave (152, 166). A spike does not undershoot a slow wave on its repolarization phase, but it does undershoot a prepotential. Rabbit intestine shows multiple spikes per slow wave, cat and dog usually one or two. In colon, slow waves are generated by the circular layer at 2.2–2.6/min (69). In stomach, slow waves occur 3/min in man and 5/min in dog (167). In turkey stomach, pressure waves mirror slow waves at 3.3/min in stomach and 3.4/min in duodenum (82). Gall bladder shows both slow waves and spikes (76). The electrical activity of stomach is complex and varies according to species. In cat, both one of the slow components and the spikes are sensitive to Ca and can trigger contractions; a second slow component resembles intestinal slow waves (171).

Whether slow waves are conducted through a sheet of smooth muscle, as are spikes, is not established. Volume recorded waves are interpreted as indicating conduction (33). In intact segments of intestine, slow waves travel for distances of a few cm at a velocity of 1.0 cm/sec along the segment and in colon at 2.6 m/sec (70, 71). Longitudinal conduction in the intestine is abolished if connection to the circular muscle is cut or if the circular muscle is transected. Slow waves are also synchronized circumferentially in a ring. However, in isolated strips of longitudinal muscle, slow waves are not conducted far and there may be many local pacemaker areas of origin of these waves.

One hypothesis as to the nature of slow waves is that they represent a rhythmic sodium pump. Slow waves in cat longitudinal muscle are very sensitive to hypoxia, to metabolic inhibitors such as DNP, CN, and to some antibiotics which block electron transport (123, 124). They have a high $Q_{10}$ for frequency and amplitude and they disappear below 25°C; they are relatively insensitive to calcium but disappear in a Na-free medium. Slow waves decrease in frequency and increase in amplitude during hyperpolarization and show the reverse effects on depolarization (221). They are very sensitive to ouabain and zero $K_o$, both of which stop the sodium pump; amplitude is maximum at a $K_o$ concentration corresponding to highest Na-K pump activity (72). A peak of efflux of $^{22}Na$ occurs in the repolarizing phase (123). Pulses applied during a slow wave in cat longitudinal muscle fail to show any conductance change, and changes in $Na_o$ do not alter the wave form as they should if there were conductance changes (221). In rabbit longitudinal muscle a conductance decrease was observed at the slow wave peak (163). This conductance change was likely to have resulted from the membrane voltage being displaced into the range for delayed rectification and spiking. When strips of longitudinal muscle are voltage clamped in a sucrose gap, current pulses are recorded corresponding to the voltage pulses. From these current pulses and membrane constants it has been possible by a computer program to reconstruct slow waves (221).

One may conclude that true slow waves or pacesetter potentials are generated, not by a membrane conductance change, but by a rhythmic electrogenic Na-K pump. The nature of the primary pacemaker reaction is unknown, it may be an intracellular sodium threshold or a threshold of ATP. It has been possible to drive the slow waves electrically in rabbit longitudinal muscle over the range of 13–22/min (163), in dog stomach at 4.2–8/min, and in cat colon at 2.5/min (132); what part of the generating mechanism is being driven is unknown. The mode of synchronisation of waves in a sheet of longitudinal muscle fibers is unknown as is the mode of spread to circular muscle.

Uterine muscle, particularly in pregnant rat, shows slow waves and spikes. In guinea pig oviduct, hyperpolarization increases the amplitude of slow waves; a calcium pump has been postulated to control potassium in an oscillatory fashion (209).

In intact segments of guinea pig intestine, spontaneous slow oscillations occur which differ from slow waves and prepotentials in that they are sensitive to TTX and atropine (145, 146). Acetylcholine is known to be liberated from the myenteric plexus of guinea pig intestine (173). When acetylcholine (or carbachol together with depolarization) is applied to strips of the longitudinal layer of guinea pig ileum, slow oscillations are induced. They are steeper in form than the slow waves of cat and rabbit, may be induced by depolarization, are insensitive to ouabain, and are not sensitive to TTX. They are not affected by ganglion blockers but are abolished by atropine, which does not alter slow waves. The ACh-induced oscillations are sensitive to low Na, but not to low Ca (27, 28, 31). In cat longitudinal muscle in which slow waves are absent or have been blocked by ouabain, oscillations resembling those of guinea pig can be induced by ACh or by depolarization and can be blocked by atropine. In guinea pig stomach, Na-sensitive slow potentials are increased in frequency by ACh at $10^{-7}$ and are abolished in Na-free medium (157).

Thus, in guinea pig, acetylcholine, whether exogenous or liberated from plexus neurons, initiates oscillations which may involve a sodium conductance change. In cat the Na-K pump slow waves normally prevent the ACh type of oscillation. Whether guinea pig has the rhythmic Na-K pump is unknown.

Still other types of slow electrical activity have been reported. In taenia and some intestinal preparations, depolarizing waves and bursts of spikes lasting 1–2 min and recurring every few min have been recorded (96–99). The nature of these is unknown but high $CO_2$ decreases the activity (228). Another rhythm has been seen only in intact starved dogs and consists of complexes of action potentials passing in bursts down the intestine at 1.2–3 cm/min and traversing the entire small bowel in 115–183 min. These waves of action seem to depend on activation of muscle via autonomic nerves (203). Another ganglion-dependent slow rhythm is in the chicken gizzard where spontaneous slow depolarizations precede spikes; these depolarizations represent excitatory postsynaptic potentials that are dependent on plexus neurons (24, 25).

In summary, gastrointestinal muscle shows spikes and prepotentials which represent increased Ca conductance. Longitudinal muscle of some species shows 5–6 second slow waves which appear to be generated by a rhythmic Na-K pump. In other species (guinea pig especially) the longitudinal muscle manifests oscillations due to acetylcholine liberated from plexus neurons, which are sensitive to Na rather than to Ca. The basis for minute-long rhythms remains to be studied. The greater dependence on plexus neurons in guinea pig than in cat and rabbit is indicated by opposite effects of the GI hormones cholecystokinin (CCK) and gastrin in these species. In guinea pig these hormones are excitatory and their action is blocked by TTX, whereas in cat the hormones have a relaxing action directly on the muscle (232). There is evidence that various regions of the human gastrointestinal tract are controlled in different degrees by the neural plexus (14).

## MODULATION OF SMOOTH MUSCLE
## BY NEURAL TRANSMITTERS

Visceral smooth muscles in general receive both cholinergic parasympathetic and adrenergic sympathetic innervation. Some muscles, particularly those of stomach and small intestine, have in addition a nonadrenergic inhibitory innervation. Regulatory nerve fibers do not innervate each fiber in a sheet of smooth muscle, but transmitters liberated from varicosities in axons of an autonomic ground plexus can diffuse through distances of several muscle fiber diameters, and the electrical effect of a transmitter can spread via the low resistance connections between muscle cells (22, 53, 115, 214). The myogenic spontaneous activity is modulated by nerves, and there may also be local reflex actions.

Smooth muscles differ in their density of innervation; vas deferens and some sphincters are densely innervated, ureter and uterus sparsely. Counts of nerve cells per 100 $\mu m^2$ of muscle area in rat are as follows: esophagus 0.8–1.6, cardiac stomach 2.2, pylorus 1.5, pyloric sphincter 10.7, duodenum 3.0, jejunum 2.4, ileum 1.7, cecum 1.8, rectum 1.5, anal sphincter 5.1, and anococcygeus muscle 17.2 (93). Identification of particular endings with regard to transmitter is uncertain. A detailed description of Auerbach's plexus in large intestine of several species indicates (a) axon endings with small clear vesicles, probably cholinergic, (b) endings with small granular vesicles, probably adrenergic, (c) endings and varicosities with large granular vesicles surrounded by halos and a few opaque vesicles which take up DOPA and which may be neurosecretory (18), and (d) large granules without halos which may be purinergic (50). Guinea pig vas deferens has a rich plexus of dense-cored adrenergic endings and other endings with agranular vesicles which may be cholinergic (88). Fluorescence microscopy shows that most of the adrenergic endings are in the plexus of the intestine, a few on circular muscle, few or none on longitudinal muscle (74, 121, 192).

Transmural stimulation of caecum causes contractions which are abolished by TTX and atropine, and are prolonged by eserine. Hence they are mediated by cholinergic neurons (195). Transmural stimulation of guinea pig ileum causes release of acetylcholine (ACh) from plexus cells; the hormones gastrin and cholecystokinin (CCK) likewise cause release of ACh in guinea pig; norepinephrine (NE), acting via $\alpha$ receptors, reduces the amount of ACh released (173, 219). The contractile response in opossum to gastrin, a slight relaxation in pylorus, is greater in the esophagus than in the antrum (151). Transmural stimulation of intestine causes inhibition which is not blocked by either $\alpha$- or $\beta$-adrenergic blocking agents; evidence is accumulating that this inhibition may be from purinergic (ATP releasing) neurons (50, 51). Following neuronal inhibition a rebound excitation is commonly seen; this is a release of myogenic activity, distinct from primary excitation due to cholinergic neurons (85).

In some isolated smooth muscles, spontaneous miniature postsynaptic potentials (psp's) have been recorded: excitatory and depolarizing in vas deferens (23), and inhibitory and hyperpolarizing in taenia (145) and colon (84). The sling muscle (part of the esophageal sphincter) shows both excitatory and inhibitory postsynaptic potentials (ipsp's and epsp's) and is neurally controlled (20). When the intrinsic nonadrenergic inhibitory neurons were stimulated in taenia coli and jejunum, ipsp's were recorded of 10–20 mV hyperpolarization; These reversed when the membrane was polarized by 25–40 mV. From effects of $K_o$ it was concluded that the ipsp's are due to increase in $G_K$ and that the ipsp amplitude is determined by $K_o$, not $Cl_o$ (208). In jejunum the epsp's in response to stimulation of intrinsic nerves are due to increase in $G_{Na}$ and in $G_K$; they are abolished in absence of $Ca_o$ (113). Treatment of taenia with epinephrine increases membrane conductance, hyperpolarizes by some 8 mV (depending on resting potential), and decreases spread of electrotonic potential. These effects are diminished when $K_o$ or $Cl_o$ is reduced. Equilibrium potentials are as follows: $E_{Epi}$ –75 mV, $E_K$ –91 mV, $E_{Cl}$ –31 mV, and $E_m$ –60 mV; thus epinephrine opens ion paths for $K^+$ and $Cl^-$ (169). The ratio of $\Delta G_{Cl}/\Delta G_K$ is 0.36, i.e. the effect on $G_K$ is predominant. Strips of aorta contract in response to NE and show an increased Ca influx, a response diminished by Mn, therefore in this smooth muscle NE increases $G_{Ca}$ (131). In intestine, hyperpolarization due to NE and sympathetic stimulation is less than that due to the nonadrenergic inhibitor (possibly ATP) because the catecholamines increase $G_{Cl}$ as well as $G_K$ whereas the nonadrenergic inhibitor increases $G_K$ only. In guinea pig uterus an important action of catecholamines is to depolarize by increasing $G_{Cl}$ (204).

The action of ACh (or its analog carbachol) on longitudinal muscle of guinea pig ileum is to depolarize with an $E_{ACh}$ of about –9 mV. Reduction in $Na_o$ shifts the peak depolarization to a more negative voltage, reduction in $Cl_o$ has no effect, and decrease in $K_o$ shifts the peak depolarization to less negative values. It is concluded that carbachol opens ion channels for Na, K, and possibly Ca (29). The stimulating action of carbachol on ileum increases with elevation of $Ca_o$ to a maximum at 2.5 m$M$ and decreases at higher $Ca_o$ (49). In ileal muscle ACh and carbachol increase K efflux and decrease K influx, hence there is net loss of K; atropine reduces the effect on K efflux (12). In pigeon ileum the response to ACh decreases when $Ca_o$ is reduced (184). Longitudinal muscle of rabbit colon is more sensitive to ACh than is circular muscle (161). In intestinal muscles of guinea pig, ACh increases $G_{Na}$, $G_K$, and $G_{Ca}$ but not $G_{Cl}$ (28). ACh can release bound Ca and can increase influx of Ca without causing depolarization (141). In guinea pig uterus, ACh depolarizes by increasing both $G_{Na}$ and $G_{Ca}$ (204).

Catecholamines (CA) act via $\alpha$ and $\beta$ receptors. The two classes of receptor are distinguished by observing the relative efficacy of different agents and the effects of specific blockers (14). The mechanisms of CA action on smooth muscle appear to differ according to whether $\alpha$ or $\beta$ sites are involved. Guinea pig taenia coli has both $\alpha$ and $\beta$ receptors and catecholamines relax the muscle by different mechanisms for each. The $\alpha$ action hyperpolarizes from normal RP's with a reversal when the membrane is hyperpolarized by 20 mV. It increases the flux (both in and out) for K, decreases $R_m$ as judged by spread of electrotonic potentials, and blocks both spontaneous and evoked spikes; its effect is reduced by procaine. The decrease in $R_m$ is due to increase in conductance for both K and Cl as shown by ion replacements. The $\alpha$ action is best shown by epinephrine (E) and not at all by isoprenaline; it is blocked by phentolamine. After $\alpha$ block CA's, especially isoprenaline, act on $\beta$ receptors and this action is blocked by propranolol; spontaneous pacemaker potentials and resulting spikes are blocked without action on membrane resistance. Both actions require Ca, but the $\alpha$ action is at the membrane, possibly on Ca binding, and the $\beta$ action is internal, affecting the pacemaker mechanisms (45–47, 122). The $\beta$ action has a parallel, possibly secondary effect on oxygen consumption. In taenia, which is relaxed by CA, $O_2$ consumption drops; in aorta, which is contracted by CA, $O_2$ consumption increases (226, 227).

In several smooth muscles (uterus, aorta, rabbit colon, and, to a lesser extent, taenia) correlations of $\beta$ action with cyclic AMP have been established. There is disagreement whether the $\beta$ receptor is membrane adenyl cyclase or a nearby site, but all $\beta$ action increases activity of adenyl cyclase. This is followed by increase in cyclic AMP (cAMP), decrease in ATP, increased phosphorylase-A activity, and an increase in hexose phosphate and lactic acid. The $\beta$ action can occur in muscle which has been depolarized by K and the $\beta$ action is mimicked by cAMP (6, 7, 212, 213). In rabbit colon, the time for maximum relaxation is 15 sec by $\alpha$ action and 1–2 min by $\beta$ action and the time for change in cAMP is similar to the $\beta$ mechanical effect (6). The blocker sotalol inhibits both the relaxation and the increase in cAMP. In some other muscles the time correlation is less good. cAMP increases the binding of Ca by aortic microsomes and $\beta$ CA action decreases Ca binding; hence, in aorta cAMP does not parallel the $\beta$ action (17).

The actions of CA's on uterine muscle vary with hormonal state and species. In an estrogen primed guinea pig the action via $\alpha$ receptor is excitatory, depolarizing with an increase in membrane conductance; increase in spiking is due mainly to increase in $P_{Cl}$. In virgin cat uterus CA's and ATP cause relaxation, while in early pregnant cat uterus they both cause contraction (204). In cat uterus under progesterone dominance, inhibition is by $\beta$ action; under estrogen dominance, excitation is by $\alpha$ action (1). In estrogen primed rat uterus, E increases cAMP, an effect antagonized by ACh, but ACh alone has no effect on cAMP content (211). In late pregnant rat uterus, $\beta$ inhibition is the predominant CA action: isoprenaline at $10^{-7}$ $M$ causes some hyperpolarization which is Ca dependent and is abolished by La, but is not affected by K or Cl; cAMP concentration increases. The $\beta$ relaxation can occur without hyperpolarization, as in high K; hence the observed hyperpolarization could be due to outward Ca current stimulated by cAMP (159).

In bladder smooth muscle, CA's induce relaxation and counteract ACh contraction; the CA effect is via $\beta$ receptors (55, 77). In vas deferens NE is excitatory, and spontaneous epsp's occur as a result of pelvic nerve activity; these cease when NE synthesis is blocked (21). Mouse vas deferens shows excitatory junction potentials due to sympathetic impulses; after NE synthesis is blocked the amplitude of epsp's declines with a time constant of 4 min at 10 Hz stimulation. Blocking of reuptake of NE at the nerve terminals also reduces epsp size; hence the amount of transmitter available depends on both synthesis and reuptake (23). The anoccygeus of rat, a multiunit smooth muscle, is stimulated to contract by $\alpha$-adrenergic receptors and muscarinic ACh receptors, and it receives some nonadrenergic inhibitors (91, 92). In another multiunit muscle, the chicken expansor secundariorum, contraction is initiated by release of NE; after nerve transection the muscle shows supersensitivity for two days, possibly due to loss of uptake mechanism in the nerve terminals (90). The esophagus of the opossum, like that of man and unlike that of most mammals, has smooth muscle in the lower third of its length. The circular fibers are stimulated directly by stretch but give an "off" contraction mediated by noncholinergic nerves and the longitudinal fibers give a tonic contraction in response to cholinergic nerve impulses (68).

Strips of guinea pig stomach respond to CA with relaxation effected via $\beta$ receptors and blocked by propranolol, and, in addition, relaxation via $\alpha$ receptors and blocked by phentolamine; in some conditions, particularly after removal of the mucosa, the muscle contracts in response to stimulation of $\alpha$ receptors (11). A dual effect occurs also in the terminal ileum of guinea pig where E excites via $\alpha$ receptors and relaxes via $\beta$ receptors; the motor action is blocked by phentolamine and the inhibitory action by propranolol (181).

Muscle fibers of chicken and pigeon gizzard vary in their innervation patterns. Many show cholinergic epsp's in response to vagal impulses, and ipsp's secondary to perivascular stimulation (sympathetic impulses). Other cells manifest reverse junction potentials with nerve stimulation, or epsp's or ipsp's in response to each nerve; hence the nerves are mixed cholinergic and adrenergic (24–26). Rat portal vein is stimulated to contract by sympathetic impulses and also by NE; 8 × $10^{-6}$ $M$ NE corresponds to 4 impulses/sec and 2 × $10^{-5}$ $M$ NE to 16 imp/sec (153).

In summary, catecholamines act on smooth muscle by at least two mechanisms. The $\alpha$ action is primarily on cell membranes and may be either hyperpolarizing or depolarizing, and the $\beta$ action is primarily intracellular and may involve an increasing of cAMP as one step. The $\beta$ receptor may be adenyl cyclase, but the $\alpha$ receptor is unknown. The end effect of each action may be either relaxation or contraction. One unifying hypothesis is that $\beta$ action enhances intracellular binding of Ca and that $\alpha$ action increases release of membrane Ca which affects permeabilities to other ions and a Ca pump (43). This is probably an oversimplification and the diversity of effects of catecholamines emphasizes the variation and lability in ionic control in smooth muscle.

Serotonin (5HT) has been suggested as an excitatory transmitter in smooth muscle. In guinea pig stomach, 5HT increases resting tension of longitudinal strips and decreases that of circular strips; the action is not mediated by nerves (231). In taenia and caecum, 5HT causes contraction, an action converted to relaxation by TTX, hexamethonium, and hyoscine; thus the action of 5HT is via neural elements. Since relaxation due to NE is not affected by TTX, it is acting on muscle; NE can also block liberation of ACh by field stimulation, an effect on neurons (81). A noncholinergic excitor of intestinal muscle detected by transmural stimulation could be 5HT (84), and it has been suggested as a possible transmitter to cholinergic excitor neurons of the myenteric plexus (42). The cellular function of the 5HT, which is present in considerable amounts, remains undetermined.

There is much evidence for nonadrenergic inhibitory neurons in gastrointestinal tract and probably similar neurons occur in bladder, lung, and elsewhere. Evidence that the transmitter may be ATP has been summarized and the neurons characterized as purinergic (50). ATP decreases contractions induced by ACh in frog stomach and guinea pig taenia, and reduced spiking parallels the reduction in tension (175). Action of vagal inhibitory fibers is not blocked by atropine or by guanethidine, and thus it could be via ATP (86). In guinea pig taenia coli, ATP at $10^{-6}$–$10^{-7}M$ reduces spontaneity and relaxes; low $Cl_o$, which diminishes CA inhibition, does not alter inhibition by ATP. The inhibitory junction potentials resulting from transmural stimulation, and probably those from ATP, are due to increase in $G_K$ (210). In rabbit colon more than 90% of fibers show ipsp's when intrinsic nerves are stimulated and these are not altered by guanethidine; a few cells show epsp's which are blocked by hyoscine (83).

Many visceral smooth muscles show postinhibitory rebound or excitation on cessation of inhibition. These secondary contractions are not affected by TTX and are apparently myogenic (85). In other intestinal preparations, atropine decreases contractile response to transmural stimulation, an effect removed by TTX. This is interpreted as due to cholinergic activation of nonadrenergic inhibitors (229). The mechanisms of action of hormones and of other agents such as prostaglandins are beyond the scope of this review.

## MECHANICS AND CONTRACTILE PROPERTIES

Most studies on the mechanical properties of smooth muscles have employed tension-length and force-velocity measurements, i.e. the kinds of measurements commonly used with striated muscles. Little attention has been given to the unique properties of smooth muscles: how tension is developed, how tension is transmitted throughout a short-fibered system, the differences between phasic and tonic contractions, stimulation by stretch, contraction without depolarization. Equivalent mechanical models for sheets of smooth muscle are lacking.

One unique property of most unitary smooth muscles is activation by stretch. Stretch at a critical velocity depolarizes and initiates repetitive spikes, e.g. in taenia, portal vein, and intestinal longitudinal muscle. Slow stretch may not initiate spikes, i.e. the membrane accommodates (8). Thus some smooth muscle membranes behave as mechanoreceptors; why multiunit muscles are not activated by stretch while most unitary ones are is not known. Many mammalian visceral muscles are activated by cooling.

When a strip of smooth muscle is stretched, the fibers lengthen and become thinner but do not slide past one another. In taenia, single fibers may become 30% longer when stretched. On stretching, the dense bodies consolidate with filaments and become concentrated in the center of fibers as if interconnected in a network (73).

Rapid cooling of guinea pig stomach from 32 to 10°C induces depolarization and increase in $R_m$; cooling of taenia depolarizes with initial decrease in $R_m$ followed by a prolonged increase in $R_m$. Contracture, which may begin before the depolarization, is not altered by induced hyperpolarization and the tension is not proportional to the depolarization. Hence cold induced contracture is unlike that in high K and may be caused by release of bound $Ca^{2+}$ (156).

Tension-length curves and force-velocity curves resemble those of striated muscle, hence a sheet of contractile cells behaves mechanically like a bundle of long fibers. Active tension curves for smooth muscles rise at shorter lengths than for striated muscles. The force-velocity relation obeys Hill's equation with $b$ values, in lengths per second of 0.03 for taenia, 0.073 for uterus (188), and 0.06 for trachealis muscle (202). The rate of tension development for muscle such as taenia ($dP/dt$) increases linearly with tension ($P$) and for a given load increases to a maximum as log $Ca_o$ increases (104). Isotonic contraction is slow: $V_{max}$ in lengths per second is 0.03 for rabbit taenia and 0.3 for guinea pig taenia, as compared with 1.3 for frog sartorius (191). Work curves for smooth muscles go through a maximum at a given load as with striated muscles (8).

In portal vein the force developed is proportional to Ca concentration but velocity of shortening is independent of Ca level (109). In portal vein, $V_{max}$ is less in a K contracture than in a phasic contraction (by action potentials), i.e. velocity varies according to mode of activation.

A surprising property of many unitary smooth muscles is the capacity to contract in response to chemical stimulation after depolarization in high K concentrations. Intestinal muscles in depolarizing concentrations of KCl contract in response to ACh. K-depolarized taenia contracts in response to carbachol and the contractile tension is proportional to Ca influx. Similarly E and NE can cause contraction of stomach without action potentials or depolarization. Catecholamines can relax K-depolarized intestinal muscles by a $\beta$ action (122). Limited contractions can occur in response to these agents in Ca-free medium, presumably by release of internally bound Ca (8). Toad bladder contracts in response to cooling, even after depolarization by K (187). NE causes contraction of dogfish spiral valve retractor without initiating spikes, but not in Ca-free or depolarized muscle (172). Tonic K-induced contractions conform to a graded depolarization; they occur without spikes in pulmonary artery. In mesenteric vein, K induces spike-like potentials and fast contractions (199). In summary, pharmacomechanical coupling can occur without spikes, sometimes by triggering Ca release and sometimes by increasing Ca influx.

Smooth muscles show some unusual mechanical properties following contraction or stretch. When taenia is subjected to repeated sinusoidal stretches, it shows resonance; tension follows extension with maxima at 35–55/min and 0.5–3/min; hence mechanical coupling occurs between the fibers (95). When aortic smooth muscle is stretched, it shows an instantaneous elongation followed by slower elongation or creep (230). Passive tension-length curves of ureter show a hysteresis, tension being less for a given length on shortening than on lengthening, i.e. it is stiffer initially. The circumferential tension is also greater than the longitudinal tension

(224). Helical strips of portal vein show a similar hysteresis in passive tension-length curves (2). Cat circular intestinal muscle shows a regular increase in tension during repeated sinusoidal stretches, but after a contraction and relaxation the stretch reveals enhanced stiffness, an effect which may persist for more than one minute and which depends on prior contraction, not merely shortening (162).

Much evidence indicates a close relation between Ca and contractile coupling. The relative importance of extracellular, membrane bound, and intracellular Ca varies according to the muscle. Since fiber diameters are small, T-tubules are absent, and the spike involves an influx of Ca, there is a more direct relation between action potential and contraction than in skeletal muscle. In myometrium, both the contraction in response to stretch and spontaneous contractions are abolished in Ca-free solution, and are blocked by Mn (170). In strips of frog stomach the contractile force decreases during a period of bathing in Ca-free Ringer, but some intracellular stores appear to be present (35). The contraction of guinea pig ileal longitudinal muscle in response to carbachol is maximal at 2.5 m$M$ Ca and decreases at both higher and lower Ca concentrations (49). In rabbit taenia at 22°C the response to electrical stimulation increases sigmoidally as a function of log Ca$_o$ up to 8 m$M$ (191).

After portal vein is depleted of Ca, the isometric tension is proportional to [Ca]$^2$ in the bathing medium; hence force is regulated by the binding of 2 Ca ions per receptor molecule (109). Depolarization by K$_o$ causes contraction which is dependent on Ca in the presence of Na (19). Mesenteric artery gives fast and slow contractions in response to K depolarization; the fast response persists longer at low Ca concentrations, and high calcium initiates contractions in a Na-free but not in normal Na medium, hence the two calcium sources are differently affected by Na (193). In cat circular intestinal muscle, action potentials trigger contractions for which Sr cannot substitute for Ca, whereas for large contractions due to field stimulation, Sr can replace Ca, i.e. Sr cannot replace Ca in membrane-induced contractions (201).

Muscle of sheep carotid arteries responds to NE in a Ca-free solution by contracting with slight depolarization; in a Ca-free medium plus EDTA, NE elicits some contraction and this response declines rapidly after 36 min, apparently as the limited Ca stores are depleted. It is calculated that after 30 min in such a Ca-free medium, Ca remaining in the center of the preparation is equivalent to a concentration of 0.049 m$M$. The threshold for contraction is 0.005 m$M$ extracellular Ca and therefore most of the Ca used in contraction is extracellular or in exchangeable stores. Small residual stores remain, however, and these can be activated by NE without depolarization (131). Angiotensin causes release of $Ca^{2+}$ from microsomes of rabbit aortae (16).

It appears that all smooth muscles require Ca for contraction; the different requirements for Ca in various muscles reflect differences in stores. Ca may enter during the action potential, it may be released from cell membrane, or it may be released from internal stores.

Further evidence regarding the participation of Ca in contraction comes from measurements of Ca influx and from the effects of agents which block contraction. In taenia the Ca content increases in tonic contraction. In aortic smooth muscle K stimulates Ca influx and La blocks this influx. Lanthanum also blocks contractions produced by adding Ca to a Ca-free medium. Epinephrine causes contraction by releasing Ca from intracellular stores and La blocks replenishment of these stores from membrane Ca (216). In longitudinal muscle of ileum, La reduces muscle tone and contractions due to ACh and K (223). The contractions of arterial smooth muscle due to NE are reduced by cinnarizine, an effect antagonized by Ca (94).

In several muscles the compound verapamil (isoveratril) blocks contractions in response to high K, but not those due to NE (174); it blocks Ca induced contractions (107a). Papavarine blocks contractions at the level of intracellular coupling (Ca liberation) and is effective on contractions elicited by a variety of means. Norepinephrine can cause contraction of arterial smooth muscle without depolarization, an action blocked by α-blockers, by decreased pH, and by cooling; thus it acts to liberate calcium beyond the cell membrane. Contractions due to depolarization, as by K or by spontaneous action potentials, are blocked by verapamil and Ca-free medium because these reduce Ca influx (105, 174). In uterus, verapamil blocks contractions resulting from depolarization by K, ACh, electrical stimuli, and oxytocin; its action is antagonized by Ca (106). Lanthanum reduces contractions in response to K more effectively than those induced by ACh (103).

When ileum is treated with high Ca (36 m$M$) and then transferred to zero Ca medium, a tonic contraction occurs; this is apparently a result of release of Ca from internal stores on removal of the surface Ca. The internal stores can be depleted by bathing in La saline (118).

Relaxation requires the sequestering of Ca, as in striated muscle. Microsomes from the rough ER of myometrium (69) or aorta (3, 17) take up Ca ions. Bound microsomal Ca can be displaced by other divalent cations. Microsomal particulates from cell membranes of guinea pig ileum bind Ca in the presence of Mg and ATP (117). Both mitochondria and microsomes from rat myometrium bind Ca in the presence of ATP; microsomes can bind from a Ca concentration of $6 \times 10^{-7}$ $M$ and the total amount bound can account for relaxation (15). It is concluded that Ca sequestering is correlated with membrane or intracellular storage sites of varying amounts in different smooth muscles.

A method commonly used to block contractions while leaving relatively normal electrical activity is to treat smooth muscle with physiological saline made 50% hypertonic by addition of sucrose. There is some shrinkage of cells, disruption of nexuses, membrane hyperpolarization, and disruption of the calcium coupling to contractile elements, but microelectrodes can remain inside the cells long enough to permit measurements of ionic effects (8, 36). Many of the results reported above on action potentials were obtained in hypertonic solutions.

Muscle fibers of portal vein in hyperosmotic solution shrink and decrease their contractions but show apparently normal spikes; in hypo-osmotic solution, leakage causes them to swell less than predicted and they show increase in $P_{Na}/P_K$ and in spontaneity (127, 128). In a given hypo-osmotic solution, the intracellular water increased by 14% in stretched and 35% in unstretched portal vein fibers; swelling was less in low $Na_o$ than in normal Krebs (129).

The osmotic behavior of smooth muscle depends on a variety of conditions, and the use of hypertonic solutions to diminish muscle movement during recording by microelectrodes must be viewed with caution.

## GENERAL SUMMARY

Emphasis in research has been on similarities of smooth muscle to striated muscle rather than on differences. Smooth muscles are very diverse in their properties. Some of the features shown most strikingly by smooth muscles and least well understood are the following:

Membrane vesicles or caveolae; nexuses.

Lability of thick filaments in fixation.

Dense bodies; intermediate size filaments.

Ion fluxes variable with concentrations; high resting $P_{Na}/P_K$.

Ion fluxes not corresponding to identifiable compartments.

Active electrogenic Na-K pump at cell membrane.

Intercellular electrical conduction; low resistance connections.

Several kinds of active electrical events in one cell.

Spikes more dependent on Ca than on Na.

Several types of spontaneous slow potential changes.

Multiple actions of neurotransmitters, especially catecholamines.

Complex modulation of activity by hormones and other agents.

Stimulation by rapid stretch.

Activation of contraction without membrane depolarization.

Tension development without apparent filament attachments.

Anomolous mechanical behavior; intercellular mechanical transmission.

*Literature Cited*

1. Abe, Y. 1971. Hormonal control and effects of drugs and ions on uterus. *Smooth Muscle,* ed. E. Bülbring, A. F. Brading, A. W. Jones, T. Tomita, 396–417. London: Arnold. 676 pp.
2. Alexander, R. S. 1969. Action of acid on the plasticity of venous smooth muscle. *Microvasc. Res.* 1:317–28
3. Allen, J. C., Daniel, E. E. 1970. Adenosinetriphosphatase activities of rat myometrial tissue. *Arch. Int. Pharmacodyn. Ther.* 188:213–25
4. Anderson, N. C. 1969. Voltage-clamp studies on uterine smooth muscle. *J. Gen. Physiol.* 54:145–65
5. Anderson, N. C., Ramon, P., Snyder, A. 1971. Voltage clamp of uterine smooth muscle. *J. Gen. Physiol.* 58: 322–39
6. Andersson, R. 1972. Role of cyclic AMP and calcium in metabolic and relaxing effects of catecholamines in intestinal smooth muscle. *Acta Physiol. Scand.* 85:312–22
7. Andersson, R., Mohme-Lundholm, E. 1970. Metabolic actions in intestinal smooth muscle associated with relaxation mediated by adrenergic α- and β-receptors. *Acta Physiol. Scand.* 79: 244–61
8. Axelsson, J. 1971. Mechanical properties of smooth muscle, and the relationship between mechanical and electrical activity. See Ref. 1, 289–315
9. Axelsson, J., Holmberg, B. 1971. The effects of K⁺-free solution on tension development in the smooth muscle of taenia coli from the guinea pig. *Acta Physiol. Scand.* 82:322–32
10. Bagby, R., Fisher, B. 1973. Graded contractions in muscle strips and single cells from *Bufo marinus* stomach. *Am. J. Physiol.* 225:105–9

11. Bailey, D. M. 1971. Inhibitory and excitatory effects of sympathomimetic amines on muscle strips from stomach of guinea pig. *Brit. J. Pharmacol.* 41: 227–38

12. Banerjee, A. K. 1972. Drug effects on K$^{42}$ fluxes in guinea pig ileum *in vitro. Arch. Int. Pharmacodyn. Ther.* 198:173–86

13. Bass, P. 1971. Relation of electrical activity to contraction. *Gastrointestinal Motility,* ed. L. Demling, R. Ottenjang, 59–71. Rieme: Stuttgart

14. Bass, P., Weisbrodt, N. W. 1971. Current concepts in pharmacology of gastrointestinal motility. See Ref. 13, 149–67

15. Batra, S. C., Daniel, E. E. 1971. ATP-dependent Ca uptake by subcellular fractions of uterine smooth muscle. *Comp. Biochem. Physiol.* 38:369–85

16. Baudouin, M., Meyer, P., Fermandijian, S., Morgat, J. L. 1972. Calcium release induced by interaction of angiotensin with its receptors in smooth muscle cell microsomes. *Nature* 235: 336–38

17. Baudouin-Legros, M., Meyer, P. 1973. Effects of angiotensin, catecholamines and cyclic AMP on Ca storage in aortic microsomes. *Brit. J. Pharmacol.* 47:377–85

18. Baumgarten, H. G., Holstein, A. F., Owman, C. 1970. Auerbach's plexus of mammals and man: electron microscopic identification of three different types of neuronal processes in myenteric ganglia of large intestine from rhesus monkeys, guinea pigs and man. *Z. Zellforsch.* 106:376–97

19. Beamino, G., Johansson, B. 1970. Effects of calcium on contracture tension in the smooth muscle of the rat portal vein. *Pfluegers Arch.* 321: 143–58

20. Beck, C. S., Osa, T. 1971. Membrane activity of the guinea pig gastric sling muscle—a nerve dependent phenomenon. *Am. J. Physiol.* 220:1397–403

21. Bennett, M. R. 1967. Effect of cations on electrical properties of smooth muscle cells of guinea pig vas deferens. *J. Physiol. London* 190:465–79

22. Bennett, M. R. 1972. *Autonomic Neuromuscular Transmission.* Cambridge: Cambridge Univ. Press. 274 pp.

23. Bennett, M. R. 1973. Storage and release of noradrenaline. *J. Physiol. London* 229:515–31

24. Bennett, T. 1969. The effects of hyoscine and anticholinesterases on cholinergic transmission to the smooth muscle cells of the avian gizzard. *Brit. J. Pharmacol.* 37:585–94

25. Bennett, T. 1969. Nerve-mediated excitation and inhibition of the smooth muscle cells of the avian gizzard. *J. Physiol. London* 204:669–86

26. Bennett, T. 1970. Interaction of nerve-mediated excitation and inhibition of single smooth muscle cells of the avian gizzard. *Comp. Biochem. Physiol.* 32: 669–80

27. Bolton, T. B. 1971. Oscillations of membrane potential (slow waves) produced by acetylcholine or carbachol in intestinal smooth muscle. *J. Physiol. London* 216:403–18

28. Bolton, T. B. 1972. Depolarizing action of acetylcholine or carbachol in intestinal smooth muscle. *J. Physiol. London* 220:647–71

29. Bolton, T. B. 1972. Effects of varying the concentrations of ions in the external solution on the oscillations of the membrane potential produced by carbachol in longitudinal ileal muscle. *Pfleugers Arch.* 335:85–96

30. Bolton, T. B. 1973. Effects of electrogenic sodium pumping on membrane potential of the longitudinal smooth muscle from terminal ileum of guinea pig. *J. Physiol. London* 228:693–712

31. Bolton, T. B. 1973. The role of electrogenic sodium pumping in the response of smooth muscle to acetylcholine. *J. Physiol. London* 228:713–31

32. Bortoff, A. 1972. Digestion: Motility. *Ann. Rev. Physiol.* 34:261–90

33. Bortoff, A., Sachs, F. 1970. Electrotonic spread of slow waves in circular muscle of small intestine. *Am. J. Physiol.* 218:576–81

34. Bose, D., Innes, I. R. 1972. Influence of Na pumping on smooth muscle contraction. *Brit. J. Pharmacol.* 45: 689–90

35. Bozler, E. 1969. Role of calcium in initation of activity of smooth muscle. *Am. J. Physiol.* 616:271–74

36. Brading, A. F. 1971. Osmotic phenomena in smooth muscle. See Ref. 1, 166–96

37. Brading, A. F. 1971. Analysis of the effluxes of Na, K and Cl ions from smooth muscle in normal and hypertonic solutions. *J. Physiol. London* 214:393–416

38. Brading, A. F. 1973. The role of calcium in cellular function. Ion distribution and ion movements in smooth muscle. *Phil. Trans. Roy. Soc. B* 265: 35–46

39. Brading, A. F., Bülbring, E., Tomita, T. 1969. The effect of temperature on

membrane conductance of the smooth muscle of the guinea pig. *J. Physiol. London* 200:621–35

40. Brading, A. F., Bülbring, E., Tomita, T. 1969. The effect of sodium and calcium on the action potential of the smooth muscle of the guinea-pig taenia coli. *J. Physiol. London* 200:637–54

41. Bülbring, E., Brading, A., Jones, A. W., Tomita, T., Eds. 1971. *Smooth Muscle.* London: Arnold. 676 pp.

42. Bülbring, E., Gershon, M. D. 1967. 5-Hydroxytryptamine participation in vagal inhibitory innervation of stomach. *J. Physiol. London* 192:823–46

43. Bülbring, E., Kuriyama, H. 1973. The action of catecholamines on guinea-pig taenia coli. *Phil. Trans. Roy. Soc. B* 265:115–21

44. Bülbring, E., Needham, D. M. 1973. A discussion on recent developments in vertebrate smooth muscle physiology. *Phil. Trans. Roy. Soc. B* 265:1–231

45. Bülbring, E., Tomita, T. 1969. Increase of membrane conductance by adrenaline in the smooth muscle of guinea-pig taenia coli. *Proc. Roy. Soc. B* 172:89–102

46. Bülbring, E., Tomita, T. 1969. Suppression of spontaneous spike generation by catecholamines in smooth muscle of guinea-pig taenia coli. *Proc. Roy. Soc. B* 172:103–19

47. Bülbring, E., Tomita, T. 1969. Effect of Ca, Ba and Mn on the action of adrenaline in smooth muscle of guinea-pig taenia coli. *Proc. Roy. Soc. B* 172:121–36

48. Bülbring, E., Tomita, T. 1970. Effects of Ca removal on the smooth muscle of the guinea-pig taenia coli. *J. Physiol. London* 210:217–32

49. Burgen, A. S. V., Spero, L. 1970. Effects of calcium and magnesium on the response of intestinal smooth muscle to drugs. *Brit. J. Pharmacol.* 40:492–500

50. Burnstock, G. 1972. Purinergic nerves. *Pharmacol. Rev.* 24:509–81

51. Burnstock, G., Campbell, G., Satchell, D., Smythe, A. 1970. Evidence that ATP or a related nucleotide is the transmitter substance released by nonadrenergic inhibitory nerves in the gut. *Brit. J. Pharmacol. Chemother.* 40:668–88

52. Burton, J., Godfraind, T. 1972. The action of ouabain upon smooth muscle cell during restoration. *Arch. Int. Pharmacol. Ther. Suppl.* 196:95–98

53. Campbell, G. R. 1971. Autonomic nervous supply to effector tissues. See Ref. 1, 451–95

54. Campbell, G. R., Uehara, Y., Mark, G., Burnstock, G. 1971. Fine structure of smooth muscle cells grown in tissue culture. *J. Cell Biol.* 49:21–34

55. Carpenter, F. G. 1970. Antagonism of smooth muscle contractility by catecholamines. *Am. J. Physiol.* 219:1539–43

56. Carsten, M. 1969. Role of Ca binding by sarcoplasmic reticulum in the contraction and relaxation of uterine smooth muscle. *J. Gen. Physiol.* 53:414–26

57. Casteels, R. 1966. Action of ouabain on smooth muscle cells of guinea-pig's taenia coli. *J. Physiol. London* 184:131–42

58. Casteels, R. 1969. Ion content and ion fluxes in the smooth muscle cells of the longitudinal layers of the guinea pig's vas deferens. *Pfluegers Arch.* 313:95–105

59. Casteels, R. 1971. The distribution of chloride ions in smooth muscle cells of the guinea pig's taenia coli. *J. Physiol. London* 214:225–43

60. Casteels, R., Droogmans, G., Hendrickx, H. 1971. Membrane potentials of smooth muscle cells in K-free solution. *J. Physiol. London* 217:281–95

61. Casteels, R., Droogmans, G., Hendrickx, H. 1971. Electrogenic Na pump in smooth muscle cells of the guinea pig's taenia coli. *J. Physiol. London* 217:297–313

62. Casteels, R., Droogmans, G., Hendrickx, H. 1972. Membrane potential of K-depleted smooth muscle cells of the guinea pig's taenia coli in solutions containing Li or choline. *J. Physiol. London* 224:61P–62P

63. Casteels, R., Droogmans, G., Hendrickx, H. 1973. Effect of Na and Na substitutes on the active ion transport and on the membrane potential of smooth muscle cells. *J. Physiol. London* 228:733–48

64. Casteels, R., Droogmans, G., Hendrickx, H. 1973. Active ion transport and resting potentials in smooth muscle cells. *Phil. Trans. Roy. Soc. London B* 265:47–56

65. Casteels, R., Kuriyama, H. 1966. Membrane potentials and ion content in smooth muscle of guinea pig's taenia coli at different external potassium concentrations. *J. Physiol. London* 184:120–30

66. Casteels, R. et al 1973. A study of factors affecting the cellular calcium content of smooth muscle cells. *Arch. Int. Pharmacodyn. Ther.* 201:191–92

67. Casteels, R., van Breemen, C., Mayer, C. J. 1972. A study of the calcium distribution in smooth muscle cells of the guinea-pig taenia coli using La³⁺. *Arch. Int. Pharmacodyn. Ther.* 199:193–94

68. Christensen, J. 1970. Responses of the smooth muscle segment of the opossum esophagus to distension and electrical stimulation, and their modification by antagonists. See Ref. 13, 167–74

69. Christensen, J., Caprilli, R., Lund, G. F. 1969. Electric slow waves from the colon of cat. *Am. J. Physiol.* 217:771–76

70. Christensen, J., Hauser, R. L. 1971. Longitudinal axial coupling of slow waves in proximal cat colon. *Am. J. Physiol.* 221:246–50

71. Christensen, J., Hauser, R. L. 1971. Circumferential coupling of electric slow waves in circular muscle of cat colon. *Am. J. Physiol.* 221:1033–37

72. Connor, C., Prosser, C. L. 1974. Comparison of longitudinal and circular intestinal muscle with respect to effects of K and Ca. *Am. J. Physiol.* In press

73. Cooke, P. H., Fay, F. S. 1972. Correlation between fiber length, ultrastructure, and the length-tension relationship of mammalian smooth muscle. *J. Cell Biol.* 52:105–16

74. Costa, M., Gabella, G. 1971. Adrenergic innervation of alimentary canal. *Z. Zellforsch.* 122:357–77

75. Creed, K. E. 1971. Membrane properties of the smooth muscle membrane of the guinea pig urinary bladder. *Pfluegers Arch.* 326:115–26

76. Creed, K. E., Kuriyama, H. 1971. Electrophysiological properties of smooth muscle cells of the biliary system of guinea pig. *Jap. J. Physiol.* 21:333–48

77. DeSy, W. 1970. Receptor responses in isolated smooth muscle of the urinary bladder. *Arch. Int. Pharmacol. Ther.* 186:188–89

78. Devine, C. E., Somlyo, A. P. 1971. Thick filaments in vascular smooth muscle. *J. Cell Biol.* 49:636–49

79. Devine, C. E., Somlyo, A. V., Somlyo, A. P. 1973. Sarcoplasmic reticulum and mitochondria as cation accumulation sites in smooth muscle. *Phil. Trans. Roy. Soc. B* 265:17–23

80. Dewey, M. M., Barr, L. 1964. A study of the structure and distribution of the nexus. *J. Cell Biol.* 23:553–85

81. Drakontides, A. B., Gershon, M. D. 1972. Studies on the interaction of

82. Duke, G. E., Djuk, H. E., Evanson, O. A. 1972. Gastric pressure and smooth muscle electrical potential changes in turkeys. *Am. J. Physiol.* 222:167–73

83. Furness, J. B. 1969. An electrophysiological study of the innervation of the smooth muscle of the colon. *J. Physiol. London* 205:549–62

84. Furness, J. B. 1970. The excitatory input to a single smooth muscle cell. *Pfluegers Arch.* 314:1–13

85. Furness, J. B. 1971. Secondary excitation of intestinal smooth muscle. *Brit. J. Pharmacol.* 41:213–26

86. Furness, J. B., Costa, M. 1973. Nonadrenergic inhibitory neurons to the intestine. *Phil. Trans. Roy. Soc. B* 265:123–33

87. Gabella, G. 1972. Intercellular junctions between circular and longitudinal intestinal muscle layers. *Z. Zellforsch.* 125:191–99

88. Gabella, G. 1972. Cellular structures of smooth muscle junctions. *Phil. Trans. Roy. Soc. B* 265:7–16

89. Garamvölgyi, N., Vizi, E. S., Knoll, J. 1971. Regular occurrence of thick filaments in stretched mammalian smooth muscle. *J. Ultrastruct. Res.* 34:135–43

90. Geffen, L. B., Hughes, C. H. 1972. Degeneraion of sympathetic nerves *in vitro* and development of smooth muscle supersensitivity to noradrenaline. *J. Physiol. London* 221:71–84

91. Gillespie, J. S. 1972. The rat anococcygeus muscle and its response to nerve stimulation and to some drugs. *Brit. J. Pharmacol.* 45:404–16

92. Gillespie, J. S., Creed, K. E., Muir, T. C. 1973. The mechanisms of action of neurotransmitters. *Phil. Trans. Roy Soc. B* 265:95–106

93. Gillespie, J. S., Maxwell, J. D. 1971. Adrenergic innervation of smooth muscle of the rat intestine. *J. Histochem. Cytochem.* 19:676–81

94. Godfraind, T., Kaba, A., Van Dorsser, W. 1972. The action of cinnarizine on the contraction induced by calcium in depolarized arterial and intestinal smooth muscle preparations. *Arch. Int. Pharmacodyn. Ther.* 197:399–400

95. Golenhofen, K. 1965. Rhythmische Dehnung der glatten Muskulatur vom Blinddarm des Meerschweinchens. *Pfluegers Arch.* 284:327–46

96. Golenhofen, K. 1971. Intrinsic rhythms of gastrointestinal tract. See Ref. 13, 71–79

97. Golenhofen, K. 1971. Slow rhythms in smooth muscle (minute rhythm). See Ref. 1, 316–42

98. Golenhofen, K., von Loh, D. 1970. Elektrophysiologische Untersuchungen zur normalen Spontanaktivität der isolierten Taenia coli des Meerschweinchens. *Pfluegers Arch.* 314: 312–28

99. Golenhofen, K., von Loh, D., Milenov, K. 1970. Spontaneous activity of isolated smooth muscle preparation from different regions of the guinea-pig stomach. *Pfluegers Arch.* 315: 336–56

100. Goodford, P. J. 1966. An interaction between K and Na in the smooth muscle of the guinea-pig taenia coli. *J. Physiol. London* 186:11–26

101. Goodford, P., Wolowyk, M. W. 1971. Counter-cation interaction at the smooth muscle cell membrane of guinea pig taenia coli. *J. Physiol. London* 218:36P–37P

102. Goodford, P. J., Wolowyk, M. W. 1972. Localization of cation interactions in the smooth muscle of the guinea pig taenia coli. *J. Physiol. London* 224:521–35

103. Goodman, F. R., Weiss, G. B. 1971. Dissociation by lanthanum of smooth muscle responses to potassium and acetylcholine. *Am. J. Physiol.* 220: 759–66

104. Gordon, A. R., Siegman, M. J. 1971. Mechanical properties of smooth muscle. I. Length-tension and force-velocity relations. II. Active state. *Am. J. Physiol.* 221:1243–49, 1250–54

105. Griebel, L., Peiper, U., Wende, W., Glaser, B., Wasner, E. 1971. Activation of the vascular smooth muscle by noradrenaline, vasopressin or depolarization in the presence of graded blockade of the adrenergic alpha-receptors. *Naynyn-Schmiedebergs Arch. Pharmacol.* 220:248–61

106. Grun, G., Fleckenstein, A., Tritthart, H. 1969. Excitation-contraction uncoupling on the rat's uterus by some "musculotropic" smooth muscle relaxants. *Naynyn-Schmiedebergs Arch. Pharmacol.* 264:239–40

107. Gunn, M. 1972. Structure of smooth muscle of gut. *Acta Anat.* 82:473–96

107a. Haeusler, G. 1972. Differential effect of verapamil on excitation-contraction coupling in smooth muscle and on excitation-secretion coupling in adrenergic nerve terminals. *J. Pharmacol. Exp. Ther.* 180:672–82

108. Haljamae, H. et al 1970. The distribution of sodium, potassium and chloride in the smooth muscle of the rat portal vein. *Acta Physiol. Scand.* 78: 255–68

109. Hellstrand, P., Johansson, B., Ringberg, A. 1972. Influence of extracellular calcium on isometric force and velocity of shortening in depolarized venous smooth muscle. *Acta Physiol. Scand.* 84:528–37

110. Henderson, R. M., Duchon, G., Daniel, E. E. 1971. Cell contacts in duodenal smooth muscle layers. *Am. J. Physiol.* 221:564–74

111. Heumann, H. G. 1971. Mechanism of smooth muscle contraction: An electron microscope study of the mouse large intestine. *Cytobiology* 3: 259–81

112. Heumann, H. G. 1971. Thick filaments in freeze-etched smooth muscle. *Z. Zellforsch.* 122:139–44

113. Hidaka, T., Kuriyama, H. 1969. Responses of the smooth muscle membrane of guinea pig jejunum elicited by field stimulation. *J. Gen. Physiol.* 53:471–86

114. Hodgson, B. J., Daniel, E. E. 1972. Effects of excitatory drugs on K fluxes in uterine smooth muscle. *Can. J. Physiol. Pharmacol.* 50:725–30

115. Holman, M. E. 1970. Junction potentials in smooth muscle. See Ref. 1, 244–88

116. Horn, L., Kumamoto, M. 1970. Effects of 2,4-dinitrophenol on the electrical and mechanical activity of vascular smooth muscle. *Microvasc. Res.* 2: 182–87

117. Hurwitz, L., Fitzpatrick, D. F., Debbas, G., Landon, E. J. 1973. Localization of calcium pump activity in smooth muscle. *Science* 179:384–86

118. Hurwitz, L., Joiner, P. D. 1970. Mobilization of cellular calcium for contraction in intestinal smooth muscle. *Am. J. Physiol.* 218:12–19

119. Ito, Y., Kuriyama, H. 1971. Membrane properties of smooth muscle fibers of guinea pig portal vein. *J. Physiol. London* 214:427–41

120. Ito, Y., Kuriyama, H., Sakamoto, Y. 1970. Effects of tetraethylammoniun chloride on the membrane activity of guinea-pig stomach smooth muscle. *J. Physiol. London* 211:445–60

121. Jacobowitz, D. 1965. Histochemical studies of autonomic innervation of the gut. *J. Pharmacol. Exp. Ther.* 149:358–64

122. Jenkinson, G. H., Morton, I. K. M. 1967. The role of alpha and beta adrenergic receptors in some actions of catecholamines on intestinal smooth

muscle. *J. Physiol. London* 188:387–402

123. Job, D. D. 1969. Ionic basis of intestinal electrical activity. *Am. J. Physiol.* 217:1534–41

124. Job, D. D. 1971. Effects of antibiotics and selective inhibitors of ATP on intestinal slow waves. *Am. J. Physiol.* 220:299–306

125. Johnson, E. A., Lieberman, M. 1971. Heart: Excitation and Contraction. *Ann. Rev. Physiol.* 33:479–532

126. Jones, A. W., Somlyo, A. P., Somlyo, A. V. 1973. Potassium accumulation in smooth muscle and associated ultrastructural changes. *J. Physiol. London* 32:247–73

127. Jonsson, O. 1969. Changes in the activity of isolated vascular smooth muscle in response to reduced osmolarity. *Acta Physiol. Scand.* 77:191–200

128. Jonsson, O. 1970. Extracellular osmolality and vascular smooth muscle activity. *Acta Physiol. Scand. Suppl.* 359:5–48

129. Jonsson, O. 1971. Effects of variations in the extracellular osmolality of the ionic permeability of vascular smooth muscle. *Acta Physiol. Scand.* 81:405–21

130. Katase, K., Tomita, T. 1972. Influence of Na and Ca on the recovery process from K contracture in the guinea pig taenia coli. *J. Physiol. London* 224:489–500

131. Keatinge, W. R. 1972. Mechanical response with reversed electrical response to noradrenaline by Ca-deprived arterial smooth muscle. *J. Physiol. London* 224:21–34

132. Kelly, K. A., LaForce, R. C. 1972. Pacing the canine stomach with electrical stimulation. *Am. J. Physiol.* 222:588–94

133. Kelly, R. E., Rice, R. V. 1969. Ultrastructural studies on the contractile mechanism of smooth muscle. *J. Cell Biol.* 42:683–94

134. Kobayashi, M. 1969. Effects of calcium on the electrical activity in smooth muscle cells of cat ureter. *Am. J. Physiol.* 216:1279–85

135. Kobayashi, M. 1971. Relationship between membrane potential and spike configuration recorded by sucrose gap method in ureter smooth muscle. *Comp. Biochem. Physiol.* 38A:301–8

136. Kobayashi, M., Prosser, C. L., Nagai, T. 1967. Electrical properties of intestinal muscle as measured intracellularly and extracellularly. *Am. J. Physiol.* 213:275–86

137. Kristensen, B. I., Nielsen, L. E. 1971. Two-filament system and interaction of heavy meromyosin with thin filaments in smooth muscle. *Z. Zellforsch.* 122:350–56

138. Kumamoto, M., Horn, L. 1970. Voltage clamping of smooth muscle from taenia coli. *Microvasc. Res.* 2:188–201

139. Kurihara, S., Creed. K. E. 1972. Changes in the membrane potential of the smooth muscle cells of the guinea pig urinary bladder in various environments. *Jap. J. Physiol.* 22:667–83

140. Kuriyama, H. 1963. Influence of potassium, sodium and chloride on membrane potential of smooth muscle of taenia coli. *J. Physiol. London* 166:15–28

141. Kuriyama, H. 1971. Effects of ions and drugs on smooth muscle. See Ref. 1, 366–95

142. Kuriyama, H., Mekata, F. 1971. Biophysical properties of the longitudinal smooth muscles of the guinea-pig rectum. *J. Physiol. London* 212:667–83

143. Kuriyama, H., Ohshima, K., Sakamoto, K. 1971. The membrane properties of the smooth muscle of the guinea-pig portal vein in isotonic and hypertonic solutions. *J. Physiol. London* 217:179–99

144. Kuriyama, H., Osa, T., Toida, N. 1967. Electrophysiological study of the intestinal smooth muscle of the guinea-pig. *J. Physiol. London* 191:239–55

145. Kuriyama, H., Osa, T., Toida, N. 1967. Nervous factors influencing the membrane activity of intestinal smooth muscle. *J. Physiol. London* 191:257–70

146. Kuriyama, H., Tomita, T. 1965. Responses of single smooth muscle cells of guinea pig taenia coli to intracellularly applied currents, and their effect on spontaneous electrical activity. *J. Physiol. London* 178:270–89

147. Kuriyama, H., Tomita, T. 1970. Action potential in smooth muscle of guinea pig taenia coli and ureter studied by double sucrose-gap method. *J. Gen. Physiol.* 55:147–62

148. Lammel, E., Golenhofen, K. 1971. Erregbarkeit und Ca-Austausch intestinaler glatter Muskulatur (taenia coli des Meerschweinschens) unterhalb der kritischen Temperatur für die Spontanaktivität. *Pfluegers Arch.* 329:258–68

149. Lammel, E., Golenhofen, K. 1971. Messungen der $^{45}$ Ca-Aufnahme an intestinaler glatter Muskulatur. Zur Hypothese eines von Ca-Ionen getra-

genen Aktionsstromes. *Pfluegers Arch.* 329:269–82

150. Lane, B. P. 1967. Localization of products of ATP hydrolysis in mammalian smooth muscle cells. *J. Cell Biol.* 34:713–20

151. Lipshutz, W., Cohen, S. 1972. Action of gastrin I and secretin on gastrointestinal circular muscle. *Am. J. Physiol.* 222:775–81

152. Liu, J., Prosser, C. L., Job. D. D. 1969. Ionic requirements of slow waves and spikes. *Am. J. Physiol.* 217:1542–47

153. Ljung, B. 1969. Local transmitter concentrations in vascular smooth muscle during vasoconstrictor nerve activity. *Acta Physiol. Scand.* 77:212–23

154. Lowy, J., Vibert, P. J., Haselgrove, J. C., Poulsen, F. R. 1973. The structure of myosin elements in vertebrate smooth muscles. *Phil. Trans. Roy. Soc. B* 265:191–96

155. Lullman, H., Siegfriedt, A. 1968. Uber den Calcium-Gehalt und den $^{45}$Ca Austausch im Langsmuskulatur des Meerschweindunndarms. *Pfluegers Arch.* 300:108–19

156. Magaribuchi, T., Ito, Y., Kuriyama, H. 1973. Effects of rapid cooling on the mechanical and electrical activities of smooth muscles of guinea-pig stomach and taenia coli. *J. Gen. Physiol.* 61:323–41

157. Magaribuchi, T. et al 1972. Electrical properties of the slow potential changes recorded from the guinea pig stomach in relation to drug actions. *Jap. J. Physiol.* 22:333–52

158. Marshall, J. M. 1965. Calcium and uterine smooth muscle membrane potentials. *Muscle,* ed. W. M. Paul, E. E. Daniel, C. M. Kay, G. Manckton, 229–38. New York: Pergamon

159. Marshall, J. M., Kroeger, E. A. 1973. Adrenergic influences on uterine smooth muscle of pregnant rat. *Phil. Trans. Roy. Soc. B* 265:135–48

160. Mayer, C. J., van Breemen, C., Casteels, R. 1972. The action of La and D600 (iso N Me N homoveratryl γaminopropyl-3,4,5 trimethophenylacetonitril) on Ca exchange in the smooth muscle of guinea pig taenia coli. *Pfluegers Arch.* 337:333–50

161. McKirdy, H. C. 1972. Relation of logitudinal and circular layers of rabbit colon. *J. Physiol. London* 227:839–54

162. Meiss, R. 1971. Some mechanical properties of cat intestinal muscle. *Am. J. Physiol.* 220:2000–7

163. Mills, R. G., Taylor, G. S. 1971. Studies of intestinal slow wave activity with

a double sucrose gap apparatus. *Life Sci.* 10:347–53

164. Mironneau, J., Lefant, J. 1972. Activité électrique du faisceau musculaire lisse de l'uterus. *J. Physiol. Paris* 64:97–105

165. Munson, J. L., Paton, D. M. 1972. Na-K pump in rabbit detrusor muscle. *Comp. Biochem. Physiol.* 43B:97–108

166. Nagai, T., Prosser, C. L. 1963. Electrical parameters of smooth muscle cells. *Am. J. Physiol.* 204:915–24

167. Nelsen, T. S., Kohatsu, S. 1968. Clinical electrogastrography. *Am. J. Surg.* 116:215–21

168. Ohashi, H. 1970. An estimate of the proportion of the resting membrane conductance of the smooth muscle of guinea-pig taenia coli attributable to chloride. *J. Physiol. London* 210:405–19

169. Ohashi, H. 1971. Relative contribution of K and Cl to the total increase of membrane conductance produced by adrenaline on the smooth muscle of guinea-pig taenia coli. *J. Physiol. London* 212:561–75

170. Orlov, R. S., Vasil'ev, A. J. 1972. Mechanism of formation of functional characteristics of the membrane of myometrium cells. *Dok. Akad. Nauk SSSR* 206:1482–84

171. Papasova, M., Nagai, T., Prosser, C. L. 1968. Two-component slow waves in smooth muscle of cat stomach. *Am. J. Physiol.* 214:695–702

172. Parnas, I., Prosser, C. L., Rice, R. V. Electrical responses and fiber structure in a tonic smooth muscle of dogfish. *Am. J. Physiol.* In press

173. Paton, W. D. M., Zar, M. A. 1968. The origin of acetylcholine released from guinea-pig intestine and longitudinal muscle strips. *J. Physiol. London* 194:13–33

174. Peiper, U., Griebel, L., Wende, W. 1971. Activation of vascular smooth muscle of rat aorta by noradrenaline and depolarization: two different mechanisms. *Pfluegers Arch.* 330:74–89

175. Poskonova, M. A., Mal'chikova, L. S. 1970. Effect of adenine nucleotides on the electrical and mechanical activity of guinea pig taenia coli and frog stomach circular muscle. *Dok. Akad. Nauk SSSR* 190:1494–97 *DK BSAS* 190:132–35

176. Potter, J. M., Sparrow, M. P. 1968. The relationship between the calcium content of depolarized mammalian smooth muscle and its contrac-

tility in response to acetylcholine. *Austral. J. Exp. Biol. Med. Sci.* 46: 435–46

177. Potter, J. M., Sparrow, M. P., Simmonds, W. J. 1970. Increased uptake and efflux of calcium with acetylcholine stimulation in smooth muscle of toad stomach. *Aust. J. Exp. Biol. Med. Sci.* 48:429–43

178. Prosser, C. L., Bortoff, A. 1968. Electrical activity of intestinal muscle under in vitro conditions. *Handb. Physiol., Sect. 6, Aliment. Canal,* ed. C. F. Code, 4:2025–50. Washington DC: Am. Physiol. Soc.

179. Rangachari, P. K., Paton, D. M., Daniel, E. E. 1972. Potassium: ATP ratios in smooth muscle of the rat myometrium. *Biochim. Biophys. Acta* 274: 462–65

180. Reisen, I. L., Gulati, J. 1972. Cooperative critical thermal transition of potassium accumulation in smooth muscle. *Science* 176:1137–39

181. Reynolds, D. G., Demarec, G. E., Heiffer, M. H. 1967. An excitatory adrenergic alpha receptor mechanism of terminal guinea-pig ileum. *Proc. Soc. Exp. Biol. Med.* 125:73–78

182. Rice, R. V., Brady, A. C. 1972. Biochemical and ultrastructural studies on vertebrate smooth muscles. *Cold Spring Harbor Symp.* 429–38

183. Rice, R. V., Moses, J. A., McManus, G. M., Brady, A. C., Blasik, L. M. 1970. The organization of contractile filaments in a mammalian smooth muscle. *J. Cell Biol.* 47:183–96

184. Rico, J. M. G. T. 1971. L'influence de la temperature sur l'activité agoniste de l'acetylcholine etudiée sur le muscle longitudinal isolé de l'ileon de cobaye. *CR Soc. Biol.* 165:2475–79

185. Robson, R. 1973. Alpha-actinin in smooth muscle. Personal communication

186. Rogers, D. C. 1972. Cell contacts and smooth muscle bundle formation in tissue transplants into the anterior eye chamber. *Z. Zellforsch.* 133:21–33

187. Sakai, T., Iizuka, T. 1972. Effect of caffeine and cooling on smooth muscle of toad bladder. *Jap. J. Physiol.* 22: 135–45

188. Schatzmann, J. J. 1964. Erregung und Kontraktion glatter Vertebratenmuskeln. *Ergeb. Physiol.* 55:28–130

189. Shoenberg, C. F. 1969. An electron microscope study of the influence of divalent ions on myosin filament formation in chicken gizzard extracts and homogenates. *Tissue Cell* 1:83–96

190. Shoenberg, C. F. 1973. The influence of temperature on the thick filaments of vertebrate smooth muscle. *Phil. Trans. Roy. Soc. B* 265:197–202

191. Siegman, M. J., Gordon, A. R. 1972. Potentiation of contraction; effects of calcium and caffeine on active state. *Am. J. Physiol.* 222:1587–93

192. Silva, D. G., Ross, G., Osborne, L. W. 1971. Adrenergic innervation of ileum of cat. *Am. J. Physiol.* 220: 347–52

193. Sitrin, M. D., Bohr, D. F. 1971. Ca and Na interaction in vascular smooth muscle contraction. *Am. J. Physiol.* 220:1124–28

194. Small, J. V., Squire, J. M. 1972. Structural basis of contraction in vertebrate smooth muscle. *J. Mol. Biol.* 67: 117–49

195. Small, R. C. 1971. Transmission from cholinergic neurones to circular smooth muscle obtained from the rabbit caecum. *Brit. J. Pharmacol. Chemother.* 42:656P–657P

196. Sobieszeh, A., Small, J. V. 1973. The assembly of ribbon-shaped structures in low ionic strength extracts obtained from vertebrate smooth muscles. *Phil. Trans. Roy Soc. B* 265:203–12

197. Somlyo, A. P., Devine, C. E., Somlyo, A. V. 1971. Thick filaments in unstretched mammalian smooth muscle. *Nature New Biol.* 233:218–19

198. Somlyo, A. P., Devine, C. E., Somlyo, A. V., North, S. R. 1971. Sarcoplasmic reticulum and the temperature-dependent contraction of smooth muscle in calcium-free solutions. *J. Cell Biol.* 51:722–41

199. Somlyo, A. V., Vinall, P., Somlyo, A. P. 1969. Excitation-contraction coupling and electrical events in two types of vascular smooth muscle. *Microvasc. Res.* 1:354–73

200. Sparrow, M. P. 1969. Interaction of $^{28}Mg$ with Ca and K in the smooth muscle of guinea pig taenia coli. *J. Physiol. London* 205:19–38

201. Sperelakis, N. 1962. $Ca^{45}$ and $Sr^{89}$ movements with contraction of depolarized smooth muscle. *Am. J. Physiol.* 203:860–66

202. Stephens, N. L., Chiu, B. S. 1970. Mechanical properties of tracheal smooth muscle and effects of $O_2$, $CO_2$, and pH. *Am. J. Physiol.* 219:1001–8

203. Szurszewski, J. H. 1969. Migrating electrical complex in canine small intestine. *Am. J. Physiol.* 217:1757–63

204. Szurszewski, J. H., Bülbring, E. 1973. The stimulant action of acetylcholine

and catecholamines on the uterus. *Phil. Trans. Roy. Soc B* 265:149–56

205. Taylor, G. S., Paton, D. M., Daniel, E. E. 1969. Evidence for an electrogenic sodium pump in smooth muscle. *Life Sci.* 8:769–73

206. Taylor, G. S., Paton, D. M., Daniel, E. E. 1970. Characteristics of electrogenic sodium pumping in rat myometrium. *J. Gen. Physiol.* 56:360–75

207. Taylor, G. S., Paton, D. M., Daniel, E. E. 1971. Effect of rubidium and caesium on electrogenic sodium pumping in rat myometrium. *Comp. Biochem. Physiol. A* 38:251–64

207a. Tomita, T. 1971. Electrical properties of mammalian smooth muscle. See Ref. 1, 197–243

208. Tomita, T. 1972. Conductance change during inhibitory potential in the guinea-pig taenia coli. *J. Physiol. London* 225:693–703

209. Tomita, T., Watanabe, H. 1973. Factors controlling myogenic activity in smooth muscle. *Phil. Trans. Roy. Soc. B* 265:73–85

210. Tomita, T., Watanabe, H. 1973. A comparison of the effects of adenosine triphosphate with noradrenaline and with the inhibitory potential of the guinea pig taenia coli. *J. Physiol. London* 231:167–77

211. Tomita, T., Yamamoto, T. 1971. Effects of removing the external K on the smooth muscle of guinea-pig taenia coli. *J. Physiol. London* 212:851–68

212. Triner, L. et al 1971. Cyclic AMP and smooth muscle functions. *Ann. NY Acad. Sci.* 185:458–76

213. Triner, L. et al 1972. Acetylcholine and the cyclic AMP system in smooth muscle. *Biochem. Biophys. Res. Commun.* 46:1866–73

214. Uehara, Y., Burnstock, G. 1972. Postsynaptic specialization of smooth muscle at close neuromuscular junctions in the guinea pig sphincter pupillae. *J. Cell Biol.* 53:849–53

215. Uehara, Y., Campbell, G. R., Burnstock, G. 1971. Cytoplasmic filaments in developing and adult vertebrate smooth muscle. *J. Cell Biol.* 50:484–97

216. van Breemen, C. et al 1973. Factors controlling cytoplasmic $Ca^{++}$ concentration. *Phil. Trans. Roy. Soc. B* 265: 57–71

217. van Breemen, C., Daniel, E. E., van Breemen, D. 1968. Calcium distribution and exchange in rat uterus. *J. Gen. Physiol.* 49:1265–97

218. van Breemen, C. et al 1972. Excitation-contraction coupling in rabbit aorta studied by the La method for measuring cellular Ca influx. *Circ. Res.* 30:44–54

219. Vizi, E. S. et al 1973. Evidence that acetylcholine released by gastrin and related polypeptides contributes to their effect on gastrointestinal motility. *Gastroenterology* 64:268–77

220. von Hagen, S., Hurwitz, L. 1967. Effects of extracellular Na and Ca on longitudinal muscle from guinea pig ileum. *Am. J. Physiol.* 213:579–86

221. Weems, W. 1973. Evidence for electrogenic Na-K pump as basis for slow waves in cat longitudinal intestinal muscle. PhD thesis. Univ. Illinois

222. Weiss, G. B. 1969. Alterations in $^{22}Na$ distribution in ileal smooth muscle. *Am. J. Physiol.* 217:828–34

223. Weiss, G. B., Goodman, F. R. 1969. Effects of $Ca^{++}$ on contraction, calcium distribution and movement in intestinal smooth muscle. *J. Pharmacol. Exp. Ther.* 169:46–55

224. Weiss, R. M., Bassett, A. L., Hoffman, B. F. 1972. Dynamic length-tension curves of cat ureter. *Am. J. Physiol.* 222:388–93

225. Wells, G. S., Wolwyk, M. W. 1971. Freeze-etch pictures of membrane of taenia coli. *J. Physiol. London* 218:11P–13P

226. Weston, A. H. 1971. Inhibition of the longitudinal muscle of rabbit duodenum. *Brit. J. Pharmacol.* 43:428–429

227. Weston, A. H. 1972. Effects of isoprenaline and phenylephrine on $O_2$ consumption in isolated smooth muscle. *Brit. J. Pharmacol.* 45:95–103

228. Wienbeck, M., Golenhofen, K., Lammel, E. 1972. Effects of $CO_2$ and pH on the spontaneous activity of the taenia coli of guinea pig. *Pfluegers Arch.* 334:181–92

229. Wood, J. D., Marsh, D. R. 1973. Effects of atropine, TTX and lidocaine on rebound excitation of guinea pig small intestine. *J. Pharmacol. Exp. Ther.* 184:590–98

230. Wurzel, M., Cowper, G. R., McCook, M. M. 1970. Smooth muscle contraction and viscoelasticity of arterial wall. *Can. J. Physiol. Pharmacol.* 48: 510–23

231. Yamaguchi, T. 1972. Effects of 5HT on isolated strips of guinea pig stomach. *Brit. I. Pharmacol.* 44:100–8

232. Yau, W. M., Farrar, J. T., Prosser, C. L. 1974. Effects of cholecystokinin and related peptides on electrical activity of intestinal muscle. In press

# RELATED ARTICLES APPEARING
# IN OTHER *ANNUAL REVIEWS*

From the *Annual Review of Biochemistry,* Volume 43 (1974)
  *Synaptic Macromolecules: Identification and Metabolism,* S. H. Barondes
  *Bacterial Transport,* W. Boos
  *The Biosynthesis of Collagen,* P. Bornstein
  *Membrane Receptors,* P. Cuatrecasas
  *Regulation of Steroid Biosynthesis,* M. E. Dempsey
  *Phosphoglyceride Metabolism,* H. J. von den Bosch and L. L. M. van
    Deenen
From the *Annual Review of Biophysics and Bioengineering,* Volume 3
(1974)
  *Scintillation Scanning of the Brain,* G. Brownell, J. A. Correia, and
  B. Hoop, Jr.
  *Models for Flow and Transport in Capillary Beds,* E. F. Leonard and S. B.
    Jorgensen
  *Blood Preservation,* H. T. Meryman
  *Collagen as a Biomaterial,* A. L. Rubin and K. H. Stenzel
From the *Annual Review of Fluid Mechanics,* Volume 6 (1974)
  *The Meaning of Viscometry in Fluid Dynamics,* C. A. Truesdell
From the *Annual Review of Genetics,* Volume 8 (1974)
  *Regulation: Positive Control,* E. Englesberg
  *Origin of Life,* N. H. Horowitz
From the *Annual Review of Medicine,* Volume 25 (1974)
  *Animal Models of the Asthmatic State,* R. Patterson and J. F. Kelly
  *Physiological Aspects of Exercise on the Heart,* J. H. Mitchell and
    K. Wildenthal
  *Physiological Effects of Scuba Diving,* J. P. Sanford
  *Disorders in Tridothyronine Metabolism,* R. Utiger
  *Vasopressin in Osmotic Regulation in Man,* G. L. Robertson
  *Role of Gastrin in Hypersecretory Disorders in Man,* J. E. McGuigan
  *Intravascular Coagulation in Liver,* M. Verstraete
  *2,3-DPG and the Oxygen Dissociation Curve,* G. J. Brewer
  *Control of Platelet Production,* L. Harker
  *Immuno-Prevention of Rh Hemolytic Disease of the Newborn,* R. B.
    McConnell and J. C. Woodrow
  *Mechanism of Action of Hemoglobin,* A. Arnone
  *Cell Surface Changes Associated with Malignant Transformation,* R. A.
    Pollack
  *Biogenic Amines and Affective Disorders,* J. J. Schildkraut

*(Continued next page)*

From the *Annual Review of Pharmacology*, Volume 14 (1974)
  *Regulation of Biosynthesis of Catecholamines and Serotonin in the CNS*,
    E. Costa and J. L. Meek
  *Movement of Drugs Across the Gills of Fishes*, J. B. Hunn and J. L. Allen
  *Renal Pharmacology:* Comparative, Developmental and Cellular Aspects,
    Y. V. Natochin
  *Blood Brain Barrier Permeability to Drugs*, W. H. Oldendorf
  *Mechanism of Action of Insulin*, S. J. Pilkis and C. R. Park
  *Cyclic AMP and GMP*, T. Posternak
  *The Use of Neuropoisons in the Study of Cholinergic Transmission*, L. L.
    Simpson
  *Relationships Between Chemical Structure and Biological Activity of
    Convulsants*, J. R. Smythies

From the Annual Review of *Physical Chemistry*, Volume 25 (1974)
  *Molecular Process in Membranes*, D. A. Haydon
  *Excitable Membranes*, R. E. Taylor

From the Annual Review of *Psychology*, Volume 25 (1974)
  *Brain Functions*, R. B. Masterton and M. Berkeley

# REPRINTS

The conspicuous number aligned in the margin with the title of each article in this volume is a key for use in ordering reprints.

Available reprints are priced at the uniform rate of $1 each postpaid. Payment must accompany orders less than $10. A discount of 20% will be given on orders of 20 or more. For orders of 200 or more, any Annual Reviews article will be specially printed.

The sale of reprints of articles published in the Reviews has been expanded in the belief that reprints as individual copies, as sets covering stated topics, and in quantity for classroom use will have a special appeal to students and teachers.

# AUTHOR INDEX

542     AUTHOR INDEX

# SUBJECT INDEX

## A

Abortion
  prostaglandin analogues and,
    401, 402
  prostaglandins and, 399-
    402
  administration routes and,
    399-402
  mechanism of action of,
    403-5
Acetates
  heart utilization of, 444
Acetylcholine
  see ACh
Acetyl-CoA
  production of
    heart metabolism and,
    418
Acetyl units
  transfer of
    heart metabolism and,
    444, 445
ACh
  ductus arteriosus response
    to, 202
  fetal circulation and, 197
  fetal pulmonary circulation
    and, 201
  hypersensitivity to
    muscle denervation and,
    252, 253, 256, 259, 260,
    267
  invertebrate heart effects
    of, 177
  lung metabolism of, 225,
    226
  skeletal muscle maintenance
    and, 285
  smooth muscle effects of,
    518-20
  transmitter role of, 519,
    522
    invertebrates and, 179,
    181, 182
Actin
  muscle contraction and,
    477-93
Actomyosin
  ATPase activity of, 487-89,
    491
  muscle contraction and, 477,
    487
Acyl-CoA synthetases
  heart lipid metabolism and,
    436, 438, 439, 448
Acyl units
  heart lipid metabolism and,
    441-43
Adenine nucleotides

lung removal of, 228
mitochondrial translocation
  of
  acyl-CoA and, 417
Adenohypophysis
  extracts of
    diabetes production and,
    347
Adenylcyclase-cAMP system
  insulin and, 343, 344
ADH
  see Antidiuretic hormone
Adipose tissue
  enzymes of
    insulin and, 340
  insulin effects on, 337
  lipid metabolism in, 437
  protein synthesis in
    insulin and, 340
Adrenal cortical hormones
  glucocorticoids
    calcium absorption and,
    370
  heart electrical properties
    and, 157
  lung maturation and, 223,
    224
  tyrosine amino transferase
    and
    insulin and, 339
Adrenergic blocking agents,
  alpha
  fetal circulatory effects of,
    198
Adrenergic blocking agents,
  beta
  fetal heart rate and, 197,
    198
  see also individual agents
Adrenergic neurons
  axoplasmic transport in,
    282, 286
Adrenergic receptors
  beta
    cAMP and, 521
    mechanism of action of
      calcium and, 522
    smooth muscle action of,
      520-22
Aequorin
  photoprotein, 472
Aging
  skeletal muscle changes in,
    268
Amiloride
  sodium transport and, 26,
    30, 31
Amines
  lung metabolism of, 225
Amino acids

active intestinal absorption
  of
  sodium transport and, 74-
    76, 79
  insulin secretion and, 333
  intestinal transport of,
    78
  intracellular accumulation of
    invertebrate osmoregulation
    and, 171
  sodium transport and, 68-
    76
  transport of
    insulin and, 338
γ-Aminobutyric acid
  see GABA
Aminopeptidase
  forms of, 316
  testis content of, 316
Amphotericin B
  epithelia and
    potassium transport across,
    30
Ampullae of Lorenzini
  function of, 240
Androgens
  LH secretion and, 322,
    323
  spermatogenesis and, 319
  synthesis of, 319-21
  testis cell origin of, 319,
    320, 323
  testis production of, 319-
    21
  see also Testosterone
Aneurysms
  elasticity of, 145
Angiotensin
  converting enzyme for, 226,
    227
  lung metabolism of, 226,
    227
Antidiuretic hormone
  intestinal absorption and,
    77
  lithium transport and, 31
  sodium transport and, 26,
    30-32
  toad bladder permeability
    and, 19
Aorta
  atherosclerosis of
    location of, 130
  balloon counterpulsation in,
    142
  bifurcation of
    endothelial damage at,
    134
    flow pattern at, 134,
    140

# CUMULATIVE INDEXES

## CONTRIBUTING AUTHORS VOLUMES 32-36

# CHAPTER TITLES VOLUMES 32-36

COMPARATIVE PHYSIOLOGY